THE DAVE NICHOL COOKBOOK

The Home Ranch: Our vineyard in the Stag's Leap District of Napa Valley, California. Eight acres of grapevines planted on rich soil produce our reserve Cabernet Sauvignon.

THE
NO L
SINCERE
THE L
FO

RE IS

OVE

R THAN

OVE OF

OD.

— George Bernard Shaw

THE DAVE NICHOL COOKBOOK

CELEBRATING THE 10TH ANNIVERSARY
OF DAVE NICHOL'S INSIDER'S REPORT AND
FEATURING CANADA'S FAMOUS
PRESIDENT'S CHOICE PRODUCTS

The Cookbook Team (from left):
David Scott, Photographer;
Dori Burchat, Creative Director/Designer;
Olga Truchan, Food Stylist;
Doug Bradshaw, Photographer;
Carol White, Editor;
Dave and Terri Nichol;
Russ Rudd, Director of Photography;
François Baillargeon, Production;
Frances Litwin, Writer;
Ted Reader, Test Kitchen Chef;
Janet Watkinshaw, Props Coordinator;
Jennifer McLagan, Food Stylist;
Alison Jarvest, Test Kitchen Chef.

Canadian Cataloguing in Publication Data
Nichol, Dave, 1940-
   The Dave Nichol Cookbook : celebrating the 10th anniversary of Dave Nichol's Insider's
report and featuring Canada's famous President's choice products
Includes index.
ISBN 0-9697259-0-6
1. Cookery. I. Loblaw Companies Limited. II. Title.
TX715.6.N53 1993   641.5   C93-090398-6

The following are trademarks of Loblaw Companies Limited or its affiliated companies:
President's Choice™, PC®, Insider's Report®, Dave Nichol's Insider's Report®, La Elección
del Presidente®, 'Too Good To Be True!'®, Memories Of®, Splendido™, Out of Africa™,
The Decadent™, The Decadent Chocolate Fudge Crackle®, Uncommonly Light™, The
World's Best™, Gigantico™, Zipper-Back®, Special Trim™, G·R·E·E·N G·O·U·R·M·E·T®,
Pizzazz™, Esplendido™, Passion Blend™, 2-Minute Miracle®.
Rustico™, Lamburghini™, Splenda®, Swiss Water™ and Texmati® are trademarks used under licence.

Director of Photography: Russ Rudd, Vice President, Loblaw International Merchants
Art Direction/Design: Dori Burchat, Creative Director, Loblaw International Merchants
Production: François Baillargeon
Production Director: R.W. Pohlak & Associates Inc.
Photography: Doug Bradshaw and David Scott
Food Stylists: Olga Truchan and Jennifer McLagan
Props Coordinator: Janet Watkinshaw
Editor: Carol White
Writer: Frances Litwin
Test Kitchen Chefs: Alison Jarvest and Ted Reader

A Word About Product Availability
PC, President's Choice and President's Blend products are available in Canada at
Loblaws, Loblaws Superstores, Supercentres, Zehrs, Food Plus Markets from Zehrs,
no frills, mr. grocer, valu-mart, freshmart, Your Independent Grocer, Fortinos,
the real Canadian Superstore, Extra Foods, O.K. Economy, Tom Boy, Lucky
Dollar, Shop Rite, Super Value, Shop Easy, save-easy, the real atlantic Superstore
and Super Valu. **Please note that some products featured in this book may not be
available at all stores. For questions concerning specific products, contact the
manager of the store nearest you.**

CONTENTS

I would like to dedicate this book
to the three seminal influences upon my lifelong obsession
with fine food:

My mother, who trained my palate for almost 20 years
and built the solid foundation for my love of food.

Jean and Pierre Troisgros, who taught me that
something we do at least three times a day can be done on
an extraordinary and relatively uncomplicated plane
of quality that I never realized existed.

And my wife, Terri, my best friend and the person
without whose help and enthusiasm this book could
never have been written.

*I*t has always seemed to me that the purchase of any book represents an act of faith. No one, not even a best friend or spouse, can guarantee that a book will please another person, however well and long the acquaintance may be. Elements of style, choice of vocabulary, and subject matter are among the variables that make it difficult to forecast the satisfaction that a book may provide.

The recommendation is almost like a blind date; hence my comment about the purchase of a book, be it given by a commentator, a respected friend, a book review in a reliable literary journal.

If this proposition be true, then the acquisition of a cookbook is a double act of faith, for in addition to the same general ties that apply to other books, the process is intensified by the addition of recipes for the preparation of food. As sensitive as is the human mind on matters relating to intellectual taste, the mouth and palate are even more responsive to the variations of seasonings, cooking time, and methodology of preparation. Nonetheless, I have the temerity to commend Dave Nichol's latest achievement to cookbook readers and users.

As a longtime collector of cookbooks, I have been interested in the introductions to them, as well as the recipes the authors have either invented or collected. Since cooking has been going on for quite a long time, there is more adaptation and improving than sheer inventions of a totally new way of cooking. This is in no way a criticism, for a constructive refinement of an old recipe requires talent equal to the creation of a completely new one.

This book is noteworthy in that it may be the first cookbook put forth by a chain of supermarkets, the first cookbook edited by the irrepressible Dave Nichol, an accomplished chef, head of Loblaw International Merchants and the originator of the exclusive retailer-controlled brand that his stores label President's Choice. Indeed, the recipes are his careful selections, for he has insatiable curiosity, boundless energy, the courage of his convictions to take action, and a stomach and digestive system that permits the rigorous food experimentation in which he indulges.

I have read many of the recipes, but I haven't actually tried any of them, which I shall do when this book is published. Knowing Dave Nichol for a number of years, though, I have complete faith in him, in his integrity and in any cookbook to which he would give his name.

Besides, any man who will go on the record he has, with his list of favorite restaurants around the world (and I'm familiar with most of them), knows his gastronomy.

Bon appetit.

Stanley Marcus
September 1993

In moments of considerable strain,
I tend to take to bread-and-butter pudding.
There is something about the blandness of soggy bread,
the crispness of the golden outer crust and
the unadulterated pleasure of a lightly set custard that
makes the world seem a better place to live.
— Clement Freud
Freud on Food, 1978

I wrote this cookbook for three basic reasons.

Since most of us eat three times a day for our entire lives, I've come to the conclusion that it's a worthwhile investment in time to learn how to cook well. I also believe that every human being has an inherent need to express his or her own creativity, and cooking well is an everyday activity that meets that need. And, finally, "breaking bread" with people you hold dear, when you've done the preparation, is still one of life's most pleasurable undertakings. It's always about more than just food.

Over the years, I've met many bright and enthusiastic people who are terrified of going near their kitchens because they regard cooking as some kind of alchemy and recipes as thinly disguised incantations. In my opinion, cooking for yourself or for your friends should never be cause for alarm. I wouldn't like to think anyone takes it that seriously. But who isn't serious about eating? (Credit cards, after all, were originally invented exclusively for use at restaurants. Isn't it mind-boggling to think that the entire premise for the West's cashless society was the Diner's Club?!)

If this cookbook makes a difference to anyone, I hope it will be those individuals who view cooking as a daily labor — their rock of Sisyphus — and the kitchen as that infernal region where, as they stand in the doorway agonizing over what to make for dinner, they hear the Sibyl whisper in their ear, "Now summon up your courage, for you will need it."

One of the most common reasons I hear for not bothering to learn to cook well is the fact that, in this hectic era, everyone is so "time poor" that even if they could develop their culinary skills, they'd never have the time to demonstrate them!

With more than 200 recipes in this book and a vast array of quality, easy-to-use President's Choice products, you won't have that problem anymore. The book you hold in your hands is the ultimate in speed cooking. My anniversary cookbook team combed through 10 years of *Insider's Report* recipes to find all of the old favorites so that you could finally get rid of the dog-eared originals you've been holding on to but can barely read anymore. (Marie Saffery, are you paying attention?) Now the classic *Insider's Report* recipes are all here in one book. Many of these recipes have been updated. And almost all of them can be prepared in 30 minutes or less. That should silence the Sibyl. I've even persuaded my wife, Terri, to divulge some of the very special, never-before-revealed dishes that she lovingly prepares on special occasions for family and friends.

In addition to the scores of President's Choice products featured on these pages, there are literally hundreds more at your favorite supermarket with which you can experiment. My basic motto behind President's Choice is, and has always been: "If Terri and I won't use it in our home, I'm not interested in it being a President's Choice product."

The *Insider's Report* team has developed more than 1,000 President's Choice products since 1984 because I know what it means to confront the "what-do-we-make-for-dinner" dilemma. We all know what it's like to be held hostage by terrible food prepared by indifferent or incompetent cooks. And we're all acquainted with the sacrifice to our wallets when we dine at the altar of the high priests and priestesses of cuisine, where our chances for a good meal are infinitely better. Whenever you can get past the question of what to make for supper without grabbing your coat and the kids, and making a dash for the nearest fast-food outlet — whatever that may be — you've achieved another great moment in self-sufficiency. And the best thing about feeding yourself and your family is that you can do it according to your own whims and inclinations. Tastebuds, after all, are as temperamental as we humans can be from one day to the next.

What is sauce for the goose may be sauce for the gander, but it is not necessarily sauce for the chicken, the duck, the turkey or the Guinea hen.
— Alice B. Toklas

In our house, the kitchen is a playroom. (For sheer organization, however, it's a model of military exactitude. Everything is at hand, right where we want it.) From the kitchen, Terri and I can look into the glass dome that we had built to enclose our own piece of Hawaii (we were married at Mauna Kea on the Big Island). "The Dome," as we call it, is our tropical island fantasy escape. At the end of a day, I find that cooking at home is relaxing. It's liberating. And it can transport you to any place in the world. I learned that years ago as a bachelor, when I taught myself to cook by working through Julia Child's first cookbook (co-authored with Simone Beck and Louisette Bertholle) while I was selling industrial bearings and seals and living in Saskatoon, Saskatchewan. I can still remember the joy of discovering how simple it is to prepare what I had always perceived to be impossibly complex recipes, such as Julia's incomparable chocolate soufflé.

But more than anything else, I find that cooking is a matter of time. Like everyone else, Terri and I don't have nearly enough hours in a day, so I'm always looking for ways to simplify mealtime without sacrificing quality or flavor. Lately, President's Choice customers have made our "Memories of..." sauces one of our best-selling ranges of PC products. I created the first President's Choice "memory" in 1989 — Memories of Szechwan Peanut Sauce. Today, we have a Loblaw store around the corner from our home that, some weeks, sells more bottles of this sauce than they do of the entire ketchup category! And we've extended the "Memories of..." line to include more than two dozen exotic sauces representing many international cuisines.

In the desperate '90s, with few households apart from the very rich or the very royal employing full-time family cooks, the convenience of President's Choice products helps make the servantless life easier to manage. For instance, stir-fries are often too much of a production for the time-compressed world we're living in. Who has the time for a stir-fry if you first have to prepare the vegetables? That's why, in 1990, I developed President's Choice Shanghai Stir-Fry Frozen Oriental Vegetable Mix. Almost from day one, it has been our best-selling specialty frozen vegetable (recipe, page 152). Does unexpected company accompany you home? A box of PC "Lamburghini" Hot & Spicy Lamb Meatballs in the freezer and a bottle of PC Memories of Ancient Damascus Tangy Pomegranate Glaze in the cupboard will come to the aid of your impromptu gathering (recipe, page 36).

The destiny of nations depends upon what and how they eat.
— Jean-Anthelme Brillat-Savarin
La Physiologie du goût, 1825

I was amused to read the article about me in *Toronto Life* magazine last year that claimed, tongue in cheek, that I was The Only Person Who Can Save Canada. The essence of the article, as I interpreted it, is that anyone who can solve all of the problems involved in creating a product as sensational as President's Choice "The Decadent" Chocolate Fudge Crackle Ice Cream should have no difficulty straightening out the Canadian economic conundrum!

Well, it's already been said that every country gets the governments it deserves. And quite possibly, the supermarkets it deserves, too. Although I haven't the answers for our politicians, I've made it my life to try to give Canadians the supermarkets and the food products they deserve.

President's Choice has its roots in No Name, which we launched in Ontario in March 1978. There were 16 products in this initial lineup, which was inspired by a visit to France during which I toured several Carrefour stores — the originator of so-called "generics." I was very impressed with Carrefour's line of *Produits Libres,* which roughly means products that are free of additional advertising and marketing costs because they're in-house, as opposed to nationally branded, products.

In the 20 years since I first entered the grocery business, I've personally approved more than 3,000 house-brand products (about 2,000 No Name products and 1,000 President's Choice) that have helped to create a revolution in North America retailing. Our world-famous corporate labels — No Name, President's Choice, G·R·E·E·N, G·R·E·E·N

G·O·U·R·M·E·T and 'Too Good To Be True!' — have radically changed supermarket shopping in this country.

When we started President's Choice, most large Canadian manufacturers wouldn't have anything to do with us, so we frequently turned to small manufacturers to produce our products. Today, there's global demand for the President's Choice. We're in California, New York, Boston, Philadelphia, Chicago, Phoenix, New Orleans, St. Louis, Dallas and the Carolinas, and products made from our special President's Choice recipes are available elsewhere in the United States. Internationally, our PC signature products can be found as far afield as Bermuda, Singapore, Hong Kong and Australia.

Food which is worth eating is worth discussing.
— X. Marcel Boulestin
Simple French Cooking for English Homes, 1923

In the fall of 1982, I was among a group of supermarket executives that visited a fascinating specialty food store in Los Angeles called Trader Joe's, which, at the time, had about two dozen small stores scattered around Los Angeles county. One unique aspect of its operation was a bi-monthly publication called "Trader Joe's Insider's Report," which showcased a series of economical, good-quality foods and beverages that founder Joe Coulombe, a brilliant merchandiser, had sourced from around the world. Joe's report was jammed with information and anecdotes about the products he was featuring.

On the flight home, we all agreed that an *Insider's Report* was one of the most exciting grocery ideas we had ever seen, and a powerful vehicle for merchandising our corporate-label products. I was so impresssed that I bought the North

American rights for the name, *The Insider's Report,* and set about creating my own version for our customers. (Today, Trader Joe's, which has 52 stores in California and Arizona, calls its quarterly publication *Trader Joe's Fearless Flyer.*)

In November 1983, I wrote my first *Dave Nichol's Insider's Report* to make the holiday season more exciting and help people save money. Our French bulldog, Georgie Girl, appeared on the cover with me, as she did for every subsequent *Insider's Report*, until last summer, when she passed away at the ripe old age of 12. (Georgie Girl left a living legacy of four generations — daughter Bonnie, and our three French bulldogs: grand-daughter Kathryn, aka "Stinky," Stinky's son, The Great Buckaroo, and Buckaroo's daughter, The Jazz.)

My *Insider's Report* has been a culinary phenomenon. Famous for its comic-book appearance, it's published four times a year and is read by about 6 out of 10 Ontario householders. (And they spend about four hours browsing through it!) Every year, we print more than 10 million copies. It only took a few editions to realize that the *Insider's Report* was a major undertaking, and that I would need help. As a result, I hired Jim White, an award-winning food writer with the *Toronto Star.* For five years before he left to set up his own food consultancy, Jim led the team of *Insider's Report* writers and played an active role in the development of the first flight of President's Choice products.

During the time that he worked with me, one of the greatest contributions Jim made was to insist that the ingredients going into our President's Choice products were as clean as possible. Jim had a vendetta against ingredients such as MSG, artificial colors and flavors, and preservatives. Whenever possible, I listened to him. For years I was skeptical that healthy eating was a genuine consumer trend. Perhaps our success with the PC The Decadent Chocolate Chip Cookie had something to do with that skepticism. But time proved Jim right. In the past few years, health has become a major consumer concern. Even the *Guinness Book of Records* scrapped its gluttony records; "unhealthy and outmoded," the editors said, in a world that has become so health-conscious.

In 1991, I realized that the healthy eating movement was gaining momentum, so I made up my mind to develop a special group of nutritious President's Choice products that I called 'Too Good To Be True!' To help me identify the products, I hired Barbie Casselman, one of Canada's best-known nutrition consultants and author of *Barbie Casselman's Good-For-You Cooking: A Healthy Eating Guide* (Random House, 1993).

In January 1992, we launched the first 'Too Good To Be True!' products. Today we have about 90 PC 'Too Good To Be True!' products, and we're continually adding more.

In that minefield of temptation that's called the supermarket, isn't it reassuring to know that someone has already taken the time to count the fat and the calories for you — and make sure that there's enough flavor to keep you satisfied?

All people are made alike.
They are made of bones, flesh and dinners.
Only the dinners are different.
— Gertrude Louise Cheney
People, 1927

When I graduated from Harvard law school and m.... Toronto 25 years ago, one of my favorite restaurants was the main dining room at the Three Small Rooms in the Windsor Arms Hotel. My favorite dish on the menu was Chef Dante Rota's fantastic wild mushroom soup. (Unfortunately, Three Small Rooms no longer exists, but you can now find Dante at his haven of traditional Italian cooking, Da Dante, on Yonge Street in North Toronto.)

Terri's son, Michael, loves Dante's soup so much, and the recipe is so simple, that he made it for a Loblaw's in-store recipe video when he was only 9 years old. That was the start of Michael's culinary aspirations. He's 21 now and for several years has been garnering experience on the front lines of cooking (i.e., in restaurant kitchens such as North 44°) in preparation for studies at the Culinary Institute of America.

WILD MUSHROOM SOUP

The Madeira is what heightens this soup's exotic "woodsy" flavor. Cream sherry is a good second choice.

1 oz	dried wild mushrooms (porcini, morels, cèpes)	30 g
4 tbsp	PC Normandy-Style Cultured Butter	50 mL
1	onion, finely chopped	1
1/4 cup	all-purpose flour	50 mL
8 cups	chicken stock, homemade or made with PC Fresh Concentrated Chicken Stock	2 L
2	pkg (each 8 oz/227 g) PC Sliced Mushrooms OR 1 lb (454 g) fresh white mushrooms, sliced	2
1/2 cup	whipping cream	125 mL
2 tbsp	Madeira or cream sherry	25 mL
	Salt and freshly ground pepper	
	Chopped fresh Italian parsley	

♦ Soak dried mushrooms in warm water to cover for about 15 minutes to soften; drain, reserving soaking liquid. Chop mushrooms and set aside. Strain liquid.
♦ In large soup pot, heat butter. Add onion and cook, stirring often, just until soft. Stir in flour and continue cooking, stirring often, for about 5 minutes.
♦ Add chicken stock, white mushrooms, wild mushrooms, soaking liquid and salt and pepper to taste. Simmer, uncovered, until mushrooms are tender, about 20 to 30 minutes.
♦ In blender or food processor, purée soup in batches. Heat until hot. Add whipping cream, Madeira and salt and pepper to taste. Just before serving, sprinkle with chopped parsley.
Makes 6 to 8 servings

▲
Super-Quick Mushroom Soup

SAUTÉ 1 JAR (113g) PC CHOPPED SHALLOTS IN OIL UNTIL FRAGRANT. ADD 2 PKGS (EACH 8 OZ) PC SLICED MUSHROOMS AND COOK UNTIL SOFT. ADD 2 CUPS (500 mL) BOILING WATER MIXED WITH 2 TSP (10 mL) PC CONCENTRATED CHICKEN STOCK. BRING TO BOIL AND REMOVE FROM HEAT. PURÉE UNTIL SMOOTH. ADD 1 BOTTLE (350 mL) PC MEMORIES OF FUJI SHIITAKE MUSHROOM SAUCE, 2 CUPS (500 mL) LIGHT OR HEAVY CREAM AND 1/3 CUP (75 mL) CREAM SHERRY. BRING TO BOIL, REDUCE HEAT AND SIMMER 10 MINUTES. HEAT UNTIL HOT. PURÉE. ADD SALT AND PEPPER TO TASTE. MAKES 4 TO 6 SERVINGS.

▼

To be "full of beans" is a wonderful thing. It implies that you're full of energy, zip, get-up-and-go. It's also wonderful to be full of beans in another sense; it means that you're getting enough dietary fibre in your diet — particularly soluble fibre. For several years now, there have been rumblings among scientific circles about the importance of soluble fibre in your diet. Soluble fibre includes pectins, certain gums and the fibre found in oat products, beans and legumes. As part of healthy eating, nutritional authorities now recommend diets low in saturated fat and rich in vegetables, fruits and grains that contain various types of dietary fibre.

Three years ago, when I asked Canada's pre-eminent fibre researcher, David Jenkins, what products he'd like to see the *Insider's Report* team produce for the PC 'Too Good To Be True!' line of healthful foods, he said without hesitation, "Foods that contain soluble fibre — like beans."

David Jenkins, a professor of medicine and nutritional science at the University of Toronto, has spent two decades investigating the benefits of soluble fibre in the diet and headed the government's Expert Advisory Committee on Dietary Fibre in 1985. Recently, he has been conducting fibre research for the National Institutes of Health in the U.S., which we help fund, and on July 1, 1993, he published the results of his findings in the *New England Journal of Medicine* (Vol. 329). To summarize, the study shows that consciously selecting foods with soluble fibre is of significant importance to men and post-menopausal women *who already follow healthy eating habits*.

We've developed a number of great-tasting PC 'Too Good To Be True!' bean-based products in consultation with David Jenkins and his group at the University of Toronto's Nutritional Sciences Department for use in the *New England Journal of Medicine* study, including PC 'Too Good To Be True!' Frozen Vegetarian Chili, Precooked 7-Bean Mix and Spicy Black Bean Instant Soup.

David Jenkins recommends eating them as they come. But I find these bean products are a wonderful convenience in cooking, in recipes such as 7-Bean Soup with Bacon & Beer (pictured at left), Pasta e Fagiole (at right) and 20-Bean Gazpacho.

Turn page for recipes.

7-Bean Soup with Bacon & Beer

The flavor of the beer is subtle — it helps round out the flavors and underscores this soup's hearty robustness.

3 tbsp	PC Extra-Virgin Olive Oil	45 mL
1 tbsp	PC Chopped Garlic in Oil	15 mL
2 cups	finely chopped onions	500 mL
2/3 cup	chopped red pepper	150 mL
1/2 lb	PC Special-Trim Bacon, chopped	250 g
2 tbsp	PC Splendido Pizzazz	25 mL
1	bottle (341 mL) PC Premium Draft Beer	1
2	jars (28 oz/796 mL) PC 'Too Good To Be True!' 7-Bean Mix	2
4 tsp	PC Fresh Concentrated Chicken Stock	20 mL
3 cups	boiling water	750 mL
2 tbsp	PC Memories of Jaipur Curry & Passion Fruit Sauce	25 mL
	Salt and freshly ground pepper	

• In saucepan, heat oil until hot. Add garlic, onions, red pepper and bacon and cook, stirring, until onion is translucent. Stir in Pizzazz.
• Add beer, bring to boil and cook until liquid is reduced by half. Stir in beans.
• Dissolve chicken stock in boiling water and add to soup mixture. Return to boil, reduce heat and let simmer for 30 minutes, stirring occasionally; soup should be quite thick. If not, continue cooking for about 15 minutes longer.
• Stir in Memories of Jaipur sauce and season with salt and pepper to taste.

Makes 6 servings

20-Bean Gazpacho

This hearty version of gazpacho can be served hot or cold.

1/2	English cucumber, coarsely chopped	1/2
1/2	red onion, coarsely chopped	1/2
1/2	red pepper, seeded and coarsely chopped	1/2
1 cup	fresh coriander	250 mL
1 tbsp	PC Chopped Garlic in Oil	15 mL
1	jar (19 oz/540 mL) PC 'Too Good To Be True!' 20-Bean Soup	1
1 cup	PC La Elección del Presidente Chunky Salsa Picante, Mild or Hot	250 mL
2 tbsp	fresh lemon juice	25 mL
	Salt and freshly ground pepper	

• In food processor or blender, lightly pulse cucumber, red onion, red pepper, coriander and garlic. Combine with bean soup and salsa. Add lemon juice and salt and pepper to taste. Chill before serving.

Makes 4 servings

PASTA E FAGIOLE

"Fagioli" is the Italian word for beans. You can make this classic Italian soup as thick with beans and pasta as you wish — until a spoon stands upright in it.

2 tbsp	PC Extra-Virgin Olive Oil	25 mL
1 tbsp	PC Chopped Garlic in Oil	15 mL
2 cups	chopped onions	500 mL
2 cups	sliced carrots	500 mL
1 cup	sliced celery	250 mL
1 cup	chopped red pepper	250 mL
¼ cup	chopped fresh basil	50 mL
2 tsp	dried oregano	10 mL
1 tsp	dried red pepper flakes	5 mL
	Salt and freshly ground pepper	
1	can (28 oz/796 mL) PC Italian-Style Plum Tomatoes	1
4 tsp	PC Fresh Concentrated Chicken Stock	20 mL
3 cups	boiling water	750 mL
1½ cups	PC World's Best Elbow Macaroni OR Farfalle	375 mL
1	jar (28 oz/796 mL) PC Great Northern Beans	1
	Shaved Parmesan cheese	
	(preferably Parmigiano Reggiano)	

• In saucepan, heat oil. Add garlic, onions, carrots, celery and red pepper and cook, stirring, for a few minutes until onions are translucent.
• Stir in basil, oregano, red pepper flakes and salt and pepper to taste. Add tomatoes with their liquid and concentrated chicken stock dissolved in boiling water. Bring to boil, reduce heat and simmer for 15 to 20 minutes.
• Add pasta and let cook about 15 minutes, stirring often. Taste and adjust seasoning. Stir in beans and cook 5 minutes longer until heated through.
• Ladle into soup bowls and top with a few shavings of Parmesan cheese.

Makes 4 to 6 servings

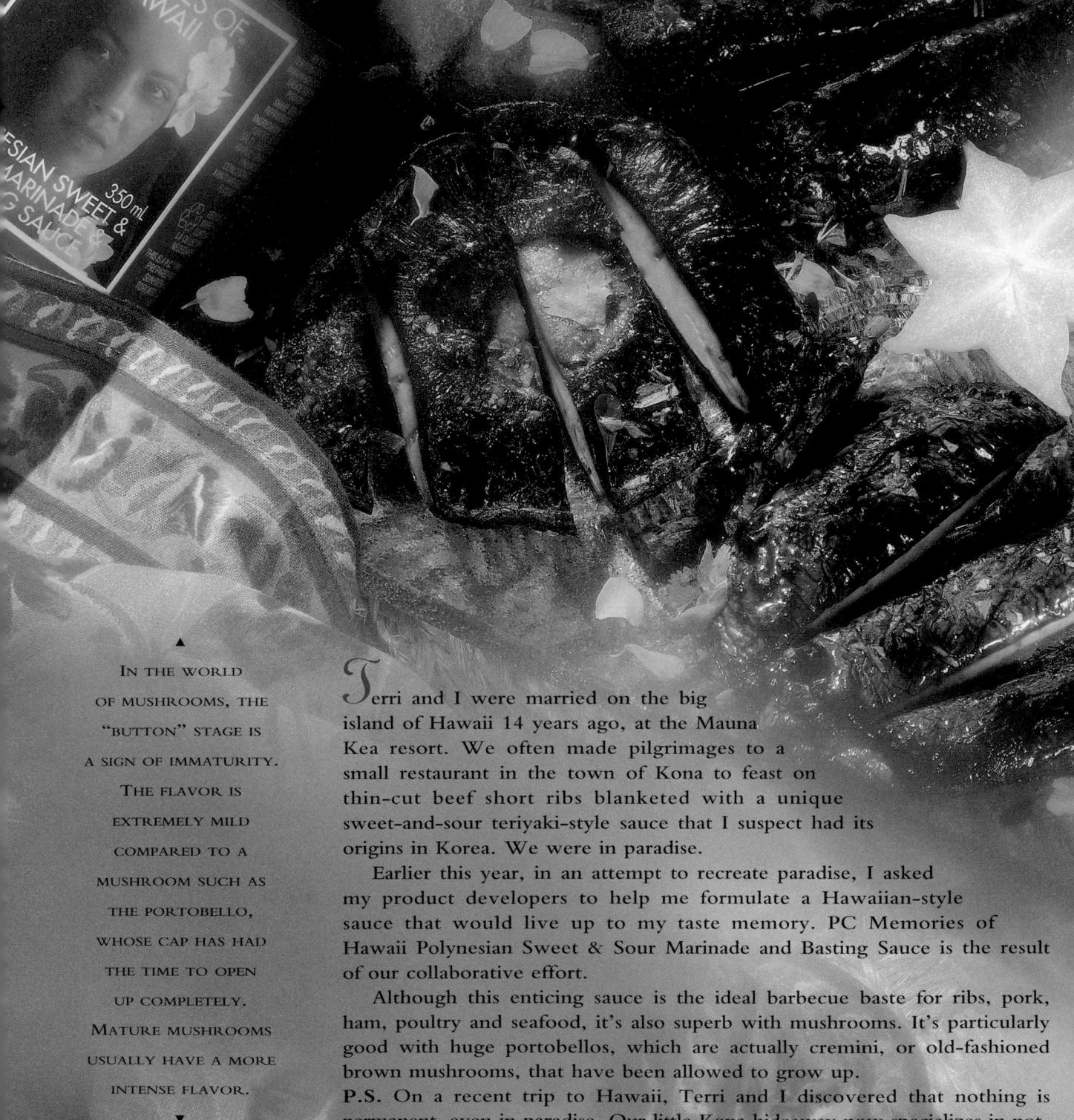

Terri and I were married on the big island of Hawaii 14 years ago, at the Mauna Kea resort. We often made pilgrimages to a small restaurant in the town of Kona to feast on thin-cut beef short ribs blanketed with a unique sweet-and-sour teriyaki-style sauce that I suspect had its origins in Korea. We were in paradise.

Earlier this year, in an attempt to recreate paradise, I asked my product developers to help me formulate a Hawaiian-style sauce that would live up to my taste memory. PC Memories of Hawaii Polynesian Sweet & Sour Marinade and Basting Sauce is the result of our collaborative effort.

Although this enticing sauce is the ideal barbecue baste for ribs, pork, ham, poultry and seafood, it's also superb with mushrooms. It's particularly good with huge portobellos, which are actually cremini, or old-fashioned brown mushrooms, that have been allowed to grow up.

P.S. On a recent trip to Hawaii, Terri and I discovered that nothing is permanent, even in paradise. Our little Kona hideaway now specializes in not-very-good deli sandwiches, and has eliminated short ribs from the menu.

ROASTED PORTOBELLO MUSHROOMS

The surgical precision which test kitchen chef Ted Reader brings to the job of slicing portobello mushrooms is very impressive. His secret? "Place them gill side down and use your sharpest knife. Try to keep the slices no more than $1/4$ inch (5 mm) thick," he advises.

6	large portobello mushrooms, stems removed	6
1 cup	PC Memories of Hawaii Polynesian Sweet & Sour Sauce	250 mL
$1/3$ cup	PC Memories of Kobe The 2-Minute Miracle Tamari Garlic Marinade	75 mL
1 tsp	PC Chopped Garlic in Oil	5 mL
1 tbsp	chopped fresh coriander	15 mL
1 cup	PC Extra-Virgin Olive Oil Salt and freshly ground pepper	250 mL

• Clean mushrooms with damp cloth or paper towel; do not immerse in water.
• Mix together Memories of Hawaii sauce, Memories of Kobe sauce, garlic, coriander, olive oil and salt and pepper to taste.
• Brush mushrooms all over with sauce mixture. Arrange gill-side up in shallow baking dish and bake in 400°F (200°C) oven for 15 to 20 minutes or until mushrooms are tender.
• Slice mushrooms but do not separate slices. Brush again with sauce mixture and return to oven for 5 minutes longer. (Refrigerate any remaining sauce and reuse if desired.)

Makes 6 appetizer servings

▲

Lamborghini
meets
Lamburghini

◆

UNINHIBITED STYLE IS
WHAT THE LAMBORGHINI
IS ABOUT, FROM THE
SPORTS CAR'S POST-
WAR GLORY DAYS TO
THE LAMBORGHINI-
BERTONE EFFORT,
THE COUNTACH, THE
WORLD'S FASTEST
PRODUCTION CAR AT
300 KM PER HOUR PLUS!
(WHEN YOU NAME
DROP, MAKE SURE YOU
PRONOUNCE IT
CORRECTLY. SAY
"COON-TASH.")

▼

My friend Serge Darkazanli (Serge and I go all the way back to our days at McKinsey and Co., a leading business consulting firm), who runs our real Canadian Superstores in Western Canada, spent his boyhood years in Damascus. One weekend, when we were poking around a Middle Eastern food shop in Seattle's famous Pike Place Market, Serge triumphantly held up a jar of a mysterious dark liquid and gave me my first lesson in the virtues of concentrated pomegranate juice.

The deep red pomegranate, some conjecture, was the original forbidden fruit in the Garden of Eden. Its juice is a prized flavor enhancer in Syrian cuisine because its sourness is balanced by just the right amount of sweetness. In the Middle East, concentrated pomegranate juice perks up foods when acidic ingredients such as fresh citrus products are out of season. Acidity or "tang" balanced with sweetness, in my opinion, is the backbone of all great cooking.

15-MINUTE
SPICY LAMB MEATBALLS
IN TANGY POMEGRANATE SAUCE

Put the contents of 1 box (2 lb/907 g) PC Lamburghini Hot & Spicy Lamb Meatballs in shallow ovenproof dish. Stir in 1 bottle (350 mL) PC Memories of Ancient Damascus Tangy Pomegranate Sauce and heat in 400°F (200°C) oven for 15 minutes or until heated through. Serve with toothpicks.
Makes 65 hors d'oeuvres

la chips ·38·

BORIS'S BARBECUE WARM-UP

Serve this with PC Guacamole, our frozen Haas avocado dip, or our lower-fat version made with PC Petits Pois (recipe follows).

1	bag (300 g) PC 'The Restaurant Blues' Blue Corn Tortilla Chips	1
3	green onions, thinly sliced	3
1	red pepper, cut in small pieces	1
1	container (68 g) PC 'Too Good To Be True!' Instant Spicy Black Bean Soup, prepared according to pkg directions	1
1	bag (250 g) PC Splendido 2-Cheese Blend	1
1 cup	PC La Elección del Presidente Extra-Chunky Salsa Picante, Mild or Hot	250 mL
1 cup	sour cream	250 mL

• Arrange tortilla chips on large ovenproof platter.
• Sprinkle with green onions and red pepper. Spoon black bean soup over top.
• Sprinkle with 2-cheese blend and heat in 400°F (200°C) oven until cheese melts, about 8 to 10 minutes.
• Top with PC Salsa and sour cream.

Makes 4 to 6 servings

SWEET PEA GUACAMOLE

Not all of us can afford to indulge in guacamole as often as we want, so here's a version that contains only 33% calories from fat. Compare with 77% calories from fat in regular guacamole (at least it's mostly monounsaturated fat)! Apparently, taco stands along the U.S.-Mexican border occasionally use sweet peas to counter the high price of avocados.

1	handful fresh coriander (about ¼ bunch)	1
1	jalapeño pepper, seeded	1
3 tbsp	fresh lime juice	45 mL
1 tbsp	PC Extra-Virgin Olive Oil	15 mL
2 cups	PC Petits Pois Frozen Peas, thawed	500 mL
¼ tsp	ground cumin	1 mL
1 tsp	salt	5 mL
¼	red onion, finely diced	¼

• In blender or food processor, combine coriander, jalapeño, lime juice and oil and process until roughly puréed.
• Add peas, cumin and salt and process until smooth.
• Stir in onion and serve.

Makes 2½ cups (625 mL)

▲

THIS SPECIAL APPETIZER COMES COURTESY OF BORIS AND JAN POLAKOW. BORIS IS MY VP OF CORPORATE BRAND SALES, THE GUY WHO QUARTERBACKS THE ORDERING OF *INSIDER'S REPORT* PRODUCTS ACROSS CANADA. HE'S ALSO THE "BO" OF MY "BO KNOWS" TV SPECIALS ON WUTV (FOX CHANNEL 29) AND THE VALUE PLUS NETWORK ON YOUR LOCAL CABLE. BORIS'S WIFE, JAN, SPENT SOME TIME IN CALIFORNIA AND DEVELOPED A TASTE FOR THIS CALIFORNIA-STYLE NACHO DISH.

▼

One of our favorite places in Toronto for brunch or informal weekend lunches is Allen's Restaurant on the Danforth, which is associated with the famous Manhattan eatery, Joe Allen. John Maxwell, who owns the Toronto restaurant, is related by his aunt's marriage to the Lea family of Lea & Perrins, who have been making the world's most famous Worcestershire sauce commercially since 1896.

John's restaurant serves Manhattan chicken wings made with meaty capon wings and plenty of heat. When I told John that I loved their fiery flavor, he said, "You should! With the exception of Lea & Perrins Worcestershire sauce, we use only President's Choice products to make them." If you love wings, try this recipe. Then make a pilgrimage to Allen's to see if John gave me the "real" secret. Regardless, it's one heck of a wing recipe.

ALLEN'S AMAZING MANHATTAN CHICKEN WINGS

Allen's is the only restaurant I know that uses big, succulent capon wings, which are next to impossible to find in commercial quantities. Instead, I use PC Gigantico Frozen Winglets and Wing Drumettes, cut from jumbo roasters.

New refrigerated PC The Decadent Blue Cheese Dressing, made with Roquefort cheese, is a quick alternative to the blue cheese dip.

1	bottle (270 mL) PC Gourmet Steak & Burger Sauce	1
2/3 cup	Worcestershire sauce	150 mL
1/4 cup	PC Louisiana Hot Sauce	50 mL
2 tbsp	PC Premium Alfalfa Honey	25 mL
1/2	bag (4 lb/1.81 kg) PC Gigantico Frozen Chicken Winglets and Wing Drumettes, thawed	1/2

BLUE CHEESE DIP

3/4 cup	sour cream	175 mL
3/4 cup	PC The Ultimate Mayonnaise	175 mL
3/4 cup	crumbled Danish blue cheese	175 mL

• In large bowl, mix together steak sauce, Worcestershire sauce, Louisiana sauce and honey.
• Add chicken, stir to coat evenly and marinate 2 to 4 hours.
• Prepare Blue Cheese Dip: In small bowl, mix together sour cream, mayonnaise and blue cheese; cover and refrigerate until serving.
• Place chicken wings in grill basket and grill over medium-hot coals 10 minutes per side, brushing with marinade frequently during cooking and just before removing from grill.
• Arrange on platter. Serve with Blue Cheese Dip.
• *Dave's Tip:* This recipe can also be made with 1 box (2.4 lb/1.1 kg) PC Seasoned Chicken Winglets and Drumettes, thawed.
Makes 4 to 6 servings

PESTO TORTA

To vary the theme, Sandra McKenzie suggests substituting thinly sliced smoked salmon for the shredded cheese, or salmon pâté from a deli or specialty food store for the pesto mixture.

2	pkg (each 8 oz/250 g) PC Memories of Winnipeg Old-Fashioned Cream Cheese	2
1	pkg (250 g) PC Lightly Salted Normandy-Style Cultured Butter	1
6 tbsp	PC Splendido Sundried Tomato Pesto	75 mL
½ cup	PC Splendido 2-Cheese Blend	125 mL

• Blend together cream cheese and butter until smooth. Set aside.
• Line a loaf pan or straight-sided round mould with plastic wrap so it covers bottom and sides and overhangs edge by a few inches.
• Spread one-third of cream cheese mixture along bottom of mould; spread half of tomato pesto on top. Sprinkle with cheese.
• Spread with another one-third of cream cheese mixture, then remaining tomato pesto. Top with remaining cream cheese mixture.
• Cover with plastic wrap and refrigerate 3 to 4 hours, preferably overnight.
• About 20 to 30 minutes before serving, unmould torta, remove plastic wrap and invert onto serving plate. Serve with crackers or crusty bread.

Makes 6 to 8 appetizer servings

Sandra McKenzie, a journalist in British Columbia, interviewed me for *Canadian House & Home* in 1990, around the time that Terri and I had discovered a prize-winning Dried Tomato Pesto Torta made by one of our U.S. suppliers. Consisting of alternating layers of cream cheese and a special pesto sauce, this unusually good "cream cheese pâté" was the perfect appetizer. Unfortunately, it was too costly for us to develop as a President's Choice product.

In one serendipitous moment during the interview, Sandra told me that "Torta Basilica" happened to be a Christmas breakfast tradition in her home. Her recipe, I soon learned, produces an incredibly smooth and unctuous torta, owing to the fact that it's made with genuine Winnipeg cream cheese (PC "Memories of Winnipeg" Old-Fashioned Cream Cheese is one and the same) and scented with a flavorful basil pesto. The basic recipe came from friends of hers who run a catering service in Napa, California, and she generously shared it with us.

Asparagus Strudel with Goat Cheese and Memories of Asiago

This strudel has the potential of becoming a culinary ritual in your home during asparagus season. The asparagus continues to cook in the oven, so it only needs to be parboiled before the strudel is assembled.

Make this for brunch, a light lunch or serve it beside simply prepared meat, poultry or fish.

▲

THE SIMPLEST WAY TO COOK ASPARAGUS IS STILL THE BEST: PUT IT IN SALTED BOILING WATER TO COVER (A LARGE SAUTÉ PAN IS PERFECT FOR THIS) AND COOK ABOUT 4 MINUTES OR UNTIL TENDER BUT FIRM, LID OFF! THIS WILL PREVENT VOLATILE PLANT ACIDS FROM CONDENSING ON THE LID AND FALLING BACK INTO THE WATER, WHERE THEY'LL CAUSE THE BRIGHT GREEN CHLOROPHYLL IN THE ASPARAGUS TO FADE TO A DRAB OLIVE COLOR. FOR THIS REASON, YOU SHOULD ALWAYS KEEP THE LID OFF WHEN COOKING ANY GREEN VEGETABLE.

▼

1/3 cup	whole milk ricotta	75 mL
1/3 cup	PC Memories of Asiago Tangy Asiago Cheese Sauce	75 mL
4 oz	goat cheese	125 g
1	large egg yolk	1
3 tbsp	minced fresh chives	45 mL
	Salt and freshly ground pepper	
1 lb	thin asparagus, trimmed	500 g
8	sheets PC Phyllo Pastry	8
4 tbsp	PC Unsalted Normandy-Style Cultured Butter, melted	50 mL
2 tbsp	PC Gourmet Blend 100% Grated Parmesan Cheese	25 mL
8	slices PC Splendido Prosciutto	8
1/2	red pepper, sliced in thin julienne strips	1/2

• In medium-sized bowl, mix together ricotta, Memories of Asiago sauce, goat cheese, egg yolk, chives and salt and pepper to taste.

• Bring a pot of salted water to boil. Add asparagus and cook, uncovered, until tender but firm, about 2 to 3 minutes; do not overcook. Drain well and pat with paper towels.

• Place 1 sheet of phyllo pastry on work surface. Brush with some of the melted butter. (Keep remaining phyllo covered with damp towel.) Arrange another sheet on top; brush with melted butter. Place a third sheet on top; brush with melted butter and sprinkle with 1 tbsp (15 mL) grated Parmesan cheese. Top with a fourth sheet of phyllo; brush again with butter.

• Arrange 4 slices of prosciutto, slightly overlapping, along one short end of phyllo, leaving a 1½ inch (4 cm) margin along bottom and both sides. Spread half of goat cheese mixture on top.

• Arrange half of asparagus spears on top of cheese, running parallel to short end of phyllo. Arrange half of red pepper strips in between asparagus spears.

• Fold in sides and bottom edge of phyllo over filling. Roll up strudel, starting at bottom end, to form strudel roll. Arrange seam side down on ungreased baking sheet. Repeat with remaining ingredients to make a second strudel.

• Brush top and sides of strudels with butter and cut several vents in top of each. Place in 400°F (200°C) oven for about 25 minutes until golden brown. Let cool on wire rack for 5 to 10 minutes before slicing with serrated knife.

Makes 8 appetizer, 4 main course servings

I have Russ Rudd, Vice-President of Design Services, and his team to thank for our many award-winning President's Choice package designs over the years — to name a few, the PC The Most Beautiful Black Bowl in the World, PC Memories of Kobe beef burgers, PC Tuxedo Crackers, our PC Raspberry, Lemon and Peanut Butter & Raspberry Temptations, PC English-Style Ginger Snap Cookies, PC 'Too Good To Be True!' Ancient Grains Cereal — and, along with Dori Burchat, the design of this book.

I also have Russ to thank for collaborating with test kitchen chef Alison Jarvest on the creation of this staggeringly good Asparagus Strudel with PC Memories of Asiago cheese sauce while I was out of the country on business earlier this year. This version sent my tastebuds into ecstasy.

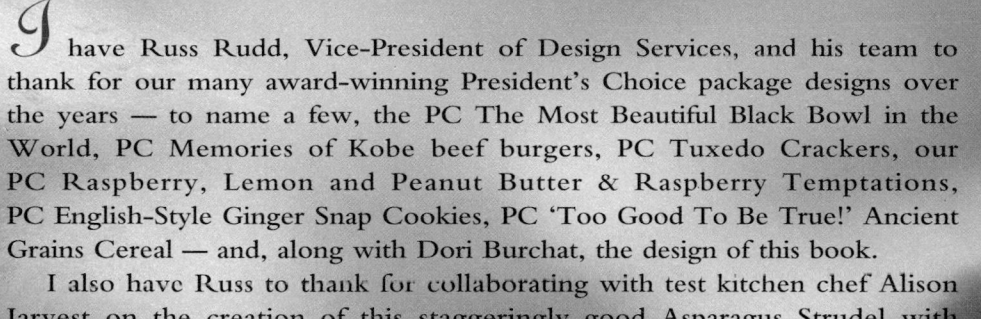

Smoked salmon is a special seasonal item we bring in subject to cost, quality and availability. It can come from different parts of the world and its quality varies from one year to the next. Before making my President's Choice selection, we look around at the premium sources, do a comparison tasting and then decide which one offers absolutely the best quality for the price.

One of my favorite smoked salmons is prepared for us literally at the border of England and Scotland, although we've had superb product from Norway, where salmon farming was pioneered in the 1960s. And a few years ago I tasted an unforgettable smoked salmon during a trip to the southern tip of Chile, where a Swiss company has established its base of operations on a beautiful fjord. It took me a two-hour trip by light aircraft down the spectacularly rugged coast of Chile to get to that company town!

SMOKED SALMON & GOAT CHEESE PINWHEELS

Serve these at room temperature for the most enjoyment. Cold only diminishes the flavor of smoked salmon.

1 cup	goat cheese, softened (about $1/2$ lb/250 g)	250 mL
1 cup	PC Unsalted Normandy-Style Cultured Butter, softened	250 mL
1	small red onion, finely chopped	1
$1/3$ cup	chopped fresh dill	75 mL
1	side (1 lb/454 g) frozen PC Smoked Salmon, thawed	1

• With wooden spoon or in food processor, blend together goat cheese and butter until smooth. Set aside.
• In small bowl, combine onion and dill. Set aside.
• Tear off two sheets of plastic wrap, each about 24 inches (60 cm) long. Arrange lengthwise on work surface with long sides overlapping by about 2 inches (5 cm).
• With overlapping slices of smoked salmon, create a rectangular "blanket," about 16 x 12 inches (40 x 30 cm), running lengthwise and centred on plastic wrap.
• Spread all over with goat cheese mixture to about $1/2$ inch (1 cm) from edges. Spoon onion-dill mixture in long narrow strip running lengthwise along centre of goat cheese.
• Starting at long end nearest edge of counter, roll up salmon into tight log, using plastic wrap as a guide. Tear off another sheet of plastic wrap and seal log inside, twisting ends to tighten. Refrigerate 8 to 10 hours, preferably overnight.
• While cold, remove plastic wrap and cut log into thin slices. Arrange on serving platter and let warm to room temperature before serving.
Makes about 15 portions

TERRI'S TWICE-BAKED
GOAT CHEESE & GARLIC SOUFFLÉ

Terri perfected this recipe and her version is one of the best appetizers I've ever tasted. The secret to the light-tasting creamy tomato sauce is PC Italian Magic from Italy. This authentic, home-style tomato sauce never overpowers the natural flavors of foods.

2 tbsp	PC Unsalted Normandy-Style Butter	25 mL
3 tbsp	all-purpose flour	45 mL
¾ cup	milk	175 mL
6 oz	goat cheese, crumbled	175 g
3	large eggs, separated	3
	Roasted Garlic (see recipe at left)	
1 cup	PC Italian Magic	250 mL
1 cup	whipping cream	250 mL
¼ cup	chopped fresh parsley	50 mL
3 tbsp	grated Parmesan cheese	45 mL
3 tbsp	shredded Gruyère cheese	45 mL

• In medium saucepan over low heat, melt butter. Whisk in flour and cook for 1 minute. Whisk in milk and bring to simmer, stirring.

• Add goat cheese, stir until melted, and simmer for 2 minutes, stirring occasionally. Remove from heat.

• Whisk egg yolks in small bowl. Whisk in 1 cup (250 mL) of goat cheese mixture, then whisk back into saucepan. Stir over low heat until slightly thickened, about 30 seconds, being careful not to let mixture curdle. Strain into bowl and place plastic wrap directly on surface.

• Generously butter six ½-cup (125 mL) ramekins and place in large baking pan.

• Prepare Roasted Garlic. When cool, peel cloves and push through sieve into goat cheese mixture.

• Beat egg whites with electric mixer until stiff but not dry. Fold into goat cheese mixture and divide among ramekins. Pour enough boiling water into baking pan to come halfway up sides of ramekins. Bake in centre of 350°F (180°C) oven until soufflés are firm in centre, about 25 minutes. Cool in water bath for 10 minutes. Transfer ramekins to wire rack.

• In small saucepan, heat together PC Italian Magic and whipping cream until hot. Stir in parsley and keep warm.

• Unmould soufflés and place on baking sheet. Sprinkle with Parmesan and Gruyère cheeses and place under preheated broiler just until cheese is melted and tops are golden. Watch carefully to avoid burning.

• Spoon tomato mixture onto each of 6 individual serving plates. Arrange soufflés on top.

Makes 6 servings

▲
Roasted Garlic
◆

SEPARATE 2 MEDIUM HEADS OF GARLIC INTO CLOVES, REMOVING OUTER LAYER OF SKIN BUT LEAVING PEEL ON CLOVES. PLACE CLOVES IN SHALLOW ROASTING PAN AND TOSS WITH 1 TBSP (15 mL) PC EXTRA-VIRGIN OLIVE OIL, 1 TBSP (15 mL) DRY WHITE WINE AND SALT AND FRESHLY GROUND PEPPER TO TASTE. ROAST IN CENTRE OF 350°F (180°C) OVEN, STIRRING OCCASIONALLY, UNTIL CLOVES ARE SOFT, 25 TO 30 MINUTES. LET COOL.

▼

$\mathcal{W}$hoever said goat cheese, or chèvre, has to kick you in the head with flavor was wrong.

Some years ago, Terri and I were having lunch at a lovely restaurant on the Bahnhofstrasse in Zurich, Switzerland, when we were served a fabulous French chèvre during the cheese course. It was very creamy and had a distinctive mild flavor with just the right amount of bite. It made such an impression that I asked the waiter for the label, stuck it in my luggage, and secured the Canadian rights for it as soon as we got home. Its flavor has become the benchmark for my *Insider's Report* goat cheese.

If you've yet to acquire a taste for chèvre because of some very strong-tasting versions carried by gourmet cheese shops, look for our *Insider's Report* goat cheese from France — it makes an excellent introduction. And it's an essential ingredient in this very special recipe.

Henri Gault: As we have to play the game,
let's define our criteria. What is a good restaurant?
Christian Millau: A place where you can get
a good meal. And the best restaurant is the place
where you can get the best meal.
— "Which is the World's Greatest Restaurant?"
Holiday Magazine, 1970

My culinary base expanded when I went to law school in Boston, where I was lucky to be able to rent an apartment from a family that took a special interest in cooking. Mr. and Mrs. Swindells travelled the world extensively, and they always returned home with fascinating tales of their trips, particularly when they went to France.

My food odyssey truly began in France. I'd read an article in *Holiday* magazine by Henri Gault and Christian Millau, the esteemed French gastronomes, in which they discussed their personal choices for the title, "The Greatest Restaurant in the World." As a result, I holidayed in France immediately after graduation, planning my itinerary around three-star restaurants. The most famous was Restaurant Troisgros in Roanne, France. This apotheosis of good eating in the Rhone Valley was run by two brothers and a father who Henri Gault and Christian Millau considered "the greatest chefs in the world." (Pierre and his son Michel carry the torch today.)

Troisgros is where I had my culinary awakening. I can still remember the first meal I ordered there; it changed my entire life. Foie gras, sorrel-sauced escalope of salmon, crayfish in beurre blanc, Charolais beef with marrow in Fleurie wine sauce — the white beef cattle that's named after the

Burgundian village of Charolles is France's finest — and Dauphinois potatoes, a regional specialty made with the thinnest sliced potatoes baked with shallots, thick fresh cream and cheese. For the cheese course, they wheeled up two trolleys of cheese. I chose several small ash-covered rounds of chèvre and the waiter suggested a "soupçon of St. André."

Top: Pleasurable decision – what to order for dinner. Right: Terri and I with Pierre Troisgros in his famous kitchen in Roanne.

My tastebuds were so dazzled with this repast that I asked to be allowed into the Troisgros kitchen, where I watched brothers Jean and Pierre prepare their salmon specialty. (A few years ago, my wife Terri spent two weeks in Roanne cooking in the Troisgros kitchen.)

My dinner at Troisgros marked the beginning of my obsession with the culinary arts. After I began working for Loblaw Supermarkets, the memory of it prompted me to invite Jean Troisgros to Toronto to investigate the possibility of opening "Troisgros West" in Toronto. Jean looked at the frozen fish available at that time and, sadly shaking his head, headed back to France. Anything but "fresh" is unthinkable for a Troisgros. My earnest hopes for a Restaurant Troisgros at our doorstep were dashed. (Terri and I still make the pilgrimage to Roanne whenever we're in France. Obviously, we are lifelong acolytes.)

I sometimes think not having the Troisgros in Toronto was a blessing in disguise, as it motivated me to focus on the quality and price of food products that we eat every day. My product developers and I meet regularly for tastings. Almost daily we assemble in the test kitchen, where food samples from around the world are laid out the entire length of the long counter. I call these tastings the President's Choice "auditions." I start down the line: a glance here, a sniff there, a sip of this, a taste of that. Most of the items are quickly dismissed, but occasionally "it happens": a product stops me in my tracks. And a President's Choice product is born.

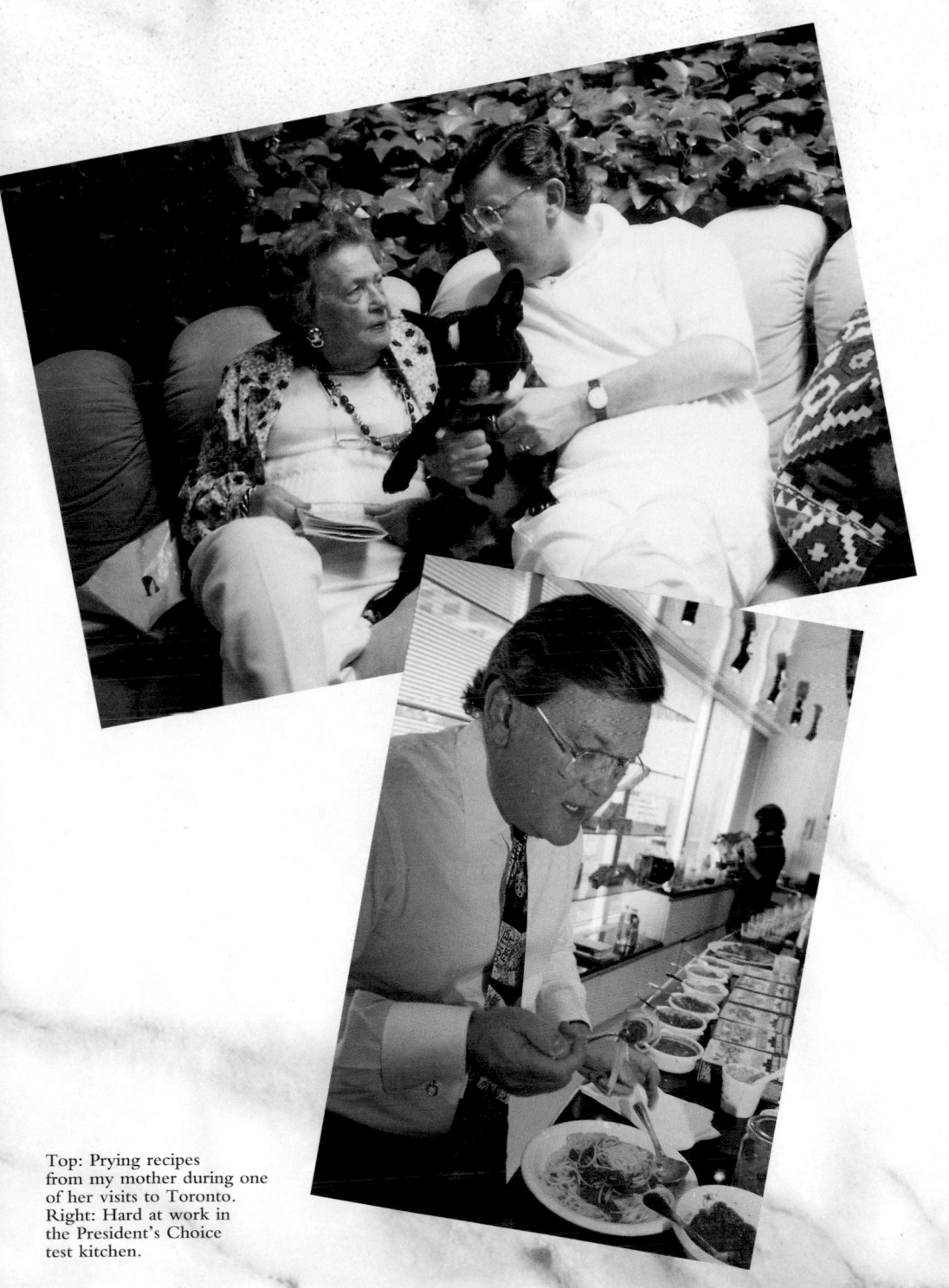

Top: Prying recipes
from my mother during one
of her visits to Toronto.
Right: Hard at work in
the President's Choice
test kitchen.

a man is as good as his nerve, they say. So when I read a *New York Times* feature on cooking for cowboys that insisted, "No bottled barbecue sauce comes near these wagons," I told the test kitchen staff to ready for the challenge. We cooked up "Chuck Wagon Pot Roast" using economical beef blade roast and our famous PC Gourmet Barbecue Sauce. It was very good, but there were a few improvements we felt we could make. (Like eliminate the half pound of butter in the original recipe.) When we were finished, we had a classic.

EXTRA-EASY TANGY CHUCK WAGON POT ROAST

This tastes even better the next day when the flavors have had a chance to develop.

1	beef blade roast (approx. 3 lb/1.5 kg)	1
	Salt	
	All-purpose flour	
1 tbsp	PC Uncommonly Light Pure Olive Oil	15 mL
1 cup	PC Gourmet Barbecue Sauce	250 mL
½ tsp	coarsely ground pepper	2 mL
¼ cup	PC 'Too Good To Be True!' Light Worcestershire sauce	50 mL
1 tsp	dry mustard	5 mL
½ cup	fresh lemon juice	125 mL
1 tbsp	PC Chopped Garlic in Oil	15 mL
1 cup	beef stock, homemade or made with PC Fresh Concentrated Beef Stock	250 mL
6 to 8	potatoes, peeled and quartered	6 to 8
6 to 8	carrots, peeled and sliced	6 to 8
20	pearl onions, peeled	20

• Sprinkle beef blade roast lightly with salt and flour.
• In Dutch oven or flameproof casserole, heat oil until hot; add roast and cook, turning, until browned all over. Remove from pan and keep warm.
• Pour off any excess fat from pan. Add barbecue sauce, pepper, Worcestershire sauce, dry mustard, lemon juice, garlic and beef stock; mix well.
• Return beef to pan; cover and cook in 350°F (180°C) oven for approximately 1½ hours.
• Spoon off excess fat. Stir in potatoes, carrots and onions. Bring to boil, reduce heat, cover and simmer for 1 hour or until meat is fork-tender.
• Slice meat and arrange on platter or individual plates. Surround with vegetables and spoon sauce on top.
• *Dave's Tip:* This is a great recipe for the slow-cooker. Brown the meat and combine with all other ingredients in cooker. Cook on Low for 8 to 9 hours.
• *Dave's Tip:* To loosen the skins on pearl onions, blanch in boiling water for 30 to 60 seconds before peeling.
Makes 6 to 8 servings

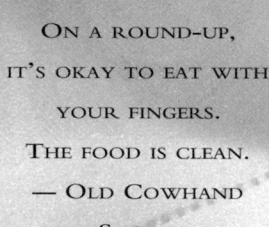

ON A ROUND-UP, IT'S OKAY TO EAT WITH YOUR FINGERS. THE FOOD IS CLEAN.
— OLD COWHAND SAYING

▲

Gracie Allen's Perfect Roast Beef

◆

TAKE ONE LARGE ROAST
OF BEEF AND ONE SMALL
ROAST OF BEEF, AND PUT
THEM IN THE OVEN, SIDE
BY SIDE. WHEN THE
LITTLE ONE BURNS, THE
BIG ONE IS DONE!!!

▼

THE SECRET OF "PERFECT" ROAST BEEF

Roasting is the simplest, most elementary form of cooking known to man — and it's also one of the most unforgiving for the home cook. There's no turning back the clock on a ruined roast.

Medieval chefs in Treviso, Italy, "the garden of Venice" where radicchio originated and huge plantations of kiwifruit now grow, devised a musical spit for the kitchen of Count de Castel Maria to make sure their roasts turned out perfect every time. The spit could turn 100 roasts at a time and played a number of tunes, depending on the cut of meat. Cooks knew the meat was done when the spit reached a certain point in a song!

In the event that you lack a musical spit, we've narrowed the odds of producing a perfect roast with our Eight Secrets to Perfect Roast Beef. They're detailed on the next page. Follow them closely and you'll produce a perfect roast, one with a crusty brown exterior and a juicy interior.

EIGHT SECRETS TO PERFECT ROAST BEEF

◆ **Secret No.1:** A roast must start out tender or all is lost. My favorite beef roast is prime rib because for my taste, it has the perfect distribution of lean to fat. Although it may offend the "food police," the truth is that most of the flavor in roasted meat comes from special flavor compounds in the fat.

◆ **Secret No. 2:** Remove the roast from the refrigerator and let come to room temperature before cooking. A 4- to 5-lb (2 to 2.5 kg) roast takes about 1½ to 2 hours to reach room temperature.

◆ **Secret No. 3:** Half an hour before cooking, generously brush roast all over with 1 cup (250 mL) President's Choice Memories of Kobe Tamari Garlic Marinade. Let marinate 30 minutes. Do not omit this step — it's critical to your success! The mystery of Memories of Kobe is how it accentuates all of the natural beef flavors.

◆ **Secret No. 4:** Using paper towel, pat roast dry and place rib side down in small roasting pan. (If rib roast is boneless, place on rack to keep meat from touching pan bottom where juices collect and where heat from the pan can cause roast to cook unevenly.) LEAVE THE LID OFF! You need dry heat to produce a roast with a crusty texture and deep brown color.

◆ **Secret No. 5:** Sear in preheated 475°F (240°C) oven for 15 minutes. Reduce heat to 350°F (180°C) and cook roast about 12 to 15 minutes per pound, or almost to desired degree of doneness. Since the roast will continue to cook while it stands, remove from oven while slightly underdone, or when internal temperature reaches 125°F (50°C) for rare or 135°F (55°C) for medium-rare on a meat thermometer. About 15 minutes before removing from oven, brush roast all over with pan juices.

◆ **Secret No. 6:** Let roast stand in warm place for 15 to 20 minutes before carving to allow the savory juices that the heat of the oven has driven to the roast's surface to redistribute. This resting period also makes the meat easier to slice.

◆ **Secret No. 7:** Meanwhile, pour off any pan juices into small skillet. Add ½ cup (125 mL) PC Memories of Lyon 4-Peppercorn Sauce, 3 tbsp (45 mL) dry white wine and 1 tsp (5 mL) PC Memories of Kobe Marinade; add a little more wine or Kobe Sauce if desired. Heat, stirring, just until hot.

◆ **Secret No. 8:** Slice meat and arrange on platter. Serve with sauce and accompany with Mashed Potatoes with Leeks and Sun-Dried Tomatoes (see opposite page for recipe).

Makes 4 to 6 servings

Mashed Potatoes with Leeks and Sun-Dried Tomatoes

This is a perfect accompaniment to beef. Your guests might be put off momentarily by the unusual pink color imparted by the sun-dried tomatoes, but the flavor of these potatoes will win you their accolades — and requests for your "secret recipe."

2½ lb	PC Yukon Gold Potatoes, peeled and cut in cubes	1.2 kg
	Salt	
3 tbsp	PC Unsalted Normandy-Style Cultured Butter	45 mL
2 tsp	PC Chopped Garlic in Oil	10 mL
¾ cup	finely chopped onion	175 mL
1½ cups	thinly sliced leeks (white and light green part only)	375 mL
⅔ cup	milk	150 mL
1 cup	crumbled goat cheese	250 mL
¼ cup	minced chives	50 mL
¾	pkg (85 g) PC Splendido Sun-Dried Tomatoes, soaked in water for 10 minutes and puréed	¾
	Freshly ground pepper	
	Extra crumbled goat cheese for topping	

• Place potatoes in saucepan. Add cold water to cover and 2 tsp (10 mL) salt. Bring to boil, reduce heat and simmer, partially covered, for 10 to 15 minutes until tender.
• Meanwhile, in heavy skillet, heat 2 tbsp (30 mL) butter. Add garlic, onion and leeks and cook just until tender. Remove from heat.
• Drain potatoes and return to saucepan. Shake pan over low heat for about 10 seconds to remove remaining moisture.
• Using a ricer or food mill, mash potatoes. Stir in milk and remaining 1 tbsp (15 mL) butter, leek mixture, goat cheese, chives and sun-dried tomatoes. Season with salt and pepper to taste.
• Spoon into shallow baking dish. Top with a little crumbled goat cheese and place in 350°F (180°C) oven for 20 minutes or until heated through.

Makes 4 to 6 servings

▲
Roasted Elephant Garlic
◆

ELEPHANT GARLIC, A RELATIVE OF THE LEEK, IS MILDER IN FLAVOR THAN TRUE GARLIC. HERE'S AN EXCELLENT SIDE DISH FOR ROASTED AND GRILLED MEATS. PLACE 2 OR 3 HEADS OF ELEPHANT GARLIC IN A SMALL BOWL. ADD 2 TBSP (25 mL) PC EXTRA-VIRGIN OLIVE OIL AND 1 TSP (5 mL) PC BALSAMIC VINEGAR; TOSS WELL. PLACE ON BAKING SHEET AND BAKE IN 350°F (180°C) OVEN FOR 20 TO 30 MINUTES OR UNTIL SKIN IS CRISP AND GOLDEN BROWN. ADD SALT AND PEPPER TO TASTE. (NOTE: IF ELEPHANT GARLIC ISN'T AVAILABLE, USE THE MORE UBIQUITOUS VARIETY FOR THIS RECIPE.) MAKES 4 TO 6 SERVINGS.

▼

HERE'S HOW NANCY
PENCER (HER HUSBAND,
GERRY, MAKES OUR
PC COLA) MAKES
BRISKET. (IT'S FABULOUS,
TOO!) MARINATE MEAT
OVERNIGHT IN A PASTE
MADE WITH DRIED
ONION SOUP MIX, DRY
MUSTARD, GARLIC
POWDER AND CHICKEN
FAT OR VEGETABLE OIL.
PLACE ON BED OF SLICED
SPANISH ONIONS, CELERY
AND CARROTS IN
ROASTING PAN; ADD RED
WINE AND BEEF BROTH.
BRUSH BRISKET WITH
PC MEMORIES OF KOBE.
COVER PAN WITH FOIL
AND COOK AT 500°F
(260°C) FOR
30 MINUTES. REDUCE
HEAT TO 325°F (160°C)
AND COOK A FEW HOURS
UNTIL FORK-TENDER.
ABOUT 30 MINUTES
BEFORE MEAT IS DONE,
REMOVE FOIL AND
LET MEAT BROWN.
SERVE WITH DEFATTED
PAN DRIPPINGS.

▼

*I*n 1980, Terri and I made the pilgrimage to the Great Chefs of France cooking school at the Robert Mondavi Winery in California's Napa Valley for a three-day cooking course with Jean Troisgros. Among the worshippers at the late great chef's feet was "Big Al," a microbiologist from Tyler, Texas, for whom food has been a lifelong hobby. We've been friends ever since.

Big Al has great instincts as a cook, so it's always a treat for Terri and me when he comes to visit and takes over our kitchen. One of his recipe "greats" is Texas brisket. We've given up asking our friend why he insists on using all those dried ingredients instead of fresh seasonings. Big Al simply refuses to back down on this one! He is passionate that if someone is going to make brisket, this is the recipe they should use.

BIG AL'S FAVORITE BRISKET

This is the only way that my friend "Big Al" Morris will make brisket. People may accuse me of being culinarily incorrect, but my advice is: Just try it for yourself. I must confess that it tastes very, very good.

1	beef brisket point (4 to 5 lb/2 to 2.5 kg)	1
1 tbsp	garlic powder	15 mL
1 tbsp	onion powder	15 mL
1 tbsp	celery seed	15 mL
1 tsp	freshly ground pepper	5 mL
1½ tsp	Knorr Aromat Seasoning	7 mL
1	bay leaf	1
1 tsp	thyme	5 mL
1 tbsp	dry parsley flakes	15 mL
1 cup	beef broth, homemade or made with PC Fresh Concentrated Beef Stock	250 mL
1 tbsp	Kitchen Bouquet	15 mL
1 tbsp	Worcestershire sauce	15 mL

• Wipe beef with damp cloth and pat dry.
• Mix together garlic powder, onion powder, celery seed, pepper and Knorr Aromat. Rub meat all over with spice mixture. Place in shallow roasting pan.
• Mix together bay leaf, thyme, parsley, beef broth, Kitchen Bouquet and Worcestershire sauce. Pour over brisket.
• Cover pan with foil wrap and perforate in a few places to let steam escape. Place in 325°F (160°C) oven and cook 2 to 2½ hours or until tender, about 30 minutes per pound. About 30 minutes before meat is done, remove foil and allow brisket to brown.
• Remove brisket from pan and keep warm. Let rest 10 to 15 minutes before slicing.
• Drain off excess fat from pan drippings. Heat and serve with meat.
Makes 8 to 10 servings

$\mathcal{A}$fter 40 years of exploring French gastronomy, respected food and wine authority Richard Olney maintains that simple home-style cooking is always the best. Softly scrambled eggs. Sautéed green beans. Bread and squash soup. These are the foods that command the respect of Olney, who was chief series consultant of *The Good Cook* series for Time Life Books and wrote the award-winning *Simple French Food* in 1974, now in its fourth printing.

Few dishes are more simple, or satisfying, than beef stew. Plus, you don't need fancy ingredients to make it.

FAVORITE BEEF STEW

Every culture loves stew. France has its daubes, *Italy its* spezzatino, *Hungary its* gulyás. *This version is a family favorite of cookbook editor Carol White.*

2 to 2½ lb	boneless lean beef, cut in cubes	1 kg
2 tbsp	PC Uncommonly Light Pure Olive Oil	25 mL
2 tbsp	PC Normandy-Style Cultured Butter	25 mL
1	onion, finely chopped	1
¼ cup	all-purpose flour	50 mL
1	bay leaf	1
2 tsp	chopped fresh thyme OR 1 tsp (5 mL) dried	10 mL
4 cups	beef stock, homemade or made with PC Fresh Concentrated Beef Stock	1 L
	Salt and freshly ground pepper	
¼ cup	dry red wine (optional)	50 mL
6 to 8	carrots, coarsely chopped	6 to 8
6 to 8	potatoes, coarsely chopped	6 to 8
6 to 8	onions, coarsely chopped	6 to 8
1	can (28 oz/796 mL) PC Italian-Style Plum Tomatoes, drained and coarsely chopped	1
¼ cup	chopped fresh Italian parsley	50 mL

• Pat meat with paper towel. In large saucepan, heat together oil and butter. Add meat and cook, stirring, until browned all over. Remove from pan and set aside.
• To juices remaining in pan, add onion and cook, stirring, until tender (add a little more butter if necessary). Stir in flour and cook, stirring, until flour is golden.
• Return meat to pan. Add bay leaf, thyme, beef stock, salt and pepper to taste and wine, if using; bring to boil, stirring up browned bits from pan bottom. Reduce heat and simmer, covered, until meat is tender, about 1½ to 2 hours.
• Add carrots, potatoes, onions and tomatoes and continue to simmer until vegetables are tender, about 30 minutes. Taste and adjust seasoning. Sprinkle with parsley.

Makes 6 to 8 servings

MEMORIES OF KOBE RIB-EYE STEAKS

Brushed on before cooking, PC Memories of Kobe (pronounced either KO-bay or KO-bee) lifts the natural flavors of foods. Like magic, it intensifies the steak's natural beef flavors.

4	rib-eye steaks, each 4 to 6 oz (125 to 175 g)	4
1/2 cup	PC Memories of Kobe The 2 Minute Miracle Tamari Garlic Marinade	125 mL

• Brush steaks all over with Memories of Kobe marinade. Let stand about 2 minutes, or longer if time permits.
• Place steaks on grill over very hot coals and cook about 3 minutes per side for medium-rare, or to desired doneness. Garnish with Fried Red Onion Rings (recipe follows).
Makes 4 servings

FRIED RED ONION RINGS

Start this recipe one hour ahead to give the onions time to soak in milk.

1	large or 2 medium red onions, cut in 1/4-inch (5 mm) rings	1
1 1/2 cups	milk	375 mL
1 cup	all-purpose flour	250 mL
1 tsp	salt	5 mL
1 tbsp	chili powder	15 mL
	PC Peanut Oil for frying	

• Soak onion rings in milk for 1 hour. Drain and lay on paper towels to dry.
• In shallow bowl, mix together flour, salt and chili powder.
• Pour oil into large heavy skillet to a depth of about 2 inches (5 cm). Heat until hot.
• Dredge onions in flour mixture, shake off excess and cook in oil, stirring often, until golden brown and crispy. (You may have to do this in batches.) Drain on paper towels.
• *Dave's Secret:* Milk helps retain moisture in onions during cooking and tones down the harsh oils that make your eyes water.
Makes 4 servings

At a famous steakhouse in Japan, the chef prepared a Kobe steak at our table. He made his own marinade and dipped the steak into it for only two minutes! Then he quickly grilled it over charcoal. I was amazed that in only two minutes his marinade could impart such a unique flavor to the meat.

I couldn't decide what impressed me more: the famous Japanese beef of Kobe or the secret marinade. Of the two, I'd have to say that the chef's dipping marinade is the right product for our times.

Thanks to the chef's generosity in sharing his secret recipe with mc, you can add a wonderful marinated flavor to meat, poultry and even vegetables in minutes — not days.

$\mathcal{I}$'m not always on the other side of the globe, planning to dazzle your tastebuds with a new "Memories of Kookamonga." When I'm back in the office and the day has been particularly trying, I just want to go home and relax in "The Dome," my French bull dogs curled up beside me, and watch Peter Jennings on ABC TV's 6:30 news.

On these occasions, I often opt for meals that Terri and I enjoyed as youngsters, such as meat loaf. Few foods are as comforting as meat loaf after a challenging day and, what's more, we've discovered that it doesn't have to be boring.

My current favorite is this recipe for layered meat loaf, devised by Terri and refined by Alison Jarvest, our test kitchen chef. Everybody who tastes it is crazy about the flavor.

MEAT LOAF WITH MEMORIES OF KOBE

Our versatile PC Memories of Kobe The 2 Minute Miracle Tamari Garlic Marinade brings out all the meaty flavors in this rich, moist meat loaf.

2 lb	PC 3-Meat Meat Loaf Mixture or your choice of mixed lean ground beef, veal and pork	900 g
1	large egg	1
1 tsp	PC Chopped Garlic in Oil	5 mL
1/2 cup	finely chopped onion	125 mL
1 cup	sliced fresh mushrooms	250 mL
1/4 cup	PC Memories of Kobe Tamari Garlic Marinade	50 mL
1/4 cup	light cream (10%)	50 mL
1 cup	PC Gourmet Barbecue Sauce	250 mL
1/4 cup	PC Splendido Pizzazz	50 mL
1 cup	PC Splendido 2-Cheese Blend	250 mL

• In large bowl, mix together ground meat, egg, chopped garlic, onion, mushrooms, Memories of Kobe sauce and cream.
• In small bowl, mix together barbecue sauce and Pizzazz (a flavorful sauce made with sun-dried tomatoes and fermented black beans).
• Spoon 1/4 cup (50 mL) of sauce mixture along bottom of 9 x 5-inch (2 L) loaf pan. Add half the meat mixture, packing well with hands.
• Cover with another 1/4 cup (50 mL) of sauce mixture, sprinkle with 2-cheese blend and top with another 1/4 cup (50 mL) of sauce mixture.
• Pack remaining meat mixture into pan and spread remaining sauce over top.
• Bake in 400°F (200°C) oven for 40 to 50 minutes or to desired doneness. Pour off excess fat and let stand 10 minutes before slicing.
• *Dave's Tip:* My instincts tell me that PC Memories of Fuji Shiitake Mushroom Sauce would be a great accompaniment to this meat loaf.
Makes 8 servings

▲
Terri's Leek & Shiitake Variation

◆

FOLLOW RECIPE AT RIGHT WITH THE FOLLOWING CHANGES: RATHER THAN FILLING MEAT LOAF WITH 2-CHEESE BLEND, SUBSTITUTE 1 CUP (250 mL) THINLY SLICED LEEKS AND 2 CUPS (500 mL) SLICED SHIITAKE MUSHROOMS. IF DESIRED, YOU CAN LIGHTLY SAUTÉ MUSHROOMS AND LEEKS IN PC UNSALTED NORMANDY-STYLE CULTURED BUTTER.

▼

MY 12 FAVORITE RESTAURANTS IN THE WORLD

The way a restaurant greets you and takes care of you is just as important as the food. Of course, the food has to be sensational. But if they don't make you feel like part of their family, you won't find them on this list. These restaurants are not ranked in any particular order, except for Les Frères Troisgros which, because of the many special memories associated with it over the years, will always be my favorite restaurant in the world.

Les Frères Troisgros
Roanne, France

The Troisgros brothers, Jean and Pierre, taught me that something we do three times every day — eating — could be done on an entirely different level. This was my first culinary epiphany, and like your first love, you can never forget it.

Zuni Café
San Francisco, California

The secret to happiness in life is this equation: $H = R/E$; that is, happiness equals reality over expectation.

When you walk into the Zuni bar & grill, your E (expectation) will be low. But when they bring you their incredible Caesar Salad, followed by their spectacular chicken baked in a mesquite-fueled oven, served with a sourdough bread salad dressed with champagne vinaigrette, your R (reality) will be about 100 times greater than your E (expectation). AND YOU WILL BE VERY HAPPY!

The Grill Room of the Connaught Hotel
London, England

Not the main dining room. The Grill Room. It's the best restaurant in England. Very small. Almost impossible to get into. Originally, I was spoiled by Mr. Bovo, a former maitre d' who is now at the Gritti Palace in Venice. His successors in the Grill Room have admirably upheld the tradition of making their guests feel especially welcome. This is remarkable in light of the fact that the Connaught is probably the stuffiest hotel in the world. They're very proud that there are no minibars in their rooms!

The Grill Room has the best smoked salmon — it's sliced at your table, and it's like watching a world-class surgeon at work. Treat the waiter with respect and he'll offer you seconds. Irritate him and you'll get one thin slice. I particularly recommend that you go for lunch on Friday when they serve their puff-pastry-swaddled Coulibiac of Salmon off the trolley. I guarantee that this traditional Russian wedding dish served with a wonderful beurre blanc will become your personal "Memories of London!"

Gotham Bar and Grill
New York, New York

The best restaurant in North America.

Chef Alfred Portale, from Buffalo, NY, trained with the Troisgros brothers.

The great thing about Alfred is that he's not only a wonderful cook with a great palate, but he also has an astonishing sense of style and presentation.

Order his seafood salad and you'll understand what the Japanese mean when they say that "first you eat with your eyes, then with your palate."

Alfred is starting up other restaurants in New York City, and it'll be interesting to see if he can maintain his creative juices.

Four Seasons
New York, New York

The great thing about New York's Four Seasons restaurant (not related to the fabulous Toronto-based Four Seasons hotel group) is that, in a city where most "hot" restaurants have their tables arranged cheek by jowl (for example, Le Cirque), architect Philip Johnson designed a tremendous luxury of space into the dining rooms (I've heard the place was originally designed to be a car showroom).

The food is great, not sensational, but the restaurant's general managers are another matter altogether. It's a tremendous pleasure to watch the antics of Julian Niccolini and to observe Alex Von Bidder trying to control him.

One thing: If you're a lover of wine, be careful. Julian has a habit of dropping very expensive bottles of wine on your table whether you want them or not.

One of the world's unique dining experiences is to go to the Four Seasons Grill Room for a "power" lunch and the Pool Room for supper (make sure you ask for a table near the fountain pool).

Harry's Bar
Venice, Italy

A favorite for 32 years!

I first went to Venice in 1961. I was a sophomore at the University of Western Ontario and had spent the summer working for the Deutscher supermarket chain in Germany — they assigned me a non-lingually-demanding job: looking after bottle returns!

For my return trip to Canada, I started by taking a train to Venice. This trip took me over the Brenner Pass and into Italy at three in the morning. At the first Italian station stop, I was jolted awake by a man selling salami sandwiches and singing operatic arias at the top of his lungs. Deciding he was a lunatic, I slipped back into the arms of Morpheus, only to be jolted back to reality by Italians singing opera at every station during the night. Finally, it sank in — Italians are not lunatics. They're just happy — quite a shock for a Canadian! Before my boat sailed for Halifax, I spent three days in Venice, and I've been in love with it ever since.

My favorite restaurant — Harry's Bar, of course. Do not sit in the downstairs bar unless you're an obsessive people watcher. The best place is the corner table upstairs overlooking the Grand Canal. That's where Arrigo "Harry" Cipriani always has his picture taken for the press.

Some consider Harry's Bar to be an overpriced, insensitive tourist trap because it was made famous by Hemingway and Charlie Chaplin, among others. But the maitre d'hotel I met — Johnny — had the ability to take a second-year university student and make him feel that it was the greatest pleasure in the world to feed him. Most maitre d's consider it their place to put you in your place; they won't let you get too close to the altar lest you uncover the mystique and the secret of the food. Johnny now runs the Hotel Monaco across the alley from Harry's Bar. You mustn't go to Venice without eating at the Monaco with Johnny.

Have the formula lunch at Harry's: a Bellini (sparkling spumante with the rosy juice of white peaches); green tagliolini with ham, cream and cheese sauce; carpaccio (lightly dusted with sea salt and then refrigerated to bring out the gorgeous red color of the beef); tiny sautéed Adriatic scampi (the secret to this recipe is that at the very last moment they're flambéed in Cognac, which makes them sweet); any one of the house cakes (I know — they're all too sweet); a carafe of house white wine (the Italians are dead set against making a religion of wine); and a double espresso.

I remember a New Year's Eve dinner at Harry's Bar based on white truffles. Arrigo was there at the end of the meal. He handed out beautiful books with black-and-white photos of Venice as New Year's gifts to everyone in the bar. How could you ever forget that?

La Lampada da Tonino
Rome, Italy

This is a restaurant run by owner/cook Tonino Fereale and his family. Very small place, very simple, almost a hole in the wall. Specializes in porcini mushrooms, white truffles, black truffles and variations.

Tonino is a great connoisseur of Italian wine. Warm up to him and he'll dazzle you with his selections. If you request it, he will do a salad of white truffles that will live in your memory forever.

Look at the walls and you'll see currency from around the world with names on it. Look for the Canadian $10 bill above my table with "Memories of Rome" written on it.

Roy's
Honolulu, Oahu, Hawaii

One of the great trends in food today — and even more so in the future — is East meets West. Chef Roy Yamaguchi is the Hawaiian master of Eurasian.

Spago-style with baseball caps and open kitchen. Tremendous energy and a tremendous feel for exotic sauces. Staff appears to be there just to have fun. Lots of energy to explore other cuisines.

For years, Hawaii was a gastronomic wasteland. Now we're starting to see the first signs of enormous culinary energy. Roy is a mover — he recently opened restaurants in Waikiki and on the island of Maui.

Five Feet
Laguna Beach, California

Another East-meets-West restaurant run by a young chef, Michael Kang. Very unpretentious. Very reasonably priced. I found it by reading *Vogue* magazine, which said that it had perhaps the best Chinese food in North America.

I recommend it because of one supreme dish — fried whole catfish. They fly the catfish in fresh from Louisiana every day. After they pick it up from the airport, they put it (head-on) in seasoned flour, deep fry it, put it on a plate and then bring it to the table, where a waiter separates the flesh from the skeleton and pours an incredible fruited sweet-and-sour sauce over it. Also beg Michael to prepare his New Zealand green-lipped mussels in black bean sauce.

Anywhere in Canada
where Michael Städtlander is cooking

One of the really naturally blessed culinary talents in the world.

At the time we went to press, Michael was planning to open a bed & breakfast in Rob Roy, Ont. (near Collingwood) and offer lessons in organic cooking. I wish he'd forget about this organic stuff, though... and also learn how to cook a meal fast enough to satisfy a person with my abbreviated attention span.

Restaurant Bareiss
Kurhotel Mitteltal, Baiersbronn-Mitteltal, Germany

Every two years I go to Cologne for Anuga, the world's biggest food fair, and frankly, over the years, I've been "underwhelmed" by my encounters with German cuisine.

But then my good friend Ziggy Wauro took me to the Black Forest. (Ziggy, who's one of the happiest people I've ever met, worked as a master butcher in Germany before emigrating to Canada, where he set up Ziggys specialty butcher shops; he later sold them to Loblaw Companies and now lives in Phoenix, Ariz.) In my opinion, the Black Forest is one of the most beautiful areas in the world. Bucolic. Chalet homes with hanging geraniums spilling out of tiers of window boxes.

Germans love this low and sprawling, chalet-style "Kur" ("Cure" or spa) hotel. They go off during the day for their fill of fresh air and exercise in the Black Forest Valley and come back at night, ravenous.

The Bareiss family's objective was to try to create the best restaurant in Germany. Be warned: There are three restaurants in the hotel. Make sure your reservations are in the gourmet restaurant. It's small, just a few tables, but the food will astound you. Maybe because it's so close to the French border. (Two hours from Strasbourg.) Thanks, Zigger.

Schwarzwaldstube
Kurhotel Traube-Tonbach, Tonbach, Germany

Fifteen minutes down the way from Mitteltal, in Tonbach, is Kurhotel Traube and its magnificent French restaurant, Schwarzwaldstube, run by the very capable Herr Heiner Finkbeiner.

Schwarzwaldstube's chef, Willi Finkbeiner, has just been awarded his third Michelin star. Need I say more? Do not miss these two German restaurants!

BONELESS WHITE VEAL ROAST WITH LINGONBERRY AND MUSHROOM SAUCE

The sauce in this dish is superb, but if you're rushed for time, try this speedy version: In saucepan, bring to boil 1 bottle (350 mL) Memories of Fuji Shiitake Mushroom Sauce and ⅔ cup (150 mL) whipping cream. Stir in ⅓ cup (75 mL) PC Swedish-Style Lingonberry Sauce. Makes 2⅓ cups (575 mL). By the way, this sauce is also wonderful with The President's Cut Boneless Pork Shoulder Roast.

1	PC Boneless Fancy White Veal Roast (4 to 6 lb/2 to 3 kg)	1
4 tbsp	PC Extra-Virgin Olive Oil	50 mL
	Salt and freshly ground pepper	
2 tsp	dry mustard powder	10 mL

LINGONBERRY & MUSHROOM SAUCE

¼ cup	PC Normandy-Style Cultured Butter	50 mL
1 tbsp	PC Chopped Garlic in Oil	15 mL
1	small shallot, finely chopped	1
2 cups	sliced Cremini (Italian brown) OR white mushrooms	500 mL
½ cup	cream sherry	125 mL
½ cup	undiluted beef consommé	125 mL
2 cups	whipping cream	500 mL
3 tbsp	fresh lemon juice	45 mL
¼ cup	PC Swedish-Style Lingonberry Sauce	50 mL

• Rub veal roast all over with 2 tbsp (25 mL) olive oil. Season lightly with salt and pepper and sprinkle with mustard powder.

• Heat remaining 2 tbsp (25 mL) PC Extra-Virgin Olive Oil in large skillet over high heat; add veal roast and cook, turning, until browned all over.

• Place meat on rack in roasting pan and roast in 450°F (230°C) oven for 15 minutes. Reduce heat to 325°F (160°C) and continue cooking for about 2 hours or until internal temperature reaches 160°F (70°C) on a meat thermometer. Cover loosely with foil and let stand 15 to 20 minutes before slicing.

• Meanwhile, prepare Lingonberry & Mushroom Sauce: In skillet over medium heat, melt butter. Add garlic and shallot and cook about 1 minute until fragrant; do not brown.

• Add mushrooms and cook, stirring, for 2 to 3 minutes until tender. Stir in cream sherry and undiluted beef consommé. Cook over medium heat, stirring occasionally, until liquid is reduced by half.

• Stir in whipping cream and 2 tbsp (25 mL) fresh lemon juice; continue cooking until thick and creamy. (You should be able to see bottom of pan as you draw spoon across it.)

• Just before serving, stir in lingonberries and remaining lemon juice. Season with salt and pepper to taste.

• Slice meat and arrange on platter. Spoon sauce on top.

Makes 6 to 8 servings

ONLY 14 CALORIES PER 1/2 CUP SERVING
PRESIDENT'S CHOICE
GOURMET
MIXED MUSHROOM
PIECES AND STEMS
a unique blend of fine imported
gourmet mushrooms
19 fl oz 540 mL

Jhere are 120,000 identified species of fungi in the world, the most notorious being the monster mushrooms in Upper Michigan and Washington state. These single-organism mushroom mats cover thousands and thousands of acres!

As I'm particularly fond of mushrooms, I make a point of cooking with them whenever I get a chance. One of the most convenient and tasty assortments of mushrooms is President's Choice Gourmet Mixed Mushrooms Pieces and Stems. Each jar contains a selection of European-grown nameko, oyster and "champignons de Paris," or white button mushrooms. What a convenience! And the entire 540 mL jar contains only 75 calories.

Keep them handy to add real mushroom flavor to your favorite casseroles, sauces, stews, soups, rice, vegetables, hors d'oeuvres, pizzas and egg dishes.

I especially like to use them to dress up beautiful veal chops. (Ask your butcher for chops with as much tenderloin as possible.)

▲
Side Show
◆
Sauté one jar rinsed and drained PC Gourmet Mixed Mushrooms Pieces and Stems in 1 tbsp (15 mL) PC Pure Olive Oil with Garlic Essence. Just before serving, drizzle with a little PC Pure Olive Oil with Hot Pepper Essence.

Makes 4 to 6 servings.
▼

Veal Chops with Mushrooms & Onions

If you spin-dry rinsed PC Gourmet Mixed Mushrooms Pieces and Stems in a salad spinner before cooking, they won't throw off as much moisture.

4	veal rib chops, about 1 inch (2.5 cm) thick	4
	Salt and freshly ground pepper	
3 tbsp	PC Extra-Virgin Olive Oil	45 mL
2 tbsp	butter	25 mL
1 tbsp	PC Chopped Garlic in Oil	15 mL
1	large onion (Vidalia, if available), thinly sliced	1
1	jar (19 oz/540 mL) PC Gourmet Mixed Mushrooms Pieces and Stems, drained	1

• Season veal lightly with salt and pepper. In large ovenproof heavy skillet, heat oil until hot. Add chops and cook over high heat until browned on both sides.
• Place skillet in 375°F (190°C) oven and continue cooking for about 10 to 15 minutes or until desired doneness. Transfer meat to serving platter and keep warm.
• Add butter to juices remaining in skillet and cook garlic over medium-high heat for about 30 seconds. Stir in onion and mushrooms and cook 3 or 4 minutes until onion is tender. Spoon over veal chops and serve.
• *Terri's Tip:* Mustard Sauce is a great accompaniment for these chops: Blend 1 cup (250 mL) PC The Ultimate Mayonnaise, 2 tsp (10 mL) dry mustard, 2/3 cup (150 mL) light cream, 1 1/2 tsp (7 mL) each of Worcestershire sauce and PC Gourmet Steak & Burger Sauce, a few drops of PC Louisiana Hot Sauce and lemon juice to taste. Stir well.
Makes 4 servings

FANCY WHITE VEAL LIVER WITH SWEDISH LINGONBERRIES

I find that the tartness of lingonberries, a type of European cranberry, balances perfectly with the sweetness of liver.

2 lb	fancy white veal or calf's liver	1 kg
¼ cup	cornstarch	50 mL
	Salt and freshly ground pepper	
2 tbsp	PC Extra-Virgin Olive Oil	25 mL
¼ cup	dry white wine	50 mL
1 cup	PC Swedish-Style Lingonberry Sauce	250 mL
¼ cup	PC Aged Red Wine Vinegar	50 mL
¼ cup	PC Over 50% Fruit French-Style Pure Passion Fruit Jam	50 mL

• Wipe liver with damp cloth and pat dry.
• Dust lightly with cornstarch seasoned with salt and pepper to taste.
• In skillet, heat oil until hot. Add liver and cook until desired doneness, turning halfway through. Transfer to platter and keep warm.
• To juices remaining in pan, add white wine. Cook over medium-high heat, stirring up browned bits on pan bottom, until reduced by half.
• Stir in lingonberries, wine vinegar, jam and salt and pepper to taste. Heat to boiling. Spoon sauce over liver.

Makes 4 to 6 servings

The cook's personal *tour de main* — the attitude and culinary finesse one brings to the kitchen — can make all the difference in a recipe. For instance, consider these directions for a famous Scandinavian marriage of flavors — liver and lingonberries. Here you see it with fancy white veal liver, but there's plenty of latitude in the way you interpret "liver."

Why not use foie gras for extra fancy occasions when you want to indulge your guests? At Christmas, Terri and I like to splurge on duck foie gras, served hot from the pan with cold lingonberry sauce. Many people would have you believe that only three-star chefs can cook raw foie gras, but you shouldn't have any problem with medium-size foie gras of about one pound (500 g), which you can order directly through La Ferme in Pefferlaw, Ont. (Speak to Nadine at 1-800-263-1263.) Many local chefs order this size specifically because they find it easier to cook.

For a fine, intimate dinner, the recommended choice is fancy white veal liver, the ne plus ultra of calf's liver. For weeknights, go bistro-style: Sauté beef liver or chicken livers and serve with a side of very thin fries.

Terri and I often made James Beard's teriyaki leg of lamb for friends when we were first married and living in a one-bedroom apartment in midtown Toronto with virtually no space for entertaining. Even New Year's Eve dinners were served "buffet" style on the kitchen counter.

In those "pre-Dome days," we cooked the lamb under the broiler a few hours ahead and served it tepid or at room temperature with crusty bread and a huge green salad tossed with my special balsamic vinegar and blue cheese dressing. We concluded with Terri's famous lemon tart (recipe, page 270) followed by rich, dark espresso. It was fabulous!

MEMORIES OF JAMES BEARD
TERIYAKI LEG OF LAMB

The late James Beard was a great authority on American food and a prolific cookbook writer. This recipe, our President's Choice adaptation of a James Beard classic, is one of my favorites. Now that there's PC Memories of Kobe The 2-Minute Miracle Tamari Garlic Marinade, I always substitute it for the soy sauce.

1 cup	PC Peanut Oil	250 mL
1 cup	PC Naturally Brewed Soy Sauce OR	250 mL
	PC Memories of Kobe The 2-Minute Miracle	
	Tamari Garlic Marinade	
1 tbsp	PC Chopped Garlic in Oil	15 mL
1 tbsp	PC Puréed Ginger	15 mL
2/3 cup	dry sherry OR Madeira wine	150 mL
1	boned and butterflied leg of lamb (about 5 lb/2.5 kg)	1

• Combine oil, soy sauce or Memories of Kobe sauce, garlic, ginger and sherry or Madeira.
• Place the lamb in a glass baking dish. Add soy mixture and turn lamb to coat all over. Cover and refrigerate 6 to 8 hours, preferably overnight; turn the lamb three or four times.
• Remove lamb from marinade and pat dry. Place over well-heated coals or under preheated oven broiler and cook about 15 to 18 minutes per side or until desired doneness, basting frequently with marinade.
• Let lamb rest about 10 minutes, then slice across grain into thin slices and serve on large platter.
• *Dave's Secret:* An easy way to marinate is to place meat inside a large, clean plastic bag. Pour marinade into bag. Tie off bag as close to the meat as possible to maximize contact with the marinade. Refrigerate, preferably overnight, turning bag several times.
Makes 6 servings

▲

TRY OUR JAMES BEARD LAMB MARINADE WITH BEEF — IT'S SUPERB. AND HERE'S A TIP: IT CAN BE REUSED TWO TO THREE TIMES, AS LONG AS YOU COOK IT THOROUGHLY AFTER EACH USE. BRING TO A BOIL, SIMMER 5 MINUTES, AND THEN REFRIGERATE, COVERED.

FOR YEARS, GUESTS TO MY HOME BEGGED ME FOR MY "SECRET SALAD DRESSING." HERE'S THE RECIPE: BEAT TOGETHER 1/2 CUP (125 mL) PC BALSAMIC VINEGAR AND 1 1/2 CUPS (375 mL) PC EXTRA VIRGIN OLIVE OIL. STIR IN 4 OZ (125 g) CRUMBLED ROQUEFORT CHEESE. SEASON WITH SALT AND FRESHLY GROUND PEPPER. SERVE OVER HEARTS OF ROMAINE OR BELGIAN ENDIVE, WITH SLICED RED BELL PEPPERS. MAKES 2 1/2 CUPS (625 mL).

▼

About once a year, I take an extended trip to the Orient to visit Singapore, Bali and Thailand. (One of Terri's and my favorite resorts in the world is a tropical paradise on the island of Phuket in Thailand; an hour by plane from Bangkok, it's called Amanpuri, a Sanskrit word meaning "The Region of Tranquility.")

Because of the long distances involved, I usually lay over in Hong Kong. This cosmopolitan port city is to the Orient what Chicago's O'Hare Airport is to the United States — the hub. The layover gives me a chance to recover and to sample the colony's delicious and varied regional Chinese foods.

A favorite of mine is a garlicky black bean sauce made with fermented soya beans. Fermented beans, of course, are the original soy seasoning in Chinese cuisine. Their history predates even soy sauce,

SPICY BLACK BEAN AND GARLIC SAUCE 350 mL

and their distinctive flavor shows up in many of China's spicy dishes.

Instead of importing black bean sauce from Asia, however, we decided to develop it with the E.D. Smith Company in Winona, Ont. The small town of about 1,200 people might just become the exotic sauce capital of the world!

BARBECUED RACKS OF LAMB WITH GINGER & BLACK BEAN SAUCE

The Sanssouci Restaurant in Toronto's Sutton Place Hotel Kempinski featured this sensational dish during its salute to my Insider's Report *earlier in the year. Executive Chef Niels Kjeldsen served it with our Mushroom Risotto (recipe, page 207).*

¼ cup	PC Memories of Hong Kong Spicy Black Bean & Garlic Sauce	50 mL
¼ cup	PC Memories of Jaipur Curry & Passion Fruit Sauce	50 mL
1 cup	PC Memories of Kyoto Ginger Sauce	250 mL
¼ cup	dry sherry	50 mL
1 tbsp	grated orange peel	15 mL
¼ cup	toasted sesame seeds★	50 mL
1	box (2.75 lb/1.25 kg) frozen PC Frenched Racks of Spring Lamb, thawed	1

• In mixing bowl, combine Memories of Hong Kong, Jaipur and Kyoto sauces. Add sherry, orange peel and sesame seeds.
• Place lamb in sauce mixture and turn to coat all over. Cover and let marinate in refrigerator for 6 to 8 hours, preferably overnight.
• Place racks on grill over hot coals and cook, turning and brushing with marinade, for 12 to 15 minutes or to desired doneness.
• Place remaining marinade in saucepan and heat until boiling. Serve as sauce with lamb.
• *Dave's Tip:* Here's how Texans cut down on barbecue clean-up, according to my friend "Big Al" Morris of Tyler, Texas. They line their barbecues with a layer of regular, unscented cat litter before arranging the charcoal briquets on top. This eliminates the nasty job of having to scrape up all the fat and grease that collects on the bottom of the barbecue. When it's time for clean-up, all they have to do is dump out the charcoal ash along with the cat litter.

Makes 4 servings

★To toast sesame seeds: Place seeds on small baking sheet and toast in 350°F (180°C) oven for 3 to 5 minutes, shaking once or twice so seeds brown evenly. Watch carefully to avoid burning.

▲

PC FRENCH-STYLE SHOULDER RACKS OF LAMB FROM NEW ZEALAND CAN ALSO BE PREPARED THIS WAY. USE MEDIUM-HOT COALS AND COOK THE RACKS A BIT LONGER.

▼

Beef Stir-Fry with Memories of Hong Kong

The flank steak is easier to cut if you put it in the freezer for 30 minutes. This firms the meat and allows you to slice it as thin as possible.

1 lb	flank steak	500 g
1 tbsp	PC Naturally Brewed Soya Sauce	15 mL
1 tbsp	dry sherry	15 mL
1 tbsp	cornstarch	15 mL
1/4 tsp	granulated sugar	1 mL
2 tbsp	PC Pure Olive Oil with Lemon Essence	25 mL
1 lb	asparagus, trimmed	500 g
1/2	Spanish onion, thinly sliced	1/2
3/4 cup	PC Memories of Hong Kong Spicy Black Bean & Garlic Sauce	175 mL

• Cut meat lengthwise along the grain into 3 pieces. Then cut each piece crosswise into 1/8-inch (3 mm) slices. Set aside.

• In mixing bowl, combine soya sauce, sherry, cornstarch, sugar and 1 tbsp (15 mL) oil. Add meat and toss well. Cover and refrigerate at least 30 minutes, preferably 1 to 2 hours.

• Cook asparagus in boiling salted water for about 2 to 3 minutes or just until tender; drain well.

• Heat remaining oil in stir-fry pan or skillet over high heat. Add meat and marinade and cook, stirring constantly, about 1 to 2 minutes. Add asparagus and onion and cook about 2 minutes, stirring often, until onion is tender. Stir in Memories of Hong Kong sauce and continue cooking, about 2 minutes, until sauce is reduced and slightly thickened.

Makes 4 servings

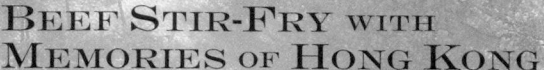

GREEN BEANS & BACON WITH MEMORIES OF HONG KONG

The sauce and seasonings in this recipe give green beans a totally new character.

1 lb	green beans, trimmed	500 g
2 tbsp	sesame seeds	25 mL
2 tbsp	PC Pure Olive Oil with Garlic Essence	25 mL
4	slices PC Special Trim Bacon, chopped	4
½	medium onion, thinly sliced	½
½ cup	PC Memories of Hong Kong Spicy Black Bean & Garlic Sauce	125 mL

• Cook green beans in boiling water to cover for about 3 to 4 minutes or just until tender. Drain, rinse under cold water, drain again and set aside.
• Toast sesame seeds in small skillet over high heat, shaking pan often, for about 2 minutes or until golden brown.
• In skillet or stir-fry pan, heat oil over medium-high heat. Add bacon and onion and cook, stirring, until onion is soft and bacon is crisp.
• Add green beans and Memories of Hong Kong and cook, stirring, until heated through. Just before serving, sprinkle with sesame seeds.

Makes 4 servings

MEMORIES OF HONG KONG ROAST CHICKEN

One of the easiest ways to dress up a chicken with minimal effort.

1	roasting chicken (3 to 4 lb/1.5 to 2 kg)	1
½ cup	PC Memories of Hong Kong Spicy Black Bean & Garlic Sauce	125 mL
2 tbsp	PC Pure Olive Oil with Lemon Essence	25 mL

• Using sharp knife or poultry shears, cut chicken down the back and lay flat on work surface.
• With fingers, gently separate skin from breast and legs. Spoon Memories of Hong Kong sauce under skin; distribute evenly.
• Place chicken on rack in shallow roasting pan and brush with oil. Bake in 350°F (180°C) oven for 20 to 25 minutes or until juices run clear when leg is pierced with fork.

Makes 3 to 4 servings

BARBECUED BACK RIBS
WITH MEMORIES OF HONG KONG

Spicy black bean sauce makes a wonderful change of pace from traditional tomato-based barbecue sauces.

4	racks pork back ribs (about 3 lb/1.5 kg)	4
1 cup	PC Memories of Hong Kong Spicy Black Bean & Garlic Sauce	250 mL

• Cut back ribs into serving-size portions. Place in shallow dish. Add Memories of Hong Kong sauce and turn to coat well.

• Remove ribs from sauce (reserve sauce) and steam or parboil in covered saucepan for 45 minutes to an hour or until meat is almost falling off the bone.

• Place ribs on grill over medium-hot coals and cook, turning and brushing with reserved sauce, until ribs are crispy and brown, about 20 minutes.

• Lightly brush with sauce before serving.

• *Dave's Tip:* Mix together equal parts PC Memories of Hong Kong and our famous PC Regular Gourmet Barbecue Sauce, and you have a fantastic new sauce that I've given the moniker "Kansas City Meets Hong Kong."

Makes 4 servings

LOBSTER WITH MEMORIES OF HONG KONG

Spicy black bean sauce is at home with seafoods such as lobster, shrimp and crab. Its pungency balances their sweetness perfectly.

2 tbsp	PC Pure Olive Oil with Lemon Essence	25 mL
1	can (11.3 oz/320 g) PC 100% Knuckle Meat Frozen Lobster Meat, thawed and drained	1
2 tbsp	sake or medium-dry white wine	25 mL
¾ cup	PC Memories of Hong Kong Spicy Black Bean & Garlic Sauce	175 mL
	Mango Salsa (see below)	

• In skillet, heat oil. Add lobster and heat just until warm. Remove from pan and set aside.

• Add sake or wine to pan and heat, stirring, until nearly evaporated. Return lobster to pan along with Memories of Hong Kong sauce. Heat, stirring, until warmed through. Serve with Mango Salsa.

Makes 3 or 4 servings

MANGO SALSA

Mangoes and passion fruit are a sensational flavor combination in this tropical-flavored salsa.

2	ripe, but firm, mangoes, peeled and cut in cubes	2
1	red pepper, finely chopped	1
3	green onions, thinly sliced on the diagonal	3
¼ cup	PC Memories of Singapore Passion Fruit Sauce	50 mL
1 tbsp	fresh lemon juice	15 mL
	Salt and freshly ground pepper	

• In small bowl, combine mangoes, red pepper, onions, Memories of Singapore sauce and lemon juice. Season with salt and pepper to taste.

Makes about 2 cups (500 mL)

The righteous are among us and they eat no fat. They forget that fat is part of the higher primate experience and that we're hard-wired at birth to seek it out. Fat for insulation, fat for concentrated calories. Fat is stored energy!

Our craving for fat is as ancient and as powerful as our craving for sugar. What possible chance does eating lean like Jack Spratt have against this primordial instinct?

Those who disdain fat forget that we are exceedingly permanent at the genetic level, heirs to the biochemistry that served our forebears so efficiently some 40,000 years ago.

In tribute to the venerableness of our fat-seeking genes, I offer up: Barbecued Pork Roast with Passion Fruit Glaze. It's made with my favorite economy cut for the barbecue: The President's Cut Boneless Pork Shoulder Roast. The meat has just the right amount of fat — yes, fat! — to make it flavorful and keep it from drying out on the grill.

BARBECUED PORK ROAST
WITH PASSION FRUIT GLAZE

Ziggy Wauro, the genius behind Ziggys food stores (he later sold the chain to Loblaw Companies Ltd.), and one of the happiest people I know, introduced me to The President's Cut Boneless Pork Shoulder Roast. Its marbling makes it juicy and flavorful.

³/₄ cup	PC Memories of Singapore Passion Fruit Sauce	175 mL
2 tbsp	PC Chopped Garlic in Oil	25 mL
	Juice of ¹/₂ lemon	
1	The President's Cut Boneless Pork Shoulder Roast	1
	(2 to 3 lb/1 to 1.5 kg)	
2 tbsp	PC Pure Olive Oil with Garlic Essence	25 mL

• In small bowl, mix together Memories of Singapore sauce, chopped garlic and lemon juice. Set aside.

• Brush pork roast all over with garlic-infused olive oil. Place in shallow baking dish and roast in 375°F (190°C) oven for 30 minutes.

• Transfer to grill over medium-hot coals. Cook for about 15 to 20 minutes, basting liberally with Memories of Singapore mixture and turning as necessary to cook evenly and prevent charring. Remove from grill when internal temperature registers 160°F (70°C) on meat thermometer. Meat may still be slightly pink.

• Let stand 10 to 15 minutes before carving. Drizzle with any leftover sauce mixture before serving.

• *Dave's Tip:* To cook entirely on barbecue, butterfly roast to reduce cooking time: Cut roast horizontally through centre nearly to opposite side so that it opens like a book. Place on grill rack and barbecue 30 minutes or to desired doneness.

Makes 4 to 6 servings

▲

PC MEMORIES OF
SINGAPORE IS THE
PERFECT GLAZE FOR
PORK ROASTS AND
HOLIDAY HAMS, AN
IDEAL COOKING SAUCE,
STIR–FRY SAUCE AND
DIPPING SAUCE FOR
CHICKEN STRIPS OR
VEGETABLES.

▼

Most of the famous Java and Sumatra coffees are distributed through Singapore. On one of my trips there to visit a broker who supplies an important component of our President's Blend Gourmet Ground Coffee, Terri and I were taken to a Malaysian restaurant where we enjoyed a fantastic barbecued chicken dish made with a sweet-and-sour sauce. The owner wouldn't disclose the recipe, but she did confirm my suspicion that the irresistible tang in the sauce came from passion fruit. It was a beginning! With that clue, the E.D. Smith Company managed to replicate perfectly my memories of that unforgettable Singapore sauce.

Don't restrict the use of this sauce to your barbecue. It makes an ideal cooking sauce with meat, fish and poultry, and an ideal dipping sauce for spring rolls and chicken fingers. Your children will love it, too.

MEMORIES OF SINGAPORE PINEAPPLE SAUCE

Spoon over hot-from-the-oven PC Breaded Chicken Balls. (Follow package directions for cooking them from frozen.) Your children will love you for it!

1	can (14 oz/398 mL) PC Pineapple Spears in Pineapple Juice, drained (reserve liquid)	1
¾ cup	PC Memories of Singapore Passion Fruit Sauce	175 mL
2 tbsp	fresh lemon juice	25 mL

• In saucepan, bring pineapple juice to boil. Boil gently until reduced by half. Add Memories of Singapore sauce and lemon juice; simmer 5 minutes.
• Cut pineapple pieces in half and add to sauce. Bring to boil, stirring often. Remove from heat and serve.
Makes 1 cup (250 mL)

MEMORIES OF
SINGAPORE
350 mL
PASSION FRUIT
SAUCE & GLAZE

MEMORIES OF
SONOMA
350 mL
DRIED TOMATO
SAUCE & DRESSING

MEMORIES OF
THAILAND
F·I·E·R·Y
THAI DIPPING SAUCE

MEMORIES OF
BANGKOK
350 mL
SPICY THAI SAUCE
& DRESSING

MEMORIES OF
ASIAGO
350 mL
TANGY ASIAGO
CH

MEMORIES OF
SZECHWAN
350 mL
PEANUT SAUCE
AND D

MEMORIES OF FUJI
富士
350 mL
SH

VAGUE MEMORIES OF
MONTEGO BAY
the timid
JERK
MARINADE AND SAUCE
A MILD VERSION OF OUR POPULAR
P.C. MEMORIES OF MONTEGO BAY
JERK MARINADE AND SAUCE

MEMORIES OF
GILROY
350 mL
CREAMY ROASTED GARLIC
SAUCE & DRESS

BARBECUED LEG OF LAMB
WITH PASSION FRUIT SAUCE

*People who know me are aware of my obsession for passion fruit. There's no better
place for its special tang than on barbecued leg of lamb.*

1	boned and butterflied leg of lamb (3 to 4 lb/1.5 to 2 kg)	1
1	bottle (350 mL) PC Memories of Singapore Passion Fruit Sauce	1
2 tsp	PC Chopped Garlic in Oil	10 mL

• Place lamb in shallow, non-reactive pan. Add Memories of Singapore sauce
and turn to coat well. Cover and refrigerate 6 to 8 hours, preferably overnight;
turn meat periodically.
• Remove lamb from marinade; reserve marinade.
• Grill lamb above medium-hot coals, turning frequently, for 30 to 40 minutes
or to desired doneness; baste frequently with marinade. Let meat rest 10 to 15
minutes before slicing.
• To make sauce, place reserved marinade in small saucepan and heat to boiling.
Stir in garlic and simmer for 5 minutes.
• Slice lamb and serve with sauce.
Makes 4 servings

MEMORIES OF
LYON
Lyon
Gastronomic
capital of the
world
50 mL
PEPPERCORN SAUCE

MEMORIES OF
MONTEGO BAY
BOB'S JERK
CHICKEN
FISH
LOBSTER
350 mL
J·E·R·K
MARINADE AND SAUCE

MEMORIES OF
SAN FRANCISCO
350 mL
GOLDEN GATE
LEMON GINGER
SAUCE

MEMORIES OF
DIJON
350 mL
MUSTARD RAISIN
SAUCE AND GLAZE

MEMORIES OF
ANCIENT DAMASCUS
350 mL
TANGY
POMEGRANATE
GLAZE & SAUCE

ROAST DUCK WITH PASSION FRUIT-LINGONBERRY SAUCE

The tartness of passion fruit and lingonberries cuts the richness of the duck.

1	whole young duck (3 to 4 lb/1.5 to 2 kg)	1
½ cup	PC Memories of Singapore Passion Fruit Sauce	125 mL
1 cup	PC Refrigerated 100% Orange Juice from Concentrate	250 mL
3 tbsp	PC Swedish-Style Lingonberry Sauce	45 mL

• Place duck on rack in shallow roasting pan and roast in 400°F (200°C) oven for 15 minutes. Reduce heat to 350°F (180°C) and continue cooking 45 minutes for medium, longer for well done.
• Meanwhile, prepare sauce: In skillet or saucepan, whisk together Memories of Singapore sauce and orange juice. Bring to boil and cook until sauce is thick enough to coat the back of a spoon.
• Remove from heat and stir in lingonberry sauce.
• Carve duck and serve with sauce.
• *Dave's Tip:* If you like duck skin extra crisp, the night before cooking, pour boiling water over duck, drain well and refrigerate, uncovered. (A trick Chinese chefs use to make Peking duck extra crispy. It really works!) Proceed with above recipe.

Makes 2 or 3 servings

SALMON STEAKS WITH PASSION FRUIT SAUCE

You can prepare these salmon packets on the grill, too. Cook parcels over hot coals 5 to 8 minutes without turning. Salmon steaks might require 1 to 2 minutes longer.

1 tbsp	PC Normandy-Style Cultured Butter	15 mL
6	salmon steaks or fillets, 1 inch (2.5 cm) thick (about 2 lb/1 kg total weight)	6
	Salt and freshly ground pepper	
½ cup	PC Memories of Singapore Passion Fruit Sauce	125 mL
¼ cup	fresh lemon juice	50 mL

• Tear off a 2-foot (60 cm) length of heavy-duty aluminum foil and place on baking sheet. Butter centre section of foil; arrange salmon on top; if using fillets, place skin side down.
• Season salmon lightly with salt and pepper.
• In small bowl, mix together Memories of Singapore sauce and lemon juice. Pour over salmon. Bring up edges of foil and seal well.
• Place in 350°F (180°C) oven for about 10 minutes or until salmon is cooked nearly through to centre; do not overcook.
• Serve salmon with cooking juices spooned on top.

Makes 6 servings

MEMORIES OF SINGAPORE MEAT LOAF

Often the test of a PC sauce is what it does for meat loaf. This garlicky version with its sophisticated passion-fruit tang is geared to adult tastes.

1 lb	lean ground pork	500 g
1 lb	lean ground beef	500 g
1 lb	ground lamb	500 g
4 tbsp	PC Chopped Shallots in Oil	50 mL
4 tbsp	PC Chopped Garlic in Oil	50 mL
3	large eggs, lightly beaten	3
1/4 cup	whipping cream	50 mL
1 cup	PC Italian-Style Breadcrumbs	250 mL
1/4 cup	chopped fresh parsley	50 mL
3/4 cup	PC Memories of Singapore Passion Fruit Sauce	175 mL
	Salt and freshly ground pepper	
	PC Gourmet Barbecue Sauce	

• In large bowl, mix together ground meats. Add shallots, garlic, eggs, cream, breadcrumbs, parsley, 1/2 cup (125 mL) Memories of Singapore sauce and salt and pepper to taste; blend well.
• Pack meat mixture into 12 x 8-inch (3 L) baking dish or two 9 x 5-inch (2 L) loaf pans. Spread remaining Memories of Singapore sauce on top.
• Place in 350°F (180°C) oven for 60 to 70 minutes or until desired doneness. During final 15 minutes of cooking time, brush with barbecue sauce.
• Pour off excess fat and let meat stand 10 to 15 minutes before slicing.

Makes 8 to 10 servings

MEMORIES OF SINGAPORE DIPPING SAUCE

Serve with PC White Breast Meat Breaded Chicken Strips or Nuggets and PC Swedish Meatballs. Sauce thickens as it cools. To thin out, reheat before serving.

3/4 cup	PC Memories of Singapore Passion Fruit Sauce	175 mL
2 tbsp	PC Over 50% Juice French-Style Pure Seville Orange Marmalade	25 mL
2 tbsp	fresh lemon juice	25 mL

• In saucepan, mix together Memories of Singapore sauce, orange marmalade and lemon juice.
• Cook over medium heat, making sure not to let sauce boil (or it will caramelize) for 2 to 3 minutes, stirring constantly.

Makes 1 cup (250 mL)

$\mathscr{P}$lenty of people have bright ideas, but few pursue them. You have to admire the pluck of dedicated tinkerers like Bertha Dlugi, inventor of diapers for birds; or Joseph Fallek, who dreamed up a grapefruit shield to prevent juice from spattering; or my great friend, the late Brian Davidson, mastermind behind the Hot Diggity Dogger, a device that cooks wieners and toasts hot dog buns at the same time.

Brian wore many hats for Loblaw Companies Ltd., of which he was Executive Vice President, but by nature he was the consummate inventor. For almost 20 years, the two of us were constant partners in crime, stalking the ultimate promotion and searching the world for unusual new products.

Despite his penchant for the unconventional, Brian appreciated basic foods, as many of the 4,000 people he knew can testify. His hands-down favorite was Pork Schnitzel "Franz Josef," made with mustard and Parmesan cheese in the coating.

PORK SCHNITZEL "FRANZ JOZEF"

We featured Russian-Style Sweet Mustard in our first Insider's Report *10 years ago. It makes a great glaze for meat or poultry, or brush it over foods on the grill. It's especially good in this schnitzel dish.*

4	thin pork cutlets	4
	Salt	
1 cup	all-purpose flour	250 mL
2	eggs, lightly beaten	2
1 cup	dry breadcrumbs	250 mL
1 cup	PC Gourmet Blend 100% Grated Parmesan Cheese	250 mL
	Grated rind of 1 lemon	
¼ cup	(approx.) PC Russian-Style Sweet Mustard	50 mL
3 tbsp	PC Normandy-Style Cultured Butter	45 mL
3 tbsp	PC Vegetable Oil	45 mL
	Lemon wedges	

• Pat pork dry with paper towels; season lightly with salt.
• Place flour in one dish, eggs in another and mixture of breadcrumbs, cheese and lemon rind in a third.
• Dip pork into flour, shake off excess. Spread mustard over one side only.
• Dip into eggs; allow excess to drip off. Press into breadcrumb mixture. Place on waxed paper and refrigerate for an hour or longer if time permits.
• In large skillet, heat butter and oil. Add pork and cook over medium-high heat for about 5 minutes per side or until crisp and golden brown. Serve with lemon wedges.

Makes 4 servings

▲

AS A DINNER HOST IN THE 1800S, FRANZ JOSEF I, AUSTRIAN EMPEROR AND KING OF HUNGARY, WAS A GUEST'S WORST NIGHTMARE. NO ONE WAS ALLOWED TO EAT ONCE HE'D FINISHED. THE PROBLEM WAS, HE ATE VERY FAST! GUESTS AT THE FAR END OF THE TABLE USUALLY FEASTED WITH THEIR EYES ONLY SINCE THE FOOD TYPICALLY ARRIVED JUST AS THE EMPEROR WAS LAYING DOWN HIS KNIFE AND FORK!

▼

PRESIDENT'S CHOICE
PREPARED
RUSSIAN-STYLE
SWEET MUSTARD
250 mL

Prizewinning Jamaican-Style Jerk Chicken Wings

MARINATE 1 BOX (1.1 kg) PC FROZEN SEASONED CHICKEN WINGLETS & DRUMETTES OR ½ BAG (1.8 kg) PC GIGANTICO FROZEN CHICKEN WINGLETS & WING DRUMETTES, THAWED, IN ½ CUP (125 mL) PC MEMORIES OF MONTEGO BAY JERK MARINADE FOR AT LEAST 4 TO 6 HOURS. PLACE IN GRILL BASKET AND GRILL OVER MEDIUM-LOW HEAT FOR 20 MINUTES, TURNING OFTEN, OR ROAST IN 400°F (200°C) OVEN FOR 20 MINUTES. MAKES 4 SERVINGS.

▼

*I*n Jamaica, you don't eat barbecue. You eat "jerk."

Some say the name comes from the way the spicy meat is turned over and over — or jerked — on the barbecue. Others claim that it's the way a serving portion of meat is torn or jerked off the bone.

Whatever the origin, for me it's the appealing sweet, salty, hot Jamaican spicing that characterizes jerk food. Jerk seasoning dates back to the 17th century when salt and hot peppers preserved meat. One thing is certain: Jerk is hot with chili peppers and pungent seasonings that reveal its African, East Indian and Islands origin.

We developed PC Memories of Montego Bay Jerk Marinade and Sauce to help people make the prizewinning Jamaican Jerk chicken wings from our 1991 *Insider's Report* barbecue contest. Contest winners Sharon and Joseph Mimran and their friends Michelle Lloyd-Berman and David Berman, all of Toronto, made their jerk marinade with a spice mixture that's only available in Jamaica. So we imported it and created our own distinctively spiced jerk sauce for chicken pork, beef and seafood.

PORK KEBABS WITH ISLAND JERK SAUCE

Pork was the original jerked food in Jamaica. You can lower the heat by substituting our milder PC "Vague Memories of Montego Bay" Timid Jerk Marinade and Sauce. For dipping, serve with refrigerated PC The Decadent Blue Cheese Dressing.

2 lb	lean boneless pork (leg or shoulder), cut in 1-inch (2.5 cm) cubes	1 kg
½ cup	PC Memories of Montego Bay Jerk Marinade and Sauce	125 mL
48	cherry tomatoes	48

• Place pork in mixing bowl. Add Memories of Montego Bay sauce and toss to coat. Let marinate 1 hour at room temperature.
• If using bamboo skewers, let soak in water for about 1 hour before using. Thread meat onto skewers, alternating with tomatoes (4 tomatoes per skewer).
• Barbecue kebabs on greased grill 4 to 6 inches (10 to 15 cm) above hot coals or on medium-high setting, turning and brushing frequently with Memories of Montego Bay sauce, for 15 to 20 minutes or until pork is no longer pink in centre. Do not overcook or meat will be dry.

Makes 4 to 6 servings

I love barbecued pork ribs. My search in '84 for the perfect barbecue sauce took me to Missouri, Texas, North Carolina, even to Mississippi. Finally, I found it — a sauce that made my taste buds stand up and salute.

I was eating pork back ribs at a famous rib house and I couldn't stop. The sauce kept drawing me back. They were the best pork ribs I'd ever tasted. It took a couple of months to get the recipe that helped us create President's Choice Gourmet Barbecue Sauce, but we had it in time for our first Barbecue Edition of the *Insider's Report* in 1984. We're still producing our original recipe almost a decade later. (We remained faithful to its perfectly balanced sweet and tangy flavor when developing PC 'Too Good To Be True!' Lite Gourmet Barbecue Sauce with half the calories.)

THE MOST ENJOYABLE WAY TO EAT RIBS IS WITH YOUR FINGERS. WHAT'S MORE, IT'S HISTORICALLY CORRECT TO EAT OUT OF HAND, AS DID QUEEN ELIZABETH I DURING HER REIGN FROM 1558 TO 1603.

"THE SEARCH FOR THE HOLY GRAIL" BABY BACK RIBS

If I were forced to choose a single President's Choice product to cook with all summer, it would be President's Choice Gourmet Barbecue Sauce because of its unique sweet and sour balance. Do not even consider attempting this recipe without it.

• Allow ½ cup (125 mL) PC Gourmet Barbecue Sauce for each rack of pork baby back ribs. (Use fresh or PC Restaurant-Cut frozen ribs).
• Cut ribs into serving-size pieces and steam, or parboil in boiling water to cover, for 45 minutes to an hour or until meat almost falls off the bone.
• Do not let steamed or parboiled ribs cool before grilling (the meat tends to toughen). To grill: While ribs are still hot, brush both sides liberally with PC Gourmet Barbecue Sauce and transfer to well-greased grill about 5 inches (13 cm) above medium-hot coals.
• Grill 3 to 5 minutes per side until sauce starts to char and caramelize. Remove from grill, brush lightly with more sauce and serve. Do not return to barbecue.
• *Dave's Secrets:* There are two essential secrets to tender, succulent ribs.
1. You must steam them until the meat starts to fall off the bones — a secret I learned from my dentist, Bob Locke.
2. After taking them off the grill, you must coat them again lightly with PC Gourmet Barbecue Sauce.
Steaming first not only results in perfect ribs, it also saves time. Ribs cooked entirely on the grill would take about 2½ hours, and you'd be guaranteed of tough rib meat! If you're pressed for time, you can microwave the ribs, but don't expect them to taste quite the same. To microwave, place in single layer in microwaveable casserole, overlapping thin pieces slightly. Add a few spoonfuls of water and cover with vented plastic wrap. Microwave at High for 5 minutes. Then continue to microwave, covered, at Medium for about 10 minutes per side, or until meat starts to fall off the bones.

AN
EXCEPTIONAL PRODUCT
CHOSEN AS OUR

President's Choice

SQUEEZABLE
GOURMET
BARBECUE
SAUCE

REFRIGERATE AFTER OPENING
INGREDIENTS: CONCENTRATED TO...
WHITE VINEGAR 14...
SPICE EXTRACTIVES 14...
PROTEIN, DERIVES FROM...

Blenheim, Ont,

Dear Joanne
Thank you very much for your very generous birthday gift. I had wanted some hockey equipment all winter, but never seemed to be able to get any so I bought the shin and shoulder pads with the money you sent me. I had my best friends in for supper and we played games then we went to the movies. It was Copper Canyon. Mother served a very nice birthday supper we had ~~roast~~ scalloped potatoes and cold roast pork and salad, birthday cake butter-scotch sundae and coke raspberry whipped cream tarts and candy. It really was the nicest birthday I have ever had. The boys gave me a hockey stick a game called pit some stamps a tie a flashlight Grandmother sent me a dollar Marjorie gave me a box of Hunts candy Mrs. Langford gave me a shirt and a tie and me a pen. Mother gave a pen also. I hope are not too lonesome

Your Brother David

x x x x x x x x x x x x

I wrote this letter to my
sister Joanne on the occasion
of my 11th birthday.

I grew up in Blenheim, Ontario, when it was a farming community of 2,500 and known affectionately by locals as the "Heart of the Golden Acres." My father worked as a station agent for the Chesapeake and Ohio railway line that ran through Canada from Buffalo to Detroit. Because station agents tend to be moved around a lot, I attended 13 different public schools in southwestern Ontario while he ran various stations. This constant uprooting and upheaval in our lives equipped me to cope with change and for that I'm grateful. (Is there anything worse for a small child than the first day at a new school?)

However, I consider that my particular good fortune was to be born into a generation when most grandparents still owned farms! My mother came from a family of fruit farmers, the McGuigans, and they owned several prosperous farms in Cedar Springs, Ontario, a small farming community on Lake Erie. The McGuigans were Irish, and they'd settled in Cedar Springs in the 1840s. Newspaper accounts from that period credit one of my relatives, Charles McGuigan, with the introduction of peaches to Cedar Springs; he planted the area's first peach tree — nursery stock that he brought back from Kentucky, where he had been visiting a brother.

I spent all my holidays at Grandmother McGuigan's Cedar Springs farm. My grandfather, W.R. McGuigan, raised Clydesdale horses, which he showed at Toronto's Royal Winter Fair. For two to three weeks every summer, I'd help to drive teams of Clydesdales — but my biggest pleasure was to dine at the backyard picnic table with the hired hands.

I suppose my lifelong devotion to food was born at my

grandmother's farmhouse table because her cooking was exemplary. It had to be. In those days, good food was the key to attracting and keeping the best hired hands. And the McGuigans had some of the best hired hands in Canada! Even now, although decades have passed, the mere smell or taste of a particular food can flood my mind with memories of my grandmother's farm kitchen.

My passions for hard work, the best-quality ingredients and cooking were rooted in those early experiences on the farm and at the boarding house that my mother subsequently ran in Chatham, Ontario, for school teachers who came from out of town.

I remember the first recipe I ever made as a child. I cooked a commercial lemon pie filling, folded in three stiffly beaten egg whites and stirred in torn-up chunks of angel food cake. (That may not be your idea of a great dessert, but as an 8-year-old, I loved it!) By high school,

I was frequently cooking for myself since, by this time, my mother had turned her considerable talent and energy to real estate.

The inevitable outcome of all this respect for food, of course, is that I thought everybody ate as well as we did, and it came as an enormous shock to me to discover that they didn't.

Opposite page: A gathering of the Nichol clan. That's my father on the far right.
Above: Yes, that's me — not much bigger than a fire hydrant.
Right: Here I am with my older brother John, now a Baptist minister in Florida.

The holidays always trigger a flood of reminiscences from my childhood, since I spent so many holidays at my Grandmother McGuigan's farm in Cedar Springs, Ontario. One of my Thanksgiving favorites was savory sage-and-onion dressing with holiday turkey. For years, I raved about it to my product developers until, one day, they announced, "Dave, we've done it. We've recreated your grandmother's dressing."

It took only a forkful to call up those days from my youth. The difference is that the perfectly seasoned stuffing that I tasted in the test kitchen was prepared in almost no time at all, using PC Rustico Bread and a delectable sage-and-onion sauce that the product developers had created with only the vaguest of hints from me.

Roast Capon with Sage-and-Onion Bread Stuffing

PC Memories of Cedar Springs sauce taps very special memories for me. Its flavor sums up what holiday feasting is all about — family and friends coming together.

2	PC Rustico Italian-Style White Breads (each 280 g), cut in ½-inch (1 cm) cubes	2
4 tbsp	PC Unsalted Normandy-Style Cultured Butter	60 mL
1	medium onion, finely chopped	1
2	bottles (each 350 mL) PC Memories of Cedar Springs Sage-and-Onion Sauce	2
	Salt and freshly ground pepper	
1	capon (about 8 lb/4 kg)	1
	PC Pure Olive Oil with Garlic Essence	

• Place bread cubes on baking sheet and heat in 400°F (200°C) oven for about 15 minutes, turning occasionally, until toasted; watch carefully so bread doesn't burn.
• In large saucepan over medium heat, melt butter. Add onion and cook, stirring, until tender. Stir in Memories of Cedar Springs sauce and bread cubes. Cook, stirring, until heated through.
• Turn off heat. Cover and let sit on burner for 5 to 10 minutes. Season with salt and pepper to taste.
• Wipe capon with damp cloth and pat dry. Sprinkle cavity with salt and pepper to taste.
• Stuff the cavity loosely with bread mixture. Skewer or sew the opening closed. Stuff the neck area and secure neck skin flap to capon with skewer. (Heat any extra stuffing in covered casserole along with capon during final 30 minutes of cooking time.)
• Rub capon all over with garlic-infused olive oil. Place on rack in shallow roasting pan and roast in 375°F (190°C) oven, basting frequently, until done. Allow about 2 hours for an 8-lb (4 kg) bird.
• Transfer capon to heated platter and let rest 15 minutes before carving. Meanwhile, strain pan juices into saucepan. Skim off excess fat and heat until hot. Season with salt and pepper to taste. Serve along with bird and stuffing.

Makes 4 to 6 servings

▲

TURN PAGE FOR OUR RECIPES FOR SAGE-AND-ONION RICE STUFFING AND TWO VERSATILE SAUCES MADE WITH PC MEMORIES OF CEDAR SPRINGS SAUCE.

▼

SAVORY SAGE-AND-ONION SAUCE

This flavorful sauce takes only a few minutes to prepare. Serve it with chicken, turkey, veal or pork.

1 tbsp	PC Unsalted Normandy-Style Cultured Butter	15 mL
1 tbsp	chopped shallot	15 mL
1/4 cup	dry white wine	50 mL
1/2 tsp	PC Fresh Concentrated Chicken Stock	2 mL
1/2 cup	boiling water	125 mL
1	bottle (350 mL) PC Memories of Cedar Springs Grandmother McGuigan's Sage-and-Onion Sauce Salt and freshly ground pepper	1

• In saucepan over medium heat, melt butter. Add shallot and cook for 30 seconds.
• Add wine, bring to boil and cook until reduced by half.
• Combine concentrated chicken stock with boiling water and add to saucepan along with Cedar Springs sauce. Bring to boil, reduce heat and cook until mixture is thick enough to coat the back of a spoon. Season with salt and pepper to taste.
Makes 4 servings

SAGE-AND-ONION SAUCE WITH CREAM AND LINGONBERRIES

This may well be the easiest and most sophisticated tasting sauce you will ever come across. Serve with poultry and other white meats.

1	bottle (350 mL) PC Memories of Cedar Springs Grandmother McGuigan's Sage-and-Onion Sauce	1
3/4 cup	whipping cream	175 mL
3 tbsp	PC Swedish-Style Lingonberry Sauce Salt and freshly ground pepper	45 mL

• In medium-sized saucepan, mix together Memories of Cedar Springs sauce, whipping cream and lingonberry sauce.
• Heat until hot. Season with salt and pepper to taste.
Makes 4 servings

SAGE-AND-ONION RICE STUFFING

Not just for the cavity of a chicken or turkey — use it to stuff pork chops or a pork loin roast, or prepare it as an accompaniment to grilled meats.

1 tbsp	PC Unsalted Normandy-Style Cultured Butter	15 mL
1	medium onion, chopped	1
1	pkg (227 g/8 oz) PC Sliced Mushrooms	1
1 tsp	PC Chopped Garlic in Oil	5 mL
1 cup	PC Royal Blend Precooked Premium Rice Mix	250 mL
1 tsp	PC Fresh Concentrated Chicken Stock	5 mL
1 cup	boiling water	250 mL
1	bottle (350 mL) PC Memories of Cedar Springs Grandmother McGuigan's Sage-and-Onion Sauce	1
	Salt and freshly ground pepper	

- In Dutch oven, melt butter. Add onion, mushrooms and garlic and cook, stirring, for 30 seconds.
- Add rice, concentrated chicken stock dissolved in boiling water and 1/2 cup (125 mL) Memories of Cedar Springs sauce.
- Cover pan and place in 400°F (200°C) oven for 40 to 50 minutes or until rice is cooked.
- Stir in remaining Memories of Cedar Springs sauce. Season with salt and pepper to taste.

Makes 4 servings

▲

PC MEMORIES OF CEDAR SPRINGS SAUCE MAKES AN EXCELLENT BREAD STUFFING FOR PLUMP, SUCCULENT CAPONS, A FAVORITE IN MY HOME, AS WELL AS TURKEYS AND CORNISH GAME HENS.

▼

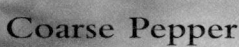

▲
Coarse Pepper
◆

MANY PEPPERMILLS HAVE
A TOP SCREW THAT
LETS YOU ADJUST THE
COARSENESS OF THE
GRIND. IF YOUR
PEPPERMILL DOESN'T
PRODUCE A COARSE
GRIND, WRAP A HANDFUL
OF PEPPERCORNS IN
A TEA TOWEL AND
WHACK A FEW TIMES
WITH A HEAVY SKILLET.
THE FLAVOR OF
GROUND PEPPER FADES
RAPIDLY, SO GRIND OR
CRACK PEPPERCORNS
JUST BEFORE USING.

▼

𝒜sk a great chef why his chicken is so flavorful, and he'll probably tell you it's because he cooks it with the skin on. That's because so much of the flavor in poultry (and meats, too) is in the fat. Not only does the fatty skin contain unique flavor compounds, but it also acts as a protective barrier to keep in moisture so that the meat stays succulent.

In this often requested *Insider's Report* recipe (a favorite for so long that we've forgotten its source), lemon juice, rosemary and a torrent of coarsely cracked pepper turn ordinary chicken breasts into a barbecue classic.

BARBECUED LEMON CHICKEN WITH CRACKED PEPPERCORNS

Many gourmets call Indian Tellicherry peppercorns, which come from India's Malabar coast, "the Cabernet of peppercorns" because of their rich flavor. They're strongly aromatic, with a juniper-like freshness and distinct spicy fruitiness.

4	boneless skin-on chicken breasts	4
1/4 cup	fresh lemon juice	50 mL
2 tbsp	PC Extra-Virgin Olive Oil	25 mL
1 tbsp	chopped fresh rosemary OR 1 tsp (5 mL) dried	15 mL
2 tsp	PC Chopped Garlic in Oil	10 mL
1/4 tsp	salt	1 mL
1 1/2 tsp	PC Black Tellicherry Peppercorns	7 mL

• Place chicken breasts in shallow glass dish.
• Mix together lemon juice, olive oil, rosemary, garlic and salt. Coarsely crush or grind peppercorns and add to lemon mixture.
• Pour lemon mixture over chicken breasts; turn chicken to coat well. Cover and refrigerate 6 to 8 hours or overnight. Let warm to room temperature before cooking.
• Place chicken breasts on lightly oiled grill over very hot coals and grill until they are cooked through but still moist, about 3 minutes per side.
Makes 4 servings

$\mathcal{N}$ormandy, the part of France that borders the English Channel, is synonymous with orchard-fresh apples, sweet cream from black-and-white cows and flavorful cultured butter — all of which come together in a wonderful regional cuisine. Apple orchards are so prevalent that, come the fall, local entrepreneurs travel from farm to farm with their own apple presses, helping farmers process the harvest.

As Canadians, we don't make much ado about our own "regional" foods, even though, for example, Ontario has an honorable apple-growing history that dates back to the 1700s. Ontario growers harvest about 10 million bushels a year, almost half of which go into cider or juice.

We use a variety of fresh-pressed, ripened apples from the Georgian Bay region to make President's Choice Sweet Apple Cider. Don't let anyone tell you that it's just for drinking. Use it to glaze roasts, or for adding flavor to soups, stews and sauces.

CHICKEN BREASTS WITH APPLE CIDER CREAM SAUCE

In the mid-1980s, we prepared a number of easy, great-tasting dishes on video for the meat departments of Loblaw stores. This was Terri's favorite.

2 cups	PC Fresh-Pressed Sweet Apple Cider	500 mL
2 tbsp	PC Dijon Mustard	25 mL
2 cups	whipping cream	500 mL
Pinch	cayenne pepper	Pinch
	Salt and freshly ground pepper	
2 tbsp	PC Extra-Virgin Olive Oil	25 mL
6	PC Frozen Boneless Skinless Seasoned Chicken Breasts, thawed	6
2 tbsp	PC Unsalted Normandy-Style Cultured Butter	25 mL
2	large tart apples, cored and cut in thin rings	2

• In saucepan over medium-high heat, bring cider to boil and continue boiling until reduced to about $\frac{1}{2}$ cup (125 mL).
• Whisk in Dijon mustard and whipping cream. Season with cayenne pepper and salt and pepper to taste. Continue boiling until reduced to about $\frac{1}{2}$ cup (125 mL). Keep warm.
• Meanwhile, in large skillet, heat oil until hot. Add chicken breasts and cook about 3 to 4 minutes per side or until done. Transfer to serving platter.
• Add butter to juices left in pan and heat until hot; cook apple slices for a few minutes, turning halfway through, until tender.
• To serve, spoon cider sauce over chicken breasts and top with apple slices.
Makes 6 servings

▲

ORDINARY NORTH AMERICAN BUTTER TYPICALLY CONTAINS 80% BUTTERFAT. EUROPE'S FAMOUS NORMANDY BUTTER, WHICH HAS BUTTERFAT LEVELS OF AT LEAST 82% (AND, THEREFORE, LESS MOISTURE), PROVIDED THE MODEL FOR PC NORMANDY-STYLE CULTURED BUTTER. IT'S EVEN MADE WITH SPECIAL CULTURES FOR EXTRA FLAVOR!

▼

*D*arly, Godolphin and Byerly. Every thoroughbred racehorse in the world has a blood line that can be traced back to these three Arabian stallions that were imported into England in the 1700s.

In the President's Choice family of products, Memories of Szechwan Peanut Sauce & Dressing is the cornerstone of our exotic line of sauces. Turn page for more great dishes made with PC Memories of Szechwan sauce.

SENSATIONAL CHICKEN WITH PEANUT SAUCE

This is probably the most effective TV recipe I ever created. In some stores our peanut sauce outsells the entire ketchup category!

¼ cup	PC Uncommonly Light Pure Olive Oil	50 mL
1	roasting chicken (about 3 to 4 lb/1.5 to 2 kg), cut in pieces	1
1	bottle (350 mL) PC 'Too Good To Be True!' Memories of Szechwan Peanut Sauce & Dressing	1
¼ cup	whipping cream	50 mL
2 tbsp	fresh lemon juice	25 mL
	Salt and freshly ground pepper	

• In heatproof skillet or Dutch oven, heat oil; add chicken pieces and cook, turning often, until browned all over. Drain off excess fat.
• Pour Memories of Szechwan sauce over chicken. Cover pan tightly and bake in 375°F (190°C) oven for 1 hour. Transfer chicken to serving platter and keep warm.
• Skim fat from accumulated pan juices. Blend in cream and lemon juice. Bring to boil and cook, uncovered, until thickened. Season with salt and pepper to taste.
• Spoon sauce over chicken and serve.

Makes 3 or 4 servings

PORK MEDALLIONS
WITH MEMORIES OF SZECHWAN

PC Memories of Szechwan Peanut Sauce & Dressing won the Gorman Best New Product Award (Condiments) in 1990 in a tasting of new condiments from all over North America.

¼ cup	PC Uncommonly Light Pure Olive Oil	50 mL
12	PC Frozen Boneless Pork Medallions, thawed (about 3 lb/1.5 kg)	12
1	bottle (350 mL) PC Memories of Szechwan Peanut Sauce	1
¼ cup	whipping cream	50 mL
2 tbsp	lemon juice	25 mL
½ cup	PC La Elección del Presidente Salsa Picante, hot or mild	125 mL

♦ In Dutch oven or ovenproof skillet, heat oil over medium-high heat. Add pork medallions and cook, turning, until browned all over. Drain off excess fat.
♦ Add Memories of Szechwan sauce, cover tightly and place in 375°F (190°C) oven for 45 minutes until meat is cooked through to centre. Remove meat from pan and set aside.
♦ Skim excess fat from pan juices. Blend in cream and lemon juice. Bring to boil over medium heat and cook, uncovered, until thickened.
♦ Just before serving, stir in salsa. Heat through but do not boil.
♦ Arrange pork on platter and spoon sauce on top.
Makes 4 to 6 servings

Szechwan Chicken with Bean Thread Noodles

Bean thread noodles are made from mung bean flour. Rice vermicelli, which is found in most supermarkets, is an excellent alternative.

1 tbsp	PC Naturally Brewed Soya Sauce	15 mL
2 tsp	dry sherry	10 mL
2	PC Frozen Boneless Skinless Seasoned Chicken Breasts, partially defrosted and cut in julienne strips	2
8 oz	bean thread noodles or rice vermicelli	250 g
2 tbsp	PC 'Too Good To Be True!' 80% Monounsaturates Sunflower Oil	25 mL
1 tsp	PC Chopped Garlic in Oil	5 mL
2 tsp	PC Puréed Ginger or grated fresh gingerroot	10 mL
½	red onion, thinly sliced	½
½	seedless cucumber, peeled and cut in julienne strips	½
1	carrot, shredded	1
½ cup	PC Memories of Szechwan Peanut Sauce	125 mL
½ cup	PC Unsalted Dry Roasted Peanuts, coarsely chopped	125 mL

• Combine soya sauce and sherry. Add chicken and let marinate 30 minutes.
• Meanwhile, cook noodles in boiling water for 30 seconds until they start to soften. Drain well. Cut in half and set aside.
• In wok or large skillet over high heat, heat oil. Add garlic and ginger and cook, stirring, until fragrant, about 30 seconds.
• Add chicken and stir-fry 1 minute. Add onion and stir-fry 1 minute longer.
• Add cucumber, carrot and Memories of Szechwan sauce. Cook, stirring, until sauce is slightly thickened. Remove from heat.
• Add noodles and peanuts and toss.
Makes 6 servings

Memories of Szechwan Fiery Ribs

PC Szechwan and Bangkok sauces make pork ribs taste especially succulent.

3 lb	pork back ribs	1.5 kg
¾ cup	PC Memories of Szechwan Peanut Sauce	175 mL
¾ cup	PC Memories of Bangkok Spicy Thai Sauce	175 mL

• Trim off excess fat from ribs. Cut ribs into serving-size pieces and steam or parboil for 45 minutes to an hour or until meat is almost falling off the bone.
• Combine Memories of Szechwan and Memories of Bangkok sauces. Brush ribs generously with sauce mixture.
• On grill over medium-hot coals, cook ribs until outside becomes crispy, turning and basting often with sauce, about 8 to 10 minutes.
• Serve with remaining sauce, if desired.
Makes 4 to 6 servings

HOLIDAY TURKEY I:
TERRI'S ROAST TURKEY WITH RICE, MUSHROOM & PINE NUT STUFFING

Butter-basting is an old chef's trick (not a poultry processor's invention!) to help keep turkey meat moist and give it a golden crispy skin. We use PC Normandy-Style Cultured Butter exclusively in our PC Butter-Basted Fresh and Frozen Young Turkeys.

1 cup	raisins	250 mL
1 cup	rum or Cognac	250 mL
2 tbsp	PC Extra-Virgin Olive Oil	25 mL
1 tsp	PC Chopped Garlic in Oil	5 mL
1	medium onion, finely chopped	1
2 cups	shiitake mushrooms, sliced	500 mL
1½ cups	PC Royal Blend Precooked Premium Rice Mix	375 mL
2 cups	chicken stock, homemade or made with PC Concentrated Chicken Stock	500 mL
1 cup	pine nuts, toasted★	250 mL
1	PC Frozen Butter-Basted Turkey (about 12 to 15 lb/5 to 7 kg), thawed	1
	PC Unsalted Normandy-Style Cultured Butter	
	Salt and freshly ground pepper	

▲

INCIDENTALLY, THIS STUFFING IS THE FINAL EVOLUTIONARY STAGE OF A MEATLESS DISH THAT MY WIFE CREATED YEARS AGO FOR HER DAUGHTER, LEIGH, 27, WHO'S CURRENTLY WORKING AS A PRODUCT DEVELOPER IN AUSTRALIA. SINCE LEIGH LOVES RICE AND PASTA, TERRI IS ALWAYS LOOKING FOR WAYS TO DOCTOR THEM UP.

▼

• Prepare stuffing: Soak raisins in rum or Cognac and set aside.
• In large skillet, heat olive oil. Add garlic, onion and mushrooms and cook, stirring, until onion is tender. Stir in raisins with soaking liquid. Remove from heat.
• Using long kitchen matches and being careful not to lean over pan, light the rum or Cognac and let flame until alcohol is evaporated. (Flames will extinguish on their own.)
• Add rice and chicken stock. Bring to boil, reduce heat and simmer, covered, for 15 minutes or until rice is cooked. Stir in pine nuts.
• Rinse turkey and pat dry. Stuff the cavity loosely with rice mixture. Skewer or sew the opening closed. Stuff the neck area and secure neck skin flap to turkey with skewer. (Place any remaining stuffing in buttered casserole and heat in oven for final 30 to 40 minutes of turkey roasting time.)
• Rub turkey all over with butter. Place on rack in shallow roasting pan and roast in 350°F (180°C) oven, basting frequently, until done. Allow 3 to 4 hours for a 12- to 15-lb (5 to 7 kg) bird.
• Transfer turkey to heated platter and let rest 15 to 20 minutes before carving. Meanwhile, strain pan juices into saucepan. Skim off as much excess fat as possible. Heat until hot, season with salt and pepper to taste and serve along with turkey and stuffing.

Makes 8 to 10 servings

★To toast pine nuts, place on baking sheet and heat in 350°F (180°C) oven for 3 to 5 minutes, just until golden. Watch carefully to avoid burning.

This wonderful stuffing, made with PC Royal Blend Precooked Premium Rice Mix, shiitake mushrooms, rum-soaked raisins and toasted pine nuts, is so elegant and has such sensational flavor that it has become one of my two favorite stuffings for our holiday turkey or capon. (The other one is my Grandmother McGuigan's Sage-&-Onion Bread Stuffing, page 103.)

LINGONBERRIES: A HOLIDAY TRADITION

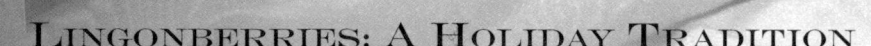

About a decade ago, I went to Sweden in the summer to scour the country for ideas for the *Insider's Report*. One evening while in Stockholm, I went to bed quite early to make sure I would not miss my early business appointments the next morning. Imagine my panic when I awoke with a start and saw a ray of sun piercing through the curtain. I jumped out of bed, raced to the window and swept back the drapery — the sun was high! I was almost finished shaving when I looked at my watch and realized that it was 3:30 — in the morning! I had fallen victim to Midnight Sun Syndrome. You see, in the summer, the sun shines 24 hours a day in Scandinavia.

That endless sunshine is one reason why lingonberries, a type of wild cranberry, grow so abundantly in Sweden. I grew extremely fond of lingonberry sauce while I was there, since it is served with almost everything — waffles, liver (see our recipe on page 76), meat loaf, ham, game (especially venison, absolutely superb!) and desserts.

In my opinion, the deep, tangy-sweet flavor of lingonberries is vastly superior to that of cranberries, and ever since that trip, lingonberry sauce has been a holiday tradition in our home.

This year, we asked E.D. Smith in Winona, Ont., to make PC Swedish-Style Lingonberry Sauce for us from lingonberries grown in Sweden; the bonus is the cost savings that we're able to pass along!

BABY BRUSSELS SPROUTS
WITH BROWN BUTTER

Did you know that a ¹/2-cup (125 mL) serving of frozen Brussels sprouts provides 50% of the recommended daily intake of vitamin C? Ours are picked small for tenderness and mild flavor. This recipe is easily doubled for a large crowd.

1	pkg (2.2 lb/1 kg) PC Frozen Baby Brussels Sprouts	1
³/4 cup	PC Unsalted Normandy-Style Cultured Butter, cut in pieces	175 mL
3 tbsp	lemon juice	45 mL
3 tbsp	chopped fresh parsley	45 mL
	Salt and freshly ground pepper	

• Boil, steam or microwave Brussels sprouts for a few minutes until tender but firm.
• In small saucepan over medium heat, melt butter. Cook for 2 to 3 minutes until butter is light brown in color and has a nutty fragrance. Add lemon juice.
• Drizzle brown butter over baby Brussels sprouts. Sprinkle with parsley.
• Season with salt and pepper to taste.

Makes about 6 servings

SWEDISH LINGONBERRIES
WITH ORANGES AND PECANS

PC Swedish-Style Lingonberry Sauce is great on its own — just chill and spoon from the jar. Or for special occasions, try this crunchy variation. Make sure nuts are fresh before you add them.

2	jars (each 250 mL) PC Swedish-Style Lingonberry Sauce	2
3	mandarin oranges, peeled	3
³/4 cup	fresh pecans, coarsely chopped	175 mL

• Place lingonberry sauce in mixing bowl.
• Cut orange sections in halves or thirds, depending on size. Discard any seeds.
• Add oranges to lingonberries. Stir in pecans.
• Refrigerate a few hours or, preferably, overnight.

Makes 6 to 8 servings

Terri and I learned years ago, when we were first married and living in a one-bedroom apartment, that lack of space needn't be a deterrent if you enjoy cooking for friends.

For instance, provided you have a table or a kitchen counter that you can use for a buffet, you can put together a fabulous turkey feast for your guests during the holidays, and let them help themselves. Our President's Choice Frozen Seasoned Boneless Thick-Slice Turkey Breasts, PC Memories of Cedar Springs Sage & Onion Sauce and PC Swedish-Style Lingonberry Sauce make it fast and fabulous. The unusually good sweet potato dressing was created by our test kitchen chef, Alison Jarvest.

You won't believe how quickly this dinner comes together!

HOLIDAY TURKEY II: BONELESS TURKEY SLICES WITH SAGE & ONION SWEET POTATO STUFFING

If your buffet includes other main-course dishes, you may wish to make the turkey portions smaller. Cut the slices in half after they've been cooked.

6 tbsp	PC Uncommonly Light Pure Olive Oil	90 mL
1	medium onion, chopped	1
1 lb	white or Cremini mushrooms, chopped	500 g
4	medium sweet potatoes, peeled and cut in $1/2$-inch (1 cm) cubes	4
2	bottles (each 350 mL) PC Memories of Cedar Springs Sage & Onion Sauce	2
	Salt and freshly ground pepper	
1	box (2.1 lb/950 g) PC Frozen Seasoned Boneless Thick-Slice Turkey Breasts, thawed	1

• In large saucepan, heat 4 tbsp (60 mL) oil. Add onion and mushrooms and cook a few minutes until onion is translucent.
• Add sweet potatoes and 1 bottle of Cedar Springs sauce. Heat, stirring, until hot. Transfer to shallow baking dish and place in 400°F (200°C) oven for 15 to 20 minutes or until potatoes are tender.
• Stir in remaining bottle of Cedar Springs sauce and season with salt and pepper to taste. Keep warm.
• Meanwhile, in large skillet, heat remaining oil. Add turkey slices (you may have to do this in batches) and cook, turning frequently, for 8 to 10 minutes or until completely cooked through; add a little more oil if necessary.
• Arrange turkey on large serving platter, separating slices with generous spoonfuls of stuffing.
Makes about 8 servings

▲

THE EXPRESSION "TO MAKE BOTH ENDS MEET" ORIGINATED IN THE DINING ROOM. ELIZABETHAN GENTLEMEN PROTECTED THEIR STARCHED WHITE RUFFLES BY TYING THEIR NAPKINS AROUND THEIR NECKS. IT WASN'T ALWAYS EASY, HOWEVER, "TO MAKE BOTH ENDS MEET."

▼

CAULIFLOWER AND BROCCOLI WITH MEMORIES OF CHEDDAR

Extra old Cheddar and Monterey Jack cheeses give PC Memories of Cheddar the characteristic tang that helps vegetables come alive with flavor. And there's no faster way to prepare them "au gratin" with this much taste appeal.

½	bag (2.2 lb/1 kg) PC Frozen Premium Quality Broccoli Spears	½
½	bag (2.2 lb/1 kg) PC Frozen Premium Quality Cauliflower	½
1	bottle (350 mL) PC Memories of Cheddar Cheese Sauce	1

• Boil or steam broccoli and cauliflower until tender but firm.
• Place vegetables in large gratin or baking dish.
• Pour Memories of Cheddar sauce over top. Place under preheated broiler for about 5 to 7 minutes or until lightly browned.

Makes about 8 servings

WHOLE BABY CARROTS WITH MEMORIES OF DIJON

The perfectly spherical shape of PC Frozen Parisienne-Style Whole Baby Carrots and their delectable glaze of mustard-raisin sauce makes them a conversation piece. Good with baked ham, too.

1	bag (2.2 lb/1 kg) PC Frozen Parisienne-Style Whole Baby Carrots	1
½ cup	(approx.) PC Memories of Dijon Mustard-Raisin Sauce Salt and freshly ground pepper	125 mL

• Boil or steam carrots until tender and heated through.
• Add Memories of Dijon sauce and toss to coat. Add more sauce, if desired.
• Season with salt and pepper to taste.

Makes 6 to 8 servings

STIR-FRIED SUGAR SNAP PEAS

Our sweet, flavor-rich PC Sugar Snap Peas are a special hybrid grown on trellises and picked by hand in the mountains of Central America. This easy-to-make vegetable dish is a superb addition to any holiday buffet.

2 tbsp	PC Extra-Virgin Olive Oil	25 mL
¼ tsp	PC Chopped Garlic in Oil	1 mL
2	bags (each 500 g) PC Frozen Sugar Snap Peas	2
	Salt and freshly ground pepper	

• In wok or skillet over medium-high heat, heat oil. Add garlic and cook, stirring, just until fragrant. Do not brown.
• Stir in sugar snap peas and cook, stirring, for about 1 to 2 minutes or just until tender but firm.
• Add salt and pepper to taste.

Makes about 8 servings

SWEET & SOUR ROASTED ONIONS

This fabulous onion dish comes from cookbook editor Carol White, who calls this her single most popular vegetable dish and one of the easiest in her repertoire.

6 to 8	red onions	6 to 8
2 tbsp	PC Extra-Virgin Olive Oil	25 mL
	Salt and freshly ground pepper	
½ cup	PC Balsamic Vinegar	125 mL

• Slice tops off onions and peel, making sure to keep root ends intact.
• Slice onions in half vertically through root. Cut each half into quarters, cutting through root so onion wedges hold together.
• Place wedges in large bowl. Add oil and toss gently with hands until all pieces are coated. Season with salt and pepper to taste.
• Arrange onion wedges in single layer in large shallow baking dish. Drizzle vinegar over tops.
• Seal well with foil and place in 450°F (230°C) oven for 40 minutes. Remove foil and continue roasting until onions are soft and juices have caramelized, about 5 to 10 minutes or longer.
• *Carol's Tip:* If you have any leftover onions (I usually make a few extra), try them cold the next day with Dijon mustard and crusty bread. You won't believe how good they are.

Makes 8 to 10 servings

10 PEOPLE
I'D LIKE TO HAVE TO A DINNER PARTY

Lucius Licinius Lucullus (117-58 B.C.)

Famous Roman general and consul. Lucullus was one of the wealthiest men of his day. In 66 B.C., he retired to a life of great culinary extravagance at a country villa featuring several dining halls. The adjective Lucullan, meaning luxurious, derives from his name.

Fernand Point (1897-1955)

At his famous restaurant, La Pyramide in Vienne, France, he ran the incubator that set the standard for France's new wave of chefs (the Troisgros brothers and Bocuse were among his pupils) who revolutionized food in the '60s and '70s. Let's face it, who can resist a man who had his barber shave him in the garden every morning accompanied by a magnum of Champagne.

Stanley Marcus (1905-   )

He was kind enough to write the foreward for this cookbook. I was totally entranced by his books, *Minding the Store* (the "store" was none other than Neiman-Marcus, where he spent more than half a century making retail history), and, especially, *Quest for the Best* (The Viking Press). I first met Mr. Marcus when I was helping Holt Renfrew launch its "Classics" line. He's everything you would imagine him to be, a total class act.

Jean-Anthelme Brillat-Savarin (1755-1826)

Author of the most famous book about eating, *The Physiology of Taste or Meditation on Transcendental Gastronomy, A Work Theoretical, Historical and Programmed* — a witty compendium of random chitchat and rubrics, of anecdotes and observations of every kind that might enhance the pleasure of the table. Jean-Anthelme's role at a dinner party would be to resolve issues of culinary consequence to gastronomes — and, after all, the guy had a heck of a triple crème cheese named after him.

M.F.K. Fisher (1908-1992)

Of course without the late M.F.K. Fisher's English translation of *The Physiology of Taste*, nobody in North America would have heard about Brillat-Savarin. So I would have to invite the brilliant and very clever Ms. Fisher as well. I expect she would more than hold her own at this table, if she deigned to show.

Alistair Cooke (1908-   )

The consummate gentleman. One of his earliest Omnibus TV shows about J-Class Yachts — the incredibly beautiful, fast sailing yachts that stole the world's imagination during the '30s — still sticks in my subconscious today. His mere presence dresses up the place.

Jean-Baptiste Troisgros (1898-1974)

I only caught glimpses of him during my early visits to Troisgros. What was the man like who spawned Jean and Pierre? How much of an influence was he in their success? His great unfulfilled longing, I hear, was to be a practising chef himself — a vocation that he enjoyed vicariously through his sons.

Is it true that he tasted and pronounced on every dish they prepared in their early days, before he would allow anything to be served forth in the family hotel restaurant?

Orson Welles (1915-1985)

A man of gargantuan appetites. People say that they just like to watch me eat because it gives them pleasure to see a person derive so much pleasure from food. Orson Welles is the person I want to watch eat.

Recently, I was talking to Michael, the head bellman at New York's wonderful Carlyle Hotel. (Isn't it amazing that a city like New York has so few great hotels?) Michael mentioned that Mr. Welles would be totally charming with celebrity guests, such as Elizabeth Taylor, and then turn around and converse with the hotel staff with exactly the same enthusiasm and personal attention.

I'd be fascinated to have the opportunity to clear up why a person of such incredible talents seemingly throws them away. My theory about Orson Welles — it's equally applicable to Marlon Brando — is that his excellence came to him so easily that he became terminally bored with his brilliance.

Julia Child (1912-   )

Julia, along with her co-authors, Louisette Bertholle and the wonderful Simone Beck, taught me how incredibly easy it is to cook well. I also love her frontal attacks on the "Food Police."

Cary Grant (1904-1986)

Elegance incorporated. Must be the greatest dinner companion imaginable (if he wants to be). Greatest head of hair in history, to be sure. I'd considered inviting Audrey Hepburn (1929-1993), a female Cary Grant, as his companion, but she never looked like much of an eater. Let's not impose on her.

POSTSCRIPT: PEOPLE *NOT* TO INVITE TO DINNER

Louis Pasteur (1822-1895)

"At the dinner table, he would wipe glassware and dinnerware in the hope of removing contaminating dirt. 'He minutely inspected the bread that was served him....Often I tried to find in my own piece of bread from the same loaf the objects found by Pasteur, but could not discover anything.'"
— Adrien Loir, Louis Pasteur's technical assistant
From *Louis Pasteur* by René J. Dubos (Charles Scribner's Sons, 1976)

POACHED SALMON WITH DAVE NICHOL'S CREAMY BEURRE BLANC

When you want to bring out the "big guns" and impress your dinner guests, take out the saucepan and whip up this incredible dish. The recipe looks intimidating, but it's unusually easy.

4	salmon fillets (each 4 to 6 oz/120 to 180 g)	4
	Dave Nichol's Creamy Beurre Blanc	
	(recipe follows on next page)	

POACHING LIQUID

3 cups	water	750 mL
½ cup	dry white wine	125 mL
1	small onion, sliced	1
1	rib celery, sliced	1
3 or 4	parsley sprigs	3 or 4
3 or 4	dill sprigs	3 or 4
½	lemon, thickly sliced	½
	Salt and coarsely ground pepper	

• Prepare Poaching Liquid: In large skillet, combine water, wine, onion, celery, parsley, dill, lemon and salt and pepper to taste. Bring to boil, reduce heat and simmer 5 to 10 minutes.

• Add salmon fillets, skin side down. Cover and poach about 8 minutes or until nearly cooked through; salmon should be slightly translucent in the centre. Keep warm.

• To serve, arrange salmon on individual plates; spoon beurre blanc over top. Or spoon a pool of beurre blanc on plate and set salmon fillet on top.

• *Dave's Tip:* Never overcook salmon. There should be a thin opalescent strip at the centre that looks slightly undercooked. You'll know you're there when you see thin white droplets — actually collagen in the fish — on the surface of the fillets. (At Troisgros, they use very thin salmon scallops and sauté them about 25 seconds one side and 15 seconds on the other. The heat of the sauce on which they're served is sufficient to finish cooking them.)

Makes 4 servings

Beurre blanc...

Two words that strike fear into so many cooks!

"Beurre blanc," which literally means "white butter," is appropriately named since this classic French sauce is principally made with white wine and butter.

My recipe for beurre blanc is virtually foolproof because I use PC Fresh Thick Double Cream (or whipping cream) to replace most of the butter. I find that the cream makes the sauce less likely to break or curdle, and it bestows an extraordinarily velvety smoothness.

IDEAL WITH FRESH FRUIT

AN EXCEPTIONAL PRODUCT CHOSEN AS OU

President's Choice

PASTEURIZED

FRESH, THICK DOUBLE CREAM

B.F. 40%

IDEAL WITH FRESH FRUIT

250 mL

Wild Atlantic salmon carries its own special cachet because out of 8,000 original eggs, perhaps only two salmon will survive the perilous journey to maturity.

In my opinion, the best-tasting salmon is farmed Atlantic salmon from the inlets and coves along the Bay of Fundy, off New Brunswick's coast.

The world-famous tides, the world's highest at more than 26 feet (8 metres), produce conditions that are most like the wild. These tides churn warm water from the bottom of the bay to the cold surface, creating steady temperatures for the salmon and stirring up nutrients that fish can thrive on in addition to their daily rations from their keepers. (Since the flavor of salmon is largely dependent on what it eats, fish farmers typically feed their salmon a marine protein diet similar to that of wild Atlantic salmon.) And the high tidal flow produces firm-fleshed fish — it's like an aquatic aerobics class for the salmon.

DAVE NICHOL'S CREAMY BEURRE BLANC

If you learn to make just one sauce in the course of your life, make it this one. Some beurre blanc recipes are tricky, but mine is nearly foolproof.

1 cup	dry white wine	250 mL
¼ cup	white wine vinegar	50 mL
⅓ cup	finely chopped shallots	75 mL
1½ cups	PC Fresh Thick Double Cream or whipping cream	375 mL
2 tbsp	PC Unsalted Normandy-Style Cultured Butter, chilled and cut in small pieces	25 mL
	Fresh lemon juice	
	Salt and freshly ground white pepper	

◆ In saucepan over high heat, combine wine, vinegar and shallots. Bring to boil and cook until liquid is almost totally evaporated, about 1 to 2 minutes.
◆ Stir in cream and cook over medium heat until mixture is thick enough to coat a spoon.
◆ Gradually whisk in butter, one piece at a time, until blended. Season to taste with lemon juice, salt and pepper.

Makes ¾ cup (175 mL)

CREAMY BEURRE BLANC IS EXCELLENT WITH CHICKEN, VEAL OR PORK. FOR A VARIATION, STIR 1 TSP (5 mL) PRESIDENT'S CHOICE CREAMED HORSERADISH FROM ENGLAND INTO THE FINISHED SAUCE.

FILLET of SALMON with BLACK BEAN SAUCE

Your friend the fantastic cook is coming for dinner. You're terrified. What are you going to do? Try this sensational salmon dish. Its preparation is literally child's play.

▲

WHEN THEY BEG
YOU FOR THIS RECIPE,
TELL THEM YOU WERE UP
ALL NIGHT FERMENTING
THE BLACK BEANS.

▼

4	salmon fillets (each about 6 oz/180 g)	4
	PC Uncommonly Light Pure Olive Oil	
2 tbsp	PC Pure Olive Oil with Lemon Essence	25 mL
6	green onions, trimmed and thinly sliced	6
¼ cup	sake (Japanese rice wine) OR dry white wine	50 mL
1 cup	PC Memories of Hong Kong Spicy Black Bean and Garlic Sauce	250 mL
	Fresh lemon or lime juice (optional)	

• Brush salmon fillets all over with light olive oil to seal in moisture. Preheat broiler.
• Arrange fish, skin side down, on broiler rack and cook about 4 inches (10 cm) below broiler element for about 8 to 10 minutes or just until a thin opalescent strip remains at centre of fish.
• Prepare sauce: In small saucepan, heat lemon-infused olive oil. Add green onions and cook for about 1 minute, stirring often. Add sake or wine and heat until hot. Stir in Memories of Hong Kong sauce, bring to boil, reduce heat and simmer for about 2 minutes. Add a little fresh lemon or lime juice, if desired.
• Arrange salmon on individual serving plates. Spoon sauce on top.
• *Dave's Tip:* If the flavor of the sauce is too intense for your taste, just add a little more sake or dry white wine.

Makes 4 servings

SKATE WITH BROWN BUTTER & CAPERS

Skate has a striated texture more like poultry than fish. The capers and vinegar perfectly balance the mild, scallop-like sweetness of the meat.

2	fresh skinless skate wing fillets (each approx. 1 lb/500 g)	2
	Salt and freshly ground pepper	
½ cup	PC Unsalted Normandy-Style Cultured Butter	125 mL
4 tbsp	PC Balsamic Vinegar	50 mL
2 tbsp	drained capers	25 mL

♦ Season skate lightly with salt and pepper.
♦ In large skillet over medium-high heat, melt half the butter. When foam subsides, add skate and cook 3 minutes per side. (You may have to cook wings separately, depending on the size of your pan.) Remove fish from pan and place on serving plate; keep warm.
♦ Add remaining butter to pan and cook over medium-high heat until butter foams and turns nutty brown in color, about 2 to 3 minutes. Blend in balsamic vinegar and capers and spoon over fish.
♦ *Dave's Secret:* A "milk bath" is a quick way to refresh many types of fish. Put the skate in a shallow dish or rimmed platter with about 1 cup (250 mL) milk; let stand for 4 minutes, turning once. Remove and pat dry before proceeding with recipe.

Makes 4 servings

I've had a few truly religious food experiences in my life, and two of them have been at the seafood paradise of Le Bernardin, an outstanding restaurant run by brother and sister Gilbert and Maguy Le Coze. They opened Le Bernardin in Paris, a Michelin-two-star restaurant, where some years ago I lunched — and then later dined — on an unforgettable seafood stew with cream and truffles. (It's tough work but somebody has to do it!)

In 1986, the Le Cozes sold their famous Paris restaurant and opened Le Bernardin in New York. They now operate what I consider to be the best French-style seafood restaurant in all of North America.

Gilbert introduced me to skate dressed the traditional way, with the classic brown butter sauce (*beurre noisette*), vinegar and capers. It tasted exotic and was priced to match — about $25. Yet in North America, that entrée-sized portion of almost a pound might cost only about $3 or $4 because there's so little demand for skate in this part of the world. (In recent months, our seafood departments have featured skate at prices as low as $1.99 a pound to encourage more people to become familiar with this great fish.) More surprising, some of the best skate is fished from Canada's cold Atlantic waters!

·133·

MEMORIES OF
JAIPUR

NET WT.14 OZ 400 g
CURRY AND PASSION
FRUIT SAUCE

MEMORIES OF
BANGKOK

350 mL
SPICY THAI SAUCE
& DRESSING

MEMORIES OF™
SZECHWAN

350 mL
PEANUT SAUCE
AND DRESSING

S auces, of course, are a cook's best secret for teasing the tastebuds at mealtime.

After France, with its refined reductions of flavor essences, I think Thailand leads the world in sauce sorcery. Thai cooks prepare a fresh sauce for almost every meal, playing with the sweet-&-sour balance to complement the central ingredient, whether it be fish, meat, poultry or vegetables.

Moving west to India, you're faced with true sauce adventure. The sauces we generally describe as "curries" are based on intricate spice blends called masalas. Like silk threads, no two masalas are alike — although most are based on spices native to India: turmeric, ginger, pepper, coriander, cumin and chilies.

No matter which cuisine you prefer, one thing's for sure. Good sauces can turn a familiar food into an epicurean epiphany that transcends all sense of place.

BARBECUED SHRIMP 2 WAYS

It's easy to prepare two completely different shrimp dishes just by changing the sauce. In this recipe, half the shrimp are marinated in a curry and passion fruit sauce, the other half in a spicy Thai sauce. We recommend our versatile PC Memories of Szechwan Peanut Sauce as a dipping sauce for both.

2 lb	PC Frozen "Zipper Back" Raw Shell-On Jumbo Black OR White Tiger Shrimp, thawed	900 g
1 cup	PC Memories of Jaipur Curry and Passion Fruit Sauce	250 mL
1 cup	PC Memories of Bangkok Spicy Thai Sauce	250 mL
1	bottle (350 mL) Memories of Szechwan Peanut Sauce	1

• Rinse shrimp under cold running water and drain well. Marinate shrimp with shells on for 1 hour at room temperature: half in Memories of Jaipur sauce, half in Memories of Bangkok. (Refrigerate in summer if kitchen is hot.)
• Place Memories of Jaipur-marinated shrimp in grill basket and grill over medium-high heat for about 3 minutes per side or until cooked through. Repeat with Memories of Bangkok-marinated shrimp. (If you have two grill baskets and a large grill, cook all of the shrimp at the same time.)
• Arrange shrimp on two platters. Pour Memories of Szechwan into small bowl and serve as a dipping sauce. (You can also serve shrimp with leftover marinades, although they should each be simmered first for about 10 minutes.)

Makes 4 to 6 servings

▲

ANCIENT CHINESE SECRET! GIVING SHRIMP A SALT-WATER BATH HELPS UNCOOKED SHRIMP MEAT STAY FIRM. GENTLY SWISH THE RAW SHRIMP IN A LARGE BOWL OF WATER TO WHICH YOU'VE ADDED 1 TBSP (15 mL) SALT. DRAIN. PREPARE FRESH SALTED WATER AND REPEAT THE PROCESS. DRAIN AGAIN. RINSE SHRIMP WELL WITH COLD WATER, DRAIN AND PAT DRY. NOW THEY'RE READY TO COOK.

▼

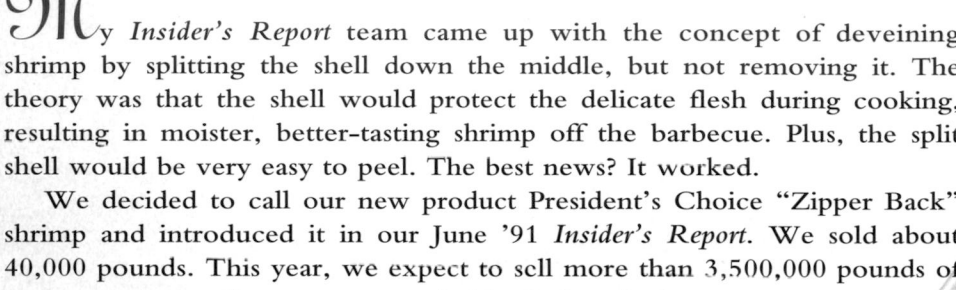

$\mathcal{M}$y *Insider's Report* team came up with the concept of deveining shrimp by splitting the shell down the middle, but not removing it. The theory was that the shell would protect the delicate flesh during cooking, resulting in moister, better-tasting shrimp off the barbecue. Plus, the split shell would be very easy to peel. The best news? It worked.

We decided to call our new product President's Choice "Zipper Back" shrimp and introduced it in our June '91 *Insider's Report*. We sold about 40,000 pounds. This year, we expect to scll more than 3,500,000 pounds of Zipper Backs to all our customers in North America!

This fantastic Zipper Back shrimp dish is the creation of John Maxwell of Toronto's Allen's Restaurant. (See recipe for Allen's Amazing Manhattan Chicken Wings on page 40.) When Terri and I serve PC Zipper Back Shrimp at home, this is how we usually prepare them!

JOHN MAXWELL'S JUMBO TIGER SHRIMP WITH GINGER AND CORIANDER

John's recipe is unbelievably good. As you can only make it with our President's Choice products, make sure you're shopping at the right supermarket!

1 cup	PC Memories of Kyoto Ginger Sauce	250 mL
1/4 cup	PC Memories of Thailand Fiery Thai Dipping Sauce	50 mL
1/4 cup	PC Naturally Brewed Soya Sauce OR tamari sauce	50 mL
1/2 cup	dry sherry	125 mL
2 tbsp	Worcestershire sauce	25 mL
2 tbsp	PC Chopped Garlic in Oil	25 mL
2 tbsp	PC Puréed Ginger	25 mL
1/4 cup	chopped fresh coriander	50 mL
2 lb	PC "Zipper Back" Raw Shell-On Jumbo White OR Black Tiger Shrimp, thawed	1 kg

♦ Mix together Memories of Kyoto sauce, Memories of Thailand sauce, soya or tamari, sherry, Worcestershire, garlic, ginger and coriander. Remove 1/2 cup (125 mL) to use as a dipping sauce and set aside.
♦ Add shrimp to marinade and let marinate 1 to 2 hours.
♦ Place shrimp in grill basket and grill over medium-hot coals for about 3 minutes per side or just until opaque. Do not overcook.
♦ Serve with reserved sauce for dipping.

Makes 4 servings

▲
Stove–Top Version:
◆

FOLLOW RECIPE BELOW BUT RATHER THAN GRILLING, SAUTÉ SHRIMP AND 2 OR 3 THINLY SLICED GREEN ONIONS IN 2 TBSP (25 mL) PC PURE OLIVE OIL WITH GARLIC ESSENCE, STIRRING OFTEN, FOR A FEW MINUTES UNTIL OPAQUE. ADD RESERVED MARINADE AND BRING TO BOIL. SERVE OVER RICE.

▼

$\mathcal{E}$arlier this year, Boris Polakow, my VP of corporate brand sales, asked me why I hadn't yet created a better ravioli. "Make it with lots more filling and call it The Decadent Ravioli," he suggested.

So I did. PC The Decadent Ravioli are overstuffed with a blend of three cheeses — ricotta, mozzarella and Parmesan. To go with them, Terri created this seafood sauce based on PC Italian Magic, the secret of great home-style Italian cooking. The mellow tomato cream sauce, teeming with pieces of lobster and shrimp, is the perfect counterpoint to our generously stuffed cheese pillows. It'll make you wish you had double your 5,500 tastebuds so that you could take in even more of the incredible flavor.

Our PC cookbook editor, Carol White, thinks this is one of the best recipes in the book.

TERRI'S RAVIOLI WITH SHRIMP & LOBSTER SAUCE

Terri held a private cooking class for six of her friends and this was the main course she served.

2 tbsp	PC Extra-Virgin Olive Oil	25 mL
1 tbsp	PC Chopped Garlic in Oil	15 mL
1	onion, finely chopped	1
1	bag (1 lb/454 g) PC Frozen Large Tail-On White OR Black Tiger Shrimp, thawed and cut in pieces	1
1	can (320 g) PC 100% Knuckle Meat Frozen Lobster Meat, thawed and drained	1
1	bottle (660 mL) PC Italian Magic	1
1 cup	whipping cream	250 mL
2	pkg (each 350 g) PC The Decadent 3-Cheese Ravioli (about 24 ravioli)	2
	Salt and freshly ground pepper	
½ cup	finely chopped parsley	125 mL

• In medium saucepan, heat oil until hot. Add garlic and onion and cook, stirring, until onion is translucent. Stir in shrimp and lobster meat and cook, stirring, for 1 minute.
• Add Italian Magic and cream. Bring to boil, reduce heat and let simmer for 5 minutes.
• Meanwhile, bring large pot of boiling salted water to boil. Add ravioli and cook a few minutes until done. Season with salt and pepper to taste. Stir in parsley.
• Drain ravioli and serve with sauce.

Makes 4 servings

AN EVERYDAY TOMATO SAUCE IN ITALY IS MADE WITH PURÉED TOMATO, ONION, SALT AND A PINCH OF SUGAR (TO BALANCE THE ACIDITY OF THE TOMATO). SOUNDS UNBELIEVABLY SIMPLE, BUT THE FLAVOR IT IMPARTS IS MAGIC. TRY PC ITALIAN MAGIC AND YOU'LL DISCOVER THE SECRET OF HOME-STYLE ITALIAN TOMATO SAUCE.

$\mathcal{T}$hree years ago, I asked Barbie Casselman what her clients craved most in wholesome foods. Barbie, of course, is one of Canada's best known nutrition consultants and author of *Barbie Casselman's Good-For-You Cooking* (Random House, 1993).

She told me "flavor" — that the most common complaint she hears is that foods designed for optimal nutrition don't always satisfy people's flavor cravings. Low-fat "flavor hits," she said, are what she wanted me to develop to make it easier for people to cut back on calories.

Shortly after that conversation, I persuaded Barbie to give us her input on a new line of products that I was going to call 'Too Good To Be True!' I would make sure that they tasted exciting if she would make sure that they were nutritionally sound.

Today we have about 90 'Too Good To Be True!' products on the shelves. In my opinion, some of our most successful marriages of taste and nutrition are the low-calorie versions of our most popular "Memories of..." sauces, made with Splenda Brand Sweetener. PC 'Too Good To Be True!' Memories of Hong Kong is one of my favorites.

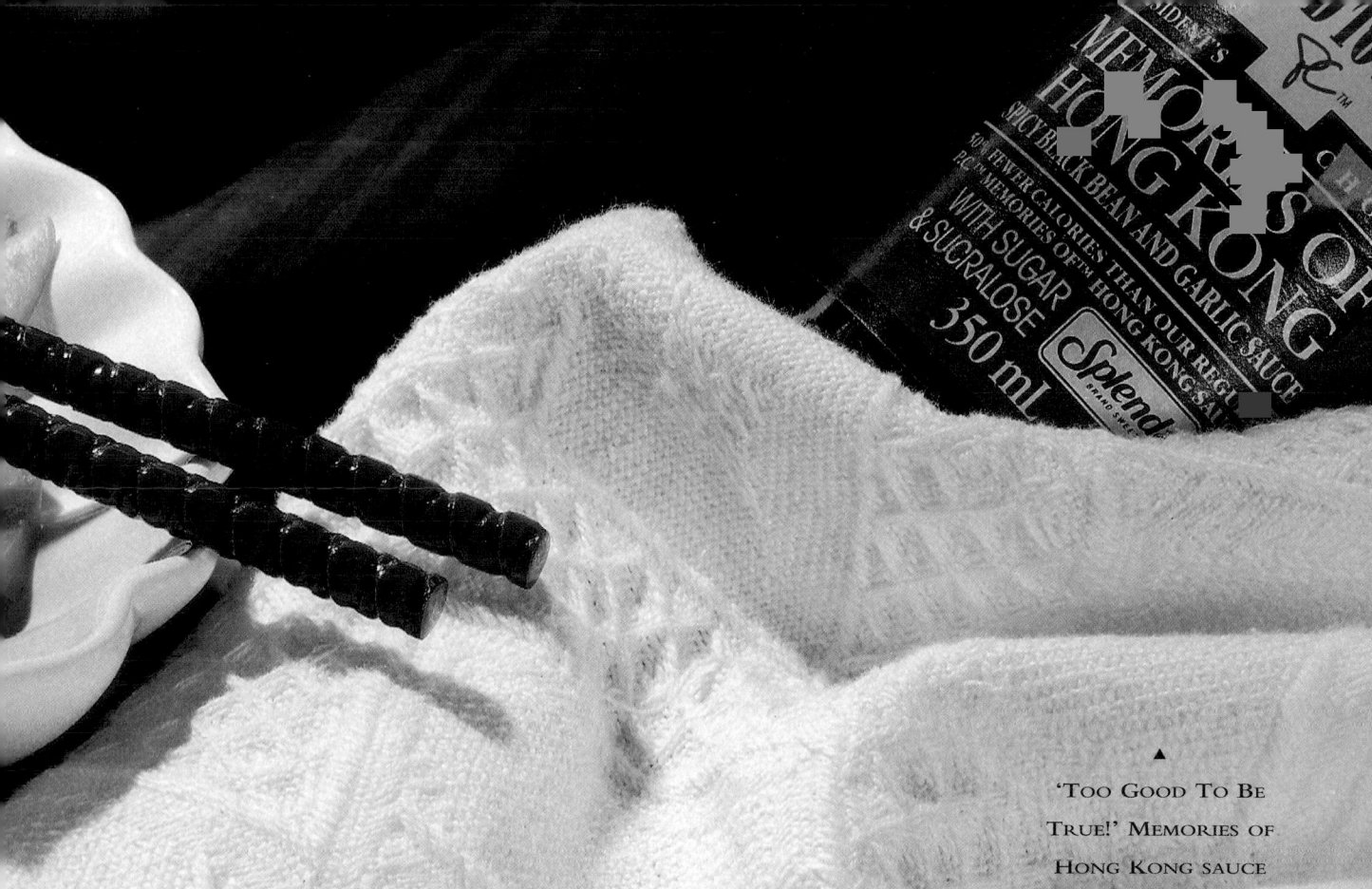

5-MINUTE GINGER SCALLOPS
WITH BLACK BEAN & GARLIC SAUCE

It's hard to imagine that anything this tasty could be so simple to make!

1 tsp	sesame oil	5 mL
1 tbsp	PC Puréed Ginger	15 mL
½ tsp	PC Chopped Garlic in Oil	2 mL
1 lb	snow peas, trimmed	500 g
2	medium carrots, thinly sliced	2
¼ cup	water	50 mL
1 lb	scallops	500 g
½ cup	PC 'Too Good To Be True!' Memories of Hong Kong	125 mL
	Spicy Black Bean & Garlic Sauce	

• In large skillet or stir-fry pan, heat oil. Add ginger and garlic and cook, stirring, for about 30 seconds.
• Add snow peas, carrots and water and stir-fry for 2 minutes.
• Add scallops and stir-fry for 3 minutes.
• Add 'Too Good To Be True!' Hong Kong sauce and bring to boil, stirring often. Serve with boiled or steamed rice.

Makes 4 servings

▲

'TOO GOOD TO BE TRUE!' MEMORIES OF HONG KONG SAUCE ADDS A RICH & SPICY FLAVOR — BUT ONLY 19 CALORIES PER TABLESPOON (15 mL) — TO MEAT, FISH, POULTRY AND VEGETABLE DISHES.

▼

Some of the product developers insist that they like the flavors of our 'Too Good To Be True!' "Memories of..." sauces made with Splenda Brand Sweetener even better than the originals.

'Too Good To Be True!' Baked Chicken

You won't believe this dish contains only 268 calories per serving! And only 23% of the calories are from fat.

4	PC Frozen Boneless Skinless Seasoned Chicken Breasts, thawed	4
1 cup	PC 'Too Good To Be True!' Memories of Szechwan Peanut Sauce	250 mL
1	medium red onion, sliced	1
1	pkg (8 oz/227 g) PC Sliced Mushrooms	1
1	red pepper, cut in julienne strips	1

◆ Wipe chicken breasts with damp cloth and pat dry. Place in shallow baking dish.
◆ In small bowl, mix together Memories of Szechwan sauce, onion, mushrooms and red pepper. Spoon over chicken breasts.
◆ Cover and bake in 375°F (190°C) oven for 40 to 50 minutes or until chicken is cooked through.
Makes 4 servings

'TOO GOOD TO BE TRUE!' SPICY PASTA

This pasta dish offers an exciting hit of flavors with only 16% calories from fat. If most fat-controlled entrées leave you hungry, I think you'll be satisfied with a portion of this pasta (547 calories per serving). Add as much as you want in the way of steamed vegetables such as broccoli, snow peas or asparagus.

1 cup	PC 'Too Good To Be True!' Memories of Szechwan Peanut Sauce	250 mL
2 tbsp	PC 'Too Good To Be True!' Memories of Bangkok Spicy Thai Sauce	25 mL
6 to 8	green onions, sliced	6 to 8
½ tsp	dried red pepper flakes (or more to taste)	2 mL
2 tbsp	sesame seeds	25 mL
1	pkg (15.9 oz/450 g) PC World's Best Capelli d'Angelo OR Spaghetti	1

• In mixing bowl, combine Memories of Szechwan and Memories of Bangkok sauces, green onions, red pepper flakes and sesame seeds. Set aside.
• In large pot of boiling salted water, cook pasta until tender but firm; drain and toss with sauce mixture.

Makes 4 servings

SALMON FILLETS WITH 'TOO GOOD TO BE TRUE!' MANGO SALSA

This is a glamorous treatment for salmon fillets or steaks. Our PC 'Too Good To True!' Memories of Singapore Passion Fruit Sauce supplies the exotic flavor and a hint of heat. There are only 282 calories per serving and 31% calories from fat.

4	salmon fillets (each 4 oz/120 g)	4
2 tsp	PC Uncommonly Light Pure Olive Oil	10 mL
	Salt and freshly ground pepper	
2	ripe mangoes, peeled and finely chopped	2
1	red pepper, finely chopped	1
1	bunch green onions, finely chopped	1
¼ cup	PC 'Too Good To Be True!' Memories of Singapore Passion Fruit Sauce	50 mL

• Brush salmon lightly with oil. Season with salt and pepper to taste. Set aside.
• Prepare mango salsa: In small bowl, mix together mangoes, red pepper, green onions and Memories of Singapore sauce.
• Place fish under preheated oven broiler for 7 to 10 minutes or to desired doneness; be careful not to overcook.
• Arrange salmon on individual plates. Spoon mango salsa on top.

Makes 4 servings

$\mathcal{M}$ost of us spend five years of our lives waiting in line, according to time studies. It's estimated that we spend, on average, one year searching for misplaced objects, four years doing housework and up to two years trying to return telephone calls! Barely time for breakfast — we're on the run from early on — and no time to fix lunch!

That's what makes our "tote cuisine" for the office 'Too Good To Be True!' Consider it fuel for the frenzied.

Here's how to brown bag it to the office in ways that will reward you with great taste and maximum nutrition. By the way, PC 'Too Good To Be True!' Frozen Vegetarian Chili, Precooked 7-Bean Mix and three of our instant soups — Spicy Black Bean, Split Pea and Lentil with Curry — were all selected for use in a soluble-fibre study that was conducted by David Jenkins, a professor of medicine and nutritional science at the University of Toronto, for the National Institutes of Health in the United States.

Even if you're eating at home, you'll welcome these satisfying lunch suggestions, especially if you've fallen victim to the calorie wars. They're all fat-controlled.

• Make a deli sandwich with your choice of PC 'Too Good To Be True!' packaged low-fat sliced meats (select from cooked ham, smoked ham, smoked chicken breast, smoked turkey breast, smoked turkey & ham and smoked turkey) on PC 'Too Good To Be True!' Bran, Multi-Grain or 11-Reasons White Loaf. Spread bread with PC mustard of choice. Serve with assorted raw vegetables. For dessert, pack PC 'Too Good To Be True!' Almond-Flavored Tofu Dessert.

• Make a pita sandwich. Spread pita pocket with PC 'Too Good To Be True!' Tzatziki Greek-style yogurt and cucumber dip, or Salsa Tzatziki. Fill with PC Precooked 7-Bean Mix or Great Northern Beans, alfalfa sprouts, cucumber and tomato. Serve with PC 'Too Good To Be True!' Beta Blast Beta Carotene Cocktail.

• Make a tuna sandwich with PC Albacore Solid White Tuna packed in water and PC 'Too Good To Be True!' No Cholesterol Whipped Dressing or Mayonnaise-Type Dressing. Dress with lettuce and grated raw vegetables. Pack a couple of PC "Thunder Crunch" Baby Dill Pickles (they contain 45% less sodium than our regular dill pickles and only 7 calories for the two!). To drink? PC 'Too Good To Be True!' Beta Blast Beta Carotene Cocktail.

• Heat PC 'Too Good To Be True!' 2-Minute Miracle Beef Stew in microwave as per directions. Eat with a few slices of PC 'Too Good To Be True!' Multi-Grain Bread. Finish with a banana.

• Prepare PC 'Too Good To Be True!' Instant Soup of choice as per directions on label and serve with PC 'Too Good To Be True!' Snack Crackers. For dessert, PC 'Too Good To Be True!' Fat-Free Plain Yogurt flavored with 1 tsp (5 mL) of PC 'Too Good To Be True!' Jam-Type Spread.

• Make a 'Too Good To Be True!' burrito: Prepare 'Too Good To Be True!' Instant Vegetarian Chili as per directions on label and spread in centre of PC Flour Tortilla. Roll up. Heat in microwave at office and enjoy with assorted raw vegetables or PC 'Too Good To Be True!' Beta Blast Beta Carotene Cocktail.

• Try a "bean bagel." On a whole wheat bagel, spread a few tablespoons of thick bean spread made with 'Too Good To Be True!' Instant Spicy Black Bean Soup. (Add boiling water to within one inch of top of container — don't fill all the way.) Finish with a crunchy apple, any variety.

• Heat a bowl of PC 'Too Good To Be True!' 20-Bean Soup in microwave at office and accompany with assorted raw vegetables.

THE GREATEST FOOD MARKETS IN THE WORLD

The Tsukiji Fish Market
Tokyo, Japan

If you don't get there by 4 a.m. for the tuna auction, forget it. After the auction, you wander through acres of fish stalls selling fresh and frozen seafood from every corner of the globe. A riot of color and activity. Definitely the ultimate food marketing experience in the world. Not to be missed!

The Mercat de Sant Josep (aka "Bocquería")
Barcelona, Spain

The best merchandising of fresh seafood I've ever seen. In the city's huge food market off the Ramblas, the great street for Barcelona's boulevardiers. Roofed in by a 19th-century ironwork structure, this market feels like a train station. You won't see anything like it in North America.

Ka-De-We
Berlin, Germany

A department store on Berlin's major shopping street, Tauentzienstrasse. The name "Ka-De-We" is an abbreviation of the German expression for "the largest store of the West." Ka-De-We has two or three floors of nothing but food with small, intimate food bars where you can purchase and eat dishes made from the products on sale in that area. My longtime friend Ziggy Wauro (the founder of Ziggy stores; he now lives in Arizona) considers this to be the best food store in the world. A must-see.

Dallmayr and Käfer
Munich, Germany

As Ziggy puts it, Dallmayr is the Mercedes 600 of food stores in southern Germany and Käfer is the BMW 850i. For Dallmayr, think of a small Harrods food hall. For Käfer, picture a warren of little rooms, beautifully merchandised, and a number of small but excellent restaurants spread throughout the store.

Fauchon
Paris, France

Too precious for me.

Fortnum & Mason, Harrods Food Halls
London, England

Fortnum & Mason's food floor should be seen. Salesmen in morning coats make it something of a food museum. The Harrods Food Halls should also be seen. Great theatre, although it doesn't make me want to buy.

Peck
Milan, Italy

Peck is a series of small shops grouped together on Via Spadari, a back street of Milan. Should not be missed by aficionados of Italian cuisine. There's also a wonderful delicatessen on Via Montenapoleane (this is the top street for fashion shopping in Milan). I've forgotten the name, but it's a short street, and the window displays are so exciting that you can't fail to recognize it.

Oakville Grocery
Oakville, Napa Valley, California

Terri and I own a small vineyard near the Oakville Grocery, a tiny old-time grocery store in the Napa crossroads called Oakville. I've probably found more leads for President's Choice products here than anywhere else in the world.

The Pike Place Market
Seattle, Washington

The Pike Place Market has been Disney-ized since I first went there as a law student at the University of British Columbia in Vancouver. Still, if you're in Seattle, it's worth paying a visit.

Dean & DeLuca, Balducci's, Grace Balducci's
New York, New York

Dean & DeLuca is a food store in Soho that specializes in food as an art form. I go there everytime I'm in New York, and on the way back to the hotel, I stop at Balducci's in Greenwich Village. Great salads, white truffles in season, Kobe beef, etc. On the way to the airport, I stop at the "breakaway" Grace Balducci's. Not as good as the original, but it will certainly do in a pinch. For the best bread in North America, stop at Eli Zabar's E.A.T. on Madison Avenue. Whatever you do, don't start up with Eli — you've been warned!!

Pusateri's, Ziggys St. Clair Market
Toronto, Ontario

Pusateri's is on Avenue Road just north of Lawrence. The staff is very nice and they really try. Pusateri's is a great training ground for future President's Choice customers. And, needless to say, Ziggys St. Clair Market, in its new incarnation, at the corner of Yonge St. and St. Clair Ave. E.

crusty italian-style
white bread made with extra virgin olive oil

RUSTICO

pain blanc croustillant de style italien, préparé avec
de l'huile d'olive extra vierge

This authentic, generations-old fondue, a family treasure of Swiss-raised company executive Rob Chenaux, has the distinction of being the first recipe to appear in my *Insider's Report*. We featured it in our first edition, back in November 1983.

Rob Chenaux is Executive Vice-President of Intersave Buying & Merchandising Services for Loblaw Companies Ltd. and is responsible for purchasing our President's Choice products. Somehow, he also manages to find time to train as a triathlete. (Rob didn't come late to sports; he was in Rome in 1960 competing on the Swiss Olympic swim team.)

Rob's family lived for a number of years in Switzerland, where every family has its own special fondue recipe. "It's a tradition in the Chenaux family that the men make the fondue," says Rob. "The recipe itself was handed down from my father's father. My father taught me. It was the only thing he cooked — usually he didn't even go near the kitchen. We always made ours with four cheeses, including a uniquely Swiss variety called Fribourg Vacherin, which isn't available in Canada. But Tilsit tastes very similar.

"The romance of this recipe is that it has been passed on for four generations. I've taught my sons, Eric, 23, and Peter, 20, how to make it — they're fondue freaks.

"PC Swiss Fondue is also very good," Rob continues. "Ellen (Rob's wife) and I eat it all the time — at least once a week. Sometimes I add a splash of kirsch and, always, five or six cloves of garlic. Traditionalists use one or two cloves to rub and toss into the pot, but I add more because I love to eat the garlic that has cooked in the cheese. That's my idiosyncrasy — but I'd never do it for Swiss guests because they'd chastise me!"

Swiss Fondue Chenaux

Dry white wine, not too chilled, and hot tea are traditional drinks with fondue. Rob suggests starting with an appetizer like PC Splendido Bündnerfleisch, a dark red air-dried beef.

2	cloves garlic (or more to taste)	2
1½ cups	dry white wine	375 mL
1¼ lb	Gruyère cheese, shredded	625 g
1 lb	Emmenthal cheese, shredded	450 g
½ lb	Appenzeller cheese, shredded	225 g
1 tsp	cornstarch	5 mL
¼ cup	kirsch	50 mL
⅓ lb	Tilsit cheese, cut in cubes	150 g
Pinch	baking soda	Pinch
	Freshly ground white pepper	
3	PC Rustico Crusty Italian-Style White Breads (each 280 g), heated in 400°F (200°C) oven for 10 minutes, cooled and cut in cubes	3

▲

WHAT TURNS A GOOD FONDUE INTO A GREAT ONE, ROB SAYS, IS THE CHEESE. "THAT'S THE SECRET — TO GET THE RIGHT AGE AND THE RIGHT BLEND OF CHEESES. NOT TOO YOUNG OR THEY MAY GO STRINGY, AND NOT TOO OILY. IF A CHEESE IS TOO OLD, IT CAN LOSE ITS FLAVOR. YOU HAVE TO TASTE IT FIRST — IDEALLY, IN THE STORE, BEFORE YOU BUY."

▼

• Rub inside of ceramic or enamel fondue pot with garlic and place cloves in pot.

• Pour in wine and place over low heat (do not allow wine to boil). When wine starts to steam, gradually stir in Gruyère, Emmenthal and Appenzeller cheeses, waiting for one handful to melt before adding the next. After the last handful of cheese is added, continue stirring and let cook an additional 3 to 5 minutes.

• Dissolve cornstarch in kirsch and add to fondue mixture. Add Tilsit cubes and cook until melted.

• Add baking soda and stir until foam subsides. Season with pepper to taste.

• Place pot on table heating unit. Spear a piece of Rustico bread and dunk in fondue with a deep stirring motion (Chenaux tradition demands constant clockwise stirring), then place bread cube in your mouth and listen to the angels sing.

• *Rob's Tip:* If the fondue starts to separate and become stringy, you can restore its smoothness by stirring in a little lemon juice.

Makes 6 to 8 servings

·151·

Rainbow Pepper
Stir-Fry

◆

HEAT 2 TBSP (25 mL)
PC EXTRA-VIRGIN
OLIVE OIL IN LARGE
SKILLET OR STIR-FRY PAN
OVER MEDIUM HEAT
UNTIL HOT. ADD 1 TSP
(5 mL) PC CHOPPED
GARLIC IN OIL AND
¼ TSP (1 mL) DRIED
RED PEPPER FLAKES;
COOK, STIRRING, FOR
ABOUT 30 SECONDS
UNTIL FRAGRANT.
DO NOT BROWN. ADD
¼ RED ONION, THINLY
SLICED, AND 1 PKG
(500 g) PC FROZEN
MIXED PEPPER STRIPS.
COOK FOR ABOUT 10 TO
12 MINUTES, UNTIL
VEGETABLES ARE TENDER
AND ALL OF LIQUID
IS EVAPORATED.
MAKES 3 OR 4
SERVINGS

▼

Apprentice cooks in China spend months learning how to cut vegetables with surgical precision before they're allowed to get near a stove. But in the fast-paced '90s, stir-fries can lose their appeal when you end up spending half the night peeling, chopping, slicing and dicing.

When I find myself alone at home for the evening, I'm not always inspired to spend a lot of time in the kitchen. On these occasions, I often opt for a quick stir-fry made with President's Choice Shanghai Stir-Fry Vegetables. It contains sugar snap peas, bamboo shoots, bean sprouts, green soybeans, water chestnuts, carrots, whole baby ears of corn, button or straw mushrooms, leek flowers and "Cloud Ears," or Tree Ears as these mushrooms are often called. I don't know where else you can get this kind of variety, ready to use, at the drop of a chef's toque.

10-MINUTE CHICKEN STIR-FRY

PC Shanghai Stir-Fry Vegetables is our best-selling frozen specialty vegetable. This flavorful dish is a special favorite of Paul Uys, Senior Director of Unique Product Development, and his family. They enjoy it for dinner at least once a week.

4 tbsp	PC Uncommonly Light Pure Olive Oil	50 mL
4	PC Boneless Skinless Seasoned Frozen Chicken Breasts, thawed and cut in strips	4
2	pkg (each 375 g) PC Shanghai Stir-Fry Frozen Vegetables	2
1 cup	PC Memories of Bangkok Spicy Thai Dressing	250 mL
	Juice of ½ lemon	

• In large skillet or stir-fry pan, heat oil until hot; add chicken and stir-fry for 2 minutes until cooked through; remove from pan and keep warm.
• Add frozen vegetables to oil remaining in pan and cook, turning frequently, until heated through, about 2 to 3 minutes. Add vegetables to chicken and keep warm.
• To juices remaining in pan, add Spicy Thai Dressing and lemon juice. Over medium-high heat, reduce until thickened. Return chicken and vegetables to pan and toss until coated with sauce and heated through.
• *Dave's Tip:* This is also excellent with PC Memories of San Francisco Golden Gate Lemon Ginger Sauce. Or try a few spoonfuls of Memories of Hong Kong Spicy Black Bean & Garlic Sauce. Adjust lemon juice to taste.
• *Dave's Tip:* For a variation, substitute a 1 kg bag of our PC Classic Cantonese Stir-Fry Frozen Vegetable Mix for the Shanghai vegetables. This economical blend contains sugar snap peas, Thai baby corn, carrots, bean sprouts, water chestnuts, mushrooms, lima beans, onions and red peppers.
Makes 4 servings

President's Choice

Stir-Fry
Vegetables

In 1985, I read an *Esquire* magazine article titled "The World's Best Hotels." It claimed that the Tawaraya Inn in Kyoto, Japan, was unsurpassed for its hospitality. After learning that the English translation of Tawaraya is "old rice bag," Terri and I were intrigued enough to make a special pilgrimage to this gracious and gardened *ryokan* — the Japanese word for inn — in the ancient city of Kyoto.

Japan has been crisscrossed with ryokan for several centuries, since all feudal lords in the country's last great Samurai dynasty were required by royal edict to travel to Tokyo (then called Edo) every other year. Inns had to be built to accommodate the lords and their many servants.

You can imagine our surprise when we arrived at the Tawaraya and discovered it has no dining room. Instead, meals are prepared in your room by a Japanese woman cooking on a charcoal hibachi, leaving you free to meditate on the beauty of your private garden until dinner is ready.

It was at the Tawaraya that my tastebuds were exposed to a special soy and ginger sauce that was the inspiration for our PC Memories of Kyoto Ginger Sauce & Glaze.

BEEF STIR-FRY WITH GINGER SAUCE

Ginger is to Chinese, Japanese and Southeast Asian food what salt is to Western cuisine. It adds essential flavor.

4 tbsp	PC Uncommonly Light Pure Olive Oil	60 mL
2 tbsp	PC Chopped Garlic in Oil	30 mL
¾ lb	lean beef, sliced in thin strips	375 g
2	red or green peppers, cut in thin julienne strips	2
4	carrots, thinly sliced on the diagonal	4
4	stalks celery, thinly sliced on the diagonal	4
1	red onion, thinly sliced	1
4	shiitake mushrooms, sliced	4
1 cup	PC Memories of Kyoto Ginger Sauce	250 mL

• Heat skillet or stir-fry pan until very hot. Add 2 tbsp (30 mL) oil, 1 tbsp (15 mL) garlic and beef strips. Cook, stirring, for 2 minutes. Remove meat from pan and set aside.

• Add remaining oil and garlic to pan and heat. Add red or green peppers, carrots, celery, onion and mushrooms and stir-fry, tossing frequently, for about 5 to 7 minutes, until tender but crunchy.

• Add Memories of Kyoto sauce and heat to boiling; return meat to pan and toss well.

Makes 4 servings

▲

SEE OUR RECIPE FOR LAMB CHEVRE BURGERS GLAZED WITH PC MEMORIES OF KYOTO (PAGE 161). AS WELL, NEXT TIME YOU GRILL PC THICK & JUICY BEEF BURGERS, BRUSH THEM WITH MEMORIES OF KYOTO THE MOMENT THEY'RE FINISHED COOKING. FABULOUS!

▼

GRILLED SWORDFISH WITH MEMORIES OF KYOTO

It's long been known that the flavor of ginger cuts the "fishiness" of fish.

4	swordfish steaks (about 6 oz/150 g each)	4
1	bottle (350 mL) PC Memories of Kyoto Ginger Sauce	1
2 tbsp	PC Puréed Ginger	25 mL

• Marinate swordfish in ¾ cup (175 mL) Memories of Kyoto sauce for 1 to 2 hours in refrigerator.
• On greased grill over medium-hot coals, cook swordfish about 3 to 4 minutes per side or to desired doneness.
• Just before serving, brush fish with remaining Kyoto sauce combined with ginger.

Makes 4 servings

ASPARAGUS WITH MEMORIES OF KYOTO

East meets West in this sensational vegetable dish.

½ cup	PC Memories of Kyoto Ginger Sauce	125 mL
2 tbsp	freshly squeezed orange juice OR PC Refrigerated 100% Orange Juice from Concentrate	25 mL
1 tbsp	fresh lemon juice	15 mL
2 tbsp	grated orange zest	25 mL
1 lb	asparagus, trimmed	500 g

• Mix together Memories of Kyoto sauce, orange juice, lemon juice and orange zest. Set aside.
• In pot of boiling salted water, cook asparagus, uncovered, for 3 to 4 minutes or just until tender. Drain and toss with sauce mixture.

Makes 4 servings

BARBECUED DUCK BREASTS WITH MEMORIES OF KYOTO

Don't overcook duck — for the most flavor, aim for rare or medium-rare. For a light lunch, add slices of this warm grilled duck to dressed mixed salad greens.

4	boneless skin-on duck breasts	4
	Salt and freshly ground pepper	
6 tbsp	PC Uncommonly Light Pure Olive Oil	75 mL
½ cup	PC Memories of Kyoto Ginger Sauce	125 mL

• Season duck with salt and pepper to taste.
• In small ovenproof skillet, heat oil until hot. Add duck breasts, skin side down, and cook briefly until skin is crisp, about 2 minutes.
• Brush all over with Memories of Kyoto sauce and place on greased grill over medium-hot coals. Cook for 4 to 5 minutes, turning and brushing often with remaining Kyoto sauce.
• Let rest 10 minutes. Slice and serve.
Makes 4 servings

THICK & JUICY KYOTO BURGERS

A good dish to make when the countdown to dinner is only minutes away. PC Frozen Thick & Juicy Beef Burgers cook from frozen in 3 to 5 minutes! No need to thaw.

| 1 | box (3 lb/1.36 kg) PC Frozen Thick & Juicy Beef Burgers (8 patties) | 1 |
| 1 cup | PC Memories of Kyoto Ginger Sauce | 250 mL |

• Place frozen burgers on greased grill over medium-hot coals for 3 to 5 minutes per side or to desired doneness, brushing all over with Memories of Kyoto sauce during last few minutes of cooking.
Makes 6 to 8 servings

SHRIMP & VEGETABLE KEBABS
WITH CORIANDER COUSCOUS

Memories of Kyoto is a superb marinade for shrimp and vegetables.

2 lb	PC Zipper Back Raw Shell-On Jumbo Black OR White Tiger Shrimp, thawed	900 g
½ lb	shiitake mushrooms	250 g
2	red peppers, cut in 1-inch (2.5 cm) squares	2
1	yellow pepper, cut in 1-inch (2.5 cm) squares	1
1	medium zucchini, cut in ½-inch (1 cm) slices	1
1	bottle (350 mL) PC Memories of Kyoto Ginger Sauce	1
2 tsp	PC Fresh Concentrated Chicken Stock	10 mL
4 tbsp	PC Normandy-Style Cultured Butter	60 mL
½ cup	finely chopped green onions	125 mL
1	pkg (340 g) PC Memories of Marrakech Couscous	1
½ cup	chopped fresh coriander or parsley	125 mL

• Marinate shrimp, shiitake mushrooms, red and yellow peppers and zucchini in 1 cup (250 mL) Memories of Kyoto sauce for 1 hour. Do not marinate longer or shrimp meat will start to break down.

• Alternately thread shrimp, mushrooms, red and yellow peppers and zucchini onto skewers.

• Barbecue skewers on greased grill 4 inches (10 cm) from medium-hot coals, turning and brushing often with remaining Memories of Kyoto sauce, until shrimp are cooked through and vegetables are tender, about 8 to 10 minutes.

• Meanwhile, bring 2½ cups (625 mL) water to boil in medium-size saucepan. Add concentrated chicken stock, butter and green onions. Stir in couscous, cover and remove from heat.

• Let couscous stand for 5 minutes. Fluff with fork. Stir in coriander or parsley. Serve with kebabs.

Makes 4 servings

QUICK & EASY BARBECUED RACKS OF LAMB

Glazing the lamb racks with Memories of Kyoto sauce gives them an appetizing sheen and great flavor.

1	box (2¾ lb/1.25 kg) PC Frozen Frenched Racks of Spring Lamb, thawed (4 racks)	1
1 cup	PC Memories of Kyoto Ginger Sauce	250 mL

• On greased grill over medium-hot coals, cook lamb for 15 to 20 minutes, turning, or to desired doneness. During final 10 minutes of cooking, brush lamb all over with Memories of Kyoto sauce.
• Remove from grill and let rest 10 minutes; brush again with Kyoto sauce and serve.
Makes 4 servings

BARBECUED PORK BACK RIBS

Something different to try for your next ribfest.

3 lb	pork back ribs	1.5 kg
1	bottle (350 mL) PC Memories of Kyoto Ginger Sauce	1
3 tbsp	PC Over 50% Juice French-Style Pure Seville Orange Marmalade	45 mL

• Cut ribs into serving-size portions. In large saucepan, combine ribs, Memories of Kyoto sauce and orange marmalade. Bring to boil, reduce heat and simmer, covered, for 1 hour, until meat starts to fall off the bone.
• Transfer ribs to greased grill over medium-hot coals and cook about 2 minutes per side, brushing frequently with remaining Kyoto sauce mixture. Brush again with sauce just before serving.
Makes 4 servings

$\mathcal{I}$n the summer, Terri and I probably eat more lamburgers than we do hamburgers. This is one of our favorite recipes.

The secret to barbecuing burgers is to keep them all the same size so that they cook evenly. I mastered the art of hand-pattying after reading *The Chef's Secrets Cook Book* by Louis Szathmary, a now-out-of-print cookbook that I treasure to this day.

Here's Chef Louis's technique: Spread out meat mixture evenly (you can use a cutting board or baking sheet). Divide into two, then four, then eight, etc., until you have equal portions in the size you wish. Wet your hands with cold water from time to time to keep the meat from sticking to your hands.

LAMB CHÈVRE BURGERS ON GRILLED RUSTICO BREAD

There are two secrets to the great flavor of these burgers: the goat cheese, or chèvre, that's mixed right into the meat and the PC Memories of Kyoto Ginger Sauce with which they're glazed.

3 lb	ground lamb	1.5 kg
¾ cup	crumbled goat cheese	175 mL
2	PC Rustico Crusty Italian-Style White Breads (each 280 g)	2
	Melted butter	
¾ cup	PC Memories of Kyoto Ginger Sauce	175 mL
	Lettuce leaves, tomato slices, onion slices (optional)	

• Mix together lamb and goat cheese. Shape into patties.
• Place on grill and cook about 5 minutes per side or until desired doneness.
• Meanwhile, cut each Rustico in half lengthwise. Brush cut surfaces with melted butter and grill, turning frequently, for 1 to 2 minutes until lightly toasted. Cut each half into 4 wedges.
• Brush burgers with Memories of Kyoto sauce. Arrange Rustico wedges on counter. Cover with lettuce leaves. Add burgers and top with tomato and onion slices, if using. Top with remaining Rustico wedges.
Makes 8 servings

▲

TORONTO'S SUTTON PLACE HOTEL KEMPINSKI FEATURED THESE BURGERS, WITH A SIDE OF SPICY FRIES, ON ITS PASTA BAR MENU DURING ITS SPRING '93 SALUTE TO THE *INSIDER'S REPORT.*

▼

Vegetarian Chili Burritos

When you want a light lunch that's loaded with flavor, make these tasty tortilla roll-ups. Or slice the burritos into 1-inch-thick (2.5 cm) rounds and serve as appetizers or snacks.

1	pkg (65 g) PC 'Too Good To Be True!' Instant Vegetarian Chili	1
4	PC Esplendido "Fajita Size" Flour Tortillas	4
1 cup	PC Splendido 2-Cheese Blend	250 mL
1/4 cup	PC La Elección del Presidente Extra-Chunky Salsa Picante, Hot or Mild	50 mL
1 cup	shredded lettuce	250 mL
1/4 cup	sour cream OR PC 'Too Good To Be True!' Fat-Free Plain Yogurt	50 mL
1/4 cup	chopped fresh coriander (optional)	50 mL

• Prepare instant vegetarian chili: Pull back lid halfway across top of cup. Fill cup with boiling water, stir well and return lid to original position. Let stand for 5 to 7 minutes, stirring occasionally.

• Arrange tortillas on microwaveable plates. Spread each with a few spoonfuls of chili. Sprinkle with cheese. Microwave on high for 30 to 40 seconds or until cheese melts.

• Top each with salsa, shredded lettuce and a dollop of sour cream or yogurt. Add coriander, if desired. Roll and serve whole or cut in pieces.

• *Dave's Tip:* For variation, substitute PC 'Too Good To Be True!' Instant Spicy Black Bean Soup for the vegetarian chili. It's excellent.

Makes 4 servings

▲

You choose salsa according to its "strength." That's why PC La Elección del Presidente Salsa Picante comes in Extra Mild, Mild, Hot and "Volcano," as well as Hot or Mild Extra Chunky. Last year, the four top-selling salsas in Ontario were President's Choice.

▼

We launched PC 'Too Good To Be True!' Instant Vegetarian Chili in 1991, the same year that salsa finally outsold ketchup in the United States. It was an amazing turn of events, considering that ketchup has been, and probably still is for most people, the most important condiment in the kitchen. I think it's because salsa delivers so much flavor for so few calories; ours is only 4 calories per tablespoon (15 mL). And when you can use it in tandem with a vegetarian chili that derives only 8% of its calories from fat, how can you lose?

VIP Cornbread

Everyone in my family is passionately interested in food — and good at it. This recipe comes from the personal recipe file of my sister, Joanne Ridley. She often makes it for guests at her Ridley's Bed & Breakfast in Victoria, B.C. (Joanne also makes absolutely the best peach pie Terri and I have ever tasted!)

³/₄ cup	cornmeal	175 mL
1¹/₄ cups	milk	300 mL
¹/₂ cup	PC 'Too Good To Be True!' Fat-Free Plain Yogurt	125 mL
2	eggs, lightly beaten	2
¹/₄ cup	PC Normandy-Style Cultured Butter, melted	50 mL
1 cup	all-purpose flour	250 mL
1 tbsp	baking powder	15 mL
1 tsp	salt	5 mL
4 tbsp	granulated sugar	60 mL
¹/₂ cup	PC Frozen Peaches and Cream Corn, thawed (optional)	125 mL
	Extra PC Normandy-Style Cultured Butter	

• In mixing bowl, mix together cornmeal, milk and yogurt. Let stand for 5 minutes.
• Blend in eggs and melted butter.
• Mix together flour, baking powder, salt and sugar. Add to cornmeal mixture and stir until blended. Stir in corn, if using.
• Pour into greased 9 x 5-inch (2 L) loaf pan and bake in 400°F (200°C) oven for 40 to 45 minutes or until toothpick inserted in centre comes out clean. Serve warm with butter.
• *Joanne's Tip:* This cornbread bakes faster in a 9-inch (2.5 L) square baking dish or a cast-iron frying pan; it will cook in 25 to 30 minutes. For breakfast, I sometimes dot the top with fresh or frozen blueberries because I like the way that they burst open in the oven and spill their juice. It makes the cornbread look very attractive.

Makes 6 to 8 servings

"Chili is not going to come and go, like kiwi fruit. It is going to stay, like rock and roll."
— Dr. Paul Bosland, Famous North American Chili Breeder
New Mexico State University in Las Cruces

TED'S FAVORITE BOWL OF RED

In Texas, they call chili a "bowl of red." Here's test kitchen chef and assistant product developer Ted Reader's favorite version.

2 lb	boneless lean beef, cut in cubes	1 kg
¾ lb	lean ground pork	375 g
2 tbsp	ground cumin	25 mL
2 tbsp	chili powder	25 mL
2 tbsp	dried oregano	25 mL
½ tsp	dried red pepper flakes	2 mL
½ cup	PC Soya Oil	125 mL
3	medium onions, chopped	3
1	pkg (8 oz/227 g) PC Sliced Mushrooms	1
4 tbsp	PC Chopped Garlic in Oil	60 mL
2	sweet red bell peppers, chopped	2
1 tbsp	salt	15 mL
2 tbsp	coarsely ground pepper	25 mL
1	can (28 oz/796 mL) PC Italian-Style Plum Tomatoes	1
1	can (5½ oz/156 mL) tomato paste	1
1	jar (850 mL) PC Extra-Chunky Mild Salsa Picante	1
1 tbsp	PC Fresh Concentrated Beef Stock	15 mL
2 cups	boiling water	500 mL
	Extra salsa, chopped green onions, sour cream	

▲

IN TEXAS,
EVERYONE KNOWS THAT
THE BEST BOWL OF RED
IS THE ONE THAT
YOU ENJOY!

▼

• In large bowl, mix together beef, pork, cumin, chili powder, oregano, red pepper flakes, soya oil, onions, mushrooms, chopped garlic, red peppers, salt and pepper. Cover and refrigerate for 6 to 8 hours, preferably overnight.
• Remove meat mixture from refrigerator and let warm to room temperature. Place in large stewpot over medium heat and cook, stirring, for about 15 minutes.
• Add plum tomatoes with their liquid, tomato paste and extra-chunky salsa. Mix well.
• Combine concentrated beef stock with boiling water and add to stewpot. Bring to boil, reduce heat and simmer for 2 to 3 hours, stirring every 15 minutes, until meat is tender and sauce is thickened.
• Serve with salsa, green onions and sour cream.

Makes 6 to 8 servings

This is one of the best appetizers I've ever tasted. In Mexico and the American southwest, a quesadilla (pronounced "kay-sa-DEE-ya") is a flour tortilla turnover filled with melted cheese. The word, in fact, suggests "a little something made of cheese." It's one of many Mexican snack foods regarded as "antojitos" or "little whims" because they're primarily designed to use up leftover bits of various ingredients. (Much the same way that cheese straws are often borne from scraps of puff pastry.)

This version, made with PC Esplendido Flour Tortillas, is no trifle, however. It's loaded with our flavorful fontina-and-mozzarella President's Choice Splendido 2-Cheese Blend and President's Choice frozen white shrimp — uncooked, peeled and deveined shrimp with all the great flavor of more expensive cold-water salad shrimp.

▲

MY FAVORITE SPLENDIDO PIZZA RECIPE GAVE ME THE IDEA FOR PC SPLENDIDO PIZZAZZ. BRINGING TOGETHER DRIED TOMATO PESTO AND BLACK BEAN SAUCE MAY SEEM LIKE AN OUTRAGEOUS EXPERIMENT, BUT THE TWO FLAVORS COME TOGETHER LIKE HAPPILY REUNITED COUSINS FROM TWO DISTANT LANDS. THE TASTE COMBINES THE BEST OF BOTH WORLDS: THE FAMILIAR AND THE EXOTIC. IT IS, AS THEY'D SAY IN MEXICO, THE *TOQUE FINAL* — OR SPECIAL FINISHING TOUCH.

▼

SHRIMP QUESADILLAS

Instead of folding the tortillas over the filling, we recommend the "sandwich" approach (i.e., use one whole tortilla on the bottom and another on top).

2 tbsp	PC Uncommonly Light Pure Olive Oil	25 mL
1 tbsp	PC Chopped Garlic in Oil	15 mL
1 lb	PC Uncooked Medium White Shrimp, thawed	500 g
4 tbsp	PC Splendido Pizzazz	60 mL
1	pkg (250 g) PC Splendido 2-Cheese Blend	1
6	PC Esplendido "Fajita Size" Flour Tortillas	6
3 tbsp	PC Normandy-Style Cultured Butter	45 mL
	PC La Elección del Presidente Salsa Picante, Hot or Mild	

• In skillet over medium heat, heat oil. Add garlic and cook for about 30 seconds. Add shrimp and cook, stirring often, for about 1 minute; add Pizzazz and continue cooking until shrimp are firm and turn opaque; do not overcook. Remove from heat.
• Add cheese to shrimp and mix well.
• Spoon one-third of shrimp mixture onto one PC Flour Tortilla. Top with another tortilla, pressing firmly to make a tight "package." Repeat with remaining tortillas and shrimp mixture to make a total of 3 quesadillas.
• On hot griddle or in large sauté pan over medium heat, heat 1 tbsp (15 mL) butter. Add one quesadilla and cook 1 to 2 minutes per side or until crisp and golden brown. Repeat with remaining quesadillas.
• Slice each quesadilla into six pieces and serve with salsa.
Makes 6 appetizer servings

$\mathcal{E}$lizabeth and Richard Fujas make our President's Choice Splendido Sun-Dried Tomato Pesto for the United States at their organic herb farm in Oregon. It's a second career for both of these seafarers-turned-farmers. (They sold their yacht rental business.) For their first five years on terra firma, they and their two children lived in a "yurt," a tent traditionally used by nomadic tribes in the Middle East.

Elizabeth showed me many different ways to enjoy the special sweet-sour tang of sun-dried tomatoes in foods. You can imagine their intensity of flavor considering that it takes about 17 pounds of fresh tomatoes to make only one pound of dried tomatoes!

WARMED SALAMI & PROVOLONE SANDWICH WITH SUN-DRIED TOMATO PESTO

The secret to this sandwich is our PC Splendido Sun-Dried Tomato Pesto ("al pesto" means "by pounding," which used to be how pesto was made) and my favorite "personal recipe" pizza sauce, PC Splendido Pizzazz, made with spicy black bean sauce for emphasis.

1	PC Rustico Crusty Italian-Style White Bread (280 g)	1
4 tbsp	PC Sun-Dried Tomato Pesto	50 mL
2 tbsp	PC Splendido Pizzazz	25 mL
4 tbsp	PC Extra-Virgin Olive Oil	50 mL
6	slices PC Splendido Capocollo Ham	6
4	slices each PC Splendido Mortadella, Genoa Salami and Peppered Salami	4
6	thin slices Provolone cheese, mild or strong	6
4	lettuce leaves	4
6	slices ripe tomato	6
1	small red onion, thinly sliced	1

• Slice bread in half lengthwise and arrange cut-side up on work surface.
• Mix together tomato pesto, Pizzazz and olive oil and spread over cut surfaces of bread.
• Arrange Splendido meats and Provolone cheese on bottom half. Top with lettuce, tomato, onion and top half of Rustico.
• Place on baking sheet and heat in 400°F (200°C) oven for 10 minutes. Slice on the diagonal into four wedges.

Makes 4 servings

OPEN-FACED RIB-EYE STEAK SANDWICH WITH ONIONS AND MULTI-COLORED PEPPER STRIPS

Our Cheddar and sweet pepper topping makes this a meal of a sandwich.

3 tbsp	PC Extra-Virgin Olive Oil	45 mL
1	onion, sliced	1
2 cups	PC Frozen Mixed Pepper Strips	500 mL
1 cup	PC Memories of Cheddar Cheese Sauce	250 mL
4	rib-eye steaks (each 4 oz/125 g)	4
1	PC Rustico Crusty Italian-Style White Bread (280 g), sliced in half lengthwise	1

• Heat 1 tbsp (15 mL) olive oil in skillet. Cook onion, stirring, until golden brown. Add pepper strips and cook, stirring, about 1 minute. Stir in Memories of Cheddar sauce and set aside.

• Cook rib-eye steaks on greased grill over medium-hot coals until desired doneness, turning halfway through. Shortly before steaks are finished cooking, brush cut surfaces of Rustico with olive oil. Place cut-side down on grill and heat just until golden brown. Cut each Rustico half in two.

• Arrange steaks on Rustico wedges. Spoon Cheddar mixture on top.

Makes 4 servings

SPLENDIDO MEATS ON RUSTICO

Splendido 4-Cheese Blend contains Edam, Parmesan, fontina and white Cheddar.

1	PC Rustico Crusty Italian-Style White Bread (280 g), sliced in half lengthwise	1
2 tbsp	PC Extra-Virgin Olive Oil	25 mL
1 tbsp	PC Red Wine Vinegar	15 mL
1/3 cup	PC Russian-Style Sweet Mustard	75 mL
3/4 cup	PC Splendido 4-Cheese Blend	175 mL
3 or 4	slices each: PC Splendido Sliced Ham, Capocollo, Genoa Salami, Spicy Italian Salami	3 or 4
3	slices red onion	3
1/2 cup	alfalfa sprouts	125 mL
1	handful watercress	1
2	tomatoes, thinly sliced	2

• Hollow out bottom half of Rustico, leaving a shell about 1 inch (2.5 cm) thick.

• Combine olive oil and vinegar. Brush evenly on cut surfaces of bread. Place on baking sheet and bake in 350°F (180°C) oven for 10 to 12 minutes until golden brown. Spread bread with mustard.

• Sprinkle 4-cheese blend over bottom half of bread. Layer with half the meats, onion slices, alfalfa sprouts and remaining meats. Cover with watercress and tomatoes. Top with bread and slice into 4.

Makes 2 or 3 servings

WARM GRILLED VEGETABLE SANDWICH WITH OLIVE VINAIGRETTE

If you can never get your fill of vegetables, then this is the sandwich for you.

1	small eggplant, cut lengthwise in ¼-in (5 mm) slices	1
1	medium zucchini, cut lengthwise in ¼-in (5 mm) slices	1
1	red pepper, cut in quarters	1
1	yellow pepper, cut in quarters	1
2	green onions	2
4	shiitake mushrooms	4
3 tbsp	PC Jalapeño Pepper Jelly, melted	45 mL
	Salt and freshly ground pepper	
1	PC Rustico Crusty Italian-Style White Bread (280 g), sliced in half lengthwise	1
2 tbsp	PC Extra-Virgin Olive Oil	25 mL
2	tomatoes, thinly sliced	2
2 tbsp	PC Gourmet Blend 100% Grated Parmesan Cheese	25 mL
¼ cup	PC Prepared Stoneground Mustard with Horseradish	50 mL
½	bunch fresh arugula	½

OLIVE VINAIGRETTE

¾ cup	PC Super Colossal Pitted Black Olives, finely chopped	175 mL
2 tbsp	PC Extra-Virgin Olive Oil	25 mL
1 tsp	PC Chopped Garlic in Oil	5 mL
2 tsp	PC Balsamic Vinegar	10 mL
	Freshly ground pepper	

• Brush eggplant, zucchini, red and yellow peppers, green onions and mushrooms all over with jalapeño jelly. Place in grill basket over medium-hot coals for a few minutes per side. Season with salt and pepper to taste.
• Hollow out bottom half of Rustico, leaving a shell about 1 inch (2.5 cm) thick. Brush cut surfaces of Rustico with olive oil and place in 350°F (180°C) oven for 10 to 12 minutes until heated through.
• Meanwhile, prepare Olive Vinaigrette: Combine ingredients, adding freshly ground pepper to taste, and mix well.
• Spoon vinaigrette mixture on Rustico bottom. Layer with tomato slices, eggplant, green onions, red pepper, zucchini, mushrooms and yellow pepper. Sprinkle with Parmesan cheese.
• Place in 350°F (180°C) oven for 5 minutes longer or until cheese starts to turn golden.
• Brush top of Rustico with mustard. Top grilled vegetables with arugula, then top of bread. Slice into 4.

Makes 2 or 3 servings

NORTHERN BEAN AND WHITE TUNA SALAD

The dressing will surprise you with its creaminess and rich flavor.

2 cups	PC 'Too Good to be True!' Precooked Great Northern Beans, rinsed and drained	500 mL
1	can (5.5 oz/155 g) PC Albacore Solid White Tuna, drained	1
1	large ripe tomato, chopped	1
¼ cup	finely chopped red onion	50 mL
¼ cup	chopped fresh parsley	50 mL

DRESSING

2 tbsp	fresh lemon juice	25 mL
1 tsp	PC Chopped Garlic in Oil	5 mL
2 tbsp	PC Dijon Mustard	25 mL
2 tbsp	PC Russian-Style Sweet Mustard	25 mL
½ cup	PC Extra-Virgin Olive Oil	125 mL
	Salt and freshly ground pepper	

• In medium-sized bowl, combine beans, tuna, tomato, onion and parsley.
• Prepare Dressing: Whisk together lemon juice, garlic and Dijon and Russian-Style mustards. Gradually whisk in oil. Add salt and pepper to taste.
• Toss bean mixture with dressing. Serve on a bed of lettuce, if desired.

Makes 4 servings

In Italy, people eat more fish than meat — especially "tunny fish" or *tonno*, which can be purchased by the kilo from big barrel drums as well as in cans. They also have a great affection and a prodigious appetite for beans, or *fagioli*. It's no wonder that both these foods make an appearance in one of Italy's famous salads, tonno con fagioli, or tuna with beans.

The wonderful thing about using beans in salads is that they absorb the flavors that surround them — from the tuna fish that you choose (PC White Albacore Tuna is ideal) right down to the olive oil.

In fact, the flavor of olive oil, a monounsaturated oil, is important to the success of this salad. I recommend PC Extra-Virgin Olive Oil from Italy. If you prefer your oil to sing a little more softly, or *sotto voce*, mix it half and half with a light-tasting vegetable oil such as PC 'Too Good To Be True!' 80% Monounsaturates Sunflower Oil, a unique oil that's extracted from a special hybrid sunflower. (Ordinary sunflower oil contains about 20 to 25% monounsaturates.)

▲

PC 'TOO GOOD TO BE TRUE!' PRECOOKED GREAT NORTHERN BEANS HAVE A DELICATE FLAVOR AND SMOOTH TEXTURE. THEY'RE FROM THE SAME FAMILY OF HARICOT BEANS AS WHITE CANNELLINI BEANS, WHICH ARE POPULAR IN ITALIAN DISHES.

▼

DUFFLET'S SPLENDIDO BREAKFAST BREAD

Toronto's pre-eminent dessert inventor, Dufflet Rosenberg, devised a very clever recipe for our Splendido that I think makes the perfect holiday breakfast. It's also perfect for weekend brunches.

▲

IF YOU CAN'T FIND FRESH BLUEBERRIES OR NECTARINES, DUFFLET SUGGESTS USING WELL-DRAINED CANNED APRICOTS AND THAWED AND DRAINED FROZEN BLUEBERRIES.

IF USING OTHER FROZEN FRUIT, SUCH AS PEACHES, DEFROST AND DRAIN OFF EXCESS JUICES BEFORE PLACING ON SPLENDIDO.

▼

1	PC Original Splendido (11 in/28cm) Italian-Style Flatbread	1
1 cup	ricotta cheese	250 mL
1	egg yolk	1
6 tbsp	granulated sugar	90 mL
1 tsp	grated lemon zest	5 mL
3	nectarines, sliced	3
1 cup	fresh blueberries	250 mL
1 tbsp	PC Normandy-Style Cultured Butter, cut in small pieces	15 mL
	Sifted icing sugar (optional)	

• Place Splendido on parchment-lined baking sheet.
• Mix together ricotta, egg yolk, 4 tbsp (60 mL) sugar and lemon zest until blended. Spread evenly over Splendido.
• Arrange nectarine slices, slightly overlapping, in concentric rings, starting at outside and working toward centre.
• Sprinkle blueberries over top. Dot with butter.
• Sprinkle with remaining 2 tbsp (30 mL) sugar.
• Bake in 425°F (220°C) oven for about 10 minutes or until fruit starts to bubble. Let cool 10 minutes before serving. If desired, dust top with a little icing sugar.

Makes 4 to 6 servings

Dufflet (pronounced duff-LET) Rosenberg is one of Toronto's most high-profile dessert-makers. Her company, Dufflet Pastries, supplies many of the city's fine restaurants and food emporiums with exquisite patisserie-style and homey desserts. Her real name is Arlene, but her family nicknamed her Dufflet because she looks so much like her older brother "Duff."

Her earliest dessert memory? Vacherin Glacé — meringue nest filled with ice-cream — made by her mother.

DAVE NICHOL'S
GRILLED SPLENDIDO PORTOFINO

The terrace of the Splendido Hotel is one of the most idyllic spots in the world. You sit at the top of gently rolling hills that cascade down through the lush gardens to a small Mediterranean fishing village whose harbor is filled with beautiful yachts. (So many dolphins once swam in this port that it was called Portus Dolphinus, or Dolphins' Port.)

I had lunch there for the first time 20 years ago, and I can still remember the wonderful pizza-like bread that the Italians call "focaccia." The Splendido served it with an unctuous goat cheese spread.

²⁄₃ cup	soft goat cheese	150 mL
¹⁄₃ cup	PC Unsalted Normandy-Style Cultured Butter	75 mL
1	PC Original Splendido (11 in/28 cm) Italian-Style Flatbread	1
	PC Pure Olive Oil with Hot Pepper Essence	

• In blender or food processor, combine goat cheese and butter and process until smooth. Set aside.

• Brush Splendido lightly with olive oil and place on grill over medium-hot coals, turning frequently to prevent burning, for about 2 to 3 minutes or until outside is crusty.

• Cut into wedges and serve with goat cheese butter.

Makes 4 to 6 servings

In 1972, the Ajmera brothers, Sam and Shreyas, arrived in Canada with only $200 in their pockets. Since then, they've built one of the most successful bakeries in North America — and they helped us create the President's Choice Splendido Italian-Style Flatbread. Since its introduction in 1991, we've sold more than eight million Splendidos across North America! In addition to its obvious use as a pizza base, you can toast it or use it with various dips, and it's perfect with cheese fondue.

Naming the Splendido was easy. It took only one bite to know that I had finally found the chewy pizza-type flatbread I'd enjoyed more than 20 years ago at the Hotel Splendido in Portofino, on the Italian Riviera. The hotel was once a private villa, but the owners converted it into a hotel to accommodate British and other expatriates who took up residence there at the turn of the century.

JAMIE KENNEDY'S
FETA SPLENDIDO WITH BLACK OLIVE PASTE

Jamie Kennedy, chef and co-owner of Palmerston Restaurant, is one of the country's most innovative chefs.

1	PC Original Splendido (11 in/28 cm) Italian-Style Flatbread	1
6 tbsp	PC Extra-Virgin Olive Oil	75 mL
1 tbsp	finely chopped fresh rosemary	15 mL
	Freshly ground pepper	
¾ cup	crumbled Feta cheese	175 mL
1 cup	pitted Kalamata olives OR PC Super Colossal Pitted Black Olives	250 mL
1	clove garlic, finely chopped, OR ½ tsp (2 mL) PC Chopped Garlic in Oil	1
¼ cup	vegetable or chicken stock	50 mL

• Place Splendido on lightly oiled baking sheet. Brush with 2 tbsp (25 mL) olive oil. Sprinkle with rosemary and pepper to taste.
• Top with Feta cheese and place in 425°F (220°C) oven for 10 minutes or until heated through.
• Meanwhile, in food processor, combine olives, garlic, ¼ cup (50 mL) olive oil and stock; process until smooth. Transfer to small serving bowl.
• Cut Splendido into thin slices. Arrange on platter and set bowl of olive paste in middle for dipping or spreading.
Makes 8 appetizer servings

ALISON JARVEST'S
3-CHEESE SPLENDIDO WITH SALAMI

Cut into wedges, this is the perfect party finger-food. It was developed by our test kitchen chef, Alison Jarvest. The PC Splendido Salami with Prosciutto she uses is one of the best prepared meat products I've ever tasted.

1	PC Splendido (6 in/15 cm) Italian-Style Flatbread	1
1 tbsp	PC Pure Olive Oil with Garlic Essence	15 mL
1 tsp	PC Chopped Garlic in Oil	5 mL
3	slices PC Splendido Salami with Prosciutto, sliced in thin strips	3
¼	red onion, thinly sliced	¼
1 tbsp	PC Gourmet Blend 100% Grated Parmesan Cheese	15 mL
½ cup	PC Splendido 2-Cheese Blend	125 mL
2 or 3	leaves fresh basil, chopped	2 or 3
1 tbsp	PC La Elección del Presidente Salsa Picante	15 mL

• Place Splendido on lightly oiled baking sheet. Spread with garlic-infused olive oil and chopped garlic.

• Top with salami with prosciutto, onion, Parmesan and 2-cheese blend.

• Sprinkle with basil. Dot with salsa. Place in 425°F (220°C) oven for 7 to 10 minutes or until cheese is melted.

Makes 1 or 2 servings

SPLENDIDO WITH PC ITALIAN-STYLE SALSA

Mini pizza slices packed with full-scale pizza flavor. (The secret is PC Italian-Style Salsa.)

2	PC Splendido (6 in/15 cm) Italian-Style Flatbreads	2
¼ cup	PC Italian-Style Salsa	50 mL
1 cup	PC Splendido 2-Cheese Blend	250 mL

• Arrange Splendidos on baking sheet. Spread with salsa. Top with cheese.
• Place on baking sheet and bake in 425°F (220°C) oven for 10 to 12 minutes until cheese is melted and golden brown.

Makes 4 to 6 appetizer servings

ARPI MAYGAR'S MUSHROOM SPLENDIDO

I happen to love mushrooms. Hungarian-born Arpi, chef and co-owner of the restaurant Splendido (no connection), makes a pizza with mushrooms that I think is just fantastic.

1	PC Original Splendido (11 in/28 cm) Italian-Style Flatbread	1
2 tbsp	PC Pure Olive Oil with Hot Pepper Essence	25 mL
3 or 4	large white mushrooms, sliced	3 or 4
1 oz	porcini mushrooms, soaked, drained and sliced (tough stems removed)	30 g
½ cup	PC Splendido Sun-Dried Tomatoes, soaked, drained and sliced	125 mL
½	red pepper, thinly sliced	½
1 tbsp	coarsely cracked black pepper	15 mL
¼ cup	freshly grated Parmesan cheese	50 mL
¼ cup	freshly grated Pecorino Romano cheese	50 mL
3 or 4	leaves fresh basil, shredded	3 or 4

• Place Splendido on lightly oiled baking sheet and brush with 1 tbsp (15 mL) hot pepper-infused oil.
• Top with white mushrooms, porcini, sun-dried tomatoes, red pepper, black pepper, Parmesan and Romano cheeses.
• Place in 425°F (220°C) oven for 10 to 15 minutes or until done. Before serving, brush edges of Splendido with remaining oil. Sprinkle with basil.

Makes 4 to 6 servings

▲

WHAT IS PC ITALIAN-STYLE SALSA? IT'S A DELICIOUS BLEND OF CHOPPED FRESH RED PEPPERS (INSTEAD OF TOMATOES) AND GREEN AND BLACK OLIVES, WITH THE ZING OF PC BALSAMIC VINEGAR. IT'S PERFECT ON CRACKERS, SALADS, GRILLED MEATS, SANDWICHES — AND IT MAKES A HECK OF A PIZZA!

▼

MARK McEWAN'S SPLENDIDO DINNER BREAD

It's worth having roasted garlic on hand so that you can enjoy this bread at a moment's notice. Alternatively, you can sauté thinly sliced garlic in a bit of olive oil in a small frying pan until golden.

2 tbsp	raisins	25 mL
2 tbsp	PC Balsamic Vinegar	25 mL
1	PC Original Splendido (11 in/28 cm) Italian-Style Flatbread	1
1 tbsp	PC Extra-Virgin Olive Oil	15 mL
Pinch	salt	Pinch
Pinch	coarsely cracked black pepper	Pinch
¼	onion, sliced and lightly sautéed in oil	¼
1	serrano chili pepper, cut in fine julienne strips	1
2	cloves garlic, roasted★ and sliced	2
1 tsp	chopped fresh rosemary, thyme or oregano	5 mL
¼ cup	grated Pecorino Romano cheese	50 mL

• Soak raisins in balsamic vinegar for about 5 minutes.
• Place Splendido on lightly oiled baking sheet. Brush with olive oil. Sprinkle with salt and pepper.
• Top Splendido with onion, raisins, chili pepper, garlic and fresh herbs. Sprinkle with Pecorino Romano.
• Place in 425°F (220°C) oven for about 5 to 8 minutes or until heated through. Alternatively, this may be cooked on a covered grill for 2 or 3 minutes.

Makes 4 to 6 servings

★ To roast garlic, place whole head in 350°F (180°C) oven for 1 hour.

KEITH FROGGETT'S CARAMELIZED ONION SPLENDIDO

Terri and I love Keith Froggett's food at Scaramouche, a "neighborhood" restaurant that's within walking distance of our home.

3 tbsp	PC Extra-Virgin Olive Oil	45 mL
2	medium Vidalia onions, halved and sliced	2
1 tbsp	PC Balsamic Vinegar	15 mL
1	PC Original Splendido (11 in/28 cm) Italian-Style Flatbread	1
6	pitted Kalamata olives OR PC Super Colossal Pitted Black Olives, sliced	6
⅓ cup	crumbled Gorgonzola cheese	75 mL
1 tbsp	chopped fresh thyme	15 mL

• In skillet, heat 2 tbsp (30 mL) olive oil. Add onions and cook over low heat for 35 to 40 minutes, stirring occasionally, until soft and golden brown. Stir in vinegar. Set aside.
• Place Splendido on lightly oiled baking sheet. Brush with remaining olive oil. Top with onions, olives and Gorgonzola. Sprinkle with thyme.
• Place in 425°F (220°C) oven for 10 minutes or until cheese is melted.

Makes 4 to 6 servings

MASSIMO'S EGGPLANT PIZZA

There's no elixir like enthusiasm, and I think Massimo's enthusiasm is the secret of his culinary successes at Toronto's Prego Della Piazza.

1	PC Original Splendido (11 in/28 cm) Italian-Style Flatbread	1
3 tbsp	puréed PC Splendido Sun-Dried Tomatoes★	45 mL
1 cup	crumbled Feta cheese	250 mL
5	slices eggplant, lightly oiled and grilled until golden	5
4 or 5	pitted Kalamata olives OR PC Super Colossal Pitted Black Olives, sliced	4 or 5
1 tbsp	chopped fresh oregano	15 mL
	PC Pure Olive Oil with Hot Pepper Essence	

• Place Splendido on lightly oiled baking sheet. Spread with puréed tomatoes. Top with Feta and eggplant slices.
• Arrange olives on cheese. Sprinkle with oregano.
• Drizzle with a little oil. Place in 400°F (200°C) oven for 10 to 15 minutes.

Makes 4 to 6 servings

★ To purée PC Splendido Sun-Dried Tomatoes, place 1 pkg (85 g) in hot water to cover for 20 minutes. Drain and purée in food processor. Thin with a little olive oil, if desired. Makes enough for 2 or 3 pizzas.

WENDY BASKERVILLE'S
GREEK MELT WITH SPLENDIDO

Wendy catered a supper at our home and I asked her to develop a special recipe for the PC Splendido. The cheese dip she created was an absolute sensation. It's perfect for entertaining.

1	PC Original Splendido (11 in/28 cm) Italian-Style Flatbread	1
1 tbsp	PC Pure Olive Oil with Garlic Essence	15 mL
3 to 4 tbsp	each crumbled feta and Gorgonzola cheeses	45 to 60 mL
3 to 4 tbsp	each shredded Cheddar, Havarti, Havarti with Jalapeño, Spiced Gouda and mozzarella cheeses	45 to 60 mL
1 tsp	PC Chopped Garlic in Oil	5 mL
2 tbsp	fresh lemon juice	25 mL
1 tsp	lemon zest	5 mL

• Brush Splendido with oil and place in 425°F (220°C) oven for 5 minutes.

• Meanwhile, in skillet over medium-high heat, heat together cheeses, garlic, lemon juice and lemon zest until cheeses are melted, shaking pan vigorously all the while; do not stir. (Watch carefully to prevent mixture from burning on bottom.) Remove from heat.

• Keep cheese mixture in pan or pour into serving bowl. Slice Splendido into bite-sized pieces or small wedges and dip into cheese sauce.

Makes 4 to 6 servings

DANTE ROTA'S TUNA SPLENDIDO

Chef Dante Rota inspired my favorite mushroom soup recipe (see page 29). I was not disappointed to see what he did with the Splendido.

1	PC Original Splendido (11 in/28 cm) Italian-Style Flatbread PC Pure Olive Oil with Garlic Essence	1
2 tsp	PC Extra-Virgin Olive Oil	10 mL
½	medium red onion, chopped	½
4 tbsp	PC Spaghetti & Pasta Sauce	60 mL
1	can (5.5 oz/155 g) PC Albacore Solid White Tuna, drained and flaked	1
4	pitted Kalamata olives, halved	4
1 cup	PC Splendido 2-Cheese Blend	250 mL
½ cup	roasted red pepper slices	125 mL

• Place Splendido on lightly oiled baking sheet. Brush with garlic-flavored olive oil.
• In small skillet, heat extra-virgin olive oil. Add onion and cook, stirring, until tender; set aside.
• Spread spaghetti sauce over top of pizza. Evenly distribute tuna, olives, onions, 2-cheese blend and red pepper slices.
• Place in 425°F (220°C) oven for 5 to 7 minutes until cheese is melted and pizza is heated through. If desired, drizzle a little olive oil over top.
Makes 4 to 6 servings

GRANO'S SPLENDIDO PIZZA

Roberto Martella, owner of one of Toronto's most popular Italian eateries, Grano, says one of the greatest gifts you can give your children is to show them, at the earliest age possible, how easy it is to prepare fantastic food.

1	PC Original Splendido (11 in/28 cm) Italian-Style Flatbread	1
3 tbsp	PC Spaghetti & Pasta Sauce	45 mL
1 cup	PC Splendido 2-Cheese Blend	250 mL
3	leaves fresh basil, chopped	3
½ cup	grilled or sautéed zucchini slices	125 mL
3 or 4	slices grilled or sautéed eggplant	3 or 4
3 or 4	grilled or sautéed mushrooms, sliced	3 or 4
½	roasted red pepper, cut in strips	½

• Place Splendido on lightly oiled baking sheet. Spread with spaghetti sauce. Add cheese and basil.
• Arrange zucchini and eggplant around edges. Put mushrooms and pepper strips in centre.
• Cook in 400°F (200°C) oven for 10 minutes.
Makes 4 to 6 servings

Wendy Baskerville is a prominent society caterer who's known for being innovative and offbeat. She created four fabulous appetizer breads — Tomato Bruschetta, Memories of Gilroy Focaccia, Wild Mushroom Bruschetta and Pissaladière — especially for my recipe video, *Dave Nichol and the Toronto Gang of Eleven Splendido Secrets.*

This page and the next feature Wendy's wonderful recipes. The next time you're planning to entertain, turn to this part of the book for her surefire successes.

TOMATO BRUSCHETTA

"Bruscare" in Italian means "to roast over coals" — deemed the original and still the best way to toast the bread for this quick snack.

4	ripe tomatoes, coarsely chopped	4
1 tbsp	chopped fresh basil	15 mL
2 tbsp	PC Chopped Garlic in Oil	25 mL
1/2 cup	PC Gourmet Blend 100% Grated Parmesan Cheese	125 mL
1	PC Cheese Splendido (11 in/28 cm) Italian-Style Flatbread	1
	PC Extra-Virgin Olive Oil	
	Chopped fresh Italian parsley	

• Mix together tomatoes, basil, garlic and Parmesan cheese. Set aside.
• Generously brush Splendido with olive oil. Spread tomato mixture evenly over top. Heat in 450°F (230°C) oven for 3 to 4 minutes until heated through.
• Sprinkle with parsley.
Makes 4 to 6 servings

Salsa Bruschetta

HALVE LENGTHWISE 1 PC RUSTICO ITALIAN-STYLE WHITE BREAD (280 g). PLACE ON BAKING SHEET AND TOAST IN 400°F (200°C) OVEN FOR 10 MINUTES. SPREAD 1/4 CUP (50 mL) PC ITALIAN-STYLE SALSA OVER TOASTED BREAD AND SPRINKLE WITH 1/4 CUP (50 mL) PC GOURMET BLEND 100% GRATED PARMESAN CHEESE. RETURN TO OVEN FOR AN ADDITIONAL 5 MINUTES. SLICE INTO WEDGES. MAKES 4 TO 6 APPETIZER SERVINGS.

MEMORIES OF GILROY FOCACCIA

The bread "focaccia" is basically pizza-type dough, patted flat and rubbed with olive oil and herbs.

1	PC Original Splendido (11 in/28 cm) Italian-Style Flatbread	1
1/4 cup	PC Memories of Gilroy Creamy Roasted Garlic Sauce	50 mL
2 tbsp	chopped fresh herbs, such as rosemary, thyme and/or parsley	25 mL
1/4 cup	PC Gourmet Blend 100% Grated Parmesan Cheese	50 mL

- Spread Splendido with Memories of Gilroy sauce.
- Sprinkle with chopped fresh herbs and Parmesan cheese.
- Heat in 450°F (230°C) oven for 3 to 4 minutes until heated through.

Makes 4 to 6 servings

PISSALADIÈRE

Pissaladière is a snack food, a specialty of Provence, in the south of France. The name comes from "pissalat," a pungent anchovy-based spread.

1	PC Original Splendido (11 in/28 cm) Italian-Style Flatbread	1
2 tbsp	PC Pure Olive Oil with Garlic Essence	25 mL
6 to 8	Kalamata olives, pitted and halved, OR PC Super Colossal Pitted Black Olives, sliced	6 to 8
6 to 8	PC Mammoth Stuffed Queen Olives, sliced	6 or 8
1/2	Vidalia or other sweet onion, thinly sliced	1/2
1 tbsp	(or more) chopped anchovies	15 mL

- Brush Splendido with oil.
- Top with Kalamata or black olives and stuffed queen olives. Add onion and anchovies.
- Heat in 450°F (230°C) oven for 3 to 4 minutes until heated through.
- *Dave's Tip:* I find it even easier to use 1/3 cup (75 mL) PC Italian-Style Salsa instead of the olives. Just spoon out and spread, then carry on with the recipe.

Makes 4 to 6 servings

WILD
MUSHROOM
BRUSCHETTA

Cut this into wedges or fingers to serve as an appetizer. Or call it a pizza and share it with a friend.

2 tbsp	PC Pure Olive Oil with Lemon Essence	25 mL
1	pkg (12 oz/336 g) PC Assorted Gourmet Mushrooms, sliced, or 4 cups (1 L) mixed mushrooms (cremini, shiitake, oyster, white), sliced	1
1	PC Original Splendido (11 in/28 cm) Italian-Style Flatbread	1
	PC Memories of Gilroy Creamy Roasted Garlic Sauce	
1 tbsp	chopped fresh thyme or 1 tsp (5 mL) dried	15 mL
1/4 cup	PC Gourmet Blend 100% Grated Parmesan Cheese	50 mL

• In skillet, heat oil. Add mushrooms and cook, stirring, until tender, about 5 minutes.

• Spread Splendido with Memories of Gilroy sauce. Arrange mushrooms on top. Sprinkle with thyme and Parmesan cheese.

• Heat in 450°F (230°C) oven for 3 to 4 minutes until heated through.

Makes 4 to 6 servings

Spaghetti Carbonara

This famous pasta dish was named for Italy's "carbonari" — the charcoal makers who used to work in the forests of central Italy. This is a sensational version.

½ lb	PC Splendido Pancetta OR PC Special Trim Bacon	250 g
1	pkg (15.9 oz/450 g) PC World's Best Spaghetti OR Linguine	1
1	bottle (350 mL) PC Memories of Reggiano Parmigiano Reggiano Caesar Dressing	1
¼ cup	chopped fresh parsley	50 mL
	Salt and freshly ground pepper	
	Freshly shaved Parmesan cheese	

• Place pancetta or bacon on baking sheet and bake in 350°F (180°C) oven for 10 to 15 minutes until brown and crispy. Drain off excess fat and tear into pieces.
• In large pot of boiling salted water, cook pasta until tender but firm. Drain and place in pasta bowl. Add Memories of Reggiano dressing, pancetta or bacon, parsley and salt and pepper to taste; toss well.
• Garnish with shavings of Parmesan cheese.

Makes 4 servings

▲

"AL DENTE" MEANS
"TO THE TOOTH," OR
SLIGHTLY RESISTANT
TO THE BITE.
PASTA THAT'S
COOKED TO THE "FILO
DE FERRO," OR
"IRON STRING" STAGE,
IS A LITTLE FIRMER —
AND BETTER SUITED
TO RECIPES WHERE IT'S
SAUCED AND TOSSED
OVER HEAT FOR A
MINUTE OR TWO, WHICH
CONTINUES TO COOK
THE PASTA.

▼

PENNE WITH SHIITAKE MUSHROOM SAUCE

Serve this superb pasta dish with a salad and warmed Rustico bread.

2 tbsp	PC Extra-Virgin Olive Oil	25 mL
1 tbsp	PC Chopped Garlic in Oil	15 mL
1	medium onion, sliced	1
1/2 lb	white mushrooms, sliced	250 g
1/2 lb	shiitake mushrooms, sliced	250 g
1/4 cup	dry white wine	50 mL
1 cup	PC Memories of Fuji Shiitake Mushroom Sauce	250 mL
1/4 cup	whipping cream	50 mL
2 tsp	chopped fresh thyme OR 1 tsp (5 mL) dried	10 mL
	Salt and freshly ground pepper	
1	pkg (15.9 oz/450 g) PC World's Best Penne OR Radiatore	1
1/4 cup	PC Gourmet Blend 100% Grated Parmesan Cheese	50 mL
	Freshly shaved Parmesan cheese	

• In skillet, heat oil. Add garlic and onion and cook, stirring, until tender.
• Add white and shiitake mushrooms, white wine, Memories of Fuji sauce, whipping cream and thyme. Cook, stirring, until mushrooms are tender and sauce thickens. Season with salt and pepper to taste.
• Meanwhile, in large pot of boiling salted water, cook penne or radiatore until tender but firm; drain well. Place in large pasta bowl.
• Add mushroom mixture and toss. Sprinkle with grated Parmesan; toss again. Taste and adjust seasoning. Top with shaved Parmesan.
Makes 4 servings

MACARONI AND FOUR CHEESES

The four cheeses in this flavorful dish are Edam, Parmesan, Fontina and Cheddar.

3 tbsp	PC Normandy-Style Cultured Butter	45 mL
1 tbsp	PC Chopped Garlic in Oil	15 mL
3	shallots, finely chopped	3
3 tbsp	all-purpose flour	45 mL
3 cups	chicken stock, homemade or made with	750 mL
	PC Fresh Concentrated Chicken Stock	
1 cup	whipping cream	250 mL
	Salt and freshly ground pepper	
2	pkg (each 250 g) PC Splendido 4-Cheese Blend	2
1	pkg (15.9 oz/450 g) PC World's Best Macaroni	1
1 cup	PC Gourmet Blend 100% Grated Parmesan Cheese	250 mL

• In saucepan, heat butter. Add garlic and shallots and cook, stirring, until tender. Add flour and cook, stirring constantly, for 3 minutes.
• Gradually whisk in chicken stock and continue whisking to remove any lumps. Bring to boil. Stir in cream and season with salt and pepper to taste. Return to

boil, reduce heat and simmer for 15 minutes, stirring occasionally.
• Stir in 4-cheese blend and continue stirring until melted. Remove from heat.
• In large pot of boiling salted water, cook pasta until tender but firm. Drain. Place in large bowl. Add cheese sauce and toss.
• Place in baking dish, top with Parmesan cheese and bake in 350°F (180°C) oven for 25 to 30 minutes until top is crisp and golden brown.

Makes 6 to 8 servings

PASTA WITH CHICKEN AND MEMORIES OF CHEDDAR

Mild-flavored red onions become quite sweet when cooked. Apparently, heat converts some of the onion's odor compounds into complex molecules that are 50 to 70 times sweeter than sugar! To lock in the vivid red color, sauté onions with a bit of wine or vinegar.

2 tbsp	PC 'Too Good To Be True!' 80% Monounsaturates Sunflower Oil	25 mL
4	PC Frozen Boneless Skinless Seasoned Chicken Breasts, thawed and cut in 1-inch (2.5 cm) cubes	4
2 tsp	PC Chopped Garlic in Oil	10 mL
1/2	red onion, thinly sliced	1/2
1/2 cup	sliced shiitake mushrooms	125 mL
1/2 cup	sliced white mushrooms	125 mL
1/4 cup	chopped fresh basil	50 mL
1/4 cup	chopped fresh parsley	50 mL
	Salt and coarsely ground pepper	
1/4 cup	dry white wine	50 mL
1 1/2 cups	whipping cream	375 mL
1 cup	PC Memories of Cheddar Cheese Sauce	250 mL
1	box (15.9 oz/450 g) PC World's Best Farfalle OR Fusilli	1

• In large skillet or stir-fry pan, heat oil. Add chicken and cook, stirring, for about 2 minutes.
• Add garlic, red onion, shiitake and white mushrooms and continue cooking for 3 minutes more. Season with basil, parsley and salt and pepper to taste.
• Stir in wine and continue cooking until liquid is reduced by half. Add whipping cream, bring to boil and cook until cream mixture is reduced by half. Stir in Memories of Cheddar sauce.
• Meanwhile, in large pot of boiling salted water, cook pasta until tender but firm. Drain well.
• Combine pasta with Cheddar mixture. Toss well.

Makes 4 to 6 servings

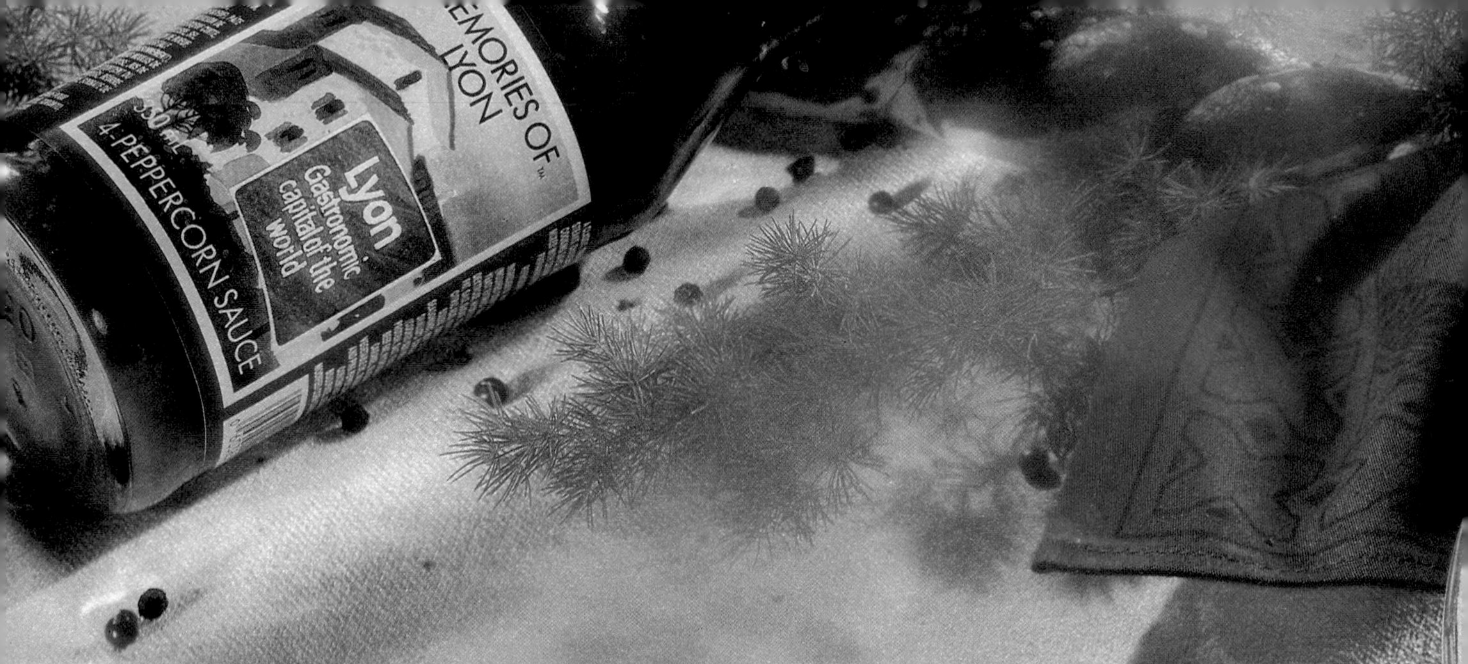

Turkey Strogonoff

In this update of a 200-year-old Russian dish, turkey replaces beef for a lighter-eating entrée. Some experts say the name of the dish derives from the Russian verb, strogat, *which means "to cut into pieces." Strogonoff may have been invented by a French cook employed by the Stroganov family in imperial Russia.*

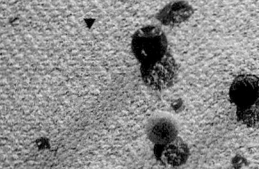

4	slices PC Frozen Seasoned Boneless Thick-Slice Turkey Breasts, thawed	4
2 tbsp	PC Pure Olive Oil with Garlic Essence	25 mL
2 tbsp	PC Chopped Garlic in Oil	25 mL
½	medium onion, thinly sliced	½
1	pkg (12 oz/336 g) PC Assorted Fresh Gourmet Mushrooms, sliced, OR 1 jar (19 oz/540 mL) PC Gourmet Mixed Mushrooms, drained	1
¼ cup	dry Sherry	50 mL
1	bottle (350 mL) PC Memories of Lyon 4-Peppercorn Sauce	1
½ cup	sour cream	125 mL
1	pkg (375 g) egg noodles	1
½ cup	sour cream	125 mL

- Cut turkey into 1-inch (2.5 cm) cubes.
- In skillet, heat oil until hot. Add garlic, onion, mushrooms and turkey and cook, stirring, for a few minutes until onion is tender and turkey is cooked through.
- Add sherry and continue cooking until alcohol is evaporated.
- Add Memories of Lyon sauce, bring to boil, reduce heat and simmer, stirring occasionally, for 10 to 15 minutes.
- In large pot of boiling salted water, cook egg noodles until tender; drain and place on platter. Whisk sour cream into turkey mixture until blended; do not boil. Spoon over noodles.
- *Dave's Tip:* The turkey mixture is also delicious served over mashed potatoes, rather than noodles.

Makes 4 servings

▲

PC Memories of Lyon 4-Peppercorn Sauce is ideal with beef, but it's also a superb cooking sauce for chicken, pork, vegetables and pasta.

Turn page for more recipes using Memories of Lyon sauce.

▼

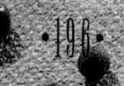

*I*n Paris, the chefs say, "Paris cooking is good, but if you want real food, go to Lyon!"

A five-hour drive from Paris on the road to the Riviera, Lyon is a mecca for food lovers and widely regarded as the gastronomic capital of France, if not the world. The city's reputation was built on a tradition of women cooks, "les mères Lyonnaises," whose knowledge of traditional French cooking has been passed down through generations of French chefs.

Lyon's chefs are renowned for their ability with the classic sauces that form the foundation of French cuisine. One of these is *poivrade*, or peppercorn sauce, a classic with beef. It inspired our PC Memories of Lyon 4-Peppercorn Sauce, made with white, black, green and pink peppercorns in a rich-tasting brown sauce.

4-PEPPERCORN SCALLOPED POTATOES

An exciting treatment for potatoes. With every forkful, you get the pungency and heat of pepper. For adventurous palates only!

1 cup	PC Memories of Lyon 4-Peppercorn Sauce	250 mL
1/4 cup	whipping cream	50 mL
4	large baking potatoes, peeled and thinly sliced	4
1/4 cup	(or more to taste) PC Gourmet Blend 100% Grated Parmesan Cheese	50 mL
1/2 cup	PC Splendido 2-Cheese Blend	125 mL

• Mix together Memories of Lyon sauce and whipping cream.
• Line a greased 11 x 7-inch (2 L) baking dish with one layer of potato slices. Sprinkle with some of the Parmesan cheese and drizzle with some of the Memories of Lyon mixture. Repeat layers until all ingredients are used up, finishing with Memories of Lyon mixture.
• Top with 2-cheese blend.
• Place in 375°F (190°C) oven for 45 to 55 minutes or until potatoes are tender and topping is golden brown.
Makes 4 to 6 servings

GRILLED SALMON WITH 4-PEPPERCORN SAUCE

Although the recipe specifies salmon, you can make this with any firm white fish, such as swordfish, shark, halibut or marlin.

4	salmon fillets (each 4 to 6 oz/120 to 180 g)	4
2 tbsp	PC Uncommonly Light Pure Olive Oil	25 mL
2 tbsp	PC 4-Peppercorn Steak Spice	25 mL
1/2 cup	PC Memories of Lyon 4-Peppercorn Sauce	125 mL
1/2 cup	whipping cream	125 mL

• Brush salmon with olive oil. Season with steak spice.
• On greased grill over medium-hot coals or under preheated broiler, cook salmon skin-side down for about 8 to 10 minutes, or until cooked through. Do not overcook; flesh should be translucent in the centre.
• Meanwhile, in small saucepan, combine Memories of Lyon sauce and whipping cream. Bring to boil, reduce heat and simmer for 1 to 2 minutes.
• Arrange salmon on serving platter. Spoon sauce on top.

Makes 4 servings

BAKED CHICKEN WITH 4-PEPPERCORN SAUCE

An incredibly easy chicken dish with the bold flavor of four peppercorns — white, black, green and pink. Sensational!

1	whole chicken (3 to 4 lb/1.5 to 2 kg), cut in serving pieces	1
	Salt and freshly ground pepper	
2 tbsp	PC Uncommonly Light Pure Olive Oil	25 mL
1	bottle (350 mL) PC Memories of Lyon 4-Peppercorn Sauce	1

• Wipe chicken with damp cloth and pat dry. Season with salt and pepper to taste.
• In Dutch oven, heat oil until hot. Add chicken and cook, stirring, until browned all over. Drain off excess fat.
• Add Memories of Lyon sauce, cover and place in 375°F (190°C) oven for about 50 to 60 minutes until done.
• Arrange chicken on serving platter. Drain off excess fat from sauce. Spoon sauce over chicken.

Makes 3 or 4 servings

▲

Grilled Rib-Eye Steak with 4-Peppercorn Sauce

IF YOU DON'T KNOW BY NOW THAT BEEF WITH CRUSHED PEPPERCORNS IS A MATCHLESS AFFINITY OF FLAVORS, THIS RECIPE WILL CONVINCE YOU. SEASON 4 RIB-EYE STEAKS, ABOUT 1/2 INCH (1 cm) THICK, ALL OVER WITH PC 4-PEPPERCORN STEAK SPICE. ON GREASED GRILL OVER MEDIUM-HOT COALS, COOK STEAKS UNTIL DESIRED DONENESS. MEANWHILE, IN SMALL SAUCEPAN, HEAT 1 CUP (250 mL) PC MEMORIES OF LYON 4-PEPPERCORN SAUCE AND, IF DESIRED, 1/2 CUP (125 mL) WHIPPING CREAM. BRING TO BOIL, REDUCE HEAT AND COOK 1 TO 2 MINUTES. ARRANGE STEAKS ON INDIVIDUAL PLATES. SPOON MEMORIES OF LYON MIXTURE ON TOP. MAKES 4 SERVINGS.

▼

Whatever its tangled origins, the pasta-and-vegetable dish we've come to know as Pasta Primavera was popularized by New York City's famous French restaurant, Le Cirque. But it was invented on Canadian soil!

In 1974, Sirio Maccioni, who at that time co-owned (and who now owns) Le Cirque with French chef Jean Vergnes, was on a fishing trip in New Brunswick. Despite the wonderful meals of venison and lobster, says Sirio, after a few days he grew nostalgic for a plate of pasta.

One night at the fishing lodge, he went into the kitchen and made a classic Italian Alfredo sauce with cream and fresh Parmesan cheese, and a simple tomato sauce to which he added asparagus and zucchini. At the last minute, he combined both sauces with spaghetti and thus created Spaghetti Primavera — "springtime" spaghetti. It was a culinary breakthrough in American-style Italian cooking!

Today, pasta primavera consists of almost any pasta shape tossed with plenty of vegetables. You can include any of your favorites provided they're at the peak of freshness and only lightly cooked to retain some crunch.

PASTA PRIMAVERA

This recipe calls for fusilli, but you can substitute any PC Pasta.

1	pkg (15.9 oz/450 g) PC World's Best Fusilli	1
2	carrots, cut in thin julienne strips	2
4 to 6	asparagus spears, cut in 1-in (2.5 cm) pieces	4 to 6
2 tbsp	PC Extra-Virgin Olive Oil	25 mL
1 tbsp	PC Chopped Garlic in Oil	15 mL
1	pkg (8 oz/227 g) PC Sliced Mushrooms	1
1	zucchini, cut in thin julienne strips	1
1/2	red pepper, cut in thin julienne strips	1/2
1	bottle (350 mL) PC Memories of Sonoma Dried Tomato Sauce	1
	Salt and freshly ground pepper	
	PC Gourmet Blend 100% Grated Parmesan Cheese	

• In large pot of boiling salted water, cook pasta until slightly underdone; drain and set aside. If desired, toss with a spoonful of olive oil to prevent sticking.
• While pasta is cooking, bring small pot of salted water to boil. Add carrots and boil for 2 minutes. Add asparagus and continue cooking 2 minutes more. Drain and refresh under cold water. Set aside.
• Heat oil in large skillet or stir-fry pan over medium heat. Add garlic, mushrooms, zucchini, red pepper, carrots and asparagus. Cook, stirring, for 2 minutes. Then add pasta, PC Memories of Sonoma sauce, and salt and pepper to taste. Toss well and sprinkle with Parmesan cheese. Toss and serve.
Makes 4 servings

▲

NORTHERN CALIFORNIA'S SONOMA VALLEY, WHERE SOME OF AMERICA'S BEST WINES ARE PRODUCED, LEADS THE U.S. IN DRIED TOMATO PRODUCTION. PC MEMORIES OF SONOMA DRIED TOMATO SAUCE GIVES OUR VERSION OF PASTA PRIMAVERA A LIGHT-TASTING TOMATO FLAVOR SUITABLE FOR THE FAMILY TABLE.

◆

SEE MORE RECIPES USING PC MEMORIES OF SONOMA SAUCE ON PAGES 202 TO 205.

▼

GRILLED CHICKEN
WITH STIR-FRIED VEGETABLES

To prepare this on the stove, cut the chicken breasts into strips and stir-fry in basil-infused olive oil for a few minutes before adding the vegetables. Of course, you forfeit the barbecued flavor.

4	PC Skinless Boneless Seasoned Frozen Chicken Breasts, thawed	4
1 cup	PC Memories of Sonoma Dried Tomato Sauce	250 mL
2 tbsp	PC Pure Olive Oil with Basil Essence	25 mL
½	bag (1 kg) PC Classic Cantonese Stir-Fry Vegetable Mix	½
	PC La Elección del Presidente Salsa Picante, Hot or Mild	

• Place chicken in shallow bowl. Add ¾ cup (175 mL) Memories of Sonoma sauce and toss to coat well. Cover and let marinate in refrigerator for 6 to 8 hours, preferably overnight.
• Cook chicken on grill over medium-hot coals, turning and basting often with marinade, for 10 to 15 minutes or until cooked through. Brush with remaining Memories of Sonoma sauce just before removing from grill.
• In skillet or stir-fry pan, heat basil-infused olive oil until hot. Add Cantonese vegetable mix and cook, stirring, for 2 to 3 minutes.
• Serve chicken with vegetables and salsa.

Makes 4 servings

PARSLEY & PARMESAN SALAD
WITH SUN-DRIED TOMATOES

Until you taste it, you won't know how sensational parsley, Parmesan and sun-dried tomatoes taste together. If you insist on using a food processor, give it only about two quick turns of a few milliseconds each, or you'll end up with relish — not salad.

4 cups	curly-leafed parsley (stems removed)	1 L
8	leaves fresh basil	8
½ cup	PC Memories of Sonoma Dried Tomato Sauce	125 mL
½ cup	crumbled or shaved Parmesan cheese	125 mL
4 to 6	PC Splendido Sun-Dried Tomatoes, cut in thin julienne strips	4 to 6
2 tbsp	fresh lemon juice	25 mL
	Salt and freshly ground pepper	

• Using sharp knife, coarsely chop parsley and basil. Place in small bowl.
• Add Memories of Sonoma sauce, cheese, sun-dried tomatoes, lemon and salt and pepper to taste. Toss well. Taste and adjust seasoning.

Makes 3 or 4 servings

SHRIMP SALAD WITH MEMORIES OF SONOMA

Serve this as an appetizer or light main-course salad with crusty bread and a glass of dry white wine. As an alternative, you can substitute scallops or crab meat for the shrimp.

½ lb	fresh asparagus	250 g
1 lb	PC Cooked Peeled Salad Shrimp	500 g
2 tbsp	fresh lemon juice	25 mL
½ cup	diced red pepper	125 mL
½ cup	PC Memories of Sonoma Dried Tomato Sauce	125 mL
¼ cup	PC Memories of Gilroy Creamy Roasted Garlic Sauce	50 mL
1 tsp	PC Chopped Shallots in Oil	5 mL
1 tsp	PC Balsamic Vinegar	5 mL
	Salt and freshly ground pepper	
¼ cup	chopped fresh Italian parsley	50 mL

• In pot of boiling salted water, cook asparagus for 3 to 4 minutes, uncovered, until tender but firm. Drain and cut into ½-inch (1 cm) lengths. Set aside.
• In salad bowl, combine shrimp, lemon juice, asparagus and red pepper. Stir in Memories of Sonoma and Memories of Gilroy sauces, chopped shallots and balsamic vinegar. Season with salt and pepper to taste.
• Adjust lemon juice and balsamic vinegar, if desired.
• Sprinkle with parsley and serve.

Makes 3 or 4 servings

▲

IN RECENT YEARS, CURLY-LEAFED PARSLEY HAS BEEN RELEGATED TO THE SIDE OF THE PLATE AS A GARNISH, WHILE FLAT-LEAFED ITALIAN PARSLEY HAS WON FAVOR IN COOKING BECAUSE OF ITS STRONGER-TASTING TENDER LEAVES. HOWEVER, FOR OUR PARSLEY SALAD, THE CURLY VARIETY IS THE PARSLEY OF CHOICE BECAUSE OF ITS FLUFFINESS IN THE SALAD BOWL AND MILDER PARSLEY FLAVOR.

▼

POTATO AND LEEK SOUP

This soup is excellent on its own, but I find the swirl of PC Memories of Sonoma contributes an exciting taste as well as visual intrigue.

2 tbsp	PC Unsalted Normandy-Style Cultured Butter	25 mL
1 tbsp	PC Chopped Garlic in Oil	15 mL
4	PC Yukon Gold Potatoes, peeled and coarsely chopped	4
3	leeks, chopped (white and light green parts only)	3
3 cups	chicken stock, homemade or made with	750 mL
	PC Fresh Concentrated Chicken Stock	
½ cup	sour cream	125 mL
	Salt and freshly ground pepper	
	PC Memories of Sonoma Dried Tomato Sauce	

• In saucepan, melt butter. Add garlic, potatoes and leeks and cook 5 minutes, stirring constantly.
• Add stock, reduce heat and simmer, covered, for 20 minutes until potatoes are soft.
• Purée mixture in blender or food processor. Return to pot and whisk in sour cream. Season with salt and pepper to taste. Heat until hot but do not boil or soup may separate.
• Drizzle each serving with PC Memories of Sonoma sauce. Serve hot or cold.
Makes 3 or 4 servings

7-BEAN SALAD WITH
DRIED TOMATO & ROASTED GARLIC DRESSING

This mellow-tasting bean salad will make you forget all about the sharp-tasting, vinegary concoctions you've ever left on your plate.

1	jar (28 oz/796 mL) PC 'Too Good To Be True!' Precooked 7-Bean Mix	1
¼ cup	PC Memories of Sonoma Dried Tomato Sauce	50 mL
¼ cup	PC Memories of Gilroy Creamy Roasted Garlic Sauce	50 mL
1	red pepper, finely chopped	1
½	red onion, finely chopped	½

• Rinse beans under cold running water and drain well.
• In mixing bowl, combine beans with Memories of Sonoma and Memories of Gilroy sauces. Add pepper and onion.
• Toss well and serve.

Makes 4 to 6 servings

SPLENDIDO WITH MEMORIES OF SONOMA

If Asiago cheese is too strong for your taste, substitute aged white Cheddar — preferably three to four years old for best Cheddar flavor.

¼ cup	PC Memories of Sonoma Dried Tomato Sauce	50 mL
1 tbsp	PC Chopped Garlic in Oil	15 mL
1	PC Original Splendido (11 in/28 cm) Italian-Style Flatbread	1
6	slices PC Special Trim Bacon, cooked and cut in ½-inch (1 cm) pieces	6
1 cup	grated Asiago cheese	250 mL
2 tbsp	chopped fresh basil	25 mL

• Combine Memories of Sonoma sauce and garlic. Brush over Splendido.
• Top with bacon, cheese and basil.
• Place in 400°F (200°C) oven for 15 minutes or until cheese has melted.

Makes 6 to 8 appetizer servings

ALORIES PER 1/2

DENT'S ℃HO

**GOURMET
XED MUSHROOMS**
PIECES AND STEMS

*a unique blend of fine imported
gourmet mushrooms*

19 fl oz 540 mL

$\mathscr{R}$isotto aficionados believe that nothing should diminish the anticipation of that first forkful. No appetizer, no bread. Not even salad. The savory creaminess of this classic Italian rice dish is its own reward. Certainly this risotto, devised by our test kitchen chef and assistant product developer, Ted Reader, commands my undivided attention with its sensational mushroom flavor. His secret? A jar of PC Gourmet Mixed Mushrooms, our selection of European-grown nameko, oyster and "champignons de Paris," or white mushrooms.

To ensure that your risotto reaches creamy perfection, you must use arborio rice, as this short-grain rice has the necessary starch to make risotto creamy.

MUSHROOM RISOTTO

In the north of Italy, where risotto reigns supreme, they always use butter to make the dish. In the south, only olive oil. No matter what your preference, serve risotto as soon as it's ready, on warm plates. Risotto waits for no man or woman!

5 cups	(approx.) chicken stock, homemade or made with PC Fresh Concentrated Chicken Stock	1.25 L
1	jar (19 oz/540 mL) PC Gourmet Mixed Mushrooms, drained (reserve liquid)	1
1 tbsp	PC Extra-Virgin Olive Oil	15 mL
3 tbsp	finely chopped shallots	45 mL
1 tbsp	PC Chopped Garlic in Oil	15 mL
1¼ cups	arborio rice (available in many supermarkets)	300 mL
½ cup	sliced shiitake mushrooms	125 mL
½ cup	sliced white mushrooms	125 mL
1 tbsp	chopped fresh sage	15 mL
½ cup	PC Gourmet Blend 100% Grated Parmesan Cheese	125 mL
	Salt and freshly ground pepper	
	Freshly shaved Parmesan cheese (optional)	

• Prepare broth: In saucepan over medium heat, combine chicken stock and liquid reserved from mixed mushrooms; heat until hot. Let simmer while preparing risotto.

• Heat olive oil in large skillet or sauté pan over medium-high heat. Add shallots and garlic and cook, stirring, for about 30 seconds. Stir in arborio rice and cook for about 1 minute, stirring constantly, until rice is evenly coated with oil.

• Add broth, about ½ cup (125 mL) at a time, stirring continuously and waiting until most of liquid is absorbed before adding next installment. Continue in this manner until rice is tender, but slightly resistant to the bite, about 18 minutes.

• Stir in mixed mushrooms, shiitakes, white mushrooms, sage and grated Parmesan cheese. Add 1 cup (250 mL) broth and continue stirring until liquid is absorbed. Season with salt and pepper to taste.

• Serve immediately with shaved Parmesan cheese, if desired.

Makes 4 to 6 servings

THE BEST WAY TO REHEAT LEFTOVER RISOTTO? PUT IT IN THE MICROWAVE. MORE TRADITIONALLY, USE IT TO MAKE PANCAKES OR CROQUETTES FOR A LIGHT LUNCH. SERVE WITH TERRI'S CALIFORNIA-STYLE MIXED SALAD GREENS (SEE RECIPE, PAGE 234).

11 Dishes Worth A Special Trip

Potato Purée, Restaurant Jamin
Paris, France

This is no ordinary plate of mashed potatoes. My wife, Terri, calls it baby food since it melts in your mouth. If someone hadn't beat me to it, I'd say it's so ethereally light that it practically floats off the plate — to join the angels in heaven who created it! A word of caution: Do not take a member of the "food police" with you because the secret to this dish is **lots** of butter.

Spaghetti Primavera and Crème Brûlée, Le Cirque
New York, New York

Owner Sirio Maccioni removed Spaghetti Primavera from the menu of his elegant restaurant at one point because the kitchen was getting too many orders for this extraordinary pasta dish filled with broccoli, zucchini, asparagus, green beans, peas, mushrooms and tomatoes. Sirio was determined that his restaurant carry on its tradition of fine French cuisine!

As for Le Cirque's Crème Brûlée — what is there to say, other than it's the best in the world.

White Truffles and Porcini, La Lampada da Tonino
Rome, Italy

White truffles and porcini are specialties of this very tiny restaurant. I like my porcini roasted and tossed with a bit of cream. (Excellent wine list, by the way.)

Espresso, Bar Sant'eustachio
Rome, Italy

The best cup of espresso coffee in the world. Go for the "doppio" (a double). One is never enough.

Foie Gras Risotto, Le Centenaire (Michelin two star)
Les Eyzies-de-Tayac, France

The chef, Roland Mazère, melts fresh foie gras into the risotto, puts it into a round mould and tops it with four triangles of sautéed foie gras with langoustines between the triangles. Deliciously decadent!

Drunken Shrimp, Lai Ching Heen Restaurant, Regent Hotel
Hong Kong

A famous Cantonese dish traditionally prepared at the table. Great theatrics. Rice wine is poured over shrimp in a glass dish and they're allowed to "drink." When they're "drunk" (i.e., when they have absorbed as much wine as they can), they're put into a simmering pot of rice wine and stock for just a few minutes.

(A great version of this dish, Drunken Prawns, is available at Vancouver's Kirin Mandarin Restaurant. There, the "drunken" prawns are dropped one by one through a hole in the lid of a special cooking container designed especially for this dish.)

Kobe Beef Steak, Okura Hotel
Tokyo, Japan

If you make it to the main dining room of Tokyo's Okura Hotel, do not leave without ordering the Kobe beef. The tender preparation that goes into producing the famous beef from Japan's Kobe region results in the sweetest-tasting meat in the world — certainly it's the most expensive! In Japanese butcher shops, you can pay up to $150 a pound for the highest grade of Kobe beef, depending on the cut.

(The Sutton Place Hotel Kempinski surprised me earlier this year when it flew in beautifully marbled Kobe beef especially for the hotel's salute to the *Insider's Report*. For this event, diners were treated to Grade #5 strip loin Kobe beef steak, the best grade available.)

Chili Crab, Hayman Island Resort
Great Barrier Reef, Australia

The oriental seafood restaurant at this famous island resort makes a fabulous Chili Crab using Australia's Moreton Bay bugs, a type of indigenous mud crab. The "bugs," a quasi-cross between lobster and crayfish, are stir-fried Singapore-style with garlic, soy sauce, tomato and lots of chilies.

Pecorino Romano Cheese, Gallura Restaurant
Olbia, Sardinia

Eating at Rita Denza's restaurant on this Mediterranean island is one of the great culinary experiences the world has to offer. (It's rated the best restaurant in Italy right now.) The famous Italian sheep's milk cheese of Sardinia has been made since before Roman times.

Lobster Bisque, The Lobster Trap
Toronto, Ontario

First meet Anne, the most gracious waitress in Canada; charm her, then ask if her son-in-law, Gus, who's also the chef, could make you a special bowl of lobster bisque (i.e., with lots of lobster meat).

Having a dinner party? Take home a tub of Gus's bisque and add a can of PC 100% Knuckle Meat Frozen Lobster Meat. Serve with a bottle of your best dry sherry, allowing your guests to flavor their bisque according to individual preference.

Homemade Almond Brittle, Ziggys St. Clair Market
Toronto, Ontario

Terri found an amazing homemade almond brittle made with real creamery butter. Made locally by Brook's Delectable Chocolates, it consists of melt-in-your-mouth buttercrunch loaded with whole roasted almonds, coated all over with chocolate and dusted with more chopped almonds.

THE WORLD'S BEST SCALLOPED POTATOES

Ordinary whipping cream (35% B.F.) will give you excellent results, but if you use our PC Fresh Thick Double Cream (40% B.F.), you'll create a culinary epiphany.

1½ lb	baking potatoes, peeled	750 g
2 tbsp	finely chopped shallots OR onions	25 mL
	Freshly grated nutmeg	
1 tsp	salt	5 mL
	Freshly ground pepper	
1 cup	whole milk	250 mL
1 cup	PC Fresh Thick Double Cream OR whipping cream	250 mL
1 cup	grated Gruyère cheese	250 mL

• Thinly slice potatoes (about the thickness of a penny) and dry on paper towelling. (In restaurants, they use a mandoline to cut the potatoes into the thinnest possible slices.)
• In large bowl, combine potato slices, shallots, ½ tsp (2 mL) nutmeg, salt and pepper to taste; mix well.
• In large pot over medium heat, heat milk just to boiling. Add potato mixture, return to boil, reduce heat and simmer, uncovered, for about 15 minutes or until most of liquid has evaporated.
• In another pot over medium-high heat, bring double cream or whipping cream to boil; add potatoes, reduce heat to low and cook, uncovered, for about 30 minutes or until sauce is thickened. Taste and adjust seasoning.
• Transfer potato mixture to buttered baking dish; top with grated cheese, a light sprinkling of nutmeg and salt and pepper to taste.
• Place 4 inches (10 cm) beneath heated broiler element and broil for 2 to 3 minutes until top is crusty and golden brown.
• *Dave's Secret:* Be sure not to wash the sliced potatoes. The starch in them helps to thicken the cream and heighten the sensual quality of the dish.
• *Dave's Tip:* Cook potatoes slowly to avoid sticking to pan. If they absorb all the liquid before they're fully cooked, add a little more milk.

Makes 4 to 6 servings

▲

THANKS, MARIE: MARIE SAFFERY, A DIRECTOR OF ADMINISTRATION FOR NATIONAL GROCERS CO. LTD., LOVES OUR SCALLOPED POTATOES. SHE HAS NEVER DEVIATED FROM THE ORIGINAL RECIPE IN NINE YEARS, EXCEPT RECENTLY. NOW SHE TOPS OFF THE DISH WITH A GENEROUS COATING OF PRESIDENT'S CHOICE GOURMET BLEND 100% GRATED PARMESAN CHEESE. "IT'S A TASTE THING," SHE SAYS. "I LOVE CHEESE!"

◆

TURN PAGE FOR MORE POTATO RECIPE CLASSICS.

▼

*I*f you ever go to my favorite restaurant in the world — Troisgros, in Roanne, France — make sure you order their potatoes Dauphinois. In North America, we call them scalloped potatoes, and it's one of the most useful dishes you can have in your "culinary quiver."

Finding the best recipe in the world for scalloped potatoes was a challenge we undertook in 1984. We took months to sort out the confusion of methods and techniques — some recipes recommend baking potatoes, others say to use boiling potatoes; some people rinse the sliced potatoes, others warn against it, etc. In the end, The World's Best Scalloped Potatoes (see recipe on preceding page) turned out to be an adaptation of Troisgros's recipe, using North American ingredients.

TERRI'S MASHED POTATOES with GOAT CHEESE

Restaurant Jamin in Paris is one of the world's most famous restaurants — three stars in Michelin, four toques in Gault et Millau! — and its chef-owner Joël Robuchon is regarded as the best chef working in France today. Mashed potatoes are served with almost everything and are the restaurant's most talked-about dish. "Jamin uses a lot of butter," says Terri. "I use butter but I also add goat cheese. By no stretch of the imagination is this a low-calorie dish — not a bit! But it's wonderful to serve with roast beef or roast capon, along with any green vegetable."

3 lb	PC Yukon Gold Potatoes, peeled	1.5 kg
½ cup	light cream (10%)	125 mL
½ lb	soft goat cheese	250 g
½ cup	PC Unsalted Normandy-Style Cultured Butter, melted	125 mL
	Salt and freshly ground pepper	

• Place potatoes in large saucepan. Add cold water to cover and 2 tsp (10 mL) salt. Bring to boil, reduce heat and cook until potatoes are tender. Drain and return to saucepan. Shake pan over low heat for about 10 seconds to remove remaining moisture.

• Mash potatoes with potato masher. Using a spatula or hand mixer, whip potatoes, gradually blending in cream, goat cheese and butter. Taste and adjust quantities, if desired.

• Season with salt and pepper to taste.

• *Dave's Tip:* I like to swirl a tablespoon (15 mL) of PC Splendido Pizzazz into my portion. The dried tomato and fermented black bean sauce adds a rich piquancy.

Makes 6 to 8 servings

POWER POTATOES

At the Bar Room of the Four Seasons Restaurant in New York City, I was surprised to find barbecued potatoes on the menu — for just under $10 each! Apparently, many powerful Manhattanites (the investment bankers, famous members of the press, etc.) order it as an appetizer. I learned from Four Seasons' General Manager Julian Niccolini how easy it is to transform a Potater Familias into a "power lunch."

For each serving:
- Place potato in 400°F (200°C) oven for about 1 hour until tender. Then, place on grill for a few minutes, turning periodically, until skin turns golden brown; potato will develop a wonderfully charred flavor.
- To serve, slit top and squeeze gently to expose "flesh." Drizzle with PC Extra-Virgin Olive Oil. Season with salt and pepper to taste.
- *Dave's Tip:* Aged potatoes, the ones with leathery looking skin, make the best "bakers" since their sugars convert to starch during storage and they have a light and fluffy texture when cooked.

BILL WHITE'S
BEST POTATO PANCAKES

"One of the things my dad did best was potato pancakes," says food consultant Jim White, who used to help me write the Insider's Report. *Here's Jim's dad's traditional family recipe, which we revealed in the November 1984 edition.*

2 cups	unpeeled, cubed raw PC Yukon Gold OR baking potatoes	500 mL
2	eggs	2
1 tsp	salt	5 mL
¼ tsp	freshly ground pepper	1 mL
1 tbsp	all-purpose flour	15 mL
¼ tsp	baking powder	1 mL
1	small onion, chopped	1
	PC Peanut OR Corn Oil	

- In blender or food processor fitted with steel blade, combine potatoes, eggs, salt, pepper, flour, baking powder and onion. Process in short bursts until potato is finely grated but not puréed. Do not overblend; you want a relish-like consistency, not mush. Set aside.
- In saucepan or skillet, pour in peanut or corn oil to a depth of ⅓ inch (8 mm); heat until oil is hot enough to make drops of water sputter. Spoon in potato batter, 3 tablespoons (45 mL) at a time; form pancakes about 3½ inches (9 cm) in diameter. Cook 6 to 8 minutes or until golden, turning once.
- Remove with slotted spoon and drain on paper towels. Sprinkle lightly with salt and place in heated oven to keep warm while cooking additional batches.

Makes about 12 pancakes

$\mathcal{T}$erri and I "adopted" Jim White's recipe for gingered carrots when it appeared in *The Best of Canada Cookbook* (McClelland & Stewart, 1981), which Jim wrote with the late chef Tony Roldan. Tony was captain of the Canadian team that went to Frankfurt in 1976 to compete in the World Culinary Olympics. The team placed second in the world cooking competition.

"I don't know of any other way to prepare carrots that tastes as good as Tony's," says Jim of his longtime family friend and cooking mentor. "The maple syrup is quintessentially Canadian and it complements the zing of ginger. People seem to get as much pleasure out of this vegetable dish as they do dessert!

"Moreover — it's supremely simple to make."

JIM WHITE'S GINGER BABY CARROTS

My adaptation of Jim's recipe calls for even more ginger and, for convenience, uses PC Frozen Uncommonly Sweet Whole Baby Carrots, a special hybrid carrot from Israel that tastes very sweet and maintains its small size, even when mature.

2 tbsp	PC Unsalted Normandy-Style Cultured Butter	30 mL
¼ cup	finely chopped onion	50 mL
½	bag (2.2 lb/1 kg) PC Frozen Uncommonly Sweet Whole Baby Carrots OR 1 lb (500 g) fresh carrots, peeled and sliced	½
¼ cup	PC Canada No.1 Light 100% Pure Maple Syrup	50 mL
2 tbsp	PC Puréed Ginger OR grated fresh gingerroot	30 mL
½ cup	cold water	125 mL
½ tsp	salt	2 mL
	Juice of ½ lemon	
1 tbsp	chopped fresh parsley	15 mL

• In skillet over medium heat, melt butter. Add onion and cook until tender.
• Add carrots, maple syrup, ginger, water and salt.
• Cook over medium heat, stirring occasionally, until carrots are tender and water has evaporated to form a glaze, about 8 to 10 minutes for frozen whole carrots, 20 to 30 minutes for fresh sliced carrots.
• Stir in lemon juice. Sprinkle with parsley and serve.
• *Dave's Secret:* The secret of many of the world's great dishes involves achieving a perfect balance between its sweet and sour elements. In a recipe that calls for fresh lemon juice, like this one, always leave the lemon until the last, and add it a bit at a time until you achieve the sweet-and-sour balance that is most appealing to your palate.
Makes 3 or 4 servings

MY SISTER MARILYN'S FAMOUS GRILLED VEGETABLES

This is a meal in itself. All you need is a loaf of our PC Rustico Italian-Style White Bread and your favorite Chardonnay.

Since this dish is easiest to make with a barbecue basket, we had one specially designed with a tight, non-stick wire mesh to hold in the vegetables and a heatproof hardwood handle. If you don't have one of our PC Multi-Purpose Barbecue Baskets, cut the vegetables large enough to prevent them from falling through the barbecue grill.

For a grilled vegetable extravaganza, accompany with any or all of the barbecue treasures on the next page.

2	sweet peppers (red, yellow, orange or green), seeded and cut in wedges	2
1	zucchini, cut in ½-inch (1 cm) chunks	1
½ lb	PC Gourmet Fresh Mushrooms OR other mixed whole mushrooms (e.g., cremini, oyster, shiitake)	250 g
1	bunch green onions, trimmed	1
12	spears asparagus, coarse ends removed	12
2	cobs of fresh corn, cut in 1-inch (2.5 cm) lengths, OR 12 canned miniature corn cobs, drained	2
3 tbsp	PC Uncommonly Light Pure Olive Oil OR PC Pure Olive Oil with Garlic, Lemon or Hot Pepper Essence	45 mL
	Salt and freshly ground pepper	
⅓ cup	PC Memories of Sonoma Dried Tomato Sauce	75 mL
⅓ cup	PC Memories of Gilroy Creamy Roasted Garlic Sauce	75 mL
⅓ cup	crumbled goat cheese	75 mL

◆ Place vegetables in large mixing bowl. Add olive oil and salt and pepper to taste; toss gently until vegetables are all coated with oil.
◆ Place in grill basket or directly on grill and cook over medium-hot coals for about 20 to 30 minutes or until lightly charred, turning often.
◆ Transfer vegetables to serving bowl. While still hot, toss with Memories of Sonoma and Memories of Gilroy sauces and crumbled goat cheese. Mix well to melt cheese and serve.

Makes 4 servings

MEMORIES OF GILROY ™

·219·

THE BEST MUSHROOMS I'VE EVER TASTED

Whole exotic mushrooms cooked just until they absorb the rich flavor of PC Memories of Fuji Shiitake Mushroom Sauce makes a side dish with intense mushroom flavor. It's sensational with grilled meats and poultry, or over cornmeal polenta. For a pasta sauce, slice the mushrooms before cooking.

3 tbsp	PC Extra-Virgin Olive Oil	45 mL
2 lb	whole mixed fresh mushrooms (shiitake, oyster, portobello)	1 kg
½ cup	(approx.) PC Memories of Fuji Shiitake Mushroom Sauce	125 mL
	Salt and freshly ground pepper	

• Heat large skillet or stir-fry pan on grill until hot. Add oil and mushrooms and cook, stirring often, until mushrooms begin to soften, about 1 to 2 minutes.
• Gradually stir in Memories of Fuji sauce, adding just enough to coat mushrooms. (Mushrooms should not be swimming in sauce.)
• Remove from heat. Season with salt and pepper to taste.
• *Dave's Tip:* As a variation, add 2 tbsp (25 mL) chopped shallots to skillet along with the mushrooms. When mushrooms are nearly finished cooking, stir in ¼ cup (50 mL) dry white wine.

Makes 4 servings

GRILLED VIDALIA ONIONS WITH BALSAMIC VINEGAR

This classic Insider's Report *barbecue recipe is a great make-ahead dish. You can prepare the onions and wrap in foil 1 to 2 hours before tossing on the grill.*

4	Vidalia or other sweet onions	4
4 tbsp	PC Normandy-Style Cultured Butter	60 mL
4 tbsp	PC Balsamic Vinegar	60 mL
	Salt and freshly ground pepper	

• Remove onion skins. Using small sharp knife, hollow out a cone-shaped crater, about 1 inch (2.5 cm) deep, in top of each onion.
• Place each onion on a square of aluminum foil large enough to encase onion. Fill each crater with butter and balsamic vinegar. Sprinkle with salt and pepper to taste.
• Bring up ends of foil around onion and seal well to make a tight packet. Keep upright.
• Arrange onions on grill over medium hot coals until tender but firm, about 20 to 30 minutes or longer. Serve onions in foil wrap.
• *Dave's Tip:* For special occasions, I sometimes add 2 tbsp (25 mL) PC Mincemeat to each onion along with the butter and vinegar. It's surprisingly good.

Makes 4 servings

GRILLED RADICCHIO & OYSTER MUSHROOMS

This recipe is our adaptation of a John Maxwell recipe that we first tasted at Orso restaurant in Toronto. "Radicchio is so tightly bound that no washing is necessary," John notes. "Simply peel away the outermost layer of leaves."

1	head radicchio	1
	PC Extra-Virgin Olive Oil	
½ lb	oyster mushrooms	250 g
	Salt and freshly ground pepper	
2 tbsp	finely chopped fresh parsley	25 mL
2	lemons, cut in half	2

• Trim off outer layer of radicchio leaves. Cut radicchio into quarters. Brush with olive oil, coating completely; some oil should penetrate leaves. Set aside.
• Wipe mushrooms with damp towel. Trim off stems. If mushrooms are large, cut into pieces about 3 inches (7.5 cm) long and 1½ inches (4 cm) wide. Allow 4 such pieces per person. Brush with oil.
• On greased grill over medium-hot coals, arrange radicchio on one of its flat sides. After about 1½ minutes, turn onto other flat side and grill another 1½ minutes. Meanwhile, add mushrooms and cook, turning periodically.
• Turn radicchio onto rounded side. Continue to grill vegetables until nicely charred. Season with salt and pepper to taste.
• Arrange on large platter or distribute among individual plates. Sprinkle with parsley. Serve with lemon halves.
Makes 4 servings

BARBECUED ENDIVE

This exceedingly simple recipe using lemon-infused PC olive oil brings out Belgian endive's full potential.

6 to 8	heads of Belgian endive	6 to 8
	PC Pure Olive Oil with Lemon Essence	
	Salt and freshly ground pepper	

• Halve endives lengthwise. Rinse, pat dry and brush with olive oil with lemon essence.
• Place on greased grill over medium-hot coals and cook, turning often, until nicely charred.
• Arrange on platter. Season with salt and pepper to taste.
• *Dave's Secret:* Belgian endive is one of my favorite salad ingredients, but the stem end can be excessively bitter. You can find out where it stops being overly bitter by slicing rings off the stem end and tasting them until you find one that isn't so bitter. Simple!
Makes 4 to 6 servings

▲

TO BARBECUE SWEET CORN, LEAVE THE HUSK ON. SOAK IN COLD WATER 30 MINUTES, THEN PLACE ON GRILL AND LET STEAM 10 MINUTES OR UNTIL TENDER. REMOVE HUSK AND SILK AND SERVE WITH PLENTY OF PC NORMANDY-STYLE CULTURED BUTTER.

▼

Asiago Sauce from Scratch

To help you appreciate the convenience of PC Memories of Asiago sauce, here's Terri's original cheese sauce recipe: Pour 2 cups (500 mL) whipping cream into a heavy saucepan; season with a generous grinding of black pepper and nutmeg to taste. Bring to a boil, reduce heat and cook until thickened and reduced to about half. Coarsely chop ½ lb (250 g) Asiago cheese and add to the cream; continue cooking, stirring often, until cheese is melted and sauce is thick and creamy. Makes about 1⅓ cups (325 mL).

▼

Terri's sensational recipe for leeks and mushrooms inspired me to create PC "Memories of Asiago" Tangy Asiago Cheese Sauce. Its key ingredient is Asiago cheese, a sharp-tasting cheese with a tang faintly similar to extra-extra-old Cheddar. Asiago originated in the pre-Alps of Italy's Vincenza province, but it's now produced commercially around the world. In my opinion, Asiago is one of the world's finest table and cooking cheeses. Its distinctively rich flavor makes our Memories of Asiago one of the very few commercial cheese sauces that surpasses the quality of most homemade cheese sauces! For more recipes with Memories of Asiago, turn the page.

TERRI'S LEEK & MUSHROOM CASSEROLE WITH MEMORIES OF ASIAGO

There is no greater offence to the mouth than gritty leeks. To wash away trapped sand, cut the trimmed leek lengthwise through to the centre; then gently riffle the cut edges under cold running water.

2 tbsp	PC Normandy-Style Cultured Butter	25 mL
1 tsp	PC Chopped Garlic in Oil	5 mL
1	jar (19 oz/540 mL) PC Mixed Gourmet Mushrooms, drained, OR 2 cups (500 mL) sliced cremini mushrooms	1
4	leeks, halved lengthwise and sliced in 1-inch (2.5 cm) lengths (white and light green parts only)	4
1	bottle (350 mL) PC Memories of Asiago Tangy Asiago Cheese Sauce	1
⅔ cup	grated Asiago Cheese	150 mL

• In skillet, melt butter. Add garlic, mushrooms and leeks and cook, stirring, for about 10 to 12 minutes or until leeks are tender. Transfer to buttered baking dish.
• Add Memories of Asiago sauce and grated Asiago cheese; toss to coat.
• Bake in 400°F (200°C) oven for 15 to 20 minutes or until sauce bubbles and top is golden brown.
• *Dave's Tip:* A very interesting variation of this recipe is to use half Asiago, half Extra-Old Canadian White Cheddar for the grated cheese.

Makes 3 or 4 servings

Pasta with Asparagus, Shrimp & Memories of Asiago

Why eat out when you can dine in? This is beautiful to look at and it tastes sensational.

1	pkg (15.9 oz/450 g) PC World's Best Fusilli	1
3 tbsp	PC Uncommonly Light Pure Olive Oil	45 mL
1	bag (1 lb/454 g) Frozen "Zipper Back" Raw Shell-On Medium White Shrimp, thawed and shells removed	1
1	bunch asparagus, diagonally sliced in 2-inch (5 cm) lengths	1
1	bottle (350 mL) PC Memories of Asiago Tangy Asiago Cheese Sauce Salt and freshly ground pepper	1

• In large pot of boiling salted water, cook pasta until tender but firm. Drain well.
• Meanwhile, in large skillet or stir-fry pan, heat oil. Add shrimp and asparagus and cook until shrimp turn opaque. Do not overcook.
• Add Memories of Asiago sauce and cook until heated through. Add pasta and toss well. Season with salt and pepper to taste.

Makes 4 servings

MEMORIES OF ASIAGO PIZZA

Our PC Splendido and Memories of Asiago sauce make it easy to become your own "pizzaiolo" — that's Italian for pizzamaker.

¼ cup	PC Pure Olive Oil with Garlic Essence	50 mL
1 tbsp	PC Chopped Garlic in Oil	15 mL
1	red pepper, thinly sliced	1
1	PC Original Splendido (11 in/28 cm) Italian-Style Flatbread	1
½ cup	PC Memories of Asiago Tangy Asiago Cheese Sauce	125 mL
1 cup	shredded or chopped cooked chicken	250 mL
¼ cup	chopped green onions	50 mL
½ cup	PC Splendido 2-Cheese Blend Salt and freshly ground pepper	125 mL

• In skillet, heat oil. Add garlic and red pepper and cook 2 to 3 minutes, stirring, until pepper is tender. (Watch carefully to avoid burning garlic.) Remove from heat.
• Spread Splendido with Memories of Asiago sauce. Top with cooked chicken, red pepper mixture, green onions and cheese. Season with salt and pepper to taste.
• Place in 425°F (220°C) oven for 10 to 15 minutes or until cheese is melted and crust is crispy.

Makes 2 to 4 servings

GRILLED CHICKEN WITH TANGY CHEESE SAUCE

I am extremely fond of eating chicken when it tastes this good. You can also use the onion-cheese sauce for steaks.

4	PC Frozen Boneless Skinless Seasoned Chicken Breasts, thawed	4
4 tbsp	PC Normandy-Style Cultured Butter	60 mL
1	onion, thinly sliced	1
2	pkgs (each 227 g/8 oz) PC Sliced Mushrooms	2
1 cup	PC Memories of Asiago Tangy Asiago Cheese Sauce	250 mL

• On greased grill over medium-hot coals, grill chicken for 10 to 15 minutes, turning once, or just until cooked through. Keep warm.
• In skillet, heat butter. Add onion and mushrooms and cook, stirring, until onions are lightly browned. Stir in Memories of Asiago sauce and cook until heated through.
• Arrange chicken on individual plates. Top with sauce mixture.

Makes 4 servings

5-MINUTE ASPARAGUS
WITH LEMON GINGER SAUCE

You can decorate the asparagus with finely chopped yolk of hard-cooked egg (the classic "mimosa" garnish) or simply sprinkle with PC Gourmet Blend 100% Grated Parmesan Cheese. We were lucky enough to find fresh mimosa the day we photographed this simple, superb side dish.

1 lb	asparagus, trimmed (about 20 to 25 thin spears)	500 g
½ cup	PC Memories of San Francisco Golden Gate Lemon Ginger Sauce	125 mL

• In pot of boiling salted water, cook asparagus, uncovered, until tender but firm, about 4 to 5 minutes. Drain.
• Add PC Memories of San Francisco sauce and toss gently to coat.
• *Dave's Tip:* Peel the bottoms of large asparagus for more tenderness. And cook the spears uncovered to maintain their rich green color.

Makes 3 or 4 servings

I first visited San Francisco more than two decades ago after reading an article in which Parisian gastronomes Henri Gault and Christian Millau discussed their candidates for the greatest restaurant in the world.

In passing, Henri Gault mentioned that he had discovered the world's best Chinese cooking not in the famous restaurants of Hong Kong and Singapore, but at the Imperial Palace in San Francisco.

The pilgrimage I made to the Golden Gate City as a result of that article was the start of my lifelong love affair with the restaurants in San Francisco's Chinatown. When I taste our gingery lemon sauce, PC Memories of San Francisco, it brings to mind the joy of discovering the exciting world of flavors that opened up for me in that beautiful city by the bay.

Turn the page for our flavorful chicken stir-fry, fabulous barbecued salmon and sensational grilled scallop recipes — all made with Memories of San Francisco sauce.

A POUND OF ASPARAGUS (ABOUT 500 g) CONTAINS ABOUT 20 TO 25 THIN SPEARS OR NINE THICK SPEARS.

———◆———

ASPARAGUS IS 94% WATER. THAT MEANS YOU CAN AFFORD TO INDULGE. TRY IT HOT WITH CREAMY BEURRE BLANC (PAGE 129).

▼

MEMORIES OF SAN FRANCISCO CHICKEN STIR-FRY

The quantity of PC Memories of San Francisco sauce called for may sound like a lot, but it's not. Its lemon-ginger flavor is subtle, and mild enough that even children can enjoy it.

4	PC Frozen Boneless Skinless Seasoned Chicken Breasts, thawed	4
1	bottle (350 mL) PC Memories of San Francisco Golden Gate Lemon Ginger Sauce	1
8 oz	rice vermicelli	227 g
1 tbsp	PC G·r·e·e·n G·o·u·r·m·e·t The Virtuous Oil	15 mL
½	red onion, thinly sliced	½
½ lb	snow peas, trimmed	250 g
1	red pepper, thinly sliced	1
	Salt and freshly ground pepper	

• Cut chicken into thin strips. Combine with ½ cup (125 mL) Memories of San Francisco sauce and marinate for about 1 to 2 hours.
• In large pot of boiling salted water, cook rice vermicelli for 1 minute, stirring gently. Drain and set aside.
• In large skillet or stir-fry pan, heat oil. Add chicken with marinade and cook, stirring, for 2 minutes. Add onion, snow peas and red pepper; toss well and cook 2 minutes or until vegetables are tender-crisp and chicken is fully cooked.
• Add noodles and remaining Memories of San Francisco sauce. Toss for 30 seconds until heated through.
• Season with salt and pepper to taste.

Makes 4 servings

BARBECUED SALMON IN FOIL PACKETS

Serve with Asparagus Strudel with Goat Cheese and Memories of Asiago on page 44.

| 4 | salmon fillets (each about 6 oz/175 g) | 4 |
| ½ cup | PC Memories of San Francisco Golden Gate Lemon Ginger Sauce | 125 mL |

• Tear off 4 sheets of foil wrap, each large enough to enclose one fish fillet. Place one fillet in the middle of each sheet of foil.
• Drizzle Memories of San Francisco sauce over fish and seal packets well.
• Place on grill over medium-hot coals, or in 375°F (190°C) oven, and cook about 10 minutes or until fish is just cooked through; do not overcook.

Makes 4 servings

GRILLED SCALLOPS WITH VEGETABLES

What we call a "scallop" is actually the white muscle that the bivalve uses to open and close its shell. That's how a scallop propels itself through water.

1 lb	sea scallops	500 g
1 cup	PC Memories of San Francisco Golden Gate Lemon Ginger Sauce	250 mL
3 tbsp	PC Unsalted Normandy-Style Cultured Butter	45 mL
2 cups	julienne strips of assorted vegetables: carrots, celery, red pepper, yellow pepper, leeks, cucumber	500 mL

• Toss scallops with 3 tbsp (45 mL) Memories of San Francisco sauce.
• Thread scallops onto skewers. Place on greased grill over medium-hot coals and cook, turning once, for about 3 to 5 minutes, or just until firm; do not overcook.
• In saucepan, melt butter. Add vegetables and cook, stirring, for about 1 minute. Stir in remaining Memories of San Francisco sauce.
• Arrange scallops on plate and surround with vegetables. Serve with basmati rice.

Makes 4 servings

ith its dark color and concentrated sweet flavor, the vintage wine vinegar called "aceto balsamico" is unlike any other vinegar in the world. It's made in northern Italy — in the provinces of Modena and Reggio Emilia — and is named for the Italian word for "balm," which refers to the smooth, mellow nature of this superb vinegar.

In this colorful salad, from Terri's personal recipe collection, PC Balsamic Vinegar adds a rich, fruity character to the dressing and lends just the right counterpoint to the roasted peppers. The recipe is our adaptation of one we pried out of chef Dante Rota when he was at Toronto's Noodles restaurant in the '80s.

NOODLES' ROASTED RED PEPPERS
WITH ANCHOVIES AND GARLIC

Serve this flavor-rich salad as an appetizer or as a light main dish with crusty PC Rustico Italian-Style White Bread.

4	sweet red peppers	4
3	anchovy fillets, chopped	3
1/2 cup	chopped fresh parsley	125 mL
2 tsp	PC Chopped Garlic in Oil	10 mL
2 tbsp	PC Balsamic Vinegar	25 mL
1/4 cup	PC Extra-Virgin Olive Oil	50 mL
	Salt and freshly ground pepper	

• Slice peppers in half lengthwise and remove seeds. Arrange skin side up on broiler pan. Place 2 to 3 inches (5 to 7 cm) below preheated broiler element and broil until skins are black.
• Using tongs, transfer peppers to a plastic bag and seal well with twist tie. Let peppers steam in bag for 15 to 20 minutes. Then remove from bag and peel off skin. Slice peppers into thin strips and place in serving bowl.
• In separate bowl, mix together anchovies, parsley, garlic, balsamic vinegar and olive oil. Season with salt and pepper to taste.
• Add anchovy mixture to peppers and toss. Serve at room temperature.
• *Dave's Tip:* If time is at a premium, substitute a bag (500 g) of PC Frozen Mixed Pepper Strips for the roasted red peppers. Just heat in a little olive oil until heated through, then toss with the dressing and let cool to room temperature before serving.
Makes 4 servings

DID YOU KNOW THAT THERE ARE TWO DISTINCTLY DIFFERENT BALSAMIC VINEGAR PRODUCTS IN ITALY, THE PRODUCTION OF EACH GOVERNED BY SEPARATE MINISTERIAL DECREES. DON'T PAY FOR FANCY LABELS WITHOUT KNOWING WHAT'S INSIDE! FOR MORE ON BALSAMIC VINEGAR, SEE INDEX.

California-style salad mixes are North America's answer to France's ritual of spring: the "mesclun" salad. These colorful mixes can include anything from baby romaine, arugula, mâche, radicchio and red oak leaf lettuce, to tiny mustard greens, blue kale, even red Swiss chard. (A true mesclun, or mesclum, salad, of course, is totally random; you simply gather whatever leafy greens or reds poke their heads out of the ground and pop them into a salad bowl.)

Exotic greens make salad an experience, not just a side dish. But what sets Terri's salad apart from the rest — it was the single best-selling item at the Sanssouci restaurant during the Sutton Place Hotel's spring tribute to my *Insider's Report*! — is her choice of dressing: PC "Memories of Reggiano" Parmigiano Reggiano Caesar Salad Dressing, a luxuriously thick, flavorful dressing made with real Parmigiano Reggiano cheese from Italy.

TERRI'S CALIFORNIA-STYLE MIXED GREENS WITH MEMORIES OF REGGIANO CAESAR DRESSING

If you can't find our "pre-mixed" PC California-Style greens, make your own selection. Look for contrasting colors and textures and balance the more pungent or bitter-tasting greens (i.e., mustard greens, chicory, arugula) with mild and sweet varieties (i.e., romaine, red oak leaf, baby spinach).

2	bags (each 125 g) PC California-Style Fresh Salad Mixed Greens or 4 to 6 cups (1 to 1.5 L) mixed greens and reds of your choice	2
1	pint ripe cherry tomatoes, cut in half	1
1/3 cup	pine nuts, toasted*	75 mL
1 cup	PC Memories of Reggiano Parmigiano Reggiano Caesar Dressing	250 mL
	Freshly shaved Parmesan cheese	
8 to 12	Rustico Croutons (recipe follows)	8 to 12

• Arrange mixed greens on 4 to 6 salad plates. Add cherry tomatoes and pine nuts.
• Drizzle with Memories of Reggiano dressing. Garnish with shaved Parmesan cheese.
• Place 2 Rustico croutons on each plate.

Makes 4 to 6 servings

*To toast pine nuts: Place on baking sheet and toast in 350°F (180°C) oven for about 5 minutes or until golden; watch carefully so nuts don't burn.

RUSTICO CROUTONS

Cut 1 PC Rustico Italian-Style White Bread (280 g) on the diagonal into 1/4-inch (5 mm) slices. Brush each slice with PC Extra-Virgin Olive Oil, arrange on baking sheet and toast in 350°F (180°C) oven for 5 to 10 minutes or until golden brown. Watch carefully to avoid burning.

Makes 24 to 30

TENDER GREENS GET WATERLOGGED EASILY, SO RINSE BRIEFLY AND DRY WELL. FIRM GREENS, LIKE ARUGULA, RADICCHIO AND SPINACH, CAN SOAK IN COLD WATER FOR 5 TO 10 MINUTES (A GOOD TRICK FOR REVIVING TIRED SPINACH LEAVES).

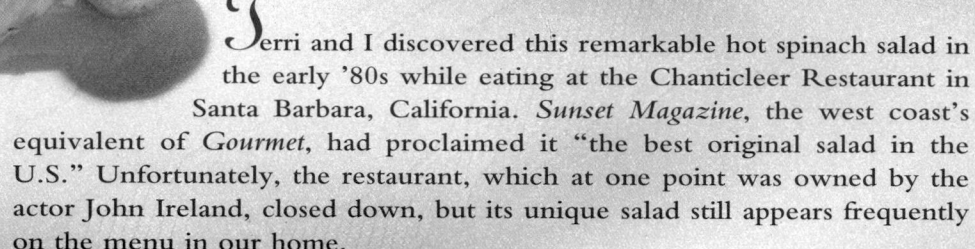

*T*erri and I discovered this remarkable hot spinach salad in the early '80s while eating at the Chanticleer Restaurant in Santa Barbara, California. *Sunset Magazine*, the west coast's equivalent of *Gourmet*, had proclaimed it "the best original salad in the U.S." Unfortunately, the restaurant, which at one point was owned by the actor John Ireland, closed down, but its unique salad still appears frequently on the menu in our home.

SANTA BARBARA WILTED SPINACH SALAD

This is the perfect salad to serve with summer barbecues. While the meat's cooking on one side of the grill, you can cook the bacon, mushrooms and dressing in a skillet on the other side.

1	pkg (250 g) PC Special-Trim Bacon, cut in bite-sized pieces	1
1	pkg (8 oz/250 g) PC Sliced Mushrooms	1
4 tbsp	PC Balsamic Vinegar	60 mL
2 tbsp	fresh lemon juice	25 mL
2 tbsp	PC Dijon Mustard	25 mL
1 tbsp	PC Russian-Style Sweet Mustard	15 mL
1	bundle or bag (10 oz/284 g) fresh spinach, stems removed	1
	Salt and freshly ground pepper	

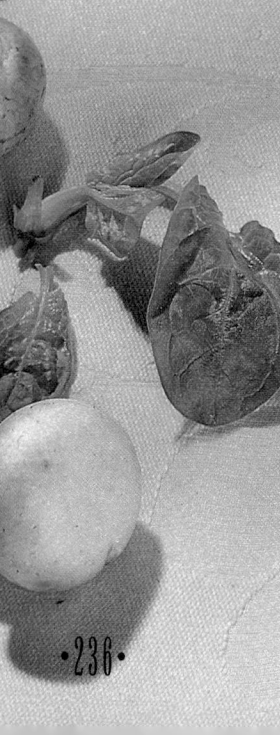

• In large skillet over medium heat, fry bacon until cooked through but not crisp. Remove from pan and keep warm.
• Pour off all but 3 tbsp (45 mL) of bacon fat. Add mushrooms and cook for about 3 to 4 minutes or until tender. Add vinegar and lemon juice and cook 1 to 2 minutes longer until mixture is reduced by half.
• Add Dijon and Russian-style mustards; blend well and reduce to a syrupy consistency. Taste and adjust lemon, vinegar and mustards, if desired. Remove from heat.
• Tear spinach into pieces and place in heatproof bowl (such as a stainless steel mixing bowl). Add dressing and toss to coat. Sprinkle with bacon and place bottom of heated skillet over salad bowl for about 1 minute or until spinach "steams" and starts to wilt.
• Season with salt and pepper to taste. Serve warm.
• *Dave's Tip:* An interesting and colorful variation is to use half the spinach and add 1 medium head of radicchio and 3 Begian endives, leaves separated, rinsed and torn in bite-sized pieces.
• *Dave's Minute-Minded Version:* Cook bacon and mushrooms as above. Pour off fat and add ¾ cup (175 mL) PC Memories of Szechwan Peanut Sauce OR PC Memories of Bangkok Spicy Thai Sauce to skillet. Heat, stirring, until hot. Remove from heat. Tear spinach into pieces and finish as above.

Makes 3 or 4 servings

*B*efore tuna in cans, there was tuna in amphoras. The ancient Greeks and Romans ate tuna fish that was salted and then marinated in oil. (In Italy, you can still buy tuna out of barrels, much like you do anchovies.) The best quality tuna had to be caught between the rising of the star cluster Pleiades and the setting of the star Arcturus. A gourmet, it was said, could tell the difference.

Tuna aficionados still discriminate when it comes to choosing tuna. Albacore is the finest of all the varieties — it's the only one that can be called "white" — although I often make this salad with PC Tongol Tuna, our original "PC tuna" and the only light tuna, in my opinion, that looks and tastes essentially like albacore.

▲

OUR PC MEMORIES
OF BANGKOK
SPICY THAI SAUCE
IS MY RECOLLECTION
OF A DELICIOUS
SWEET AND SOUR
HOT SAUCE THAT
I'VE ENCOUNTERED
FREQUENTLY IN
BANGKOK.
▼

SPICY THAI TUNA SALAD

You can use PC Memories of Bangkok on everything from fish, chicken and vegetables to noodles and dumplings. You can even use it to make tuna salad. Try our version — it's a snap to make and tastes terrific.

1	pkg (375 g) PC Shanghai Frozen Stir-Fry Oriental Vegetable Mix	1
1	can (5.5 oz/155 g) PC Albacore Solid White Tuna, drained	1
2	stalks celery, sliced	2
1/2	red bell pepper, coarsely diced	1/2
2/3 cup	PC 'Too Good To Be True!' Memories of Bangkok Spicy Thai Sauce	150 mL
2 tbsp	fresh lemon juice	25 mL
	Salt and freshly ground pepper	

• Bring 2 cups (500 mL) water to boil. Add Shanghai vegetables and cook for 1 minute. Drain, rinse with cold water to stop cooking and drain again. Pat dry with paper towel.
• Place tuna in salad bowl; flake with fork. Add Shanghai vegetables, celery and red pepper; toss gently.
• Mix together Memories of Bangkok sauce and lemon juice. Add to tuna mixture and toss. Season with salt and pepper to taste.

Makes 4 servings

CORN SALSA

This is served warm — wonderful with chicken or fish, or spooned into a hot, fluffy baked potato! Or try it over vegetables such as broccoli and cauliflower.

2 tsp	PC Normandy-Style Cultured Butter	10 mL
2 tsp	PC Chopped Garlic in Oil	10 mL
1	red pepper, seeded and finely chopped	1
2 cups	PC Frozen Peaches and Cream Corn	500 mL
1 cup	PC Memories Of Gilroy Creamy Roasted Garlic Sauce	250 mL

• In medium saucepan over medium-high heat, melt butter. Add garlic and red pepper and cook for 1 minute. Add frozen corn and continue cooking until vegetable mixture is warm.

• Stir in Memories of Gilroy sauce and cook until heated through. Serve warm.

Makes 4 servings

We named our PC Creamy Roasted Garlic Sauce & Dressing after Gilroy, California, the uncontested garlic capital of North America. Located 100 miles south of San Francisco in the Santa Clara Valley, a major garlic-producing region, Gilroy is known to alliophiles (i.e., garlic aficionados) all over the globe.

Every summer, they descend on the town by the hundreds of thousands to indulge in a three-day extravaganza of garlic-laden foods ranging from garlic steak to garlic ice cream.

Will Rogers, the great American humorist, described Gilroy as the only place he knew "where you can marinate a steak by hanging it on the clothesline."

Herewith, a trio of salads for your next garlic festival, all made with our unique PC Memories of Gilroy. The recipes for the Warm Potato Salad and Gilroy Coleslaw, pictured at right with Corn Salsa, are on the following page.

GILROY COLESLAW

Toss this coleslaw with the dressing just before serving to prevent the color of the red cabbage from bleeding. You can make the salad with white cabbage only, if preferred. If the cabbage is particularly pungent, make the salad a few hours ahead to give the flavors time to tone down.

1	medium white cabbage, thinly sliced	1
1	medium red cabbage, thinly sliced	1
1/4 cup	PC Memories of Gilroy Creamy Roasted Garlic Sauce	50 mL
1/2 cup	PC Whipped Salad Dressing	125 mL
	Salt and freshly ground pepper	
	Juice of 1/2 lemon	

• In large bowl, combine white and red cabbages.
• In small bowl, whisk together Memories of Gilroy sauce and whipped salad dressing; pour over cabbage. Toss.
• Season with salt and pepper to taste and lemon juice. Toss well.

Makes 6 to 8 servings

LE CHOIX DU

PRESIDENT'S CHOICE™

BLACK PEPPERCORNS

TELLICHERRY

GRAINS DE POIVRE NOIR

COR 94

IDS NET WT. 10.2 OZ 290 g

WARM POTATO SALAD

It's important to use a moderately starchy potato for this recipe, such as the PC Yukon Gold, so that the cubes of potato stay intact. Baking potatoes are too starchy and will fall apart, making a mess of your salad.

2 lb	PC Yukon Gold Potatoes OR other yellow-fleshed potatoes	1 kg
6	slices PC Special Trim Bacon, chopped	6
1	small onion, coarsely chopped	1
1 tsp	PC Chopped Garlic in Oil	5 mL
½	bunch fresh spinach, stems removed	½
½ cup	PC Memories of Gilroy Creamy Roasted Garlic Sauce	125 mL
	Salt and freshly ground pepper	

• Cook potatoes with skins on in boiling salted water to cover for about 20 minutes or just until tender; do not overcook. Remove from heat but do not drain.
• In small skillet, cook bacon until it begins to soften and render its fat. Add onion and garlic and continue cooking, stirring often, until bacon is crisp. Remove from heat.
• Stir in spinach and Memories of Gilroy sauce. Season with salt and pepper to taste.
• Drain potatoes and cut into ½-inch (1 cm) cubes. Place in serving dish. Add spinach mixture and toss.

Makes 4 to 6 servings

Mixed Bean Salad

COMBINE 1 JAR (28 OZ/796 mL) PC 'TOO GOOD TO BE TRUE!' PRECOOKED 7-BEAN MIX, RINSED AND DRAINED, ¼ CUP (50 mL) FINELY CHOPPED RED ONION, 1 RED PEPPER, FINELY CHOPPED, ¼ CUP (50 mL) EACH PC MEMORIES OF SONOMA DRIED TOMATO SAUCE AND PC MEMORIES OF GILROY CREAMY ROASTED GARLIC SAUCE. TOSS. MAKES 4 TO 6 SERVINGS.

SPLENDIDO WITH ONIONS AND MUSHROOMS

Here's our version of pizza bianca, or "white pizza" — i.e. without tomatoes.

1 tbsp	PC Uncommonly Light Pure Olive Oil	15 mL
2	onions, thinly sliced	2
5	shiitake mushrooms, trimmed and sliced	5
½ cup	PC Memories of Gilroy Creamy Roasted Garlic Sauce	125 mL
1 tbsp	chopped fresh thyme or 1 tsp (5 mL) dried	15 mL
	Salt and freshly ground pepper	
1	PC Original or Cheese Splendido (11 in/28 cm) Italian-Style Flatbread	1
2 tbsp	PC Gourmet Blend 100% Grated Parmesan Cheese	25 mL

• In skillet, heat oil. Add onions and mushrooms and cook, stirring often, until onions are tender. Turn off heat. Add Memories of Gilroy sauce, thyme and salt and pepper to taste; mix well.

• Spoon onion mixture onto Splendido. Sprinkle with Parmesan cheese.

• Place directly on rack in 400°F (200°C) oven for 10 to 15 minutes or until heated through.

Makes 4 to 6 appetizer servings

LE CHOIX DU PRÉSIDENT™MC

PRESIDENT'S CHOICE™

BLACK PEPPERCORNS

TELLICHERRY

GRAINS DE POIVRE NOIR

COR 94

POIDS NET WT. 10.2 OZ 290 g

CAPELLI D'ANGELO WITH SWEDISH MEATBALLS AND MEMORIES OF GILROY

A new twist on spaghetti and meatballs, made with our unique PC creamy roasted garlic sauce — now one of our Top 10 "Memories of..." sauces in Ontario!

20 to 25	PC Frozen Fully Cooked Swedish Meatballs (about ⅓ of a 2 lb/907 g pkg)	20 to 25
1	pkg (15.9 oz/450 g) PC World's Best Capelli d'Angelo Pasta	1
1	bottle (350 mL) PC Memories of Gilroy Creamy Roasted Garlic Sauce	1
1 cup	finely chopped tomato	250 mL
½ cup	chopped fresh parsley	125 mL
	Salt and freshly ground pepper	

• Arrange frozen meatballs in shallow ovenproof dish. Heat in 400°F (200°C) oven for 15 minutes or until heated through.
• Meanwhile, bring large pot of salted water to boil. Add pasta and cook until tender but firm; drain well.
• Place pasta in serving bowl. Add Memories of Gilroy sauce, tomato, parsley and meatballs. Toss well.
• Season with salt and freshly ground pepper to taste.

Makes 4 to 6 servings

Grilled Mixed Mushrooms with Roasted Garlic Dressing

IN LARGE BOWL, COMBINE ½ LB (250 g) EACH WHOLE CREMINI, OYSTER AND SHIITAKE MUSHROOMS. ADD 2 TBSP (25 mL) PC EXTRA-VIRGIN OLIVE OIL AND TOSS. PLACE IN GRILL BASKET AND GRILL OVER MEDIUM-HOT COALS FOR 15 TO 20 MINUTES UNTIL TENDER. TOSS WITH ½ CUP (125 mL) PC MEMORIES OF GILROY CREAMY ROASTED GARLIC SAUCE AND SPRINKLE LIGHTLY WITH PC GOURMET BLEND 100% GRATED PARMESAN CHEESE. MAKES 4 TO 6 SERVINGS.

▼

We were staying at the Rambagh Palace Hotel in Jaipur, a landmark in India's "pink city," so-named because of the preponderance of pink paint within the city walls. The Rambagh was once the home of the famous polo-playing Maharaja Man Singh II of Jaipur, who died in 1970. (It's now managed by the The Taj Group of Hotels.)

We were served shrimp grilled with a sweet-and-sour curry sauce that easily surpassed every curry dish we had tasted before. The sauce was alive with fragrance and heat — aromatic with the manifold spices favored by Indian cooks and tantalizingly seductive with the savor of passion fruit.

Even with the help of the Maharaja's chef, the sauce from the Rambagh wasn't easy to duplicate, but after many attempts in our President's Choice test kitchen, we finally discovered its mouth-watering secret and bottled it as the President's Choice "Memories of Jaipur" Curry and Passion Fruit Sauce. This sauce is delectable with rice, or as a spicy sauce or glaze for meat, poultry and seafood.

MEMORIES OF JAIPUR CHICKEN SALAD

This salad is medium-hot. Add more or less PC Memories of Jaipur sauce according to your preference for "heat."

Rice, of course, is an antidote to the effects of the hot and spicy foods found in many cuisines in the Far East. Milk also cools the mouth because it contains the protein casein, which binds with capsaicin, the "heat factor" in hot peppers.

4 cups	chicken stock, homemade or made with PC Fresh Concentrated Chicken Stock	1 L
4	PC Frozen Boneless Skinless Seasoned Chicken Breasts, thawed	4
1	medium cucumber, cut in 1/2-inch (2 cm) cubes	1
1 cup	PC Lightly Seasoned Dry Roasted Peanuts	250 mL
4 tbsp	PC The Ultimate Mayonnaise	50 mL
4 tbsp	sour cream or PC 'Too Good To Be True!' Fat-Free Plain Yogurt	50 mL
4 tbsp	PC Memories of Jaipur Curry & Passion Fruit Sauce Salt and freshly ground pepper	50 mL

• In large deep skillet, bring chicken stock to boil. Add chicken, reduce heat and simmer for 10 to 15 minutes or until chicken is cooked through. Remove from broth and let cool.

• Cut chicken into cubes. Place in bowl and toss with cucumber, peanuts, mayonnaise, sour cream, Memories of Jaipur sauce and salt and pepper to taste.

Makes 4 servings

▲

IF YOU MAKE IT TO THE RAMBAGH, BE SURE TO DROP BY THE HOTEL'S POLO BAR. IT IS TO JAIPUR WHAT HARRY'S BAR IS TO VENICE.

—————

FOR MORE SPICY DISHES FLAVORED WITH PC MEMORIES OF JAIPUR SAUCE, SEE THE NEXT FOUR PAGES.

▼

JAIPUR RICE SALAD

Indian rice dishes are fragrant with many aromatic spices — supplied here by our authentically inspired PC Memories of Jaipur Curry & Passion Fruit Sauce.

1 tbsp	PC Unsalted Normandy-Style Cultured Butter	15 mL
1 tsp	PC Chopped Garlic in Oil	5 mL
1 tsp	PC Chopped Shallots in Oil	5 mL
1/2	Spanish onion, finely chopped	1/2
1	red pepper, finely chopped	1
2 cups	PC American Basmati Rice, rinsed and drained	500 mL
1/2 cup	PC Whole Cashews	125 mL
1/4 cup	raisins	50 mL
1/2 cup	PC Memories of Jaipur Curry & Passion Fruit Sauce	125 mL

♦ In deep skillet or large saucepan, heat butter. Add garlic, shallots, onion and red pepper and cook, stirring, until onion is soft; do not brown.
♦ Add rice and 4 cups (1 L) water; bring to boil. Reduce heat to medium and cook, covered, for about 25 minutes or until all of water is absorbed. Remove from heat.
♦ Add cashews, raisins and Memories of Jaipur sauce. Stir well.
♦ Serve hot or cold.

Makes 4 servings

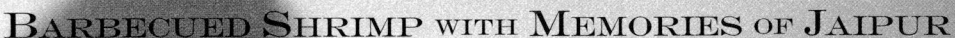

BARBECUED SHRIMP WITH MEMORIES OF JAIPUR

Our colossal-size shrimp make impressive barbecue fare. They're huge — only 10 or fewer per pound (500 g).

1	pkg (16 oz/454 g) PC Frozen "Zipper Back" Raw Shell-On Colossal Black Tiger Shrimp, thawed	1
½ cup	PC Memories of Jaipur Curry & Passion Fruit Sauce	125 mL
	Additional PC Memories of Jaipur sauce OR PC Memories of Szechwan Peanut Sauce for dipping	

• Marinate shrimp in PC Memories of Jaipur sauce for 30 to 60 minutes; do not marinate longer than one hour or flesh will start to break down. Drain shrimp and place in grill basket.
• Place grill basket over medium-hot coals and cook for 3 to 5 minutes per side or until cooked through; do not overcook.
• Serve shrimp in their shells with additional Memories of Jaipur sauce or Memories of Szechwan sauce for dipping.

Makes 4 servings

LENTILS WITH MEMORIES OF JAIPUR

In India, lentils are nearly as important as rice. The country grows dozens of different kinds that are valued for their individual flavor characteristics.

1 tbsp	PC Unsalted Normandy-Style Cultured Butter	15 mL
1 tsp	PC Chopped Garlic in Oil	5 mL
1	onion, coarsely chopped	1
1 cup	green lentils, rinsed and drained	250 mL
¼ cup	PC Memories of Jaipur Curry & Passion Fruit Sauce	50 mL
3 tbsp	crumbled goat cheese	45 mL
½	tomato, finely chopped	½
	Salt and freshly ground pepper	

• In medium saucepan, heat butter. Add garlic and onion and cook over medium heat, stirring occasionally, until tender.
• Add lentils and 2 cups (500 mL) water. Bring to boil, reduce heat to medium, and cook, covered, for about 20 minutes, until lentils are tender but firm. Most of the liquid will have been absorbed.
• Remove from heat. Stir in Memories of Jaipur sauce, goat cheese, tomato and salt and pepper to taste.

Makes 4 servings

▲

THE WORD CURRY, COINED BY BRITISH COLONIALS IN INDIA, IS USED TO DESCRIBE SAVORY DISHES OF MEAT, FISH OR VEGETABLES IN SPICY SAUCES THAT VARY FROM HOT TO MILD. THE SAUCES ARE BASED ON DIFFERENT MIXES OF SPICES, KNOWN AS MASALAS. MOST MASALAS ARE BLENDED FROM TWO OR MORE SPICES NATIVE TO INDIA, INCLUDING TURMERIC, GINGER, CORIANDER SEEDS, CUMIN, CHILIES, CLOVES, CINNAMON AND NUTMEG.

▼

BANANA CURRY SAUCE

A sensational sauce for shrimp, scallops, chicken or turkey. It tastes extravagantly rich, but there's actually very little butter or cream in it.

2 tbsp	PC Unsalted Normandy-Style Cultured Butter	25 mL
1 tbsp	PC Chopped Garlic in Oil	15 mL
1	medium onion, coarsely chopped	1
1	apple, peeled, seeded and coarsely chopped	1
2	bananas, coarsely chopped	2
2 cups	chicken stock, homemade or made with	500 mL
	PC Fresh Concentrated Chicken Stock	
¾ cup	PC Memories of Jaipur Curry & Passion Fruit Sauce	175 mL
¼ cup	whipping cream	50 mL
	Salt and freshly ground pepper	

• In saucepan over medium-high heat, melt butter. Add garlic, onion, apple and bananas and cook, stirring occasionally, for about 5 minutes.
• Stir in chicken stock and Memories of Jaipur sauce and bring to boil; reduce heat and simmer, uncovered, for 20 to 30 minutes.
• Using food processor or blender, purée mixture until smooth. Return to saucepan and add cream and salt and pepper to taste. If desired, thin sauce with a little broth or water.

Makes 4 to 6 servings

CARROT SOUP WITH MEMORIES OF JAIPUR

Curry and carrots are a marriage of flavors made in heaven.

2 tbsp	PC Unsalted Normandy-Style Cultured Butter	25 mL
1 tbsp	PC Chopped Garlic in Oil	15 mL
1	medium onion, coarsely chopped	1
1	pkg (2.2 lb/1 kg) PC Frozen Uncommonly Sweet Whole Baby Carrots	1
1 cup	PC Memories of Jaipur Curry & Passion Fruit Sauce	250 mL
3 cups	chicken stock, homemade or made with PC Fresh Concentrated Chicken Stock	750 mL
	Salt and freshly ground pepper	

• In large saucepan over medium-high heat, melt butter. Add garlic and onion and cook, stirring occasionally, until onion is tender.
• Add carrots and cook, stirring, for about 5 minutes.
• Stir in Memories of Jaipur sauce and chicken stock. Bring to boil, reduce heat and simmer, uncovered, for about 15 to 20 minutes.
• Using food processor or blender, purée soup until smooth. Season with salt and pepper to taste.

Makes 6 to 8 servings

CAULIFLOWER AND POTATOES WITH MEMORIES OF JAIPUR

Be warned: these curried vegetables will set your mouth on fire! To tame the fire, serve with plenty of rice, or with cold milk (true!) or PC Brew De-Alcoholized Beer Beverage.

3	PC Yukon Gold Potatoes, peeled and cut in cubes	3
1	bottle (350 mL) PC Memories of Jaipur Curry & Passion Fruit Sauce	1
1	medium head cauliflower, separated in florets	1
2 tbsp	sour cream	25 mL
	Salt and freshly ground pepper	

• In medium saucepan, combine potatoes and Memories of Jaipur sauce. Bring to boil, reduce heat and simmer, covered, for about 10 minutes. Add cauliflower and continue cooking, covered, for 10 minutes longer or until vegetables are soft, but not mushy.
• Remove from heat and let stand for about 5 minutes. Using strainer, separate vegetables from sauce, reserving sauce.
• Return reserved sauce to saucepan and boil for about 2 minutes until slightly thickened. Remove from heat and whisk in sour cream.
• Return potatoes and cauliflower to sauce. Mix well.

Makes 4 servings

THE EDITORIAL STAFF'S FAVORITE RECIPES

Carol White, Editor

Wild Mushroom Soup (p. 29)
It's hard to resist the intense, earthy flavor of wild mushrooms in a flavor-rich broth thickened with cream.

Favorite Beef Stew (p. 63)
This is a long-time family favorite. Perfect comfort food. (Frances Litwin was away when we tested this dish and doesn't believe me when I tell her how good it is.) Serve with broad noodles and a bottle of your favorite French Burgundy.

Veal Chops with Mushrooms & Onions (p. 74)
Can you ever improve on simple dishes made with the best ingredients around.

Poached Salmon with Dave Nichol's Creamy Beurre Blanc (p. 126)
Dave Nichol's Creamy Beurre Blanc has that wonderful sour tang I can't resist. The best part is that you only need a spoonful to brighten up poached salmon.

Terri's Ravioli with Shrimp & Lobster Sauce (p. 138)
A creamy tomato sauce abundant with chunks of lobster and shrimp spooned over pillows of cheese ravioli. Fabulous!

Shrimp Quesadillas (p. 166)
You simply have to try these to understand how good they are. Make plenty and serve with chilled PC Premium Draft Beer.

Northern Bean and White Tuna Salad (p. 175)
This salad has it all — white albacore tuna (which I love), beans (which I adore), tomatoes (my favorite), all tossed with a sensational mustard vinaigrette.

Spaghetti Carbonara (p. 192)
I especially like it with pancetta and generous shavings of Parmigiano Reggiano. Simple and delicious.

Devon Custard Trifle (p. 266)
I never understood all the fuss about trifle until I tasted this one.

Memories of Terri's Chocolate Mousse Cake (p. 258)
This fits my definition of the perfect chocolate cake: (1) dense texture; (2) intense, rich chocolate flavor. (If I'm going to spend calories on a chocolate dessert, I want the best.)

La Crème de la Crème Brûlée (p. 262)
Luxuriously smooth and creamy beneath a crust of caramelized sugar.

Frances Litwin, Writer

Parsley & Parmesan Salad with Sun-Dried Tomatoes (p. 203)
Wonderful. I could eat bowlfuls of it.

Shrimp Quesadillas (p. 166)
You won't know how good these are until you bite into one. In one mouthful you get tender crunch (from the crisply fried flour tortillas), appealing chewiness (from the shrimp) and exciting flavor (from the PC Splendido 2-Cheese Blend and PC Splendido Pizzazz, a sun-dried tomato and fermented black bean sauce.)

Roast Capon with Sage-and-Onion Bread Stuffing (p. 103)
There are times when you long for familiar flavors, and this recipe has all the shortcuts. One of the simple perfect recipes.

Fillet of Salmon with Black Bean Sauce (p. 131)
Fermented black beans were created for fish and seafood. Of that I'm firmly convinced. They're the perfect match.

My Sister Marilyn's Famous Grilled Vegetables (p. 218)
These are a vegetable awakening. Fabulous and flamboyant, like Dave Nichol's sister Marilyn herself in her dazzling purple hat.

4-Peppercorn Scalloped Potatoes (p. 198)
A very sophisticated rendition, yet virtually effortless. Learn to make it and open your own restaurant.

Memories of Copenhagen Apple Purée & Browned Butter (p. 273)
It looks deceptively ordinary, but your tastebuds soon put a lie to that notion. It's nutty and sweet. (Carol White was away when we tested this recipe; she doesn't believe that it tastes as good as I say.)

Memories of Harry's Bar Bittersweet Chocolate Ice Cream (p. 278)
The words "deep chocolate" could have been coined to describe this smooth and creamy ice cream. Homemade ice cream never tasted so luxurious. (Believe me, I know, I've tried 'em all.)

High-Fibre Muesli Muffins (p. 290)
Few muffins come together this quickly. They're moist and chockful of fruit.

Memories of Terri's Chocolate Mousse Cake (p. 258)
This is so-o-o good. I think it can console me until the test kitchen cracks the secret of Terri Nichol's famous chocolate mousse cake. (It's o.k., Terri, I know you're not holding anything back.)

WARM TRUFFLE-FILLED CHOCOLATE SOUFFLÉ CAKES

This recipe for individual warm chocolate soufflé cakes that ooze a rich truffle filling when you cut into them comes from Elka Gilmore, chef-proprietor of San Francisco's famous restaurant in the Miyako Hotel. We've adapted it using President's Choice products.

9 oz	PC Bittersweet Rich Dark Chocolate, coarsely chopped	250 g
¾ cup	PC Unsalted Normandy-Style Cultured Butter	175 mL
6	eggs, separated	6
1 cup	granulated sugar	250 mL
½ tsp	salt	2 mL
4 to 8	Teuscher Champagne Truffles	4 to 8
	PC Vanilla Crème Anglaise	
	Sifted icing sugar	

• Butter four 1-cup (250 mL) or eight ½-cup (125 mL) ramekins and dust with sugar.
• Melt together chocolate and butter over gently simmering water.
• Whip egg yolks and ¾ cup (175 mL) of sugar until well blended. Add melted chocolate-butter mixture and mix well.
• Whip egg whites and salt until soft peaks form; fold into chocolate mixture.
• Spoon into ramekins and insert one truffle into centre of each. Place in 350°F (180°C) oven for 20 to 30 minutes or until firm to the touch and top is slightly crusty.
• Let cool slightly. Spoon a little crème anglaise onto each dessert plate. Unmould soufflés and place on top. Sprinkle with sifted icing sugar.
• *Dave's Tip:* To gild this lily, serve the warm soufflé cake beside a pool of strawberry purée and a few puffs of softly whipped cream, lightly sweetened to taste.

Makes 4 to 8 servings

Terri and I were in San Francisco with Jim and Carol White. We dined at one of the city's top restaurants, Elka Definite Seafood.

Chef-proprietor Elka Gilmore is considered to be the best East–West chef in San Francisco. After sampling her French-Japanese treatment of seafood, I instantly knew why!

For dessert, a few of us ordered the restaurant's revered warm chocolate soufflé cake. From the first mouthful, I recognized that this was no ordinary chocolate dessert — it was a classic. When I asked Elka for her secret, she revealed that the pastry chef tucked a bittersweet chocolate truffle into the heart of each individual cake just before baking.

We've tested this recipe using every available type of truffle known to man. As far as I'm concerned, the best is Teuscher's Champagne Truffle (available in Toronto at Teuscher of Switzerland, 55 Avenue Road). An extravagant touch? Of course. And it's worth every bite.

MEMORIES OF
TERRI'S CHOCOLATE MOUSSE CAKE

Don't even attempt to make this luxurious chocolate cake with ordinary cooking chocolate. The secret of the intense flavor is PC Bittersweet Rich Dark Chocolate from France.

10 oz	PC Bittersweet Rich Dark Chocolate (30 squares)	300 g
½ cup	PC Unsalted Normandy-Style Cultured Butter	125 mL
6	large eggs, separated	6
1 cup	granulated sugar	250 mL
	Sifted icing sugar	
	PC Vanilla Crème Anglaise	

▲

REFRIGERATE THIS
CAKE OVERNIGHT SO
THAT IT ACQUIRES
A PROPERLY DENSE AND
FUDGY TEXTURE.
AND SLICE IT THIN
— IT'S RICH!

▼

• In top of double boiler over simmering water, melt together chocolate and butter. Let cool slightly.
• Beat together egg yolks and ¾ cup (175 mL) sugar until very light and lemon colored. Beat in melted chocolate mixture until well blended.
• In separate bowl, beat egg whites until mounds begin to form. Slowly beat in remaining sugar until firm (but not brittle). Fold one-third of egg whites into chocolate mixture; gently fold in remaining whites.
• Butter an 8-inch (20 cm) springform pan; line with parchment and butter again; dust lightly with flour. Pour batter into prepared pan. Line outside with double thickness of heavy-duty foil to prevent leaking. Place springform in larger pan. Pour in hot water to halfway up sides of springform.
• Place in lower half of 375°F (190°C) oven for 15 minutes; reduce heat to 350°F (180°C) and continue baking for 15 minutes longer. Reduce heat to 275°F (140°C) and cook 30 minutes longer. Turn off heat and prop open oven door for 30 to 40 minutes. Remove from water bath and let cool in springform.
• Refrigerate at least 2 hours, preferably overnight, until cake sets. Carefully remove from pan and invert onto serving platter. Let warm to room temperature.
• Dust lightly with icing sugar, slice and serve on a pool of crème anglaise.

Makes 8 to 10 servings

$\mathcal{W}$hy is dessert and a good cup of coffee so important? Because the human brain always remembers most keenly *what happens last* — especially when there's meaning attached.

Meaning, of course, is what determines our ability to remember anything. My wife, Terri, makes a very "meaningful" chocolate mousse cake. Meaningful because it's the cake she makes to celebrate the birthdays of family and special friends. And meaningful because its single dominant flavor is CHOCOLATE in the superlative.

Terri was going to reveal the recipe for her famous chocolate mousse cake in the pages of my President's Choice anniversary cookbook. But every time the test kitchen chefs made it — at least half a dozen times, and even after watching Terri make it at our home! — something continually went awry. We simply can't bake a cake as good as my wife's!

This recipe evolved during our many kitchen trials and errors. It's so close to Terri's legendary chocolate mousse cake, however, that I was persuaded to include it here.

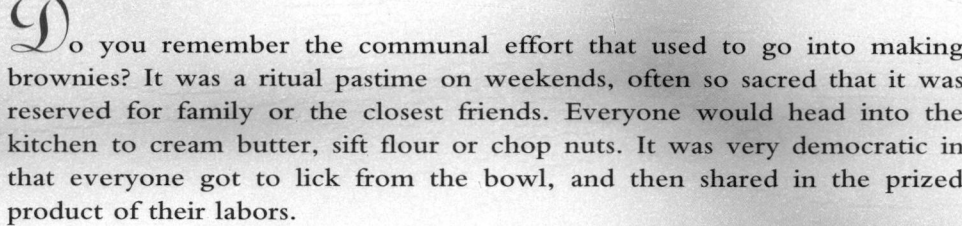

*D*o you remember the communal effort that used to go into making brownies? It was a ritual pastime on weekends, often so sacred that it was reserved for family or the closest friends. Everyone would head into the kitchen to cream butter, sift flour or chop nuts. It was very democratic in that everyone got to lick from the bowl, and then shared in the prized product of their labors.

My friend "Big Al" Morris, who hails from Tyler, Texas (you'll find his Texas brisket recipe on page 60), considers this to be "The World's Best Brownie Recipe," which is big praise, indeed, from a Texan. The recipe, which has gone through several evolutions, originated with product developer Christine Mullen.

THE WORLD'S BEST BROWNIE RECIPE

The addition of PC Chocolate Hazelnut or Chocolate Almond Spread produces a fudgy moistness and rich chocolate flavor that are irresistible. WARNING: If you are a chocoholic, then we are legally and morally obligated to inform you beforehand that should you try this recipe, you may spend the rest of your life at home, making these brownies!

4	large eggs	4
2	containers (each 400 g) PC Chocolate Hazelnut OR Chocolate Almond Spread	2
½ cup	PC Unsalted Normandy-Style Cultured Butter, melted	125 mL
2 tsp	pure vanilla extract	10 mL
⅔ cup	all-purpose flour	150 mL
1 tsp	baking powder	5 mL
Pinch	salt	Pinch
1 cup	PC 'The Decadent' Semisweet Chocolate Chips	250 mL
2 cups	chopped fresh pecans	500 mL

♦ In medium bowl, beat eggs until light and frothy. Blend in chocolate hazelnut or chocolate almond spread, butter and vanilla.
♦ In separate bowl, combine flour, baking powder and salt. Add to chocolate mixture and mix well. Stir in chocolate chips and pecans.
♦ Spread in buttered 13 x 9-inch (3.5 L) baking dish and bake in 350°F (180°C) oven for 30 to 40 minutes; brownies should appear slightly underbaked in centre. Let cool. Then, for best flavor and texture, refrigerate overnight. Cut into squares before serving.
♦ *Dave's Tip:* Always taste nuts before using in baking to make sure they're fresh.
Makes 30 squares

La Crème de la Crème Brûlée

This Le Cirque-inspired dessert has the most incredible "mouth feel" of any dessert in the world. The custard is as smooth as satin beneath the golden crackling, caramelized sugar glaze. We use PC Fresh Thick Double Cream, athough you can also use whipping cream and the results will still be stellar.

Before you start calculating the quantity of eggs and cream, remember: This is a very special occasion dessert!

3 cups	PC Fresh Thick Double Cream OR whipping cream	750 mL
1 cup	whole milk	250 mL
1	vanilla bean OR 2 tsp (10 mL) pure vanilla extract	1
Pinch	salt	Pinch
7	egg yolks	7
1/2 cup	granulated sugar	125 mL
1 cup	brown sugar	250 mL

• In saucepan, heat together thick double cream or whipping cream, whole milk, vanilla bean (if using vanilla extract, don't add yet) and salt. Bring to boil and turn off heat. Remove vanilla bean. (Use it to make vanilla sugar).

• In large bowl, beat egg yolks with granulated sugar until light and lemony. Slowly whisk in cream mixture. If using vanilla extract, add at this point.

• Divide mixture into 8 ramekins. Set ramekins in large baking dish. Pour in hot water to halfway up sides of ramekins. Bake in 300°F (150°C) oven for 50 to 60 minutes or until set; let cool for 30 minutes.

• Before serving, press brown sugar through a strainer and sprinkle evenly over surface of custards. Place custards on baking sheet and broil about 6 inches (15 cm) beneath preheated broiler until sugar melts and starts to look like a sheet of ice. Sugar may burn in a few places but watch carefully so it doesn't burn too much. Refrigerate a few minutes to firm up custard.

• *Dave's Tip:* Do not refrigerate for more than 5 to 10 minutes after you have broiled the top or the caramel will soften and liquefy.

Makes 8 servings

▲

TERRI FREQUENTLY USES WHITE SUGAR FOR THE CARAMELIZED TOPPING. TO MELT THE SUGAR INTO AN EVEN GLAZE, SHE USES A SMALL BLOWTORCH THAT SHE BOUGHT AT A HARDWARE STORE (THE KIND YOU USE TO LIFT FLOOR TILES). TO CARAMELIZE SUGAR: ADJUST FLAME TO MEDIUM-LOW, THEN HOLD BLOWTORCH 3 TO 4 INCHES (8 TO 10 CM) ABOVE TOPPING, MOVING IT ALONG AS SUGAR MELTS. THEN, TO FIRM UP THE CUSTARD, PUT THE DESSERT IN THE REFRIGERATOR FOR ABOUT 5 MINUTES BEFORE SERVING. (IF YOU DON'T HAVE A BLOWTORCH, YOU CAN USE AN ELECTRIC CHARCOAL STARTER.)

▼

Brillat-Savarin, the 18th century French gastronome, once said, "Tell me what you eat and I shall tell you what you are."

For fear of revealing too much about myself, I'll only tell you what my candidate for the best dessert in the world is: the crème brûlée at Le Cirque in New York City.

Terri and I have been devotées of Le Cirque's crème brûlée through successive administrations of its chefs de cuisine. Alain Sailhac gave us Le Cirque's recipe for the *Insider's Report* at a time when few other restaurants in North America had crème brûlée on their menus.

The one constant for us at Le Cirque all these years, aside from the overall quality of its food, has been its stunningly good crème brûlée!

FRESH FRUIT

AN EXCEPTIONAL PRODUCT CHOSEN AS OUR

President's Choice™

PASTEURIZED
FRESH, THICK
DOUBLE CREAM
B.F. 40%
IDEAL WITH FRESH FRUIT
250 mL

▲

FOR A TENDER, MOIST
INTERIOR AND A FLAKY
EXTERIOR, DON'T
OVERKNEAD THE DOUGH
BEFORE PATTING IT
OUT. ABOUT 5 TO
10 SECONDS WILL DO.
ANY LONGER AND
YOU'LL OVERWORK THE
GLUTEN, WHICH
TOUGHENS THE PASTRY.
WHAT'S MORE, THE
HEAT FROM YOUR
HANDS WILL START TO
MELT THE BUTTER
TRAPPED IN THE DOUGH,
QUASHING ANY CHANCE
OF FLAKINESS.

▼

WORLD'S BEST MIXED BERRY SHORTCAKE

This mouth-watering dessert is an update of a recipe that appeared in our June 1986
Insider's Report.

3½ cups	all-purpose flour	875 mL
2 tbsp	baking powder	25 mL
¼ cup	granulated sugar	50 mL
1½ tsp	salt	7 mL
½ cup	PC Unsalted Normandy-Style Cultured Butter	125 mL
¾ cup	2% milk	175 mL
2 cups	PC Fresh Thick Double Cream OR whipping cream	500 mL
	Mixed berries of your choice, lightly sweetened with sugar: blueberries, raspberries, blackberries, sliced strawberries, red currants	

• In mixing bowl, combine flour, baking powder, sugar and salt.
• Using fingers or pastry blender, cut in butter until mixture resembles coarse meal.
• In separate bowl, mix together milk and ¾ cup (175 mL) thick double cream or whipping cream. Gradually stir in flour mixture. Turn dough out onto floured board and knead for a few seconds until smooth.
• Pat dough into circle about 1-inch (2.5 cm) thick. Using knife, cut into pie-shaped wedges; alternatively, you can cut into rounds with a 3-inch (8 cm) cookie cutter. Arrange on ungreased baking sheet and bake in 400°F (200°C) oven for about 20 to 25 minutes or until baked through in centre and golden brown.
• To serve, split shortcakes in half with fork. Slather bottoms with remaining double cream or whipping cream that has been whipped to soft peaks; spoon on mixed berries. Add tops and decorate with dollops of cream and a few berries.
Makes 8 servings

DEVON CUSTARD TRIFLE

Our Twice The Fruit Raspberry Jam-Type Spread contains only 7 calories per teaspoon (5 mL) and has twice the raspberries and half the sugar of regular jam.

1	PC 'The Classic' All-Butter Pound Cake	1
1½ cups	sherry	375 mL
2	cans (each 15 oz/425 g) PC Devon Custard	2
1	jar (500 mL) PC 'Too Good To Be True!' Twice The Fruit Raspberry Jam-Type Spread	1
2 cups	whipping cream, whipped	500 mL
1	pint strawberries, sliced	1
1	pint raspberries	1
2 oz	PC Bittersweet Rich Dark Chocolate, shaved	60 g

◆ Cut or tear pound cake into pieces. Line a large glass bowl with half the cubes. Sprinkle with half the sherry.
◆ Combine half of one can of Devon custard with raspberry jam-type spread. Spoon half of jam mixture onto cake cubes in bowl and toss gently to coat evenly.
◆ Mix together half the whipped cream with remaining 1½ cans of Devon custard. Spread half of custard-whipped cream mixture on top of cake layer. Top with half the strawberries.
◆ Repeat layering, starting with cake cubes and ending with remaining strawberries.
◆ Slather remaining whipped cream on top. Cover and refrigerate 4 to 6 hours, preferably overnight.
◆ Just before serving, decorate with raspberries and grated chocolate.

Makes 10 to 12 servings

$\mathcal{I}$n Paris, around the turn of the century, there was a group called the Club of the One Hundred. This could well be the 20th century's first "gourmet dining club," according to Louis Szathmary, an American chef whom I've long admired. A "Club des Cents" continues to meet even today in Paris — for lunch! (Fifty years later, on this side of the Atlantic, the cultured palates of America thrilled at an invitation to join the prestigious Lucullus Circle, a group of distinguished epicures that dined at the Waldorf Hotel in New York. Its menus are carefully preserved in the New York Public Library.)

The Club of One Hundred met once a month for an entirely new menu — except for the dessert, which, Chef Szathmary points out, was always the same. "It consisted of raspberry sherbet towering over a number of crêpes folded around slices of sherbet, laid at the foot of the sherbet mountain, all strewn with fresh sugared raspberries and decorated with whipped cream."

Trifle is easier.

10 More Ways To Use PC Devon Custard

• **5-Minute Trifle:** Prepare jelly powder, any flavor, according to instructions. Pour over sliced Swiss jelly rolls in serving dish. Let set. Top with PC Devon Custard, canned fruit cocktail, drained, and whipped cream.

• **Crunchy Banana Custard:** Mix 3 sliced bananas and 1 can PC Devon Custard. Put in shallow baking dish. Top with enough crumbled PC Raisins First or Butter First Oatmeal Cookies to cover. Broil until topping is golden.

• **Brandy Butter Dessert Sauce:** Cream $^1/_3$ cup (75 mL) PC Unsalted Normandy-Style Cultured Butter and $^3/_4$ cup (175 mL) icing sugar. Stir in $^1/_4$ cup (50 mL) PC Devon Custard and 2 tbsp (25 mL) brandy.

• **Raspberry Ripple:** Mix 1 cup (250 mL) frozen whipped topping, $^1/_2$ can PC Devon Custard and $^1/_4$ cup (50 mL) PC Over 50% Fruit French-Style Raspberry Jam OR PC 'Too Good To Be True!' Twice The Fruit Raspberry Jam-Type Spread. Layer with fresh raspberries and chill before serving.

• **Frozen Custard Pops:** Mix one single-serving container PC Appletreet, any flavor, with ½ can PC Devon Custard. Freeze in 3 or 4 frozen pop moulds until nearly frozen. Insert a wooden stick into each. Continue freezing until firm.

• **Bananas, Custard & Maple Syrup:** Sauté 2 sliced bananas in 1 tbsp (15 mL) butter. Stir in 3 tbsp (45 mL) PC Canada No. 1 Light Maple Syrup and remove from heat. Drizzle PC Devon Custard over top.

• **Chocolate-Strawberry Milkshake:** In blender, combine 1 can PC Devon Custard, 3 or 4 strawberries, 2 scoops premium-quality chocolate ice cream and 1 cup (250 mL) milk. Blend until smooth.

• **Fresh Fruit Flan:** Spread 1 can PC Devon Custard in store-bought shortcake flan shell. Arrange slices of fresh fruit on top. (For a firmer custard base, chill PC Devon Custard 8 to 10 hours before using. This will make flan easier to serve.)

• **Fruit & Custard:** Cut assorted fresh fruit into bite-sized chunks. Place in bowl and cover with blanket of PC Devon Custard.

• **Glazed Angle Food Cake:** Cut store-bought angel food cake in half crosswise and spread with PC 'Too Good To Be True!' Twice The Fruit Jam-Type Spread, any flavor. Reassemble cake and glaze with more PC jam-type spread. Drizzle PC Devon Custard over top, letting it run down sides. Serve with remaining custard.

TERRI'S LEMON TART

My wife pried this recipe from Fredy Girardet, who runs a three-star restaurant in Crissier, Switzerland. Her rendition is definitely a showstopper. Make it when you want to make a big impression.

PASTRY

2 cups	all-purpose flour	500 mL
1/4 cup	granulated sugar	50 mL
3/4 cup	chilled PC Unsalted Normandy-Style Cultured Butter, cut in cubes	175 mL
1	egg, lightly beaten	1

FILLING

4	eggs	4
3/4 cup	granulated sugar	175 mL
2/3 cup	fresh lemon juice	150 mL
1/2 cup	PC 100% Pure Florida-Squeezed Pasteurized Orange Juice	125 mL
	Grated rind of 2 lemons	
1/4 cup	PC Unsalted Normandy-Style Cultured Butter	50 mL
1/4 cup	whipping cream	50 mL
	Sifted icing sugar	

◆ **Pastry:** In large bowl, sift together flour and sugar. Using pastry blender or 2 knives, cut in butter until mixture resembles coarse crumbs. Stir in egg and blend until well combined.

◆ Shape dough into ball and knead lightly with heel of hand to evenly distribute butter. Reshape into ball, dust lightly with flour and wrap loosely in waxed paper. Refrigerate at least 1 hour.

◆ On lightly floured surface, roll out dough to 1/8-inch (3 mm) thickness. Fit into 10-inch (25 cm) tart pan with removable bottom. Trim edges, prick bottom with fork and line with parchment or waxed paper. Fill evenly with dried beans or pie weights.

◆ Bake pastry in lower third of 400°F (200°C) oven for 10 to 15 minutes or until slightly golden in color. Remove weights and parchment and let cool on wire rack.

◆ **Filling:** In bowl, whisk together eggs, sugar, lemon juice, orange juice and lemon rind. Set aside.

◆ In saucepan over low heat, melt butter; stir in cream. Add egg mixture and cook over low heat, stirring constantly, just until mixture thickens; do not boil. Transfer to clean bowl, cover surface directly with buttered round of waxed paper or parchment and let cool, about 15 minutes.

◆ Pour custard into pie shell and bake in upper third of 375°F (190°C) oven for 20 minutes. Remove from oven.

◆ Serve warm or at room temperature. Just before serving, sprinkle with icing sugar. Alternatively, sprinkle with icing sugar, cover pastry edge with strip of foil to prevent burning and place under preheated broiler for a minute or more until sugar turns golden. Remove foil.

Makes 10 servings

Terri's Tip:

YOUR PIE CRUST WILL HAVE A BETTER COLOR AND A FLAKIER TEXTURE IF YOU MAKE THE PASTRY DOUGH AHEAD AND REFRIGERATE IT. I MAKE MY DOUGH IN THE MORNING AND THEN GIVE IT A FEW HOURS IN THE REFRIGERATOR BEFORE ROLLING IT OUT. OR YOU CAN CHILL IT OVERNIGHT AND LET THE DOUGH SOFTEN AT ROOM TEMPERATURE FOR 20 TO 30 MINUTES BEFORE ROLLING IT OUT.

This dessert made my wife's reputation as a great cook. Until you taste it, I don't think you can imagine how much luxury a "lemon filling" carries with it. The difference is like comparing dyed lumpfish roe with malossol ("little salt") beluga caviar from the Caspian Sea. Or ordinary button mushrooms with exotic white truffles!

Terri's Lemon Tart contains a true lemon cream with a sparkling tartness and a velvety smoothness. In my opinion, this dessert is right up there with Le Cirque's Crème Brûlée. Its flavor will astound you.

*I*f you're thinking that this looks like ordinary apple sauce, you're right. But you'd be wrong to presume that it tastes ordinary. This is the "quintessential" apple accompaniment which we discovered at the Tivoli Gardens Restaurant in Copenhagen. It inspired me to develop PC Memories of Copenhagen Apple Purée & Browned Butter.

A favorite of Terri's and mine, this easy-to-prepare apple purée is very complex in its component flavors. Its taste literally unfolds in your mouth! The secret is the caramelized sugars and the addition of browned butter for nuttiness, which gives it an ineffable flavor you won't find in any other sauce.

Serve it as a side dish with meats or poultry, or as a tantalizing conclusion to any meal.

MEMORIES OF COPENHAGEN APPLE PURÉE & BROWNED BUTTER

If there were an apple sauce hall of fame, this would be the only exhibit. Its superb flavor will startle your tastebuds.

2 lb	Granny Smith or other tart apples	1 kg
2/3 cup	PC Unsalted Normandy-Style Cultured Butter	150 mL
2/3 cup	cold water	150 mL
1 cup	granulated sugar (or to taste)	250 mL
1	vanilla bean, cut in half lengthwise	1
	Juice of 2 lemons	

• Peel and core apples. Cut into small chunks.
• In saucepan, melt 2 tbsp (25 mL) butter. Add apples, water, sugar and vanilla bean. Cook over medium-low heat for about 30 minutes, stirring occasionally, until apples are tender.
• Remove vanilla bean (it can be reused to make vanilla sugar). In food processor or blender, purée apples until smooth. Stir in lemon juice.
• In small saucepan over medium heat, melt remaining butter. Cook for 2 to 3 minutes until it is light brown in color and has a nutty fragrance; watch carefully to prevent burning.
• Stir butter into apple purée. Serve warm or at room temperature.
Makes 4 to 6 servings

▲

TERRI SERVES THIS PURÉE WITH ANY CUT OF PORK, FROM CROWN ROAST TO CHOPS, OR WITH CHICKEN. OR AS A DESSERT — ON ITS OWN OR SERVED WARM OVER ICE CREAM.

▼

ESPRESSO COFFEE REFERS ONLY TO THE DARK ROAST OF A BEAN, NOT THE TYPE OF BEAN OR WHERE IT COMES FROM. PRESIDENT'S BLEND IS A SELECTION OF DARK-ROASTED BEANS FROM INDONESIA, CENTRAL AMERICA AND COLOMBIA.

*T*en years ago, I read an article in *Connoisseur* magazine that listed all the best restaurants and hotels in Rome and even suggested where to find the best libations. In Italy, a glass of Sambuca, Scotch or even a cup of coffee and a sandwich can be enjoyed under the same roof — in a bar. (The Spanish have a name for people who spend long hours in the bars of Europe, drinking espresso and solving the world's problems. They're called *los estadistas de cafe*, or coffee statesmen.)

"If you want the best cup of espresso coffee in the world," the article said, "go to the Bar Sant'eustachio, located in Rome's Piazza Sant'eustachio."

I did, and to my everlasting delight, they were right. I was so impressed with the espresso, in fact, that I brought home several pounds of their coffee beans and set about creating a President's Blend Espresso Coffee with the same taste profile. Every time we tasted new samples, I extracted a few of the precious Sant'eustachio beans from my freezer.

As soon as we perfected our version, we sent a sample to Alberto Ottolini, owner of Bar Sant'eustachio. He wrote back to say, "What an excellent product! (You) could conquer North America with (your) espresso."

TIRAMISU

Nobody knows the true origins of tiramisu (pronounced teer-a-mee-SOO), a luxurious Italian dessert made with ladyfingers and a velvety Italian cream cheese called mascarpone. Some Italians wickedly suggest that it was devised as a restorative at an 18th century Venetian bordello. Tira Mi Su literally means "pick me up."

6	eggs, separated	6
½ cup	granulated sugar	125 mL
1 lb	mascarpone cheese	500 g
½ cup	strongly brewed President's Blend Espresso Coffee, at room temperature	125 mL
⅓ cup	coffee-flavored liqueur, such as Kahlua OR Tia Maria	75 mL
24	Italian-style ladyfingers (such as Savoiardo)	24
	Unsweetened cocoa powder	

• Using electric mixer, beat together egg yolks and sugar until thick and lemon colored. Add mascarpone and beat until thick and smooth.

• In separate bowl, beat egg whites until soft peaks form. Fold into mascarpone mixture.

• Combine espresso coffee and coffee-flavored liqueur. Briefly dip half the ladyfingers into coffee mixture and arrange in single layer in glass serving bowl. Cover with half of mascarpone mixture.

• Repeat with remaining ladyfingers and mascarpone mixture.

• Dust with cocoa powder. Cover with plastic wrap and refrigerate 6 to 8 hours, preferably overnight.

Makes 6 to 8 servings

AN EXCEPTIONAL PRODUCT
CHOSEN AS OUR
President's Blend
ESPRESSO
COFFEE

CHOCOLATE FUDGE CRACKLE
TORSADES AU FUDGE
LATE CHOCOLATE FUDGE C
OCOLAT HOLLANDAIS À TO

THE DECADENT ICE CREAM PIE

Make this with any flavor of our PC The Decadent chocolate fudge crackle ice cream.

10	PC The Decadent Chocolate Chip Cookies	10
½ cup	PC The Decadent Semisweet Chocolate Chips, melted	125 mL
½	tub (2 L) PC The Decadent Chocolate Fudge Crackle Ice Cream OR PC Beyond Decadence Dutch Chocolate Chocolate Fudge Crackle Ice Cream, slightly softened	½

• In food processor or blender, process cookies to a medium crumb (be careful not to process too fine). Add melted chocolate chips and pulse on and off a few times to blend.
• Press mixture onto bottom of 7-inch (18 cm) fluted tart or springform pan.
• Spread softened ice cream over crust, being careful not to disturb cookie crust (a hot spoon will make this easier). Cover pie and freeze until firm, at least 2 hours.
• Let pie stand at room temperature for 10 to 15 minutes to soften slightly before serving.

Makes 4 servings

This is the story of one of the most exciting products we've ever launched: PC "The Decadent" Chocolate Fudge Crackle Ice Cream.

One day an inventor, Cornelis ("Cort") Kortschot, walked into my office and explained why chocolate is so tasteless and waxy when it's added to ice cream. It seems that chocolate must be almost at body temperature before it can release all of its flavor. Since ice cream is so tempting to eat quickly, we rarely give the chocolate in it a chance to get to this point. Cort then described how he could modify pure chocolate so that it would melt rapidly in the mouth even when frozen. I said, "That sounds great in theory — let's make up a batch."

Weeks later, he showed me and Larry Griffin, our VP of Quality Assurance, how he had distributed strands of his unique chocolate mixture throughout a velvety vanilla ice cream. "They crackle," Larry said when I scooped some out. He was right. And they melted quickly with every mouthful, releasing an explosion of rich chocolate flavor that I never dreamed possible.

We subsequently used the same technology to create our other unique chocolate fudge crackle ice creams — Beyond Decadence Dutch Chocolate, Peanut Butter Decadence and, our *Insider's Report* 10th anniversary holiday offering, a devastatingly good version made with peppermint stick and bittersweet chocolate!

Thanks, Cort, for the ice cream experience of a lifetime.

*F*or years, the bittersweet chocolate ice cream served at Harry's Bar in Venice was my benchmark for the very best ice cream. Harry's bittersweet chocolate ice cream was so wonderful that I naturally assumed it would be difficult, if not impossible, to replicate. However, after weeks of experimenting, we discovered a recipe that was fast, incredibly simple, and, in my opinion, measured up to Harry's!

MEMORIES OF HARRY'S BAR
BITTERSWEET CHOCOLATE ICE CREAM

It's hard to imagine that anything that tastes this good can be so quick and easy to make. I personally prefer the version made with PC Crème Anglaise, our English-style pourable vanilla custard sauce.

½	bar (17.6 oz/500 g) PC Bittersweet Rich Dark Chocolate, broken in small chunks	½
4 tsp	unsweetened cocoa powder	20 mL
1½ tsp	President's Blend 100% Arabica Gourmet Instant Coffee grains	7 mL
1	container (500 mL) PC Vanilla Crème Anglaise OR 1 can (15 oz/425 g) PC Devon Custard	1

• In top of double boiler over simmering water, heat together chocolate, cocoa powder and coffee grains, stirring occasionally, until melted. Let cool to room temperature.
• Stir crème anglaise or Devon custard into chocolate mixture. Cover and refrigerate until thoroughly chilled.
• Freeze in ice cream maker following manufacturer's instructions.
Makes about 4 cups (1 L)

PRESIDENT'S CHOICE™

MEMORIES OF WINNIPEG
OLD-FASHIONED CREAM CHEESE
perfect for cheesecakes · contains no stabilizers

250 g ⓦⓚ

30% M.F.
55% MOISTURE

PASTEURIZED
KEEP REFRIGERATED

MEMORIES OF WINNIPEG CREAMY CHEESECAKE

THE NORTH END OF WINNIPEG ENCOMPASSES ALL THAT IS GREAT ABOUT HOME-STYLE ETHNIC COOKING, INCLUDING THE CO-OP DAIRIES, WHICH PRODUCES OUR MEMORIES OF WINNIPEG CREAM CHEESE. UNLIKE MOST ORDINARY CREAM CHEESES, OURS – WHICH HAS A CULTURED, SLIGHTLY TANGY FLAVOR – CONTAINS NO CAROB BEAN GUM OR OTHER STABILIZERS TO HELP IT SET.

The fresh dairy flavor and light creamy texture of PC Memories of Winnipeg cream cheese are showcased in this award-winning recipe from Heather Cram, which appeared in Across the Table, *Cynthia Wine's 1985 paean to Canadian food. (Wine, the* Toronto Star *restaurant critic, has a new book out from Penguin, titled* Eating For A Living.)

¾ cup	graham cracker crumbs	175 mL
⅓ cup	brown sugar	75 mL
	Grated peel of 1 lemon	
¼ tsp	ground cardamom	1 mL
⅓ cup	melted butter	75 mL
4	pkg (each 250 g) PC Memories of Winnipeg Old-Fashioned Cream Cheese, at room temperature	4
4	eggs	4
¾ cup	granulated sugar	175 mL
	Juice of ½ lemon	
1 tsp	pure vanilla extract	5 mL

• In medium bowl, mix together graham cracker crumbs, brown sugar, lemon peel, cardamom and butter. Pat firmly and evenly onto bottom of 10-inch (25 cm) springform pan.

• In large bowl, combine cream cheese, eggs, granulated sugar, lemon juice and vanilla; beat until smooth.

• Pour cream cheese mixture over crust in springform pan. Heat in 350°F (180°C) oven for 35 minutes. Turn off heat and prop open oven door with folded tea towel; let cake stand for about 1 hour.

• Refrigerate several hours before serving.

Makes 10 to 12 servings

ALISON'S BREAD PUDDING

Created by test kitchen chef Alison Jarvest, this may be the best bread pudding I've ever tasted. (Does it compare with Anton Mosimann's fabled version from his days at London's Dorchester Hotel? YES.) For sure it's one of the easiest to prepare when you make it with PC Vanilla Crème Anglaise.

12	slices plain white bread	12
6 tbsp	softened butter	90 mL
½ cup	PC Over 50% Fruit French-Style Pure Apricot Jam	125 mL
6 tbsp	currants	90 mL
1	container (500 mL) PC Vanilla Crème Anglaise	1
	OR 2 cups (500 mL) Crème Anglaise From Scratch	
	(see recipe, page 285)	
1	egg	1
¼ tsp	salt	1 mL
	Additional Crème Anglaise for topping	

• Trim crust off bread and spread one side of each slice with butter and jam.
• Arrange 6 bread slices, buttered side up, in one layer in 11 x 7-inch (2 L) baking dish. (Trim bread, as required, to fit.) Sprinkle with 3 tbsp (45 mL) of currants. Repeat with remaining bread and currants. (Alternatively, divide bread and currants into three layers in 8-inch [2 L] square or round baking dish.)
• Mix together crème anglaise, egg and salt. Pour evenly over bread.
• Place in 350°F (180°C) oven for 40 to 50 minutes or until custard is set and top is golden brown. Serve warm with additional crème anglaise.

Makes 6 to 8 servings

*B*y giving up rich food, wine and late nights, you'll live to be 100 — at least it will feel like 100.

I don't remember where I stumbled across that quote, but I think we'd all agree that life would lose its zest if we gave up all of its enjoyments.

Julia Child, one of my favorite food people, proclaims herself to be a card-carrying carnivore and will not bend to those members of the "food police" who would have us believe that meat should not pass our lips. (Julia, may I add, is in her early eighties and is still going strong!)

For my part, I will never renounce cream in cooking. I particularly like what it does to a sauce. For instance, strip away the mystery of a Crème Anglaise — and you find that it's essentially cream thickened with egg yolks and sweetened with sugar. Even more, Crème Anglaise is an essential ingredient in ice cream, fruit Bavarians and rice pudding. And it transforms simple bread pudding into a dazzling dessert.

10 Simple Ways to use PC Vanilla Crème Anglaise

- Spoon over fresh fruit.
- Drizzle over fruit crisps, crumbles, shortcakes and cakes.
- Add cinnamon, nutmeg and a splash of rum for a rich and creamy eggnog.
- Use as the custard base for great homemade ice cream.
- Use instead of milk in homemade rice pudding.
- Spike with brandy and pour over plum pudding.
- Decorate your dessert plates with a pool of PC Vanilla Crème Anglaise and a few spoonfuls of PC Over 50% Fruit French-Style Jam.
- Make Rum Custard: Stir 1 tbsp (15 mL) rum into 1 container (500 mL) PC Vanilla Crème Anglaise.
- Make Coffee Custard: At least one hour before serving, stir 1 tbsp (15 mL) PC 100% Arabica Gourmet Instant Coffee into 1 cup (250 mL) PC Vanilla Crème Anglaise. Stir before using to ensure granules have dissolved.
- Make Quick Chocolate Fondant for dipping fresh strawberries or to spread over chilled PC New-York-Style Cheesecake for a sumptuous glaze: Stir ½ cup (125 mL) PC Vanilla Crème Anglaise into 8 oz (250 g) PC Bittersweet Rich Dark OR Rich Milk Chocolate, melted. Stir until smooth. Makes about 1¼ cups (300 mL).
- *Dave's Tip:* For a quick and easy way to melt 8 oz (250 g) of chocolate, put it in the microwave at Medium for 3 to 5 minutes, stirring occasionally.

CRÈME ANGLAISE FROM SCRATCH

Serve this vanilla custard sauce warm or chilled over ice cream, fruit desserts or puddings.

½ cup	granulated sugar	125 mL
4	egg yolks	4
1¾ cups	light cream	425 mL
1 tbsp	pure vanilla extract	15 mL

• In heavy-bottomed saucepan, beat sugar and egg yolks until thick and lemon-colored. Mixture will fall in ribbons.
• Beat in cream until blended.
• Cook over low heat, stirring constantly with wooden spoon in figure 8 pattern to prevent lumping, until mixture is thick enough to coat the back of a spoon; do not boil or eggs will scramble.
• Strain custard into bowl. Set bowl in ice water to stop the cooking. Keep stirring for about 5 minutes or until cool. Stir in vanilla.
• *Dave's Tip:* Add 2 tsp (10 mL) cornstarch to egg yolks along with the sugar as a safeguard to prevent sauce from curdling in the event custard gets too hot while cooking.

Makes about 2 cups (500 mL)

Chocolate pâté is one of those luxurious chocolate desserts that have acquired a number of metaphorical aliases, such as "Chocolate Velour" or "Death By Chocolate." You'll sometimes see it on restaurant menus as simply "Chocolate Terrine." Whatever it's called, chocolate pâté was invented for raging chocoholics who want every mouthful to be a caress. In my estimation, Jimmy Schmidt, owner-chef of the Rattlesnake Club in Detroit, Michigan, created the chocolate pâté that set the standard for the rest of the culinary world when he was an up-and-coming chef at Detroit's London Chop House in the early '80s.

PÂTÉ OF BITTERSWEET CHOCOLATE WITH GRAND MARNIER SAUCE

PC Vanilla Crème Anglaise cuts preparation time to a minimum. If your store doesn't carry it, you can make it from scratch (see recipe, page 285).

1	bar (17.6 oz/500 g) PC Bittersweet Rich Dark Chocolate, broken in pieces	1
1 cup	whipping cream	250 mL
1/4 cup	PC Unsalted Normandy-Style Cultured Butter	50 mL
4	egg yolks	4
3/4 cup	sifted icing sugar	175 mL
4 tbsp	dark rum	50 mL
1	container (500 mL) PC Vanilla Crème Anglaise	1
1/4 cup	Grand Marnier or other orange-flavored liqueur	50 mL

• In top of double boiler over simmering water, heat chocolate, cream and butter until melted. Whisk until well blended and glossy. Remove from heat.
• Whisk in egg yolks, one at a time, blending well after each. Gradually whisk in icing sugar and continue whisking until thick and glossy. Whisk in rum.
• Line a greased 4-cup (1 L) mould or loaf pan with parchment or waxed paper, allowing paper to extend 2 inches (5 cm) beyond rim of pan. Butter paper. Pour chocolate mixture into pan, cover with plastic wrap and refrigerate 8 hours or overnight.
• To serve, remove pâté from mould by lifting with paper. If chocolate ran into mould and pâté does not easily lift out, dip mould into hot water for a few seconds to help loosen. Remove paper and, using a knife dipped in hot water or a cheese wire, cut pâté into 1/2-inch (1 cm) slices. Let stand at room temperature about 30 minutes before serving.
• Slice pâté and arrange on dessert plates. Combine crème anglaise with Grand Marnier and drizzle over each slice. Or, if desired, spoon sauce onto dessert plates and place pâté slice on top.
Makes 8 to 10 servings

▲

WE USE PC BITTERSWEET RICH DARK CHOCOLATE FROM FRANCE AND PC VANILLA CRÈME ANGLAISE IN OUR ADAPTATION OF JIMMY SCHMIDT'S RECIPE, WHICH APPEARED IN ELLEN BROWN'S *COOKING WITH THE NEW AMERICAN CHEFS* (HARPER AND ROW, 1985).

▼

I was looking for a place to stay in Boston while I was attending the graduate program at Harvard Law School when I came across an advertisement from a Mr. and Mrs. Swindells. Their son had gone to Switzerland to study and I happily took over his apartment on their 15-acre estate with a private lake, located in the Boston suburb of Dedham. The best part of the arrangement was the Swindells's family cook, a wonderful German lady by the name of Amelia. Her cooking left indelible marks on my gastronomic memories of those student days.

Amelia's signature dessert was something she called "Lemon Angel Pie" — lemon cream served in an extravagant dessert shell made from meringue. It wasn't meringue as I knew it, slathered over baked Alaska or lemon pie. Amelia's meringue was done in the French style, beaten into stiff peaks, shaped into a pie-size nest with the back of a wet spoon, and baked in what she described as "a very slow oven." There it was transformed into a snowy white shell of crunchy meringue with a moist and chewy interior.

One summer I asked Alison Jarvest, our test kitchen chef, to recreate Amelia's specialty using President's Choice Meringue Nests. Her version can be prepared in about 10 minutes.

MEMORIES OF AMELIA
MERINGUE NESTS FILLED WITH LEMON CREAM

If raspberries are hard to come by, substitute any fresh berries you can find.

4	large egg yolks	4
¾ cup	fresh lemon juice (do not use reconstituted)	175 mL
1 tbsp	grated lemon zest	15 mL
1	can (300 mL) PC Sweetened Condensed Milk	1
1	pkg (125 g) PC Meringue Nests (8 nests)	1
1 cup	PC Fresh Thick Double Cream OR whipped cream	250 mL
1 cup	fresh raspberries	250 mL

• Prepare lemon cream: In top of double boiler, whisk together egg yolks, lemon juice and lemon zest. Set over simmering water and cook for 8 to 10 minutes, whisking constantly, until mixture is thick and pale yellow in color. Remove from heat and let cool to room temperature.
• Whisk in condensed milk. (Recipe can be made several hours ahead to this point; cover and refrigerate lemon cream until serving.)
• Just before serving, spoon lemon cream into meringue nests. Top each with a dollop of thick double cream or whipped cream and fresh raspberries.

Makes 8 servings

MERINGUE NESTGUE

AN EXCEPTIONAL PRODU

MADE WITH PURE EGG WHITES

8 NESTS

PRODUCT OF SCOTLAND

$\mathscr{N}$obody ever really has time for breakfast, which explains why Terri and I often take time to indulge in a leisurely, luxurious breakfast at the elegant Campton Place Hotel whenever we're in San Francisco.

Breakfast at Campton Place is never banal; it's sybaritic. "Fruit cocktail" is an assortment of tropical fruit in passion fruit purée; "pancakes" are whole-wheat apple walnut, served with spiced persimmon butter; "French toast" is lemon poppyseed, and it comes with Concord grape syrup!

Wonderful if you have an hour or so for an unhurried "breaking of the fast." But when you need to fortify yourself quickly in the morning, then make our President's Choice "power breakfast" — high-fibre muesli muffins made with PC 30% Fruit, Nuts and Seeds Muesli. You won't believe that anything that takes so little time to make can have so much flavor.

HIGH-FIBRE MUESLI MUFFINS

These muffins are packed with fruit and nuts. Fibre never tasted so good!

1	pkg (450 g) PC 30% Fruit, Nuts and Seeds Muesli Cereal	1
2 cups	PC 'Too Good To Be True!' Whole Wheat Flour	500 mL
1 cup	packed brown sugar	250 mL
2 tbsp	baking powder	25 mL
½ tsp	salt	2 mL
2 cups	1% milk	500 mL
2	eggs	2
½ cup	PC 'Too Good To Be True!' 100% Pure Safflower Oil	125 mL

• In medium-sized bowl, mix together muesli, whole wheat flour, brown sugar, baking powder and salt.
• In separate bowl, combine milk, eggs and safflower oil; mix well.
• Add liquid to dry ingredients all at once, stirring just until moistened.
• Spoon into buttered muffin tins and bake in 400°F (200°C) oven for about 20 minutes or until tops spring back when lightly touched.
Makes 18 muffins

*I*f you've ever eaten Greek baklava or Hungarian apple strudel, you know what phyllo pastry is — very thin sheets of dough that are piled one on top of another and buttered to produce impressive layers of flakiness.

Why some people are afraid of phyllo pastry I'll never know, since it's actually easier to work with than pie dough. It's more forgiving; it never gets tough, and the only layer you have to worry about not breaking is the one on the outside!

Once you've tried it, there's no turning back.

PEARS WRAPPED IN PHYLLO PASTRY

Did you know that pears ripen better off the tree? To ripen, keep at room temperature until they yield to gentle pressure at the stem end.

4	ripe pears	4
8	sheets PC Frozen Phyllo Pastry, thawed in refrigerator	8
4 tbsp	PC Unsalted Normandy-Style Cultured Butter, melted	60 mL
2 tsp	granulated sugar	10 mL
	PC Gourmet Chocolate Ice Cream & Dessert Topping, heated until warm	

• Carefully peel and core pears; if possible, core from base to keep stems intact. If pears do not stand level, trim bases as required.
• Cut 2 sheets of phyllo in half lengthwise. Brush each half with some of butter and sprinkle lightly with some of sugar. Arrange sheets on top of one another, fanning slightly so corners aren't lined up.
• Stand one pear in centre and, working your way around pear, gently pull up pastry so corners meet at top of pear, pleating or folding pastry sides to take on the form of the pear.
• Pinch top of pastry around stem of pear, allowing stem to show. Carefully open out corners at top and fold one or two down to create an attractive appearance. Repeat with remaining pears and phyllo.
• Place on baking sheet and bake in 350°F (180°C) oven for 25 to 30 minutes or just until pastry is golden. Serve with warm gourmet chocolate topping.
Makes 4 servings

▲

YOU CAN USE PHYLLO DOUGH IN MOST RECIPES THAT CALL FOR PIE DOUGH, WHETHER IT'S FOR APPLE PIE, FOR DUMPLINGS, FOR ENCLOSING FRUIT OR VEGETABLE FILLINGS, OR FOR MAKING EDIBLE CUPS FOR DESSERTS OR SALADS. ALWAYS DEFROST PHYLLO SLOWLY, PREFERABLY IN THE REFRIGERATOR; OTHERWISE MOISTURE DEVELOPS AND MAKES THE SHEETS STICK TOGETHER. AND DON'T REFREEZE OR THE LAYERS WILL BECOME BRITTLE.

▼

PRESIDENT'S CHOICE™

PHYLLO PASTR

phyllo pastry dough made with 100% vegetable oil

NET WT. 16 OZ (1 LB) 454 g

MY FAVORITE CREATURE COMFORTS

A Great Shower

For me, one of life's great pleasures is a high-pressure shower first thing in the morning. When you get to be 53 — although, as I remember, it was the same at 23 — you tend to wake up with a few aches and pains, and there is no quicker or better cure than a "power shower."

To achieve the right pressure, I installed a Jacuzzi Water Pressure Pump with its own 50-gallon pressure tank. (It can drill holes through you if you're not careful.) You match that with the best-made showerhead in the world, the Speakman — use the largest model that will still allow you to maintain as much pressure as possible. Obviously, men need a mirror in the shower for shaving. And, of course, it should be a steamless mirror because the high humidity in the shower enables you to get a much closer shave.

It goes without saying that before you can do any of this, you need to call in an expert plumber to make sure you don't blow any pipes.

One thing I lack is an anti-beading solution spray to keep the water beads off the mirror. For now, I use PC Out of Africa Botanical Secrets Shampoo with shea butter, which keeps the mirror clear for at least half the shave.

A Featherbed

I believe you should do everything you can to get a great night's sleep. One of the easiest ways is with a featherbed.

Terri and I were staying at the Sherman House in San Francisco where they have featherbeds on all their beds. Essentially, a featherbed is a huge baffled pillow that covers the entire mattress. You put your sheets on top of it. Featherbeds make beds so soft and luxurious that you feel like you're sleeping on clouds. (You still have the support of the mattress.) Naturally, I asked the hotel where I could get them and was told I'd find them in San Francisco at Warm Things (isn't that a great name for a store?). Now all the beds in our house have featherbeds on them.

The Dome

The greatest creature comfort Terri and I have is The Dome (see photo, page 300). We were married in Hawaii at the Mauna Kea Resort on the big island of Hawaii — one of my favorite places in the world.

For me to survive — I'm energized by sunlight — I need a respite from the onerously grey Canadian winters. One winter, Terri and I went to California and visited Michael's Restaurant in Santa Monica. We sat under oversized Verona market umbrellas in a room surrounded by wonderful flower beds with bamboo growing in them. There's a frame over the room and when it starts to rain or get cold, a huge canvas automatically caps the entire courtyard.

When we returned home, we took our backyard and converted it into a "Michael's of Santa Monica" version of Hawaii. Since the seasons in Toronto are different than in Santa Monica or Hawaii, we naturally had to glass it in. For winter comfort, we installed a raised fireplace in the middle that draws out those hunker-down, Neanderthal instincts that all Canadians possess.

French Bulldogs

French Bulldogs are indispensable — they're four-legged tranquilizers.

One day, I went to the Sportsman's Dog Show in Toronto and I saw this French bulldog puppy in a cage. It was love at first sight. The next day, I called the dog's handler, and he arranged for me to buy "George."

George was our very first French bulldog. Tragically, this wonderful dog accidentally drowned in our hot tub. The next day, I found out that George, who was bred in Georgia, had a sister who lived in Toronto. Fortunately, circumstances were such that we were able to adopt her immediately. That was in 1980 and in memory of her brother we decided to call her Georgie Girl. She and her four generations of offspring have owned Terri and me ever since. (Sadly, Georgie Girl passed away in April 1992. But she lives on in our Insider's Report.)

A few years ago, a survey of top Fortune 500 corporate executives found that 94 per cent of them credited a childhood pet with contributing to their success as adults. They believed that having a pet shaped their personalities in positive ways that helped them to get where they wanted to go!

To come home at the end of the day, open a bottle of Dave Nichol's Personal Selection Cabernet Sauvignon, and settle back on the couch with my French bulldogs lying up against my leg is total relaxation for me.

Gravol

There are one or two miracle drugs in the world today for the traveler. Gravol is definitely one of them.

I accepted early in life that once or twice a year I'd get the stomach flu. Nothing serious, just 24 hours of hell. There have been days when I could have used a monorail between my bed and the bathroom.

After eating my way through France's three-star restaurants a few years back, I realized that I was about to spend the next 24 hours paying the price. Fortunately, Patti Watt was there. (Patti and Don Watt of Toronto's The Watt Group are among the world's pre-eminent industrial design consultants and over the years they've helped us develop many packaging and merchandising concepts.) Patti gave me some Gravol. I couldn't believe how effective it was. I was cured and I've never had the 24-hour traveler's flu since!

Shahtoosh

"Shah" means ruler and "toosh" means cloth — the cloth of the king.

Ever since I read Stanley Marcus's book, *Quest For The Best* (Viking Press, 1979), I've been intrigued with the fabric called Shahtoosh. Whereas cashmere, strictly speaking, comes from the soft underhair of the Kashmir goat, Shahtoosh is made from the precious neck hair of the ibex goat in the Himalayas. Shahtoosh is sheer when woven, and so fine that a 54-inch-wide Shahtoosh shawl can be drawn through a wedding band. (That's why it's called "the ring shawl.")

When I went to Bombay a few years ago, an exhaustive search revealed a store that had a few precious Shahtoosh scarves. I bought two, one black and one maroon. I love to look at them. Despite the fineness of Shahtoosh, however, they're incredibly warm, and as I'm hot-blooded, I can't wear them! But Terri does, and that gives me great pleasure.

GOOD ICED COFFEE
DOESN'T START WITH
YESTERDAY'S LEFTOVER
COFFEE. BREW IT FRESH.
USE 2 TBSP (30 mL)
PRESIDENT'S BLEND
GOURMET GROUND
COFFEE FOR EACH
¾ CUP (175 mL)
COLD WATER. POUR
IT OVER ICE CUBES
MADE FROM THE SAME
STRENGTH BREW.

On my trips to Japan, I've discovered that vending machines are as numerous there as cherry blossoms in the spring. One item that you're bound to find in them is iced coffee. The Japanese drink more iced coffee than soft drinks!

Before we developed ready-to-pour refrigerated President's Choice Iced Café au Lait Beverage, this is how we made killer iced coffee — using President's Blend Espresso Ground Coffee and sweetening it Thai-style with PC Sweetened Condensed Milk, which gives it a delectable cappuccino color.

KILLER ICED COFFEE

Insider's Report *writer/editor Frances Litwin discovered the inspiration for this incredible iced coffee in a Thai restaurant in Dallas, where President's Choice products are carried in Tom Thumb stores.*

For each serving:
Pour about ¼ cup (50 mL) PC Sweetened Condensed Milk into a glass. Add 3 or 4 ice cubes and fill to the top with freshly prepared President's Blend Espresso Coffee. (If you don't have an espresso machine, use a plunger-type coffee maker or prepare coffee double strength in your drip pot.) Stir well and serve immediately.
• *Dave's Tip:* For an extra flavor hit, serve over espresso ice cubes. Just pour espresso coffee into your ice cube tray and freeze.

At one time, I intended to teach law, so I went to Boston to get a Master's of Law degree; while there, I lived with the Swindells family. Mrs. Swindells made a superb iced tea with a pronounced citrusy flavor. She insisted on using bottled spring water for a clearer-tasting iced tea, the sweetest and most flavorful oranges, and English Breakfast tea. President's Blend English Breakfast Tea combines flavor-rich Kenyan and Ceylon teas for a smooth-tasting beverage that's strong enough to get you going in the morning. Its depth of flavor makes it ideal for iced tea, as this compensates for the fact that ice melts and, in so doing, dilutes the brew.

MRS. SWINDELLS'S FAMOUS FRUITED ICED TEA

Always use 50% more tea than usual when making tea you plan to "ice."

½ cup	granulated sugar	125 mL
½ cup	PC Natural Spring Water	125 mL
6	bags President's Blend English Breakfast Tea	6
4 cups	boiling water	1 L
1½ cups	freshly squeezed and unstrained Valencia orange juice	375 mL
	Unstrained juice of 2 lemons	
¾ cup	pineapple juice	175 mL

• In saucepan, combine sugar and spring water and bring to boil; continue boiling until liquid is clear, about 5 minutes. Chill thoroughly.
• Place tea bags in heat-resistant pitcher; add boiling water and let steep about 5 minutes. Remove and discard tea bags. Let tea cool and refrigerate until chilled.
• Add orange juice, lemon juice, pineapple juice and chilled sugar syrup. Refrigerate a few hours, preferably overnight. Serve over ice in tall glasses.

Makes 6 to 8 servings

▲

YEARS AGO, THE NAME "ENGLISH BREAKFAST" REFERRED TO A HEARTY CHINA BLACK TEA CALLED KEEMUN. NOWADAYS, IT USUALLY DENOTES A SPECIAL FULL-BODIED BLEND OF TEAS.

▼

FESTIVE CRANBERRY PEACH PUNCH

Jean Paumier, the product development director who brings our famous PC cookies to market, created this non-alcoholic Insider's Report recipe. If desired, you can add a few fresh cranberries to the punch bowl for color.

¼ cup	granulated sugar	50 mL
½ tsp	cinnamon	2 mL
¼ tsp	whole cloves	1 mL
½ cup	PC Natural Spring Water	125 mL
3 cups	PC Cranberry Cocktail	750 mL
3 cups	PC Peach Cocktail	750 mL
½ cup	freshly squeezed lemon juice	125 mL
1	bottle (750 mL) PC Memories of Champagne Sparkling Non-Alcoholic White Grape Cocktail OR 3 cans (each 12 oz/355 mL) PC Ginger Ale	1
1	each orange and lemon, thinly sliced	1
	Ice cubes	

◆ In small saucepan over medium heat, combine sugar, cinnamon, cloves and natural spring water. Heat for 5 minutes or until sugar and cinnamon are dissolved. Strain and let cool.
◆ In punch bowl, combine cinnamon mixture, cranberry cocktail, peach cocktail, lemon juice and Memories of Champagne grape cocktail or ginger ale.
◆ Add fruit slices and ice cubes.
◆ *Dave's Tip:* You can also make this by substituting PC Tropical Cranberry Cocktail for the PC Cranberry and PC Peach Cocktails.
Makes 16 to 18 servings

▲
Peach Bellini
◆──────

NEXT TIME YOU HAVE GUESTS IN FOR A FESTIVE GATHERING, BE SURE TO OFFER ALCOHOL-FREE BEVERAGES LIKE THIS ONE: COMBINE 1 BOTTLE (750 mL) PC MEMORIES OF CHAMPAGNE SPARKLING NON-ALCOHOLIC WHITE GRAPE COCKTAIL, CHILLED, AND 3 CUPS (750 mL) PC PEACH COCKTAIL, CHILLED. POUR INTO CHAMPAGNE FLUTES. MAKES 10 TO 12 COCKTAILS.

▼

APPLE CITRUS REFRESHER

An all-occasion beverage — fruity and effervescent. Make sure juices and ginger ale are well chilled at the start.

2 cups	PC Cox's Orange Pippin Apple Juice	500 mL
2 cups	PC 100% Florida Squeezed Pasteurized Orange Juice	500 mL
2 cups	PC 100% Florida Squeezed Pasteurized Grapefruit Juice	500 mL
½ cup	Freshly squeezed lime juice	125 mL
2	cans (each 12 oz/355 mL) PC Ginger Ale	2
	Ice cubes	

◆ In large pitcher or punch bowl, combine apple, orange, grapefruit and lime juices.
◆ Just before serving, pour in ginger ale.
◆ Serve over ice cubes in tall juice glasses.
Makes 8 to 10 servings

MEMORIES OF SOUVENIRS de
CHAMPAGNE

750 mL

President's Choice

Le Choix du President

Sparkling non-alcoholic white grape cocktail
mousseux de raisins blanc non alcoolise

President's Choice
CRANBERRY

President's Choice
PEACH COCKTAIL
PEACH

OZ

The Dome at our home in Toronto: During a howling blizzard, there's no place I'd rather be than The Dome, settled in front of the fireplace with my French bulldogs beside me and strains of Hawaiian music in the background — the President's choice for those long winter nights.

BACK TO BASICS

It's not mandatory to know how to cook if your supermarket carries the President's Choice, but it can be a lot of fun. And it goes faster when your kitchen cupboard, refrigerator and freezer are stocked with the foodstuffs that are basic to any culinary adventure — from the oil and vinegar you use, to the mineral water you serve. In no particular order of importance, here are the President's Choice products that, by virtue of their value and quality, fulfill the requirements of every well-intentioned cook.

Incidentally, throughout this cookbook, where the size of produce (e.g., apple, onion, bunch spinach) is not specified in a recipe, it's understood that we mean "medium."

President's Choice 'Too Good to Be True!' Bean Products

Fibre-padding our diet with various types of dietary fibre — in particular, soluble fibre, the type found in the pectin of some fruits, certain gums, oat products, beans and legumes — may be one of the easiest ways we can improve our diet. As well as containing soluble fibre, beans are a source of complex carbohydrates, and they're an alternate source of protein — one cup (250 mL) of beans can stand in for two to three ounces (60 to 90 grams) of meat.

Think of beans as an investment in health, and plan your mixed portfolio around these President's Choice bean products:

PC 'Too Good To Be True!' Precooked 7-Bean Mix: Small red beans, navy beans, light red kidney beans, black-eyed peas, great northern beans, green peas and baby lima beans. Great in bean dips, burritos, soups, even chili.

PC 'Too Good To Be True!' Precooked Great Northern Beans: Mild tasting. Can be used in any recipe that calls for great northern, navy or pea beans, small white beans, cannellini or white kidney beans.

PC 'Too Good To Be True!' 20-Bean Soup: Contains beans, peas and lentils. High in dietary fibre and low in fat. Suitable for vegetarian diets. One jar contains two 270 mL servings (9 grams dietary fibre per serving) at 203 calories each and only 3% calories from fat.

PC 'Too Good To Be True!' Frozen Chili: Home-made style, with red kidney beans, chunks of tomatoes, onions and soya, in a zesty sauce seasoned with coriander, mixed spices and garlic. A very high source of dietary fibre, with only 13% calories from fat and less than 350 calories per 350 gram portion. Suitable for vegetarian diets.

PC 'Too Good To Be True!' Instant Soups — Spicy Black Bean, Minestrone Pasta, Vegetarian Chili, Split Pea, Lentil with Curry and new Vegetable Couscous and Chicken Flavor Noodle Soup: These instant soups are all under 250 calories per serving, high or very high in dietary fibre, low in fat, free of added preservatives and meatless.

President's Choice Normandy-Style Cultured Butter

Years ago, while attending cooking classes with the late Jean Troisgros, I walked into class early and caught the great chef with a rolling pin in his hand — battering a slab of butter that he'd rolled up in a towel. "What are you doing?" I asked in astonishment. Jean replied, "North American butter has too much moisture in it. I always have to pound out the excess before I can bake with it!"

Jean was right. For years the only really good pastry butter came from Normandy, France, a butter that contains special cultures for flavor and contains less moisture and more butterfat than ordinary North American butters — 82% B.F. vs 80% B.F. in North American butter. Normandy butter provided the model for our **President's Choice Normandy-Style Cultured Butter,** a butter with 82% B.F. and all the richness and flavorful character of a Normandy butter. And you don't have to beat out the excess moisture to ensure success in cakes, puff pastry or pie crusts! It's also my all-around favorite for sautéeing since its lower moisture content means it doesn't sputter as much in the pan as ordinary butter.

The only dilemma: Do you choose Unsalted or Lightly Salted? In our home, we use the Unsalted version almost exclusively. Many people, however, prefer a salted butter for pan-frying because they feel the salt in butter encourages foods to turn an attractive golden brown — not unlike the color of certain Stradivari violins — when subjected to high heat.

President's Blend Gourmet 100% Arabica Bean Coffees

Travel can't last forever — and even though I love coming home, it's often with a tiny pang of sadness. But that feeling lifts when I awaken the first morning back and realize that I have my favorite coffee to look forward to, President's Blend Gourmet Ground Coffee. This coffee is formulated from six different varieties of premium Arabica beans from around the world, including very special Sumatra Mandhelings from Indonesia — a hard-to-get variety that gives our mellow blend a deep taste and rich aroma. It comes in Regular and Decaffeinated.

The Perfect Brew

You want your coffee to have body, not just flavor and color, so be generous. Listen to Beethoven. The great composer's rule of thumb was to use 60 coffee beans per cup. That works out to about 2 tbsp (30 mL) ground coffee for ¾ cup (175 mL) water — exactly what today's experts recommend. It goes without saying that for best flavor, serve immediately after brewing. You should never let your coffee boil or try to reheat it. And if you can use filtered or PC Natural Spring Water, thereby eliminating the off-flavors you can get in tap water, the flavor of your coffee will be all the better for it.

Instant

Of all the revolutionary products that debuted in 1938 — the ballpoint pen, Nylon, Teflon, fluorescent lighting, the Xerox machine — perhaps the most mundane one today is instant coffee. It was inevitable that we would create a President's Blend instant coffee although, naturally, we went out of our way to ensure that **President's Blend 100% Arabica Instant Gourmet Coffee** doesn't taste like the old days. Those early instant coffees were produced by subjecting prepared coffee to a stream of hot air to remove the water; they were so pale and so powdery that manufacturers often resorted to bulking them up with carbohydrate fillers so that you could find them in your teaspoon!

President's Blend 100% Arabica Instant Gourmet Coffee is made exclusively from high-quality Arabica bean coffee and absolutely no Robustas, those run-of-the-mill tasting beans that find their way into many instant coffees because they grow hardy in many regions of the world, which makes them cheap and plentiful.

Decaf

To remove caffeine from coffee, many coffee manufacturers use either ethyl acetate (you will see it stated in the ingredient list), which occurs naturally in many fruits, or methylene chloride, a chemical solvent. Only manufacturers who use water or carbon dioxide to decaffeinate coffee are allowed to make the claim "naturally decaffeinated" on the label.

President's Blend Swiss-Water-Process Decaffeinated Ground Coffee, which uses the same gourmet blend of 100% Arabica coffee beans as our regular gourmet ground coffee, is manufactured in Canada using a unique water-based decaffeination process called Swiss Water®, a trademark that we use under licence.

Using only pure water and carbon filters, a batch of unroasted coffee beans is soaked in water to dissolve the caffeine and flavor components. This water is then passed through carbon filters to remove only the caffeine. The beans used to create the decaffeinated "flavor-charged" water are now discarded; they have done their job. In the next stage, premium coffee beans are soaked in the flavor-laden water; this draws off the caffeine but not the original flavor of the beans, since their flavor components can't pass into the water that's already saturated with flavor components. The newly decaffeinated beans are then dried, polished and ready for roasting to our specifications.

President's Choice Over 50% Fruit Pure French-Style Fruit Jams

There is a multitude of uses for PC Over 50% Fruit Pure Fruit Jams that have nothing to do with toast. You can combine them with cream to make ice cream, or with fresh puréed fruit to make sorbet. Their wonderful fresh fruit flavor comes from their "Over 50%" fruit content. They're made in Canada in the French style, which means *more fruit.* Most jams in North America contain only 45% real fruit.

To get you started, try these suggestions for using PC jams to make fast work of desserts.

Easy Fruit Filling for Crêpes
• For 8 servings, heat together ½ cup (125 mL) each President's Choice Over 50% Fruit French-Style Pure Apricot Jam and water until jam is melted. Stir in 4 tsp (20 mL) rum; heat 1 minute longer.
• Spread on 8 crêpes, fold and place on plate. Keep warm till serving.

Strawberry Dessert Shells
• Brush sponge cake flan shells with PC Over 50% Fruit French-Style Pure Strawberry Jam OR PC 'Too Good To Be True!' Strawberry Jam-Type Spread, thinned with a little water if necessary.
• Fill with fresh berries.
• Slather whipped cream on top or drizzle with PC Devon Custard OR PC Vanilla Crème Anglaise.

Condiments and Seasonings

The most precious commodity is time. No one finds enough of it. Yet recipes invariably call for chopped garlic — or shallots or ginger — and chopping takes time! That's why I introduced ready-to-use PC seasonings in oil.

PC Chopped Garlic in Oil: A true time-saver. Half a teaspoon (2 mL) is equivalent to one garlic clove.

PC Chopped Shallots in Oil: In France, Thailand, Malaysia, Indonesia, Laos, Vietnam and Kampuchea, cooking would grind to a halt without shallots. There's really no substitute for the flavor of these small garlic-shaped bulbs with a reddish skin (and don't believe cookbooks that tell you otherwise). For all their delicacy of flavor, however, shallots can make your eyes water like no other member of the onion family (all of which, by the way — bulb onions, leeks, garlic, chives, scallions and shallots — are related to the lily). One teaspoon (5 mL) of PC Chopped Shallots is equivalent to ¼ to ½ medium shallot.

PC Puréed Ginger: Did you know that cooking fish with a bit of ginger helps to minimize the "fishy" taste? Try it for yourself. Be sure to start with the freshest fish possible — you're not likely to improve on fish that's already past its prime! One teaspoon (5 mL) PC Puréed Ginger is equivalent to the same amount of freshly grated gingerroot. Use to taste.

PC Coarse Sea Salts: These purified but non-iodized salt crystals are harvested from vast salt ponds on the coast of California that are constantly being fed with sea water. Subjected to the heat of the sun and the prevailing winds, the sea water slowly evaporates and the salt begins to form crystals. Our salt crystals, which dissolve easily during cooking, are free of the anti-caking agents commonly added to fine-grained salt to keep it free-flowing.

PC Tellicherry Black Peppercorns: Strongly aromatic, Tellicherry peppercorns come from India's Malabar coast. Whole peppercorns are always recommended in dishes requiring long, slow cooking, as fresh ground pepper turns bitter when exposed to prolonged heat.

PC Sarawak White Peppercorns: These peppercorns come from Borneo in Malaysia and are true white peppercorns from fully vine-ripened pepper berries, as opposed to those produced from black peppercorns that have been polished to remove the black skin (this is known as "decorticated" white pepper). PC Sarawak White Peppercorns have an earthy fragrance and subdued spicy-sweetness, yet retain pepper's characteristic heat. Ideal in light-colored sauces or mayonnaise, as they flavor but won't discolor the sauce.

PC 'Too Good To Be True!' Lemon Pepper Seasoning: Did you know that you can "boost" the effect of salt simply by adding a little lemon juice to a dish? We took that principle further and created a special lemon-pepper seasoning that contains *no salt.* It really is 'Too Good To Be True!' Naturally, there's no MSG added.

PC 4-Peppercorn Steak Spice: The ideal barbecue seasoning. You can also use it in marinades and sauces. It's made with salt, dehydrated garlic, four kinds of ground peppercorns — Lampong black, Sarawak white, Madagascar green and Mauritius pink — and dehydrated red and green bell peppers. There's no added MSG.

PC Lime-Cilantro Seasoning: This was a popular choice among the top Toronto chefs who shared their backyard barbecue secrets with me on my summer Value Plus Network infomercial. They sprinkled it on grilled chicken, skate and endives, and used it to flavor PC Shanghai Frozen Stir-Fry Vegetables! You can use it on pork, too. No MSG added.

PC Spicy Barbecue Seasoning: An award-winning professional rib-cooker taught me that you can use this spicy blend as a "dry rub" on spareribs that you want to slow-cook on the barbecue. In the southern United States, real barbecue often starts with meats that are flavored with dry spices about one hour before they hit the fire. The sauce comes much later. No MSG added.

Vegetable Oils

PC Extra-Virgin Olive Oil from Italy: Our PC Extra-Virgin Olive Oil from Italy comes from the first pressing of the olives. Full flavored and lightly fruity, it's the oil of choice for salads, marinades, poultry, veal and fish.

PC Flavored Pure Olive Oils: An oil change at the supermarket? Why not? Engineers have known since the turn of the century that vegetable oil makes a perfectly acceptable alternative to diesel fuel. And it's cleaner. Of course, if you lean toward the exotic, you'll choose our President's Choice flavored pure olive oils. They're infused with the flavor essences that give stir-fries and vinaigrettes extra mileage. Try **PC Pure Olive Oil with Lemon** (a natural with fish and seafood), **Garlic or Basil Essence.** Or, for a turbo version, **Pure Olive Oil with Hot Pepper Essence.**

PC Uncommonly Light Pure Olive Oil: A delicate tasting, all-purpose olive oil for those who prefer subtlety in their olive oil. It's recommended for sautéeing vegetables and for leafy green salads. Or, use it for deep-frying — one of the great secrets of Spanish cuisine that we revealed in our September 1988 *Insider's Report.* Many cultures know that foods fried in olive oil don't necessarily taste "heavy." In April 1990, the original *Cook's* magazine tested pure olive oil and pure corn oil to deep-fry French fries, doughnuts, chicken and fish. In each taste test, four of the magazine's six tasters actually preferred the foods that had been fried in the olive oil.

PC 'Too Good To Be True!' 80% Monounsaturates Sunflower Oil: This unique oil comes from a special hybrid sunflower specifically created for its high monounsaturates content. Ordinary sunflower oil is only 20% to 25% monounsaturates. (The amount of saturated fat in oils from both the hybrid and ordinary sunflower is equivalent, about 10% to 11%.)

PC G·R·E·E·N G·O·U·R·M·E·T "The Virtuous Oil" 100% Pure Canola Oil: Canola oil is Canada's success story. It's an all-purpose vegetable oil that's high in monounsaturates. Only olive and avocado oils, and oils from some specialty seed plants developed for high monounsaturates — such as our PC 80% Monounsaturates Sunflower Oil — contain more. And it's lowest in saturated fat of any commonly used vegetable oil. Canadians developed the canola plant or LEAR (Low-Erucic-Acid Rapeseed) decades ago, but it skyrocketed to prominence only in recent years, when people began to welcome the nutritional benefits of the oil pressed from its seeds. The Virtuous Oil is pressed exclusively from Canada No. 1 Grade canola seeds.

PC Soya Oil Vegetable Oil: A mild-tasting oil for salads, cooking, baking and frying.

PC Peanut Oil: Excellent for fondues and for deep-frying as it has a high smoking point and there's minimal transfer of flavors from food to oil (and vice versa, if you decide to strain it and reuse it for deep-frying).

PC 'Too Good To Be True!' 100% Pure Safflower Oil: A neutral-tasting oil with the highest smoking temperature of any oil, which makes it ideal for salads, baking and stir-frying. Safflower oil is the highest source of polyunsaturated fats.

PC Corn Oil: A longtime favorite and all-purpose oil. Especially good for deep-frying. Many people prefer the flavor of foods fried in corn oil to any other oil.

Vinegars

Chinese poet Yuan Mei (1715-1797) devoted 20 pages of his cookbook, *Shih Tan*, or *The Menu*, to choosing the appropriate vinegar for a dish. Since the differences in character among vinegars are appreciable, we offer a variety of President's Choice vinegars with which you can experiment.

PC Aged Raspberry-Flavored Vinegar has a delicate fruitiness that imparts a unique taste to sauces and salads. It also adds superb flavor to chicken and meat dishes.

PC Aged Red Wine Vinegar is made from red wine and then matured in oak barrels to give it a mellow character. It's essential for salads, and a spoonful will enliven a pot roast. Or try **PC Aged Red Wine Vinegar with Shallots** to add flavor distinction. Here's a recipe for a vinegar-flavored basting sauce that I picked up on my travels to the Southern U.S.

Seasoned Vinegar Basting Sauce for the Barbecue
In the South, tomatoes aren't the last word in barbecue sauce. A basting sauce can be as simple as seasoned vinegar, which imparts a spicy hot flavor.

• Mix together 1 cup (250 mL) **PC Aged Red Wine Vinegar**, 1 tbsp (15 mL) chili powder OR paprika, 1 tsp (5 mL) each dry mustard, salt and pepper. (For a less pungent flavor, substitute water for half the vinegar.)
Makes about 1 cup (250 mL).

PC Aged White Wine Vinegar with Garlic is an excellent choice for salads because it's already permeated with the flavor of garlic. Just add oil! We also have **PC Aged White Wine Vinegar with Tarragon**, a natural for chicken and summer salads.

President's Choice Balsamic Vinegar of Modena: Do you know what you're getting when you buy balsamic vinegar? A tremendous amount of confusion surrounds this unique vinegar. Not many people know that there are two balsamic vinegar products made in Modena, Italy, and each is governed by separate ministerial decrees. Both products start with the boiled-down must, or juice, of grapes grown only in the provinces of Modena and Reggio Emilia (the latter is also the epicentre of Parmigiano Reggiano cheese), and each is aged in open barrels made from specified woods native to the region.

"Traditional" or "artisanal" balsamic vinegar is more condiment than vinegar: dark, syrupy, very sweet and expensive. Made in limited amounts by a society of small producers, traditional balsamic vinegar is aged a minimum of 12 years and judged on its color, taste and body like a fine liqueur. A tiny vial from a very good year, they say, can cost as much as a very old Barolo ("the king of wines and the wine of kings"). Obviously, you're lucky to get your hands on some. However, many people find it too sweet for salad, unless used by the drop.

Commercial balsamic vinegar is widely available; be careful you're not being overcharged, as its price varies. It must meet specific levels of acetic acid — that's what makes it vinegar — as well as standards of flavor and color. It's aged in oak, juniper and/or chestnut, at the discretion of the manufacturer, and wine and/or balsamic vinegars of different ages can be added periodically to develop the flavor. The final product, therefore, can be a mixture of many ages, which is why you won't see any specific age mentioned on the label. Sometimes caramel coloring is added — for example, if the grapes are too low in natural sugars one year to caramelize sufficiently during the boiling-down stage to produce the rich dark brown color that characterizes this vinegar.

President's Choice Balsamic Vinegar of Modena is made from white Trebbiano and red Lambrusco grapes. The juice is boiled down to a syrupy consistency and then fermented in open oak casks to round out its rich flavor. (Oak is favored because its tannin gives color.) The natural sweetness of the grape juice and the weather determine the fermentation period. The final product, the one that bears our President's Choice label, is a melding of various vintages of vinegar. It may or may not contain caramel color.

Barbecued Chicken Wings with PC Balsamic Vinegar
Here's something quick to try with PC Balsamic Vinegar that you wouldn't make with ordinary vinegar. The recipe is easily multiplied.
- Toss 1 lb (500 g) of chicken wings with ⅓ cup (75 mL) PC Balsamic Vinegar. Cover and let marinate 2 to 3 hours at room temperature or, preferably, overnight in the refrigerator.
- Grill over medium-hot coals for 8 to 10 minutes per side or until cooked through. Alternatively, bake in a 450°F (230°C) oven for about 25 minutes, turning halfway through.
- Serve hot or at room temperature.
Makes 2 or 3 servings.

President's Choice Raspberry-Flavored Balsamic Vinegar: This superb new addition to our vinegar collection is ideal for preparing sauce for skate or for making warm vinaigrettes for mixed green salads. It can also be used to marinate chicken or lamb.

Mustard
More mustard seed is sold around the world than pepper (most of it is grown in Canada) yet the amount of mustard we consume is still miniscule compared to what people used to eat. Imagine being a householder in 13th century England and taking delivery of 10 gallons of mustard a month! And if you were a guest at a banquet given by the Duke of Burgundy in 14th century France, you would have helped polish off 70 gallons of mustard. There even was a time when people used to keep mustard grinders on their tables!

PC Dijon Mustard and **PC Old-Fashioned Dijon Mustard** (a milder-tasting, grainy version) are essential in cooking. A teaspoon (5 mL) of either mustard in a vinaigrette will thicken the mixture as well as season it so that it clings better to salad greens.

PC Russian-Style Sweet Mustard is a sweet and tangy mustard with a smooth texture all its own.

Use it for sandwiches, for glazing ham, roast beef or poultry, and for flavoring dipping sauces for vegetable sticks. Mix with **PC Plum Sauce**, according to taste, to create an exciting dipping sauce for chicken nuggets, spring rolls and other finger foods.

Mustard Barbecue Basting Sauce
This flavorful blend is especially good on chicken.
◆ Mix ½ cup (125 mL) **PC Russian-Style Sweet Mustard** with enough **PC Vegetable Oil** to make it flow easily.
◆ Add a squeeze of lemon juice to give the mixture an acidic zip, and a dash or two of **PC Louisiana Hot Sauce** for zing.
◆ Just before finishing chicken on the barbecue, paint with this mixture and let it caramelize to a beautiful golden glaze. Refrigerate leftover baste.
Makes about ⅔ cup (150 mL).

Three-Mustard Butter
Serve this with grilled chicken, barbecued meats or as a dip for vegetables.
◆ In bowl, combine 1 pkg (250 g) slightly softened **PC Lightly Salted Normandy-Style Cultured Butter,** ⅓ cup (75 mL) **PC Dijon Mustard,** ⅓ cup (75 mL) **PC Old-Fashioned Dijon Mustard** and ⅔ cup (150 mL) **PC Russian-Style Sweet Mustard.**
◆ Mix well. Add freshly squeezed lemon juice to taste.
◆ Refrigerate at least 4 hours to let flavors develop.
Makes about 2 cups (500 mL).

Bottled Water
The dinner is under control. The table is set. There's only one thing missing: the refreshment. You go into your cellar and, after pondering the selection, you pull out a most special bottle — of mineral water!

This scene is being played out every day somewhere in France, where they're as respectful of their water as they are of their wine. A good water cellar, they say, should contain an assortment of waters — spring water (**PC Natural Spring Water**, for example) for frequent consumption, and mineral waters that differ in their mineral content and degree of effervescence. One end of the scale would be represented by a mineral water that's light-tasting and ideal for everyday enjoyment (**PC Carbonated Natural Mineral Water** is perfect); the other by a mineral water that has real mineral tang — perhaps too heavy in minerals for anything but occasional enjoyment!

From The Deep-Freeze: Hors d'Oeuvres
"Brought in from the outside." That's what hors d'oeuvre means translated from the French.

According to one of my favorite cookbook chefs, Louis Szathmary, Russian noblemen émigrés to Paris longed for a taste of the foods that reminded them of their homeland. With French chefs reluctant to prepare these foods, restaurateurs who wanted the business "brought in from the outside" the items these noblemen pined for out of nostalgia.

Today, guests at three-star restaurants are customarily greeted with complimentary hors d'oeuvres to enjoy while pondering the elaborate menus. These little morsels are frequently called "amuse-gueule" (literally "amuse the palate") because they keep your tastebuds tantalized while the serious food is being prepared.

We'll leave the three-star meal preparations to you, but you can let President's Choice cater the appetizers. Look what you can pull from the freezer at a moment's notice:
PC Silver Platter Hors d'Oeuvre Collection (Quiche Lorraine, Spinach-&-Cheese and Italian-style mini tarts); bite-size **PC Oriental-Style Spring Rolls**, vegetable, shrimp or beef; **PC Swiss Cheese**

Hors d'Oeuvres breaded cheese sticks, as well as two new varieties — breaded Cheddar sticks and Swiss cheese wrapped in bacon; **PC Savory Cocktail Sausage Rolls**; the **PC Special Occasion Hors d'Oeuvre Collection** with four phyllo appetizers (Spinach & Cheese Triangles, Pastry Cheese Twists, Mushroom Turnovers and Chevre & Sundried Tomatoes); several oriental-style appetizers (also available as part of our **PC Oriental-Style Club Pack Collection**); **PC Shrimp Toasts**, made from a seasoned paste of shrimp and vegetables spread on bread and baked; **PC "Pot Stickers" Oriental-Style Pork & Vegetable Dumplings**, our pan-fried version of the popular crescent-shaped dumplings called "jiao zi" (technically speaking, once they're fried, they become "guo tie!"); and **PC Oriental-Style Seafood Rangoon**, wonton dough wrappers filled with a delicious blend of cream cheese, pollock and snow crab. We've even developed a Club Pack of hors d'oeuvre-sized pastry turnovers flavored with our own PC "Memories of..." sauces.

Pasta

I love our PC Splendido fresh and frozen pastas, but dried pasta can be the superior choice in pasta dishes that have a lot of sauce, since dry pasta retains its texture better and absorbs less sauce than the fresh pasta. We call our PC dried pasta "The World's Best" because its taste and texture are the result of four critical factors:

• Although ordinary pasta can be made from many types of wheat, durum wheat is the premier choice for a perfect *al dente* texture — tender but firm. And PC pasta is made exclusively from the most desirable durum wheat semolina of all, hard amber durum wheat.

• In order to get only the best grade of selected varieties of hard amber durum wheat, the wheat for our pasta is hand-selected by experts who go into the fields of individual farmers.

• Using the most modern Italian equipment, the golden heart of the durum wheat is milled into extra-fine semolina. This extra milling gives PC pasta its distinctive rich golden color and superior *al dente* texture.

• It's dried using special high-temperature drying equipment, so that it won't turn sticky or starchy when cooked.

PC "Memories of..." Sauce Suggestions

The following is a list of various foods and the suggested PC "Memories of..." sauces that can turn them into culinary events.

Beef (roasts, steaks, burgers, meat loaf)
Suggested Sauces: Lyon 4-Peppercorn Sauce, Fuji Shiitake Mushroom Sauce, Bangkok Spicy Thai, Jaipur Curry & Passion Fruit Sauce, Kyoto Ginger Glaze, Savannah Hot Red Pepper Jelly (for sandwiches), Sonoma Dried Tomato Sauce (in meat loaf), Kansas City Meets Hong Kong BBQ Sauce.

Veal (breast, roast, chops, steaks)
Suggested Sauces: Fuji Shiitake Mushroom Sauce, Lyon 4-Peppercorn Sauce, Cedar Springs Sage & Onion Sauce.

Lamb (chops, leg, roast, rack, kebabs)
Suggested Sauces: Singapore Passion Fruit Sauce, Szechwan Peanut Sauce, Ancient Damascus Tangy Pomegranate Glaze, Bangkok Spicy Thai Sauce, Hong Kong Spicy Black Bean Sauce, Jaipur Curry & Passion Fruit Sauce, Kobe 2-Minute Miracle Tamari Garlic Marinade, Kyoto Ginger Sauce, Jaipur Curry & Passion Fruit Sauce, Singapore Passion Fruit Sauce, Kansas City Meets Hong Kong BBQ Sauce.

Pork (roasts, chops, tenderloin, spareribs, baby back or country-style)
Suggested Sauces: Cedar Springs Sage & Onion Sauce, Fuji Shiitake Mushroom Sauce, Hawaii

Sweet & Sour Sauce, Szechwan Peanut Sauce, Lyon 4-Peppercorn Sauce, Ancient Damascus Tangy Pomegranate Glaze, Hong Kong Spicy Black Bean Sauce, Jaipur Curry & Passion Fruit Sauce, Montego Bay Jerk Sauce or Timid Jerk Sauce (marinade), Singapore Passion Fruit Sauce, Dallas Meets Singapore BBQ Sauce.

Ham
Suggested Sauces: Dijon Mustard & Raisin Sauce, Savannah Hot Red Pepper Jelly, Ancient Damascus Tangy Pomegranate Glaze, Hawaii Sweet & Sour Sauce, Singapore Passion Fruit Sauce.

Poultry (chicken, Cornish game hen, duck, goose, turkey)
Suggested Sauces: Cedar Springs Sage & Onion Sauce, Fuji Shiitake Mushroom Sauce, Szechwan Peanut Sauce, Gilroy Creamy Roasted Garlic Sauce, Lyon 4-Peppercorn Sauce, Hawaii Sweet & Sour Sauce, Ancient Damascus Tangy Pomegranate Glaze, Bangkok Spicy Thai Sauce, Montego Bay Jerk Sauce or Timid Jerk Sauce (marinade), Canton Spicy Plum Sauce, Hong Kong Spicy Black Bean Sauce, Jaipur Curry & Passion Fruit Sauce, San Francisco Lemon Ginger Sauce, Kyoto Ginger Glaze, Savannah Hot Red Pepper Jelly, Singapore Passion Fruit Sauce, Kansas City Meets Hong Kong BBQ Sauce.

Fish (steaks, fillets)
Suggested Sauces: Hong Kong Spicy Black Bean Sauce, Jaipur Curry & Passion Fruit Sauce, Asiago Cheese Sauce, Cheddar Cheese Sauce, San Francisco Lemon Ginger Sauce, Singapore Passion Fruit Sauce.

Shellfish (shrimp, lobster, crab)
Suggested Sauces: Bangkok Spicy Thai Sauce, Hong Kong Spicy Black Bean Sauce, Jaipur Curry & Passion Fruit Sauce, Szechwan Peanut Sauce, Ancient Damascus Tangy Pomegranate Glaze, Hawaii Sweet & Sour Sauce, Canton Spicy Plum Sauce, Gilroy Creamy Roasted Garlic Sauce (for seafood salads), Kyoto Ginger Glaze, Singapore Passion Fruit Sauce.

Eggs
Suggested Sauces: Asiago Cheese Sauce, Cheddar Cheese Sauce, Jaipur Curry & Passion Fruit Sauce, Savannah Hot Red Pepper Jelly.

Pasta
Suggested Sauces: Fuji Shiitake Mushroom Sauce, Cheddar Cheese Sauce, Gilroy Creamy Roasted Garlic Sauce, Bangkok Spicy Thai Sauce, Lyon 4-Peppercorn Sauce, Szechwan Peanut Sauce.

Pizza & Bruschetta
Suggested Sauces: Gilroy Creamy Roasted Garlic Sauce, Asiago Cheese Sauce, Sonoma Dried Tomato Sauce.

Salads
Suggested Sauces: Reggiano Caesar Dressing, Gilroy Creamy Roasted Garlic Sauce, Bangkok Spicy Thai Sauce, Kyoto Ginger Glaze, Sonoma Dried Tomato Sauce, Szechwan Peanut Sauce.

Stir Fries
Suggested Sauces: San Francisco Lemon Ginger Sauce, Bangkok Spicy Thai Sauce, Hong Kong Spicy Black Bean Sauce, Canton Spicy Plum Sauce, Kyoto Ginger Glaze, Szechwan Peanut Sauce.

Stuffings
Suggested Sauces: Cedar Springs Sage & Onion Sauce, Fuji Shiitake Mushroom Sauce.

Vegetables
Suggested Sauces: Asiago Cheese Sauce, Cheddar Cheese Sauce, Reggiano Caesar Dressing (as a dip), Sonoma Dried Tomato Sauce, San Francisco Lemon Ginger Sauce, Fuji Shiitake Mushroom Sauce, Gilroy Creamy Roasted Garlic Sauce, Lyon 4-Peppercorn Sauce, Bangkok Spicy Thai Sauce,

Hong Kong Spicy Black Bean Sauce, Jaipur Curry & Passion Fruit Sauce, Kyoto Ginger Glaze.

Finger Foods (e.g., chicken nuggets, meatballs, spring or egg rolls)
Suggested Sauces: Canton Spicy Plum Sauce, Kyoto Ginger Glaze, Singapore Passion Fruit Sauce, Savannah Hot Red Pepper Jelly (try it on cream cheese and crackers), Fiery Thai Dipping Sauce.

The Language of Cooks

Al dente: Cooked until tender but still resilient to the bite. Used mostly for pasta or rice.

Baste: To moisten food while it cooks, usually with pan juices or a flavorful liquid.

Blanch: To plunge food into rapidly boiling water for a minute or two.

Blend: To mix thoroughly.

Braise: To cook food in some liquid or in its natural juices in a covered pan.

Caramelize: Sugar and water cooked to a certain temperature will turn a golden brown, or caramelize. The same thing happens to the natural sugars in vegetables (e.g., carrots) or meat dishes (e.g., barbecued ribs) during cooking.

Deglaze: To add wine or water to the sauté pan to dissolve the flavorful deposits created during sautéing or pan-frying. These browned bits add flavor to a sauce.

Fillet: "To fillet" means to remove the bones from chicken or fish. Fillet describes a boneless piece of meat or fish — fillet of salmon, fillet of cod, etc. A "fillet of beef" is the whole tenderloin; trimmed of its thick layer of suet, it weighs about 7 pounds (3 kg). A "filet mignon," on the other hand, is cut from the narrow end of the beef fillet and it weighs only a few ounces. Filet mignon steaks are prized because only two or three can be cut from a beef fillet.

Fold in: To combine gently and carefully.

Flake: To break into small pieces.

Flambé: To douse with spirits and ignite. The intent is to burn off the alcohol and leave just the flavor, but recent studies by the U.S Department of Agriculture (USDA) show that much of the alcohol in a dish remains after the flames die down — 75% in the case of Cherries Jubilee! (If you add a splash of wine to the stewpot, bear in mind that it might not completely cook away. In the same USDA study, traces of red wine were found in a pot roast that cooked for $2\frac{1}{2}$ hours. Scalloped oysters flavored with dry sherry retained 45% of the alcohol after cooking 25 minutes!)

Glaze: To give food a shiny coating of sauce just before serving.

Julienne: To cut food into thin matchstick-size strips.

Knead: To work dough using the heel of the hand while gently pressing down, stretching and folding the dough.

Marinate: To let food stand in a marinade to season and to tenderize; don't marinate fish longer than one hour or the tender flesh will break down. Marinades cannot be reused but some can be brought to a boil and used as a sauce.

Mix: To combine ingredients by stirring.

Non-reactive cookware: This refers to stainless steel, glass, ceramic, enameled steel or cast iron and anodized aluminum — materials that will not react with the acids in foods such as tomatoes or vinegar and thereby discolor food and ruin its flavor. Aluminum and cast iron will react with these ingredients. (Hollandaise sauce made in an aluminum pot will turn greyish-green!)

Parboil: To precook food in boiling water.

Plump: To soak a food in liquid until full and round (e.g., raisins or currants).

Reduce: To boil liquid down over high heat, driving off moisture until the liquid decreases in volume. Use a pan with a large enough cooking surface so that the liquid can boil down quickly. A sauté pan is perfect.

Sauté: Sautéing is fast and very versatile. The secret lies in knowing how long it takes each ingredient to cook perfectly. The higher the heat (start medium high for comfort, then move to high), the more flavor can be sealed in, and the better the food cooks through. To keep food from burning, keep it moving; you've probably seen experienced chefs jerk the sauté pan away from them in order to toss the food off the side of the pan. To thoroughly cook sautéed chicken or pork, first sear the outside on high heat, then cover the pan and finish cooking on medium heat.

Scald: To heat almost to the boiling point, as in heating milk for custard. It can also mean to pour boiling liquid over food.

Sear: To brown food, usually meats, over high heat in a hot skillet or on a grill. This seals in juices and, therefore, flavor.

Shred: To cut with a knife or pull apart with two forks into long narrow pieces. For example, try shredding oven-braised beef brisket and reheating it in some of its pan juices and PC Gourmet Hickory-Flavor Barbecue Sauce to make Southern-style barbecued beef sandwiches.

Season: To give food more flavor by adding seasoning or savory ingredients.

Simmer: To cook slowly just below the boiling point.

Steam: To cook food over boiling water in a covered pot.

Stir-fry: The Chinese term for frying (what the French call sautéing).

Sweating: The French use the word "Vichy" to describe this technique for quickly softening vegetables such as onions, leeks or mirepoix — the mixture of diced onion, garlic, carrot and celery that's used to add flavor to stocks and casseroles. Basically, sweating consists of placing buttered parchment directly on top of the vegetables in the pan, then covering the pan with a lid or foil, and letting them cook over medium heat until softened.

Tender-crisp: Cooked until tender but not soft or limp.

Toss: A way to mix ingredients using two forks or spoons while tossing ingredients upward as if you were making a salad.

Whisk: To beat ingredients with a whisk until well combined.

Whip: To beat rapidly with a whisk or an electric mixer.

Zest: The colored rind, technically the flavedo, of citrus fruit. It's usually grated or cut into thin slivers. The white pith, or albedo, that lies under the peel is bitter and not used.

10 RULES OF ROASTING

• **Use a meat roasting time chart only as a guide.** Many variables affect the time required to cook a roast. Bone lengthens cooking time; fat shortens it; and a narrow roast cooks faster than a thick one. Even the accuracy of your oven thermometer and starting temperature of the meat are factors.

• **Start at room temperature.** For even doneness, allow the meat to come to room temperature all the way through before you begin roasting it. It will taste better. If you must cook a frozen roast (it won't look or taste as good), increase cooking time by 50%.

• **Use a meat thermometer.** Preferably a small instant-read thermometer instead of one you leave in during cooking. Insert it into the thickest part of the roast, not near fat or bone. Leave in 15 seconds to register.

• **Take seasoning advice with a grain of salt.** Some say salt the roast before, some say to salt it after cooking. There is no clear answer, so follow your mother's advice on this one. You should always, however, add pepper afterward, since dry heat above 325°F (160°C) can make it bitter. Like pepper, other seasonings can be heat-sensitive. Add them when you turn the meat, to the side that's been cooked.

• **Wipe meat dry before you put it in the oven.** Surface moisture turns to steam before it evaporates, which causes the meat to turn grey or brown unevenly.

• **Sear the meat.** The brief cooking at a high oven temperature seals in juices and enhances the flavor and color of the meat's surface and sauces made from the drippings.

• **Use a rack.** To avoid a soggy-bottomed roast, don't put it on the bottom of a pan where juices collect. The pan's bottom also conducts heat, which can result in uneven cooking. A rack ensures drier, more even roasting.

• **Leave the lid off!** To achieve the crisp texture and deep brown color of a properly cooked roast, you must use dry heat — and that means leaving the lid off the roasting pan. To stop meat from drying out, baste it often, about every 15 to 30 minutes.

• **Take your roast out before it reaches the desired temperature.** That's because the internal temperature will rise a few degrees after the roast is out of the oven — the higher temperature of the exterior will continue to cook the interior. Use a "tent" of aluminum foil to keep your roast warm and protect it from "thermal shock," which can draw out much of the natural juices.

• **Let roast rest 15 to 25 minutes before carving.** If you slice your roast immediately, you will lose a substantial portion of its natural juices, which are driven from the centre during roasting. A resting period allows these juices to be reabsorbed.

Roasting Beef

Cut	Weight (lb)	Oven Temp.	Cooking Time (minutes per lb)	Interior Meat Temp. (in oven)
Standing Rib	6 to 8	350°F/180°C	18	125°F/50°C (rare)
			22	135°F/55°C (medium)
			25	160°F/70°C (well done)
Rolled Boneless Rib	4 to 6	325°F/160°C	24	125°F/50°C (rare)
			27	135°F/55°C (medium)
			30	160°F/70°C (well done)
Strip Loin	6	400°F/200°C	12	125°F/50°C (rare)
			15	135°F/55°C (medium)
			18	160°F/70°C (well done)
Top Sirloin	4	325°F/160°C	20 to 25	125°F/50°C (rare)
			25 to 30	135°F/55°C (medium)
			30 to 35	160°F/70°C (well done)
Tenderloin	4 to 6	500°F/260°C	7	125°F/50°C (rare)
			10	135°F/55°C (medium)
Eye of Round	5	325°F/160°C	20	135°F/55°C (medium)
			25	160°F/70°C (well done)

Roasting Lamb: The North American Way

Cut	Weight (lb)	Oven Temp.	Cooking Time (minutes per lb)	Interior Meat Temp. (in oven)
Leg, bone-in	4 to 6	400°F/200°C	12 to 15	145°F/63°C (medium)
		325°F/160°C	30	160°F/70°C (well done)
Loin, bone-in	3 to 4	400°F/200°C	12 to 15	145°F/63°C (medium)
		325°F/160°C	25 to 30	160°F/70°C (well done)
Saddle	6 to 8	325°F/160°C	15 to 18	145°F/63°C (medium)
Rack (6 chops)	1¾ to 2	400°F/200°C	40 to 45 total	145°F/63°C (medium)
		325°F/160°C	30	160°F/70°C (well done)
Leg, boned	4 to 6	400°F/200°C	20	145°F/63° (medium)
		325°F/160°C	40	160°F/70°C (well done)
Shoulder, boneless, rolled	3 to 5	400°F/200°C	20 to 25	145°F/63°C (medium)
		325°F/160°C	40	160°F/70°C (well done)

Roasting Lamb: The French Way

Most North Americans prefer lamb that's "barely pink." The French prefer theirs "rosy rare." They take lamb out of the oven at relatively low interior temperatures (in-oven), then let it rest 10 to 15 minutes before serving.

Degree of Doneness	Internal Temperature of Meat (in oven)
Very rare to rosy rare	120°F to 125°F/50°C
Medium rare (pink to pinky grey)	130°F to 140°F/60°C★

★140°F/60°C is the temperature at which all harmful bacteria are killed.

Roasting Pork

Cut	Weight (lb)	Oven Temp.	Cooking Time (minutes per lb)	Interior Meat Temp. (in oven)
Loin				
centre	3 to 5	325°F/160°C	30 to 35	160°F/75°C
blade or sirloin	3 to 4	325°F/160°C	35 to 40	160°F/75°C
rolled	3 to 5	325°F/160°C	35 to 40	160°F/75°C
Leg				
whole	12 to 16	325°F/160°C	20 to 25	160°F/75°C
half	5 to 8	325°F/160°C	30 to 35	160°F/75°C
Shoulder				
picnic	5 to 8	325°F/160°C	25 to 30	160°F/75°C
butt	4 to 6	325°F/160°C	35 to 40	160°F/75°C

Insider's Report Team: These are some of the people who have contributed to the success of President's Choice and the *Insider's Report*. Turn page for key.

Insider's Report Team (see photo on preceding page)

1. Terri Nichol
2. Bill Clubine, Product Development Meat Specialist
3. Dave Nichol, President, Loblaw International Merchants
4. Mary-Pat Hearn, Product Developer
5. Alison Jarvest, Development Chef
6. Rob Chenaux, Executive VP, Intersave
7. Jim Phillips, Advertising Art Director & famous *Insider's Report* cartoonist
8. Salina Strangway, Freelance Artist
9. Barbara Druxerman, Product Developer
10. Dorothy Leamen, VP, Finance
11. Sara Innes, Former Category Manager
12. Lori Fournier, Freelance Writer
13. Ted Reader, Assistant Product Developer
14. Dean Collinson, VP, Perishables, Buying & Merchandising
15. Peter Trollope, Freelance Artist
16. Tom Stephens, VP, Unique Product Development
17. Dominique Corriero, Category Manager
18. Brian Dalfen, Category Manager
19. Brad Wakutz, Director, Corporate Brands
20. Nancy Hall, Senior Product Developer
21. Maria Charvat, Director, Product Development
22. Gordana Vulevic, Manager, Design Services
23. Cathy Healey, Senior Category Manager
24. Bill Snelling, Senior Director, Quality Assurance
25. Michelle Guerrero, Product Developer, General Merchandise
26. Cathy Paull, Receptionist
27. Paul Uys, Senior Director, Unique Product Development
28. Julie Henn, Product Development Coordinator
29. Kathi Leteta, Advertising Production Manager
30. Frances Litwin, Senior Writer-Editor
31. Brian Farb, Director of Packaging
32. Doug Lunau, Former President, Intersave
33. Larry Griffin, VP, Quality Assurance
34. Lena Mattei, Secretary to Mr. Nichol
35. Robin Periana, Television Producer-Director
36. Dori Burchat, Creative Director, Design Services
37. Jeff McCullough, Product Development Assistant
38. Alison Butlin, Freelance Writer
39. Nora Snikvalds, Coordinator, Corporate Brands
40. Chris Keppy, Former Video Editor
41. Jim Grosso, Freelance Assistant Producer
42. Denise Mackenzie, Director, Corporate Brands
43. Edmund O'Keefe, Director of Strategy & Development
44. Margaret Jeffery, Senior Product Developer
45. Jimmy Graham, Gardening Category Specialist
46. Ragnar Pohlak, Production Director
47. Anne Doremus, Executive Assistant to Mr. Nichol
48. Scott Lindsay, VP, Corporate Brands
49. Boris Polakow, VP, Corporate Brand Sales
50. Russ Rudd, VP, Design Services

13. 14. 15. 16. 17. 18. 19. 20. 21. 22. 24. 23.

9. 11.

42. 34. 44. 45. 36. 37. 46. 47. 39. 48. 40. 50. 41.

43. 35. 28. 30. 38. 49.

5. 6. 7. 8. 10. 12.

4. 27. 29. 31. 32.

1. 2. 3. 25. 26. 33.

Recommended Dietary Allowances (RDA) and Adequate Intakes (AI) for Vitamins

Age (yr)	Thiamin RDA (mg/d)	Riboflavin RDA (mg/d)	Niacin RDA (mg/d)[a]	Biotin AI (µg/d)	Pantothenic acid AI (mg/d)	Vitamin B6 RDA (mg/d)	Folate RDA (µg/d)[b]	Vitamin B12 RDA (µg/d)	Choline AI (mg/d)	Vitamin C RDA (mg/d)	Vitamin A RDA (µg/d)[c]	Vitamin D RDA (µg/d)[d]	Vitamin E RDA (mg/d)[e]	Vitamin K AI (µg/d)
Infants														
0–0.5	0.2	0.3	2	5	1.7	0.1	65	0.4	125	40	400	10*	4	2.0
0.5–1	0.3	0.4	4	6	1.8	0.3	80	0.5	150	50	500	10*	5	2.5
Children														
1–3	0.5	0.5	6	8	2	0.5	150	0.9	200	15	300	15	6	30
4–8	0.6	0.6	8	12	3	0.6	200	1.2	250	25	400	15	7	55
Males														
9–13	0.9	0.9	12	20	4	1.0	300	1.8	375	45	600	15	11	60
14–18	1.2	1.3	16	25	5	1.3	400	2.4	550	75	900	15	15	75
19–30	1.2	1.3	16	30	5	1.3	400	2.4	550	90	900	15	15	120
31–50	1.2	1.3	16	30	5	1.3	400	2.4	550	90	900	15	15	120
51–70	1.2	1.3	16	30	5	1.7	400	2.4	550	90	900	15	15	120
>70	1.2	1.3	16	30	5	1.7	400	2.4	550	90	900	20	15	120
Females														
9–13	0.9	0.9	12	20	4	1.0	300	1.8	375	45	600	15	11	60
14–18	1.0	1.0	14	25	5	1.2	400	2.4	400	65	700	15	15	75
19–30	1.1	1.1	14	30	5	1.3	400	2.4	425	75	700	15	15	90
31–50	1.1	1.1	14	30	5	1.3	400	2.4	425	75	700	15	15	90
51–70	1.1	1.1	14	30	5	1.5	400	2.4	425	75	700	15	15	90
>70	1.1	1.1	14	30	5	1.5	400	2.4	425	75	700	20	15	90
Pregnancy														
≤18	1.4	1.4	18	30	6	1.9	600	2.6	450	80	750	15	15	75
19–30	1.4	1.4	18	30	6	1.9	600	2.6	450	85	770	15	15	90
31–50	1.4	1.4	18	30	6	1.9	600	2.6	450	85	770	15	15	90
Lactation														
≤18	1.4	1.6	17	35	7	2.0	500	2.8	550	115	1,200	15	19	75
19–30	1.4	1.6	17	35	7	2.0	500	2.8	550	120	1,300	15	19	90
31–50	1.4	1.6	17	35	7	2.0	500	2.8	550	120	1,300	15	19	90

NOTE: For all nutrients, values for infants are AI. The glossary on page Y at the back of the book defines units of nutrient measure.
[a] Niacin recommendations are expressed as niacin equivalents (NE), except for recommendations for infants younger than 6 months, which are expressed as preformed niacin.
[b] Folate recommendations are expressed as dietary folate equivalents (DFE).
[c] Vitamin A recommendations are expressed as retinol activity equivalents (RAE).
[d] Vitamin D recommendations are expressed as cholecalciferol and assume an absence of adequate exposure to sunlight.
[e] Vitamin E recommendations are expressed as α-tocopherol. *Adequate Intake

Recommended Dietary Allowances (RDA) and Adequate Intakes (AI) for Minerals

Age (yr)	Sodium AI (mg/d)	Chloride AI (mg/d)	Potassium AI (mg/d)	Calcium RDA (mg/d)	Phosphorus RDA (mg/d)	Magnesium RDA (mg/d)	Iron RDA (mg/d)	Zinc RDA (mg/d)	Iodine RDA (µg/d)	Selenium RDA (µg/d)	Copper RDA (µg/d)	Manganese AI (mg/d)	Fluoride AI (mg/d)	Chromium AI (µg/d)	Molybdenum RDA (µg/d)
Infants															
0–0.5	120	180	400	200*	100	30	0.27	2	110	15	200	0.003	0.01	0.2	2
0.5–1	370	570	700	260*	275	75	11	3	130	20	220	0.6	0.5	5.5	3
Children															
1–3	1,000	1,500	3,000	700	460	80	7	3	90	20	340	1.2	0.7	11	17
4–8	1,200	1,900	3,800	1,000	500	130	10	5	90	30	440	1.5	1.0	15	22
Males															
9–13	1,500	2,300	4,500	1,300	1,250	240	8	8	120	40	700	1.9	2	25	34
14–18	1,500	2,300	4,700	1,300	1,250	410	11	11	150	55	890	2.2	3	35	43
19–30	1,500	2,300	4,700	1,000	700	400	8	11	150	55	900	2.3	4	35	45
31–50	1,500	2,300	4,700	1,000	700	420	8	11	150	55	900	2.3	4	35	45
51–70	1,300	2,000	4,700	100	700	420	8	11	150	55	900	2.3	4	30	45
>70	1,200	1,800	4,700	1,200	700	420	8	11	150	55	900	2.3	4	30	45
Females															
9–13	1,500	2,300	4,500	1,300	1,250	240	8	8	120	40	700	1.6	2	21	34
14–18	1,500	2,300	4,700	1,300	1,250	360	15	9	150	55	890	1.6	3	24	43
19–30	1,500	2,300	4,700	1,000	700	310	18	8	150	55	900	1.8	3	25	45
31–50	1,500	2,300	4,700	1,000	700	320	18	8	150	55	900	1.8	3	25	45
51–70	1,300	2,000	4,700	1,200	700	320	8	8	150	55	900	1.8	3	20	45
>70	1,200	1,800	4,700	1,200	700	320	8	8	150	55	900	1.8	3	20	45
Pregnancy															
≤18	1,500	2,300	4,700	1,300	1,250	400	27	12	220	60	1000	2.0	3	29	50
19–30	1,500	2,300	4,700	1,000	700	350	27	11	220	60	1000	2.0	3	30	50
31–50	1,500	2,300	4,700	1,000	700	360	27	11	220	60	1000	2.0	3	30	50
Lactation															
≤18	1,500	2,300	5,100	1,300	1,250	360	10	14	290	70	1300	2.6	3	44	50
19–30	1,500	2,300	5,100	1,000	700	310	9	12	290	70	1300	2.6	3	45	50
31–50	1,500	2,300	5,100	1,000	700	320	9	12	290	70	1300	2.6	3	45	50

Source: Reprinted with permission from Dietary Reference Intakes: Recommended Dietary Allowances and Adequate Intake, 2011 by the National Academy of Sciences, Courtesy of the National Academies Press, Washington, D.C.

B

Tolerable Upper Intake Levels (UL) for Vitamins

Age (yr)	Niacin (mg/d)[a]	Vitamin B_6 (mg/d)	Folate (µg/d)[a]	Choline (mg/d)	Vitamin C (mg/d)	Vitamin A (µg/d)[b]	Vitamin D (µg/d)	Vitamin E (mg/d)[c]
Infants								
0–0.5	—	—	—	—	—	600	25	—
0.5–1	—	—	—	—	—	600	37.5	—
Children								
1–3	10	30	300	1,000	400	600	62.5	200
4–8	15	40	400	1,000	650	900	100	300
9–13	20	60	600	2,000	1,200	1,700	100	600
Adolescents								
14–18	30	80	800	3,000	1,800	2,800	100	800
Adults								
19–70	35	100	1,000	3,500	2,000	3,000	100	1,000
>70	35	100	1,000	3,500	2,000	3,000	100	1,000
Pregnancy								
≤18	30	80	800	3,000	1,800	2,800	100	800
19–50	35	100	1,000	3,500	2,000	3,000	100	1,000
Lactation								
≤18	30	80	800	3,000	1,800	2,800	100	800
19–50	35	100	1,000	3,500	2,000	3,000	100	1,000

[a]The UL for niacin and folate apply to synthetic forms obtained from supplements, fortified foods, or a combination of the two.

[b]The UL for vitamin A applies to the preformed vitamin only.
[c]The UL for vitamin E applies to any form of supplemental α-tocopherol, fortified foods, or a combination of the two.

Tolerable Upper Intake Levels (UL) for Minerals

Age (yr)	Sodium (mg/d)	Chloride (mg/d)	Calcium (mg/d)	Phosphorus (mg/d)	Magnesium (mg/d)[d]	Iron (mg/d)	Zinc (mg/d)	Iodine (µg/d)	Selenium (µg/d)	Copper (µg/d)	Manganese (mg/d)	Fluoride (mg/d)	Molybdenum (µg/d)	Boron (mg/d)	Nickel (mg/d)	Vanadium (mg/d)
Infants																
0–0.5	—[e]	—[e]	1,500	—	—	40	4	—	45	—	—	0.7	—	—	—	—
0.5–1	—[e]	—[e]	1,500	—	—	40	5	—	60	—	—	0.9	—	—	—	—
Children																
1–3	1,500	2,300	2,500	3,000	65	40	7	200	90	1,000	2	1.3	300	3	0.2	—
4–8	1,900	2,900	2,500	3,000	110	40	12	300	150	3,000	3	2.2	600	6	0.3	—
9–13	2,200	3,400	3,000	4,000	350	40	23	600	280	5,000	6	10	1,100	11	0.6	—
Adolescents																
14–18	2,300	3,600	3,000	4,000	350	45	34	900	400	8,000	9	10	1,700	17	1.0	—
Adults																
19–50	2,300	3,600	2,500	4,000	350	45	40	1,100	400	10,000	11	10	2,000	20	1.0	1.8
51–70	2,300	3,600	2,000	3,000	350	45	40	1,100	400	10,000	11	10	2,000	20	1.0	1.8
>70	2,300	3,600	2,000	3,000	350	45	40	1,100	400	10,000	11	10	2,000	20	1.0	1.8
Pregnancy																
≤18	2,300	3,600	3,000	3,500	350	45	34	900	400	8,000	9	10	1,700	17	1.0	—
19–50	2,300	3,600	3,000	3,500	350	45	40	1,100	400	10,000	11	10	2,000	20	1.0	—
Lactation																
≤18	2,300	3,600	3,000	4,000	350	45	34	900	400	8,000	9	10	1,700	17	1.0	—
19–50	2,300	3,600	3,000	4,000	350	45	40	1,100	400	10,000	11	10	2,000	20	1.0	—

[d]The UL for magnesium applies to synthetic forms obtained from supplements or drugs only.
[e]Source of intake should be from human milk (or formula) and food only.

NOTE: An Upper Limit was not established for vitamins and minerals not listed and for those age groups listed with a dash (—) because of a lack of data, not because these nutrients are safe to consume at any level of intake. All nutrients can have adverse effects when intakes are excessive.

Source: Reprinted with permission from Dietary Reference Intakes: Recommended Dietary Allowances and Adequate Intake, 2011 by the National Academy of Sciences, Courtesy of the National Academies Press, Washington, D.C.

THIRD CANADIAN EDITION

NUTRITION

CONCEPTS AND CONTROVERSIES

FRANCES SIENKIEWICZ SIZER

ELLIE WHITNEY

LEONARD A. PICHÉ

NELSON EDUCATION

CELEBRATE LIFELONG LEARNING

1914–2014: Nelson Education celebrates 100 years of Canadian publishing

NELSON / EDUCATION

Nutrition: Concepts and Controversies,
Third Canadian Edition

by Frances Sienkiewicz Sizer, Ellie Whitney,
and Leonard A. Piché

Vice President, Editorial Higher Education:
Anne Williams

Publisher:
Paul Fam

Executive Editor:
Jackie Wood

Marketing Manager:
Cara Cortese

Developmental Editor:
Candace Morrison

Photo Researcher and Permissions Coordinator:
David Strand

Senior Production Project Manager:
Natalia Denesiuk Harris

Production Service:
Integra

Copy Editor:
Julia Cochrane

Proofreader:
Integra

Indexer:
Stephanie Bilodeau

Design Director:
Ken Phipps

Managing Designer:
Franca Amore

Interior Design:
tani hasegawa

Cover Design:
Cathy Mayer

Cover Image:
© Mascarucci/Corbis

Compositor:
Integra

Library and Archives Canada Cataloguing in Publication Data

Sizer, Frances Sienkiewicz, author
   Nutrition : concepts & controversies / Frances Sienkiewicz Sizer, Ellie Whitney, Leonard A. Piché. — Third Canadian edition.

   Revision of: Nutrition : concepts and controversies / Frances Sienkiewicz Sizer, Ellie Whitney, Leonard A. Piché. — 2nd Canadian ed. — Toronto : Nelson Education, ©2012.
Includes bibliographical references and index.
ISBN 978-0-17-653077-8 (pbk.)

   1. Nutrition—Textbooks.
2. Nutrition—Canada—Textbooks.
3. Nutrition—Requirements—Textbooks. 4. Food—Textbooks.
5. Food—Canada—Textbooks.
I. Whitney, Eleanor Noss, author
II. Piché, Leonard A., 1950–, author
III. Title.

QP141.S5365 2014   613.2
C2013-907361-2

ISBN-13: 978-0-17-653077-8
ISBN-10: 0-17-653077-0

About the Authors

Leonard A. Piché

Leonard A. Piché, Ph.D., R.D., nutritional scientist, received his Ph.D. in human nutrition from the University of Guelph in 1987. He is Professor Emeritus in the Division of Foods and Nutritional Sciences, Brescia University College, responsible for developing and teaching basic and advanced undergraduate and graduate courses in nutrition. He was also an adjunct Full Professor in the School of Kinesiology, University of Western Ontario. He is a member of eight professional national organizations, including the Canadian Society of Nutrition and the Sports Nutrition Network of the Dietitians of Canada.

Dr. Piché was a contributor for two recent editions of *Mosby's Medical Dictionary* and a consultant for a Canadian edition of a high school food and nutrition text. His publications as a coauthor include two publications on Canada's Food Guide and a number of Canadian Student Information (CSI) documents to accompany entry-level university nutrition texts. He has been involved in and coauthored peer-reviewed articles on experiments in humans looking at the relationship between diet and heart disease risk (e.g., orange juice and good cholesterol and the effects of a high-protein diet on risk factors for cardiovascular disease).

Dr. Piché has provided feedback to Health Canada on more than five dozen occasions regarding food- and nutrition-related issues (e.g., nutrition labelling, the 2007 Food Guide, the discretionary addition of vitamins and minerals to foods, and updating the Canadian Nutrient File). He was an advisor on three of Dietitians of Canada's online courses for health-care professionals (Sport Supplements, Vitamins and Minerals, and Herbal Supplements). He has supervised the nutrient analysis of more than a dozen recipe books targeted at different segments of the general public. He has recently been involved, as a team member, in studies looking at children's beverage consumption and other factors that contribute to children's screen-related sedentary behaviours (one of the studies involved a national survey of family physicians and pediatricians about their views, practices, needs, and barriers when treating childhood obesity), which have resulted in a number of peer-reviewed publications, of which he is coauthor. He was also a member (Fall 2006–Spring 2010) of the Expert Advisory Committee for Health Canada's Natural Health Products Directorate. His current areas of interest include local food maps, supervising the generation of online galleries of "local foods" and "functional foods," the nutrient content of restaurant foods, meals served to residents in long-term care, sport supplement intake by university students, and caffeine intake of adolescents.

To my children's children, Angela, Riley and Isaac, who continue to wonder, Why should I eat this stuff?
    —Your loving Pappa

Frances Sienkiewicz Sizer

Frances Sienkiewicz Sizer, M.S., R.D., F.A.D.A., attended Florida State
University, where, in 1980, she received her B.S. and, in 1982, her M.S.
in nutrition. She is certified as a charter Fellow of the American Dietetic
Association. She is a founding member and vice-president of Nutrition
and Health Associates, an information and resource centre in Tallahassee,
Florida, that maintains an ongoing bibliographic database tracking research
in more than 1,000 topic areas of nutrition. Her textbooks include *Life
Choices: Health Concepts and Strategies; Making Life Choices; The Fitness Triad:
Motivation, Training, and Nutrition;* and others. She is a primary author of
Nutrition Interactive, an instructional college-level nutrition CD-ROM. In addition to writing, she lectures at universities and at national and regional con-
ferences and serves actively on the board of directors of ECHO, a local hunger
and homelessness relief organization in her community.

Eleanor Noss Whitney

Eleanor Noss Whitney, Ph.D., received her B.A. in biology from Radcliffe
College in 1960 and her Ph.D. in biology from Washington University,
St. Louis, in 1970. Formerly on the faculty at Florida State University and a
dietitian registered with the American Dietetic Association, she now devotes
her full time to research, writing, and consulting in nutrition, health, and
environmental issues. Her earlier publications include articles in *Science,
Genetics,* and other journals. Her textbooks include *Understanding Nutrition,
Understanding Normal and Clinical Nutrition, Nutrition and Diet Therapy,* and
Essential Life Choices for college students and *Making Life Choices* for high
school students. Her most intense interests include energy conservation,
solar energy uses, alternatively fuelled vehicles, and ecosystem restoration.
She is an activist who volunteers full-time for the Citizens Climate Lobby.

Contents in Brief

David Malan/Getty Images

Contents

© Julián Rovagnati/Dreamstime.com

© John A. Rizzo/Photodisc/Getty Images

© Elena Schweitzer/Shutterstock

CHAPTER 10
Nutrients, Physical Activity, and the Body's Responses   418

© Sarah Bossert/Thinkstock

Preface

You've probably heard the phrase "you are what you eat." This text gives you a better understanding of the phrase and hits home with the simple but obvious truth: you really are what you eat! *Nutrition: Concepts and Controversies* has been a cornerstone in nutrition classes across North America, serving the needs of students and professors in building a healthier future. In keeping with our tradition, in this, the third Canadian edition, we explore the ever-changing frontier of nutrition science in Canada while maintaining our sense of personal connection with students and instructors alike. We address the learner in clear, engaging writing but with a crispness that we hope you will enjoy.

Pedagogical Features

Throughout these chapters, features tickle the reader's interest and inform. For both verbal and visual learners, our logical presentation and clearly designed figures keep interest high and understanding at a peak. New figures in many chapters demonstrate current concepts from a Canadian perspective, and improvements to classic figures enhance their usefulness to the learner. A new margin feature, a "Tool" symbol 🔧, provides the reader with close to 200 information nuggets and websites they will find valuable for learning and teaching nutrition-related topics/concepts that affect every stage throughout the life cycle and give the reader an opportunity to dig deeper into the topic. New photos also adorn many of our pages, adding Canadian brands and imagery to provide a level of familiarity to a Canadian readership.

© Benjamin F. Fink Jr./Brand X Pictures/Getty Images

Canada's Food Guide and the Canadian Nutrient File, 2010, are discussed, referenced, and sourced throughout the book, adding a new level of understanding to nutrition for Canadian students. Demographics and data from the Canadian Community Health Surveys (CCHS) and Canadian Health Measures Surveys (CHMS) provide real data on our population.

Many tried-and-true features remain in this edition. Each chapter begins with a listing of the chapter contents to prepare students for what's to come. "Do You Ever . . ." questions pique interest and set a personal tone for the information that follows.

The practical *Food Feature*, revised for the multicultural society that is Canada, invites students to apply chapter concepts in their everyday encounters with food. The *Food Feature* sections that appear in most chapters act as bridges between theory and practice; they are practical applications of the chapter concepts that help readers choose foods according to nutrition principles.

New key terms have been added and defined in the margins of the pages where they are introduced and in the Glossary at the end of the book. *Key Point* boxes throughout the chapters are a popular study tool for students.

The *Consumer Corner* feature presents information on whole-grain breads, fat replacers, amino acid supplements, vitamin C and the common cold, bottled water, irradiation of foods, and other nutrition-related marketplace issues to empower students to make informed decisions.

Snapshot boxes are concentrated capsules of information depicting food sources of vitamins and minerals. They present the recommended Dietary Reference Intakes (DRI) for young adults, the latest known intakes (based on CCHS data), and Tolerable Upper Intake Levels (UL) and offer the chief biological roles of each nutrient, along with deficiency and toxicity symptoms.

A little reminder called *Think Fitness* appears from time to time to alert readers to ways in which physical activity links with nutrition to support health. This feature emphasizes the role of nutrients in supporting physical activity and spells out the advantage of an active lifestyle throughout life.

The *Self-Check* features provide chapter-specific review questions.

The *Controversy* features invite you to explore beyond the safe boundaries of established nutrition knowledge and examine numerous nutrition controversies, as indicated in the book's title. These optional readings, which appear near the end of each chapter and are printed on coloured pages, delve into current scientific topics and emerging controversies.

Diet Analysis Plus

Dynamic and rewarding, the newly updated Diet Analysis Plus software contains all of the food items in the Canadian Nutrient File (which are easily identified by the Canadian flag next to them) and encourages active learning by making it easier for students to track diet and activity through personalized profiles. The interactive nutrition labs respect diverse ways of learning and encourage students to practise in order to achieve concept mastery. With Diet Analysis Plus, students can analyze the nutritional value of the food they eat in order to adjust their diets to reach personal health goals—all while gaining a better understanding of how nutrition relates to, and impacts, their lives.

Diet Analysis Plus is integrated into this third edition of *Nutrition: Concepts and Controversies* through activities in most chapters that show students how the chapter concepts relate to their diet and health goals. Instructors can use these activities for assignments or extra credit.

Canadian students can access/turn on the Canadian food selections (identified by the Canadian flag icon) by selecting the box found as a subheading when you click Edit Selected Profile → select: Canadian Profile (see the screenshot below).

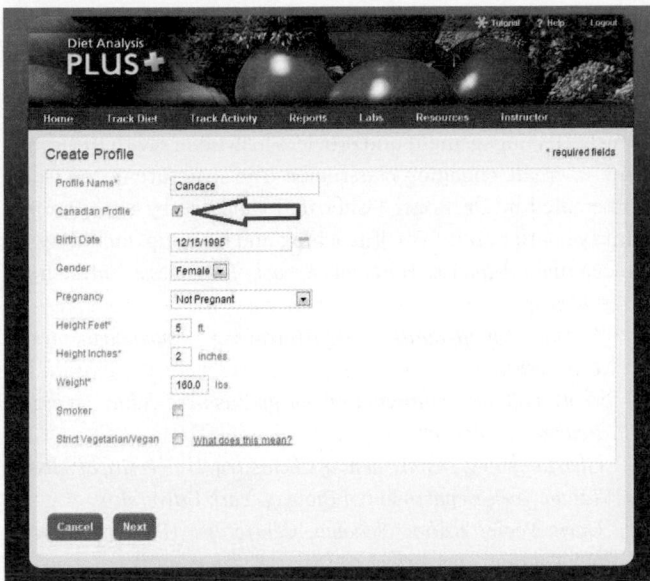

The appendixes are collections of useful resources to enhance your understanding of food and nutrition science. **Appendix A**, Canadian Nutrition Recommendations, supplies the recommended nutrient intake levels, nutrition guidelines, and Nutrition Facts label information for a Canadian audience. **Appendix B** demonstrates nutrition calculations, with special emphasis on finding the percentage of calories from fat in a diet and other percentages. **Appendix C** is the Canadian Diabetes Foundation–"Beyond the Basics" chart. **Appendix D** provides answers to the Self-Check questions. **Appendix E**, Physical Activity and Energy Requirements, helps students accurately calculate energy expenditures. **Appendix F** presents the Dietary Approaches to Stop Hypertension (DASH) Eating Plan and the discretionary calorie allowance for weight management. **Appendix G**, available online at http://www.nelson.com/nutrition3ce, offers an invaluable list of contact information for Canadian, U.S., and international nutrition resources for those interested in additional information.

New in the Third Canadian Edition

In addition to the new features mentioned above, **overall**, the third Canadian edition provides more up-to-date data on health (e.g., nutrient status) and nutrient intake of Canadians, more references to Canadian research, and numerous new and corrected weblinks. **Chapter 1** includes updated information on leading causes of death in Canada; information about personalized genetic tests available through Registered Dietitians; more information about recent Canadian Health Measures

Surveys; updates to some of the credible weblinks and Canadian Community Health Survey data sets; and updates to contact information for provincial regulatory bodies for dietetic practice. **Chapter 2** provides an update on the various translations of *Eating Well with Canada's Food Guide*, and includes recent information on the recent Institute of Medicine report on calcium and vitamin D; updated information on Health Canada's recent policy on labelling the Calories from fibre; more information on carbohydrate-counting using the Canadian Diabetes Association carb-counting poster; new information about apps for looking up the nutrient content of foods; more information on weblinks to credible interactive websites to help consumers better understand food labels; updated health claims for cardiovascular disease to include plant sterols, oats and other fibres, and unsaturated fatty acids; and updated info about the latest Canadian Physical Activity Guidelines. **Chapter 3** includes better descriptions of digestive enzymes, for example, for genetic material; new Canada's Low-Risk Alcohol Drinking Guidelines; updated information on alcohol consumption; and more information about how alcohol is metabolized, along with numerous updated weblinks and references. **Chapter 4** includes new estimates of the added sugar content of our diet and guidelines to limit its consumption; additional information about dietary fibres such as those regarded as prebiotics; excerpts and references to the 2013 Clinical Practice Guidelines from the Canadian Diabetes Association; information on the availability of certain sugars, for example, raw sugar and turbinado sugar, to the Canadian consumer; and information on the approval of the addition of Stevia glycosides to foods. **Chapter 5** includes updated position statements and numerous references to studies on dietary fat and disease and more information on health/therapeutic claims for dietary components that affect blood lipids. **Chapter 6** includes additional information about amino acid and protein metabolism; updated information about the allowable addition of small amounts of some amino acids to caffeinated energy drinks that are regulated as foods; and a weblink to a YouTube video about exercising in space. **Chapter 7** includes margin notes in each vitamin section showing the Maximum Daily Dose (MDD) specified by the Natural Health Products Directorate (NHPD) for vitamins when sold in single-ingredient formulas. The *Snapshots* for vitamins are now displayed as bar graphs showing the nutrient contribution of one Food Guide serving of foods from each food group (and a few other unusual sources) as well as the CCHS 2.2 mean intakes of vitamins by young adults. **Chapter 8** includes updated information about Drinking Water Quality Guidelines and the safety of bottled water; updated information and weblinks on calcium and phosphorus bone metabolism; additional information and weblinks on dietary guidance on sodium and the recent Institute of Medicine report on sodium; and margin notes in each mineral section showing the Maximum Daily Dose (MDD) specified by the NHPD for minerals when sold in single-ingredient formulas. As is the case for vitamins, the *Snapshots* for minerals are now displayed as bar graphs showing the nutrient contribution of one Food Guide Serving of foods from each Food Group (and a few other unusual sources) as well as the CCHS 2.2 mean intakes of minerals by young adults. **Chapter 9** includes updated information and weblinks for overweight and obesity in Canada and updated information from the *Diagnostic and Statistical Manual of Mental Disorders*, Fifth Edition (DSM V), for anorexia and bulimia nervosa. **Chapter 10** includes updated information on Canadian Physical Activity and Sedentary Guidelines as well as online interactive tools, more information about the use of dietary sources of energy by metabolic pathways, and new information about the transition of many caffeinated energy drinks that were once regulated as natural health products to now being regulated (and subsequently labelled) as foods. **Chapter 11** includes updated information on the leading causes of death in Canada; cautionary information about the use of vitamin E supplements by older Canadians with diabetes or cardiovascular disease; the 2013 Canadian Cardiovascular Society Guidelines for the diagnosis and treatment of dyslipidemia; and weblinks to the 2013 Canadian Diabetes Guidelines. **Chapter 12** now includes updated information on foodborne illness outbreaks like listeriosis and *E. coli* and more information on food safety in the kitchen; more information on how final decisions are made regarding the re-evaluation and setting of pesticide levels, a brief discussion of the chemical Bisphenol A (BPA) in beverage containers and what Health Canada is doing about the issue; and updated information and weblinks on domestic foodborne illness. **Chapter 13** includes updated information and weblinks about Canadian pre- and postnatal statistics; information about a screening tool for exercise during pregnancy; and more recommendations about alcohol and smoking during breastfeeding. **Chapter 14** includes Canadian Physical Activity and Sedentary Behaviour Guidelines for children, youth, and older adults; CHMS data on blood lead levels for children; and updated information and weblinks about food allergy labelling as well as overweight and obesity among children. The chapter includes updated data on soft-drink consumption by Canadian youth and more information about recommendations regarding consumption of caffeinated beverages by children and youth. New information about the levels of those Canadians living in their own homes who are at nutritional risk is also provided. **Chapter 15** includes updated information (as well as a map) on the estimate of regional undernourishment globally. The chapter also includes updated information about the level of food insecurity in Canada, the number of Canadians using food banks, the number of isolated communities eligible for subsidies from the Nutrition North Canada program, our level of air quality, our recent decline in the level of residential water use, and changes to the available Hunger Relief programs in Canada.

Ancillary Materials
Introducing NETA

The **Nelson Education Teaching Advantage (NETA)** program delivers research-based resources that promote student engagement and higher-order thinking and enable the success of Canadian students and educators. The primary NETA components are NETA Engagement (enriched instructor's manuals and other teaching aids for instructors) and NETA Assessment (test banks and computerized test banks). Details about the NETA components specifically prepared for *Nutrition: Concepts and Controversies* are included in the description of the Instructor's Resource CD below.

NETA Engagement's foundational principles are based on student-centred learning, deep learning, active learning, and creating positive classroom environments. Resources supporting NETA Engagement include enriched instructor manuals, classroom engagement activities, and the *Instructor's Guide to Classroom Engagement*, a manual that sets out the research underlying NETA Engagement and provides instructors with the framework to create engaging classrooms. The structure of the Guide was created by Dr. Roger Fisher and validated by an interdisciplinary board of scholars of teaching and learning, including

> *Norman Althouse, Haskayne School of Business, University of Calgary*
>
> *Brenda Chant-Smith, Department of Psychology, Trent University*
>
> *Scott Follows, Manning School of Business Administration, Acadia University*
>
> *Glen Loppnow, Department of Chemistry, University of Alberta*
>
> *Tanya Noel, Department of Biology, York University*
>
> *Gary Poole, Senior Scholar, Centre for Health Education Scholarship, and Associate Director, School of Population and Public Health, University of British Columbia*
>
> *Dan Pratt, Department of Educational Studies, University of British Columbia*

NETA Assessment is a research-based program that was created in partnership with David DiBattista, a 3M National Teaching Fellow, professor of psychology at Brock University, and researcher in the area of multiple-choice testing. Working with Prof. DiBattista, Nelson Education has developed and enforced guidelines that improve the quality of our test banks by ensuring they measure not just recall (as is typical with test banks) but *higher-level thinking* skills as well. In addition, Prof. DiBattista's *Multiple-Choice Tests: Getting beyond Remembering* established guidelines to help our test bank authors and copyeditors recalibrate poorly worded questions that students might find confusing or ambiguous. Questions and answers developed under NETA test students' knowledge and understanding, not their skill at predicting answer outcomes based on unconscious clues in wording or playing the odds.

Instructor Ancillaries

Instructor's Resources available online: All instructor supplements are available on the instructor companion site for easy access:

- The *NETA Test Bank* in printable and Cognero® computerized formats. The NETA Test Bank is available in a new, cloud-based platform. Testing Powered by Cognero® is a secure online testing system that allows you to author, edit, and manage test bank content from any place you have Internet access. No special installations or downloads are needed, and the desktop-inspired interface, with its drop-down menus and familiar, intuitive tools, allows you to create and manage tests with ease. You can create multiple test versions in an instant, and import or export content into other systems. Tests can be delivered from your learning management system, your classroom, or wherever you want.

Prepared by Carla D'Andreamatteo, the NETA Test Bank includes over 1,200 questions in multiple-choice, true–false, and short-answer formats. Test Bank files are provided in rich text format for easy editing and printing with all common word-processing formats. The NETA Test Bank is accompanied by *Multiple-Choice Tests: Getting beyond Remembering*.

- An *Enriched Instructor's Manual*. Prepared under the NETA program, the *Enriched Instructor's Manual* focuses on key educational concerns—unlike traditional manuals that reiterate chapter outlines and key terms from the text. Instead, you'll find detailed learning outcomes, discussion of key concepts, suggestions on how to motivate and engage students, strategies for addressing barriers to learning, notes on additional resources, and more! The *Enriched Instructor's Manual* is accompanied by the *Instructor's Guide to Classroom Engagement*, and was prepared by Danny Pincivero.
- Microsoft *PowerPoint®* lecture slides. Key concepts from *Nutrition: Concepts and Controversies* are presented in PowerPoint format, with generous use of figures, photographs, and short tables from the text. The PowerPoint presentations were prepared by Carla D'Andreamatteo.
- An *Image Library*. This resource allows you to customize your own PowerPoint presentations using figures, tables, illustrations, and photographs provided from the book in jpeg format.

Student Ancillaries

CengageNOW™: This CengageNOW product for students is the perfect diagnostic tool to help you gain a true understanding of nutrition concepts through testing and examples. CengageNOW features chapter-specific pretests, study plans, and posttests that empower students to master concepts, prepare for exams, and be more involved in class. It provides immediate and ongoing feedback about which topics students have mastered and which ones are causing them difficulty. The pretest generates a study plan that provides links to an integrated eBook so students can easily review topics and examine additional resources to improve their understanding. The posttest confirms that they have mastered the content. CengageNOW tests were written by Michelle Mackenzie. It's all here in CengageNOW!

CourseMate: The more you study, the better the results. Make the most of your study time by accessing everything you need to succeed in one place. The *Nutrition: Concepts and Controversies* CourseMate includes

- An interactive ebook with highlighting, note-taking, and an interactive glossary
- Interactive learning tools, including the following:
  1. Quizzes, written by Michelle Mackenzie
  2. Flashcards
  3. Activities
  4. Videos
  5. . . . and more!

Closing Thoughts

As always, our purpose in writing this text is to enhance our readers' understanding of nutrition science and their motivation to apply it. We hope the information on this book's pages will reach beyond the classroom to our readers' lives. Take the information you find inside this book home with you. Use it in your life: nourish yourself, educate your loved ones, and nurture others to be healthy. Stay up to date with the news, too. For, despite all the conflicting messages, inflated claims, and even quackery that abound in the marketplace, true nutrition knowledge progresses with a genuine scientific spirit, and important new truths are constantly unfolding.

Acknowledgments

My thanks to Frances Sienkiewicz Sizer and Eleanor Noss Whitney, authors of *Nutrition: Concepts and Controversies* in the United States, for providing a solid thirteenth edition on which this text is based; to Alicia Garcia for contributing to the University of Western Ontario version of the first Canadian edition of this text; and to my son, Leonard A. Piché Jr., for updating the weblinks to Health Canada's websites and online documents. Thank you to Gail Hammond and Kimberly Zammit-Francis for providing up-to-date nutrient data for the foods listed in the numerous Snapshots for the vitamins and minerals and to Nick Woods for constructive feedback on the Diet Analysis Plus exercises.

Special thanks to our executive editor, Jackie Wood, and our developmental editor, Candace Morrison, for their gentle persuasion and encouragement to ensure the highest quality in all facets of this book. Deep gratitude is extended to Natalia Denesiuk Harris, Julia Cochrane, and Indumathy Gunasekaran for making sense of the final manuscript, to June Trusty for her careful review of the page proofs, and to David Strand for his photo research and permission clearance. Thank you, Carmen Brosseau and Cara Cortese, for your excellent work in marketing this text and providing support for the sales team.

To our reviewers, a heartfelt thank-you for your many thoughtful ideas and suggestions in guiding the development of recent Canadian editions:

Wendy Benson   Athabasca University

Sébastien Boyas   University of Ottawa

Sandra Dorman   Laurentian University

Jess Haines   University of Guelph

Rhona Hanning   University of Waterloo

Kristin Hildahl-Shawn   University of Manitoba

Lynne Lafave   Mount Royal University

Paul LeBlanc   Brock University

Karen McLaren   Canadore College

Csilla Reszegi   George Brown College

Norman Temple   Athabasca University

Peter Tiidus   Wilfrid Laurier University

Vivienne A. Vance   University of Waterloo

Amandio Vieira   Simon Fraser University

Marie Weingartshofer   Athabasca University

Christine Wellington   University of Windsor

1 Food Choices and Human Health

Do You Ever . . .

Question whether your diet can make a real difference between getting sick and staying healthy?

Purchase supplements, believing that they are more powerful than food for ensuring good nutrition?

Wonder why you prefer the foods you do?

Become alarmed or confused by the news and media reports of nutrition science?

Keep Reading . . .

Learning Objectives

After completing this chapter, you should be able to

LO 1.1 Discuss how a particular lifestyle choice can either positively impact or harm overall health.

LO 1.2 Define the term *nutrient* and list the six major nutrients.

LO 1.3 Recognize the five characteristics of a healthy diet and give suggestions for using them.

LO 1.4 Summarize how a particular culture or circumstance can impact a person's food choices.

LO 1.5 Describe and give an example of the major types of research studies.

LO 1.6 Discuss why national nutrition survey data are important for the health of the population.

LO 1.7 List the major steps in behaviour change and devise a plan for making successful long-term changes in the diet.

LO 1.8 Recognize misleading nutrition claims in advertisements for dietary supplements and in the popular media.

Contents

When you choose foods with nutrition in mind, you can enhance your own well-being.

© iStockphoto/Thinkstock

I f you care about your body, and if you have strong feelings about **food**, then you have much to gain from learning about **nutrition**—the study of how food nourishes the body. Nutrition is a fascinating, much-talked-about subject. Each day, newspapers, radio, and television (and their websites) present stories of new findings on nutrition and heart health or nutrition and cancer prevention, and at the same time advertisements and commercials bombard us with multicoloured pictures of tempting foods—pizza, burgers, cakes, and chips. If you are like most people, when you eat you sometimes wonder, "Is this food good for me?"

When you study nutrition, you learn which foods serve you best, and you can work out ways of choosing foods, planning meals, and designing your **diet** wisely. Knowing the facts can enhance your health and your enjoyment of eating while relieving your feelings of guilt or worry that you aren't eating well.

This chapter addresses these "why, what, and how" questions about nutrition:

- *Why* care about nutrition? The **nutrients** interact with body tissues, adding a little or subtracting a little, day by day, and thus change the very foundations upon which the health of the body is built.

- *What* are the nutrients in foods, and what roles do they play in the body? Meet the nutrients and discover their general roles in building body tissues and maintaining health.

- *What* constitutes a nutritious diet? Can you choose foods wisely, for nutrition's sake? And what motivates your choices?

- *How* do governments suggest that their citizens choose their diets to meet the national health objectives?

- And, finally, *how* do we know what we know about nutrition? Scientific research reports provide an important foundation for understanding nutrition science.

The Controversy section demonstrates the differences between trustworthy sources of nutrition information and those that are less reliable.

A Lifetime of Nourishment

If you live for 65 years or longer, you will have consumed more than 70,000 meals, and your remarkable body will have disposed of 50 tonnes of food. The foods you choose have cumulative effects on your body. As you age, you will see and feel those effects—if you know what to look for.

Your body renews its structures continuously, and each day it builds a little muscle, bone, skin, and blood, replacing old tissues with new. It may also add a little fat, if you consume excess food energy (Calories), or subtract a little, if you consume less than you require. Some of the food you eat today becomes part of "you" tomorrow. The best food for you, then, is the kind that supports the growth and maintenance of strong muscles, sound bones, healthy skin, and sufficient blood to cleanse and nourish all parts of your body. This means you need food that provides not only energy but also sufficient nutrients, that is, enough water, carbohydrates, fats, protein, vitamins, and minerals. If the foods you eat provide too little or too much of any nutrient today, your health may suffer just a little today. If the foods you eat provide too little or too much of one or more nutrients every day for years, then, in later life, you may suffer severe disease effects.

A well-chosen array of foods supplies enough energy and enough of each nutrient to prevent **malnutrition**. Malnutrition includes deficiencies, imbalances, and excesses of nutrients, any of which can take a toll on health over time.

KEY POINT

- The nutrients in food support growth, maintenance, and repair of the body. Deficiencies, excesses, and imbalances of nutrients bring on the diseases of malnutrition.

How Powerful Is a Nutritious Diet in Preventing Diseases?

Your choice of diet profoundly influences your long-term health prospects.[1,*] Only two common lifestyle habits are more influential: smoking and other tobacco use and excessive drinking of alcohol. Of the leading causes of death listed in Table 1–1, two are related to nutrition, and motor vehicle accidents are related to drinking alcohol.

Many older people suffer from debilitating conditions that could have been largely prevented had they known and applied the nutrition principles of today. The **chronic diseases**—heart disease, diabetes, some kinds of cancer, dental disease, and adult bone loss—all have a connection to poor diet. These diseases cannot be prevented by a good diet alone; they are to some extent determined by a person's genetic constitution,

---

*Reference notes are found at the end of this chapter.

Table 1–1

Leading Causes of Death in Canada, 2009*

	Male	Female	Total
1. Cancer**	37,452	33,673	71,125
2. Heart Disease**	25,950	23,321	49,271
3. Cerebrovascular Diseases (stroke)**	5,823	8,282	14,105
4. Chronic Lower Respiratory Diseases	5,525	5,334	10,859
5. Accidents	6,045	4,205	10,250
Total Deaths (all causes)	80,795	74,815	155,610

*Data from Statistics Canada, Mortality, Summary List of Causes, 2009, Catalogue no. 84-215-X, http://www. statcan.gc.ca/pub/84-215-x/2012001/table-tableau/tbl002-eng.htm. Reproduced and distributed on an "as is" basis with the permission of Statistics Canada.

**Diet-related chronic diseases.

food medically, any substance that the body can take in and assimilate that will enable it to stay alive and to grow; the carrier of nourishment; socially, a more limited number of such substances defined as acceptable by each culture.

nutrition the study of the nutrients and other biologically active compounds in foods and in the body; sometimes also the study of human behaviours related to food.

diet the foods (including beverages) a person usually eats and drinks.

nutrients components of food that are indispensable to the body's functioning. They provide energy, serve as building material, help maintain or repair body parts, and support growth. The nutrients include water, carbohydrates, fat, protein, vitamins, and minerals.

malnutrition any condition caused by excess or deficient food energy or nutrient intake or by an imbalance of nutrients. Nutrient or energy deficiencies are classed as forms of undernutrition; nutrient or energy excesses are classed as forms of overnutrition.

chronic diseases long-duration degenerative diseases characterized by deterioration of the body organs. Examples include heart disease, cancer, and diabetes.

Figure 1–1
Nutrition and Disease

Not all diseases are equally influenced by diet. Some are almost purely genetic, like the anemia of sickle cell disease. Some may be inherited (or the tendency to develop them may be inherited in the genes) but may be influenced by diet, like some forms of diabetes. Some are purely dietary, like the vitamin and mineral deficiency diseases.

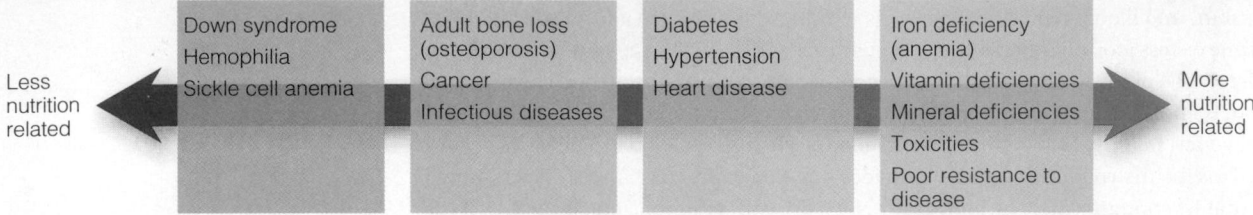

| Less nutrition related ← | Down syndrome
Hemophilia
Sickle cell anemia | Adult bone loss (osteoporosis)
Cancer
Infectious diseases | Diabetes
Hypertension
Heart disease | Iron deficiency (anemia)
Vitamin deficiencies
Mineral deficiencies
Toxicities
Poor resistance to disease | → More nutrition related |

activities, and lifestyle. Within the range set by your genetic inheritance, however, the likelihood of developing these diseases is strongly influenced by your food choices.

KEY POINT
- Nutrition profoundly affects health.

Genetics and Individuality

Consider the role of genetics. Genetics and nutrition affect different diseases to varying degrees (see Figure 1–1). The anemia caused by sickle cell disease, for example, is purely hereditary and thus appears at the left of Figure 1–1 as a genetic disease unrelated to nutrition. Nothing a person eats affects the person's chances of developing this anemia, although nutrition therapy may help ease its course. At the other end of the spectrum in Figure 1–1, iron-deficiency anemia most often results from undernutrition. Diseases and conditions of poor health appear all along this continuum from almost entirely genetic to almost purely nutritional; the more nutrition related a disease or health condition is, the more successfully sound nutrition can prevent it.

> Read more about sickle cell anemia in Chapter 6; iron-deficiency anemia is described in Chapter 8.

Furthermore, some diseases, such as heart disease and cancer, are not one disease but many. Two people may both have heart disease, but not the same form. One person's heart disease or cancer may be nutrition related, but another's may not be. Individual people differ genetically from each other in thousands of subtle ways, so no simple statement can be made about the extent to which diet can help any one person avoid a disease or slow its progress.

The recent completion of the Human Genome Project establishes the entire sequence of human **DNA** that holds the **genes**, bits of genetic material that hold the instructions for making a human being. This leap of knowledge promises greater control over health and disease as well as a greatly increased understanding of the interactions between a person's genetic makeup and the nutrients in the body.[2] Furthermore, a vast amount of research is going on in the area of science concerned with environmental influences, including diet, on genetic expression, an area known as *epigenetics*.

KEY POINT
- Choice of diet influences long-term health within the range set by genetic inheritance. Nutrition has little influence on some diseases but strongly affects others.

The Importance of Nutritional Genomics

The integration of nutrition, genomic science, and molecular biology has launched a new area of study, **nutritional genomics**. Scientists working in this area are describing how nutrients affect the activities of genes and how genes affect the activities of nutrients.[3] Soon, such revelations are expected to help pinpoint nutrient needs more precisely for growing children, healthy adults, and those fighting diseases, among others.[4]

- Anemia is a blood condition in which red blood cells, the body's oxygen carriers, are inadequate or impaired and so cannot meet the oxygen demands of the body.

- The human **genome** is 99.9 percent the same in all people; all of the normal variations, such as differences in hair colour, as well as variations that result in diseases, lie in the 0.1 percent that varies.

- Only about 2 percent of the human genome contains genes. Scientists are asking, "What does the rest do?"

genome (GEE-nome) the full complement of genetic material in the chromosomes of a cell. The study of genomes is *genomics*.

DNA an abbreviation for deoxyribonucleic (dee-OX-ee-RYE-bow-nu-CLAY-ick) acid, the molecule that encodes genetic information in its structure.

genes units of a cell's inheritance, made of the chemical DNA (deoxyribonucleic acid). Each gene directs the making of one or more proteins, which perform important tasks in the body.

nutritional genomics the science of how nutrients affect the activities of genes and how genes affect the activities of nutrients. Also called *molecular nutrition* or *nutrigenomics*.

Food manufacturers look forward to providing food and supplement products tailored to an individual's specific nutrient needs.[5] Later chapters expand the story of nutritional genomics, beginning in Chapter 6 with a description of the link between the body's proteins and the activities of genes. Also, authorized Registered Dietitians are able to offer personalized genetic testing and feedback on how several food components interact with your genes to increase or decrease your risk of chronic diseases (e.g., caffeine and heart disease) using the Nutrigenomix test kit (see http://nutrigenomix.com).

KEY POINT

- Nutritional genomics holds great promise for advances in nutrition science.

Other Lifestyle Choices

Besides food choices, other lifestyle choices also affect people's health. Tobacco use and alcohol and other substance abuse can destroy health. Physical activity, sleep, lowered

> Alcohol use and abuse and their effects on body tissues are topics of Controversy 3 in Chapter 3.

stress levels, and improved conditions at home and at work, including the quality of the air and water and other aspects of the environment, can help prevent or reduce the severity of some diseases.

Putting together a diet that supports health depends partly on knowing which foods to choose. The next section provides an overview of the nutrients in foods, and later sections present dietary guidelines that can provide goals to shoot for.

KEY POINT

- Personal life choices, such as staying physically active or using tobacco or alcohol, also affect health for the better or worse.

The Human Body and Its Food

As your body moves and works each day, it must use **energy**. The energy that fuels the body's work comes indirectly from the sun by way of plants. Plants capture and store the sun's energy in their tissues as they grow. When you eat plant-derived foods such as fruit, grains, or vegetables, you obtain and use the solar energy they have stored, for example, in the carbon-carbon bonds of glucose and starch. Plant-eating animals obtain their energy in the same way, so when you eat animal tissues, you are eating compounds containing energy that came originally from the sun.

The body requires six kinds of nutrients—families of molecules indispensable to its functioning—and foods deliver these. Table 1–2 lists the six classes of nutrients. Four

Table 1–2

Elements in the Six Classes of Nutrients

The nutrients that contain carbon are organic.

	Carbon	Oxygen	Hydrogen	Nitrogen	Minerals
Water		√	√		
Carbohydrate	√	√	√		
Fat	√	√	√		
Protein	√	√	√	√	b
Vitamins	√	√	√	√[a]	b
Minerals					√

[a]All of the B vitamins contain nitrogen; amine means nitrogen.
[b]Protein and some vitamins contain the mineral sulphur; vitamin B_{12} contains the mineral cobalt.

energy the capacity to do work. The energy in food is chemical energy; it can be converted to mechanical, electrical, heat, or other forms of energy in the body. Food energy is measured in Calories, defined in the next section.

Figure 1–2

Materials of Food and the Human Body

Foods and the human body are made of the same materials.

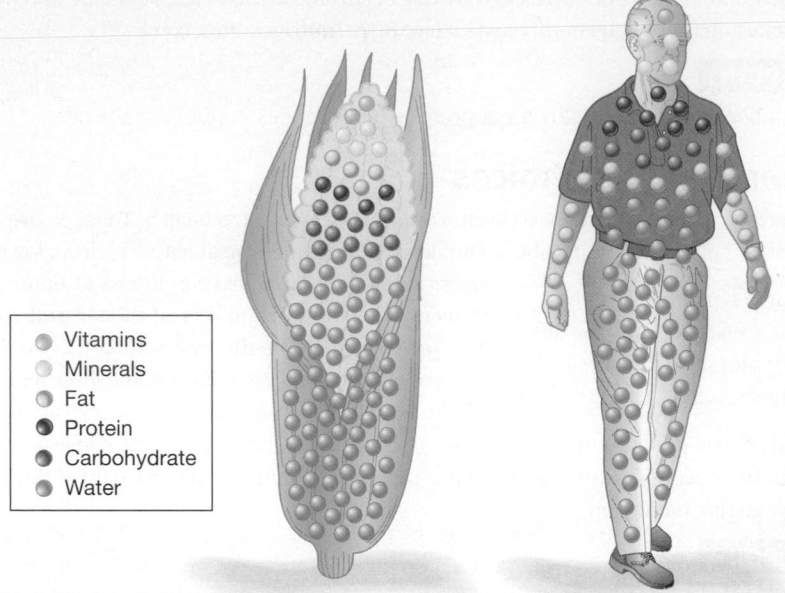

- Vitamins
- Minerals
- Fat
- Protein
- Carbohydrate
- Water

of these six are **organic**; that is, the nutrients contain the element carbon derived from living things. The human body and foods are made of the same materials, arranged in different ways (see Figure 1–2).

The Nutrients in Foods

Foremost among the six classes of nutrients in foods is *water*, which is constantly lost from the body and must constantly be replaced. Of the four organic nutrients, three are **energy-yielding nutrients**, meaning that the body can use the energy stored in the carbon-carbon bonds they contain. The *carbohydrates* (e.g., sugar and starch) and *fats* (e.g., saturated and polyunsaturated fats; fats are properly called *lipids*) are especially important energy-yielding nutrients. As for *protein* (chains of amino acids), it does double duty: it can yield energy, but it also provides materials that form structures and working parts of body tissues. (Alcohol yields energy, too, but it is a toxin, not a nutrient—see the note to Table 1–3.)

The fifth and sixth classes of nutrients are the *vitamins* (e.g., vitamin C and vitamin D) and the *minerals* (e.g., calcium and iron). These provide no energy *per se* to the body. A few minerals serve as parts of body structures (calcium and phosphorus, for example, are major constituents of bone), but all vitamins and minerals act as regulators. As regulators, the vitamins and minerals assist in all body processes: digesting food; moving muscles; disposing of wastes; growing new tissues; healing wounds; obtaining energy from carbohydrate, fat, and protein; and participating in every other process necessary to maintain life. Later chapters are devoted to these six classes of nutrients.

When you eat food, then, you are providing your body with energy and nutrients. Furthermore, some of the nutrients are **essential nutrients**, meaning that if you do not ingest them, you will develop deficiencies; the body cannot make these nutrients for itself. Essential nutrients are found in all six classes of nutrients. Water is an essential nutrient; so is a form of carbohydrate; so are some lipids, some parts of protein, all of the vitamins, and the minerals important in human nutrition.

organic carbon containing. Four of the six classes of nutrients are organic: carbohydrate, fat, protein, and vitamins. Strictly speaking, organic compounds include only those made by living things and do not include carbon dioxide and a few carbon salts.

energy-yielding nutrients the nutrients the body can use for energy. They may also supply building blocks for body structures.

essential nutrients the nutrients the body cannot make for itself (or cannot make fast enough) from other raw materials; nutrients that must be obtained from food to prevent deficiencies.

To support understanding of discussions throughout this book, two definitions and a set of numbers are useful. Food scientists measure food energy in **Calories**, units of heat. Food and nutrient quantities are often measured in **grams**, units of mass. The most energy rich of the nutrients is fat, which contains 9 Calories in each gram. Carbohydrate and protein each contain only 4 Calories in a gram (see Table 1–3).

Scientists have worked out ways to measure the energy and nutrient contents of foods. They have also calculated the amounts of energy and nutrients various types of people need—by gender, age, life stage, and activity. Thus, after studying human nutrient requirements (in Chapter 2), you will be able to state with some accuracy just what your own body needs—this much water, that much carbohydrate and fat, so much protein, and so forth. So why not simply take pills or **dietary supplements** in place of food? Because, as it turns out, food offers more than just the six basic nutrients.

KEY POINT

- Food supplies energy and nutrients. Foremost among the nutrients is water. The energy-yielding nutrients are carbohydrates, fats (lipids), and protein. The regulator nutrients are vitamins and minerals. Food energy is measured in Calories; food and nutrient quantities are often measured in grams.

Can I Live on Just Supplements?

Nutrition science can state what nutrients human beings need to survive—at least for a time. Scientists are becoming skilled at making **elemental diets**—diets with a precise chemical composition that are lifesaving for people in the hospital who cannot eat ordinary food. These formulas, administered to severely ill people for days or weeks, support not only continued life but also recovery from nutrient deficiencies, infections, and wounds.

Lately, marketers have taken these liquid formulas out of the medical setting and have advertised them heavily to healthy people of all ages as "meal replacers" or "insurance" against malnutrition. The truth is that such products are not superior to a sound diet of real foods. Formula diets are essential to help sick people survive, but they do not enable people to thrive over long periods. Elemental diet formulas do not support optimal growth and health, and they often lead to medical complications.[6] Although these problems are rare and can be detected and corrected, they show that the composition of these diets is not yet perfect for all people in all settings. Healthy people who eat a healthful diet do not need such formulas, and, in fact, most need no dietary supplements.[7]

Even if a person's basic nutrient needs are perfectly understood and met, concoctions of nutrients still lack something that foods provide. Hospitalized clients who are fed nutrient mixtures through a vein often improve dramatically when they can finally eat food. Something in real food is important to health—but what is it? What does food offer that cannot be provided through a needle or a tube? Science has some partial explanations, some physical and some psychological.

In the digestive tract, the stomach and intestine are dynamic, living organs, changing constantly in response to the foods they receive—even to just the sight, aroma, and taste of food. When a person is fed through a vein, the digestive organs, like unused muscles, weaken and grow smaller. A lack of digestive tract stimulation may even weaken the body's defences against certain infections, such as infections of the respiratory tract.[8] Medical wisdom now dictates that a person should be fed through a vein for as short a time as possible and that real food taken by mouth should be reintroduced as early as possible. The digestive organs also release hormones in response to food, and these send messages to the brain that bring the eater a feeling of satisfaction: "There, that was good. Now I'm full." Eating offers both physical and emotional comfort.

Food does still more than maintain the intestine and convey messages of comfort to the brain. Foods are chemically complex. In addition to their nutrients, they contain

---
*1 Calorie/kcalorie = 4.2 kilojoules

Table 1–3

Calorie Values of Energy-Yielding Nutrients

The energy a person consumes in a day's meals comes from these three energy-yielding nutrients; alcohol, if consumed, also contributes energy.

Energy Nutrient	Energy
Carbohydrate	4 Cal/g
Fat (lipid)*	9 Cal/g
Protein	4 Cal/g

NOTE: Alcohol contributes 7 Cal/g that the human body can use for energy. Alcohol is not classed as a nutrient, however, because it interferes with growth, maintenance, and repair of body tissues.

*See Example 6 in Appendix B.

Calories/kcalories units of energy. Strictly speaking, the unit used to measure the energy in foods is a kilocalorie (*kcalorie* or *Calorie*): it is the amount of heat energy necessary to raise the temperature of a kilogram (a litre) of water by one degree Celsius. This book follows the common practice of using the term *Calorie** (abbreviated *Cal/kcal*) to mean the same thing.

grams units of mass. A gram (g) is the mass of a cubic centimetre (cc) or millilitre (mL) of water under defined conditions of temperature and pressure. About 28 grams equals an ounce.

dietary supplements pills, liquids, or powders that contain purified nutrients or other ingredients (see Controversy 7 in Chapter 7).

elemental diets diets composed of purified ingredients of known chemical composition; intended to supply all essential nutrients to people who cannot eat foods.

When you eat foods, you are receiving more than just nutrients.

nonnutrients, including the **phytochemicals**. These compounds confer colour, taste, and other characteristics on foods, and many are believed to affect health by reducing disease risks (see Controversy 2 in Chapter 2). Even an ordinary baked potato contains hundreds of different compounds. In view of all of this, it is not surprising that food gives us more than just nutrients. If it were otherwise, that would be surprising.

KEY POINT

- In addition to nutrients, food conveys emotional satisfaction and hormonal stimuli that contribute to health. Foods also contain phytochemicals that give them their tastes, aromas, colours, and other characteristics. Some phytochemicals may play roles in reducing disease risks.

The Challenge of Choosing Foods

Well-planned meals convey pleasure and are nutritious, too, fitting your tastes, personality, family and cultural traditions, lifestyle, and budget. Given the astounding numbers and varieties available, consumers can lose track of what individual foods contain and how to put them together into health-promoting diets. A few guidelines can help.

The Abundance of Foods to Choose From

A list of the foods available a hundred years ago would be relatively short. It would consist of **basic foods**—foods that have been around for a long time, such as vegetables, fruit, meats, milk, and grains. These foods have also been called unprocessed, natural, whole, or farm foods. An easy way to obtain a nutritious diet is to consume a variety of selections from among these foods each day. On a given day, however, almost half of our population consumes no fruit or fruit juices. Also, although people generally consume a few servings of vegetables, the vegetable they most often choose is potatoes, usually prepared as French fries. Such dietary patterns increase the risk of chronic disease.[9]

The number of foods supplied by the food industry today is astounding. Thousands of foods now line the market shelves—many are processed mixtures of the basic ones, and some are even constructed mostly from artificial ingredients. This abundance may make it more difficult, rather than easier, to plan a nutritious diet.

Table 1–4 presents a glossary of terms related to foods. The terms reveal that all types of food—including **fast foods** and **processed foods**—offer various constituents to the eater. You may also hear about **functional foods**, a term coined in an attempt to identify those foods that might lend protection against chronic diseases by way of the nutrients or nonnutrients they contain. The trouble is that scientists trying to single out the most health-promoting foods find that almost every naturally occurring food—even chocolate—is functional in some way with regard to human health. Controversy 2 provides more information about functional foods.

The extent to which foods support good health depends on the Calories, nutrients, and nonnutrients they contain. In short, to select well among foods, you need to know more than their names; you need to know the foods' inner qualities.

Even more important, you need to know how to combine foods into nutritious diets. Foods are not nutritious by themselves; each is of value only insofar as it contributes to a nutritious diet. A key to wise diet planning is to make sure that the foods you eat daily, your **staple foods**, are especially nutritious.

Some foods offer beneficial nonnutrients called phytochemicals.

- In 1900, Canadians chose from among 500 or so different foods; today, they choose from more than 50,000.

nonnutrients a term used in this book to mean compounds other than the six nutrients that are present in foods and have biological activity in the body.

phytochemicals nonnutrient compounds in plant-derived foods that have biological activity in the body (*phyto* means "plant").

Table 1–4

Glossary of Food Types

The purpose of this little glossary is to show that good-sounding food names don't necessarily signify that foods are nutritious. Read the comment at the end of each definition.

- **basic foods** milk and milk products; meats and similar foods such as fish and poultry; vegetables, including dried beans and peas; fruit; and grains. These foods are generally considered to form the basis of a nutritious diet. Also called *whole foods*.
- **enriched foods** and **fortified foods** foods to which nutrients have been added. If the starting material is a whole, basic food such as milk or whole grain, the result may be highly nutritious. If the starting material is a concentrated form of sugar or fat, the result may be less nutritious.
- **fast foods** restaurant foods that are available within minutes after customers order them—traditionally, hamburgers, French fries, and milkshakes; more recently, salads and other vegetable dishes as well. These foods may or may not meet people's nutrient needs, depending on the selections made and on the energy allowances and nutrient needs of the eaters.
- **functional foods** a term that reflects an attempt to define as a group the foods known to possess nutrients or nonnutrients that might lend protection against diseases. However, all nutritious foods can support health in some ways; Controversy 2 provides details.

- **natural foods** a term that has no legal definition but is often used to imply wholesomeness.
- **nutraceutical** a term used to describe a product that has been isolated from food, often sold in pill form and believed to have medicinal effects (see Chapter 2).
- **organic foods** understood to mean foods grown without synthetic pesticides or fertilizers. In chemistry, however, all foods are made mostly of organic (carbon-containing) compounds. (See Controversy 12 in Chapter 12 for details.)
- **partitioned foods** foods composed of parts of whole foods, such as butter (from milk), sugar (from beets or cane), or corn oil (from corn). Partitioned foods are generally overused and provide few nutrients with many Calories.
- **processed foods** foods subjected to any process, such as milling, alteration of texture, addition of additives, cooking, or others. Depending on the starting material and the process, a processed food may or may not be nutritious.
- **staple foods** foods used frequently or daily, for example, rice (in East and Southeast Asia) or potatoes (in Ireland). If well chosen, these foods are nutritious.

All foods once looked like this . . .

. . . but now many foods often look like this.

KEY POINT

- Foods come in a bewildering variety in the marketplace, but the foods that form the basis of a nutritious diet are basic foods, such as ordinary milk and milk products; meats, fish, and poultry; vegetables and dried peas and beans; fruit; and grains.

How Exactly Can I Recognize a Nutritious Diet?

A nutritious diet has five characteristics. First is **adequacy**: the foods provide enough of each essential nutrient, fibre, and energy. Second is **balance**: the choices do not overemphasize one nutrient or food type at the expense of another. Third is **Calorie control**: the foods provide the amount of energy you need to maintain appropriate weight—not more, not less. Fourth is **moderation**: the foods do not provide excess fat, salt, sugar, or other unwanted constituents. Fifth is **variety**: the foods chosen differ from one day to the next. In addition, to maintain a steady supply of nutrients, meals should occur with regular timing throughout the day.

adequacy the dietary characteristic of providing all of the essential nutrients, fibre, and energy in amounts sufficient to maintain health and body weight.

balance the dietary characteristic of providing foods of a number of types in proportion to each other, such that foods rich in some nutrients do not replace foods that are rich in other nutrients. Also called *proportionality*.

Calorie control control of energy intake; a feature of a sound diet plan.

moderation the dietary characteristic of providing constituents within set limits, not to excess.

variety the dietary characteristic of providing a wide selection of foods—the opposite of monotony.

Adequacy   Any nutrient could be used to demonstrate the importance of dietary *adequacy*. Iron provides a familiar example. It is an essential nutrient: you lose some every day, so you have to keep replacing it, and you can get it into your body only by eating foods that contain it.* If you eat too few of the iron-containing foods, you can develop iron-deficiency anemia (See Figure 8–9, page 331): with anemia, you may feel weak, tired, cold, sad, and unenthusiastic; you may have frequent headaches; and you can do very little muscular work without disabling fatigue. Some foods are rich in iron; others are notoriously poor. If you add iron-rich foods to your diet, you soon feel more energetic. Meat, fish, poultry, and **legumes** are in the iron-rich category, and an easy way to obtain the needed iron is to include these foods in your diet regularly. Note: According to the Canadian Community Health Survey (CCHS) (Cycle 2.2) data, about 17 percent of Canadian females aged 19–30 years have an inadequate intake of iron (http://www.hc-sc.gc.ca/fn-an/surveill/nutrition/commun/cchs_focus-volet_escc-eng.php).

Balance   To appreciate the importance of dietary *balance*, consider a second essential nutrient, calcium. A diet lacking calcium causes poor bone development during the growing years and increases a person's susceptibility to disabling bone loss in adult life. Most foods that are rich in iron are poor in calcium. Calcium's richest food sources are milk and milk products, which happen to be extraordinarily poor iron sources. Clearly, to obtain enough of both iron and calcium, people have to balance their food choices. Balancing the whole diet to provide enough but not too much of every one of the 40-odd nutrients the body needs for health requires considerable juggling. As you will see in Chapter 2, food group plans can help you achieve dietary adequacy and balance because they recommend specific amounts of foods of each type.

Calorie-Controlled Diets   Energy intakes should not exceed energy needs. Nicknamed *Calorie-controlled diets*, this diet characteristic ensures that energy intakes from food balance energy expenditures in activity. Eating such a diet helps control body fat content and weight. The many strategies that promote weight maintenance and weight loss appear in Chapter 9.

Moderation   Intakes of certain food constituents such as fat, cholesterol, sugar, and salt should be limited for health's sake. A major guideline for healthy people is to keep fat intake below 35 percent of total Calories.[10] Some people take this to mean that they must never indulge in a delicious beefsteak or hot-fudge sundae, but they are misinformed: *moderation*, not total abstinence, is the key. A steady diet of steak and ice cream might be harmful, but once a week as part of an otherwise moderate diet plan, these foods may have little impact; as once-a-month treats, these foods would have practically no effect at all. Moderation also means that limits are necessary, even for desirable food constituents. For example, a certain amount of fibre in foods contributes to the health of the digestive system, but too much fibre leads to nutrient losses.

Variety   As for *variety*, nutrition scientists agree that people should not eat the same foods, even highly nutritious ones, day after day. One reason is that variety increases the likelihood that diet will be adequate in nutrients.[11] In addition, some nonnutrient food components are probably important to health; some foods may be better sources of these than others. Another reason is that a monotonous diet may deliver large amounts of toxins or contaminants. Each such undesirable item in a food is diluted by all of the other foods eaten with it and is even further diluted if the food is not eaten again for several days. Last, variety adds interest—trying new foods can be a source of pleasure. Table 1–5 takes an honest look at obstacles to eating well.

   A caution is in order. Any one of these dietary principles alone cannot ensure a healthful diet. For example, the most likely outcome of relying solely on variety could easily be a low-nutrient, high-Calorie diet consisting of a variety of snack foods and nutrient-poor sweets.[12] If you establish the habit of using all of the principles just described, you will find that choosing a healthful diet becomes as automatic as brushing your teeth or falling asleep.

---

legumes (leg-GOOMS, LEG-yooms) beans, peas, and lentils, valued as inexpensive sources of protein, vitamins, minerals, and fibre that contribute little fat to the diet. Also defined in Chapter 6.

*A person can also take supplements of iron, but as later discussions demonstrate, this is not as effective as eating iron-rich foods.

Table 1-5

What's Today's Excuse for Not Eating Well?

If you find yourself saying, "I know I should eat well, but I'm too busy" (or too fond of fast food, or have too little money, or a dozen other excuses), take note:

- *No time.* Everyone is busy. In truth, eating well takes little time. Convenience packages of frozen vegetables, jars of pasta sauce, and prepared meats and salads are abundant in markets today and take no longer to pick up than snack chips and colas. Priorities change drastically and instantly when illness strikes—better to spend a little time now nourishing your body's defences than to spend time later treating illness.
- *Crave fast food.* Occasional fast-food meals can support health, if you choose wisely (see Chapter 5).
- *Too little money.* For example, a single parent making minimum wage. In many cases, with proper planning, eating right can cost little more than eating poorly. Chips, colas, fast food, and premium ice cream are expensive. And serious illness costs more than a well person can imagine.
- *Like to eat large portions.* An occasional splurge, say, once a month, is a healthy part of moderation.
- *Take vitamins instead.* Vitamin pills cannot make up for consistently poor food choices. Food constituents such as fibre and phytochemicals are also important to good health.
- *Love sweets.* Sweets in moderation are an acceptable, and even desirable, part of a balanced diet.

A nutritious diet follows the A, B, C, M, V principles:

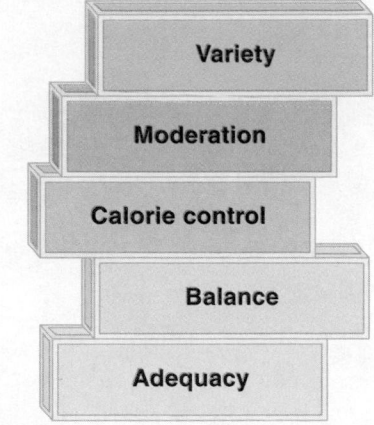

These factors are the building blocks of a nutritious diet.

KEY POINT

- A well-planned diet is adequate in nutrients, is balanced with regard to food types, offers food energy that matches energy expended in activity, is moderate in unwanted constituents, and offers a variety of nutritious foods.

Why People Choose Foods

Eating is an intentional act. Each day, people choose from the available foods, prepare the foods, and decide where to eat, which customs to follow, and with whom to dine. Many factors influence food-related choices.

Cultural and Social Meanings Attached to Food Like wearing traditional clothing or speaking a native language, enjoying traditional **cuisines** and **foodways** can be a celebration of your own or a friend's heritage. Sharing **ethnic food** can be symbolic: people offering foods are expressing a willingness to share cherished values with others. People accepting those foods are symbolically accepting not only the person doing the offering but also the person's culture.

> Figure 2–8 in Chapter 2 depicts some ethnic foods that have become an integral part of the "North American diet."

Cultural traditions regarding food are not inflexible; they keep evolving as people move about, learn about new foods, and teach each other. Today, some people are ceasing to be **omnivores** and are becoming **vegetarians** and **vegans**. Vegetarians often choose this lifestyle because they honour the lives of animals or because they have discovered the health and other advantages associated with diets rich in beans, whole grains, fruits, nuts, and vegetables. Controversy 6 in Chapter 6 explores the pros and cons of both the vegetarian's and the meat eater's diets.

Factors That Drive Food Choices Consumers today value convenience so highly that they are willing to spend over half of their food budget on meals that require little or no preparation.[13] They frequently eat out, bring home ready-to-eat meals, or have food delivered. In their own kitchens, they want to prepare a meal in 15 to 20 minutes, using only four to six ingredients. Such convenience limits food choices but doesn't necessarily mean that nutrition is out the window. This chapter's Food Feature addresses the time and nutrition tradeoff.

cuisines styles of cooking.

foodways the sum of a culture's habits, customs, beliefs, and preferences concerning food.

ethnic foods foods associated with particular cultural subgroups within a population.

omnivores people who eat foods of both plant and animal origin, including animal flesh.

vegetarians people who exclude from their diets animal flesh and possibly other animal products such as milk, cheese, and eggs.

vegans people who include only food from plant sources: vegetables, grains, legumes, fruit, seeds and nuts; also called *strict vegetarians*.

Sharing ethnic food is a way of sharing culture.

Convenience is only one consideration.[14] Physical, psychological, social, cultural, and philosophical factors all influence how you choose the foods you generally eat:

- *Advertising.* The media have persuaded you to eat these foods.
- *Availability.* There are no others to choose from (for example, no access to large supermarkets).
- *Economy.* They are within your means.
- *Emotional comfort.* They can make you feel better for a while.
- *Habit.* They are familiar; you always eat them.
- *Personal preference and genetic inheritance.* You like the way these foods taste, with some preferences possibly determined by the genes.[15]
- *Positive associations.* They are eaten by people you admire, or they indicate status, or they remind you of fun.
- *Region of the country.* They are foods favoured in your area (for example, seafood).
- *Social pressure.* They are offered; you feel you can't refuse them.
- *Values or beliefs.* They fit your religious tradition, square with your political views, or honour the environmental ethic.
- *Weight.* You think they will help control body weight.
- *Nutritional value.* You think they are good for you.

Only the last two of these reasons for choosing foods assign a high priority to nutritional health. Similarly, the choice of where, as well as what, to eat is often based more on social considerations than on nutrition judgments. University and college students often choose to eat at fast-food and other restaurants to socialize, to get out, to save time, or to date; they are not always conscious of the need to obtain healthful food.

If you wish to choose intentionally for health's sake, the final section of this chapter delivers some broad guidelines for choosing an adequate diet and some larger goals for the nutrition of the nation. Setting goals for our national nutritional health depends upon a firm base of scientific knowledge. The next section describes how such knowledge comes to light and addresses the final "how" question of this chapter: How do we know what we know about nutrition?

KEY POINT
- Cultural traditions and social values revolve around food. Some values are expressed through foodways. Many factors other than nutrition drive food choices.

The Science of Nutrition

Nutrition is a science—a field of knowledge composed of organized facts. Unlike sciences such as astronomy and physics, nutrition is a relatively young science and includes studies in areas such as clinical nutrition, community nutrition, public health and food policy, and food science. Most nutrition research has been conducted since 1900. The first vitamin was identified in 1897 and the last one in 1948, and the first protein structure was not fully described until the mid-1940s. Because nutrition science is an active, changing, growing body of knowledge, scientific findings often seem to contradict one another or are subject to conflicting interpretations.

For this reason, people may despair as they try to decipher current reports to learn what is really going on: "When the scientists themselves can't agree on what is true, how am I supposed to know?" Yet many facts in nutrition are known with great certainty. To understand why apparent contradictions sometimes arise in nutrition science, we need to look first at what scientists do.

What Nutrition Scientists Do

Everyone stampedes for oat bran, red wine, or fish oil based on today's news that these products are good for health. Then tomorrow's news reports, "It isn't true after all," and everyone drops oat bran, red wine, or fish oil and takes up the next craze. Meanwhile, bewildered consumers complain in frustration, "Those scientists don't know anything."

In truth, though, it is a scientist's business not to know. Scientists obtain facts by systematically asking questions—that's their job. They use the scientific method outlined in Figure 1–3. To answer the questions, they design and conduct experiments to test for various possible answers (see Figure 1–4 and Table 1–6). When they have ruled out some possibilities and found evidence for others, they submit their findings, not to the news media but to boards of reviewers composed of their peers, other scientists who try to pick the findings apart. If these peer-reviewers consider the conclusions to be well supported by the evidence, they endorse the work for publication in scientific journals, where still more scientists can read it. Then the news media read and summarize it and you can read it, too; Table 1–7 explains what you can expect to find in a journal article.

As you study nutrition, you are likely to hear of findings based on a national survey of Canadians' eating habits, the 2004 Canadian Community Health Survey (CCHS) (Cycle 2.2). It gathered information on the eating habits of more than 35,000 Canadians. Preliminary data from this survey indicate that most Canadians are eating fewer than five servings of vegetables and fruit each day (http://www.statcan.gc.ca/daily-quotidien/060706/dq060706b-eng.htm). For an overview of what has been and is being done regarding food and nutrition surveillance in Canada, see http://www.hc-sc.gc.ca/fn-an/surveill/environmental_scan_table_e.html. Data sources include various provincial surveys, the Family Food Expenditure Survey, the Food Habits of Canadians survey, and the biennial Canadian Health Measures Surveys (CHMS) 2007–2009; 2009–2011; 2011–2013.

Nutrition monitoring makes it possible for researchers to assess the nutrient status, health indicators, and dietary intakes of the Canadian population.

Scientific Challenge

Once a new finding is published, it is still only preliminary. One experiment does not "prove" or "disprove" anything. The next step is for other scientists to attempt to duplicate and support the work of the first researchers or to challenge the finding by designing experiments to refute it.

Only when a finding has stood up to rigorous, repeated testing in several kinds of experiments performed by several different researchers is it finally considered

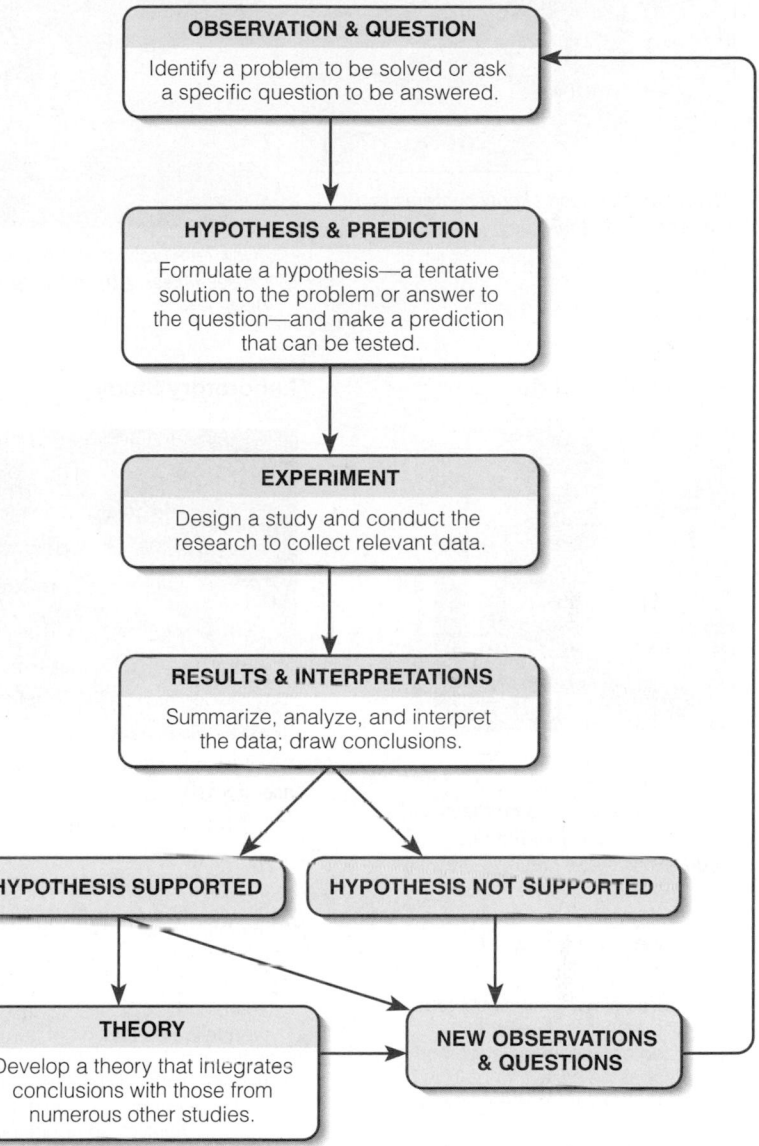

FIGURE 1–3

The Scientific Method

Research scientists follow the scientific method. Note that most research projects result in new questions, not final answers. Thus, research continues in a somewhat cyclical manner.

OBSERVATION & QUESTION
Identify a problem to be solved or ask a specific question to be answered.

HYPOTHESIS & PREDICTION
Formulate a hypothesis—a tentative solution to the problem or answer to the question—and make a prediction that can be tested.

EXPERIMENT
Design a study and conduct the research to collect relevant data.

RESULTS & INTERPRETATIONS
Summarize, analyze, and interpret the data; draw conclusions.

HYPOTHESIS SUPPORTED

HYPOTHESIS NOT SUPPORTED

THEORY
Develop a theory that integrates conclusions with those from numerous other studies.

NEW OBSERVATIONS & QUESTIONS

Government Agencies Responsible for Nutrition and Physical Activity Policies, Research, Monitoring, and Health Reports

- Health Canada's Office of Nutrition Policy and Promotion (ONPP): http://www.hc-sc.gc.ca/ahc-asc/branch-dirgen/hpfb-dgpsa/onpp-bppn/index-eng.php
- Canadian Institutes of Health Research (CIHR): http://www.cihr-irsc.gc.ca
- Canadian Fitness and Lifestyle Research Institute (CFLRI): http://www.cflri.ca/index.php
- Physical Activity Unit of the Public Health Agency of Canada (PHAC): http://www.phac-aspc.gc.ca/hp-ps/hl-mvs/index-eng.php
- Statistics Canada (Stats Can): http://www.statcan.gc.ca/start-debut-eng.html

FIGURE 1-4

Examples of Research Design

Epidemiological Study

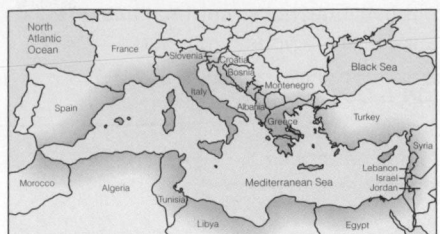

"This country's food supply contains more nutrient X, and these people suffer less illness Y."

Case Study

"Now let's prove that a nutrient X deficiency causes illness Y by inducing a deficiency in these rats."

© Alexander Raths/Shutterstock

Intervention Study

© David Buffington/Photodisc/Getty Images

"Let's add foods containing nutrient X to some people's food supply and compare their rates of illness Y with the rates of others who don't receive the nutrient."

Laboratory Study

© Brandon Laufenberg/iStockphoto

"This person eats too little of nutrient X and has illness Y."

The source of valid nutrition information is scientific research. Nutrition is a science, an organized body of knowledge composed of facts that we believe to be true because they have been supported, time and again, in experiments designed to rule out all other possibilities. Each fact has been established by many different kinds of experiments. For example, we know that eyesight depends partly on vitamin A because animals deprived of that vitamin and only that vitamin begin to go blind; when it is restored soon enough to their diet, they regain their sight. The same fact holds true in observations of human beings.

Studies of whole populations (**epidemiological studies**) provide another sort of information. Such a study can reveal a **correlation**. For example,

an epidemiological study might find no worldwide correlation of gumdrop eating with fancy footwork but, unexpectedly, might reveal a correlation with tooth decay. A *cohort study* is one in which the investigators do not manipulate the study variables of interest; instead, they monitor them over time (thus, the study is prospective in nature, a longitudinal study in which data are collected at more than one point in time). For example, such a design could be used to monitor the relationship between milk product consumption and growth in a *cohort* of children (often a single group of individuals with similar characteristics, e.g., boys or girls within a defined age range).

The type of study chosen for research depends upon what sort of information the

researchers require. Studies of individuals (**case studies**) yield observations that may lead to possible avenues of research. A study of a man who ate gumdrops and became a famous dancer might suggest that an experiment be done to see if gumdrops contain dance-enhancing power. *A case-control study* (case-comparison, an epidemiological study) is one in which the investigators do not manipulate the study variables of interest. Cases are the individuals with the condition of interest, for example, some form of cancer, and the controls are cancer-free individuals and are usually matched with cases in terms of age, gender, and other characteristics. For example, such a design could be used to study the association between past whole-grain food consumption and colon cancer. These studies are most often conducted by looking back in time, which means that the outcome for the subjects is already known, thus, retrospective.

Studies in which researchers actively intervene to alter people's eating habits (**intervention studies**) go a step further. In such a study, one set of subjects (the **experimental group**) receives a treatment, and another set (the **control group**) goes untreated or receives a **placebo** or sham treatment. If the study is a **blind experiment**, the subjects do not know who among the members receives the treatment and who receives the sham. A double-blind experiment is one in which neither the experimenter nor the subjects know who receives the treatment and who receives the placebo. If the two groups experience different effects, then the treatment's effect can be pinpointed. For example, an intervention study might show that withholding gumdrops, together with other candies and confections, reduced the incidence of tooth decay in an experimental population compared with that in a control population.

Finally, **laboratory studies** can pinpoint the mechanisms by which nutrition acts. What is it about gumdrops that contributes to tooth decay: their size, shape, temperature, colour, ingredients? Feeding various forms of gumdrops to rats might yield the information that sugar, in a gummy carrier, promotes tooth decay. In the laboratory, using animals or plants or cells, scientists can inoculate with diseases, induce deficiencies, and experiment with variations on treatments to obtain in-depth knowledge of the process under study. Intervention studies, **randomized controlled trials (RCT)**, and laboratory experiments are among the most powerful tools in nutrition research because they show the effects of treatments.

Table 1–6

Research Design Terms

- **blind experiment** an experiment in which the subjects do not know whether they are members of the experimental group or the control group. In a *double-blind experiment*, neither the subjects nor the researchers know to which group the members belong until the end of the experiment.
- **case studies** studies of individuals. In clinical settings, researchers can observe treatments and their *apparent* effects. To prove that a treatment has produced an effect requires simultaneous observation of an untreated similar subject (a *case control*).
- **control group** a group of individuals who are similar in all possible respects to the group being treated in an experiment but who receive a sham treatment instead of the real one. Also called *control subjects*. See also *experimental group* and *intervention studies*.
- **correlation** the simultaneous change of two factors, such as the increase in weight with increasing height (a *direct* or *positive* correlation) or the decrease in cancer incidence with increasing fibre intake (an *inverse* or *negative* correlation). A correlation between two factors suggests that one may cause the other but does not rule out the possibility that both may be caused by chance or by a third factor.
- **epidemiological studies** studies of populations; often used in nutrition to search for correlations between dietary habits and disease incidence; a first step in seeking nutrition-related causes of diseases.
- **experimental group** the people or animals participating in an experiment who receive the treatment under investigation. Also called *experimental subjects*. See also *control group* and *intervention studies*.
- **intervention studies** studies of populations in which observation is accompanied by experimental manipulation of some population members—for example, a study in which half of the subjects (the *experimental subjects*) follow diet advice to reduce fat intakes while the other half (the *control subjects*) do not, and both groups' heart health is monitored.
- **laboratory studies** studies that are performed under tightly controlled conditions and are designed to pinpoint causes and effects. Such studies often use animals as subjects.
- **placebo** a sham treatment often used in scientific studies; an inert harmless medication. The *placebo effect* is the healing effect that the act of treatment, rather than the treatment itself, often has.
- **randomized controlled trials (RCT)** sometimes also referred to as clinical trials, studies in which the subjects are selected in such a way that they have an equal chance of being included in the experimental/treatment group or the control group. This type of study is considered the gold standard in research.

Table 1–7

The Anatomy of a Research Article

Here's what you can expect to find inside a research article:

- *Abstract.* The abstract provides a brief overview of the article.
- *Introduction.* The introduction clearly states the purpose of the current study.
- *Review of literature.* A review of the literature reveals what science has uncovered on the subject to date.
- *Methodology.* The methodology section defines key terms and describes the procedures used in the study.
- *Results.* The results report the findings and may include summary tables and figures.
- *Conclusions.* The conclusions drawn are those supported by the data and reflect the original purpose as stated in the introduction. Usually, they answer a few questions and raise several more.
- *References.* The references list relevant studies (including key studies several years old as well as current ones).

confirmed. Even then, strictly speaking, science consists not of facts that are set in stone but of *theories* that can always be challenged and revised. Some findings, though, like the theory that the earth revolves about the sun, are so well supported by observations and experimental findings that they are generally accepted as facts. What we "know" in nutrition is confirmed in the same way—through years of replicating study findings. This slow path of repeated studies stands in sharp contrast to the media's desire for today's latest news.

Nutritional Assessment

Nutritional assessment of individuals is an essential component of their nutritional care. These assessments are conducted by Registered Dietitians or other health-care professionals and may include the client's/patient's (a) health and diet history (e.g., a person's medical record/food intake records); (b) anthropometric measurements (e.g., weight, height, skinfold measurements); and (c) laboratory test data (e.g., blood iron, glucose levels). This information is then interpreted in relation to current standards for the person's age, gender, life stage, etc.

Can I Trust the Media to Deliver Nutrition News?

● Some newspapers, magazines, talk shows, websites, and other media strive for accuracy in reporting, but others specialize in sensationalism that borders on quackery—see this chapter's Controversy feature for details.

The news media are hungry for new findings, and reporters often latch onto ideas from scientific laboratories before they have been fully tested. Also, a reporter who lacks a strong understanding of science may misunderstand complex scientific principles. To tell the truth, sometimes scientists get excited about their findings, too, and leak them to the press before they have been through a rigorous review by the scientists' peers. As a result, the public is often exposed to late-breaking nutrition news stories before the findings are fully confirmed.[16] Then, when the hypothesis being tested fails to hold up to a later challenge, consumers feel betrayed by what is simply the normal course of science at work.

It also follows that people who take action based on single studies are almost always acting impulsively, not scientifically. The real scientists are trend watchers. They evaluate the methods used in each study, assess each study in light of the evidence gleaned from other studies, and, little by little, modify their picture of what is true. As evidence accumulates, the scientists become more and more confident about their ability to make recommendations that apply to people's health and lives. The Consumer Corner later in this chapter offers some tips for evaluating news stories about nutrition.

Sometimes media sensationalism overrates the importance of even true, replicated findings. For example, a few years ago the media eagerly reported that oat bran lowers blood cholesterol, a lipid indicative of heart disease risk. Although the reports were true, oat bran is only one of several hundred factors that affect blood cholesterol. News reports on oat bran often failed to mention that cutting intakes of certain fats is still the major step to take to lower blood cholesterol.

> The links between lipids and heart disease are discussed in Chapter 5.

Also, new findings need refinements. Oat bran is truly a cholesterol reducer in those with high blood cholesterol, but how much bran must a person eat to produce the desired effects? Do oat bran pills or powders meet the need? Do oat bran cookies? If so, how many cookies must be eaten? As for oatmeal, it takes a bowl-and-a-half daily to affect blood lipids. A few cookies cannot provide nearly that much and certainly cannot undo all of the damage from a high-fat meal.

Today, oat bran's cholesterol-lowering effect is considered to be established, and labels on food packages in the United States (but not Canada, as yet) can proclaim that a diet high in oats may reduce the risk of heart disease. The whole process of discovery, challenge, and vindication took almost 10 years of research. Some other lines of research have taken many years longer. In science, a single finding almost never makes a crucial difference to our knowledge as a whole, but like each individual frame in a movie, it contributes a little to the big picture. Many such frames are needed to tell the whole story.

KEY POINT

- Nutritional scientists use tried and tested research designs to collect data and are continuously challenging and revising their own theories and those of other scientists, and then, where necessary, developing *new* theories that better explain the latest findings in the field.

Dietary Guidelines and Nutrition Objectives

Many countries set forth dietary guidelines to help their citizens answer the question "What should I eat to stay healthy?" Governments also set health objectives for the nation. The guidelines and objectives are related: ideally, if everyone followed the guidelines for individuals, many of the goals for the nation would fall into place.

Dietary Guidelines

Many of Canada's *Dietary Guidelines* are embedded in *Eating Well with Canada's Food Guide* and are listed in Table 1–8. These guidelines, along with those included in the Dietary Reference Intake (DRI) reports, are messages designed to help Canadians achieve a healthy balanced diet. Note: The DRI reports were developed by committees of American and Canadian nutritional scientists with guidance from the U.S. Food and Nutrition Board of the Institute of Medicine. Progress on Canada's food guidance system can be monitored by visiting the following weblink on Health Canada's website: http://www.hc-sc.gc.ca/fn-an/food-guide-aliment/index-eng.php.

Food guides for many countries, including ours, contain statements about the importance of physical activity. To see electronic versions of them or to order your own copy of the physical activity guides for Canadians, see http://www.phac-aspc.gc.ca/hp-ps/hl-mvs/pa-ap/index-eng.php. In addition, the 2007–2008 CCHS not only revealed the good news that physical inactivity decreased between the late 1990s and 2002, it also revealed that much work remained because an estimated 53 percent of Canadian adults were still physically inactive (http://www.statcan.gc.ca/pub/82-625-x/2011001/article/11552-eng.htm). The report further indicated that between the ages of 20 and 39 years more women than men are physically inactive and that physical inactivity increases with age. These latter results prompted an almost immediate response from the ministers responsible for physical activity, recreation, and sport. The latest goal set by them was to increase the proportion of Canadians

---

Table 1–8

Summary of Nutrition Recommendations in *Eating Well with Canada's Food Guide*

Along with recommending a specific number or range of Food Guide Servings each day for your gender and six different age categories that will allow Canadians to obtain the necessary nutrients that contribute to overall health (including a healthy body weight) and vitality and help reduce the development of chronic diseases, it also

- Recommends that we "Eat Well" in the following ways:
  - "Enjoy a variety of foods from the four food groups" every day
  - "Satisfy your thirst with water"
  - Limit foods and beverages high in
    - Calories
    - Fat
    - Sugar (including that found in sweetened hot and cold drinks)
    - Sodium (salt)
    - Alcohol
- Provides 10 "directional statements" and more than a dozen "actionable tips" to help us make wise choices among the foods represented in the four food groups
- Recommends that we include a small amount of "Oils and Fat" such as unsaturated fat each day
- Provides some additional advice for different age groups and stages of the life cycle: children [e.g., "Serve small nutritious meals and snacks"]; women of childbearing age [e.g., take a multivitamin that contains folic acid and iron]; and men and women over 50 [e.g., "take a daily vitamin D supplement of 10 μg (400 IU)"]
- Recommends that we read and compare food labels to help us make informed and wise food choices; for example, those that contain less
  - Total fat
  - Saturated fat
  - *Trans* fat
  - Sugar
  - Sodium
- Provides advice on physical activity (e.g., how long we should "Be active" every day) and inactivity (e.g., "Spend less time ... watching TV or playing computer games")

Source: Eating Well with Canada's Food Guide. *Health Canada, 2011. Reproduced with permission from Her Majesty the Queen in Right of Canada ©, represented by the Minister of Health, 2013.*

Reading Nutrition News with an Educated Eye

A news reader, who had sworn off butter years ago for his heart's sake, bemoaned this headline: "Margarine Fat as Bad as Butter for Heart Health." "Do you mean to say that I could have been eating butter all these years? That's it. I quit. No more diet changes for me." His response is understandable—diet changes, after all, take effort to make and commitment to sustain. Those who do make changes may feel betrayed when, years later, science appears to have turned its advice upside down.

It bears repeating that the findings of a single study never prove or disprove anything. Study results may constitute strong supporting evidence for one view or another, but they rarely merit the sort of finality implied by journalistic phrases such as "Now we know" or "The answer has been found." Misinformed readers who look for simple answers to complex nutrition problems often take such phrases literally.

To read news stories with an educated eye, keep these points in mind:

- The study being described should be published in a peer-reviewed journal such as the *Canadian Journal of Dietetic Practice and Research*. An unpublished study or one from a less credible source may or may not be valid; the reader has no way of knowing because the study has not been challenged or reviewed by other experts in the field.

- The news report should state the purpose of the study and describe the research methods used to obtain the data, although, in truth, few provide these details.[1,*] It should also note their limitations (in the Methodology section—look again at Table 1–7 on page 15). For example, it matters whether the study participants numbered 8 or 8,000 or whether the researchers personally observed the participants' behaviours or relied on self-reports collected over the telephone.

- The report should clearly define the subjects of the study—single cells, animals, or human beings. If the study subjects were human beings, the more you have in common with them (age and gender, for example), the more applicable the findings may be for you.

- Valid reports also describe previous research and put the current research in the proper context. Some reporters regularly follow developments in a research area and thus acquire the background knowledge to report meaningfully in that area.

- Useful for their broad perspective on a single topic are review articles appearing in journals such as *Nutrition Reviews*. Such articles allow judgment about a single study within the context of many other studies on the same topic.

Finally, ask yourself if the study makes common sense. Even if it turns out that the fat of margarine is damaging to the heart,

Consumer Corner references are listed separately at the end of the chapter.

do you eat enough margarine to worry about its effects? Before making a decision, learn more about the effects of fats on the arteries in Chapters 5 and 11 and then ask the critical questions about yourself.

When a headline touts a shocking new "answer" to a nutrition question, read the story with a critical eye. It may indeed be a carefully researched report, but often it is a sensational story intended to catch the attention of newspaper and magazine buyers, not to offer useful nutrition information.

A person wanting the whole story on a nutrition topic is wise to seek articles from peer-reviewed journals such as these. A review journal examines all available evidence on major topics. Other journals report details of the methods, results, and conclusions of single studies.

Courtesy of Dietitians of Canada

who participate in regular activity by 20 percent by 2015 (http://www.phac-aspc.gc.ca/hp-ps/hl-mvs/ipchls-spimmvs/sum-res-eng.php). *A basic premise of any dietary guidelines* is that foods, not supplements, should provide the needed nutrients whenever possible.

Another focus of *dietary guidelines* is to limit potentially harmful dietary constituents. A healthful diet is carefully chosen to supply the kinds of carbohydrates that the body needs but little sugar and to offer the needed fats and oils while limiting saturated fat, *trans* fat, and cholesterol (Chapters 4 and 5 explain these distinctions). People are also asked to consume less salt and choose sensibly if they use alcohol. Finally, foods should be kept safe from spoilage or contamination (see Chapter 12).

Notice that *Eating Well with Canada's Food Guide* does not require that you give up your favourite foods or eat strange, unappealing foods (see Chapter 2). With some planning and adjustments, almost anyone's diet and lifestyle can fit most of these recommendations.

If the experts who develop such guidelines were to ask us, we would add one more recommendation to their lists: take time to enjoy and savour your food. The joys of eating are physically beneficial to the body because they trigger health-promoting changes in the nervous, hormonal, and immune systems. When the food is nutritious as well as enjoyable, then the eater obtains all of the nutrients needed for the healthy skin, glossy hair, and natural good looks that accompany good health. Remember to enjoy your food.

© Kzenon/Shutterstock

Health Canada suggests that physical activity should be part of a healthy lifestyle.

KEY POINT

- The most recent nutrition recommendations for Canadians, which are based for the most part on the Dietary Reference Intake reports, address the problems of overnutrition and undernutrition.

Potential Benefits of Physical Activity

- Reduced risk of cardiovascular diseases
- Increased cardiovascular endurance
- Increased muscle strength and endurance
- Increased flexibility
- Reduced risk of type 2 diabetes
- Reduced risk of some types of cancer (especially colon and breast)
- Improved mental outlook and lessened likelihood of depression
- Improved mental functioning
- Feeling of vigour
- Feeling of belonging—the companionship of sports
- Strong self-image and belief in one's abilities
- Reduced body fatness and increased lean tissue
- A more youthful appearance, healthy skin, and improved muscle tone
- Greater bone density and lessened risk of adult bone loss in later life
- Increased independence in the elderly
- Sound, beneficial sleep
- Faster wound healing
- Lessening or elimination of menstrual pain
- Improved resistance to infection

Think Fitness  Why Be Physically Active?

Why should people bother to be physically active? Although a person's daily food choices can powerfully affect health, the combination of nutrition and physical activity is more powerful still. People who are physically active can expect to receive at least some of the benefits listed above. If even half of these benefits were yours for the asking, wouldn't you step up to claim them? In truth, they are yours to claim, at the price of including physical activity in your day. Chapter 10 comes back to the benefits of fitness and provides scientific evidence to support them.

Conclusion

According to the experts, people in Canada are not very successful at meeting the nutrition goals set forth in this chapter. In particular, most Canadians are not eating five or more servings of vegetables and fruit each day. Such a finding defines a challenge for the health-conscious eater: try to achieve adequacy and moderation at the same time. Because this challenge is the key to good nutrition, this chapter's Food Feature offers a tool to help make it easier—the concept of **nutrient density**. The next chapter takes up the challenge again, offering details about diet planning for adequacy and moderation.

nutrient density a measure of nutrients provided per Calorie of food.

How Can I Get Enough Nutrients without Consuming Too Many Calories?

In trying to control Calories while balancing the diet and making it adequate, certain foods are especially useful. These foods are rich in nutrients relative to their energy contents; that is, they are foods with high nutrient density. Figure 1–5 is a simple depiction of this concept. Consider calcium sources, for example. Ice cream and fat-free milk both supply calcium, but the milk is "denser" in calcium per Calorie. A cup of rich ice cream contributes more than 350 Calories, a cup of skim milk only 85—and with almost double the calcium. Most people cannot, for their health's sake, afford to choose foods without regard to their energy contents. Those who do very often exceed Calorie allowances while leaving nutrient needs unmet.

Nutrient density is such a useful concept in diet planning that this book encourages you to think in these terms. Watch for the tables and figures in later chapters that show the best buys among foods, not necessarily in nutrients per dollar (although Calorie-dense foods are often among the least expensive) but in nutrients per Calorie. This viewpoint can help you distinguish between more and less nutritious foods. For people who wish to eat larger meals yet not exceed their energy budgets, the concept of nutrient density can help them identify foods that provide bulk without a lot of Calories.

The foods that offer the most nutrients per Calorie are the vegetables, especially the nonstarchy vegetables such as broccoli, carrots, mushrooms, peppers, and tomatoes. These foods are also rich in phytochemicals, which are thought to protect against diseases. These inexpensive foods take time to prepare, but time invested this way pays off in nutritional health. Twenty minutes spent peeling and slicing vegetables for a salad is a better investment in nutrition than 20 minutes spent fixing a fancy, high-fat, high-sugar dessert. Besides, the dessert ingredients cost more money and strain the Calorie budget, too.

In today's households, although both men and women spend some 70 hours a week sleeping and taking care of personal needs, women still do most of the cooking and food shopping. Few households can afford a stay-at-home spouse, so families have very little time for food preparation. Busy chefs should seek out convenience foods that are nutrient dense, such as bags of ready-to-serve salads, refrigerated prepared meats, and frozen vegetables. To round out the meal, skim milk is both nutritious and convenient. Other selections, such as most pot pies, many frozen pizzas, and "pocket" style sandwiches, are less nutritious overall because they contain too few vegetables and too much fat, making them high in Calories and low in nutrient density.

All of this discussion leads to a principle that is central to achieving nutritional health: it is not the individual foods you choose but the way you combine them into meals and the way you arrange meals to follow one another over days and weeks that determines how well you are nourishing yourself. Nutrition is both a science and an art, and it can be used artfully to create a pleasing, nourishing diet. The remainder of this book is dedicated to helping you make informed choices and combine them artfully to meet all of the body's needs.

Note: A recent symposium was held, titled "Nutrient Profiling—Global Approaches, Policies and Perspectives," at the 18th annual Experimental Biology meeting in San Diego. Among the

Figure 1–5

A Way to Judge Which Foods Are the Most Nutritious

Some foods deliver more nutrients for the same number of Calories than others do. These two breakfasts provide about 500 Calories each, but they differ greatly in the nutrients they provide per Calorie. Note that the sausage in the larger breakfast is lower-Calorie turkey sausage, not the high-Calorie pork variety. Making small choices like this at each meal can add up to large Calorie savings, making room in the diet for more servings of nutritious foods and even some treats.

© Matthew Farruggio

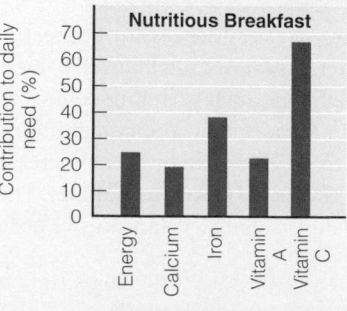

Higher Nutrient Density

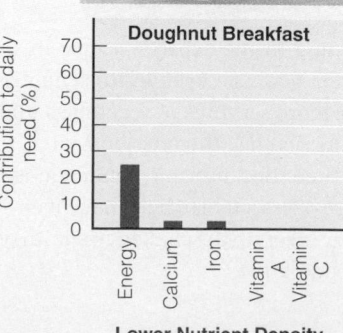
© Matthew Farruggio

Lower Nutrient Density

topics discussed were the concepts of "nutrient-rich foods"* and the U.S. Department of Agriculture (USDA) Healthy Eating Index (HEI), concepts that are expected to soon find their way into tools for both health-care professionals and consumers that will make selecting healthier foods much easier for all of us.

In fact, in August 2009, the results of a Canadian adaptation of the HEI (HEI-C) to the 2004 CCHS data set revealed a score of just under 60 (58.8) out of a possible score of 100 (http://www.statcan.gc.ca/pub/82-003-x/2009003/article/10914-eng.pdf). Not only did women's scores exceed those of men, how frequently we consume fruits and vegetables was also linked to the scores. In addition, older adolescents and younger adults had among the lowest scores.

*A. Drewnowski, Concept of a nutritious food: Toward a nutrient density score. American Journal of Clinical Nutrition 82 (2005): 721–732.

CONTROVERSY 1

Sorting the Impostors from the Real Nutrition Experts

Nutrition quackery has plagued this nation from the era of the snake oil salesman hawking wares from the back of a wagon to today's global Internet marketplace. Despite decades of attempts at regulation and enforcement, nutrition consumers today must still learn to distinguish among dishonest scams, well-meaning but misinformed advice, and honest and helpful ideas and products.

Research shows that people rely on television to provide most of their nutrition information, with magazines a close second and the Internet gaining quickly in popularity.[1,*] Innumerable products are sold on late-night television **infomercials**, in magazine and newspaper **advertorials**, and on the Internet as **urban legends** promising astonishing results with minimal effort and at bargain prices. When scam products are garden tools or stain removers, hoodwinked consumers may lose a few dollars and some pride. But when lapses in judgment lead to consumption of ineffective, untested, or even hazardous "dietary supplements," a person stands to lose much more. The sham products and procedures of

*Controversy references are listed separately at the end of the chapter.

Who is speaking on nutrition?

© Creatas/Picture Quest

quacks not only rob people of the very health they are seeking but also delay their use of legitimate strategies that could be of real help.

People want to know what nutrition news they can believe and safely use. This heightened interest in nutrition translates into a deluge of dollars spent on services and products peddled by both legitimate and fraudulent businesses. Unfortunately, nutrition and other health **fraud** (or **quackery**, defined in Table C1–1) rings cash registers to the

Table C1–1

Misinformation Terms

- **advertorials** lengthy advertisements in newspapers and magazines and their websites that read like feature articles but are written for the purpose of touting the virtues of products and may or may not be accurate.
- **anecdotal evidence** information based on interesting and entertaining, but not scientific, personal accounts of events.
- **fraud** or **quackery** the promotion, for financial gain, of devices, treatments, services, plans, or products (including diets and supplements) that alter or claim to alter a human condition without proof of safety or effectiveness. (The word *quackery* comes from the term *quacksalver*, meaning a person who quacks loudly about a miracle product—a lotion or a salve.)
- **infomercials** feature-length television commercials that follow the format of regular programs but are intended to convince viewers to buy products and not to educate or entertain them. The statements made may or may not be accurate.
- **urban legends** stories, usually false, that may travel rapidly throughout the world via the Internet, gaining strength of conviction solely on the basis of repetition.

tune of $27 billion annually. Consumers with questions about fraud or suspicions about a product or individual can contact one of the consumer fraud organizations listed in Appendix D.

How can people learn to distinguish valid nutrition information from misinformation? Some quackery may be easy to identify—like the salesman in Figure C1-1—but most fraudulent nutrition claims are not so blatant.

Between the extremes of intentional quackery and scientific data lies an abundance of less easily recognized nutrition misinformation, and resources are available that provide an excellent survey of fraud in the marketing of supplements in Canada and the United States.[2] An instructor at a gym, a physician, a health-store clerk, and an author of a book (and seller of juice machines) may all believe that the nutrition regimens they recommend are beneficial. What qualifies these people to give advice? Would following the advice be helpful or harmful? To sift the meaningful nutrition information from the rubble, you must first learn to recognize quackery wherever it presents itself.

Identifying Valid Nutrition Information

Nutrition derives information from scientific research, which has these characteristics:

- Scientists test their ideas by conducting properly designed scientific experiments. They report their methods and procedures in detail so that other scientists can verify the findings through replication.

- Scientists recognize the inadequacy of **anecdotal evidence** or testimonials.

Figure C1–1

Earmarks of Nutrition Quackery

The more of these claims you hear about nutrition information, the less likely it is to be valid.

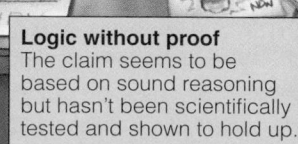

Too good to be true
Enticingly quick and simple answers to complex problems. Says what most people want to hear. Sounds magical.

Suspicions about food supply
Urges distrust of the current methods of medicine or suspicion of the regular food supply. Provides "alternatives" for sale under the guise of freedom of choice. May use the term "natural" to imply safety.

Testimonials
Support and praise by people who "felt healed," "felt younger," "lost weight," and the like as a result of using the product or treatment.

Fake credentials
Uses the title "doctor," "university," or the like but has created or bought the title—it is not legitimate.

Unpublished studies
Cites scientific studies but not studies published in reliable journals.

A **SCIENTIFIC BREAKTHROUGH**! FEEL STRONGER, LOSE WEIGHT. **IMPROVE** YOUR MEMORY ALL WITH THE HELP OF **VITE-O-MITE**! OH SURE, YOU MAY HAVE HEARD THAT **VITE-O-MITE** IS NOT ALL THAT WE SAY IT IS, BUT THAT'S WHAT THE HEALTH CANADA WANTS YOU TO THINK! **OUR DOCTORS** AND SCIENTISTS SAY IT'S THE ULTIMATE VITAMIN SUPPLEMENT. SAY NO! TO THE WEAKENED VITAMINS IN TODAY'S FOODS. **VITE-O-MITE** INCLUDES **POTENT SECRET INGREDIENTS** THAT YOU CANNOT GET WITH ANY OTHER PRODUCT! ORDER RIGHT NOW AND WE'LL SEND YOU ANOTHER FOR FREE!

Logic without proof
The claim seems to be based on sound reasoning but hasn't been scientifically tested and shown to hold up.

Persecution claims
Claims of persecution by the medical establishment or claims that physicians "want to keep you ill so that you will continue to pay for office visits."

Authority not cited
Studies cited sound valid but are not referenced, so that it is impossible to check and see if they were conducted scientifically.

Motive: Personal gain
Those making the claim stand to make a profit if it is believed.

Advertisement
Claims are made by an advertiser who is paid to promote sales of the product or procedure. (Look for the word "Advertisement," in tiny print somewhere on the page.)

Latest innovation/Time-tested
Fake scientific jargon is meant to inspire awe. Fake "ancient remedies" are meant to inspire trust.

- Scientists who use animals in their research do not apply their findings directly to human beings.
- Scientists may use specific segments of the population in their research. When they do, they are careful not to generalize the findings to all people.
- Scientists report their findings in respected scientific journals. Their work must survive a screening review by their peers before it is accepted for publication.

With each report from scientists, the field of nutrition changes a little—each finding contributes another piece to the whole body of knowledge. Table C1–2 lists some sources of credible nutrition information.

Nutrition on the Net

Hundreds of millions of websites await users of the Internet. Be forewarned: much of the nutrition "information" found on the Internet is pure fiction, aimed at separating consumers from their money. Sales of unproven and dangerous products over the Internet have reached huge proportions, partly because the Internet is not regulated.

The Internet also offers access to high-quality information, however, so it pays to learn to use it wisely. Table C1–3 provides some clues to these reliable nutrition information websites. One of the most trustworthy sites, used by scientists and others, is the U.S. National Library of Medicine's PubMed website, which provides free access to over 10 million abstracts (short descriptions) of research papers published in scientific journals around the world. Many abstracts provide links to websites from which full articles can be purchased or downloaded for free.

Table C1–2

Credible Sources of Nutrition Information

Professional health organizations, government health agencies, volunteer health agencies, and consumer groups provide consumers with reliable health and nutrition information. Credible sources of nutrition information include the following:

- Professional health organizations, especially Dietitians of Canada (http://www.dietitians.ca), the Nutrition Resource Centre (http://opha.on.ca/nrc), and the Canadian Medical Association (CMA) (http://www.cma.ca)
- Government health agencies such as Health Canada (HC) (http://www.hc-sc.gc.ca), the Public Health Agency of Canada (PHAC) (http://www.phac-aspc.gc.ca), the Canadian Food Inspection Agency (CFIA) (http://www.inspection.gc.ca/eng/1297964599443/1297965645317), the Natural Health Products Directorate (NHPD) (http://www.hc-sc.gc.ca/dhp-mps/prodnatur/index-eng.php), the Office of Nutrition Policy and Promotion (http://www.hc-sc.gc.ca/ahc asc/branch-dirgen/hpfb-dgpsa/onpp-bppn/index-eng.php), and Agriculture and Agri-Food Canada (AAFC) (http://www.agr.gc.ca)
- Canadian Nutrient File, 2010 (http://www.hc-sc.gc.ca/fn-an/nutrition/fiche-nutri-data/index-eng.php)
- Volunteer health agencies such as the Heart and Stroke Foundation of Canada (http://www.heartandstroke.ca), the Canadian Diabetes Association (http://www.diabetes.ca), and the Canadian Cancer Society (http://www.cancer.ca)
- Reputable consumer groups such as the Consumers Council Of Canada—Food Information, Labelling and Advertising Panel (http://www.consumerscouncil.com), the U.S. National Council against Health Fraud (NCAHF) (http://www.ncahf.org), and Quackwatch (http://www.quackwatch.org).

Table C1–3

Is This Site Reliable?

To judge whether an Internet site offers reliable nutrition information, answer the following questions:

- **Who is responsible for the site?** Clues can be found in the three-letter "tag" that follows the dot in the site's name. For example, "gov" and "edu" indicate government and university sites in the United States. In Canada, there is no official tag for Canadian educational institutions, but the federal government uses "gc.ca," and most provincial governments use "gov.{2-letter province abbreviation}.ca," e.g., "gov.on.ca." These are usually reliable sources of information.
- **Do the names and credentials of information providers appear? Is an editorial board identified?** Many legitimate sources provide e-mail addresses or other ways to obtain more information about the site and the information providers behind it.
- **Are links to other reliable information sites provided?** Reputable organizations almost always provide links to other similar sites because they want you to know of other experts in their area of knowledge. Caution is needed when you evaluate a site by its links, however. Anyone, even a quack, can link a Web page to a reputable site without the organization's permission. Doing so may give the quack's site the appearance of legitimacy—just the effect the quack is hoping for.
- **Is the site updated regularly?** Nutrition information changes rapidly, and sites should be updated often.
- **Is the site selling a product or service?** Commercial sites may provide accurate information, but they also may not, and their profit motive increases the risk of bias.
- **Does the site charge a fee to gain access to it?** Many academic and government sites offer the best information, usually for free. Some legitimate sites do charge fees, but before paying up, check the free sites. Chances are good you'll find what you're looking for without paying.

(continued)

Figure C1–2 provides a brief glimpse of this valuable Internet resource.

Hoaxes and scare stories abound on unsound websites and in e-mails. Be suspicious of the content of an Internet source when:

- the contents were written by someone other than the sender or some authority you know.

- something like the phrase, "Forward this to everyone you know" appears anywhere in the piece.

- the piece states something like "This is not a hoax"; chances are the opposite is true.

- the information seems shocking or something that you've never heard from legitimate sources.

- the language is overly emphatic or sprinkled with capitalized words or exclamation marks.

- no references are offered, or, if present, they are of questionable validity.

- the message has been debunked on websites such as http://www.quackwatch.com or http://urbanlegends.about.com.[3]

Of course, these hints alone are insufficient for judging material on the Internet. The user must also scrutinize "nutrition experts" who post materials, even when they possess legitimate degrees, as described next.

Figure C1–2

PubMed: Internet Resource for Scientific Nutrition References

 The U.S. National Library of Medicine's PubMed website (see the screencap below) offers tutorials to help teach the beginner to use the search system effectively. Often, simply visiting the site (www.ncbi.nlm.nih.gov/pubmed), typing a query in the "Search" box, and clicking "GO" will yield satisfactory results. For example, to find research concerning calcium and bone health, typing in "calcium bone" nets almost 3,000 results. To refine the search, try setting limits on dates, types of articles, languages, and other criteria to obtain a more manageable number of abstracts to peruse.

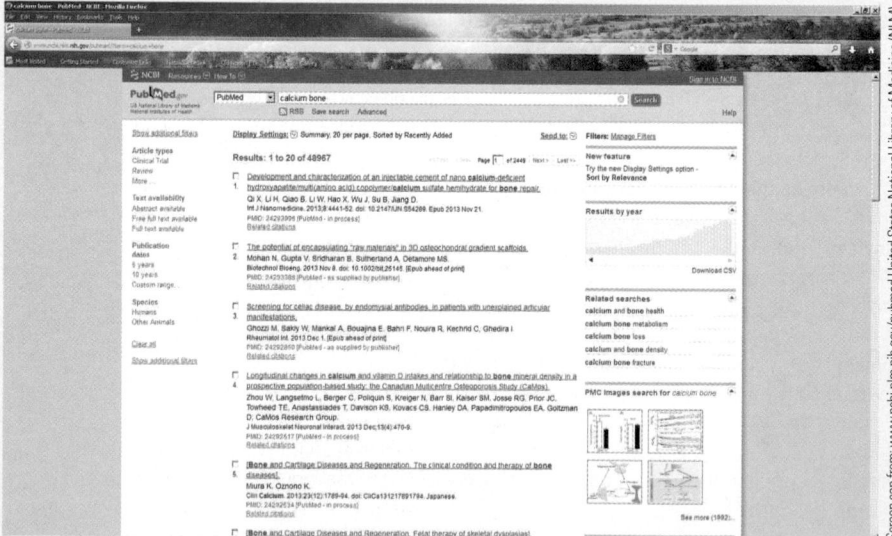

Screen cap from: www.ncbi.nlm.nih.gov/pubmed United States National Library of Medicine (NLM)

Who Are the True Nutrition Experts?

Most people turn to their physicians for dietary advice. Physicians are expected to know all about health-related matters. But only about a quarter of all medical schools in the United States require students to take even one nutrition course, and less than half provide an elective nutrition course.[4] Students attending these classes receive an average of 20 hours of nutrition instruction—an amount most graduates consider inadequate. More than a decade ago, the U.S. Congress passed a law mandating that "students enrolled in United States medical schools and physicians practicing in the United States [must] have access to adequate training in the field of nutrition and its relationship to human health." So far, this goal has not been fully achieved.

Along similar lines, one Canadian study revealed that the nutrition knowledge of Canadian physicians is weak in many important areas.[5]

Enlarging on this idea, **Dietitians of Canada (DC)**, the professional association of dietitians, asserts that nutrition education should be part of the curriculum for health-care professionals. This plan would bring access to reliable nutrition information to more people.

Physicians who specialized in clinical nutrition in medical school are highly qualified to advise on nutrition. Membership in the Canadian Nutrition Society (CNS) (http://www.cns-scn.ca) is another sign of nutrition knowledge. Still, few physicians have the knowledge, time, or experience to develop diet plans and provide detailed diet instruction for clients, and they often refer their clients to nutrition specialists.

Fortunately, the credential that indicates a qualified nutrition expert is easy to spot—you can confidently call on a **registered dietitian (RD)**. Meeting national and provincial established criteria certifies that an expert is the genuine article. See Table C1–4.

Dietitians' Credentials in Canada

Dietitians of Canada (DC) accredits university undergraduate programs and dietetic internship programs that qualify dietitians to practise. There is no single designation of title or initials for Canadian dietitians. Provincial government legislation determines the professional designation for health professionals who practise in the province.

Provincial Regulatory Bodies

Provincial regulatory bodies (i.e., colleges or **registration boards**):

- monitor the competence of members, for example, mandatory continuing education.
- protect the public from unsafe or unethical dietetic practice.
- protect the use of regulated title designation and initials, for example, RD.
- review the professional conduct of members based on complaints and discipline members where appropriate. See Table C1–5 (page 26).

Dietitians are easy to find in most communities because they perform a multitude of duties in a variety of settings. To find an RD in your area, go to http://www.dietitians.ca/Find-a-Dietitian .aspx. They work in foodservice operations, pharmaceutical companies, sports nutrition programs, corporate wellness programs, the food industry, home health agencies, long-term care institutions, private practice, community and public health settings, research centres, universities and other educational settings, hospitals, Family Health Networks (FHN), and other health-care facilities.

Public health nutritionists play key roles in delivering nutrition services to people in the community. A public health **nutritionist** may plan, coordinate, administer, and evaluate food assistance programs; inform or act as a consultant to other agencies; manage finances; set policies; and much more.

In some facilities, a **dietetic technician** assists RDs in both administrative and clinical responsibilities. A dietetic technician has been educated and trained to work under the guidance of an RD. See Table C1–6 (page 26).

Note: According to a recent national telephone Omnibus survey conducted for DC in April 2005, "… 92% of responding Canadians rated dietitians as the source of nutrition advice they trust the most"; see "Canadians trust the nutrition advice of dietitians" at https://ww2.dietitians.ca/news/media. asp?pg=24.

Dietitians in hospitals have many subspecialties. Administrative dietitians manage the foodservice system, clinical dietitians provide client care (see Table C1–7, page 27), and nutrition support team dietitians coordinate nutrition care with the efforts of other health-care professionals. In the food industry, dietitians conduct research, develop products, and market services.

Detecting Fake Credentials

In contrast to RDs, thousands of people possess fake nutrition degrees and claim to be nutrition counsellors, nutrition consultants, nutritionists, or "dietists." These and other such titles may sound meaningful, but most of these people lack the established credentials of the DC-sanctioned dietitian. If you look closely, you can see signs that their expertise is fake.

Take, for example, a nutrition expert's educational background. The minimum standards of education for a dietitian specify a bachelor of science (BSc) degree in food science and human nutrition (or related fields) from an **accredited** university (Table C1–8, page 27, defines this and two other terms). Such a degree generally requires four to five years of study. In contrast, a fake nutrition expert may display a degree from

---

Credentials of Canadian Dietitians

Alberta & the Territories	R.D. (registered dietitian/nutritionist)
British Columbia	R.D.N. (registered dietitian nutritionist)
Manitoba	R.D. (registered dietitian)
New Brunswick	P.Dt. (professional dietitian)
Newfoundland & Labrador	R.Dt. (registered dietitian)
Nova Scotia	P.Dt. (professional dietitian)
Ontario	R.D. (registered dietitian)/Dt.P. (diététiste professionnelle)
Prince Edward Island	P.Dt. (professional dietitian)
Québec	Dt.P. (diététiste professionnelle)
Saskatchewan	P.Dt. (professional dietitian)

Contacting Provincial Regulatory Bodies

The following lists the provincial regulatory bodies and their contact information in 2013. For the most current contact information, check the Dietitians of Canada website, http://www.dietitians.ca/Career/Registration-to-Practice.aspx

College of Dietitians of Alberta
#540, 10707-100 Avenue
Edmonton, AB T5J 3M1
780-448-0059; fax: 780-489-7759
cda@collegeofdietitians.ab.ca
http://collegeofdietitians.ab.ca

College of Dietitians of British Columbia
Suite 103, 1765 West 8th Avenue
Vancouver, BC V6J 5C6
604-736-2016 or toll-free within BC at
1-877-736-2016;
fax: 604-736-2018
info@collegeofdietitiansbc.org
http://www.collegeofdietitiansbc.org

College of Dietitians of Manitoba
36-1313 Border Street
Winnipeg, MB R3H 0X4
204-694-0532; fax: 204-889-1755
office.cdm@mts.net
http://manitobadietitians.ca/home.aspx

New Brunswick Association of Dietitians
P.O. Box 22024, Landsdowne Postal Outlet
Saint John, NB E2K 4T7
506-324-9396 (voice mail); fax: 506-328-2686
registrar@adnb-nbad.com
http://www.adnb-nbad.com

Newfoundland and Labrador College of Dietitians
P.O. Box 1756, Postal Station C
St. John's, NL A1C 5P5
709-753-4040 or toll free at 1-877-753-4040
http://www.nlcd.ca/default.php

Nova Scotia Dietetic Association
212-1496 Bedford Highway
Bedford, NS B4A 1E5
902-835-0253; fax: 902-835-0523
info@nsdassoc.ca
http://www.nsdassoc.ca

College of Dietitians of Ontario
438 University Avenue, Suite 1810, Box 40
Toronto, ON M5G 2K8
416-598-1725; fax: 416-598-0274
information@cdo.on.ca
http://www.cdo.on.ca

PEI Dietitians Registration Board
45 Loridale Drive
Charlottetown, PE C1E 1P2
902-569-5184; fax: 902-963-2933
info@peidietitians.ca
http://www.peidietitians.ca

Ordre professionnel des diététistes du Québec
1425 Boulevard René Levesque, ouest, Bureau 703
Montréal, QC H3G 1T7
514-393-3733; fax: 514-393-3582
opdq@opdq.org
http://www.opdq.org

Saskatchewan Dietitians Association
Box 3894
Regina, SK S4P 2R8
Phone and fax: 306-359-3040
registrar@saskdietitians.org
http://www.saskdietitians.org

Terms Associated with Nutrition Advice

- **dietetic technician** a person who has completed a two-year academic degree from an accredited college or university and an approved dietetic technician program.
- **dietitian** a person trained in nutrition, food science, and diet planning. See also *registered dietitian*.
- **Dietitians of Canada (DC)** the professional organization of dietitians in Canada.
- **medical nutrition therapy** nutrition services used in the treatment of injury, illness, or other conditions; includes assessment of nutrition status and dietary intake and corrective applications of diet, counselling, and other nutrition services.
- **nutritionist** someone who engages in the study of nutrition. Some nutritionists are registered dietitians, whereas others are self-described experts whose training is questionable and who are not qualified to give advice.

In U.S. states with responsible legislation, the term applies only to people who have a master of science (M.S.) or a doctor of philosophy (Ph.D.) degree from a properly accredited institution
- **public health nutritionist** a dietitian or other person with an advanced degree in nutrition who specializes in public health nutrition.
- **registered dietitian (R.D.)** a dietitian who has graduated from a university or college after completing a program of dietetics. The program must be approved or accredited by Dietitians of Canada. The dietitian must serve in an approved internship, coordinated program, or preprofessional practice program to practise the necessary skills.
- **registration** listing with a professional organization that requires specific course work, experience, and passing of an examination.

Table C1-7

Responsibilities of a Clinical Dietitian

The first six items on this list play essential roles in **medical nutrition therapy** as part of a medical treatment plan.

- Assesses clients' nutrition status
- Determines clients' nutrient requirements
- Monitors clients' nutrient intakes
- Develops, implements, and evaluates clients' medical nutrition therapy
- Counsels clients to cope with unique diet plans
- Teaches clients and their families about nutrition and diet plans
- Provides training for other dietitians, nurses, interns, and dietetics students
- Serves as a liaison between clients and the foodservice department
- Communicates with physicians, nurses, pharmacists, and other health-care professionals about clients' progress, needs, and treatments
- Participates in professional activities to enhance knowledge and skill

a six-month correspondence course; such a degree is simply not the same. In some cases, schools posing as legitimate **correspondence schools** offer even less. They are actually **diploma mills**—fraudulent businesses that sell certificates of competency to anyone who pays the fees, from under a thousand dollars for a bachelor's degree to several thousand for a doctorate. Buyers ordering multiple degrees are given discounts. To obtain these "degrees," a candidate need not read any books or pass any examinations.

Table C1-8

Terms Describing Institutions of Higher Learning, Legitimate and Fraudulent

- **accredited** approved; in the case of universities, certified by an agency such as provincial ministries of education or Dietitians of Canada.
- **correspondence school** a school that gives home study/career course instruction by mail, sending lessons and exams to the student's home.
- **diploma mill** an organization that awards meaningless degrees without requiring its students to meet educational standards.

A lack of proper accreditation is the identifying sign of a fake educational institution. To guard educational quality, an accrediting agency recognized by the provincial ministries of education certifies that certain schools meet the criteria defining a complete and accurate schooling, but in the case of nutrition, quack accrediting agencies cloud the picture. Fake nutrition degrees are available from schools "accredited" by more than 30 phoney accrediting agencies.*

To dramatize the case with which anyone can obtain a fake nutrition degree, one writer enrolled for $82 in a nutrition diploma mill that billed itself as a

*To find out whether a university program is properly accredited for a dietetics degree, contact Dietitians of Canada at 480 University Avenue, Suite 604, Toronto, ON M5G 1V2, call 416-596-0857, or visit its website at http://www.dietitians.ca.

To find out whether a particular university program even exists, contact your provincial Ministry of Training, Colleges, and Universities (e.g., http://www.edu.gov.on.Ca/eng/tcu).

correspondence school. She made every attempt to fail, intentionally answering all of the examination questions incorrectly. Even so, she received a "nutritionist" certificate at the end of the course, together with a letter from the "school" officials explaining that they were sure she must have misread the test. In Canada, a university degree is almost invariably legitimate. However, some private home study certificate programs are of very dubious value. Anyone with a certificate from such a program is unlikely to be properly qualified to dispense reliable nutrition advice.

In a similar stunt, Ms. Sassafras Herbert was named a "professional member" of a nutrition association. For her efforts, Sassafras received a wallet card and is listed in a fake "Who's Who in Nutrition" that is distributed at health fairs and trade shows nationwide. Sassafras is a poodle.

Summary

In summary, to stay one step ahead of the nutrition quacks, check a provider's qualifications. First look for the degrees and credentials listed after the person's name (such as M.D., R.D., M.Sc., or Ph. D.). Next find out what you can about the reputations of the institutions that awarded the degrees. Call your provincial dietetics college and ask if dietitians are licensed in your province. If they are, find out whether the person giving you dietary advice has a licence—and if not, find someone better qualified. Your health is your most precious asset, and protecting it is well worth the time and effort it takes to do so.

Self-Check

Answers to these Self-Check questions are in Appendix D.

1. Energy-yielding nutrients include all of the following *except*
   a. vitamins
   b. carbohydrates
   c. fat
   d. protein

2. Organic nutrients include all of the following *except*
   a. minerals
   b. fat
   c. carbohydrates
   d. protein

3. One of the characteristics of a nutritious diet is that the diet provides no constituent in excess. This principle of diet planning is called
   a. adequacy
   b. balance
   c. moderation
   d. variety

4. A slice of peach pie supplies 357 Calories with 48 units of vitamin A; one large peach provides 42 Calories and 53 units of vitamin A. This is an example of
   a. Calorie control
   b. nutrient density
   c. variety
   d. essential nutrients

5. Which of the following adjustments in one's diet would agree with Canada's Food Guide?
   a. eating baked potatoes rather than French fries
   b. eating fruits rather than cakes and pies
   c. drinking lower-fat milk rather than whole milk
   d. all of the above

6. Studies of populations in which observation is accompanied by experimental manipulation of some population members are referred to as
   a. case studies
   b. intervention studies
   c. laboratory studies
   d. epidemiological studies

7. Both heart disease and cancer are due to genetic causes, and diet cannot influence whether they occur.
   T   F

8. Both carbohydrates and protein have 4 Calories per gram.
   T   F

9. If a food is labelled "natural," you can be confident that it is more nutritious than a product not carrying that label.
   T   F

10. The recent goal of the ministers responsible for physical activity, recreation, and sport was to reduce physical inactivity among Canadians by 10 percent by the year 2010.
    T   F

Concepts in Action

start now! ····▸ Ready to make a change? Go to Diet Analysis Plus online and track your physical activities—all of them—for three days. After you have recorded your activities, see how much time you spent exercising at a moderate to vigorous level. Could you increase your level and amount of activity?

Track Your Diet

Exercises like this one provide an ongoing diet analysis activity that asks you to apply what you've learned in the chapter to your own diet. To do so, use the Diet Analysis Plus (DA+) program that accompanies this book. Do the following:

1. From the Home page of the DA+ program (after entering your personal data); select the Reports tab from the red navigation bar, and then select Profile DRI Goals. Click Create PDF button. You will now have a list of the appropriate DRI values for Calories, carbohydrates, and fat for your Profile.

2. For the next three days, with pencil and paper, keep track of everything you eat and drink. Be honest and careful in your record-keeping. Measure or estimate amounts of foods and beverages (including water) that you consume, as well as margarine or butter, salt, cream sauces, gravies, pasta sauce, ketchup, relish, jams, jellies, and other add-ons. Even a slice of tomato and a lettuce leaf on a sandwich count toward the day's intake. Distribute your data among five meals for each day: breakfast, lunch, dinner, and a mid-afternoon and an evening snack.

3. Keep track of your physical activity for all three of those days. Record all of the minutes spent walking or biking, working out, doing housework, washing cars, playing sports, dancing with friends, or any other nonsedentary behaviour. Hold onto this data: you'll need it in chapters to come.

4. From the Home page of DA+ select the Track Diet tab and enter each food item you recorded for Day One, Day Two, and Day Three into the Find Foods area. When finished, select the Reports tab and go to Intake vs. Goals. Click the Generate Report button, and choose all meals. What information in the report most surprised you?

5. From the Reports tab, go to Energy Balance. Using Day Two (from the three-day diet intake) choose all meals and generate a report. Was your Calorie intake more or less than the recommended Calories (kcal) for your profile? Was it higher or lower than you expected? You will analyze your energy balance in more detail later.

Endnotes

*For the full citation of a reference that is repeated in any given section of a chapter, a note is provided in square brackets that refers the reader to the full citation, for example, [see reference 11].

1. M. J. Stampfer and coauthors, Primary prevention of coronary heart disease in women through diet and lifestyle, *New England Journal of Medicine* 343 (2000): 16–22; A. K. Kant and coauthors, A prospective study of diet quality and mortality in women, *Journal of the American Medical Association* 283 (2000): 2109–2115.

2. M. Merti, Bridging genomics and genetics, *BioMedNet Conference Reporter*, American Society of Human Genetics 2000, available at http://news.bmn.com/conferences.

3. D. Shattuck, Nutritional genomics, *Journal of the American Dietetic Association* 103 (2003): 16, 18; P. Trayhurn, Nutritional genomics—"Nutrigenomics," *British Journal of Nutrition* 89 (2003): 1–2; F. P. Guengerich, Functional genomics and proteomics applied to the study of nutritional metabolism, *Nutrition Reviews* 59 (1999): 259–263.

4. B. van Ommen and R. Stierum, Nutrigenomics: Exploiting systems biology in the nutrition and health arena, *Current Opinion in Biotechnology* 13 (2002): 517–521.

5. N. Fogg-Johnson and J. Kaput, Nutrigenomics: An emerging scientific discipline, *Food Technology* 57 (2003): 60–67.

6. FDA Public Health Advisory, Reports of blue discoloration and death in patients receiving enteral feedings tinted with the dye, FD&C Blue No. 1, September 29, 2003, available at http://www.fda.gov/ForIndustry/ColorAdditives/ColorAdditivesinSpecificProducts/InMedicalDevices/ucm142395.htm.

7. Position of the American Dietetic Association: Food fortification and dietary supplements, *Journal of the American Dietetic Association* 101 (2001): 115–125.

8. C. D. Johnson and coauthors, Route of nutrition influences generation of antibody-forming cells and initial defense to an active viral infection in the upper respiratory tract, *Annals of Surgery* 237 (2003): 565–573; W. L. Biffl, E. E. Moore, and J. B. Haenel, Nutrition support of the trauma patient, *Nutrition* 18 (2002): 960–965.

9. F. B. Hu, Dietary pattern analysis: A new direction in nutritional epidemiology, *Current Opinion in Lipidology* 13 (2002): 3–9.

10. Standing Committee on the Scientific Evaluation of Dietary Reference Intakes, Food and Nutrition Board, Institute of Medicine, *Dietary Reference Intakes for Energy, Carbohydrate, Fiber, Fat, Fatty Acids, Cholesterol, Protein, and Amino Acids* (Washington, D.C.: National Academies Press, 2002), pp. 11-1–11-88.

11. J. A. Foote and coauthors, Dietary variety increases the probability of nutrient adequacy among adults, *Journal of Nutrition* 134 (2004): 1779–1785.

12. U.S. Department of Agriculture and U.S. Department of Health and Human Services, *Dietary Guidelines for Americans, 2010.* 7th Edition (Washington, DC: U.S. Government Printing Office), January 2011, http://www.ncbi.nlm.nih.gov/pmc/articles/PMC3090168.

13. J. E. Tillotson, Our ready-prepared, ready-to-eat nation, *Nutrition Today* 37: 36–38; F. Katz, "How nutritious?" meets "How convenient?" *Food Technology* 53 (1999): 44–50.

14. A. E. Sloan, What, when, and where Americans eat: 2003, *Food Technology* 57 (2003): 48–66.

15. L. L. Birch, Development of food preferences, *Annual Review of Nutrition* 19 (1999): 41–62; M. B. M. van den Bree, L. J. Eaves, and J. T. Dwyer, Genetic and environmental influences on eating patterns of twins aged > 50 y, *American Journal of Clinical Nutrition* 70 (1999): 456–465.

16. N. S. Wellman and coauthors, Do we facilitate the scientific process and the development of dietary guidance when findings from single studies are publicized? An American Society for Nutritional Sciences Controversy Session Report, *American Journal of Clinical Nutrition* 70 (1999): 802–805.

Consumer Corner 1

1. E. M. Hackman and G. L. Moe, Evaluation of newspaper reports of nutrition-related research, *Journal of the American Dietetic Association* 99 (1999): 1564–1566.

Controversy 1

1. Position of the American Dietetic Association: Food and nutrition misinformation, *Journal of the American Dietetic Association* 102 (2002): 260–266.

2. N. J. Temple and D. H. Morris, Marketing dietary supplements for health profit, in N. J. Temple, T. Wilson, and D. R. Jacobs, Jr. eds., *Nutritional Health: Strategies for Disease Prevention,* 2nd ed. (Totowa, NJ: Humana Press, 2006), pp. 299–312; Quackery-related definitions are available from the National Council Against Health Fraud, at http://www.ncahf.org/pp/definitions.html.

3. E. Cunningham and W. Marcason, Internet hoaxes: How to spot them and how to debunk them, *Journal of the American Dietetic Association* 101 (2001): 460.

4. J. A. Schulman, Nutrition education in medical schools: Trends and implications for health educators, *Med Ed Online,* http://med-ed-online.net/index.php/meo/article/view/4307.

5. N. J. Temple, Survey of nutrition knowledge of Canadian physicians, *Journal of the American College of Nutrition* 18 (1999): 26–29.

Health Canada Santé Canada

Your health and safety... our priority.   Votre santé et votre sécurité... notre priorité.

2 Nutrition Tools— Standards and Guidelines

Eating Well with Canada's Food Guide

Do You Ever . . .

Wonder how scientists decide how much of each nutrient you need to consume each day?

Dismiss government dietary recommendations as too simplistic to help you plan your diet?

Consume the portions offered in restaurants and fast-food places, believing that food professionals must offer recommended amounts?

Wish that your foods could provide a boost to health from substances beyond the nutrients they provide?

Keep Reading . . .

Learning Objectives

After completing this chapter, you should be able to

LO 2.1 Explain how RDI, AI, DV, and EAR serve different functions in describing nutrient values, and discuss how each is used.

LO 2.2 Describe how foods are grouped in Canada's Food Guide and the USDA's MyPlate.

LO 2.3 Describe the concepts of nutrient density and discretionary Calorie allowance, and identify how each may be used in diet planning.

LO 2.4 Define the term *functional foods*, and discuss some potential effects of such foods on human health.

Contents

Eating well is easy in theory—just choose a selection of foods that supply appropriate amounts of the essential nutrients, fibre, phytochemicals, and energy without excess intakes of fat, sugar, and salt, and be sure to get enough exercise to balance the foods you eat. In practice, eating well proves harder than it appears. Many people are overweight, or undernourished, or suffer from nutrient excesses or deficiencies that impair their health; that is, they are malnourished. You may not think that this statement applies to you, but you may already have less-than-optimal nutrient intakes and activity without knowing it. Accumulated over years, the effects of your habits can seriously impair the quality of your life.

Putting it positively, you can enjoy the best possible vim, vigour, and vitality throughout your life if you learn now to nourish yourself optimally. To learn how, you first need answers to several basic questions. How much energy and how much of each nutrient do you need? How much physical activity do you need to balance the energy you take in from foods? Which types of foods supply which nutrients? How much of each type of food do you have to eat to get enough? And how can you eat all of these foods without gaining weight? This chapter begins by identifying some ideals for nutrient intakes and ends by showing how to achieve them.

Nutrient Recommendations

Nutrient recommendations are sets of yardsticks used as standards for measuring healthy people's energy and nutrient intakes. Nutrition experts use the recommendations to assess intakes and to offer advice on amounts to consume. Individuals may use them to decide how much of a nutrient they need to consume and how much is too much.

The nutrition recommendations for total energy, macronutrients, vitamins, minerals, and water in use in Canada and the United States are derived from the **Dietary Reference Intakes (DRI)**. A committee of nutrition experts from Canada and the United States develops and publishes the DRI.* The DRI committee has set values for the vitamins and minerals, as well as for carbohydrates, fibre, lipids, proteins, water, and energy. Values for other food constituents that may play roles in health maintenance are forthcoming.

*This is a committee of the U.S. Food and Nutrition Board, Institute of Medicine of the U.S. National Academy of Sciences, working in association with Canadian scientists.

Dietary Reference Intakes (DRI) reports containing a set of five lists of values for measuring the nutrient intakes of healthy people in Canada and the United States. The five lists are estimated average requirements (EAR), recommended dietary allowances (RDA), adequate intakes (AI), tolerable upper intake levels (UL), and acceptable macronutrient distribution ranges (AMDR). Descriptions of the DRI values are found in Table 2–1.

A Directory of Recommendations
- DRI lists—inside front cover, pages A, B, and C
- Daily Values—page Y

Another set of nutrient standards is practical for the person striving to make wise choices among packaged foods. These are the **Daily Values**, familiar to anyone who has read a food label. (Read about the Daily Values and other nutrient standards in Table 2–1.) Nutrient standards—the DRI and Daily Values—are used and referred to so often that they are printed on the inside front cover of this book.

KEY POINT

- The DRI reports contain nutrient intake standards set for people living in Canada and the United States. The Daily Values are Canadian and U.S. standards used on food labels.

Goals of the DRI Committee

For each nutrient, the DRI establish a number of values, each serving a different purpose. Most people need to focus on only two kinds of DRI values: those that set nutrient intake goals for individuals (RDA and AI, described next) and those that define a tolerable upper intake level of safety for nutrient intakes (UL, addressed later). The following sections address the different DRI values, arranged by the goals of the DRI committee.

Goal 1. Setting Recommended Intake Values—RDA and AI One of the great advantages of the DRI recommended intakes lies in their applicability to the diets of individuals.[1] The committee offers two sets of values specifying intake goals for individuals: **recommended dietary allowances (RDA)** and **adequate intakes (AI)**.

Table 2–1

Nutrient Standards

Standards from the DRI Committee

dietary reference intakes (DRI) a set of five lists of nutrient intake values for healthy people in Canada and the United States. These values are used for planning and assessing diets:

1. **recommended dietary allowances (RDA)** nutrient intake goals for individuals; the average daily nutrient intake level that meets the needs of nearly all (97 to 98%) healthy people in a particular life stage and gender group.[a] Derived from the estimated average requirements (EAR; see below).

2. **adequate intakes (AI)** nutrient intake goals for individuals; the recommended average daily nutrient intake level based on intakes of healthy people (observed or experimentally derived) in a particular life stage and gender group and assumed to be adequate.[a] Set whenever scientific data are insufficient to allow establishment of an RDA value.

3. **tolerable upper intake levels (UL)** the highest average daily nutrient intake level that is likely to pose no risk of toxicity to almost all healthy individuals of a particular life stage and gender group. Usual intake above this level may place an individual at risk of illness from nutrient toxicity.

4. **estimated average requirements (EAR)** the average daily nutrient intake estimated to meet the requirement of half of the healthy individuals in a particular life stage and gender group; used in nutrition research and policymaking and the basis upon which RDA values are set.

5. **acceptable macronutrient distribution ranges (AMDR)** values for carbohydrate, fat, and protein expressed as percentages of total daily caloric intake; ranges of intakes set for the energy-yielding nutrients that are sufficient to provide adequate total energy and nutrients while reducing the risk of chronic diseases.

Daily Values

Daily Values (DV) nutrient standards used on food labels, in grocery stores (and on some restaurant menus and websites in Canada and the United States). The DV allow comparisons among foods with regard to their nutrient contents.

[a]For simplicity, this book combines the two sets of nutrient goals for individuals (AI and RDA) and refers to them as the DRI recommended intakes. The AI values are not the scientific equivalent of the RDA, however.

Daily Values nutrient standards that are printed on food labels. Based on nutrient and energy recommendations for a general 2,000-Calorie diet, they allow consumers to compare the nutrient and energy contents of packaged foods.

The RDA are the indisputable bedrock of the DRI recommended intakes because they are based on solid experimental evidence and reliable observations. The AI values are also as scientifically based as possible, but setting them requires some educated guesswork. The committee establishes an AI value whenever scientific evidence is insufficient to generate an RDA. Although not scientifically equivalent, both the RDA and AI values are intended to be used as nutrient goals in planning nutritious diets for individuals, so, for the consumer, there is no practical need to distinguish between them. This book refers to the RDA and AI values collectively as the DRI recommended intakes.

Goal 2. Facilitating Nutrition Research and Policy—EAR

Another set of values established by the DRI committee, the **estimated average requirements (EAR)**, establishes nutrient requirements for given life stages and gender groups that researchers and nutrition policymakers use in their work. Public health officials may also use them to assess nutrient intakes of populations and make recommendations. The EAR values form the scientific basis upon which the RDA values are set (a later section explains how).

Goal 3. Establishing Safety Guidelines—UL

Beyond a certain point, it is unwise to consume large amounts of any nutrient, so the DRI committee sets the **tolerable upper intake levels (UL)** to identify potentially hazardous levels of nutrient intake (see Table 2–1). The UL are indispensable to consumers who take supplements or consume foods and beverages to which vitamins or minerals have been added—a group that includes almost everyone. Public health officials also rely on UL values to set safe upper limits for nutrients added to our food and water supplies.

Nutrient needs fall within a range, and a danger zone exists both below and above that range. Figure 2–1 illustrates this point. People's tolerances for high doses of nutrients vary, so caution is in order when nutrient intakes approach the UL values.

Some nutrients do not have UL values. The absence of a UL for a nutrient does not imply that it is safe to consume it in any amount, however. It means only that insufficient data exist to establish a value.

Goal 4. Preventing Chronic Diseases

The DRI committee also takes into account chronic disease prevention wherever appropriate. In the last decade, abundant new research has linked nutrients in the diet with the promotion of health and the prevention of chronic diseases, and the DRI committee uses this research to set intake recommendations. For example, the committee set lifelong intake goals for the mineral calcium at the levels believed to lessen the likelihood of osteoporosis-related fractures in the later years.

The DRI committee also set healthy ranges of intake for carbohydrate, fat, and protein known as **acceptable macronutrient distribution ranges (AMDR)**. Each of these three energy-yielding nutrients contributes to the day's total Calorie intake, and their contributions can be expressed as a percentage of the total. According to the committee, a diet that provides adequate energy nutrients for healthy individuals in the following proportions can provide adequate nutrients while reducing the risk of chronic diseases:

- 45 to 65 percent from carbohydrate
- 20 to 35 percent from fat
- 10 to 35 percent from protein

Tolerable upper intake levels (UL) are listed on page C at the front of the book.

All in all, the DRI values are designed to meet the diverse needs of individuals, the scientific and medical communities, and others. Table 2–1 sums up the names and purposes of the nutrient intake standards just introduced. A later section comes back to the Daily Values, also listed in the table.

Figure 2–1

The Naive View versus the Accurate View of Optimal Nutrient Intakes

Consuming too much of a nutrient endangers health, just as consuming too little does. The DRI recommended intake values fall within a safety range, with the UL marking the tolerable upper levels.

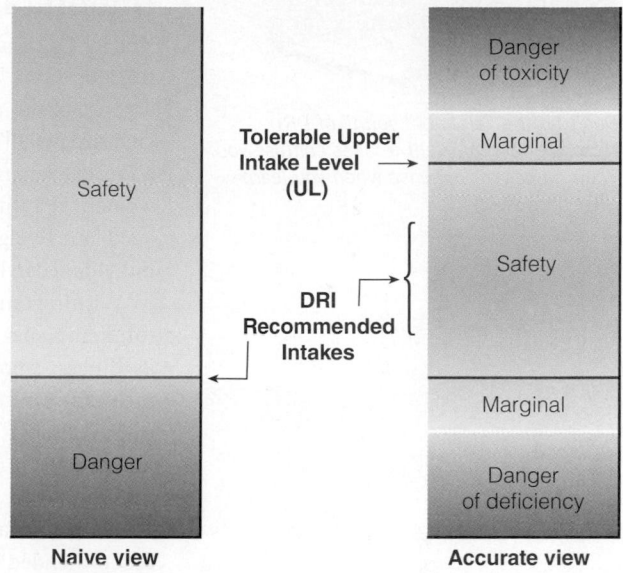

Naive view **Accurate view**

● The DRI table on the inside front cover distinguishes the RDA and AI values, but both kinds of values are intended as nutrient intake goals for individuals.

Don't let the "alphabet soup" of DRI recommended nutrient intakes confuse you. Their names make sense when you learn their purposes.

© John A. Rizzo/Photodisc/Getty Images

- Collectively, the DRI reports provide recommended nutrient intake goals for individuals, provide a set of standards for researchers and makers of public policy, establish tolerable upper intake levels (UL) for nutrients that can be toxic in excess, and take into account evidence from research on disease prevention. The DRI are composed of the RDA, AI, UL, and EAR lists of values, along with the AMDR ranges for energy-yielding nutrients.

Understanding the DRI Recommendations

Nutrient recommendations have been much misunderstood. One young woman posed this question: "Do you mean that some bureaucrat says that I need exactly the same amount of vitamin D as every other young woman in my group? Do they really think that 'one size fits all'?" The DRI committee acknowledges differences between individuals. It has made separate recommendations for specific sets of people—men, women, pregnant women, lactating women, infants, and children—and for specific age ranges. Children aged four to eight years, for example, have their own DRI recommended intakes. Each individual can look up the recommendations for his or her own age and gender group.

Within your own age and gender group, the committee advises adjusting nutrient intakes in special circumstances that may increase or decrease nutrient needs, such as illness, smoking, or vegetarianism. Later chapters provide details about which nutrients may need adjustment.

For almost all healthy people, a diet that consistently provides the RDA or AI amount for a nutrient is very likely to be adequate in that nutrient.[2] On average, you should try to get 100 percent of the DRI recommended intake for every nutrient to ensure an adequate intake over time. The following facts will help put the DRI recommended intakes into perspective:

- The values are based on available scientific research to the greatest extent possible and are updated periodically in light of new knowledge.

- The values are based on the concepts of probability and risk. The DRI recommended intakes are associated with a low probability of deficiency for people of a life stage and gender group, and they pose almost no risk of toxicity for that group.

- The values are recommendations for a level of intake shown to help prevent the development of chronic diseases, not minimum requirements. They include a generous margin of safety and meet the needs of virtually all healthy people in a specific age and gender group.

- The values are set in reference to specific indicators of nutrient adequacy, such as blood nutrient concentrations, normal growth, and reduction of certain chronic diseases or other disorders when appropriate rather than prevention of deficiency symptoms alone.

- The values reflect daily intakes to be achieved, on average, over time. They assume that intakes will vary from day to day, and they are set high enough to ensure that body nutrient stores will meet nutrient needs during periods of inadequate intakes lasting a day or two for some nutrients and up to a month or two for others.

- The recommendations apply to healthy persons only.

The DRI are designed for health maintenance and disease prevention in healthy people, not for the restoration of health or repletion of nutrients in those with deficiencies. Note: An Institute of Medicine (IOM) committee recently released a systematic evidence-based review of the effects of both vitamin D and calcium on bone health (http://www.iom.edu/Reports/2010/Dietary-Reference-Intakes-for-calcium-and-vitamin-D.aspx). The review also considered the role of vitamin D in relation to risk reduction of diseases, such as osteoporosis, cancer, and other chronic diseases. Under the stress of serious illness or malnutrition, a person may require a much higher intake of certain nutrients or may not be able to handle even the DRI amount. Therapeutic diets take into account the increased nutrient needs imposed by certain medical conditions, such as recovery from surgery, burns, fractures, illnesses, malnutrition, or addictions.

Chapter 2 Nutrition Tools—Standards and Guidelines

- The DRI recommended intakes represent up-to-date, safe levels of intake for healthy people in Canada and the United States.

How the Committee Establishes DRI Values—An RDA Example

A theoretical discussion will help explain how the DRI committee goes about its work of setting the DRI recommended intakes. Suppose we are the DRI committee members with the task of setting an RDA for nutrient X (an essential nutrient).* Ideally, our first step will be to find out how much of that nutrient various healthy individuals need. To do so, we review studies of deficiency states, nutrient stores and their depletion, and the factors influencing them. We then select the most valid data for use in our work. Of the DRI family of nutrient standards, the setting of an RDA value demands the most rigorous science and tolerates the least guesswork.

One experiment we would review or conduct is a **balance study**. In this type of study, scientists measure the body's intake and excretion of a nutrient to find out how much intake is required to balance excretion. For each individual subject, we can determine a **requirement** to achieve balance for nutrient X. With an intake below the requirement, a person will slip into negative balance or experience declining stores that could, over time, lead to deficiency of the nutrient.

We find that different individuals, even of the same age and gender, have different requirements. Mr. A needs 40 units of the nutrient each day to maintain balance, Mr. B needs 35, and Mr. C 57. If we look at enough individuals, we find that their requirements are normally distributed as shown in Figure 2–2—with most requirements near the midpoint (here 45) and only a few at the extremes (Actually, the data for most nutrients indicate a distribution that is much less symmetrical.)

To set the value, we have to decide what intake to recommend for everybody. Should we set it at the mean (45 units in Figure 2–2)? This is the estimated average requirement (EAR) for nutrient X, mentioned earlier as valuable to scientists but not appropriate as an individual's nutrient goal. The EAR value is probably close to everyone's minimum need, assuming the distribution shown in Figure 2–2. But if people took us literally and consumed exactly this amount of nutrient X each day, half the population would begin to develop internal deficiencies and possibly even observable symptoms of deficiency diseases. Mr. C (at 57) would be one of those people.

Perhaps we should set the recommendation for nutrient X at or above the extreme, say, at 70 units a day, so that everyone will be covered. (Actually, we didn't study everyone, and some individual we didn't happen to test might have an even higher requirement.) This might be a good idea in theory, but what about a person like Mr. B, who requires only 35 units a day? The recommendation would be twice his requirement, and to follow it, he might spend money needlessly on foods containing nutrient X to the exclusion of foods containing other nutrients he needs.

The decision we finally make is to set the value high enough so that 97 to 98 percent of the population will be covered but not so high as to be excessive (the graph of Figure 2–3 illustrates such a value). In this example, a reasonable choice might be 63 units a day. Moving the DRI farther toward the extreme would pick up a few additional people, but it would inflate the recommendation for most people, including Mr. A and Mr. B. The committee makes judgments of this kind when setting the DRI recommended intakes for many nutrients. Relatively few healthy people have requirements that are not covered by the DRI recommended intakes.

- The DRI recommended intakes are based on scientific data and are designed to cover the needs of virtually all healthy people in Canada and the United States.

---

*This discussion describes how an RDA value is set; to set an AI value, the committee uses some educated guesswork as well as scientific research results to determine an approximate amount of the nutrient most likely to support health.

Figure 2–2

Individuality of Nutrient Requirements

Each square represents a person. A, B, and C are Mr. A, Mr. B, and Mr. C. Each has a different requirement.

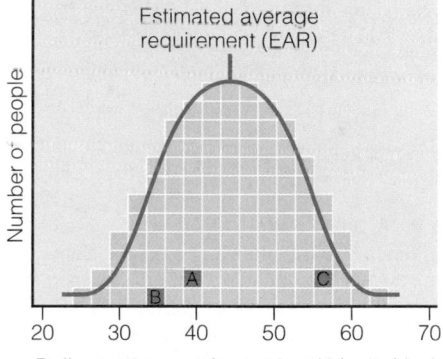

balance study a laboratory study in which a person is fed a controlled diet and the intake and excretion of a nutrient are measured. Balance studies are valid only for nutrients like calcium (chemical elements) that do not change while they are in the body.

requirement the amount of a nutrient that will just prevent the development of specific deficiency signs; distinguished from the DRI recommended intake value, which is a generous allowance with a margin of safety.

Figure 2–3

Nutrient Recommended Intake: RDA Example

Intake recommendations for most vitamins and minerals are set so that they will meet the requirements of nearly all people (boxes represent people).

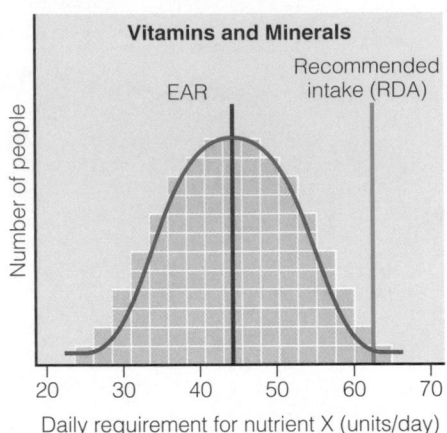

Vitamins and Minerals

EAR

Recommended intake (RDA)

Number of people

20   30   40   50   60   70

Daily requirement for nutrient X (units/day)

● A cup (250 mL) of 2% milk contains about 300 milligrams of calcium. Compared to the Canadian Reference Standard for the Daily Value for calcium of 1,100 milligrams, the %DV for calcium in 1 cup of 2% milk is 300/1100 × 100 = 27% (i.e., 27%DV).

● Appendix G (Nutrition Resources, available on the book's website) provides weblinks for the World Health Organization (WHO), the Food and Agriculture Organization (FAO), and other agencies that give nutrient recommendations for the world's people.

estimated energy requirement (EER) the average dietary energy intake predicted to maintain energy balance in a healthy adult of a certain age, gender, weight, height, and level of physical activity consistent with good health.

Setting Energy Requirements

In contrast to the recommendations for nutrients, the value set for energy, the **estimated energy requirement (EER)**, is not generous; instead, it is set at the average energy intake level predicted to maintain body weight for an individual of a particular age, gender, height, weight, and physical activity level consistent with good health. The energy DRI values reflect a balancing act: enough food energy is critical to support health and life, but too much energy causes unhealthy weight gain. Because even small amounts of excess energy consumed day after day cause weight gain and associated diseases, the DRI committee did not set a tolerable upper intake level for energy.

People don't eat energy directly. They derive energy from foods containing carbohydrate, fat, and protein, each in proportion to the others. The acceptable macronutrient distribution ranges, listed earlier, are designed to provide a healthy balance among these nutrients and to minimize a person's risks of chronic diseases. These ranges resurface in later chapters of this book wherever intakes of the energy-yielding nutrients are discussed with regard to chronic disease risks.

> The DRI recommended intake values for energy are found on page A, inside the front cover.

KEY POINT

- Estimated energy requirements are set as the average energy intake recommendation predicted to maintain body weight and to discourage unhealthy weight gain.

Why Are Daily Values Used on Labels?

Most careful diet planners are already familiar with the Daily Values because they are used on Canadian and U.S. food labels. After learning about the DRI, you may wonder why yet another set of standards is needed for food labels. One answer is that the DRI recommended intakes vary from group to group, whereas on a label, one set of values must apply to everyone. The Daily Values reflect the needs of an "average" person—someone eating 2,000 to 2,500 Calories a day. Soon, the Daily Values will be updated to reflect current DRI recommendations.[3]

Daily Values are part of the Canadian nutrition labelling regulations that took effect January 1, 2006 (http://www.hc-sc.gc.ca/fn-an/label-etiquet/nutrition/reg/index-eng.php), for large food companies and January 1, 2008, for smaller food companies (revenues of <$1 million/year from food sales). Thus, prepackaged foods will now display the mandatory nutrition facts table and other required nutrition information. Percentage of Daily Value (%DV) is used to express the food's content of macronutrients, fibre, and selected vitamins and minerals. The Daily Values reference standards for Canada are found on page Y, inside the back cover (see sample calculation in the margin). Some of the values for vitamins and minerals refer to the older recommended daily intakes (RDI) values. However, the Daily Values for fat, saturated and *trans* fatty acids, carbohydrate, fibre, sodium, and potassium are based on the appropriate Institute of Medicine (IOM) DRI report for a 2,000-Calorie diet. These differ from those for the United States in that the Daily Values on which %DV is currently calculated are different for some nutrients, the Daily Values consider the sum of both saturated and *trans* fat, and calculating a %DV for cholesterol is optional.

The nutrition education program for the nutrition labelling regulations identifies that the purpose of having %DV is to show whether the food has a "lot" or a "little" of a nutrient in a stated amount of food. The education program is available via Health Canada, Health Products and Food Branch, at http://www.hc-sc.gc.ca/fn-an/label-etiquet/nutrition/cons/dv-vq/index-eng.php.

The Daily Values are ideal for allowing comparisons among *foods*. This strength can also be a limitation, however. Because the Daily Values apply to all people, from children of age four through aging adults, they are much less useful as nutrient intake goals for individuals. Details about how to use the Daily Values appropriately in making comparisons among foods are offered in this chapter's Consumer Corner.

The Canadian Physical Activity Guidelines for Adults—18–64 years (see Figure 10–1 on page 422) makes these suggestions:

- ". . . accumulate at least 150 minutes of moderate- to vigorous-intensity aerobic physical activity per week . . ."
- ". . . add muscle and bone strengthening activities . . . at least 2 days per week."

For weight control and additional health benefits, the DRI committee recommends more than this amount—60 minutes of moderate activity each day. Other recommendations are found in Chapter 10.

KEY POINT

- The Daily Values are standards used only on food labels to enable consumers to compare the nutrient values among foods.

Other Nutrient Standards

Many nations and international groups have published sets of standards similar to the DRI. They differ from the DRI in some respects, partly because of different interpretations of the data from which they are derived and partly because people in different parts of the world have somewhat different food intakes and energy expenditures. Note: Health Canada recently changed its policy on the amount of energy attributed to fibre in foods and, unlike other countries, has set the level as 2 Calories/gram (unless demonstrated otherwise) for labelling purposes (http://www.hc-sc.gc.ca/fn-an/legislation/pol/fibre-label-etiquetage-eng.php#a7). In addition to setting nutrient standards, experts around the world recommend daily physical activity to help people stay healthy and live longer (see the Think Fitness box above).

KEY POINT

- Many nations and groups issue recommendations for nutrient and energy intakes appropriate for specific groups of people.

Eating Well with Canada's Food Guide

Diet planning connects nutrition theory with the food on the table, and a few minutes invested in meal planning can pay off in better nutrition. To help people achieve the goals set forth by Health Canada (a summary is listed in Table 1–8, page 17),[4] Canada's Food Guide provides a daily healthy eating pattern that includes foods from the four food groups. Figure 2–4 displays this plan, available at http://www.hc-sc.gc.ca/fn-an/food-guide-aliment/index-eng.php or from your local health unit as a six-page foldout document. Besides being available in both official languages, the Food Guide has now been translated into 10 other languages, including Chinese, Arabic, and Spanish. There is also a Food Guide for First Nation, Inuit, and Métis, and it too has been translated into four native languages that are common in Canada. By using the Food Guide wisely and by learning about the energy nutrients and vitamins and minerals in various foods (as you will in coming chapters), you can achieve the goals of a nutritious diet first mentioned in Chapter 1: adequacy, balance, Calorie control, moderation, and variety.

Eating Well with Canada's Food Guide is reproduced in Figure 2–4 on the next page.

Figure 2–4
Canada's Food Guide, 2011

 Health Santé
Canada Canada | Your health and safety... our priority. | Votre santé et votre sécurité... notre priorité.

Eating Well with Canada's Food Guide

GREEN BEANS

COUSCOUS

WILD RICE

Kefir

YOGURT

TOFU

Cereal

FORTIFIED SOY BEVERAGE

POWDERED MILK

MILK

SPINACH ÉPINARDS

MILK

Canada

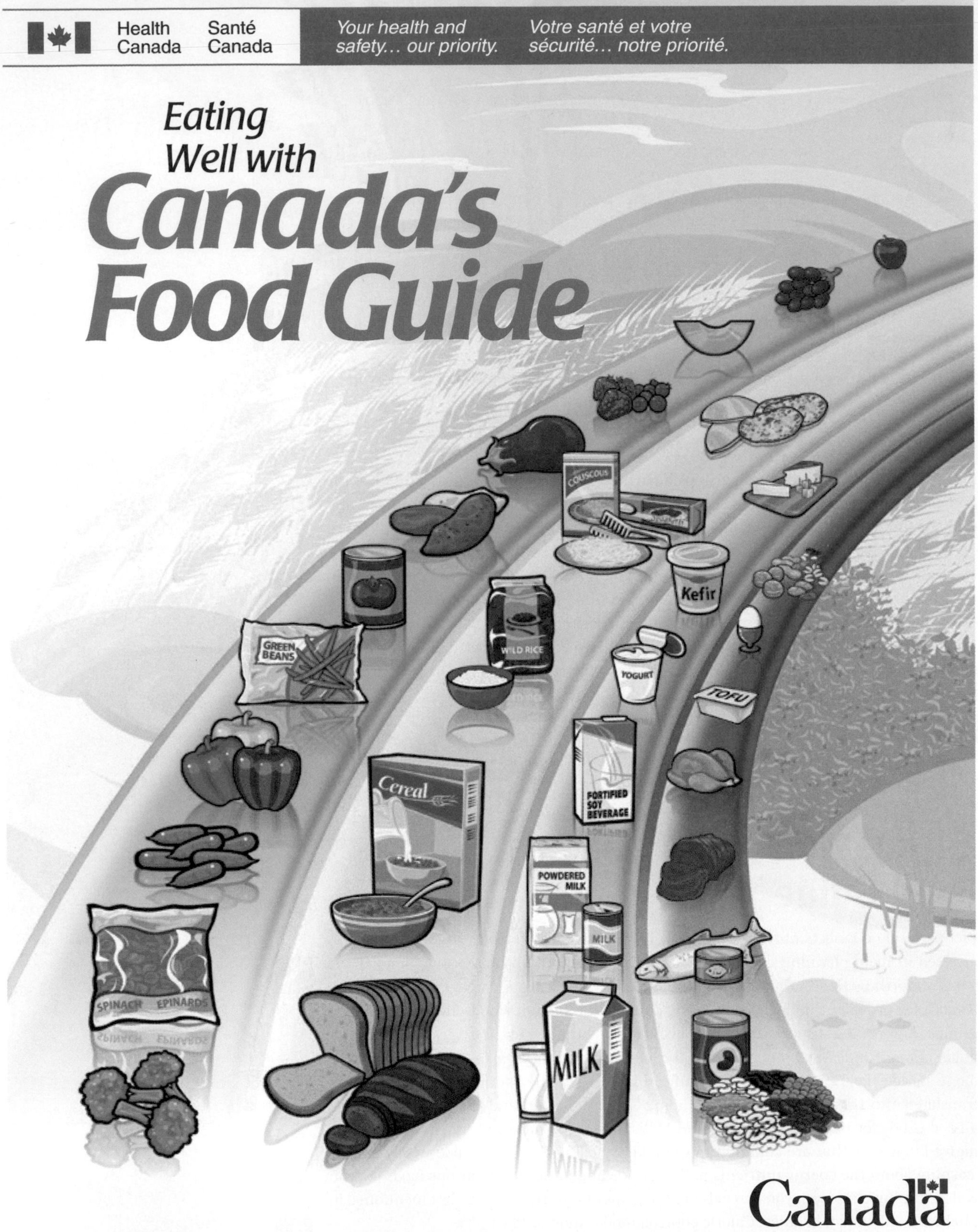

Source: Eating Well with Canada's Food Guide *(2011), Health Canada. Reproduced with the permission of the Minister of Public Works and Government Services Canada, 2013.*

Figure 2–4

Canada's Food Guide, 2011 (continued)

Recommended Number of *Food Guide Servings* per Day

	Children			Teens		Adults			
Age in Years	2-3	4-8	9-13	14-18		19-50		51+	
Sex	Girls and Boys			Females	Males	Females	Males	Females	Males
Vegetables and Fruit	4	5	6	7	8	7-8	8-10	7	7
Grain Products	3	4	6	6	7	6-7	8	6	7
Milk and Alternatives	2	2	3-4	3-4	3-4	2	2	3	3
Meat and Alternatives	1	1	1-2	2	3	2	3	2	3

The chart above shows how many Food Guide Servings you need from each of the four food groups every day.

Having the amount and type of food recommended and following the tips in *Canada's Food Guide* will help:

• Meet your needs for vitamins, minerals and other nutrients.

• Reduce your risk of obesity, type 2 diabetes, heart disease, certain types of cancer and osteoporosis.

• Contribute to your overall health and vitality.

(continued)

Figure 2–4

Canada's Food Guide, 2011 (continued)

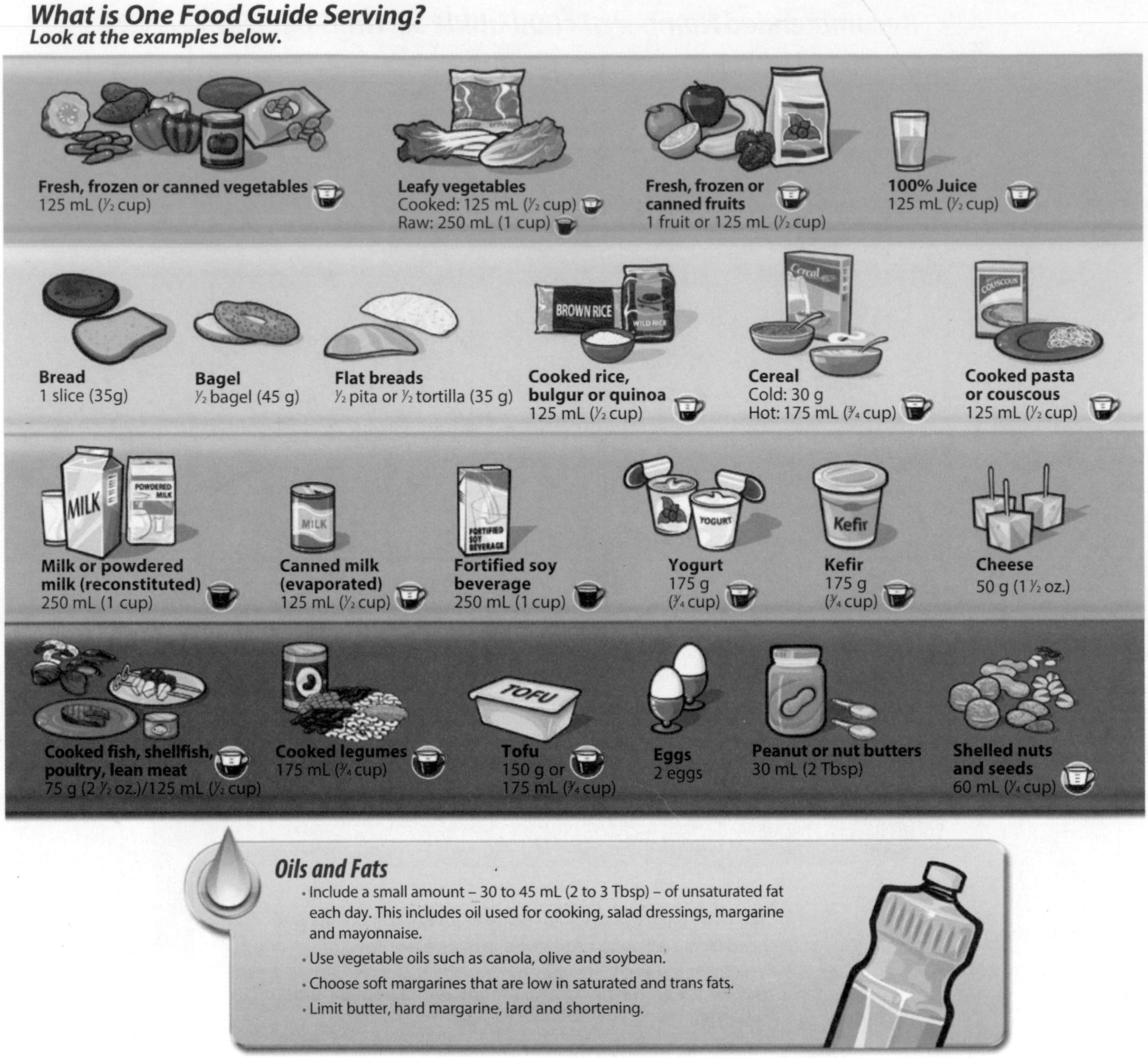

What is One Food Serving?
Look at the examples below.

Fresh, frozen or canned vegetables
125 mL (½ cup)

Leafy vegetables
Cooked: 125 mL (½ cup)
Raw: 250 mL (1 cup)

Fresh, frozen or canned fruits
1 fruit or 125 mL (½ cup)

100% Juice
125 mL (½ cup)

Bread
1 slice (35g)

Bagel
½ bagel (45 g)

Flat breads
½ pita or ½ tortilla (35 g)

Cooked rice, bulgur or quinoa
125 mL (½ cup)

Cereal
Cold: 30 g
Hot: 175 mL (¾ cup)

Cooked pasta or couscous
125 mL (½ cup)

Milk or powdered milk (reconstituted)
250 mL (1 cup)

Canned milk (evaporated)
125 mL (½ cup)

Fortified soy beverage
250 mL (1 cup)

Yogurt
175 g
(¾ cup)

Kefir
175 g
(¾ cup)

Cheese
50 g (1 ½ oz.)

Cooked fish, shellfish, poultry, lean meat
75 g (2 ½ oz.)/125 mL (½ cup)

Cooked legumes
175 mL (¾ cup)

Tofu
150 g or
175 mL (¾ cup)

Eggs
2 eggs

Peanut or nut butters
30 mL (2 Tbsp)

Shelled nuts and seeds
60 mL (¾ cup)

Oils and Fats

- Include a small amount – 30 to 45 mL (2 to 3 Tbsp) – of unsaturated fat each day. This includes oil used for cooking, salad dressings, margarine and mayonnaise.
- Use vegetable oils such as canola, olive and soybean.
- Choose soft margarines that are low in saturated and trans fats.
- Limit butter, hard margarine, lard and shortening.

Figure 2–4

Canada's Food Guide, 2011 (continued)

Make each Food Guide Serving count...
wherever you are – at home, at school, at work or when eating out!

▸ **Eat at least one dark green and one orange vegetable each day.**
- Go for dark green vegetables such as broccoli, romaine lettuce and spinach.
- Go for orange vegetables such as carrots, sweet potatoes and winter squash.

▸ **Choose vegetables and fruit prepared with little or no added fat, sugar or salt.**
- Enjoy vegetables steamed, baked or stir-fried instead of deep-fried.

▸ **Have vegetables and fruit more often than juice.**

▸ **Make at least half of your grain products whole grain each day.**
- Eat a variety of whole grains such as barley, brown rice, oats, quinoa and wild rice.
- Enjoy whole grain breads, oatmeal or whole wheat pasta.

▸ **Choose grain products that are lower in fat, sugar or salt.**
- Compare the Nutrition Facts table on labels to make wise choices.
- Enjoy the true taste of grain products. When adding sauces or spreads, use small amounts.

▸ **Drink skim, 1%, or 2% milk each day.**
- Have 500 mL (2 cups) of milk every day for adequate vitamin D.
- Drink fortified soy beverages if you do not drink milk.

▸ **Select lower fat milk alternatives.**
- Compare the Nutrition Facts table on yogurts or cheeses to make wise choices.

▸ **Have meat alternatives such as beans, lentils and tofu often.**

▸ **Eat at least two Food Guide Servings of fish each week.***
- Choose fish such as char, herring, mackerel, salmon, sardines and trout.

▸ **Select lean meat and alternatives prepared with little or no added fat or salt.**
- Trim the visible fat from meats. Remove the skin on poultry.
- Use cooking methods such as roasting, baking or poaching that require little or no added fat.
- If you eat luncheon meats, sausages or prepackaged meats, choose those lower in salt (sodium) and fat.

Enjoy a variety of foods from the four food groups.

Satisfy your thirst with water!

Drink water regularly. It's a calorie-free way to quench your thirst. Drink more water in hot weather or when you are very active.

* Health Canada provides advice for limiting exposure to mercury from certain types of fish. Refer to www.healthcanada.gc.ca for the latest information.

(continued)

Figure 2–4

Canada's Food Guide, 2011 (continued)

Advice for different ages and stages...

Children

Following *Canada's Food Guide* helps children grow and thrive.

Young children have small appetites and need calories for growth and development.

- Serve small nutritious meals and snacks each day.

- Do not restrict nutritious foods because of their fat content. Offer a variety of foods from the four food groups.

- Most of all... be a good role model.

Women of childbearing age

All women who could become pregnant and those who are pregnant or breastfeeding need a multivitamin containing **folic acid** every day. Pregnant women need to ensure that their multivitamin also contains **iron**. A health care professional can help you find the multivitamin that's right for you.

Pregnant and breastfeeding women need more calories. Include an extra 2 to 3 Food Guide Servings each day.

Here are two examples:
- Have fruit and yogurt for a snack, or
- Have an extra slice of toast at breakfast and an extra glass of milk at supper.

Men and women over 50

The need for **vitamin D** increases after the age of 50.

In addition to following *Canada's Food Guide*, everyone over the age of 50 should take a daily vitamin D supplement of 10 µg (400 IU).

How do I count Food Guide Servings in a meal?

Here is an example:

Vegetable and beef stir-fry with rice, a glass of milk and an apple for dessert		
250 mL (1 cup) mixed broccoli, carrot and sweet red pepper	=	2 **Vegetables and Fruit** Food Guide Servings
75 g (2 ½ oz.) lean beef	=	1 **Meat and Alternatives** Food Guide Serving
250 mL (1 cup) brown rice	=	2 **Grain Products** Food Guide Servings
5 mL (1 tsp) canola oil	=	part of your **Oils and Fats** intake for the day
250 mL (1 cup) 1% milk	=	1 **Milk and Alternatives** Food Guide Serving
1 apple	=	1 **Vegetables and Fruit** Food Guide Serving

Figure 2–4

Canada's Food Guide, 2011 (continued)

Eat well and be active today and every day!

The benefits of eating well and being active include:

- Better overall health.
- Lower risk of disease.
- A healthy body weight.
- Feeling and looking better.
- More energy.
- Stronger muscles and bones.

Be active

To be active every day is a step towards better health and a healthy body weight.

It is recommended that adults accumulate at least 2 ½ hours of moderate to vigorous physical activity each week and that children and youth accumulate at least 60 minutes per day. You don't have to do it all at once. Choose a variety of activities spread throughout the week.

Start slowly and build up.

Eat well

Another important step towards better health and a healthy body weight is to follow *Canada's Food Guide* by:

- Eating the recommended amount and type of food each day.
- Limiting foods and beverages high in calories, fat, sugar or salt (sodium) such as cakes and pastries, chocolate and candies, cookies and granola bars, doughnuts and muffins, ice cream and frozen desserts, french fries, potato chips, nachos and other salty snacks, alcohol, fruit flavoured drinks, soft drinks, sports and energy drinks, and sweetened hot or cold drinks.

Take a step today...

- ✔ Have breakfast every day. It may help control your hunger later in the day.
- ✔ Walk wherever you can – get off the bus early, use the stairs.
- ✔ Benefit from eating vegetables and fruit at all meals and as snacks.
- ✔ Spend less time being inactive such as watching TV or playing computer games.
- ✔ Request nutrition information about menu items when eating out to help you make healthier choices.
- ✔ Enjoy eating with family and friends!
- ✔ Take time to eat and savour every bite!

Read the label

- Compare the Nutrition Facts table on food labels to choose products that contain less fat, saturated fat, trans fat, sugar and sodium.
- Keep in mind that the calories and nutrients listed are for the amount of food found at the top of the Nutrition Facts table.

Nutrition Facts
→ Per 0 mL (0 g)

Amount	% Daily Value
Calories 0	
Fat 0 g	0 %
Saturated 0 g	0 %
+ Trans 0 g	
Cholesterol 0 mg	
Sodium 0 mg	0 %
Carbohydrate 0 g	0 %
Fibre 0 g	0 %
Sugars 0 g	
Protein 0 g	

Vitamin A 0 %		Vitamin C 0 %	
Calcium 0 %		Iron 0 %	

Limit trans fat

When a Nutrition Facts table is not available, ask for nutrition information to choose foods lower in trans and saturated fats.

For more information, interactive tools, or additional copies visit Canada's Food Guide on-line at:
www.healthcanada.gc.ca/foodguide

or contact:

Publications
Health Canada
Ottawa, Ontario K1A 0K9
E-Mail: publications@hc-sc.gc.ca
Tel.: 1-866-225-0709
Fax: (613) 941-5366
TTY: 1-800-267-1245

Également disponible en français sous le titre : Bien manger avec le Guide alimentaire canadien

This publication can be made available on request on diskette, large print, audio-cassette and braille.

How Can Canada's Food Guide Help Me Eat Well?

As a nation, Canadians eat too few servings of vegetables and fruit and, for a large segment of the adult population, too many foods that are rich in fats. For most people, then, it is recommended that they choose *more* of these:

- Vegetables (especially dark green vegetables, orange vegetables, and legumes)
- Fruit
- Meat and alternatives, such as beans, lentils, and tofu

Canadians should also choose *less* of these:

- Refined grains
- Total fats (especially saturated fat, *trans* fat, and cholesterol)
- Added sugars

Canada's Food Guide differs from the U.S. Department of Agriculture (USDA) MyPlate in the number of food groups, some serving sizes, and the graphic presentation. For the first time, our Food Guide also recommends that females of reproductive age take a multinutrient supplement that contains folic acid, and if pregnant, iron as well. In addition, it recommends that those over 50 years old take a daily 10-microgram vitamin D supplement. However, many of the drawbacks to MyPlate (e.g., multiitem foods such as pizza and stew do not fit neatly into any one food group) also apply to *Eating Well with Canada's Food Guide*. For examples of food guides used in other parts of the world, see Figure 2–8 (pages 50–51).

Canada's Food Guide was released in February 2011. Considerable research was done with consumers and nutrition educators, and the results can be accessed through the website for the Office of Nutrition Policy and Promotion (http://www.hc-sc.gc.ca/ahc-asc/branch-dirgen/hpfb-dgpsa/onpp-bppn/index-eng.php). All of the publications related to *Eating Well with Canada's Food Guide* are available from the website. Also, a history of the Food Guide from 1942 to 1992 can be accessed at http://www.hc-sc.gc.ca/fn-an/food-guide-aliment/context/hist-eng.php.

Canada's Food Guide is based on current nutritional science. The food intake pattern it describes meets the nutrient recommendations set out in the various recent DRI reports and is consistent with the latest scientific evidence linking diet with reduced risk for the development of chronic diseases. The Food Guide uses a total diet approach with a broader range of servings to accommodate the nutritional needs of female and male children, teens, and adults. This guide recognizes the use of foods that don't fit neatly into the four food groups, and we now have an "Oils and Fats" category. Table 2–2 lists the serving recommendations for *Eating Well with Canada's Food Guide* for different people.

Canadians can find helpful hints on using the Food Guide, choosing foods, maintaining healthy habits, and so on, on Health Canada's website at http://www.hc-sc.gc.ca/fn-an/food-guide-aliment/index-eng.php. Your local or provincial public health department will also have copies of Canada's Food Guide and other related resources.

● Another eating plan, the DASH eating plan discussed in Appendix F at the back of the book, also meets many of the goals set out in the Food Guide.

● For example, the Canadian Diabetes Association has produced "Beyond the Basics—Meal Planning for Healthy Eating, Diabetes Prevention and Management" to help those with diabetes choose the right foods and portions to help them manage their blood glucose and maintain a healthy weight (e.g., basic carbohydrate counting: 1 serving = 15 g of available carbohydrate or 1 carbohydrate choice); see http://www.diabetes.ca/for-professionals/resources/nutrition/beyond-basics.

Table 2–2

Number of Food Guide Servings for Different People

Food Group	Marie—5 yr old	David—17 yr old	Louise—35 yr old
Vegetables and fruit	5	8	7–8
Grain products	4	7	6–7
Milk and alternatives	2	3–4	2
Meat and alternatives	2	3	2
Oils and fats (unsaturated)	2–3 tbs	2–3 tbs	2–3 tbs

Source: Eating Well with Canada's Food Guide. *Health Canada, 2011. Reproduced with permission from Her Majesty the Queen in Right of Canada©, represented by the Minister of Health, 2013.*

Achieving Adequacy, Balance, and Variety: The Food Groups Canada's Food Guide in Figure 2–4 defines the major food groups and dictates equivalent portions of foods from each group. This standardization is needed to ensure that a diet based on the plan will deliver a certain amount of a given nutrient. Other **food group plans**, **exchange systems**, and the Dietary Approaches to Stop Hypertension (DASH) eating plan are also designed in this way. This doesn't mean that you can never choose more than 125 mL (½ cup) of pasta, for example. Instead, it means that if you choose 375 mL (1½ cup), you will have received the nutrients (and the Calories) of approximately three Food Guide servings of grains.

Eating Well with Canada's Food Guide: A Resource for Educators and Communicators also teaches people to recognize key nutrients provided by foods within the groups. These are listed in the margin for the vegetables and fruit group.

The foods in each group are well-known contributors of the key nutrients, but you can count on these foods to supply many other nutrients as well. If you design your diet around this plan, it is assumed that you will obtain adequate amounts not only of the nutrients of greatest concern but also of the other two dozen or so essential nutrients, as well as beneficial phytochemicals, because all of these are distributed among the food groups.

Applying Canada's Food Guide requires looking at foods in a new way. All vegetables provide valuable fibre and the mineral potassium, but they also reliably provide a target nutrient as well, such as vitamin A from the orange and deep yellow vegetables, the vitamin folate from the dark green vegetables, abundant carbohydrate energy from the starchy vegetables, and many of the same nutrients but fewer Calories as higher-fat food items. The diet planner should strive to vary vegetable choices among and within the vegetable and fruit group to achieve adequacy.

> Chapter 1 defined phytochemicals as nonnutrient compounds that exert biological effects on the body.
>
> Legumes were also defined in Chapter 1 as dried beans, peas, and lentils.

Spices, herbs, coffee, tea, and diet soft drinks provide few, if any, nutrients but can add flavour and pleasure to meals. They can also provide some potentially beneficial phytochemicals, such as those in tea or certain spices—see this chapter's Controversy section.

Controlling Calories: The Discretionary Calorie Allowance To help people control Calories and prevent unhealthy weight gain, the USDA developed the concept of the **discretionary Calorie allowance** (illustrated in Figure 2–5). As the figure demonstrates, a person needing 2,000 Calories a day to maintain weight may need only 1,700 Calories or so of nutrient-dense foods to supply the day's required nutrients. The difference between the Calories needed to maintain weight and those to supply nutrients from nutrient-dense foods (in this case, 267 Calories) is the person's discretionary Calorie allowance.

A person with a discretionary Calorie allowance to spend may choose to consume the following within the limits of the allowance:

1. Extra servings of the same nutrient-dense foods that make up the base of the diet, for example, an extra piece of skinless chicken or a second ear of corn

- Key nutrients and other food components found in the vegetables and fruit group include complex carbohydrates, fibre, folic acid, vitamin B$_6$, vitamin C, precursors of vitamin A (carotenes), magnesium, and potassium.

Figure 2–5

Discretionary Calorie Allowance

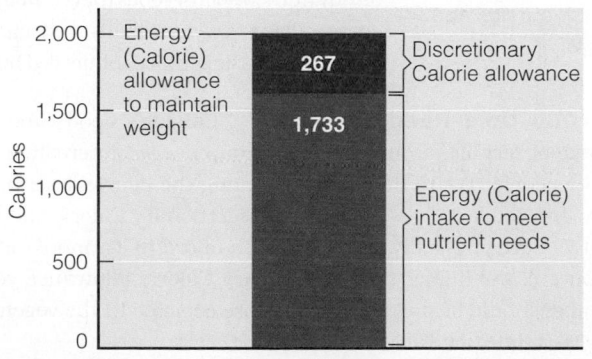

food group plan a diet-planning tool that sorts foods into groups based on their nutrient content and then specifies that people should eat certain minimum numbers of servings of foods from each group.

exchange system a diet-planning tool that organizes foods with respect to their nutrient contents and Calorie amounts.

discretionary Calorie allowance the balance of Calories remaining in a person's energy allowance after accounting for the number of Calories needed to meet recommended nutrient intakes through consumption of nutrient-dense foods.

Eating Well with Canada's Food Guide

2. Fats from two sources (within the limits recommended for health):
   - Foods higher in naturally occurring fats such as regular hamburger instead of lean hamburger or whole milk or 1 percent or 2 percent reduced-fat milk instead of skim milk
   - Added fats, including solid fats such as butter, hard margarine, lard, and shortening, and oils consumed in excess of need
3. Added sugars, such as jams, colas, and honey
4. Alcohol, within limits (some people should *not* make this choice; read Controversy 3 in Chapter 3).
5. Alternatively, a person wishing to lose weight might choose to omit the discretionary Calories from the diet. This is a safe strategy because discretionary Calories are not essential for delivering needed nutrients to the diet.

Discretionary Calories are distinguished from the Calories of the nutrient-dense foods of which they may be a part. A fried chicken leg, for example, provides discretionary Calories from two sources: the naturally occurring fat of the chicken skin and the added fat absorbed during frying. The Calories of the skinless chicken underneath are not discretionary (unless consumed in excess of need)—they are necessary to provide the nutrients of chicken.

Physical activity affects an individual's discretionary Calorie allowance. Physically active people burn more Calories (8.5 to 15.8 percent of total energy) in a day than do sedentary people and so can afford to consume more discretionary Calories each day. People who need fewer Calories to maintain their weight have fewer discretionary Calories to spend.

Achieving Moderation: Nutrient Density To control Calories and prevent overweight or obesity, it is recommended that diet planners choose the most nutrient-dense foods from each food group. Unprocessed or lightly processed foods are generally best because some processes strip foods of beneficial nutrients and fibre, while others add many Calories in the form of sugar or fat. Figure 2–4 identifies a few of the most nutrient-dense food selections in each food group. Oil is a notable exception. Oil is pure fat and therefore rich in Calories, but a small amount of oil from sources such as avocado, olives, nuts, fish, or vegetable oil provides vitamin E and other important nutrients that other foods lack.

In using Canada's Food Guide, it may help to think of the leanest meats as "meats" and to view fattier cuts as "meats with added fat." Likewise, skim (fat-free) milk is "milk," and whole milk and 1 percent or 2 percent reduced-fat milk are "milk with added fat." Pudding made with whole milk provides discretionary Calories from the naturally occurring fat of whole milk and from sugar added for sweetness. Even fruit, vegetables, and grains can carry discretionary Calories into the diet. Examples include the sugary syrup of canned peaches, the added fat of buttered corn, and the shortening added to flour to make muffins. Now it becomes clear why a diet of mostly nutrient-dense foods that contains less nutrient-dense choices delivers many discretionary Calories without increasing intakes of needed nutrients.

> Chapter 1 explained the concept of nutrient density.
>
> Chapter 9 will help you determine your energy needs. For a quick approximation, look up the DRI estimated energy requirement on the inside front cover for your age and gender group.

How Much Food Do I Need Each Day? Canada's Food Guide specifies the number or range of servings from each food group needed to create a healthful diet for most healthy people. Try to find yourself among the people described in the Food Guide in Figure 2–4. Table 2–3 also specifies a discretionary Calorie allowance for each Calorie level. If you are physically active, you can afford to eat more Calories, and the more active you are, the higher the discretionary Calorie allowance you "earn." For vegetables, intakes should be divided among those depicted in the vegetables and fruit group over a week's time (see Table 2–4).

Table 2–3

How Much Food from Each Group Daily?

	Sedentary Women: 51+ yr	Sedentary Women: 31–50 yr	Sedentary Women: 19–30 yr Active Women: 51+ yr Sedentary Men: 51+ yr	Active Women: 31–50 yr Sedentary Men: 31–50 yr	Active Women: 19–30 yr Active Men: 51+ yr Sedentary Men: 19–30 yr	Active Men: 31–50 yr	Active Men: 19–30 yr
Calories[a]	1,600	1,800	2,000	2,200	2,400	2,600	2,800
Vegetables and fruit							
Vegetables	2 c	2½ c	2½ c	3 c	3 c	3½ c	3½ c
Fruit	1½ c	1½ c	2 c	2 c	2 c	2 c	2½ c
Grain products	150 g	180 g	180 g	210 g	240 g	270 g	300 g
Meat and alternatives	150 g	150 g	165 g	180 g	195 g	195 g	210 g
Milk and alternatives	3 c	3 c	3 c	3 c	3 c	3 c	3 c
Oils and fats[b]	4½ tsp	5 tsp	5½ tsp	6 tsp	6 tsp	7 tsp	7 tsp
Discretionary Calorie allowance	132 Cal (8.5)[c]	195 Cal (10.8)	267 Cal (13.4)	290 Cal (13.2)	362 Cal (15.1)	410 Cal (15.8)	426 Cal (15.2)

NOTE: In addition to gender, age, and activity levels, energy needs vary with height and weight (see Chapter 9 and Appendix E).
[a]*Assumes high nutrient density choices– lean, low fat, and fat-free with no added sugars.*
[b]*Approximate measures; the gram values are 22, 24, 27, 29, 31, 34, and 36, respectively.*
[c]*Percentage of total energy.*

Table 2–4

Weekly Amounts from Vegetable Subgroups

Table 2–3 specifies the recommended amounts of total vegetables per *day*. This table shows those amounts dispersed among two vegetable subgroups per *week*.

Vegetable Subgroups	1,600 Cal	1,800 Cal	2,000 Cal	2,200 Cal	2,400 Cal	2,600 Cal	2,800 Cal
Dark green	2 c*	3 c	3 c	3 c	3 c	3 c	3 c
Orange and deep yellow	1½ c**	2 c	2 c	2 c	2 c	2½ c	2½ c

*Raw leafy vegetables
**Fresh, frozen, or canned

With judicious selections, the diet can supply all of the necessary nutrients and provide some luxury items as well. A sample diet plan demonstrates how the theory of Canada's Food Guide translates to food on the plate. Canada's Food Guide ensures that a certain amount from each of the food groups is represented in the diet. The diet planner begins by assigning each of the food groups to meals and snacks, as shown in Table 2–5. Then the plan can be filled out with real foods to create a menu. For example, the breakfast calls for 1 Food Guide serving of grains, 1 cup milk, and ½ cup fruit. Here's one possibility for this meal:

250 millilitres (1 cup) ready-to-eat cereal = 30 grams grains

250 millilitres (1 cup) skim (fat-free) milk = 250 millilitres (1 cup) milk

1 medium banana = 125 millilitres (½ cup) fruit

Then the planner moves on to complete the menu for lunch, supper, and snacks, as shown in Figure 2–6. This day's choices are explored further as "Monday's Meals" in the Food Feature later in this chapter.

Table 2–5

Sample Diet Plan

This diet plan is one of many possibilities for a day's meals. It follows the amounts suggested for a 2,000-Calorie diet (with an extra ½ cup of vegetables).

Food Group	Recommended Amounts	Breakfast	Lunch	Snack	Dinner	Snack
Fruit	2 c	½ c		½ c	1 c	
Vegetables	2½ c		1 c		2 c	
Grain products	4 servings	1 serving	2 servings	½ serving	1 serving	½ serving
Meat and alternatives	2 servings		1 serving		1¼ servings	
Milk and alternatives	3 c	1 c		1 c		1 c
Oils and fats	2 tbs		½ tbs		1½ tbs	
Discretionary Calorie allowance	267 Cal					

Figure 2–6

A Sample Menu

This sample menu provides about 1,850 Calories of the 2,000-Calorie plan. About 150 discretionary Calories remain available to spend on more nutrient-dense foods or luxuries such as added sugars and fats.

Amounts	Sample Menu	Energy (Cal)
Breakfast		
30 g whole grains	1 c whole-grain cereal	108
1 c milk	1 c skim (fat-free) milk	100
½ c fruit	1 medium banana (sliced)	105
Lunch		
55 g meats, 55 g whole grains	1 turkey sandwich on whole-wheat roll	272
1½ tsp oils	1½ tbs low-fat mayonnaise	71
1 c vegetables	1 c vegetable juice	50
Snack		
15 g whole grains	4 whole-wheat reduced-fat crackers	86
1 c milk	42 g low-fat cheddar cheese	74
½ c fruit	1 medium apple	72
Dinner		
½ c vegetables	1 c raw spinach leaves	8
¼ c vegetables	¼ c shredded carrots	11
30 g meats	¼ c garbanzo beans	71
2 tsp oils	2 tbs oil-based salad dressing and olives	76
¾ c vegetables, 75 g meat, 55 g enriched grains	spaghetti with meat and tomato sauce	425

Figure 2–6

A Sample Menu (continued)

Amounts	Sample Menu	Energy (Cal)
½ c vegetables	½ c green beans	22
2 tsp oils	2 tsp soft margarine	67
1 c fruit	1 c strawberries	49
	Snack	
15 g whole grains	3 graham crackers	90
1 c milk	1 c skim (fat-free) milk	100

NOTE: This plan meets the recommendations to provide 45 to 65% of Calories from carbohydrate, 20 to 35% from fat, and 10 to 35% from protein.

KEY POINT

- Canada's Food Guide specifies the amount of foods from each group that people need to consume to meet their nutrient requirements.

Conveying Health Canada's Messages to Consumers

For consumers, Health Canada makes applying its Food Guide easier through a graphic image that depicts the highlights of the Food Guide (shown in Figure 2–4). The rainbow shape dictates that nutritious foods, such as whole and enriched grains, vegetables, fruit, lean meat, and milk and milk products, should contribute the bulk of the day's Calories. It also demonstrates that fats and sugars are not typically nutrient-dense foods, so their intakes should be limited. It also conveys the idea that even nutritious foods should be eaten in limited amounts to avoid over-consuming Calories and prevent unneeded weight gain and overweight. By developing consumer messages such as these, Health Canada aims to educate Canadian consumers about how to eat well and encourage the adoption of healthy habits.

Armed with this information, consumers can make appropriate food choices, obtain needed nutrients, and stay within Calorie limits. Ideally, if all consumers in Canada began to apply the principles of Canada's Food Guide today, their rewards in terms of greater quality of life, less heart disease, less cancer, and better overall health would be well worth the effort.

KEY POINT

- The messages of Canada's Food Guide are conveyed to consumers to improve the health of the nation.

Flexibility of Canada's Food Guide

Although it may appear rigid, Canada's Food Guide can actually be very flexible once its intent is understood. For example, the user can substitute fat-free cheese for fat-free skim milk because both supply the key nutrients for the milk and alternatives group. Legumes provide many of the nutrients of the meat and alternatives group (see Figure 2–7). Consumers can adapt the plan to mixed dishes such as casseroles and to national and cultural foods as well, as Figure 2–8 demonstrates. In addition, the Japanese have had a food guide shaped like a spinning top since 2005; to see it, go to http://www.mhlw.go.jp/bunya/kenkou/pdf/eiyou-syokuji5.pdf.

Because Canada's Food Guide encourages consumption of fruit, vegetables, and whole grains and provides alternatives to meat, milk, and other animal products, it can assist vegetarians in their food choices. The food group that includes meat also includes legumes, nuts, seeds, and products made from soybeans. In the food group that includes milk, soy drinks—beverages made from soybeans—can fill the same nutrient needs, provided that

Lower-Fat Milk and Alternatives and Meat and Alternatives

© C. McGregor

© Elena Schweitzer/Shutterstock

Figure 2–8

Ethnic and Regional Foods in the Food Groups

Foods from every cuisine can fit into Canada's Food Guide. Many other countries have developed their own food guides to healthy diets, and an American research team developed the pyramid for Mediterranean diets shown on the next page.

Key: Nutrient Density

● Foods generally high in nutrient density (choose most often)

△ Foods lower in nutrient density (limit selections)

© Sarah Bossert/Thinkstock

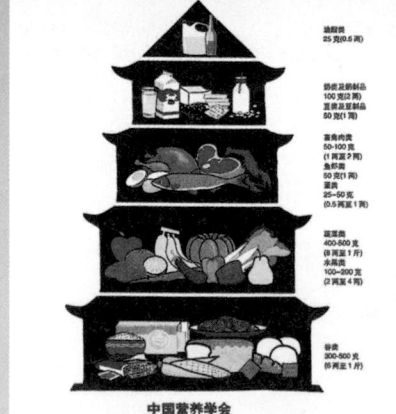

中国营养学会

China

ASIAN[a]

Grains

● Barley; glass (mung bean) noodles; millet; rice dumplings; rice or wheat noodles; rice rolls (sushi); steamed buns

△ Fried rice; fried noodles

Vegetables

● Baby corn; bamboo shoots; bean sprouts; bok choy; cabbages; dried fungus; lentils (northern Asia); lotus root; miso; scallions; seaweed; snow peas; soybeans; tempeh; water chestnuts; wild yam

△ Fried vegetables

Fruits

● Oranges, pears, plums, and other fresh fruit

Milk, Yogurt, and Cheese

● Soy milk

Meat, Poultry, Fish, Dried Peas and Beans, Eggs, and Nuts

● Broiled or stir-fried beef, fish, pork, and seafood; egg whites; egg yolks; peanuts, pine nuts, cashews, other nuts; tofu

△ Deep-fried meats and seafood; egg foo yung

Oils/Solid fats

● Vegetable oils[b]

△ Lard for deep-frying.

Seasonings and Sauces[c]

● Bean sauce; fish sauce;[d] garlic; ginger root; hoisin sauce;[d] oyster sauce;[d] plum sauce;[d] rice wine; scallions; soy sauce[d]

△ Sesame oil; other oils; oily gravies

[a]Traditional cuisines of China and of West African influence exclude fluid milk as a beverage for adults and use few or no milk products in cooking. Calcium and certain other nutrients of milk are supplied by other foods, such as small fish eaten with the bones or large servings of leafy green vegetables.

[b]Consumed in amounts recommended for caloric intakes.

[c]Many Chinese sauces are fat-free.

[d]May be high in sodium.

Figure 2–8

Ethnic and Regional Foods in the Food Groups (continued)

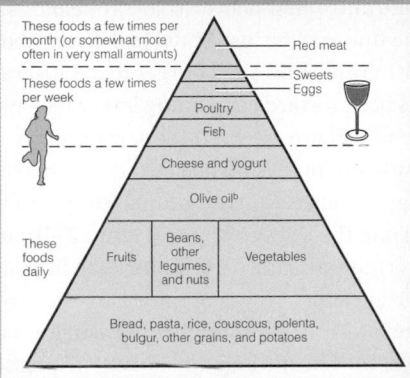

These foods a few times per month (or somewhat more often in very small amounts) — Red meat

These foods a few times per week — Sweets — Eggs

Poultry

Fish

Cheese and yogurt

Olive oil[b]

These foods daily | Fruits | Beans, other legumes, and nuts | Vegetables

Bread, pasta, rice, couscous, polenta, bulgur, other grains, and potatoes

MEDITERRANEAN

Grains
- Bulgur, couscous, focaccia, Italian bread, pasta, pita pocket bread, polenta, rice
- ▲ Baklava (honey-soaked nut pastry); cakes

Vegetables
- Cucumbers; eggplant; grape leaves; lentils and beans; onions; peppers; tomatoes
- ▲ Olives

Fruits
- Dates; figs; grapes; lemons; melons; raisins

Milk, Yogurt, and Cheese
- Fat-free or low-fat yogurt
- ▲ Feta, goat, mozzerella, parmasan, provolone, and ricotta cheeses; yogurt

Meat, Poultry, Fish, Dried Peas and Beans, Eggs, and Nuts
- Beef; eggs; fish; and seafood; lamb; lentils and beans; poultry; almonds; walnuts
- ▲ Ground lamb; ground beef; gyros (spicy roasted meat and yogurt sauce, usually rolled in flat bread); sausages

Oils
- Olive oil[a]

Seasonings and Sauces
- Garlic; herbs; lemons; egg and lemon sauce
- ▲ Olive oil

[a]Consumed in amounts recommended for caloric intakes.

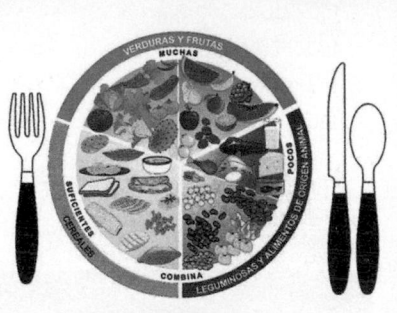

Mexico

In Mexico, Great Britain, and most European countries, a circle depicts the food guide principles.

CENTRAL AMERICAN

Grains
- Cereal; corn or flour tortillas; graham crackers; macaroni and other pasta; masa (corn flour); posole (hominy); rice
- ▲ Churros (doughnuts); fried tortilla shells; pastries; tortilla chips

Vegetables
- Cabbage; cactus; cassava; corn; iceburg lettuce; legumes; malanga; onions; potatoes; scallions; squash; tomatoes; yucca
- ▲ Olives

Fruits
- Bananas; guava; mango; oranges; papaya; pineapple
- ▲ Avocados

Milk, Yogurt, and Cheese
- Evaporated low-fat milk; powdered skim milk
- ▲ Cheddar or jack cheese; flan (caramel custard); cocoa drink; leche quemada (burnt-milk candy); queso asadero and other Mexican cheeses

Meat, Poultry, Fish, Dried Peas and Beans, Eggs, and Nuts
- Eggs; fish; lean beef, poultry, lamb, and pork; many bean varieties
- ▲ Bacon; fried fish; pork, or poultry; nuts; chorizo (sausages); refried beans

Oils/Solid Fats
- Vegetable oil[a]
- ▲ Butter, cream cheese; hard margarine; lard; sour cream

Seasonings and Sauces[b]
- Herbs; hot peppers; garlic; mole (seasoned chili and chocolate sauce); pico de gallo (finely chopped tomatoes, peppers, and onions with seasonings); salsas; spices
- ▲ Guacamole

[a]Consumed in amounts recommended for caloric intakes.
[b]May be high in sodium.

they are fortified with calcium, riboflavin, vitamin A, vitamin D, and vitamin B_{12}. Thus, people who choose to eat no meat or products taken from animals can still use Canada's Food Guide to make their diets adequate. For any careful diet planner, then, Canada's Food Guide can provide a general road map for planning a healthful diet.

KEY POINT

- Canada's Food Guide can be used with flexibility by people with different eating styles.

Portion Control

To control Calories, the diet planner must learn to control food portions (see Food Guide serving sizes, specified in Figure 2–4). Restaurants often deliver colossal helpings to ensure repeat business; a server on a cafeteria line may be instructed to deliver "about a spoonful"; fast-food burgers range from a 30-gram child-sized burger to a 350-gram triple deluxe. The trend in North America has been toward consuming larger food portions, especially of foods rich in fat and sugar (see Figure 2–9). At the same time, body weights have been creeping upward, suggesting an increasing need to control portion sizes. In contrast to the random-sized helpings found elsewhere, the quantities recommended in Canada's Food Guide (Figure 2–4) and the USDA MyPlate (Figure 2–10) are specific, precise, and reliable for delivering certain amounts of key nutrients in foods. The margin offers some tips for estimating portion sizes.

Among volumetric measures, 1 "cup" refers to a 250-millilitre measuring cup (not a teacup or drinking glass), filled to level (not heaped up, or shaken, or pressed down). Tablespoons (15 mL) and teaspoons (5 mL) refer to measuring spoons (not flatware), filled to level (not rounded or heaping). Grams/ounces signify weight, not volume. Seventy-five grams of meat, for example, would be considered one Food Guide

Portion Controller

An ice cream scoop is useful for portioning foods, including mashed potatoes, pasta, vegetables, rice, and cereal. The typical ice cream scoop filled to level holds 60 mL (¼ cup). One-half cup (two scoops) is the Food Guide equivalent amount for one Food Guide serving of 100% fruit juice. Test the size of your scoop by filling it with water and pouring it into a measuring cup.

Figure 2–9

Living Large: North American Trend toward Colossal Cuisine

Chapter 9 and Controversy 11 in Chapter 11 discuss the consequences of increasing portion sizes in terms of body fatness.

Food	Typical 1970s	Today's colossal
Cola	300 mL bottle, 120 Cal	1,200–1,800 mL fountain, 580 Cal
French fries	About 30, 475 Cal	About 50, 790 Cal
Hamburger	90–120 g meat, 330 Cal	180–360 g meat, 1,000 Cal
Bagel	30–180 g, 230 Cal	150–210 g, 550 Cal
Steak	240–300 g, 690 Cal	480–650 g, 1,260 Cal
Pasta	1 c, 200 Cal	2–3 c, 600 Cal
Baked potato	150–210 g, 180 Cal	480 g, 420 Cal
Chocolate bar	45 g, 220 Cal	90–120 g, 580 Cal
Popcorn	1½ c, 80 Cal	8–16 c tub, 880 Cal

NOTE: Calories are rounded values for the largest portions in a given range.

1970s   Today

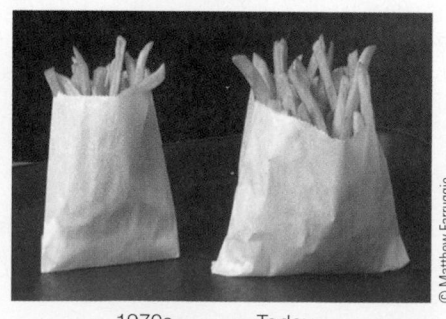

1970s   Today

1970s   Today

Figure 2–10

USDA MyPlate: Healthy Choices for a Healthier You

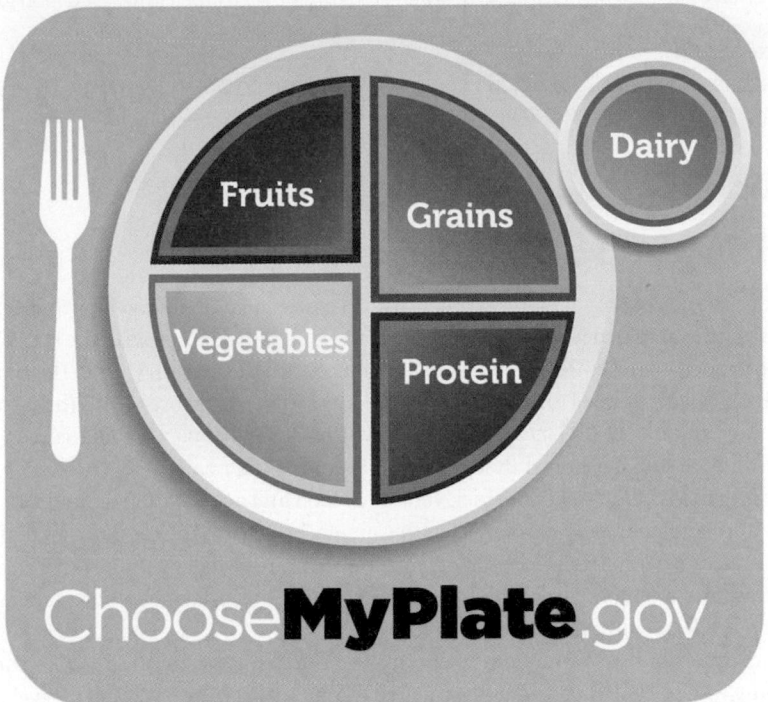

ChooseMyPlate.gov

Source: USDA, 2011, http://fnic.nal.usda.gov/dietary-guidance/myplatefood-pyramid-resources/usda-myplate-food-pyramid-resources.

To Estimate the Sizes of Food Portions, Remember These Common Objects

- 90 g of meat = the size of the palm of a woman's hand or a deck of cards
- 1 medium piece of fruit or potato = the size of a regular (60-watt) light bulb
- 45 g of cheese = the size of a nine-volt battery
- 30 g of lunch meat or cheese = 1 slice
- 1 pat (1 teaspoon) of butter or margarine = a slice from a quarter-pound stick of butter about as thick as 280 pages of this book (pressed together)

serving of cooked meat. Thirty grams (weight) of crispy rice cereal measures a full cup (volume), but take care: 30 grams of granola cereal measures only ¼ cup. Also, some foods are specified as "medium," as in "one medium apple," but the word *medium* means different things to different people. When college students are asked to bring medium-sized foods to class, they bring bagels weighing anywhere from 60 to 150 grams, muffins from about 60 to 240 grams, baked potatoes from 120 to 270 grams, and so forth. This means that if you consume a 150-gram bagel, you have consumed three Food Guide servings of grain products, not one.

KEY POINT

- People wishing to avoid overconsuming Calories must pay attention to the sizes of their food servings.

A Note about Exchange Systems

Exchange systems can be useful to careful diet planners, especially those wishing to control Calories (weight watchers), those who must control carbohydrate intakes (people with diabetes), and those who should control their intakes of fat and saturated fat (almost everyone). An exchange system may list the estimated carbohydrate, fat, saturated fat, and protein contents of food portions, as well as their Calorie values. With these estimates, exchange system users can make an educated approximation of the nutrients and Calories in almost any food they might encounter.

The Canadian Diabetes Association produces the meal planning guide "Beyond the Basics: Meal Planning Guide for Healthy Eating, Diabetes Prevention and Management." It is currently available in poster format (Appendix C) and as a 150-page document (http://www.diabetes.ca/for-professionals/resources/nutrition/beyond-basics) and involves a food group system using the exchange concept. The food groups and their nutrient content are similar to those used in Quebec and the U.S. exchange systems, and carbohydrate counting is made easier since "1 carbohydrate choice" contains about 15 grams of available carbohydrate.

© Matthew Farruggio

A serving of grains is about 30 grams, yet most bagels today weigh 100 grams or more—meaning that a single bagel can easily supply half of the total grains that many people need in a day.

Please note that there are differences compared with Canada's Food Guide when dealing with carbohydrates, lipids, and proteins. This is especially important for the carbohydrate content for foods such as chocolate milk, where ½ cup (125 mL) is "1 carbohydrate choice" instead of 1 cup (250 mL) and foods are now grouped into seven food groups.

- Exchange lists facilitate Calorie control by providing an understanding of how much carbohydrate, fat, and protein are in each food group.

The Healthy Eating Index for Assessing Diet Quality

 To judge the quality of a diet, researchers use an assessment tool known as the **Healthy Eating Index (HEI),** developed by the USDA.[5] A Canadian adaptation of the HEI (HEI-C) has been used to assess the 2004 Canadian Community Health Survey (CCHS) data set, which revealed a score of just under 60 (58.8) out of a possible score of 100 (http://www.statcan.gc.ca/pub/82-003-x/2009003/article/10914-eng.htm). Canadians can also use an online tool developed by Dietitians of Canada (DC) called "eaTracker," which, according to DC, allows you to "track your day's food and activity choices and compares them to the guidelines laid out by Health Canada." It also "assesses your food choices and provides personalized feedback on your total intake of energy (Calories) and essential nutrients and compares this to what is recommended for your age, gender, and activity level" (see http://www.eatracker.ca).

- To learn more about how to assess your own diet with the online assessment tool eaTracker, visit the Dietitians of Canada's website at http://www.eatracker.ca.

 Consumers can also find out the energy and nutrient content of the foods they eat by using either Health Canada's interactive Canadian Nutrient File (http://webprod3.hc-sc.gc.ca/cnf-fce/index-eng.jsp) or the Dietitians of Canada Eatwise food search feature at http://www.eatwise.ca, and yes, there is an app for this website.

Wise consumers also read labels on packaged foods to help them determine the foods' nutrient and energy contents and to decide how the foods may fit into their total eating plan. This chapter's Consumer Corner explains how to gain insight from the information on food labels.

- Dietitians of Canada's eaTracker is a tool for assessing diet quality.

Checking Out Food Labels

A potato is a potato and needs no label to tell you so. But what can a package of potato chips tell you about its contents? By law, its label must list the chips' ingredients—potatoes, fat, and salt—and its **Nutrition Facts** panel must also reveal details about their nutrient composition (see Table 2–6). If the oil is high in saturated fat or *trans* fat, the label will tell you so (more about fats in Chapter 5). In addition to required information, labels may make optional statements about the food. These claims are regulated by Health Canada.

This Consumer Corner introduces food labels and points out the accurate, tested, regulated, and therefore helpful information consumers need to make wise choices. It then turns the spotlight on claims whose purpose is to attract consumer dollars. Consumers must hone their label-reading skills and acquire some tools for digging out the truth from among the rubble.

What Food Labels *Must* Include

Health Canada's Food and Drug Act and Food and Drug Regulations set the requirements for certain label information to ensure that food labels truthfully inform consumers about the nutrients and ingredients in the package. This information remains reliable and true today. According to the law, most packaged food must state the following:

- The common or usual name of the product

Healthy Eating Index (HEI) a dietary assessment tool that evaluates a diet's adherence to the principles of the USDA Food Guide and the *Dietary Guidelines for Americans*, as well as the variety of foods the diet contains.

- The name and address of the manufacturer, packer, or distributor
- The net contents in terms of weight, measure, or count
- The nutrient contents of the product (Nutrition Facts panel)

Then the label must list the following in ordinary language:

- The ingredients, in descending order of predominance by weight

Not every package needs to display information about every vitamin and mineral; however, a large package, such as the box of cookies in Figure 2–11, does provide all of the information listed above.

The Nutrition Facts Panel

Most food packages are required to display a Nutrition Facts panel, like the one shown in Figure 2–11. Grocers also voluntarily post placards or offer handouts in fresh-food departments to provide consumers with similar sorts of nutrition information for the most popular types of fresh fruit, vegetables, meat, poultry, and seafood.

When you read a Nutrition Facts panel, be aware that only the top portion of the panel conveys information specific to the food inside the package. The bottom portion is identical on every label—it stands as a reminder of the Daily Values.

The items listed in this section correspond to those in Figure 2–11,

Food labels provide clues for nutrition sleuths.

which shows the location of the items listed below:

- Serving size. Common household and metric measures to allow comparison of foods within a food category. This amount of the food constitutes a single serving and the portion that contains the nutrient amounts listed. A serving of chips may be 10 chips, so if you eat 50 chips, you will have consumed five times the nutrient amounts listed on the label.
- Servings per container may be indicated. Number of servings per box, can, package, or other unit.
- Calories. Total food energy per serving.

- Nutrient amounts and percentages of Daily Values. This section provides the core information for 13 food components:
  - *Total fat.* Grams of fat per serving with a breakdown showing grams of saturated fat and *trans* fat per serving.
  - *Cholesterol.* Milligrams of cholesterol per serving.
  - *Sodium.* Milligrams of sodium per serving.
  - *Total carbohydrate.* Grams of carbohydrate per serving, including starch, fibre, and sugars, with a breakdown showing grams of dietary fibre and sugars. The sugars include those that occur naturally in the food plus any added during processing. The terms "net carbs," "impact carbs," and related terms have not been defined scientifically and are currently *not* allowed.
  - *Protein.* Grams of protein per serving.

In addition, the label must state the contents of these nutrients expressed as percentages of the Daily Values:
  - *Vitamin A*
  - *Vitamin C*
  - *Calcium*
  - *Iron*

Other nutrients present in significant amounts in the food may also be listed on the label. The Canadian Reference Standards for all of the Daily Values on food labels are provided at the back of the book on page Y and are given in terms of a person requiring 2,000 Calories each day. To help consumers better understand the %DV of nutrients on food labels Health Canada has an interactive website (http://www.hc-sc.gc.ca/fn-an/label-etiquet/nutrition/cons/dv-vq/index-eng.php) that describes what is considered "a little" or "a lot." For example, 5 percent or less is considered "a little," while 15 percent or more is considered "a lot." Consumers can use these numbers to help them select foods that have nutrients they want more of or less of for themselves or family members for health reasons.

Figure 2–11

What's on a Food Label?

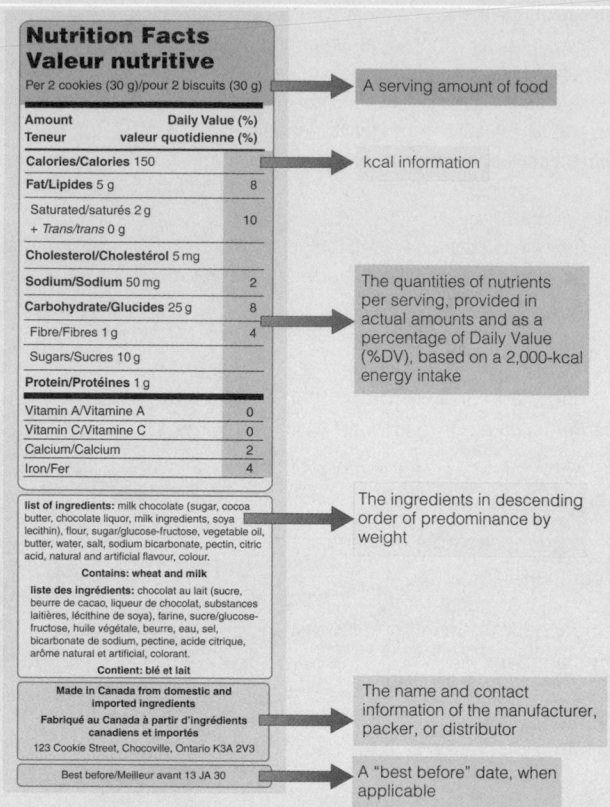

The common name of the product

Approved nutrient claims if the product meets specified criteria

The net contents in weight, measure, or count

A serving amount of food

kcal information

The quantities of nutrients per serving, provided in actual amounts and as a percentage of Daily Value (%DV), based on a 2,000-kcal energy intake

The ingredients in descending order of predominance by weight

The name and contact information of the manufacturer, packer, or distributor

A "best before" date, when applicable

English Label

Nutrition Facts

Per 1 cup (264 g)

Amount	Daily Value (%)
Calories 260	
Fat 13 g	20
Saturated Fat 3 g + *Trans* Fat 2 g	25
Cholesterol 30 mg	
Sodium 660 mg	28
Carbohydrate 31 g	10
Fibre 0 g	0
Sugars 5 g	
Protein 5 g	

Vitamin A 4	•	Vitamin C 2
Calcium 15	•	Iron 4

Bilingual Label

Nutrition Facts
Valeur nutritive

Per 1 cup (264 g)
pour 1 tasse (264 g)

Amount / Quantité	Daily Value (%) / valeur quotidienne (%)
Calories/Calories 260	
Fat/Lipides 13 g	20
Saturated/saturés 3 g + *Trans/trans* 2 g	25
Cholesterol/Cholestérol 30 mg	
Sodium/Sodium 660 mg	28
Carbohydrate/Glucides 31 g	10
Fibre/Fibres 0 g	0
Sugars/Sucres 5 g	
Protein/Protéines 5 g	

Vitamin A/Vitamine A	4
Vitamin C/Vitamine C	2
Calcium/Calcium	15
Iron/Fer	4

French Label

Valeur nutritive

pour 1 tasse (264 g)

Quantité	valeur quotidienne (%)
Calories 260	
Lipides 13 g	20
Saturés 3 g + *Trans* 2 g	25
Cholestérol 30 mg	
Sodium 660 mg	28
Glucides 31 g	10
Fibres 0 g	0
Sucres 5 g	
Protéines 5 g	

Vitamine A 4	•	Vitamine C 2
Calcium 15	•	Fer 4

The nutrition label includes:

- A title: Nutrition Facts.
- Food portions/serving sizes on which nutrient information is based.
- A list of nutrients.
- A standardized format that is bold, clear, and easy to read.
- Consistent appearance from product to product.
- Clearly identified nutrient information.
- The Daily Value, which gives a context to the nutrient values.

For more information, visit www.hc-sc.gc.ca/fn-an/label-etiquet/nutrition/index-eng.php.

Ingredients List

Often neglected but highly valuable information is contained in the list of ingredients. The product's ingredients must be listed in descending order of predominance by weight.

Knowing how to read an ingredients list puts you many steps ahead of the naive buyer. Consider the ingredients list on an orange drink powder whose first three ingredients are "sugar, citric acid, orange flavour." You can tell that sugar is the chief ingredient. Now consider a canned juice whose ingredients list begins with "water, orange juice concentrate, pineapple juice concentrate." This product is clearly made of *reconstituted* juice. Water is first on the label because it is the main constituent of juice. Sugar is nowhere to be found among the ingredients because sugar has not been added to the product. Sugar occurs naturally in juice, though, so the label does specify sugar grams; details are in Chapter 4.

Now consider a cereal whose entire list contains just one item: "100 percent shredded wheat." No question, this is a whole-grain food with nothing added. Finally, consider a cereal whose first three ingredients are "puffed milled corn, sweeteners (sugars: corn syrup, sucrose, honey, dextrose), salt." If you recognize that sugar, corn syrup, honey, and dextrose are all different versions of sugar (and you will, after Chapter 4), you might guess that this product contains close to half its weight as sugar.

More about Percentages of Daily Values

Some of the Daily Values are printed on each label in the Nutrition Facts panel. The entire list can be found at the back of this book (page Y). The calculations used to determine the %DV figures for nutrient contributions from a serving of food are based on a 2,000-Calorie diet. For example, if a food contributes 13 milligrams of vitamin C per serving and the Daily Value is 60 milligrams, then a serving of that food provides about 22 percent of the Daily Value for vitamin C.

The Daily Values are of two types. Some, such as those for fibres, proteins, vitamins, and most minerals, are akin to other nutrient intake recommendations. They suggest an intake goal to strive to reach; below that level, some people's needs may go unmet. Other Daily Values, such as those for cholesterol, total fat, the sum of saturated fat and *trans* fat, and sodium, constitute healthy daily maximums.

Of course, though the Daily Values are based on a 2,000-Calorie diet, people's actual Calorie intakes vary widely; some people need fewer Calories and some need many more. This makes the Daily Values most useful for comparing one food with another and less useful as nutrient intake targets for individuals. Still, by examining a food's general nutrient profile, you can determine whether the food contributes "a little" or "a lot" of a nutrient, whether it contributes "more" or "less" than another food, and how well it fits into your overall diet.

What Food Labels *May* Include

So far, this Consumer Corner has presented the accurate and reliable facts on nutrition labels. This section looks at reliable claims, the nutrient content descriptors, and diet-related health claims on food labels.

Nutrient Content Descriptors on Food Labels

If a food meets specified criteria, the label may display certain approved **nutrient content descriptors** concerning the product's nutritive value. The Daily Values serve as the basis for claims that a food is "low" in cholesterol or a "good source" of vitamin A. Table 2–7 provides a list of these regulated, reliable label terms along with their definitions. By remembering the meanings of these terms, consumers can make informed choices among foods. For example, any food providing 15 percent or more of the Daily Value for a nutrient (except for vitamin C, where it must contribute 30 percent or more) can boast that it is "a good source" of the nutrient; a food providing 25 percent (except for vitamin C, where it must provide 50 percent or more) is considered "an excellent source of" the nutrient.

Table 2–7

Nutrient Content Descriptor Terms on Food Labels

Certain nutrient content claims are allowable on labels if the food meets certain criteria compared with a reference amount and serving of stated size. For example, a food claiming to be "high fibre" would have to contain 4 g or more of fibre per reference amount and serving of stated size. For prepackaged meals or entrées for which no reference amount exists, the criteria for most claims would be based on 100 g of food for most claims.

Nutrient Content Claim	Compositional Criteria (per reference amount and serving of stated size)[a]
CALORIES	
Calorie-free	fewer than 5 Calories
Low in Calories	40 Calories or fewer
Reduced or lower in Calories	at least 25% less energy[b]
Source of Calories	at least 100 Calories

[a]Criteria for "reduced" or "lower in" claims are based on the reference amount of the food, and for protein claims, criteria are given per reasonable daily intake of food (Schedule K of the Food and Drug Regulations) or, in the case of breakfast cereals, per 30 g of breakfast cereal combined with 125 mL of milk.

(*continued*)

Table 2–7

Nutrient Content Descriptor Terms on Food Labels (continued)

Nutrient Content Claim	Compositional Criteria (per reference amount and serving of stated size)[a]
PROTEIN	
Source of protein	protein rating of 20 or more[c]
Excellent source of protein	protein rating of 40 or more[c]
More protein	protein rating of 20 or more,[c] at least 25% or more protein,[c] and 7 g or more protein
FAT	
Fat-free	less than 0.5 g fat
Low in fat	3 g or less fat
Reduced or lower in fat	at least 25% less fat[b]
100% fat-free	less than 0.5 g fat per 100 g, no added fat, and "free of fat"
(naming the %) fat-free	"low in fat"
SATURATED FATTY ACIDS	
Saturated fatty acid-free	less than 0.2 g saturated fatty acids and less than 0.2 g *trans* fatty acids
Low in saturated fatty acids	2 g or less saturated fatty acids and *trans* fatty acids combined and 15% or less energy from saturated fatty acids plus *trans* fatty acids
Reduced or lower in saturated fatty acids	at least 25% less saturated fatty acids and *trans* fatty acids not increased[b]
***TRANS* FATTY ACIDS**	
Free of *trans* fatty acids	less than 0.2 g *trans* fatty acids and "low in saturated fatty acids"
Reduced or lower in *trans* fatty acids	at least 25% less *trans* fatty acids and saturated fatty acids not increased[b]
POLYUNSATURATED FATTY ACIDS	
Source of omega-3 polyunsaturated fatty acids	0.3 g or more omega-3 polyunsaturated fatty acids
Source of omega-6 polyunsaturated fatty acids	2 g or more omega-6 polyunsaturated fatty acids
CHOLESTEROL	
Cholesterol-free	less than 2 mg cholesterol and "low in saturated fatty acids"
Low in cholesterol	20 mg or less cholesterol and "low in saturated fatty acids"
Reduced or lower in cholesterol	at least 25% less cholesterol[b] and "low in saturated fatty acids"
SODIUM	
Sodium-free or salt-free	less than 5 mg sodium or salt
Low in sodium or salt	140 mg or less sodium or salt
Reduced or lower in sodium or salt	at least 25% less sodium or salt[b]
No added sodium or salt	no salt or other sodium salts added during processing
Lightly salted	at least 50% less added sodium or salt[b]
SUGARS	
Sugar-free	less than 0.5 g sugars
Reduced or lower in sugar	at least 25% less sugars[b]
No added sugar	no sugars added in processing or packaging, including ingredients that contain added sugars or ingredients that functionally substitute for added sugars (e.g., concentrated fruit juice), and sugars not increased through some other means
FIBRE	
Source of fibre	2 g or more fibre or of each identified fibre
High source of fibre	4 g or more fibre or of each identified fibre
Very high source of fibre	6 g or more fibre or of each identified fibre
More fibre	at least 25% more fibre[b] and at least 2 g fibre
LIGHT	
Light	"reduced in energy" or "reduced in fat"

[b]As compared with the reference amount of a reference food. Reference food must not be "low" in subject nutrient.

[c]As determined by official method FO-1, Determination of Protein Rating, October 15, 1981.

Chapter 2 Nutrition Tools—Standards and Guidelines

For nutrients that can be harmful if consumed excessively, such as saturated and *trans* fat or sodium, foods providing less than 5 percent are desirable. For hard-to-get nutrients such as iron and calcium, a reasonable goal might be to choose foods that are "good sources of" or "excellent sources of" those nutrients several times a day. (See the Snapshot features in Chapters 7 and 8 for foods qualifying as "good sources" or better for the vitamins and minerals.)

Disease Risk Reduction Claims

In 2002, Health Canada introduced, for the first time, new disease risk reduction claims on foods, in addition to the permitted biological role claims and more nutrient content descriptors. Disease risk

---

Table 2–8

Disease Risk Reduction Claims

- Potassium, sodium, and reduced risk of high blood pressure
- Calcium, vitamin D, and regular physical activity and reduced risk of osteoporosis
- Saturated and *trans* fats and reduced risk of heart disease
- Vegetables and fruit and reduced risk of some types of cancer
- Minimal fermentable carbohydrates in products such as gum and a reduction in the risk of cavities/caries
- Over the last couple of years Health Canada has also allowed other health claims about food components (e.g., plant sterols, oat fibre, unsaturated fats) and a potential reduction in blood cholesterol levels.

Specific requirements related to the claims can be found in the Canadian Food Inspection Agency Guide to Food Labelling and Advertising, Chapter 8, Section 8.4: Disease Risk Reduction Claims.

---

reduction claims that are permitted are shown in Table 2–8.

Conclusion

The Nutrition Facts panels' nutrient content descriptors, disease risk reduction claims, and ingredients lists on food labels provide reliable information on which consumers can base their food choices.

---

try it!
Food Feature

Getting a Feel for the Nutrients in Foods

Figure 2–12 illustrates a playful contrast between two days' meals. "Monday's Meals" were selected according to the recommendations of this chapter and follow the sample menu shown earlier in Figure 2–6 (pages 48–49). "Tuesday's Meals" were chosen more for convenience and familiarity than out of concern for nutrition.

How can a person compare the nutrients that these sets of meals provide? One way is to look up each food in a food composition table, write down the food's nutrient values, and compare each one to a standard such as the DRI recommended intakes for nutrients, as we've done in Figure 2–12. By this measure, Monday's meals are the clear winners in terms of meeting nutrient needs within a Calorie budget. Tuesday's meals oversupply Calories and saturated fat while undersupplying fibre and critical vitamins and minerals.

Another useful exercise is to reverse the process of diet planning that was demonstrated in an earlier section. This time, the diet planner starts with the completed day's meals, adding up the amounts of foods from each food group consumed during the day. The result of this process is demonstrated in Table 2–9. By comparing the totals with the recommendations of Canada's Food Guide, a meaningful assessment of the adequacy of the day's meals can be made. Other evaluations, such as identifying sources of whole grains and watching for the discretionary Calories of solid fats and added sugars, complete the assessment.

In this analysis, Monday's meals again prove best for nutrition, providing the necessary amounts from each food group along with a small amount of raw oil needed for health. The Calorie intake falls well within the 2,000-Calorie

allowance. A closer look at Monday's foods reveals that the whole-grain cereal at breakfast, whole-grain sandwich roll at lunch, and whole-grain crackers at snack time meet the recommended intake of fibre. For the vegetables, dark green vegetables, orange vegetables, and legumes are represented in the dinner salad and "other vegetables" are prominent in other meals. In addition, Monday's meals have room to spare for some discretionary Calories, such as additional nutritious foods or added sugars or fats.

Tuesday's meals, though abundant in oils, meat, and enriched grains, completely lack fruit and whole grains and are too low in vegetables to provide adequate nutrients. Tuesday's meals supply too much saturated fat and sugar, as well as excess amounts of meat and enriched grains, pushing the Calorie total to well above the day's allowance.

Figure 2–12

Two Days' Meals

Breakfast

Lunch

Afternoon snack

Dinner

Bedtime snack

Monday's Meals

Monday's meals reflect nutrient-dense choices.

Foods	Energy (Cal)	Combined Saturated and *Trans* Fat (g)	Fibre (g)	Vitamin C (mg)	Calcium (mg)
Before heading off to class, a student eats breakfast:					
1 c whole-grain cold cereal	108	–	3	14	95
1 c skim milk	100	–	–	2	306
1 medium banana (sliced)	105	–	3	10	6
Then goes home for a quick lunch:					
1 roasted turkey sandwich on whole-grain roll with low-fat mayonnaise	343	4	2	–	89
1 c low-salt vegetable juice	50	–	1	60	27
While studying in the afternoon, the student eats a snack:					
4 whole-wheat reduced-fat crackers	86	1	2	–	–
45 g low-fat cheddar cheese	74	2	–	–	176
1 apple	72	–	3	6	8
That night, the student makes dinner:					
A salad:					
1 c raw spinach leaves, shredded carrots	19	–	2	18	61
¼ c garbanzo beans	71	–	3	2	19
5 lg olives and 2 tbs oil-based salad dressing	76	1	1	–	2
A main course:					
1 c spaghetti with meat sauce	425	3	5	15	56
½ c green beans	22	–	2	6	29
2 tsp soft margarine	67	1	–	–	–
And for dessert:					
1 c strawberries	49	–	3	89	24
Later that evening, the student enjoys a bedtime snack:					
3 graham crackers	90	–	–	–	–
1 c skim milk	100	–	–	2	306
Totals:	1,857	12	30	224	1,204
DRI recommended intakes:[a]	2,000	<20[b]	25	75	1,000
Percentage of DRI recommended intakes:	93	60	120	299	120

[a]*DRI values for a sedentary woman, age 19–30. Other DRI values are listed on the inside front cover.*

Figure 2–12

Two Days' Meals (continued)

Breakfast

Quest Photographic Inc.

Lunch

© JUPITERIMAGES/Brand X/Alamy

Afternoon snack

© Image Source White/Alamy

Dinner

© Dick Hemingway

Bedtime snack

© photos.com

Tuesday's Meals

Tuesday's meals are lower on the nutrient-density scale.

Foods	Energy (Cal)	Combined Saturated and *Trans* Fat (g)	Fibre (g)	Vitamin C (mg)	Calcium (mg)
Today, the student starts the day with a fast-food breakfast:					
1 c coffee	5	–	–	–	–
1 English muffin with egg, cheese, and bacon	436	9	2	–	266
Between classes, the student returns home for a quick lunch:					
1 peanut butter and jam sandwich on white bread	426	4	3	–	93
1 c whole milk	156	6	–	4	290
While studying, the student has					
360 mL diet cola	–	–	–	–	–
Bag of chips (14 chips)	105	2	–	4	–
That night for dinner, the student eats					
A salad:					
1 c lettuce					
1 tbs blue cheese dressing	84	2	1	2	23
A main course:					
180 g steak	349	6	–	–	27
½ baked potato (large)	161	–	4	17	26
1 tbs butter	102	7	–	–	3
1 tbs sour cream	31	2	–	–	17
360 mL diet cola	–	–	–	–	–
And for dessert:					
4 sandwich-type cookies	158	2	1		–
Later on, a bedtime snack:					
2 cream-filled snack cakes	250	2	2	–	20
1 c herbal tea	–	–	–	–	–
Totals:	2,263	42	13	27	765
DRI recommended intakes:[a]	2,000	< 20[b]	25	75	1,000
Percentage of DRI recommended intakes:	113%	210	52	36	1,077

[a]DRI values for a sedentary woman, age 19–30. Other DRI values are listed on the inside front cover.

[b]The 20-g value listed is the maximum allowable combined amount of saturated and trans fat for a 2,000-Calorie diet.

Table 2–9

Comparison of Monday's and Tuesday's Meals with Canada's Food Guide

Notice that Monday's meals meet the recommendations of Canada's Food Guide and include an extra cup of vegetables and fruit, with room to spare for some discretionary Calories in the 2,000-Calorie allowance. Tuesday's meals fall short of the Food Guide ideals for vegetables and fruit while overshooting the 2,000-Calorie allowance.

Monday's Meals

Food Group	Breakfast	Lunch	Snack	Dinner	Snack	Food Guide Servings	Recommended Food Guide Servings
Vegetables and fruit	1 c canned	½ c juice	1 c raw	2 c cooked	½ c fresh	9	7–10
Grain products	35 g	70 g	35 g	35 g	35 g	6	6–8
Meat and alternatives		75 g		150 g		3	3
Milk and alternatives	1 c		1 c		1 c	3	2
Oils and fats		1 tsp		2 tsp		3 tsp	2–3 tsp
Calorie allowance						1,857	2,000

Tuesday's Meals

Food Group	Breakfast	Lunch	Snack	Dinner	Snack	Totals	Food Guide Servings
Vegetables and fruit	1 c canned	2 c raw	14 potato chips[a]	1 c cooked		6	7–10
Grain products	60 g	60 g		30 g	60 g	7	6–8
Meat and alternatives	75 g	50 g		225 g		3½	2–3
Milk and alternatives	1 c	1 c				2 c	2
Oils and fats						6 tsp[b]	2–3 tsp
Calorie allowance						2,263	2,000

[a]The potato in 14 potato chips provides less than ½ cup of vegetables.

[b]Does not include solid fats.

Although a single day of such fare poses little threat to the eater, a steady diet of "Tuesday meals" presents a high probability of nutrient deficiencies and weight gain and greatly increased risks of chronic diseases in later life.

Phytochemicals and Functional Foods: What Do They Promise? What Do They Deliver?

Consumers often read exciting headlines reporting some remarkable new discovery about potential health benefits from eating foods that contain **phytochemicals—bioactive compounds** found in plants. Should we be eating more soy, tomatoes, grapes, and other foods from plants for their phytochemicals? What about taking supplements of phytochemicals—does this strategy offer benefits? Store shelves are overflowing with such supplements.

Consumers need information about the potential benefits and hazards of these substances and products, and this Controversy invites you to consider the scientific evidence concerning their effects. To begin, Table C2–1 defines some terms, and Table C2–2 provides a sampling of foods with potential phytochemical effects. In the next sections, we focus on a few food sources of the most interesting of the thousands of known phytochemicals and then discuss the concept of functional foods. The conclusion of this Controversy and of every other valid assessment of phytochemicals is that *foods*, not supplements, are the best and safest source of these potentially beneficial substances.

First, Some Cautions

Foods consist of thousands of different chemicals, and each one has the potential to be beneficial, neutral, or harmful to the body. Some may even be mixed: beneficial in some ways and harmful in others. To complicate matters further, some chemicals may exert different effects on different people or when taken in differing doses or at different life

---

Phytochemical and Functional Food Terms

- **antioxidants** (anti-OX-ih-dants) compounds that protect other compounds from damaging reactions involving oxygen by themselves reacting with oxygen (*anti* means "against"; *oxy* means "oxygen"). *Oxidation* is a potentially damaging effect of normal cell chemistry involving oxygen (more in Chapters 5 and 7).
- **bioactive compounds** defined by Health Canada as the naturally occurring chemical compounds contained in or derived from a plant, animal, or marine source that exert the desired health/wellness benefit (e.g., omega-3 fatty acids in flax or fish oils and beta-glucans from oats and barley).
- **broccoli sprouts** the sprouted seed of *Brassica italica*, or the common broccoli plant, believed to be a functional food by virtue of its high phytochemical content.
- **conjugated linoleic acid (CLA)** a type of fat in butter, milk, and other dairy products believed by some to have biological activity in the body. Not a phytochemical but a biologically active chemical produced by animals.
- **drug** any substance that when taken into a living organism may modify one or more of its functions.
- **flavonoid** (FLAY-von-oyd) any member of a chemical family of yellow pigments in foods; phytochemicals that may exert physiological effects on the body. *Flavus* means "yellow."

- **flaxseed** small brown seed of the flax plant; used in baking, cereals, or other foods; valued by industry as a source of linseed oil and fibre.
- **functional foods** defined by Health Canada as foods that appear similar to conventional foods, consumed as part of the usual diet, with demonstrated physiological benefits or with the ability to reduce chronic disease risks beyond basic nutrient functions. Also defined in Chapter 1.
- **genistein** (GEN-ih-steen) a phytoestrogen found primarily in soybeans that both mimics and blocks the action of estrogen in the body.
- **kefir** (KEE-fur) a liquid form of yogurt, based on milk, probiotic microorganisms, and flavourings.
- **lignans** phytochemicals present in flaxseed, but not in flax oil, that are converted to phytosterols by intestinal bacteria and are under study as possible anticancer agents.
- **lutein** (LOO-teen) a plant pigment of yellow hue; a phytochemical believed to play roles in eye functioning and health.
- **lycopene** (LYE-koh-peen) a pigment responsible for the red colour of tomatoes and other red-hued vegetables; a phytochemical that may act as an antioxidant in the body.
- **miso** fermented soybean paste used in Japanese cooking. Soy products are considered to be functional foods.

(continued)

Phytochemical and Functional Food Terms (continued)

- **natural health products (NHP)** defined by Health Canada to include homeopathic preparations; substances used in traditional medicines (e.g., herbal remedies); minerals or trace elements; vitamins; amino acids; essential fatty acids; or other botanical, animal-, or microorganism-derived (e.g., probiotics) substances. These products are generally sold in medicinal or "dosage" form to diagnose, treat, or prevent disease; restore or correct function; or maintain or promote health. As a product group, NHPs include nutraceuticals.
- **nutraceutical** defined by Health Canada as a product isolated or purified from foods that is generally sold in medicinal forms not usually associated with foods. A nutraceutical is demonstrated to have a physiological benefit or to provide protection against chronic disease.
- **organosulphur compounds** a large group of phytochemicals containing the mineral sulphur. Organosulphur phytochemicals are responsible for the pungent flavours and aromas of foods belonging to the onion, leek, chive, shallot, and garlic family and are thought to stimulate cancer defences in the body.
- **phytochemicals** (FIGH-toe-CHEM-ih-cals) biologically active compounds of plants believed to confer resistance to diseases on the eater, also defined in Chapter 1. *Phyto* means "plant."

- **phytoestrogens** (FIGH-toe-ESS-troh-gens) phytochemicals structurally similar to mammalian hormones, such as the female sex hormone estrogen. Phytoestrogens weakly mimic hormone activity in the human body.
- **probiotics** consumable products containing live microorganisms in sufficient numbers to alter the bacterial colonies of the body in ways believed to benefit health. A *prebiotic* product is a substance that may not be digestible by the host, such as fibre, but serves as food for probiotic bacteria and thus promotes their growth.
- **soy drink** a milklike beverage made from soybeans, claimed to be a functional food. Soy drink should be fortified with vitamin A, vitamin D, riboflavin, calcium, and vitamin B_{12} to approach the nutritional equivalency of milk. Also called *soy milk*.
- **sterol esters** compounds derived from vegetable oils that lower blood cholesterol in human beings by competing with cholesterol for absorption from the digestive tract. The term *sterol esters* often refers to both stanol esters and sterol esters.
- **tofu** a white curd made of soybeans, popular in Asian cuisines, and considered to be a functional food.

Table C2–2

A Sampling of Phytochemicals—Possible Effects and Food Sources

Name	Possible Effects	Food Sources
Capsaicin	May modulate blood clotting; may reduce the risk of fatal clots in heart and artery disease	Hot peppers
Carotenoids (including beta-carotene, lutein, lycopene, and hundreds of related compounds)[a]	Act as antioxidants; possibly reduce risks of heart disease, age-related eye disease,[b] cancer, and other diseases	Deeply pigmented fruit and vegetables (apricots, broccoli, cantaloupe, carrots, pumpkin, spinach, sweet potatoes, tomatoes)
Curcumin	May inhibit enzymes that activate carcinogens	Turmeric, a yellow-coloured spice
Flavonoids (including flavones, flavonols, isoflavones, catechins, and others)[c,d]	Act as antioxidants; may scavenge carcinogens; bind to nitrates in the stomach, preventing conversion to nitrosamines; inhibit cell proliferation; flavonoids of blueberries may improve memory	Berries, black tea, celery, chocolate, citrus fruits, green tea, olives, onions, oregano, purple grapes, purple grape juice, soybeans and soy products, vegetables, whole wheat, wine
Indoles	May trigger production of enzymes that block DNA damage from carcinogens; may inhibit estrogen action	Broccoli and other cruciferous vegetables (Brussels sprouts, cabbage, cauliflower), horseradish, mustard greens
Isothiocyanates (including sulphoraphane)	May inhibit enzymes that activate carcinogens; trigger production of enzymes that detoxify carcinogens	Broccoli and other cruciferous vegetables (Brussels sprouts, cabbage, cauliflower), horseradish, mustard greens
Monoterpenes (including limonene)	May trigger enzyme production to detoxify carcinogens; may inhibit cancer promotion and cell proliferation	Citrus fruit peels and oils
Organosulphur compounds (including allicin)	May speed production of carcinogen-destroying enzymes or slow production of carcinogen-activating enzymes	Chives, garlic, leeks, onions

A Sampling of Phytochemicals—Possible Effects and Food Sources (continued)

Name	Possible Effects	Food Sources
Phenolic acids[d] (including ellagic acid)	May trigger enzyme production to make carcinogens water soluble, facilitating excretion	Coffee beans, fruit (apples, blueberries, cherries, grapes, oranges, pears, prunes, strawberries), oats, potatoes, soybeans
Phytic acid	Binds to minerals, preventing free-radical formation, possibly reducing cancer risk	Whole grains
Phytoestrogens (members of the flavonoid family, genistein and diadzein)	May inhibit estrogen and produce these actions: inhibit cell replication in gastrointestinal tract; reduce risk of breast, colon, ovarian, prostate, and other estrogen-sensitive cancers; reduce cancer cell survival; may reduce risk of osteoporosis; may also alter blood lipids favourably and reduce heart disease risk when consumed in soy foods	Soybeans, soy flour, soy milk, tofu, textured vegetable protein, other legume products
Phytoestrogens (lignans)	Block estrogen activity in cells, possibly reducing the risk of cancer of the breast, colon, ovaries, and prostate	Flaxseed, whole grains
Protease inhibitors	May suppress enzyme production in cancer cells, slowing tumour growth; inhibit hormone binding; inhibit malignant changes in cells	Broccoli sprouts, potatoes, soybeans and other legumes, soy products
Resveratrol[e]	May offset artery-damaging effects of high-fat diets	Red wine, peanuts
Saponins	May interfere with DNA replication, preventing cancer cells from multiplying; stimulate immune response	Alfalfa sprouts, other sprouts, green vegetables, potatoes, tomatoes
Tannins[d]	May inhibit carcinogen activation and cancer promotion; act as antioxidants	Black-eyed peas, grapes, lentils, red and white wine, tea

[a]Other carotenoids include alpha-carotene, beta-cryptoxanthin, and zeaxanthin.

[b]The age-related eye disease is macular degeneration.

[c]Other flavonoids of interest include ellagic acid and ferulic acid.

[d]A subset of the larger group polyphenolic phytochemicals.

[e]A member of the chemical group stilbene, which is a subset of the larger group polyphenolic phytochemicals.

stages.[*,1] All of these possibilities have yet to be clarified by science.

Research on phytochemicals is in its infancy, and what is current today will likely be challenged a year from now by further studies. In most cases, the health benefits observed with intakes of certain foods cannot be ascribed to individual phytochemicals, much less to purified supplements of them.

When considering concentrated supplements of phytochemicals, be aware that any normally beneficial substance,

*The references for the Controversy are listed after the main chapter references at the end of the chapter.

even water, can be toxic when taken in too high a dose (Chapter 8 explains). Also, though most naturally occurring substances are assuredly safe for most healthy people when consumed in foods, virtually no safety studies exist to support the taking of any *purified* phytochemical, nor have safe dosages been established.

How Scientists View Phytochemicals in Foods

At one time, scientists believed that phytochemicals in foods played limited roles in human health. Phytochemical functions were thought to include only

their well-known sensory properties, such as taste, aroma, texture, and colour. Thank phytochemicals for the burning sensation of hot peppers, the pungent flavour of onions and garlic, the bitter tang of chocolate, the aromatic qualities of herbs, and the deep red colour of tomatoes. Today, researchers recognize that some phytochemicals have profound effects on the body by acting as **antioxidants**, mimicking hormones, and altering blood constituents in ways that may protect against some diseases. For example, cancer and heart disease are linked to processes involving oxygen (oxidation) in the body, and antioxidants are thought to oppose these actions (Chapters 5 and 7 provide details).

The scientific path to discovery often begins when scientists notice that people with a diet rich in foods that contain a particular phytochemical rarely suffer from "disease X." Researchers may then examine the diets of people with the condition to find out how much of the phytochemical they consume. If the diets are high in the substance, the researchers perform laboratory experiments in which they expose animals or cell cultures to the phytochemical and observe what happens to uncover plausible biological mechanisms for disease prevention. Science demands the answers to such questions as

- What is the function of the phytochemical in the plant tissues that produce it, and might such a function also occur in the tissues of human beings? For example, if the substance acts as an antioxidant in plant tissue, it may act the same way in human tissues.

- Can human beings absorb and metabolize enough of the phytochemical to have an effect? The substance may be present in the diet but not in a form that people can absorb or use.

- What safety issues pose concerns— is the phytochemical safe for consumption over many years or in pregnancy, childhood, or old age?

Then, if the evidence warrants, scientists may perform clinical studies to evaluate the effects of the substance on human beings. Currently, the evidence is insufficient to say with any degree of certainty whether any phytochemical is effective in fighting diseases or if it is safe to consume in concentrated doses. Research findings on a few phytochemical-rich foods that seem likely to benefit health are discussed next.

Whole Foods, Wine, and Tea

Historically, diets containing whole grains, fruit, vegetables, herbs, spices, teas, and red wine have been reputed to possess health-promoting qualities. Science has revealed that these foods and beverages

all have something in common: phytochemicals of the flavonoid family. Figure C2–1 depicts some of the best-known phytochemical-rich foods. Epidemiological evidence spanning many countries indicates that deaths from cancer, heart disease, and heart attacks are less common where these foods are plentiful in the diet, where tea is a beverage, or where red wine is consumed in moderation.[2] Many **flavonoids** act as antioxidants and may protect against cancers and heart disease by this mechanism. Nevertheless, a recent review of the literature concludes that more evidence is needed before any claims can be made for flavonoids themselves as the protective factor in foods, particularly when they are extracted from foods or herbs and sold as supplements.[3]

Research suggests that one flavonoid of grapes and red wine in particular may have disease-fighting qualities; however, the amount of this and other flavonoids in the wine may be too low to benefit human health.[4] The same flavonoid has been credited with greatly extending the life of yeast cells, but no one knows if such an effect is possible in other species.[5] Because flavonoids often impart a bitter taste to foods, food producers may refine away natural flavonoids to please consumers who generally prefer milder flavours.[6] To produce white grape juice or white wine, makers remove the red, flavonoid-rich grape skins to lighten the flavour and the colour of the product while greatly reducing its flavonoid content.

Whether or not research confirms the cancer-fighting and heart-defending nature of the flavonoids, consumers should seek out a variety of whole fruit, vegetables, and other plant-derived foods with their flavonoids intact in place of their more refined counterparts.[7] Beyond any doubt, such diets are consistently associated with low rates of diseases. Flavonoid supplements have not been proven effective or safe. As for red wine, read Controversy 3 in Chapter 3 before making a decision. The potential health benefits may not be worth alcohol's immediate and substantial risks.

Chocolate

Imagine the delight of research subjects who were instructed to eat three

ounces of dark (bittersweet) chocolate chips as part of an experiment. In a less appealing aspect of the study, researchers drew blood from the subjects for analysis. They discovered that a flavonoid antioxidant from chocolate had accumulated in the blood; at the same time, the level of certain harmful oxidizing compounds dropped substantially (40%).[8] The antioxidant effects of dark chocolate may turn out to be as powerful as those of tea or red wine.[9] In theory, chocolate may also "thin the blood" by reducing the tendency of blood to clot, and blood clots are a major cause of heart attacks and strokes (see Chapter 11).[10] No evidence exists, however, to indicate that people who eat chocolate actually suffer fewer heart attacks or strokes than people who do not.[11]

If consuming some daily chocolate sounds like a prudent and harmless idea, consider another centuries-old medicinal use of chocolate: promoting weight gain.[12] Three ounces of sweetened chocolate candy contain over 400 Calories, a significant portion of most people's daily Calorie allowance. At the same time, chocolate contributes few nutrients save two—fat and sugar. For most people, antioxidant phytochemicals are best obtained from nutrient-dense low-Calorie fruit and vegetables and Calorie-free green or black tea—with chocolate enjoyed as an occasional treat.

Soybeans

Compared with people in the West, Asians living in Asia suffer less frequently from osteoporosis (adult bone loss); cancers, especially of the breast, colon, and prostate; and heart disease. Asian women also suffer less from symptoms related to menopause, the midlife decline in women's estrogen secretion accompanied by the cessation of menstruation.[13] When Asians immigrate to the United States and adopt Western diets and habits, however, they experience these diseases and problems at the same rate as native Westerners. Among many differences between the diets of the two regions, Asians consume far more soybeans (a

An Array of Phytochemicals in a Variety of Fruit and Vegetables

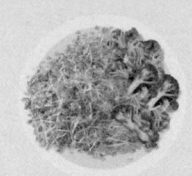

Broccoli and broccoli sprouts contain an abundance of sulfphoraphane.

An apple a day—rich in flavonoids.

The phytoestrogens genistein and diadzein are found in soybeans and soy products.

Garlic, leeks, and onions, with their abundant organosulphur compounds, may benefit health.

The phytochemicals of grapes, red wine, and peanuts include resveratrol.

Strawberries are a source of flavonoids.

Cooked tomatoes are the best source of lycopene, a carotenoid that may reduce cancer risk.

Citrus fruit provide limonene.

The flavonoids in black tea differ from those in green tea, with different potential effects on health.

The flavonoids in cocoa, chocolate, fruits and vegetables, legumes, and tea may benefit health.

Spinach and other green, orange, red, and yellow fruits and vegetables contain carotenoids.

Flaxseed is the richest source of lignans.

Blueberries are among the richest sources of flavonoids.

(spinach) © Matthew Farruggio; (apples) © PhotoDisc, Inc.; (soy products, wine, strawberries, black tea, cocoa, blueberries, tomatoes) © 2001 PhotoDisc, Inc.; (garlic, citrus fruit) © EyeWire, Inc.; (flaxseed) Courtesy of Flax Council of Canada; (broccoli and sprouts) Brassica Protection Products

Source: Data from P. M. Kris-Etherton and coauthor, "Bioactive compounds in nutrition and health–research methodologies for establishing biological function: The antioxidant and anti-inflammatory effects of flavonoids on antherosclerosis," Annual Review of Nutrition 24 (2004): 511–538.

legume) and soy products such as **miso**, **soy drink**, and **tofu** than do Westerners.

Soybeans contain phytochemicals known as **phytoestrogens**. Researchers suspect that the phytoestrogens of soy foods, their protein content, or a combination of these factors may be responsible for health effects in soy-eating peoples. However, research, though ongoing, is limited. So far, we know with certainty that phytoestrogens are plant-derived chemical relatives of the human hormone estrogen, that they weakly mimic or modulate the hormone's effects on some body tissues, and that they also act as antioxidants. We also know that breast cancer, colon cancer, and prostate cancer are estrogen sensitive—that is, they grow when exposed to estrogen. Whether any of these or other actions of phytoestrogens may alter the course of estrogen-sensitive cancers remains unknown, but recent results from breast cancer studies do not support the idea.[14]

As for symptoms of menopause, phytoestrogens may alter a woman's monthly hormonal cycle in ways that may reduce her risk of adult bone loss and the sensation of elevated body temperature known as "hot flashes," common in menopause.[15] Although more research is needed, one review of the literature concluded that a diet high in soy foods may offer bone protection rivalling that of hormone replacement therapy (HRT, the administration of female hormone drugs to prevent bone loss and symptoms of menopause).[16] Because HRT involves some serious health risks, supplements of phytoestrogens are often sold to menopausal women as a "natural" alternative, but research does not support taking phytoestrogen *supplements* for bone mineral retention or hot flashes.[17]

Not only do phytoestrogen supplements seem ineffective for preserving health, but their use may also involve some risk. While studying one soy phytoestrogen, **genistein**, researchers found that, instead of suppressing cancer growth, high doses of genistein appeared to speed division of breast cancer cells in laboratory cultures and in mice.[18] Also, the female offspring of mice treated with high doses of genistein during pregnancy seem prone to developing cancer of the uterus with an incidence even greater than that of a known cancer-causing drug.*,[19] Pregnant women should never take chances with unproven supplements of any kind. Chapter 13 provides many reasons why.

The paired, opposing findings on the health effects of phytoestrogens should raise a red warning flag against taking supplements, especially in women whose close relatives have developed breast cancer.[20] In truth, little is known about the potential effects of doses of these compounds in human beings of any age.[21] Until more is known, a safer route to obtaining soy phytoestrogens is to include moderate amounts of soy-based foods in the diet, as generations of Asian people have safely done through the ages.[22]

Flaxseed

Historically, people have used **flaxseed** for relieving constipation or digestive distress. Currently, flaxseed and its oil are

*The drug is DES, or diethylstilbestrol, once given to pregnant women before the discovery of greatly increased risk of uterine and breast cancer among their daughters.

under study for potential health benefits.[23] Flaxseed contains **lignans**, compounds converted into biologically active phytoestrogens by bacteria that normally reside in the human intestine. A review of the literature offers this evidence:[24]

- Compared with rats fed an ordinary chow, rats fed chow high in flaxseed develop fewer cancerous changes and smaller tumours in mammary tissue after exposure to chemicals known to cause cancer.

- Cancerous tumours of the lung diminish in size, and new tumour development is significantly reduced in rats fed flaxseed chow.

- Studies of populations suggest that women who excrete more phytoestrogens in the urine (an indicator of phytoestrogen intake from flaxseed and other sources) have lower rates of breast cancer.

Studies of the direct effects of giving flaxseed to *people* are lacking, however, and some risks are possible with its use. Flaxseed contains compounds that may interfere with vitamin or mineral absorption; thus, high daily intakes could cause nutrient-deficiency diseases. Large quantities of flaxseed can also cause digestive distress.

Although no clear role has been established for flaxseed in the prevention of human cancer, including a spoonful or two of ground flaxseed in the diet may not be a bad idea. Flaxseed is a rich source of linolenic acid, a needed nutrient often lacking in the North American diet (see Chapter 5).

Tomatoes

People around the world who eat the most tomatoes, say, about five tomato-containing meals per week, are less likely to suffer from cancers of the esophagus, prostate, or stomach than those who avoid tomatoes.[25] Among the phytochemical candidates for promoting this effect is **lycopene**, a red pigment with antioxidant activity found in guava, papaya, pink grapefruit, tomatoes (especially cooked tomatoes and tomato products), and watermelon.

On the one hand, while lycopene may inhibit the reproduction of cancer cells,[26] on the other hand, one of its chemical cousins, beta-carotene supplements, when given to smokers, increased lung cancer rates (see below). Some research suggests that an increased risk of breast cancer may follow blood concentrations of lycopene and related compounds that are too low.[27] Low blood lycopene also correlates with an elevated incidence of heart disease, heart attack, and stroke.[28] Lycopene may also protect against the damaging sun rays that cause skin cancer.

In one study, women who consumed a diet rich in fruit and vegetables had high blood lycopene concentrations and a greatly reduced concentration of an indicator of cervical cancer risk.[29] Do scientists conclude, therefore, that lycopene prevents cervical cancer and that women should take lycopene supplements? No, the authors of the study and another like it rightly suggest that a diet rich in fruit and vegetables, with their host of nutrients and phytochemicals, reduces women's risk of cervical cancer and many other diseases.[30]

A very important lesson about supplements can be learned from experience with lycopene's chemical cousin, the normally beneficial vitamin A relative beta-carotene. Diets high in fruit and vegetables that contain beta-carotene often correlate with low rates of lung cancer; when beta-carotene supplements were given to smokers in studies, however, lung cancer rates increased. For safety, forgo supplements of lycopene until research confirms their effectiveness and rules out hazards.

Garlic

For thousands of years, people have credited garlic with medicinal properties. Descriptions of its uses for headaches, heart disease, and tumours are recorded in early Egyptian medical writings.[31] In modern medical research, over 3,000 publications have investigated the potential health benefits of garlic, and many have reported positive findings.[32] Among garlic's active constituents are **organosulphur compounds** that are reported to inhibit cancer development in laboratory animals.[33] These compounds may work by suppressing the formation of certain harmful oxidizing compounds that damage genetic material in animal cells and trigger cancerous changes. This evidence hints that eating garlic may be beneficial against some forms of cancer in human beings.[34] Investigations into potential roles for garlic against allergies, heart disease, and even the bacterial cause of ulcers are ongoing.[35]

Other constituents of garlic also seem promising in promoting heart health. Some may fight fungal infections, reduce the clotting of the blood, or improve levels of blood cholesterol in people whose cholesterol is too high for heart health.[36] Thus, if you like garlic in foods, you can consume them with confidence; history and some research are on your side.

Although these findings hold promise, studies of garlic *supplements*, such as powders and oil, have been disappointing, save one type.[37] Positive results seem to be associated with an aged preparation of garlic that lacks garlic's characteristic odour but is rich in antioxidants and other compounds.[38] All in all, from the scientists' point of view, no certainty exists about whether large doses of concentrated chemicals from garlic may improve a person's health or injure it.[39]

Supporters and Detractors of Phytochemical/Bioactive Compound Supplements

Users and sellers of supplements argue that the existing evidence is good enough to recommend that people take supplements of purified phytochemicals. Eager for the potential benefits, they seem to discount the potential for harm. They point out that people have been consuming foods containing phytochemicals for tens of thousands of years. The body is clearly accustomed to handling phytochemicals in foods, the reasoning goes, so it follows that supplements of those phytochemicals must be safe for the body as well.

Such thinking raises concerns among scientists. They point out that although the body is equipped to handle phytochemicals when diluted among all of the other constituents of natural foods, it is not adapted to receiving concentrated doses of phytochemicals in supplement form. Consider these facts about phytochemical supplements and health:

1. Phytochemicals can alter body functions, sometimes powerfully, in ways that are only partly understood.

2. Evidence for the safety of isolated phytochemicals in human beings is lacking.

3. Health Canada (Food Directorate for Functional Foods) and Natural Health Products Directorate (for nutraceuticals)* are the regulatory bodies that oversee the safety of phytochemicals sold to consumers. Studies are required to prove that they are safe or effective before marketing them.

4. Phytochemical labels may make claims about contributing to the body's structure or functioning, but research to support such claims may be weak.

Researchers who study phytochemicals conclude that the best-known, most effective, and safest sources for phytochemicals are foods, not supplements.

If consuming whole *foods* that are rich sources of phytochemicals is wise, would it be wiser still to choose foods that have been enriched with extra doses of phytochemicals? The next section explores some issues surrounding functional foods.

The Concept of Functional Foods

Although the American food supply is being transformed by a proliferation of **functional**

*See Nutraceuticals at http://www.agr.gc.ca/misb/fb-ba/nutra/index_e.php?page=reg.

foods—foods claimed to provide health benefits beyond those of the traditional nutrients[40]—such is not the case in Canada. In truth, all of the foods mentioned so far in this Controversy, from grains to garlic, are functional—they stand out as having a potentially greater impact on the health of the body (see Table C2–3).[41]

Not long ago, most of us could agree on what was a food and what was a **drug**. As these new foods come to market, this distinction is becoming less clear.

Cholesterol-Reducing Margarine, Juice, and Candies

Consider some options for lowering high blood cholesterol, an indicator of an increased risk of heart disease. Replacing butter with ordinary liquid margarine in the diet may gradually lower blood cholesterol by a few percentage points over several months. Cholesterol-lowering medication, on the other hand, takes just weeks to dramatically lower cholesterol by as much as 40 percent—clearly, a drug action. But regular daily use of foods such as margarine, juice, or candies enhanced with **sterol esters** or *stanol esters* may achieve a sizable reduction in blood cholesterol of, say, 10 to 15 percent over a relatively short time.[42]

The sterol esters added to these foods act like a drug in the body. Also like drugs, sterol esters may have an undesirable side effect: reports link high blood levels of these compounds with early signs of heart disease in people who have an inherited disability to clear them from the blood; they may also lower the blood concentration

Table C2–3

Categories of Functional Foods[a]

1. Basic foods, e.g., oat bran (contains beta-glucan)

2. Processed foods with added ingredients, e.g., calcium- and vitamin D–fortified fruit juice

3. Foods enhanced to have more of a functional component (via special livestock feeding), e.g., omega 3-milk and omega 3-eggs

[a]Agriculture and Agri-Food Canada—Functional Foods, http://www4.agr.gc.ca/AAFC-AAC/display-afficher.do?id=1171305207040&lang=eng#s2.

of some beneficial carotenes, such as lycopene, mentioned earlier.[43]

Sterol esters may pose some degree of risk to certain people. No one yet knows how these substances may affect children and teenagers, yet children and teens may encounter them in the diet in the form of margarine, juice, and candies. As is so often true in nutrition, a cautious approach to these new, potentially beneficial products is warranted.

Yogurt

Yogurt is a special case among functional foods because it contains living *Lactobacillus* or other bacteria that ferment milk into yogurt or the liquid yogurt beverage called **kefir**. Such microorganisms, or **probiotics**, are believed to alter the native bacterial colonies or other conditions in the digestive tract in ways that may reduce diseases.[44] *Lactobacillus* organisms may be useful for improving the diarrhea that often occurs from the use of antibiotic drugs or from other causes, especially among children.[45] Some research also suggests benefits from yogurt against certain chronic intestinal diseases, colon cancer, ulcers, and other digestive problems.[46] More research is needed to verify suggestions that probiotic preparations may alleviate lactose intolerance and allergies, enhance immune function, protect against digestive tract cancers (particularly colon cancer) and ulcers, reduce urinary and vaginal infections in women, and lower blood cholesterol.[47]

Is Every Food Functional?

Many functional foods occur in nature. A serving of **broccoli sprouts**, for example, provides a concentrated source of a phytochemical associated with cancer prevention. Broccoli itself contains this type of phytochemical in less impressive but still healthy doses.[48] Drinking a half-cup of cranberry juice daily may reduce the incidence of urinary tract infections in women because cranberries contain a phytochemical that dislodges bacteria from the tract.[49] Cooked tomatoes, as mentioned, provide lycopene, along with **lutein** (an antioxidant associated with healthy eye function), vitamin C (an antioxidant vitamin), and many

other healthful attributes.[50] Lutein also occurs in leafy greens, along with other phytochemicals and beneficial nutrients. In fact, all vegetables, fruit, and whole foods of every kind possess characteristic arrays of thousands of potentially healthful constituents.

Who can say whether even butter and cheese, foods known to contain fats damaging to the heart and arteries when eaten in excess, may qualify as "functional foods" by virtue of their content of **conjugated linoleic acid (CLA)**? In some animal studies, CLA inhibits cancer, lowers cholesterol, improves diabetes, improves immune function, and nudges body composition toward leanness.[51] In other studies, the results are negative, however, and little research has been done on the effects of CLA on human beings.[52]

Virtually all foods, even a chocolate bar, have some special value in supporting health.[53] How can a consumer sort all of this out and choose wisely? The final section of this Controversy provides some guidance, but first a look at some of the problems concerning functional foods is in order.

Functional Food and Phytochemical Concerns

Serious problems exist concerning manufactured functional foods. Large doses of purified phytochemicals added to foods may produce effects vastly different from those of the phytochemicals in whole foods, and they may even be toxic. For example, concentrated cranberry tablets may significantly increase the taker's risk of developing kidney stones instead of providing the bladder benefits of cranberry juice mentioned earlier.[54]

Aside from the safety issues, conclusions about effectiveness cannot be drawn until research uncertainties are remedied. Even for soy, a popular focus of research, serious problems exist.[55] For example, soy extracts commonly used in experiments come from only the soy germ and lack many of the phytoestrogens present in whole soybeans, rendering comparisons among studies employing various soy products all but meaningless. Also, the way animals metabolize soy phytochemicals

differs substantially from the way most people do, short-circuiting human application of some animal results. Cell studies, too, continuously expose cells to 10 to 1,000 times the levels of phytochemicals typically achieved by people who eat soy foods in the diet. Until such issues are resolved, the most likely way to benefit from soy is to eat small servings of regular soy foods, such as soy drinks, tofu, or soy burgers, not by taking a large dose from a supplement or highly fortified functional food.[56]

Foods sold as functional foods often contain untested medicinal herbs. Such herbs have in recent years caused serious damage to health and even some deaths among consumers (see Chapter 11). Research has not matured nearly enough to identify which isolated phytochemicals, medicinal herbs, or other constituents may appropriately be added to foods, and consuming these substances can be risky in unimaginable ways.

One might also question the wisdom of dousing foods of low nutrient density, such as fried snack chips or candies, with phytochemicals and then labelling them "functional," implying that they will enhance health. Such products often seem to be aimed more at consumers' wallets than at improved consumer health.

Until research determines more about functional foods, consumers are on their own to make sure that the products they use are safe and effective. Start by finding answers to the following questions:[57]

- *Does it work?* Well-controlled, peer-reviewed research is generally lacking or inconclusive for manufactured functional foods (see Chapter 1 and its Controversy feature for guidelines to help identify such research).

- *Is it safe?* Check the research for well-controlled safety studies. The active ingredients of functional foods may cause allergies, drug interactions (see Chapter 14's Controversy section), dizziness, and other side effects.

- Has Health Canada issued a warning about the product or any ingredients in it? Check Health Canada's website for "Advisories, Warnings and Recalls" (http://www.hc-sc.gc.ca/ahc-asc/media/advisories-avis/index_e.html) to find out.

Some fatty acids may help reduce the risk of cardiovascular disease and help reduce inflammation, while others help with development and maintenance of brain function and normal health and development (see http://www.brescia.uwo.ca/research/food-nutrition/functional-foods/index.html).

- *How much of what does it contain?* This is currently not allowed in Canada, but U.S. manufacturers are required to list the names of added herbs and phytochemicals on labels but not the quantities added. Beware, especially, of combinations of "functional" ingredients.

- *Is the food in keeping with the current Nutrition Recommendations?* U.S. candy bars, brownies, or "smoothie" shakes may be fortified with herbs and phytochemicals, but they are still made mostly of sugar and fat.

The Final Word

In light of all of the evidence for and against phytochemicals and functional foods, it seems clear that a moderate approach is warranted. People who eat the recommended amounts of a variety of fruit and vegetables may cut their risk of many diseases by as much as half. Replacing some meat with soy foods or other legumes may also lower heart disease and cancer risks. In the context of a healthy diet, foods are time-tested for safety, posing virtually no risk of toxic levels of nutrients or phytochemicals (although some contain natural toxins: see Chapter 12). Table C2–4 offers some tips for consuming the foods known to provide phytochemicals.

Beneficial constituents are widespread among foods. Don't try to single out one phytochemical for its magical health effect. Instead, take a no-nonsense approach where your health is concerned: choose a wide variety of whole grains, legumes, fruit, and vegetables in the context of an adequate, balanced, and varied diet and receive all of the health benefits that these foods offer.

Table C2–4

Tips for Consuming Phytochemicals

- **Eat more fruit.** Remember to choose juices and raw, dried, or cooked fruit and vegetables at mealtimes as well as for snacks. Choose dried fruit in place of candy.
- **Increase vegetable portions** of raw/uncooked or cooked plain vegetables.
- **Use herbs and spices.** Cookbooks offer ways to include parsley, basil, garlic, hot peppers, oregano, and other beneficial seasonings.
- **Replace some meat.** Replace some of the meat in the diet with grains, legumes, and vegetables. Oatmeal, soy meat replacer, or grated carrots mixed with ground meat and seasonings make a luscious, nutritious meat loaf, for example.
- **Add grated vegetables.** Carrots in chili or meatballs, celery and squash in spaghetti sauce, and so on, add phytochemicals without greatly changing the taste of the food.
- **Try new foods.** Try a new fruit, vegetable, or whole grain each week. Walk through vegetable aisles and visit farmers' markets. Read recipes. Try tofu, fortified soy drink, or soybeans in cooking.

Self-Check

Answers to these Self-Check questions are in Appendix D.

1. The nutrient standards in use today include all of the following *except*
   a. Adequate Intakes (AI)
   b. Daily Minimum Requirements (DMR)
   c. Daily Values (DV)
   d. a and c

2. The Dietary Reference Intakes were devised for which of the following purposes?
   a. to set nutrient goals for individuals
   b. to suggest upper limits of intakes, above which toxicity is likely
   c. to set average nutrient requirements for use in research
   d. all of the above

3. According to Canada's Food Guide, which of the following may be counted among either the meat or the vegetables?
   a. chicken
   b. avocados
   c. cooked legumes
   d. potatoes

4. Which of the following is a source of unsaturated fatty acids?

   a. olives

   b. nuts

   c. vegetable oil

   d. all of the above

5. Which of the following values are found on food labels?

   a. Daily Values

   b. Dietary Reference Intakes

   c. Recommended Dietary Allowances

   d. Estimated Average Requirements

6. The energy intake recommendation is set at a level predicted to maintain body weight.

   T   F

7. The Dietary Reference Intakes (DRI) are for all people, regardless of their medical history.

   T   F

8. People who choose not to eat animals or their products need to find an alternative to Canada's Food Guide when planning their diets.

   T   F

9. By law, food labels must state as a percentage of the Daily Values the amounts of vitamin C, vitamin A, niacin, and thiamin present in food.

   T   F

10. To be labelled "low fat," a food must contain 3 grams of fat or less per serving.

    T   F

track it! ▸ Diet Analysis
PLUS ✚   Concepts in Action

start now! ┈┈▸ Ready to make a change? If you have access to a computer, it can be a time saver—diet analysis programs perform all of these calculations at lightning speed. This convenience may make working it out for yourself, using paper and a sharp pencil with a big eraser, seem a bit old-fashioned. But there are times when using a laptop or a diet application on a cell phone might not be practical—such as while standing in line at the cafeteria or at a fast-food counter—where real-life food decisions must be made quickly.

People who work out diet analyses for themselves on paper and those who put extra time into studying, changing, and reviewing their computer analysis often learn to "see" what constitutes a "Food Guide serving" and which foods in their diet contribute fats, sugars and the most kcalories (a skill you can fully develop by the time you reach Chapter 10). They can quickly assess their food options and make informed choices at mealtimes. People who fail to develop such skills must wait until they can access their computer programs to find out how well they did after the fact.

Compare Your Intakes with the Recommended Intakes for Canadians

The purpose of this chapter's exercise is to give you a feel for the recommended number of "Food Guide servings" for your Profile and to help you consider your sources of fats and sugars. Use the Diet Analysis Plus (DA+) program to help you evaluate your nutritional intake and needs.

1. From the Home page of DA+ select the Reports tab and under the Nutrients heading, select Daily Food Log and Choose Day Two of your three-day diet intake (from Chapter 1). Choose all meals and snacks for that day. Generate a report. Now take this opportunity to develop your skills at converting the portions of food and beverages you consumed into the serving sizes shown on Canada's Food Guide (page 38). Did your intake for that day conform to the suggested number of servings for your profile? Did you consume too few foods from any particular food group(s)? Which, if any, were lacking? Using Canada's Food Guide to help you, suggest ways that you might realistically change your intake to better conform to the recommended number of servings from each food group for you.

2. What about fat? Select the Reports tab and select Day 2 (all meals); then, under the Nutrients heading select Macronutrient Ranges. Generate a report. Did your fat intake for that day fall between 20 percent and 35 percent of your total energy? Also see the Oils and Fats category on page 38 of the Food Guide. Did you take in enough of the recommended types of oils and fats to meet your need? Change your date to include all three days of your record; generate a report to see your fat intake average. How does your single day's fat intake compare with your three-day average?

3. Breaking this information down further, which foods on your food list contribute sugars? To find out, click on the Reports tab, select Day 1 (all meals), and under the Advanced heading, select Source Analysis; then, from the pick-list use the down arrow and select Sugar, Total. If you consumed substantial calories from sugars, suggest realistic ways to reduce your intake.

4. A great feature of the DA+ program is its Source Analysis report, which allows you to list food sources of calories (kcal) or specific nutrients in order of predominance. From the Reports tab, under the Advanced heading select Source Analysis, then select Day Three (choose all meals), and then, using the pick-list down arrow, select Kilocalories. Generate a report. Which foods provided most of the calories on that day? If you consumed vegetables, where did they fall on the list? In later chapters, you'll use this report again to analyze various nutrients in your diet.

Endnotes

1. Standing Committee on the Scientific Evaluation of Dietary Reference Intakes, Food and Nutrition Board, Institute of Medicine, *Dietary Reference Intakes: Applications in Dietary Assessment* (Washington, D.C.: National Academies Press, 2000), pp. 5–7.

2. S. Murphy, S. I. Barr, and M. I. Poos, Using the new Dietary Reference Intakes to assess diets: A map to the maze, *Nutrition Reviews* 60 (2002): 267–275.

3. Committee on Use of Dietary Reference Intakes in Nutrition Labeling, *Dietary Reference Intakes: Guiding Principles for Nutrition Labeling and Fortification* (Washington, D.C.: National Academies Press, 2003), pp. ES1–ES3; Standing Committee on the Scientific Evaluation of Dietary Reference Intakes, Food and Nutrition Board, Institute of Medicine, 2003, pp. 51–52 [see reference 1].

4. Health Canada, *Eating Well with Canada's Food Guide* (Ottawa, 2007), Catalogue no. H164-38/1-2007E, available at http://www.hc-sc.gc.ca/fn-an/food-guide-aliment/index_e.html.

5. S. J. Weinstein and coauthors, Healthy Eating Index scores are associated with blood nutrient concentrations in the Third National Health and Nutrition Examination Survey, *Journal of the American Dietetic Association* 104 (2004): 576–584.

Controversy 2

1. L. Hilakivi-Clarke and coauthors, Maternal and prepubertal diet, mammary development and breast cancer risk, *Journal of Nutrition* 131 (2001): 154S–157S.

2. A. H. Wu and coauthors, Green tea and risk of breast cancer in Asian Americans, *International Journal of Cancer* 106 (2003): 574–579; L. Le Marchand and coauthors, Intake of flavonoids and lung cancer, *Journal of the National Cancer Institute* 92 (2000): 154–160; P. Knekt and coauthors, Quercetin intake and the incidence of cerebrovascular disease, *European Journal of Clinical Nutrition* 54 (2000): 415–417.

3. J. A. Ross and C. M. Kasum, Dietary flavonoids: Bioavailability, metabolic effects, and safety, *Annual Review of Nutrition* 22 (2002): 19–34.

4. J. H. M. de Vries and coauthors, Red wine is a poor source of bioavailable flavonols in men, *Journal of Nutrition* 131 (2001): 745–748; Y. Scheider and coauthors, Anti-proliferative effect of resveratrol, a natural component of grapes and wine, on human colonic cancer cells, *Cancer Letter* 158 (2000): 85–91.

5. K. T. Howitz and coauthors, Small molecule activators of sirtuins extend *Saccharomyces cerevisiae* lifespan, *Nature* 425 (2003): 191–196.

6. A. Drewnowski and C. Gomez-Carneros, Bitter taste, phytonutrients, and the consumer: A review, *American Journal of Clinical Nutrition* 72 (2000): 1424–1435.

7. U. Wenzel and coauthors, Dietary flavone is a potent apoptosis inducer in human colon carcinoma cells, *Cancer Research* 60 (2000): 3823–3831.

8. D. Rein and coauthors, Epicatechin in human plasma: In vivo determination and effect of chocolate consumption on plasma oxidation status, *Journal of Nutrition* 130 (2000): 2109S–2114S.

9. J. F. Wang and coauthors, A dose-response effect from chocolate consumption on plasma epicatechin and oxidative damage, *Journal of Nutrition* 130 (2000): 2115S–2119S.

10. F. M. Steinberg, M. M. Bearden, and C. L. Keen, Cocoa and chocolate flavonoids: Implications for cardiovascular health, *Journal of the American Dietetic Association* 103 (2003): 215–223; D. Rein and coauthors, Cocoa and wine polyphenols modulate platelet activation and function, *Journal of Nutrition* 130 (2000): 2120S–2126S.

11. Steinberg, Bearden, and Keen, 2003 [see reference 10].

12. T. L. Dillinger and coauthors, Food of the gods: Cure for humanity? A cultural history of the medicinal and ritual use of chocolate, *Journal of Nutrition* 130 (2000): 2057S–2072S.

13. K. E. Wangen and coauthors, Soy isoflavones improve plasma lipids in normo-cholesterolemic and mildly hypercholesterolemic postmenopausal women, *American Journal of Clinical Nutrition* 73 (2001): 225–231.

14. L. Keinan-Boker and coauthors, Dietary phytoestrogens and breast cancer risk, *American Journal of Clinical Nutrition* 79 (2004): 282–288; A. Cassidy, Potential risks and benefits of phytoestrogen-rich diets, *International Journal of Vitamin Nutrition Research* 73 (2003): 120–126.

15. C. Nagata and coauthors, Soy product intake and hot flashes in Japanese women: Results from a community-based prospective study, *American Journal of Epidemiology* 153 (2001): 790–793.

16. A. Cotter and K. D. Cashman, Genistein appears to prevent early post-menopausal bone loss as effectively as hormone replacement therapy, *Nutrition Reviews* 61 (2003): 346–351.

17. S. Kreijkamp-Kaspers and coauthors, Effect of soy protein containing isoflavones on cognitive function, bone mineral density, and plasma lipids in postmenopausal women, *Journal of the American Medical Association* 292 (2004): 65–74; J. A. Tice and coauthors, Phytoestrogen supplements for the treatment of hot flashes: The Isoflavone Clover Extract Study, *Journal of the American Medical Association* 290 (2003): 207–214; I. Demonty, B. Lamarche, and P. J. H. Jones, Role of isoflavones in the hypo-cholesterolemic effect of soy, *Nutrition Reviews* 61 (2003): 189–203; J. Rymer, R. Wilson, and K. Ballard, Making decisions about hormone replacement therapy, *British Journal of Medicine* 326 (2003): 322–326; J. J. Anderson and coauthors, Soy isoflavones: No effects on bone mineral content and bone mineral density in healthy, menstruating young women after one year, *Journal of the American College of Nutrition* 21 (2002): 388–393; H. D. Nelson and coauthors, Postmenopausal hormone replacement therapy, *Journal of the American Medical Association* 288 (2002): 872–881; A. St. Germain and coauthors, Isoflavone-rich or isoflavone-poor soy protein does not reduce menopausal symptoms during 24 weeks of treatment, *Menopause* 8 (2001): 17–26.

18. C. D. Allred and coauthors, Soy diets containing varying amounts of genistein stimulate growth of estrogen-dependent (MCF-7) tumors in a dose-dependent manner, *Cancer Research* 61 (2001): 5045–5050.

19. R. R. Newbold and coauthors, Uterine adenocarcinoma in mice treated neonatally with genistein, *Cancer Research* 61 (2001): 4325–4328.

20. M. S. Kurzer, Phytoestrogen supplement use by women, *Journal of Nutrition* 133 (2003): 1983S–1986S.

21. Cassidy, 2003 [see reference 14].

22. C. Munro and coauthors, Soy isoflavones: A safety review, *Nutrition Reviews* 61 (2003): 1–33.

23. M. R. Ogborn and coauthors, Dietary flax oil reduces renal injury, oxidized LDL content, and tissue n-6/n-3 FA ratio in experimental polycystic kidney disease, *Lipids* 37 (2002): 1059–1065.

24. P. E. Bown, Evaluating the health claim of flaxseed and cancer prevention, *Nutrition Today* 36 (2001): 144–158.

25. E. Giovannucci and coauthors, A prospective study of tomato products, lycopene, and prostate cancer risk, *Journal of the National Cancer Institute* 94 (2002): 391–398; L. Chen and coauthors, Oxidative DNA damage in prostate cancer patients consuming tomato sauce–based entrees as a whole-food intervention, *Journal of the National Cancer Institute* 93 (2001): 1872–1879.

26. D. Albanes and coauthors, α-Tocopherol and β-carotene supplements and lung cancer incidence in the Alpha-Tocopherol, Beta-Carotene Cancer Prevention Study: Effects of base line characteristics and study compliance, *Journal of the National Cancer Institute* 88 (1996): 1560–1570; P. Prakash, R. M. Russell, and N. I. Krinsky, In vitro inhibition of proliferation of estrogen-dependent and estrogen-independent human breast cancer cells treated with carotenoids or retinoids, *Journal of Nutrition* 131 (2001): 1574–1580.

27. P. Toniolo and coauthors, Serum carotenoids and breast cancer, *American Journal of Epidemiology* 153 (2001): 1142–1147.

28. T. H. Rissanen and coauthors, Serum lycopene concentrations and carotid atherosclerosis: The Kuopio Ischaemic Heart Disease Risk Factor Study, *American Journal of Clinical Nutrition* 77 (2003): 133–138; J. H. Dwyer and coauthors, Oxygenated carotenoid lutein and progression of early atherosclerosis: The Los Angeles Atherosclerosis Study, *Circulation* 103 (2001): 2922–2927; L. Arab and S. Steck, Lycopene and cardiovascular disease, *American Journal of Clinical Nutrition* 71 (2000): 1691S–1695S.

29. R. L. Sedjo and coauthors, Vitamin A, carotenoids, and risk of persistent oncogenic human papillomavirus infection, *Cancer Epidemiology, Biomarkers and Prevention* 11 (2002): 876–884.

30. M. A. Schiff and coauthors, Serum carotenoids and risk of cervical intraepithelial neoplasia in southwestern American Indian women, *Cancer Epidemiology, Biomarkers and Prevention* 10 (2001): 1219–1222.

31. C. Borek, Antioxidant health effects of aged garlic extract, *Journal of Nutrition* 131 (2001): 1010S–1015S.

32. H. Amagase and coauthors, Intake of garlic and its bioactive components, *Journal of Nutrition* 131 (2001): 955S–962S.

33. J. A. Milner, A historical perspective on garlic and cancer, *Journal of Nutrition* 131 (2001): 1027S–1031S.

34. D. L. Lamm and D. R. Riggs, Enhanced immunocompetence by garlic: Role in bladder cancer and other malignancies, *Journal of Nutrition* 131 (2001): 1067S–1070S.

35. E. Kyo and coauthors, Immunomodulatory effects of aged garlic extract, *Journal of Nutrition* 131 (2001): 1075S–1079S; G. P. Sivam, Protection against *Helicobacter pylori* and other bacterial infections by garlic, *Journal of Nutrition* 131 (2001): n06S–U08S.

36. H. Matsuura, Saponins in garlic as modifiers of the risk of cardiovascular disease, *Journal of Nutrition* 131 (2001): 1000S–1005S.

37. K. Rahman, Historical perspective on garlic and cardiovascular disease, *Journal of Nutrition* 131 (2001): 977S–979S.

38. Borek, 2001 [see reference 31].

39. S. K. Banerjee, P. K. Mukherjee, and S. K. Maulik, Garlic as an antioxidant: The good, the bad, and the ugly, *Phytotherapy Research* 17 (2003): 97–106.

40. C. H. Halsted, Dietary supplements and functional foods: 2 sides of a coin? *American Journal of Clinical Nutrition* 77 (2003): 1001S–1007S.

41. Position of the American Dietetic Association: Functional foods, *Journal of the American Dietetic Association* 104 (2004): 814–826.

42. R. E. Ostlund, Phytosterols in human nutrition, *Annual Review of Nutrition* 22 (2002): 533–549; N. B. Cater, Plant stanol ester foods: New tools in the dietary management of cholesterol, *Nutrition and the MD,* November 1999, pp. 1–4.

43. T. Sudhop, B. M. Gottwald, and K. von Bergmann, Serum plant sterols as potential risk factor for coronary heart disease, *Metabolism: Clinical and Experimental* 51 (2002): 1519–1521;

Ostlund, 2002 [see reference 42]; H. Gylling and coauthors, Retinol, vitamin D, carotenes and alpha-tocopherol in serum of a moderately hypercholesterolemic population consuming sitostanol ester margarine, *Atherosclerosis* 145 (1999): 279–285.

44. M. E. Sanders, Probiotics: Considerations for human health, *Nutrition Reviews* 61 (2003): 91–99; J. E. Teitelbaum and W. A. Walker, Nutritional impact of pre- and probiotics as protective gastrointestinal organisms, *Annual Review of Nutrition* 22 (2002): 107–138; J. M. Saavedra, Clinical applications of probiotic agents, *American Journal of Clinical Nutrition* 73 (2001): 1147S–1151S; J. Schrezenmeir and M. de Vrese, Probiotics, prebiotics, and synbiotics—approaching a definition, *American Journal of Clinical Nutrition* 73 (2001): 361S–364S.

45. S. L. Gorbach, Probiotics and gastrointestinal health, *American Journal of Gastroenterology* 95 (2000): S2–S4.

46. O. Adolfsson, S. N. Meydani, and R. M. Russell, Yogurt and gut function, *American Journal of Clinical Nutrition* 80 (2004): 245–256.

47. J. M. Saavedra and A. Tschernia, Human studies with probiotics and prebiotics: Clinical implications, *British Journal of Nutrition* 87 (2002): S241–S246; P. Marteau and M. C. Boutron-Ruault, Nutritional advantages of probiotics and prebiotics, *British Journal of Nutrition* 87 (2002): S153–S157; G. T. Macfarlane and J. H. Cummings, Probiotics, infection and immunity, *Current Opinion in Infectious Diseases* 15 (2002): 501–506; L. Kopp-Hoolihan, Prophylactic and therapeutic uses of probiotics: A review, *Journal of the American Dietetic Association* 101 (2001): 229–238; M. de Vrese and coauthors, Probiotics—compensation for lactase insufficiency, *American Journal of Clinical Nutrition* 73 (2001): 421S–429S; M. B. Roberfroid, Prebiotics and probiotics: Are they functional foods? *American Journal of Clinical Nutrition* 71 (2000): 1682S–1687S.

48. J. W. Lampe and S. Peterson, Brassica, biotransformation and cancer risk: Genetic polymorphisms alter the preventive effects of cruciferous vegetables, *Journal of Nutrition* 132 (2002): 2991–2994.

49. A. B. Howell and B. Foxman, Cranberry juice and adhesion of antibiotic resistant uropathogens, *Journal of the American Medical Association* 287 (2002): 3082–3083; T. Kontiokari and coauthors, Randomised trial of cranberry-lingonberry juice and *Lactobacillus* GG drink for the prevention of urinary tract infections in women, *British Medical*

Journal 322 (2001): 1571, available at http://www.bmj.com/content/322/7302/1571.

50. P. F. Jacques and coauthors, Long-term nutrient intake and early age-related nuclear lens opacities, *Archives of Ophthalmology* 119 (2001): 1009–1019; J. T. Landrum and R. A. Bone, Lutein, zeaxanthin, and the macular pigment, *Archives of Biochemistry and Biophysics* 385 (2001): 28–40.

51. B. A. Corl and coauthors, Cis-9, *trans-11* CLA derived endogenously from *trans-11* 18:1 reduces cancer risk in rats, *Journal of Nutrition* 133 (2003): 2893–2900; M. A. Belury, Dietary conjugated linoleic acid in health: Physiological effects and mechanisms of action, *Annual Review of Nutrition* 22 (2002): 505–531; L. D. Whigham, M. E. Cook, and R. L. Atkinson, Conjugated linoleic acid: Implications for human health, *Pharmacological Research* 42 (2000): 503–510.

52. J. Sher and coauthors, Dietary conjugated linoleic acid lowers plasma cholesterol during cholesterol supplementation, but accentuates the atherogenic lipid profile during the acute phase response in hamsters, *Journal of Nutrition* 133 (2003): 456–460; M. A. Belury, A. Mahon, and S. Banni, The conjugated linoleic acid (CLA) isomer, t10c12-CLA, is inversely associated with changes in body weight and serum leptin in subjects with type 2 diabetes mellitus, *Journal of Nutrition* 133 (2003): 257S–260S.

53. Steinberg, Bearden, and Keen, 2003 [see reference 10].

54. M. K. Terris, M. M. Issa, and J. R. Tacker, Dietary supplementation with cranberry concentrate tablets may increase the risk of nephrolithiasis, *Urology* 57 (2001): 26–29.

55. W. Erdman and coauthors, Not all soy products are created equal: Caution needed in interpretation of research results, *Journal of Nutrition* 134 (2004): 1229S–1233S; C. Atkinson and coauthors, Urinary equol excretion in relation to 2-hydroxyestrone and 16alpha-hydroxyestrone concentrations: An observational study of young to middle-aged women, *Journal of Steroid Biochemistry and Molecular Biology* 86 (2003): 71–77.

56. K. D. Setchell and coauthors, Bioavailability, disposition, and dose-response effects of soy isoflavones when consumed by healthy women at physiologically typical dietary intakes, *Journal of Nutrition* 133 (2003): 1027–1035.

57. C. Hasler and coauthors, How to evaluate the safety, efficacy, and quality of functional foods and their ingredients, *Journal of the American Dietetic Association* 101 (2002): 733–736; B. Brophy and D. Schardt, Functional foods, *Nutrition Action Healthletter,* April 1999, pp. 3–7.

3 The Remarkable Body

Do You Ever . . .

Feel your heart beat and wonder where the blood goes?

Hear people say, "You are what you eat," and think it is just an old saying?

Wonder how your food becomes nourishment for your body?

Take antacids to relieve heartburn?

Keep Reading . . .

Learning Objectives

After completing this chapter, you should be able to

LO 3.1 Describe the levels of organization in the body and identify some basic ways in which nutrition supports them.

LO 3.2 Define the terms *mechanical digestion* and *chemical digestion* and point out where these processes occur along the digestive tract.

LO 3.3 Trace the breakdown and absorption of carbohydrate, fat, and protein from the mouth to the colon.

LO 3.4 Explain how nutrients are transported and stored in the body.

LO 3.5 Define the term *moderate alcohol consumption*, and discuss its potential negative and positive effects.

Contents

> *DNA* was defined in Chapter 1 as the molecule that encodes genetic information in its structure; *genes* were defined as units of a cell's inheritance.

At the moment of conception, you received genes, in the form of DNA, from your mother and father. Since that moment, your genes have been working behind the scenes, directing your body's development and basic functions. Many of your genes are ancient in origin and little changed from genes of thousands of centuries ago, but here you are—living with the food, the luxuries, the smog, the additives, and all of the other pleasures and problems of the 21st century. There is no guarantee that a diet haphazardly chosen from today's foods will meet the needs of your "ancient" body. Unlike your ancestors, who nourished themselves from the wild plants and animals surrounding them, you must learn how your body works, what it needs, and how to select foods to meet its needs.

The Body's Cells

The human body is composed of trillions of **cells**, and none of them know anything about food. *You* may get hungry for fruit, milk, or bread, but each cell of your body needs nutrients—the vital components of foods. The ways in which the body's cells cooperate to obtain and use nutrients are the subjects of this chapter.

Each of the body's cells is a self-contained, living entity (see Figure 3–1), but at the same time it depends on the rest of the body's cells to supply its needs. Among the cells' most basic needs are energy and the oxygen with which to burn it. Cells also need water to maintain the environment in which they live. They need building blocks and control systems. They especially need the nutrients they cannot make for themselves, the essential nutrients first described in Chapter 1, which must be supplied from food. The first principle of diet planning is that the foods we choose must provide energy and the essential nutrients, including water.

As living things, cells also die off, although at varying rates. Some skin cells and red blood cells must replenish themselves every 10 to 120 days. Cells lining the digestive tract replace themselves every three days. Under ordinary conditions, many muscle cells reproduce themselves only once every few years. Liver cells have the ability to reproduce quickly and do so whenever repairs to the organ are needed. Certain brain cells do not reproduce at all; if damaged by injury or disease, they are lost forever.

cells the smallest units in which independent life can exist. All living things are single cells or organisms made of cells.

Figure 3–1

A Cell (Simplified Diagram)

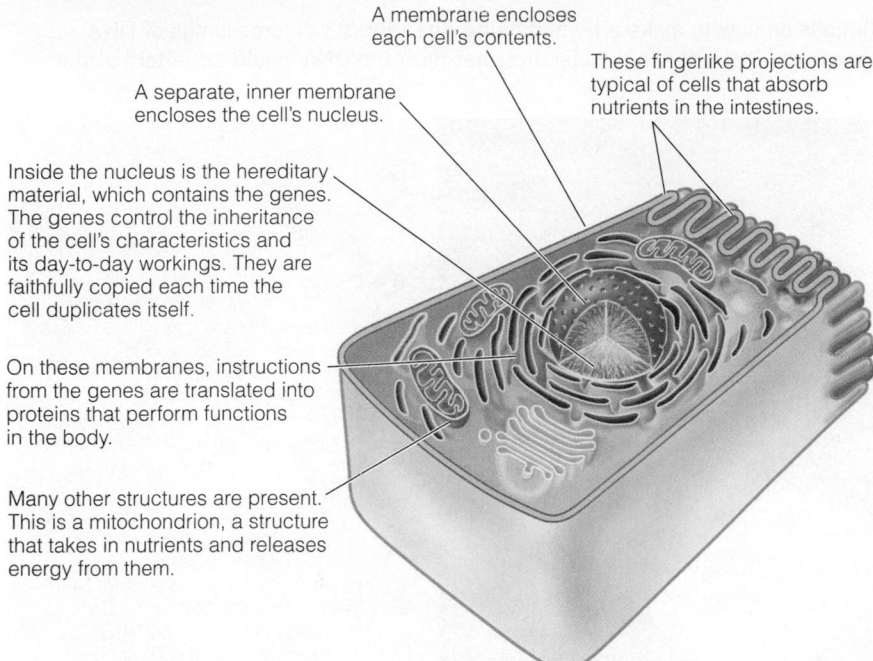

A membrane encloses each cell's contents.

These fingerlike projections are typical of cells that absorb nutrients in the intestines.

A separate, inner membrane encloses the cell's nucleus.

Inside the nucleus is the hereditary material, which contains the genes. The genes control the inheritance of the cell's characteristics and its day-to-day workings. They are faithfully copied each time the cell duplicates itself.

On these membranes, instructions from the genes are translated into proteins that perform functions in the body.

Many other structures are present. This is a mitochondrion, a structure that takes in nutrients and releases energy from them.

The Workings of the Genes

In the human body, cells work in cooperation with each other to support the whole. A cell's genes determine the nature of that work. Each gene is a blueprint that directs the production of a piece of protein machinery, often an **enzyme**, that helps do the cell's work. Genes also provide the instructions for all of the structural components cells need to survive (see Figure 3–2). Each cell contains a complete set of genes, but different ones are active in different types of cells. For example, in some intestinal cells, the genes for making digestive enzymes are active; in some of the body's **fat cells**, the genes for making enzymes that metabolize fat are active.

Genes affect the body's handling of nutrients. Certain genetic variations alter the absorption, use, or excretion of nutrients. Some variations cause lifelong maladies that require special diets to minimize damage to health. Nutrients also affect the genes. For example, the concentrations of certain vitamins and minerals influence the genes' production of nutrient-metabolizing proteins, with sweeping effects on body systems that originate at the cellular level.

Interactions between vitamins and minerals and the genes are addressed in Chapters 7 and 8; other nutrient and gene interactions or family history of disease are addressed in Chapters 11 and 13, on disease prevention and pregnancy.

● Nutritional genomics is the science of how nutrients affect the activities of genes and how genes affect the activities of nutrients. Also called *molecular nutrition or nutrigenomics*.

enzyme any of a great number of working proteins that speed up a specific chemical reaction, such as breaking the bonds of a nutrient, without undergoing change themselves. Enzymes and their actions are described in Chapter 6.

fat cells cells that specialize in the storage of fat and form the fat tissue. Fat cells also produce enzymes that metabolize fat and hormones involved in appetite and energy balance (see Chapter 9).

tissues systems of cells working together to perform specialized tasks. Examples are muscles, nerves, blood, and bone.

organs discrete structural units made of tissues that perform specific jobs. Examples are the heart, liver, and brain.

body system a group of related organs that work together to perform a function. Examples are the circulatory system, respiratory system, and nervous system.

Cells, Tissues, Organs, Systems

Cells are organized into **tissues** that perform specialized tasks. For example, individual muscle cells join to form muscle tissue, which can contract. Tissues, in turn, group to form whole **organs**. In the organ we call the heart, for example, muscle tissues, nerve tissues, connective tissues, and other types all work together to pump blood. Some body functions are performed by several related organs working together as part of a **body system**. For example, the heart, lungs, and blood vessels cooperate as parts of the cardiovascular system to deliver oxygen to all of the body's cells. The next few sections present the body systems with special significance to nutrition.

Figure 3–2

From DNA to Living Cells

If the human genome were a book of instructions on how to make a human being, then the 23 chromosomes of DNA would be chapters. Each gene would be a word, and the individual molecules that form the DNA would be letters of the alphabet.

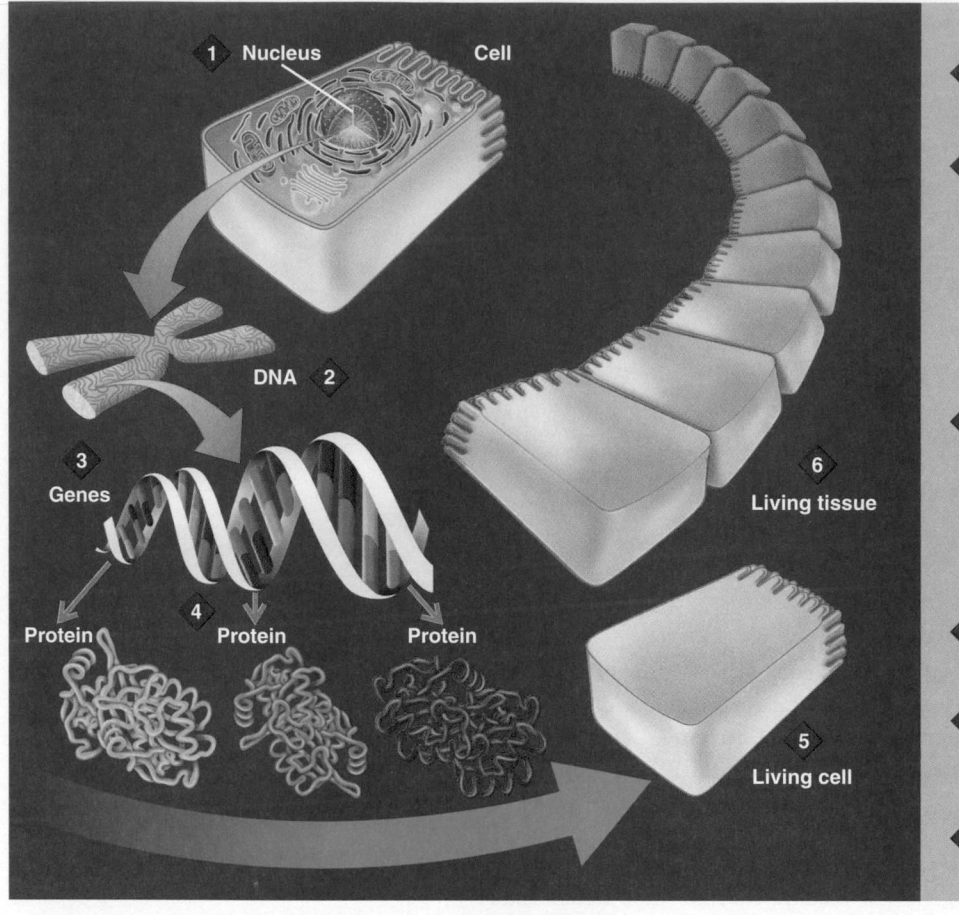

1 Each cell's nucleus contains DNA—the material of heredity in all living things.

2 Long strands of human DNA coil into 23 pairs of chromosomes. If the strands of DNA in all the body's cells were uncoiled and laid end to end, they would stretch to the sun and back four hundred times. Yet DNA strands are so tiny that about 5 million of them could be threaded at once through the eye of a needle.

3 Genes contain instructions for making proteins. Genes are sections along the strands of DNA that serve as templates for the building of proteins. Some genes are involved in building just one protein; others are involved in building more than one.

4 Many other steps are required to make a protein. See Figure 6–6 in Chapter 6 on page 212.

5 Proteins do the work of living cells. Cells employ proteins to perform essential functions and provide structures.

6 Communities of functioning cells make up the living tissue.

KEY POINT

- The body's cells need energy, oxygen, and nutrients, including water, to remain healthy and do their work. Genes direct the making of each cell's machinery, including enzymes. Genes and nutrients interact in ways that affect health. Specialized cells are grouped to form tissues and organs; organs work together in body systems.

blood the fluid of the cardiovascular system; composed of water, red and white blood cells, other formed particles, nutrients, oxygen, and other constituents.

lymph (limf) the fluid that moves from the bloodstream into tissue spaces and then travels in its own vessels, which eventually drain back into the bloodstream.

arteries blood vessels that carry blood containing fresh oxygen supplies from the heart to the tissues (see Figure 3–3).

veins blood vessels that carry blood, with the carbon dioxide it has collected, from the tissues back to the heart (see Figure 3–3).

capillaries minute, weblike blood vessels that connect arteries to veins and permit transfer of materials between blood and tissues (see Figures 3–3 and 3–4).

plasma the cell-free fluid part of blood and lymph.

extracellular fluid fluid residing outside the cells that transports materials to and from the cells.

The Body Fluids and the Cardiovascular System

Body fluids continuously supply the tissues with energy, oxygen, and nutrients, including water. The fluids constantly circulate to pick up fresh supplies and deliver wastes to points of disposal. Every cell continuously draws oxygen and nutrients from those fluids and releases carbon dioxide and other waste products into them.

The body's circulating fluids are the **blood** and the **lymph**. Blood travels within the **arteries**, **veins**, and **capillaries**, as well as within the heart's chambers (see Figure 3–3). Lymph travels in separate vessels of its own. Circulating around the cells are other fluids, such as the **plasma** of the blood, which surrounds the white and red blood cells, and the fluid surrounding muscle cells (see Figure 3–4). The fluid surrounding cells (**extracellular fluid**) is derived from the blood in the capillaries; it squeezes out through the capillary walls and flows around the outsides of cells,

Figure 3–3

Blood Flow in the Cardiovascular System

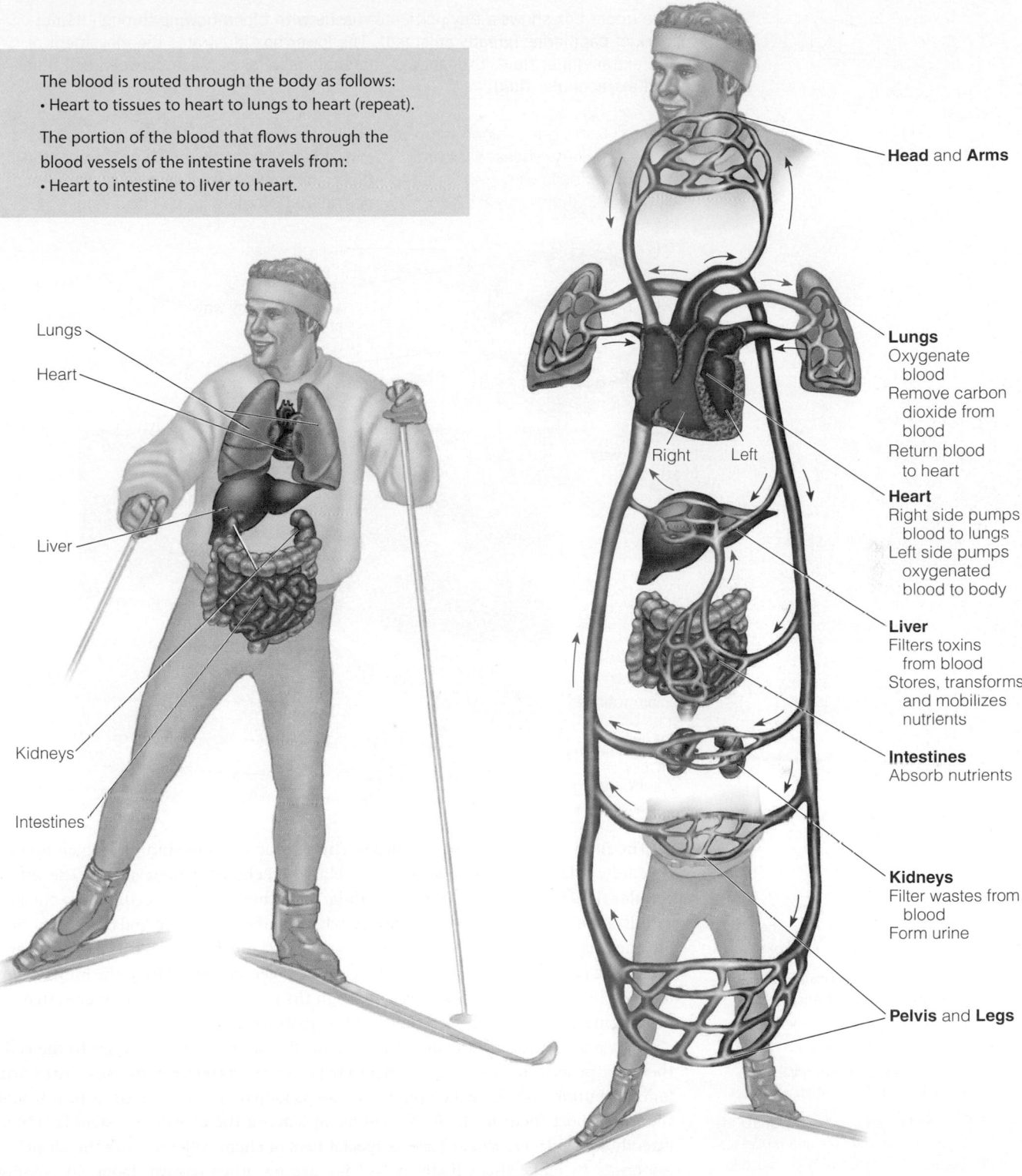

The blood is routed through the body as follows:
• Heart to tissues to heart to lungs to heart (repeat).

The portion of the blood that flows through the
blood vessels of the intestine travels from:
• Heart to intestine to liver to heart.

Lungs

Heart

Liver

Kidneys

Intestines

Head and **Arms**

Lungs
Oxygenate
  blood
Remove carbon
  dioxide from
  blood
Return blood
  to heart

Right   Left

Heart
Right side pumps
  blood to lungs
Left side pumps
  oxygenated
  blood to body

Liver
Filters toxins
  from blood
Stores, transforms,
  and mobilizes
  nutrients

Intestines
Absorb nutrients

Kidneys
Filter wastes from
  blood
Form urine

Pelvis and **Legs**

permitting exchange of materials. Some of the extracellular fluid returns to the blood
by reentering the capillaries. The fluid remaining outside the capillaries forms lymph,
which travels around the body by way of lymph vessels. The lymph eventually returns
to the bloodstream near the heart, where large lymph and blood vessels join. In this
way, all cells are served by the cardiovascular system.

Figure 3–4

How the Body Fluids Circulate around Cells

The upper box shows a tiny portion of tissue with blood flowing through its network of capillaries (greatly enlarged). The lower box illustrates the movement of the extracellular fluid. Exchange of materials also takes place between cell fluid and extracellular fluid.

1 Fluid filters out of blood through the capillary whose walls are made of cells with small spaces between them.

2 Fluid may flow back into **2** the capillary or into **3** a lymph vessel. Lymph enters the bloodstream later through a large lymphatic vessel that empties into a large vein.

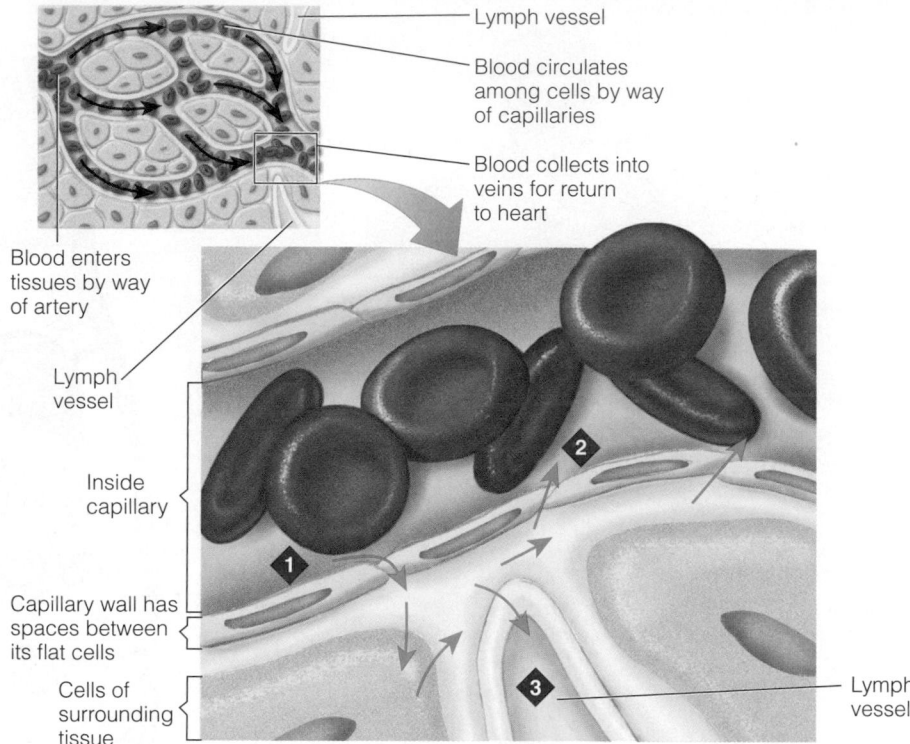

Lymph vessel

Blood circulates among cells by way of capillaries

Blood collects into veins for return to heart

Blood enters tissues by way of artery

Lymph vessel

Inside capillary

Capillary wall has spaces between its flat cells

Cells of surrounding tissue

Lymph vessel

The fluid inside cells (**intracellular fluid**) provides a medium in which all cell reactions take place. Its pressure also helps the cells hold their shape. The intracellular fluid is drawn from the extracellular fluid that bathes the cells on the outside.

All of the blood circulates to the **lungs**, where it picks up oxygen and releases carbon dioxide wastes from the cells, as Figure 3–5 shows. Then the blood returns to the heart, where the pumping heartbeats push this fresh oxygenated blood from the lungs out to all body tissues. As the blood travels through the rest of the cardiovascular system, it delivers materials that cells need and picks up their wastes.

As it passes through the digestive system, the blood delivers oxygen to the cells there and picks up most nutrients other than fats and their relatives from the **intestine** for distribution elsewhere. Lymphatic vessels pick up most fats from the intestine and then transport them to the blood. All blood leaving the digestive system is routed directly to the **liver**, which has the special task of chemically altering the absorbed materials to make them better suited for use by other tissues. Later, in passing through the **kidneys**, the blood is cleansed of wastes (look again at Figure 3–3). Note that the blood carries nutrients from the intestine to the liver, which releases them to the heart, which pumps them to the waiting body tissues.

To ensure efficient circulation of fluid to all your cells, you need an ample fluid intake. This means drinking sufficient water to replace the water lost each day. Cardiovascular fitness is essential, too, and constitutes an ongoing project that requires

intracellular fluid fluid residing inside the cells that provides the medium for cellular reactions.

lungs the body's organs of gas exchange. Blood circulating through the lungs releases its carbon dioxide and picks up fresh oxygen to carry to the tissues.

intestine the body's long, tubular organ of digestion and the site of nutrient absorption.

liver a large, lobed organ that lies just under the ribs. It filters the blood, removes and processes nutrients, manufactures materials for export to other parts of the body, destroys toxins or stores them to keep them out of the circulation, and excretes fat-soluble waste products into the small intestine.

kidneys a pair of organs that filter wastes from the blood, make urine, and release it to the bladder for excretion from the body.

Chapter 3 The Remarkable Body

Figure 3–5

Oxygen–Carbon Dioxide Exchange in the Lungs

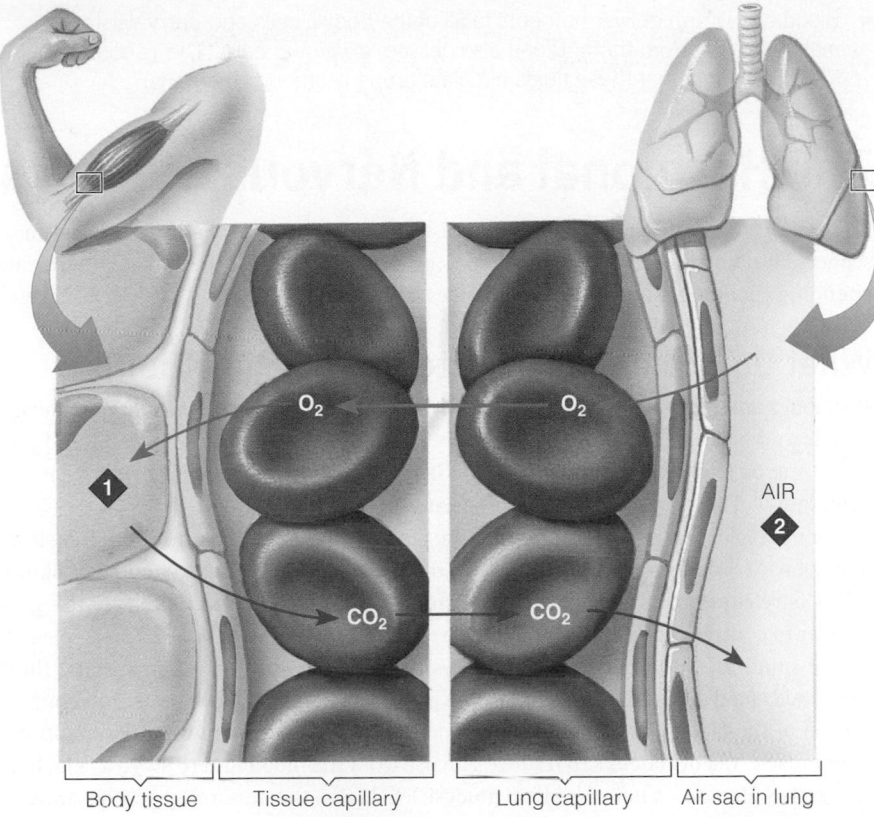

1. In body tissues, red blood cells give up their oxygen (O_2) and absorb carbon dioxide (CO_2).

2. In the air sacs of the lungs, the red blood cells give up their load of carbon dioxide (CO_2) and absorb oxygen (O_2) from air to supply to body tissues.

O_2 O_2

1 **2** AIR

CO_2 CO_2

Body tissue | Tissue capillary | Lung capillary | Air sac in lung

© Rogatnev Dmitry/iStock/Thinkstock

All of the body's cells live in water.

attention to both nutrition and physical activity. Healthy red blood cells also play a role by carrying oxygen to all of the other cells, enabling them to use fuels for energy. Since red blood cells arise, live, and die within about four months, your body replaces them constantly, a manufacturing process that requires many essential nutrients from food. Consequently, the blood is very sensitive to malnutrition and often

Chapter 8 offers guidelines for water intake.

serves as an indicator of disorders caused by dietary deficiencies or imbalances of vitamins or minerals.

KEY POINT

■ Blood and lymph deliver nutrients to all of the body's cells and carry waste materials away from them. Blood also delivers oxygen to cells. The cardiovascular system ensures that these fluids circulate properly among all organs.

The Hormonal and Nervous Systems

In addition to nutrients, oxygen, and wastes, the blood also carries chemical messengers, **hormones**, from one system of cells to another. Hormones communicate changing conditions that demand responses from the body organs.

What Do Hormones Have to Do with Nutrition?

Hormones are secreted and released directly into the blood by organs known as glands. Glands and hormones abound in the body. Each gland monitors a condition and produces one or more hormones to regulate it. Each hormone acts as a messenger that stimulates various organs to take appropriate actions.

For example, gastrin is released into the blood by the stomach and small intestines in response to food intake and stimulates the release of stomach acid; cholecytokinin (CCK) is released into the blood by the small intestine and stimulates (1) the gallbladder to contract and (2) the pancreas to release pancreatic fluid; secritin is released by the small intestine and also stimulates the pancreas to release pancreatic fluid, which aids food digestion. Also, when the **pancreas** (a gland) detects a high concentration of the blood's sugar, glucose, it releases **insulin**, a hormone. Insulin stimulates muscle and other cells to remove glucose from the blood and to store it. The liver also stores glucose. When the blood glucose level falls, the pancreas secretes another hormone, **glucagon**, to which the liver responds by releasing into the blood some of the glucose it stored earlier. Thus, normal blood glucose levels are maintained.

Nutrition affects the hormonal system. Fasting, feeding, and exercise alter hormonal balances. People who become very thin have an altered hormonal balance that may make them unable to maintain their bones, for example.

Hormones also affect nutrition. Along with the nervous system, hormones regulate hunger and affect appetite. They carry messages to regulate the digestive system, telling the digestive organs what kinds of foods have been eaten and how much of each digestive juice to secrete in response. A hormone produced by the fat tissue informs the brain about the degree of body fatness and helps regulate appetite. Hormones also regulate the menstrual cycle in women, and they affect the appetite changes many women experience during the cycle and in pregnancy. An altered hormonal state is thought to be at least partially responsible, too, for the loss of appetite that sick people experience.

Details about hormones, menstruation, and the bones appear in Controversy 8 and Controversy 9.

Hormones also regulate the body's reaction to stress, suppressing hunger and the digestion and absorption of nutrients. When there are questions about a person's nutrition or health, the state of that person's hormonal system is often part of the answer.

KEY POINT

■ Glands secrete hormones that act as messengers to help regulate body processes.

How Does the Nervous System Interact with Nutrition?

The body's other major communication system is, of course, the nervous system. With the brain and spinal cord as central controllers, the nervous system receives and integrates information from sensory receptors all over the body—sight, hearing, touch, smell, taste, and others—which communicate to the brain the state of both the outer

hormones chemicals that are secreted and released by glands directly into the blood in response to conditions in the body that require regulation. These chemicals serve as messengers, acting on other organs to maintain constant conditions.

pancreas an organ with two main functions. One is an endocrine function—the making of hormones such as insulin, which it releases directly into the blood (*endo* means "into"). The other is an exocrine function—the making of digestive enzymes, which it releases through a duct into the small intestine to assist in digestion (*exo* means "out" into a body cavity or onto the skin surface).

insulin a hormone from the pancreas that helps glucose enter cells from the blood (details in Chapter 4).

glucagon a hormone from the pancreas that stimulates the liver to release glucose into the bloodstream when blood glucose concentration dips.

Figure 3–6

Cutaway Side View of the Brain Showing the Hypothalamus and Cortex

The hypothalamus monitors the body's conditions and sends signals to the brain's thinking portion, the cortex, which decides on actions. The pituitary gland is called the body's master gland, referring to its roles in regulating the activities of other glands and organs of the body.

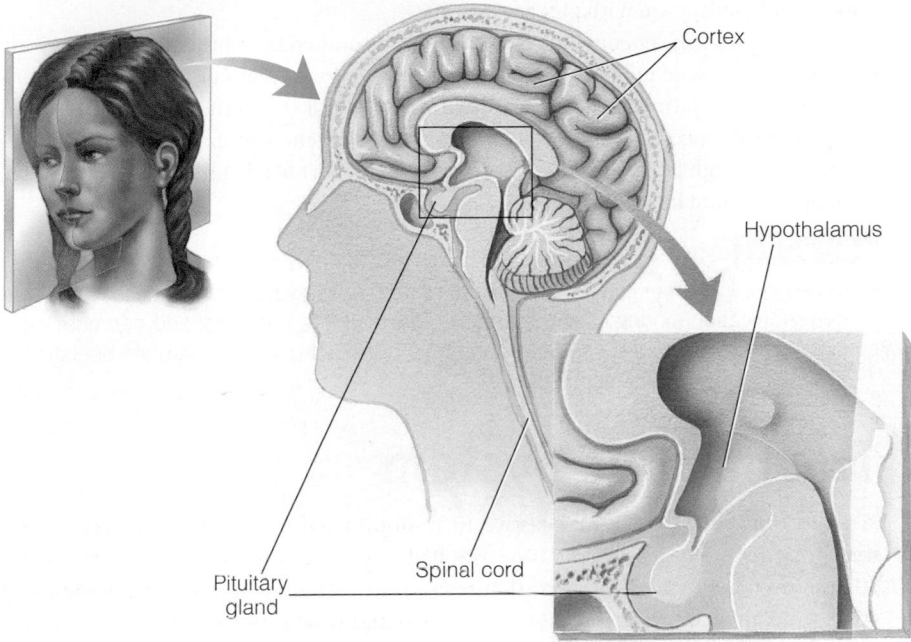

Cortex

Hypothalamus

Pituitary gland

Spinal cord

and inner worlds, including the availability of food and the need to eat. The nervous system also sends instructions to the muscles and glands, telling them what to do.

The nervous system's role in hunger regulation is coordinated by the brain. The sensations of hunger and appetite are perceived by the brain's **cortex**, the thinking, outer layer. Deep inside the brain, the **hypothalamus** (see Figure 3–6) monitors many body conditions, including the availability of nutrients and water. To signal hunger, the physiological need for food, the digestive tract sends messages to the hypothalamus by way of hormones and nerves. The signals also stimulate the stomach to intensify its contractions and secretions, causing hunger pangs (and gurgling sounds). When your brain's cortex perceives these hunger sensations, you want to eat. The conscious mind of the cortex, however, can override such signals, and a person can choose to delay eating despite hunger or to eat when hunger is absent.

In a marvellous adaptation of the human body, the hormonal and nervous systems work together to enable a person to respond to physical danger. Known as the **fight-or-flight reaction**, or the *stress response*, this adaptation is present with only minor variations in all animals, showing how universally important it is to survival. When danger is detected, nerves release **neurotransmitters**, and glands supply the compounds **epinephrine** and **norepinephrine**.* Every organ of the body responds and **metabolism** speeds up. The pupils of the eyes widen so that you can see better; the muscles tense up so that you can jump, run, or struggle with maximum strength; breathing quickens and deepens to provide more oxygen. The heart races to rush the oxygen to the muscles, and the blood pressure rises so that the fuel the muscles need for energy can be delivered efficiently. The liver pours forth glucose from its stores, and the fat cells release fat. The digestive system shuts down to permit all of the body's

---

*Strictly speaking, norepinephrine is a neurotransmitter.

cortex the outermost layer of something. The brain's cortex is the part of the brain where conscious thought takes place.

hypothalamus (high-poh-THAL-uh-mus) a part of the brain that senses a variety of conditions in the blood, such as temperature, glucose content, salt content, and others. It signals other parts of the brain or body to adjust those conditions when necessary.

fight-or-flight reaction the body's instinctive hormone- and nerve-mediated reaction to danger. Also known as the *stress response*.

neurotransmitters chemicals that are released at the end of a nerve cell when a nerve impulse arrives there. They diffuse across the gap to the next cell and alter the membrane of that second cell to either inhibit or excite it.

epinephrine (EP-ih-NEFF-rin) the major hormone that elicits the stress response.

norepinephrine (NOR-EP-ih-NEFF-rin) a compound related to epinephrine that helps elicit the stress response.

metabolism the sum of all physical and chemical changes taking place in living cells; includes all reactions by which the body obtains and spends the energy from food.

systems to serve the muscles and nerves. With all action systems at peak efficiency, the body can respond with amazing speed and strength to whatever threatens it.

In ancient times, stress usually involved physical danger, and the response to it was violent physical exertion. In the modern world, stress is seldom physical, but the body reacts the same way. What stresses you today may be a bank account out of control or a teacher who suddenly announces a pop quiz. Under these stresses, you are not supposed to fight or run as your ancient ancestor did. You smile at the "enemy" and suppress your fear. But your heart races, you feel it pounding, and hormones still flood your bloodstream with glucose and fat.

Your number-one enemy today is not a sabre-toothed tiger prowling outside your cave but a disease of modern civilization: heart disease. Years of fat and other constituents accumulating in the arteries and stresses that strain the heart often lead to heart attacks, especially when a body accustomed to chronic underexertion experiences sudden high blood pressure. Daily exercise as part of a healthy lifestyle releases pent-up stress and helps protect the heart.

KEY POINT

- The nervous system joins the hormonal system to regulate body processes through communication among all of the organs. Together, the hormonal and nervous systems respond to the need for food, govern the act of eating, regulate digestion, and call for the stress response.

The Immune System

Many of the body's tissues cooperate to maintain defences against infection. The skin presents a physical barrier, and the body's cavities (lungs, digestive tract, and others) are lined with membranes that resist penetration by invading **microbes** and other unwanted substances. These linings are highly sensitive to vitamin and other nutrient deficiencies, and health-care providers inspect both the skin and the inside of the mouth to detect signs of malnutrition. (Later chapters present details of the signs of deficiencies.) If an **antigen**, or foreign invader, penetrates the body's barriers, the **immune system** rushes in to defend the body against harm.

Of the 100 trillion cells that make up the human body, one in every hundred is a white blood cell. The actions of two types of white blood cells, the phagocytes and the **lymphocytes**, known as T cells and B cells, are of interest:

- **Phagocytes**. These scavenger cells travel throughout the body and are the first to defend body tissues against invaders. When a phagocyte recognizes a foreign particle, such as a bacterium, the phagocyte forms a pocket in its own outer membrane, engulfing the invader. Then the phagocytes may attack the invader with oxidative chemicals in an "oxidative burst" or may otherwise digest or destroy it. Phagocytes also leave a chemical trail that helps other immune cells to join the defence against infection.

- **T cells**. Killer T cells recognize chemical messages from phagocytes and "read" and "remember" the identity of an invader from the messages. The killer T cells then seek out and destroy all foreign particles with the same identity. T cells defend against fungi, viruses, parasites, some bacteria, and some cancer cells (see the photo). They also pose a formidable obstacle to a successful organ transplant—the physician must prescribe immunosuppressive drugs following surgery to hold down the T cells' attack against the "foreign" organ. Another group, helper T cells, does not attack invaders but helps other immune cells do so. People suffering from the disease AIDS (acquired immune deficiency syndrome) are rendered defenceless against other diseases because the human immunodeficiency virus (HIV) that causes AIDS selectively attacks and destroys their helper T cells.

- **B cells**. B cells respond rapidly to infection by dividing and releasing invader-fighting proteins, **antibodies**, into the bloodstream. Antibodies travel to the site of the infection and stick to the surface of the foreign particles, killing or inactivating them. Like T cells, the B cells also retain a chemical memory of each invader, and

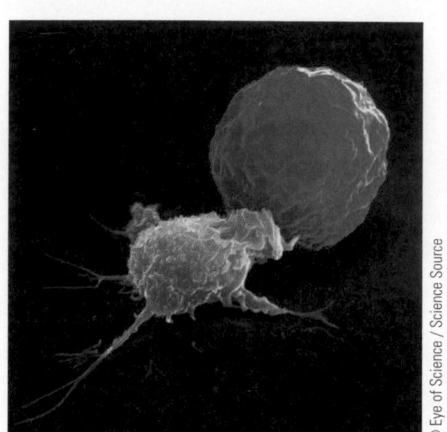

A killer T cell (the smaller cell on the bottom) has recognized a cancer cell and is releasing toxic chemicals that punch holes in the cancer cell's surface, destroying it. A nutritious diet supports immune system functioning.

© Eye of Science / Science Source

microbes bacteria, viruses, and other organisms invisible to the naked eye, some of which cause diseases. Also called *microorganisms*.

antigen a microbe or substance that is foreign to the body.

immune system a system of tissues and organs that defend the body against antigens, foreign materials that have penetrated the skin or body linings.

lymphocytes (LIM-foh-sites) white blood cells that participate in the immune response; B cells and T cells.

phagocytes (FAG-oh-sites) white blood cells that can ingest and destroy antigens. The process by which phagocytes engulf materials is called *phagocytosis*. The Greek word *phagein* means "to eat."

T cells lymphocytes that attack antigens. *T* stands for the thymus gland of the neck, where the T cells are stored and matured.

B cells lymphocytes that produce antibodies. *B* stands for bursa, an organ in the chicken where B cells were first identified.

antibodies proteins, made by cells of the immune system, that are expressly designed to combine with and inactivate specific antigens.

Read about oxidation in Chapter 5 and Chapter 7.

Chapter 11 describes the roles of nutrition in supporting the body's defence system.

if the encounter recurs, the response is swift. Immunizations work this way—a disabled or harmless form of a disease-causing organism is injected into the body so that the B cells can learn to recognize it. Later, if the real, live infectious organism invades, the B cells quickly release antibodies to destroy it.

KEY POINT

- The immune system enables the body to resist diseases.

The Digestive System

When your body needs food, your brain and hormones alert your conscious mind to the sensation of hunger (high levels of **grehlin** are associated with a fasting state and are thought to promote food intake). Then, when you eat, your taste buds guide you in judging whether foods are acceptable.

On the surfaces of the taste buds are structures that detect four basic chemical tastes: sweet, sour, bitter, and salty. A fifth taste is sometimes included on this list: the taste of monosodium glutamate, sometimes called *savoury* or *umami* (ooh-MOM-ee), its Asian name. Aroma, texture, temperature, and other flavour elements can also affect a food's flavour. In fact, the human ability to detect a food's aroma is thousands of times as sensitive as our sense of taste. The nose can detect just a few molecules responsible for the aroma of frying bacon, for example, even when they are diluted in several rooms full of air.

Why Do People Like Sugar, Fat, and Salt?

Sweet, salty, and fatty foods seem to be universally desired, but most people have aversions to bitter and sour tastes in isolation (see Figure 3–7).[1] The enjoyment of sugars and fat encourages people to consume ample energy, especially in the form of foods containing sugars, which provide energy for the brain. Likewise, foods containing fats provide energy and essential nutrients needed by all body tissues. The pleasure of a salty taste prompts

---

Figure 3–7

The Innate Preference for Sweet Taste

This newborn baby is (a) resting, (b) tasting distilled water, (c) tasting sugar, (d) tasting something sour, and (e) tasting something bitter.

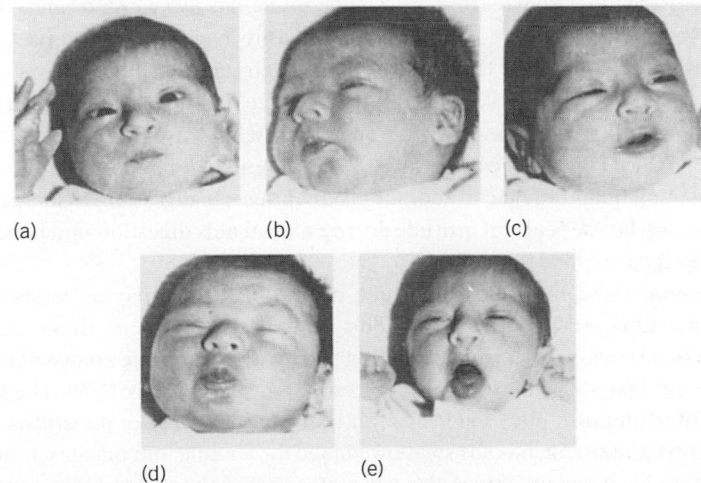

(a)   (b)   (c)

(d)   (e)

Source: Taste-induced facial expressions of neonate infants from the classic studies of J. E. Steiner, in Taste and Development: The Genesis of Sweet Preference, ed. J. M. Weiffenbach, HHS publication no. NIH 77–1068 (Bethesda, Md.: U.S. Department of Health and Human Services, 1977), pp. 173–189.

grehlin a hormone secreted by the stomach that is thought to be a "hunger hormone."

eaters to consume sufficient amounts of two very important minerals—sodium and chloride. The aversion to bitterness discourages consumption of foods containing bitter toxins and also affects people's food preferences. People born with great sensitivity to bitter tastes are apt to avoid foods with slightly bitter flavours, such as turnips and broccoli.

The instinctive liking for sugar, fat, and salt can lead to drastic overeating of these substances. Sugar has become widely available in pure form only in the last hundred years, so it is relatively new to the human diet. Although fat and salt are much older, today all three substances are being added liberally to foods by manufacturers to tempt us to eat their products.

KEY POINT

- The preference for sweet, salty, and fatty tastes seems to be inborn and can lead to overconsumption of foods that offer them.

The Digestive Tract

Once you have eaten, your brain and hormones direct the many organs of the **digestive system** to **digest** and **absorb** the complex mixture of chewed and swallowed food. A diagram showing the digestive tract and its associated organs appears in Figure 3–8. The tract itself is a flexible, muscular tube extending from the mouth through the throat, esophagus, stomach, small intestine, large intestine, and rectum to the anus, for a total length of about eight metres. The human body surrounds this digestive canal. When you swallow something, it is not inside your body—it is only inside the inner bore of this tube. Only when a nutrient or other substance passes through the wall of the digestive tract does it actually enter the body's tissues. Many things pass into the digestive tract and out again, unabsorbed. A baby playing with beads may swallow one, but the bead will not really enter the body. It will emerge from the digestive tract within a day or two.

The digestive system's job is to digest food to its components and then to absorb the nutrients and some nonnutrients, leaving behind the substances, such as fibre, that are appropriate to excrete. To do this, the system works at two levels: one, mechanical; the other, chemical.

KEY POINT

- The digestive tract is a flexible, muscular tube that digests food and absorbs its nutrients and some nonnutrients. Ancillary digestive organs aid digestion.

The Mechanical Aspect of Digestion

The job of mechanical digestion begins in the mouth, where large, solid food pieces such as bites of meat are torn into shreds that can be swallowed without choking. Chewing also adds water in the form of saliva to soften rough or sharp foods, such as fried tortilla chips, to prevent them from tearing the esophagus. Saliva also moistens and coats each bite of food, making it slippery so that it can pass easily down the esophagus.

Nutrients trapped inside indigestible skins, such as the hulls of seeds, must be liberated by breaking these skins before they can be digested. Chewing bursts open kernels of corn, for example, which would otherwise traverse the tract and exit undigested. Once food has been mashed and moistened for comfortable swallowing, longer chewing times provide no additional advantages to digestion. In fact, for digestion's sake, a relaxed, peaceful attitude during a meal aids digestion much more than chewing for an extended time.

The stomach and intestines then take up the task of liquefying foods through various mashing and squeezing actions. The best known of these actions is **peristalsis**, a series of squeezing waves that start with the tongue's movement during a swallow and pass all the way down the esophagus (see Figure 3–9). The stomach and the intestines also push food through the tract by waves of peristalsis. Besides these actions, the stomach holds swallowed food for a while and mashes it into a fine paste; the stomach and intestines also add water so that the paste becomes more fluid as it moves along. While the chyme/digesta move forward through the small intestine, further **segmentation** occurs.

digestive system the body system composed of organs that break down complex food particles into smaller, absorbable products. The *digestive tract* and *alimentary canal* are names for the tubular organs that extend from the mouth to the anus. The whole system, including the pancreas, liver, and gallbladder, is sometimes called the *gastrointestinal*, or *GI*, system.

digest to break molecules into smaller molecules; a main function of the digestive tract with respect to food.

absorb to take in, as nutrients are taken into the intestinal cells after digestion; the main function of the digestive tract with respect to nutrients.

peristalsis (perri-STALL-sis) the wavelike muscular squeezing of the esophagus, stomach, and small intestine that pushes their contents along.

segmentation alternating forward and backward movement allowing for greater contact between the partially digested food and intestinal juices and enzymes, thus resulting in virtually complete digestion of the food we eat.

Figure 3–8

The Digestive System

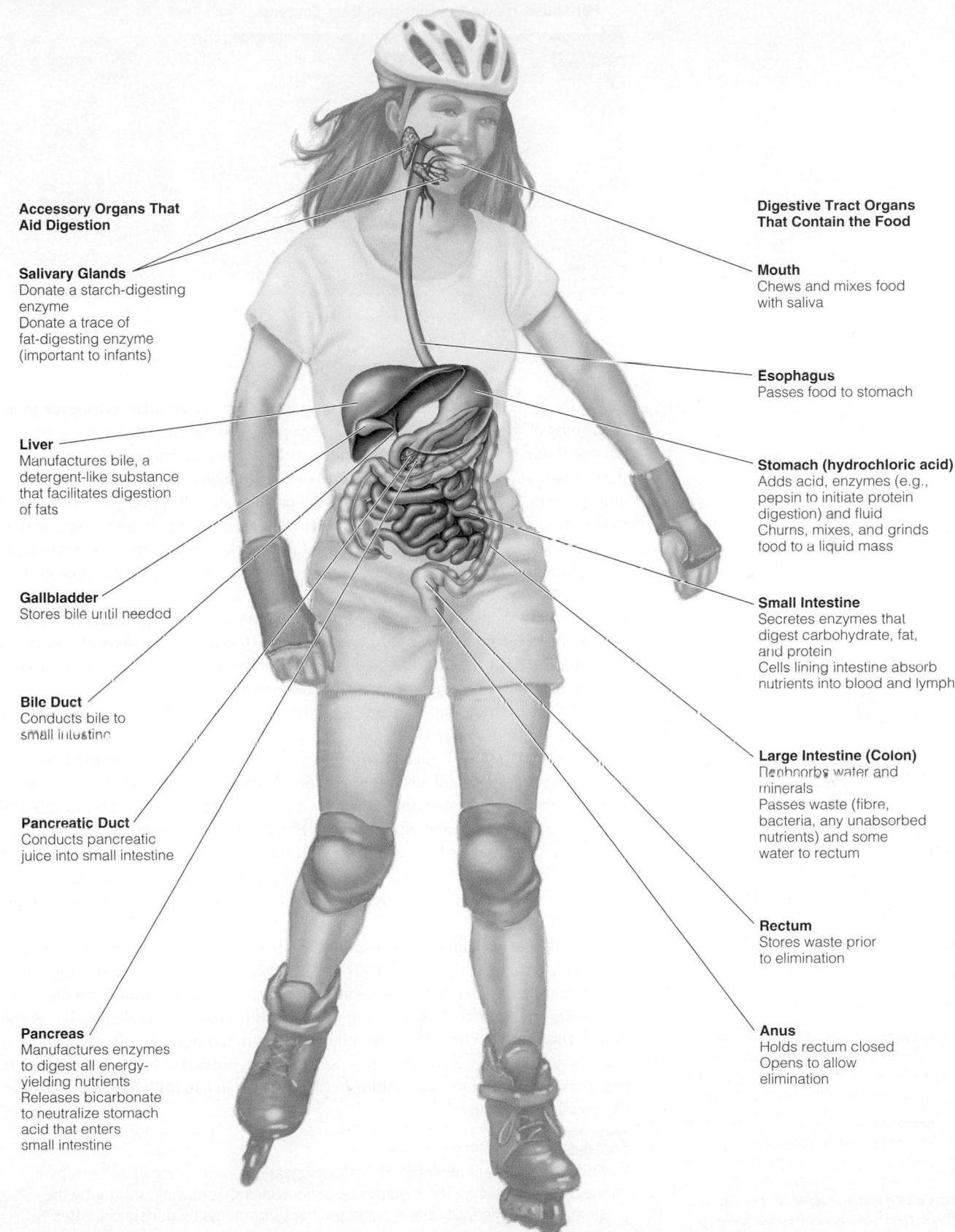

Accessory Organs That Aid Digestion

Salivary Glands
Donate a starch-digesting enzyme
Donate a trace of fat-digesting enzyme (important to infants)

Liver
Manufactures bile, a detergent-like substance that facilitates digestion of fats

Gallbladder
Stores bile until needed

Bile Duct
Conducts bile to small intestine

Pancreatic Duct
Conducts pancreatic juice into small intestine

Pancreas
Manufactures enzymes to digest all energy-yielding nutrients
Releases bicarbonate to neutralize stomach acid that enters small intestine

Digestive Tract Organs That Contain the Food

Mouth
Chews and mixes food with saliva

Esophagus
Passes food to stomach

Stomach (hydrochloric acid)
Adds acid, enzymes (e.g., pepsin to initiate protein digestion) and fluid
Churns, mixes, and grinds food to a liquid mass

Small Intestine
Secretes enzymes that digest carbohydrate, fat, and protein
Cells lining intestine absorb nutrients into blood and lymph

Large Intestine (Colon)
Reabsorbs water and minerals
Passes waste (fibre, bacteria, any unabsorbed nutrients) and some water to rectum

Rectum
Stores waste prior to elimination

Anus
Holds rectum closed
Opens to allow elimination

Figure 3–9

Peristaltic Wave Passing Down the Esophagus and Beyond

Peristalsis moves the digestive tract contents.

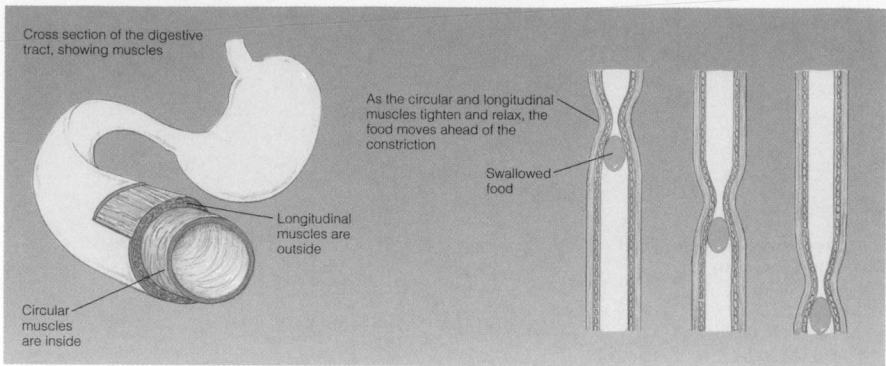

Cross section of the digestive tract, showing muscles

As the circular and longitudinal muscles tighten and relax, the food moves ahead of the constriction

Swallowed food

Longitudinal muscles are outside

Circular muscles are inside

Figure 3–10 shows the muscular **stomach**. Notice the circular **sphincter** muscle at the base of the esophagus. It squeezes the opening at the entrance to the stomach to narrow it and prevent the stomach's contents from creeping back up the esophagus as the stomach contracts. The stomach stores swallowed food in a lump in its upper portion and squeezes the food little by little (in small portions) into its lower portion. There the food is ground and mixed thoroughly, ensuring that digestive chemicals mix with the entire thick liquid mass, now called **chyme**. Chyme bears no resemblance to the original food. The starches have been partly split, proteins have been uncoiled and clipped, and fat has separated from the mass.

The stomach also acts as a holding tank. The muscular **pyloric valve** at the stomach's lower end (look again at Figure 3–10) controls the exit of the chyme, allowing only a little at a time to be squirted forcefully into the **small intestine**. Within a few hours after a meal, the stomach empties itself by means of these powerful squirts. The small intestine contracts rhythmically to move the contents along its length.

By the time the intestinal contents have arrived in the **large intestine** (also called the **colon**), digestion and absorption are nearly complete. The colon's task is mostly to reabsorb the water donated earlier by digestive organs and to absorb minerals, leaving a paste of fibre and other undigested materials, the **feces**, suitable for excretion. The fibre provides bulk against which the muscles of the colon can work. The rectum stores this fecal material to be excreted at intervals. From mouth to rectum, the transit of a meal is accomplished in as short a time as a single day or as long as three days.

Some people wonder whether the digestive tract works best at certain hours in the day and whether the timing of meals can affect how a person feels. Timing of meals is important to feeling well, not because the digestive tract is unable to digest food at certain times but because the body requires nutrients to be replenished every few hours. Digestion is virtually continuous, being limited only during sleep and exercise. For some people, eating late may interfere with normal sleep. As for exercise, it is best pursued a few hours after eating because digestion can inhibit physical work (see Chapter 10 for details).

KEY POINT

- The digestive tract moves food through its various processing chambers by mechanical means. The mechanical actions include chewing, mixing by the stomach, adding fluid, and moving the tract's contents by peristalsis. After digestion and absorption, wastes are excreted.

stomach a muscular, elastic, pouchlike organ of the digestive tract that grinds and churns swallowed food and mixes it with acid and enzymes, forming chyme.

sphincter (SFINK-ter) a circular muscle surrounding, and able to close, a body opening.

chyme (KIME) the fluid resulting from the actions of the stomach upon food.

pyloric (pye-LORE-ick) **valve** the circular muscle of the lower stomach that regulates the flow of partly digested food into the small intestine. Also called *pyloric sphincter*.

small intestine the seven-metre length of small-diameter intestine, below the stomach and above the large intestine, that is the major site of digestion of food and absorption of nutrients.

large intestine the portion of the intestine that completes the absorption process.

colon the large intestine.

feces waste material remaining after digestion and absorption are complete; eventually discharged from the body.

Figure 3–10

The Muscular Stomach

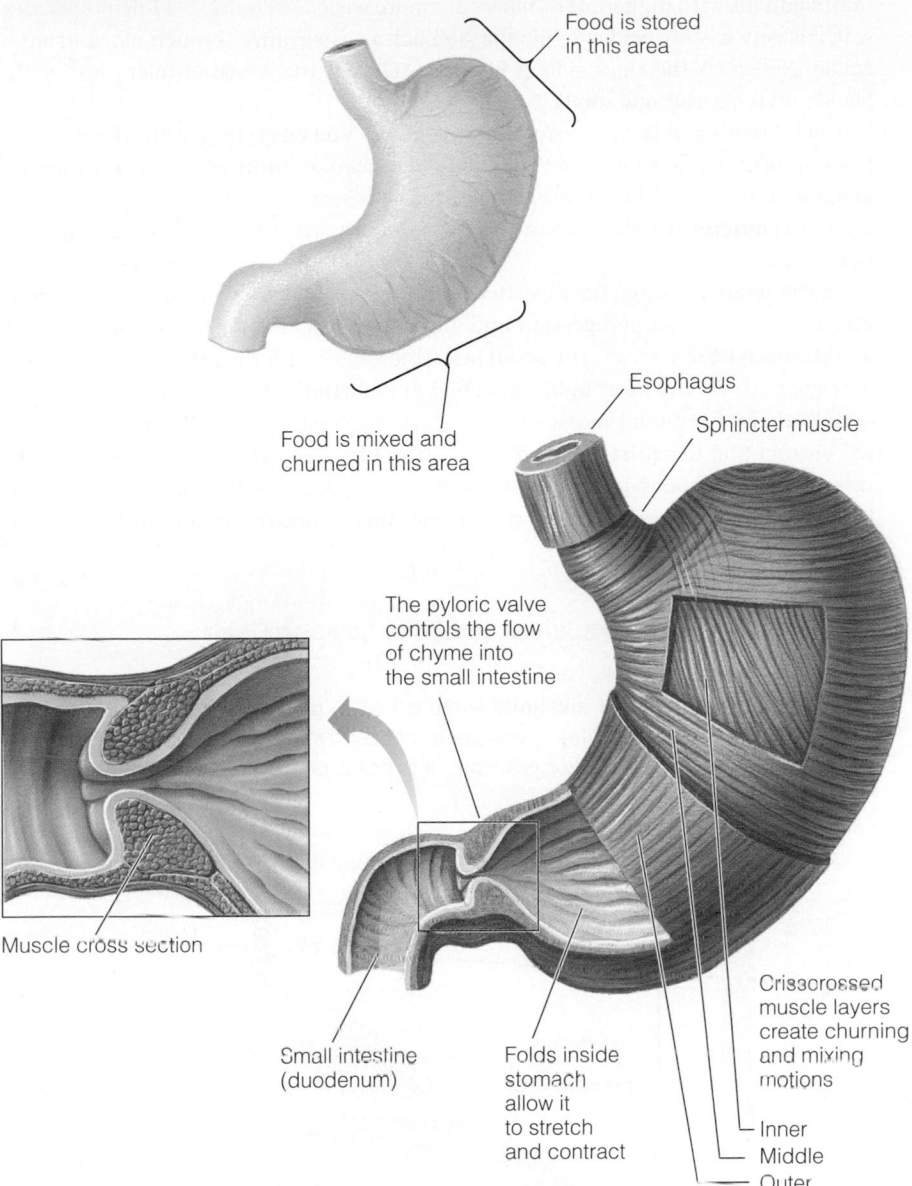

Food is stored in this area

Food is mixed and churned in this area

Esophagus

Sphincter muscle

The pyloric valve controls the flow of chyme into the small intestine

Muscle cross section

Small intestine (duodenum)

Folds inside stomach allow it to stretch and contract

Crisscrossed muscle layers create churning and mixing motions

Inner
Middle
Outer

The Chemical Aspect of Digestion

Several organs of the digestive system secrete special digestive juices that perform the complex chemical processes of digestion. Digestive juices contain enzymes that break nutrients down into their component parts. The digestive organs that release digestive juices are the salivary glands, the stomach, the pancreas, the liver, and the small intestine. Their secretions were listed previously in Figure 3–8.

How Do "Digestive Juices" Work?   Digestion begins in the mouth. An enzyme in saliva (salivary amylase) starts rapidly breaking down starch, and another enzyme (lingual lipase) initiates a little digestion of fat, especially the digestion of milk fat, important in infants. Saliva also helps maintain the health of the teeth in two ways: by washing away food particles that would otherwise foster decay and by neutralizing decay-promoting acids produced by bacteria in the mouth.

In the stomach, protein digestion begins. Cells in the stomach release **gastric juice**, a mixture of water, enzymes, and hydrochloric acid. This strong acid mixture

● Alcohol needs no assistance from digestive juices to ready it for absorption; its handling by the body is described in this chapter's Controversy section.

gastric juice the digestive secretion of the stomach.

is needed to activate a protein-digesting enzyme (pepsin) and to initiate digestion of protein—protein digestion is the stomach's main function. The strength of an acid solution is expressed as its **pH**. The lower the pH number, the more acidic the solution; solutions with higher pH numbers are more basic. As Figure 3–11 demonstrates, saliva is only weakly acidic, while the stomach's gastric juice is much more strongly acidic. Notice on the right side of Figure 3–11 that the range of tolerance for the blood's pH is exceedingly small.

Upon learning of the powerful digestive juices and enzymes within the digestive tract, students often wonder how the tract's own cellular lining escapes being digested along with the food. The answer: specialized cells secrete a thick, viscous substance known as **mucus**, which coats and protects the stomach and the rest of the digestive tract lining.

In the small intestine, the digestive process gets under way in earnest. The small intestine is *the* organ of digestion and absorption, and it finishes what the mouth and stomach have started. The small intestine works with the precision of a laboratory chemist. As the thoroughly liquefied and partially digested nutrient mixture arrives there, hormonal messengers (e.g., cholecystokinin) signal the gallbladder to contract and to squirt the right amount of **bile**, an **emulsifier**, into the intestine. Other hormones (e.g., secritin) notify the pancreas to release **pancreatic juice** containing the alkaline compound **bicarbonate** in amounts precisely

Figure 3–11

pH Values of Digestive Juices and Other Common Fluids

A substance's acidity or alkalinity is measured in pH units. Each step down the scale indicates a tenfold increase in concentration of hydrogen particles, which determine acidity. For example, a pH of 2 is 1,000 times as strong as a pH of 5.

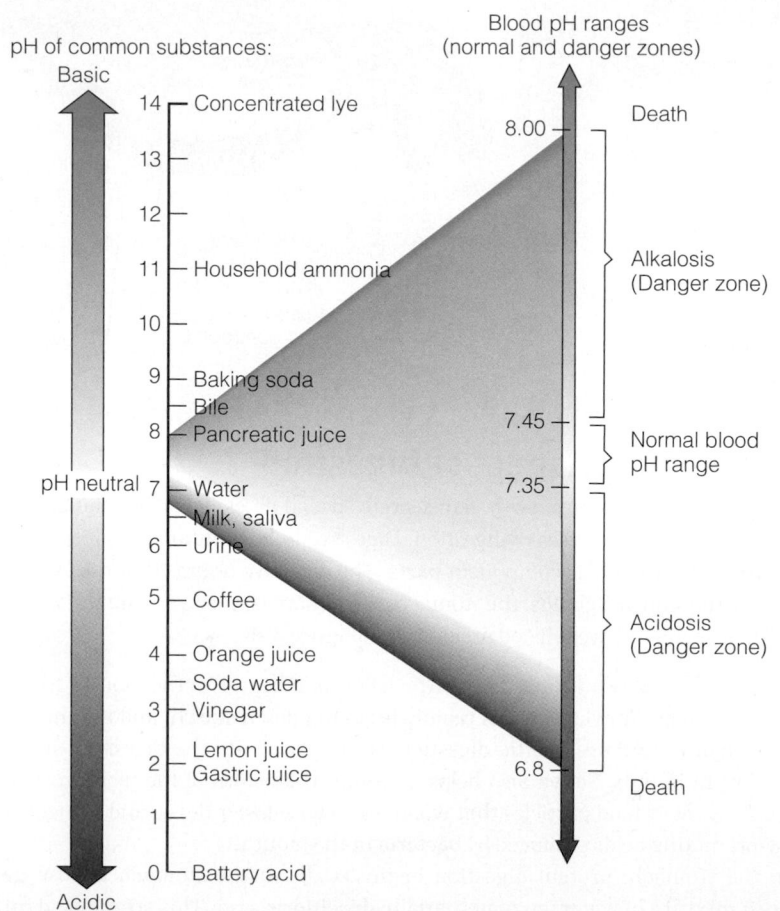

pH a measure of acidity on a point scale. A solution with a pH of 1 is a strong acid; a solution with a pH of 7 is neutral; a solution with a pH of 14 is a strong base.

mucus (MYOO-cus) a slippery coating of the digestive tract lining (and other body linings) that protects the cells from exposure to digestive juices (and other destructive agents). The adjective form is *mucous* (same pronunciation). The digestive tract lining is a *mucous membrane*.

bile a cholesterol-containing digestive fluid made by the liver, stored in the gallbladder, and released into the small intestine when needed. It emulsifies fats and oils to ready them for enzymatic digestion (described in Chapter 5).

emulsifier (ee-MULL-sih-fire) a compound with both water-soluble and fat-soluble portions that can attract fats and oils into water, combining them.

pancreatic juice fluid secreted by the pancreas that contains both sodium bicarbonate, a neutralizing agent, and enzymes to digest carbohydrate, fat, and protein.

bicarbonate a common alkaline chemical; a secretion of the pancreas; also the active ingredient of baking soda.

Chapter 3 The Remarkable Body

adjusted to neutralize the stomach acid that has reached the small intestine. All of these actions alter the intestinal environment to perfectly support the work of the digestive enzymes.

Meanwhile, as the pancreatic and intestinal enzymes act on the chemical bonds that hold the large nutrients together, smaller and smaller pieces are released into the intestinal fluids. The cells of the intestinal wall also hold some digestive enzymes (e.g., proteases) on their surfaces; these enzymes perform last-minute breakdown reactions required before nutrients can be absorbed. Finally, the digestive process releases pieces small enough for the cells to absorb and use. Digestion by human enzymes and absorption of carbohydrate, fat, and protein are essentially complete by the time the intestinal contents enter the colon. Water, fibre, and some minerals, however, remain in the tract.

Certain kinds of fibre, which cannot be digested by human enzymes, can often be broken down by the billions of living inhabitants of the human digestive tract, the resident bacteria. So active are these inhabitants in breaking down substances from food that they have been likened to an organ of intense metabolic activity that is involved in nutrient salvage. The intestinal cells then absorb the small fat fragments produced by intestinal bacteria from the fibre to provide a tiny bit of energy. Table 3–1 provides a summary of all of the processes involved.

KEY POINT

- Chemical digestion begins in the mouth, where food is mixed with an enzyme in saliva that acts on carbohydrates. Digestion continues in the stomach, where stomach enzymes and acid break down protein. Digestion then continues in the small intestine; there the liver and gallbladder contribute bile that emulsifies fat, and the pancreas and small intestine donate enzymes that continue digestion so that absorption can occur. Bacteria in the colon break down certain fibres.

Are Some Food Combinations More Easily Digested Than Others?

People sometimes wonder if the digestive tract has trouble digesting certain foods in combination—for example, fruit and meat. Proponents of fad "food-combining" diets claim that the digestive tract cannot perform certain digestive tasks at the same time, but this is a gross underestimation of the tract's capabilities. The digestive system adjusts to whatever mixture of foods is presented to it. The truth is that all foods, regardless of identity, are broken down by enzymes into the basic molecules that make them up.

Scientists who study digestion suggest that the organs of the digestive tract analyze the diet's nutrient contents and deliver juice and enzymes appropriate for digesting those nutrients. The pancreas is especially sensitive in this regard and has been observed to adjust its output of enzymes to digest carbohydrate, fat, or protein to an amazing degree. The pancreas of a person who suddenly consumes a meal unusually high in carbohydrate, for example, would begin increasing its output of carbohydrate-digesting enzymes within 24 hours while reducing outputs of other types. This sensitive mechanism ensures that foods of all types are used fully by the body. The next section reviews the major processes of digestion by showing how the nutrients in a mixture of foods are handled.

KEY POINT

- The healthy digestive system is capable of adjusting to almost any diet and can handle any combination of foods with ease.

Carbohydrates become individual sugars, mainly glucose, which is used as an immediate source of energy by all cells, especially the brain, or stored in the liver and muscles to be drawn upon when energy levels are low (Chapter 4).

If "I Am What I Eat," Then How Does a Sandwich Become "Me"?

The process of rendering foods into nutrients and absorbing them into the body fluids is remarkably efficient. Within about 24 to 48 hours of eating, a healthy body digests and absorbs about 90 percent

Table 3–1

Summary of Chemical Digestion

	Mouth	Stomach	Small Intestine, Pancreas, Liver, and Gallbladder	Large Intestine (Colon)
Sugar and Starch	The salivary glands secrete saliva to moisten and lubricate food; chewing crushes and mixes it with a salivary enzyme (salivary amylase) that initiates starch digestion.	Digestion of starch continues while food remains in the upper storage area of the stomach. In the lower digesting area of the stomach, hydrochloric acid and an enzyme of the stomach's juices halt starch digestion.	The pancreas produces a starch-digesting enzyme (pancreatic amylase) and releases it into the small intestine. Cells in the intestinal lining possess enzymes on their surfaces that break sugars (e.g., sucrase) and starch fragments into simple sugars, which are then absorbed.	Undigested carbohydrates reach the colon and are partly broken down by intestinal bacteria.
Fibre	The teeth crush fibre and mix it with saliva to moisten it for swallowing.	No action	Fibre binds cholesterol and some minerals.	Most fibre is excreted with the feces; some fibre is digested by bacteria in the colon.
Fat	Fat-rich foods are mixed with saliva. The tongue produces traces of a fat-digesting enzyme that accomplishes some breakdown, especially of milk fats. The enzyme is stable at low pH and is important to digestion in nursing infants.	Fat tends to rise from the watery stomach fluid and foods and float on top of the mixture. Only a small amount of fat is digested. Fat is last to leave the stomach.	The liver secretes bile; the gallbladder stores it and releases it into the small intestine. Bile emulsifies the fat and readies it for enzyme action. The pancreas produces fat-digesting enzymes (pancreatic lipase) and releases them into the small intestine to split fats into their component parts (primarily fatty acids), which are then absorbed.	Some fatty materials escape absorption and are carried out of the body with other wastes.
Protein	Chewing crushes and softens protein-rich foods and mixes them with saliva.	Stomach acid works to uncoil protein strands and to activate the stomach's protein-digesting enzyme (pepsin). Then the enzyme breaks the protein strands into smaller fragments.	Enzymes released into the small intestine by the pancreas (e.g., proteases) split protein fragments into smaller fragments or free amino acids. Deoxyribonuclease enzymes split the DNA molecules in food. Enzymes on the cells of the intestinal lining break some protein fragments into free amino acids; nucleotidases continue the breakdown of the building blocks of DNA, which are then absorbed. Some small protein fragments (e.g., tripeptides or dipeptides) are also absorbed.	The colon carries undigested protein residue out of the body. Normally, almost all food protein is digested and absorbed.
Water	The mouth donates watery, enzyme-containing saliva.	The stomach donates acidic, watery, enzyme-containing gastric juice.	The liver donates a watery juice containing bile. The pancreas and small intestine add watery, enzyme-containing juices; pancreatic juice is also alkaline.	The colon reabsorbs water and some minerals.

of the carbohydrate, fat, and protein in a meal. Here we follow a peanut butter and banana sandwich on whole-wheat, sesame seed bread through the tract.

In the Mouth In each bite, food components are crushed, mashed, and mixed with saliva by the teeth and the tongue. The sesame seeds are crushed and torn open by the teeth, which break through the indigestible fibre coating so that digestive enzymes can reach the nutrients inside the seeds. The peanut butter is the "extra crunchy" type, but

Fat becomes fatty acids, which are incorporated into all cell membranes to be used for energy or stored in adipose tissue (Chapter 5).

Protein becomes individual amino acids that are used to synthesize enzymes and muscle proteins and important biomolecules (Chapter 6).

Many vitamins become important components of the chemical reactions we need for normal growth, tissue maintenance, and repair and reactions that provide our tissues with energy (Chapter 7).

Minerals are important; for example, calcium and phosphorus become part of our bone tissue, and iron is needed to help carry oxygen to all our tissues (Chapter 8).

the teeth grind the chunks to a paste before the bite is swallowed. The carbohydrate-digesting enzyme of saliva begins to break down the starches of the bread, banana, and peanut butter to sugars. Each swallow triggers a peristaltic wave that travels the length of the esophagus and carries one chewed bite of sandwich to the stomach.

In the Stomach The stomach collects bite after bite in its upper storage area, where starch continues to be digested until the gastric juice mixes with the salivary enzymes and halts their action. Small portions of the mashed sandwich are pushed into the digesting area of the stomach, where gastric juice mixes with the mass. Acid in gastric juice unwinds proteins from the bread, seeds, and peanut butter; then an enzyme clips the protein strands into pieces. The sandwich has now become chyme. The watery carbohydrate- and protein-rich part of the chyme enters the small intestine first; a layer of fat follows closely behind.

In the Small Intestine Some of the sweet sugars in the banana require so little digesting that they begin to cross the linings of the small intestine immediately on contact. Nearby, the liver donates bile through a duct into the small intestine. The bile blends the fat from the peanut butter and seeds with the watery enzyme-containing digestive fluids. The nearby pancreas squirts enzymes into the small intestine to break down the fat, protein, and starch (see margin notes) in the chemical soup that just an hour ago was a sandwich. The cells of the small intestine itself produce enzymes to complete these processes. As the enzymes do their work, smaller and smaller chemical fragments are liberated from the chemical soup and are absorbed into the blood and lymph through the cells of the small intestine's wall. Vitamins and minerals (see margin notes) are absorbed here, too. They all eventually enter the bloodstream to nourish the tissues.

In the Large Intestine (Colon) Only fibre fragments, fluid, and some minerals are absorbed in the large intestine. The fibres from the seeds, whole wheat bread, peanut butter, and banana are partly digested by the bacteria living in the colon, and some of the products are absorbed. Most fibre is not absorbed, however, and, along with some other components, it passes out of the colon, excreted as feces.

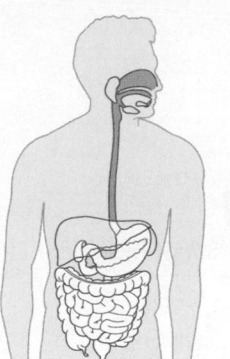
Time in mouth, less than a minute

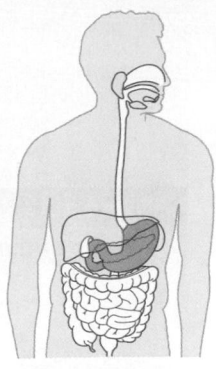
Time in stomach, about 1–2 hours

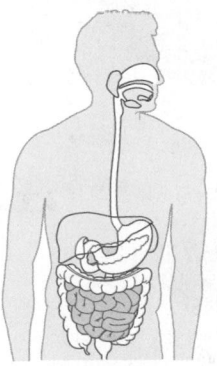
Time in small intestine, about 7–8 hours*

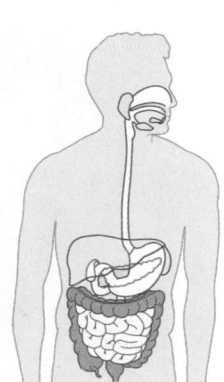
Time in colon, about 12–14 hours*

*Based on a 24-hour transit time. Actual times vary widely.

KEY POINT

- The mechanical and chemical actions of the digestive tract break foods down to nutrients and large nutrients to their smaller building blocks, with remarkable efficiency.

Absorption and Transportation of Nutrients

Once the digestive system has broken food down to its nutrient components, the rest of the body awaits their delivery. First, though, every molecule of nutrient must traverse one of the cells of the intestinal lining. These cells absorb nutrients from the mixture within the intestine and deposit them in the blood and lymph. The cells are selective: they recognize some of the nutrients that may be in short supply in the diet. The mineral calcium is an example. The less calcium in the diet, the greater the percentage of calcium the intestinal cells absorb from foods. The cells are also extraordinarily efficient: they absorb enough nutrients to nourish all of the body's other cells.

The cells of the intestinal tract lining are arranged in sheets that poke out into millions of finger-shaped projections (**villi**). Every cell on every villus has a brushlike covering of tiny hairlike projections (**microvilli**) that can trap the nutrient particles.

villi (VILL-ee, VILL-eye) fingerlike projections of the sheets of cells that line the intestinal tract. The villi make the surface area much greater than it would otherwise be (singular: *villus*).

microvilli (MY-croh-VILL-ee, MY-croh-VILL-eye) tiny, hairlike projections on each cell of every villus that greatly expand the surface area available to trap nutrient particles and absorb them into the cells (singular: *microvillus*).

The Digestive System

Each villus (projection) has its own capillary network and a lymph vessel so that as nutrients move across the cells, they can immediately mingle with the body fluids. Figure 3–12 provides a close look at these details.

Figure 3–12

Details of the Small Intestinal Lining

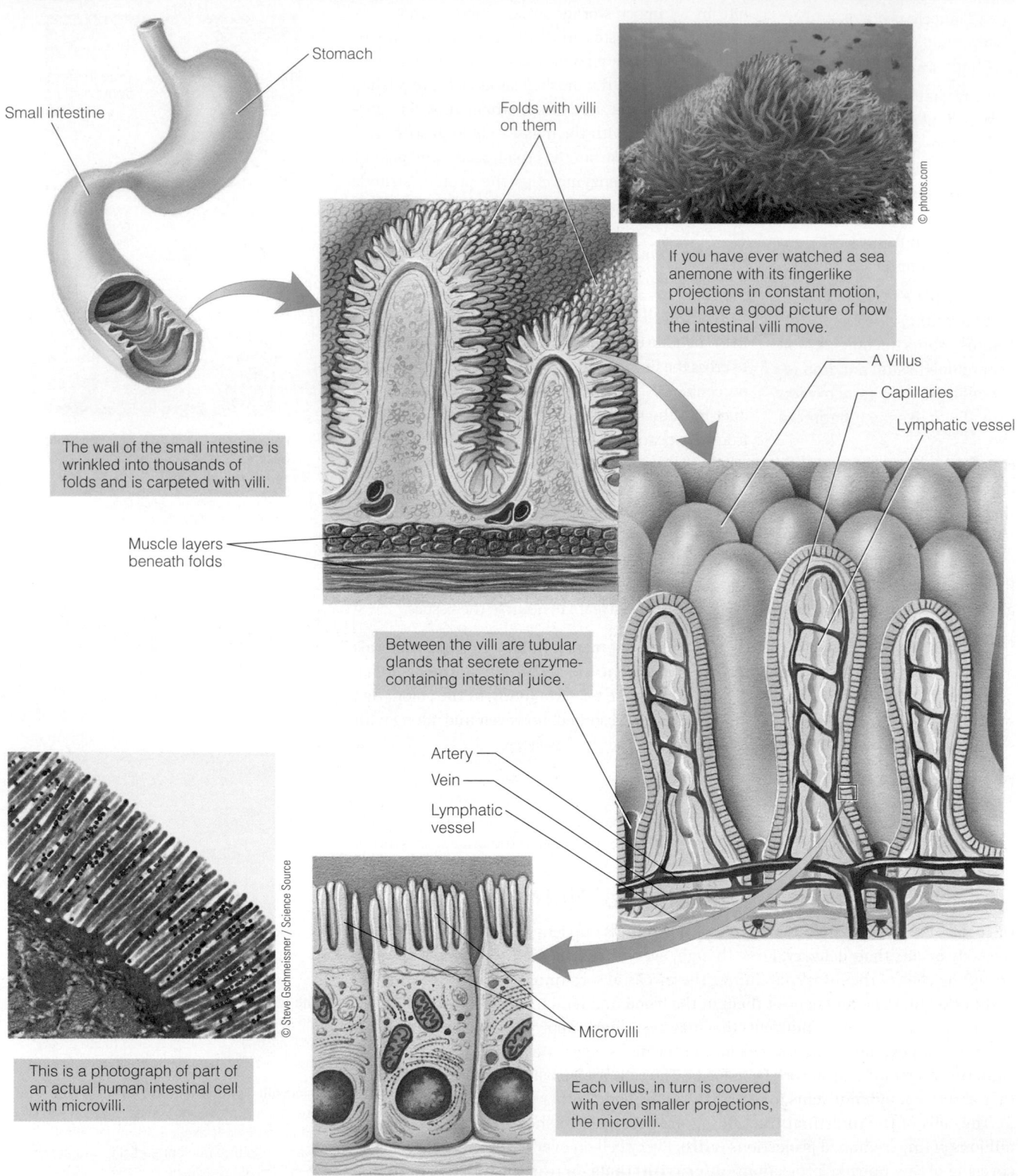

Stomach

Small intestine

Folds with villi on them

© photos.com

If you have ever watched a sea anemone with its fingerlike projections in constant motion, you have a good picture of how the intestinal villi move.

A Villus

Capillaries

Lymphatic vessel

The wall of the small intestine is wrinkled into thousands of folds and is carpeted with villi.

Muscle layers beneath folds

Between the villi are tubular glands that secrete enzyme-containing intestinal juice.

Artery

Vein

Lymphatic vessel

© Steve Gschmeissner / Science Source

This is a photograph of part of an actual human intestinal cell with microvilli.

Microvilli

Each villus, in turn is covered with even smaller projections, the microvilli.

The small intestine's lining, villi and all, is wrinkled into thousands of folds, so its absorbing surface is enormous. If the folds, and the villi that poke out from them, were spread out flat, they would cover a third of a football field. The billions of cells of that surface weigh only 2.0 to 2.5 kilograms, yet they absorb enough nutrients to nourish the other 68 kilograms of body tissues.

After the nutrients pass through the cells of the villi, the blood and lymph start transporting the nutrients to their ultimate consumers, the body's cells. The lymphatic vessels initially transport most of the products of fat digestion and a few vitamins, later delivering them to the bloodstream. The blood vessels carry the products of carbohydrate and protein digestion, most vitamins, and the minerals from the digestive tract to the liver. Thanks to these two transportation systems, every nutrient soon arrives at the place where it is needed.

The digestive system's millions of specialized cells are themselves exquisitely sensitive to an undersupply of energy, nutrients, or dietary fibre. In cases of severe undernutrition of energy and nutrients, the absorptive surface of the small intestine shrinks. The surface may be reduced to a tenth of its normal area, preventing it from absorbing what few nutrients a limited food supply may provide. Without sufficient fibre to provide an undigested bulk for the tract's muscles to push against, the muscles become weak from lack of exercise. Malnutrition that impairs digestion is self-perpetuating because impaired digestion makes malnutrition worse. In fact, the digestive system's needs are few, but important. The body has much to say to the attentive listener, stated in a language of symptoms and feelings that you would be wise to study. The next section takes a lighthearted look at what your digestive tract might be trying to tell you.

KEY POINT

- The digestive system feeds the rest of the body and is itself sensitive to malnutrition. The folds and villi of the small intestine enlarge its surface area to facilitate nutrient absorption through countless cells to the blood and lymph. These transport systems then deliver the nutrients to all of the body's cells.

use it! Consumer Corner

A Letter from Your Digestive Tract

To My Owner,

You and I are so close; I hope that I can speak frankly without offending you. I know that sometimes I *do* offend with my gurgling noises and belching at quiet times and, oh yes, the gas. But, as you can read for yourself in Table 3-2, when you chew gum, drink carbonated beverages, or eat hastily, you gulp air with each swallow. I can't help making some noise as I move the air along my length or release it upward in a noisy belch. And if you eat or drink too fast, I can't help getting **hiccups**. Please sit and relax while you dine. You will ease my task, and we'll both be happier.

Also, when someone offers you a new food, you gobble away, trusting me to

do my job. I try. It would make my life easier, and yours less gassy, if you would start with small amounts of new foods, especially those high in fibre. The breakdown of fibre by bacteria produces gas, so introduce fibre-rich foods slowly. But please: if you do notice more gas than normal from a specific food, avoid it. If the gas becomes excessive, check with a physician. The problem could be something simple—or serious.

When you eat or drink too much, it just burns me up. Overeating causes **heartburn** because the acidic juice from my stomach backs up into my esophagus. Acid poses no problem to my healthy stomach, whose walls are coated with thick mucus to protect

them. But when my too-full stomach squeezes some of its contents back up into the esophagus, the acid burns its unprotected surface. Also, those tight jeans you wear constrict my stomach,

hiccups spasms of both the vocal cords and the diaphragm, causing periodic, audible, short, inhaled coughs. Can be caused by irritation of the diaphragm, indigestion, or other causes. Hiccups usually resolve in a few minutes but can have serious effects if prolonged. Breathing into a paper bag (inhaling carbon dioxide) or dissolving a teaspoon of sugar in the mouth may stop them.

heartburn a burning sensation in the chest (in the area of the heart) area caused by backflow of stomach acid into the esophagus.

The Digestive System

Table 3-2

Foods and Intestinal Gas

Recent experiments have shed light on the causes and prevention of intestinal gas. Here are some recent findings.

- Milk intake causes gas in those who cannot digest the milk sugar lactose. Most people, however, can consume up to a cup of milk without producing excessive gas.
  Solution: Drink up to 125 mL of fluid milk at a sitting or substitute reduced-fat cheeses or yogurt without added milk solids. Use lactose-reduced products or treat regular products with lactose-reducing enzyme products.

- Beans cause gas because some of their carbohydrates are indigestible by human enzymes but are broken down by intestinal bacteria. The amount of gas may not be as much as most people fear, however.
  Solution: Use rinsed canned beans, or dried beans that are well cooked, because cooked carbohydrates are more readily digestible. Try enzyme drops that can help break down the carbohydrate before it reaches the intestine.

- Air swallowed during eating or drinking can cause gas, as can the gas of carbonated beverages. Each swallow of a beverage can carry three times as much air as fluid, which some people belch up.
  Solution: Slow down during eating and drinking and don't chew gum or suck on hard candies that may cause you to swallow air.

- Vegetables may or may not cause gas in some people, but research is lacking.
  Solution: If you feel certain vegetables cause gas, try eating small portions of the cooked product. Do try the vegetable again: the gas you experienced may have been a coincidence and have nothing to do with eating the vegetable.

Source: Based on B. Liebman, Who ya gonna call? GasBusters, an interview with Michael Levitt, Nutrition Action Healthletter, *May 2003, pp. 1, 3–5.*

antacids medications that react directly and immediately with the acid of the stomach, neutralizing it. Antacids are most suitable for treating occasional heartburn. More about antacids appears in Controversy 8.

acid reducers prescription and over-the-counter drugs that reduce the acid output of the stomach; effective for treating severe, persistent forms of heartburn but not for neutralizing acid already present. Side effects are frequent and include diarrhea, other gastrointestinal complaints, and reduction of the stomach's capacity to destroy alcohol, thereby producing higher-than-expected blood alcohol levels from each drink (see this chapter's Controversy section). Also called *acid controllers*.

ulcer an erosion in the topmost, and sometimes underlying, layers of cells that form a lining. Ulcers of the digestive tract commonly form in the esophagus, stomach, or upper small intestine.

hernia a protrusion of an organ or part of an organ through the wall of the body chamber that normally contains the organ. An example is a *hiatal* (high-AY-tal) *hernia*, in which part of the stomach protrudes up through the diaphragm into the chest cavity, which contains the esophagus, heart, and lungs.

© Matthew Ennis/Shutterstock

What is your digestive tract trying to tell you?

squeezing the contents upward into the esophagus. Just leaning over or lying down after a meal may allow the acid to escape up the esophagus because the muscular sphincter separating the

two spaces is much looser than other sphincters. And if we need to lose a few pounds, let's get at it—excess body fat can also squeeze my stomach, causing acid to back up. When heartburn is a problem, do me a favour: try to eat smaller meals; drink liquids an hour before or after, but not during, meals; wear reasonably loose clothing; and relax after eating but sit up (don't lie down).

Sometimes your food choices irritate me. Specifically, chemical irritants in foods, such as the "hot" component of chilli peppers, chemicals in coffee, fat, chocolate, carbonated soft drinks, and alcohol, may worsen heartburn in some people. Avoid the ones that cause trouble. Above all, do not smoke. Smoking makes my heartburn worse—and you should hear your lungs bellyache about it.

By the way, I can tell you've been taking heartburn medicines again. You must have been watching those misleading TV commercials. You need to know that **antacids** are designed only to temporarily relieve pain caused by heartburn by neutralizing stomach acid for a while. But when the antacids reduce my normal stomach acidity, I respond by producing *more* acid to restore the normal acid condition. Also, the ingredients in antacids can interfere with my ability to absorb nutrients. Please check with our doctor if heartburn occurs more than just occasionally and certainly before you decide that we need to take the heavily advertised **acid reducers**; these restrict my normal ability to produce acid so much that my job of digesting food becomes harder. They may also reduce our defence against certain infections.[2]

Given a chance, my powerful acid can help fight bacterial infections from contaminated food and other sources—some dangerous bacteria won't survive a bath in my caustic stomach juices.[3] Acid-reducing drugs may allow more bacteria to pass through. And even worse, self-prescribed heartburn medicine can mask the symptoms of **ulcer**, **hernia**, or the severe destructive form of chronic heartburn known as

Figure 3–13

Swallowing and Choking

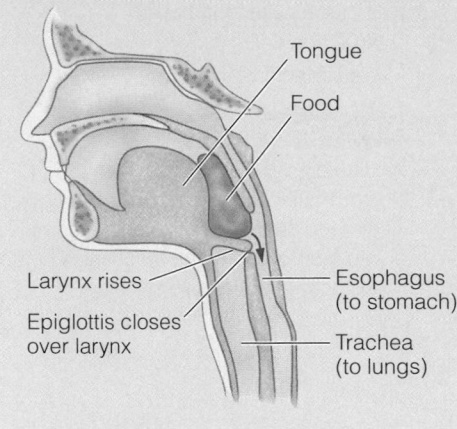

- Tongue
- Food
- Larynx rises
- Epiglottis closes over larynx
- Esophagus (to stomach)
- Trachea (to lungs)

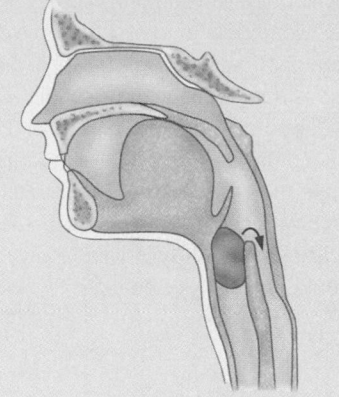

A normal swallow. The epiglottis acts as a flap to seal the entrance to the lungs (trachea) and direct food to the stomach via the esophagus.

Choking. A choking person cannot speak or gasp because food lodged in the trachea blocks the passage of air. The red arrow points to where the food should have gone to prevent choking.

gastroesophageal reflux disease (GERD).[4] This can be serious because, if not treated with antibiotic drugs, the bacterium that causes stomach ulcer may also cause stomach cancer.[5] A hernia can cause food to back up into the esophagus, so it can feel like heartburn, but many times hernias require corrective treatment by a physician. GERD can feel like heartburn, too, but requires the correct drug therapy to prevent respiratory problems, severe damage to tissues, or, less likely, cancer.[6]

When you eat too quickly, I worry about choking (see Figure 3-13). Please take time to cut your food into small pieces and chew it until it is crushed and moistened with saliva. Also, refrain from talking or laughing before swallowing and never attempt to eat when you are breathing hard. Also, for our sake and the sake of others, learn the Heimlich manoeuvre shown in Figure 3-14.

When I'm suffering, you suffer, too. When **constipation** or **diarrhea** strikes, neither of us is having fun. Slow, hard, dry bowel movements can be painful, and failing to have a movement for too

*One such stimulant, phenolphthalein, was banned because of an association with colon cancer.

Figure 3–14

The Heimlich Manoeuvre

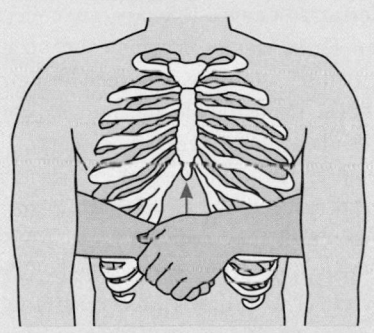

Rescuer positions fist directly against victim's abdomen as shown.

1. Rescuer stands behind victim and wraps her or his arms around victim's waist.
2. Rescuer makes a fist with one hand and places the thumb side of the fist against the victim's abdomen, slightly above the navel and below the rib cage.
3. Rescuer grasps fist with other hand and rapidly squeezes it inward and upward three or four times in rapid succession.
4. Rescuer repeats the process if necessary.

If the victim is alone, the victim positions himself or herself over edge of fixed horizontal object, such as a chair back, railing, or table edge, and presses abdomen into edge with quick movement.

- Some bacteria survive stomach conditions to cause foodborne illnesses. See Chapter 12.

- For more information concerning ulcers and medication and other digestive health issues, contact the Canadian Digestive Health Foundation at director@cdhf.ca.

- The lungs also excrete some small percentage of ingested alcohol—the basis for the "breathalyzer" test given to drivers to determine if they've been drinking.

long brings on headaches and ill feelings. Worse, chronic constipation with fewer than three bowel movements each week has been associated with a more-than-doubled risk of colon cancer.[7]

Laxatives may help in the short term, but they often contain stimulants that can cause side effects.* Instead of relying on laxatives, listen carefully for my signal that it is time to defecate and make time for it even if you are busy. The longer you ignore my signal, the more time the colon has to extract water from the feces, hardening them. Also, please choose foods that provide enough fibre (Chapter 4 lists some of these foods). Fibre attracts water, creating softer, bulkier stools that stimulate my muscles to contract, pushing the contents along. Fibre helps my muscles stay fit, too, making elimination easier. Be sure to drink enough water because

gastroesophageal (GAS-tro-eh-SOFF-ah-jee-al) **reflux disease (GERD)** a severe and chronic splashing of stomach acid and enzymes into the esophagus, throat, mouth, or airway that causes inflammation and injury to those organs. Untreated GERD may increase the risk of esophageal cancer; treatment may require surgery or management with medication.

constipation infrequent, difficult bowel movements often caused by diet, inactivity, dehydration, or medication (also defined in Chapter 4).

diarrhea frequent, watery bowel movements usually caused by diet, stress, or irritation of the colon. Severe, prolonged diarrhea robs the body of fluid and certain minerals, causing dehydration and imbalances that can be dangerous if left untreated.

dehydration causes the colon to absorb all of the water it can get from the feces. And please make time to be physically active; exercise strengthens not just the muscles of your arms, legs, and torso but those of the colon, too.

When I have the opposite problem, diarrhea, my system will rob you of water and salts. In diarrhea, my intestinal contents have moved too quickly, drawing water and minerals from your tissues into the contents. When this happens, please rest for a while and drink fluids.

To avoid diarrhea, try not to change my diet too drastically or quickly. I'm willing to work with you and learn to digest new foods, but if you suddenly change your diet, we're both in for it. I hate to even think of it, but one likely cause of diarrhea is dangerous food poisoning (*please* read, and use, the tips in Chapter 12 to keep us safe). Also, if diarrhea lasts longer than a day or two, or if it alternates with constipation, the cause could be **irritable bowel syndrome**, and you should see a physician.

Thank you for listening. I know we'll both benefit from communicating like this because you and I are in this together for the long haul.
Affectionately,
Your Digestive Tract

KEY POINT

- The digestive tract has many ways to communicate its needs. By taking the time to listen, you will obtain a complete understanding of the mechanics of the digestive tract and its signals.

The Excretory System

Cells generate a number of wastes, and all of them must be eliminated. Many of the body's organs play roles in removing wastes. Carbon dioxide waste from the cells travels in the blood to the lungs, where it is exchanged for oxygen. Other wastes are pulled out of the bloodstream by the liver. The liver processes these wastes and either tosses them out into the digestive tract with bile, to leave the body with the feces, or prepares them to be sent to the kidneys for disposal in the urine. Organ systems work together to dispose of the body's wastes, but the kidneys are waste- and water-removal specialists.

The kidneys straddle the cardiovascular system and filter the passing blood. Waste materials, dissolved in water, are collected by the kidneys' working units, the **nephrons**. These wastes become concentrated as urine, which travels through tubes to the urinary **bladder**. The bladder empties periodically, removing the wastes from the body. Thus, the blood is purified continuously throughout the day, and dissolved materials are excreted as necessary. One dissolved mineral, sodium, helps regulate blood pressure, and its excretion or retention by the kidneys is a vital part of the body's blood pressure-controlling mechanism.

Although they account for just 0.5 percent of the body's total weight, the kidneys use up to 10 percent of the body's oxygen supply, indicating intense metabolic activity.[8] The kidney's waste-excreting function rivals breathing in importance to life, but the kidneys act in other ways as well. By sorting among dissolved substances, retaining some while excreting others, the kidneys regulate the fluid volume and concentrations of substances in the blood and extracellular fluids with great precision. Through these mechanisms, the kidneys help regulate blood pressure (see Chapter 11 for details). As you might expect, the kidneys' work is regulated by hormones secreted by glands that respond to conditions in the blood (such as the sodium concentration). The kidneys also release certain hormones.

Because the kidneys remove toxins that could otherwise damage body tissues, whatever supports the health of the kidneys supports the health of the whole body. A strong cardiovascular system and an abundant supply of water are important to keep blood flushing swiftly through the kidneys. In addition, the kidneys need sufficient energy to do their complex sifting and sorting job, and many vitamins and minerals serve as the cogs in their machinery. Exercise and nutrition are vital to healthy kidney function.

KEY POINT

- The kidneys adjust the blood's composition in response to the body's needs, disposing of everyday wastes and helping remove toxins. Nutrients, including water, and exercise help keep the kidneys healthy.

irritable bowel syndrome intermittent disturbance of bowel function, especially diarrhea or alternating diarrhea and constipation; associated with diet, lack of physical activity, or psychological stress.

nephrons (NEFF-rons) the working units in the kidneys, consisting of intermeshed blood vessels and tubules.

bladder the sac that holds urine until time for elimination.

Storage Systems

The human body is designed to eat at intervals of about four to six hours, but cells need nutrients around the clock. Providing the cells with a constant flow of the needed nutrients requires the cooperation of many body systems. These systems store and release nutrients to meet the cells' needs between meals. Among the major storage sites are the liver and muscles, which store carbohydrate, and the fat cells, which store fat and other fat-related substances.

When I Eat More Than My Body Needs, What Happens to the Extra Nutrients?

Nutrients collected from the digestive system sooner or later all move through a vast network of capillaries that weave among the liver cells. This arrangement ensures that liver cells have access to the newly arriving nutrients for processing. The body tissues store excess energy-containing nutrients in two forms (details in later chapters). The liver makes some into **glycogen** (a carbohydrate), and some is stored as fat. The liver stores the glycogen to meet the body's ongoing glucose needs. Liver glycogen can sustain cell activities when the intervals between meals become long. Without glucose absorbed from food, the cells (including the muscle cells) draw on liver glycogen. Should no food be available, the liver's glycogen supply dwindles; it can be effectively depleted within as few as three to six hours. Muscle cells make and store glycogen, too, but selfishly reserve it for their own use.

Whereas the liver stores glycogen, it ships out fat in packages (see Chapter 5) to be picked up by cells that need it. All body cells may withdraw the fat they need from these packages, and the fat cells of the **adipose tissue** pick up the remainder and store it to meet long-term energy needs. Unlike the liver, fat tissue has virtually infinite storage capacity. It can continue to supply the body's cells with fat for days, weeks, or possibly even months when no food is eaten.

These storage systems for glucose and fat ensure that the body's cells will not go without energy even if the body is hungry for food. Body stores also exist for many other nutrients, each with a characteristic capacity. For example, liver and fat cells store many vitamins, and bones provide reserves of calcium and other minerals. Stores of nutrients are available to keep the blood levels constant and to meet cellular demands.

> Later chapters provide details about the storage of energy nutrients.

Variations in Nutrient Stores

Some nutrients are stored in the body in much larger quantities than others. For example, certain vitamins are stored without limit, even if they reach toxic levels within the body. Other nutrients are stored in only small amounts, regardless of the amount taken in, and these can readily be depleted. As you learn how the body handles various nutrients, pay particular attention to their storage so that you will know your tolerance limits. For example, you needn't eat fat at every meal because fat is stored abundantly. On the other hand, you normally do need to have a source of carbohydrate at intervals throughout the day because the liver stores less than one day's supply of glycogen.

KEY POINT
- The body's energy stores are of two principal kinds: glycogen in muscle and liver cells (in limited quantities) and fat in fat cells (in potentially large quantities). Other tissues store other nutrients.

Conclusion

In addition to the systems just described, the body has many more: bones, muscles, reproductive organs, and others. All of these cooperate, enabling each cell to carry on its own life. For example, the skin and body linings defend other tissues against

glycogen a storage form of carbohydrate energy (glucose), described more fully in Chapter 4.

adipose tissue the body's fat tissue, consisting of masses of fat-storing cells and blood vessels to nourish them.

microbial invaders while being nourished and cleansed by tissues specializing in these tasks. Each system needs a continuous supply of many specific nutrients to maintain itself and carry out its work. For example, calcium is particularly important for bones, iron for muscles, and glucose for the brain. But all systems need all nutrients, and every system is impaired by an undersupply or oversupply of them.

While external events clamour and vie for attention, the body quietly continues its life-sustaining work. Most of the body's work is directed automatically by the unconscious portions of the brain and nervous system, and this work is finely regulated to achieve a state of well-being. But you need to involve your brain's cortex, your conscious thinking brain, to cultivate an understanding and appreciation of your body's needs. In doing so, attend to nutrition first. The rewards are liberating—ample energy to tackle life's tasks, a robust attitude, and the glowing appearance that comes from the best of health. Read on and learn to let nutrition principles guide your food choices.

KEY POINT

■ To achieve optimal function, the body's systems require nutrients from outside. These have to be supplied through a human being's conscious food choices.

CONTROVERSY 3

Alcohol and Nutrition: Do the Benefits Outweigh the Risks?*

During 2011, just under 80 percent of Canadians over 15 years consumed alcohol, and according to Health Canada, among younger Canadians, "Less than three quarters of youth (70.8%) reported consuming alcohol in the past year. This is a decrease from 2004 when 82.9% of youth reported past-year use of alcohol" (http://www .hc-sc.gc.ca/hc-ps/drugs-drogues/ stat/index-eng.php). Also, a significantly higher proportion of males vs. females and adults vs. youth consumed alcohol in 2011. Near the end of 2011, "Canada's Low-Risk Alcohol Drinking Guidelines" were released (http:// www.ccsa.ca/Eng/Priorities/Alcohol/

*For a brief but excellent review on alcohol and health, see E. Rimm and N. J. Temple, What are the health implications of alcohol consumption? in N. J. Temple, T. Wilson, and D. R. Jacobs Jr., eds., Nutritional Health Strategies for Disease Prevention, 2nd ed. (Totowa, NJ: Humana Press, 2006), pp. 211–238.

Canada-Low-Risk-Alcohol-Drinking-Guidelines/Pages/default.aspx).

When Health Canada further examined the 2011 survey of drinking behaviours of Canadians, it was revealed that 18.7 percent exceed Guideline 1 of no more than two drinks/day for women (10 drinks/ wk) and three drinks/day for men (15 drinks/wk), and 13.1 percent exceeded Guideline 2 of no more than three drinks on any single occasion for women and four for men. However, in the latter case (i.e., Guideline 2), a significantly higher proportion of males vs. females and youths vs. adults exceeded the guideline.

Beer made up 80 percent of alcoholic beverages consumed by Canadians and has risen to the level of just over 80 litres per person over the age of 15 years. In addition, almost 14 litres of wine are consumed annually by these individuals, as are 7.5 litres of spirits. Statistics Canada notes that these levels may be understated since they do not include

homemade alcoholic beverages, those brewed on the premises, and so on.

It should also be noted that over one in five (22.6 percent) drinkers exceeded the low-risk guidelines of fewer than 14 drinks per week for males and 9 drinks per week for females, a behaviour more common among those 18 to 24 years of age. Drinking habits span a wide spectrum: many adults drink no alcohol whatsoever, some take a glass of wine only with meals, others drink on social occasions, and others take in large quantities of alcohol daily because of a life-shattering addiction.

Alcohol Consumption among Canadian University Students

According to the Centre for Addiction and Mental Health (CAMH), a 2004 Canadian campus survey funded by the Canadian

Institutes of Health Research (CIHR) of over 6,000 students from 40 universities revealed that 77 percent had consumed alcohol during the month prior to the study. Furthermore, 18.5 percent and 6.6 percent indicated that they consumed five or more or eight or more drinks (binge drinking), respectively, on a single occasion once every two weeks or more frequently (http://www.camh.ca/en/research/research_areas/ community_and_population_health/ Documents/CCS_2004_report.pdf). Also, almost one-third of students reported at least one indicator of dependent drinking (e.g., being unable to stop). Males reported drinking more often and higher amounts than females (8.9 vs. 4.5 drinks per week), as well as higher rates of episodic drinking, most of which occurred on weekends and off-campus but in private premises.

Whether or not they recognize the problem, many college students will pay a high price in terms of their health and safety as a result of episodes of heavy drinking. **Moderate drinkers** usually consume the Calories of alcohol in addition to their normal food intake, so the alcohol contributes to their daily Calorie totals.[*,1] (Alcohol-related terms are defined in Table C3–1.)

Controversy references are listed separately at the end of the chapter.

Table C3–1

Alcohol and Drinking Terms

- **acetaldehyde** (ass-et-AL-deh-hide) a substance to which ethanol is metabolized on its way to becoming harmless waste products that can be excreted.
- **alcohol dehydrogenase** (dee-high-DRAH-gen-ace) **(ADH)** an enzyme system that breaks down alcohol. The antidiuretic hormone listed below is also abbreviated ADH.
- **alcoholism** a dependency on alcohol marked by compulsive uncontrollable drinking with negative effects on physical health, family relationships, and social health.
- **antidiuretic** (AN-tee-dye-you-RET-ick) **hormone (ADH)** a hormone produced by the pituitary gland in response to dehydration (or a high sodium concentration in the blood). It stimulates the kidneys to reabsorb more water and so to excrete less. (This hormone should not be confused with the enzyme alcohol dehydrogenase, which is also abbreviated ADH.)
- **beer belly** central-body fatness associated with alcohol consumption.
- **binge drinkers** people who drink four or more drinks in a short period.
- **CAGE questions** a set of four questions often used internationally for initial screening for alcoholism. The questions relate to C, Cutting down; A, Annoyance by criticism; G, Guilty feeling; and E, Eye-openers.
- **cirrhosis** (seer-OH-sis) advanced liver disease, often associated with alcoholism, in which liver cells have died, hardened, turned an orange colour, and permanently lost their function.
- **congeners** (CON-jen-ers) chemical substances other than alcohol that account for some of the physiological effects of alcoholic beverages, such as appetite, taste, and aftereffects.
- **drink** a dose of any alcoholic beverage that delivers 15 mL of pure ethanol.
- **ethanol** the alcohol of alcoholic beverages, produced by the action of microorganisms on the carbohydrates of grape juice or other carbohydrate-containing fluids.
- **euphoria** (you-FOR-ee-uh) an inflated sense of well-being and pleasure brought on by a moderate dose of alcohol and some other drugs.
- **fatty liver** an early stage of liver deterioration seen in several diseases, including kwashiorkor and alcoholic liver disease, in which fat accumulates in the liver cells.
- **fibrosis** (fye-BROH-sis) an intermediate stage of alcoholic liver deterioration. Liver cells lose their function and assume the characteristics of connective tissue cells (fibres).
- **formaldehyde** a substance to which methanol is metabolized on the way to being converted to harmless waste products that can be excreted.
- **gout** (GOWT) a painful form of arthritis caused by the abnormal buildup of the waste product uric acid in the blood, with uric acid salt deposited as crystals in the joints.
- **MEOS** (microsomal ethanol oxidizing system) a system of enzymes in the liver that oxidize not only alcohol but also several classes of drugs.
- **methanol** an alcohol continuously produced in the body by all cells.
- **moderate drinkers** people who do not drink excessively and do not behave inappropriately because of alcohol. A moderate drinker's health is not harmed by alcohol over the long term.
- **nonalcoholic** a term used on labels of beverages, such as wine or beer, indicating that the product contains less than 0.5% alcohol. The terms *dealcoholized* and *alcohol removed* mean the same thing. *Alcohol-free* means that the product contains no detectable alcohol.
- **proof** a statement of the percentage of alcohol in an alcoholic beverage. Liquor that is 100 proof is 50% alcohol, 90 proof is 45%, and so forth.
- **social drinkers** people who drink only on social occasions. Depending on how alcohol affects a social drinker's life, the person may be a moderate drinker or a problem drinker.
- **urethane** a carcinogenic compound that commonly forms in alcoholic beverages.
- **Wernicke-Korsakoff** (VER-nik-ee KOR-sah-koff) **syndrome** a cluster of symptoms involving nerve damage arising from a deficiency of the vitamin thiamin in alcoholism. Characterized by mental confusion, disorientation, memory loss, jerky eye movements, and staggering gait.

Alcohol is not just an energy source, however; it is also a psychoactive drug and a toxin to the body.

Despite its toxicity, people want to know if there is an amount of alcohol they can drink safely or whether they may derive benefits, particularly for the health of the heart, by drinking. This Controversy first defines some terms and examines alcohol's actions within the body and its effects on the brain and other organs. It then summarizes the long-term effects of alcohol on the body and nutrition and concludes with research on moderate drinking.

Defining Drinks and Drinking

When people congregate to enjoy conversation and companionship, beverages are usually a part of that sociability. All beverages seem to ease conversation, whether they contain alcohol or not. Many people are **social drinkers** who choose alcohol over cola, juice, milk, tea, or coffee as a pleasant accompaniment to a meal, a drink of celebration, or a way to relax with friends. Taken in moderation, alcohol reduces inhibitions, encourages social interactions, and produces feelings of **euphoria**, a pleasant sensation that people seek. The term *moderation* is important because alcohol *worsens* social interactions at higher intakes. The **nonalcoholic** beers and wines now on the market also elevate mood and encourage social interaction, a testimony to the placebo effect at work.

In contrast to moderate social drinking, the effect of alcohol on problem drinkers or people with **alcoholism** is overwhelmingly negative. For these people, drinking alcohol brings irrational and often dangerous behaviour, such as driving a car while intoxicated, and regrettable human interactions, such as arguments and violence. With continued drinking, such people face psychological depression, physical illness, severe malnutrition, and demoralizing erosion of self-esteem. The Centre for Addiction and Mental Health Low-Risk Drinking Guidelines are provided in Table C3–2.

Moderation

Moderation is not easily defined because tolerance to alcohol differs among individuals. In general, women cannot handle as much alcohol as men and should not try to match drinks with male companions. Some individuals may have lower-than-average tolerance to alcohol. Health authorities have set limits at not more than two drinks a day for the average-sized, healthy man and not more than one drink a day for the average-sized, healthy woman. These amounts are supposed to be enough to elevate mood without incurring long-term harm to health—note that these are not average amounts but daily maximums. In other words, a person who drinks no alcohol during the week but then takes seven drinks on Saturday night is not a moderate drinker—instead, that alcohol intake pattern characterizes binge drinking.

Doubtless some people can safely consume slightly more than the alcohol dose called moderate; others, especially those prone to alcohol addiction, cannot handle nearly as much without significant risk.

Table C3–3 lists those people advised by the *Dietary Guidelines for Americans 2005* not to drink at all. If you think your own drinking might not be moderate or normal or if alcohol has caused problems in your life, you may want to seek a professional evaluation.* Table C3–4 contrasts some behaviours of moderate drinkers with those of problem drinkers.

Centre for Addiction and Mental Health: Addiction Assessment, 416-535-8501 ext 6166 or 1-800-463-6273 ext 6166.

Table C3–2

Canada's Low-Risk Alcohol Drinking Guidelines

Maximize Life, Minimize Risk (see excerpts from Guidelines below)

- Guideline 1:
    - Women—no more than 2 drinks/day (10 drinks/wk)
    - Men—no more than 3 drinks/day (15 drinks/wk)
- Guideline 2:
    - Women—no more than 3 drinks on any occasion
    - Men—no more than 4 drinks on any occasion
- Guideline 3: Do not drink when you are
    - Driving a motor vehicle
    - Taking medicine or other drugs that interact with alcohol
    - Living with mental or physical health problems
- Guideline 4: "If you are pregnant, planning to become pregnant, or about to breastfeed, the safest choice is to drink no alcohol at all."
- Guideline 5: "Teens should speak with their parents about drinking" and should never exceed the daily or weekly limits outline above.

One Standard Drink = 13.6 g of alcohol

- 142 mL/5 oz of wine (12% alcohol)
- 43 mL/1.5 oz of spirits (40% alcohol)
- 341 mL/12 oz of regular-strength beer (5% alcohol)

Higher-alcohol beers and coolers have more alcohol than one standard drink.

- If you don't already drink, don't start for health reasons.
- If you do drink, avoid getting intoxicated or drunk.
- Wait at least one hour between drinks.
- Have something to eat. Drink nonalcoholic beverages, such as water, soft drinks, and fruit juice.

Canada's Low-Risk Alcohol Drinking Guidelines are for people of legal drinking age.

Source: Centre for Addiction and Mental Health Canada's Low-Risk Alcohol Drinking Guidelines, http://www.ccsa.ca/Eng/Priorities/Alcohol/Canada-Low-Risk-Alcohol-Drinking-Guidelines/Pages/default.aspx

Chapter 3 The Remarkable Body

Prudent Guidelines for Those Who Should Not Drink Alcohol

These people should not drink alcoholic beverages at all:

- *Children and adolescents.* The earlier in life drinking begins, the greater the risk of alcoholism later on.
- *No one should drink on an empty stomach.*
- *People of any age who cannot restrict their drinking to moderate levels,* especially people recovering from alcoholism, problem drinkers, and people whose family members have alcohol problems.
- *Women who may become pregnant or who are pregnant or breast-feeding.* A safe level of alcohol intake has not been established for women during pregnancy (see Chapter 13), and alcohol may be especially hazardous during the first few weeks, before a woman knows she is pregnant.
- *People who plan to drive, operate machinery, or take part in other activities that require attention, skill, or coordination to remain safe.* Alcohol remains in the blood for several hours after taking even a single drink.
- *People taking medications that can interact with alcohol.* Alcohol alters the effectiveness or toxicity of many medications, and some drugs may increase blood alcohol levels.
- *People with medical conditions worsened by alcohol, such as liver disease.*
- *No one should drink when they are alone.*

U.S. Department of Agriculture and U.S. Department of Health and Human Services, 2005 Dietary Guidelines for Americans, 6th edition, (Washington, D.C.: 2005) available at http://www .usda.gov/cnpp or call (888) 878-3256; international drinking guidelines available at http://www.icap.org/ PolicyIssues/DrinkingGuidelines/ GuidelinesTable/ tabid/204/Default.aspx

Binge Drinking

Binge drinking is defined as consuming "five drinks or more in a row for a man and four drinks or more for a woman" and poses serious threats.[2]

Binge drinkers on and off school campuses may find it difficult to recognize themselves as problem drinkers (refer to

Behaviours Typical of Moderate Drinkers and Problem Drinkers[a]

Moderate Drinkers Typically	Problem Drinkers Typically
Drink slowly and casually.	Gulp or "chug" drinks.
Eat food while drinking or beforehand.	Drink on an empty stomach.
Don't binge drink; know when to stop.	Binge drink; drink to get drunk.
Respect nondrinkers.	Pressure others to drink.
Avoid drinking when solving problems or making decisions.	Turn to alcohol when facing problems or decisions.
Do not admire or encourage drunkenness.	Consider drunks to be funny or admirable.
Remain peaceful, calm, and unchanged by drinking.	Become loud, angry, violent, or silent when drinking.
Cause no problems to others or themselves by drinking.	Physically or emotionally harm themselves, family members, or others when drinking.

[a]*Canada's Food Guide recommends that Canadians limit alcohol intake.*

Table C3–4) until their drinking behaviour causes a crisis, such as a car crash, or until they've binged long enough to have caused substantial damage to their health.

What Is Alcohol?

In chemistry, the term *alcohol* refers to a class of chemical compounds whose names end in "-ol." The glycerol molecule of a triglyceride is an example. Alcohols affect living things profoundly, partly because they act as lipid solvents. Alcohols can easily penetrate a cell's outer lipid membrane, and once inside, they denature the cell's protein structures and kill the cell. Because some alcohols kill microbial cells, they make useful disinfectants and antiseptics.

The alcohol of alcoholic beverages, **ethanol**, is somewhat less toxic than others. Sufficiently diluted and taken in small enough doses, its action in the brain produces euphoria. Used in this way, alcohol is a drug, and like many drugs, alcohol presents both benefits and hazards to the taker. Its effects depend on the quantity of alcohol consumed.

What Is a "Drink"?

Alcoholic beverages contain a great deal of water and some other substances, as well as the alcohol ethanol. In wine, beer, and wine coolers, alcohol contributes a relatively low percentage of the beverage's volume. In contrast, as much as 50 percent of the volume of whiskey, vodka, rum, or brandy may be alcohol. The percentage of alcohol is stated as **proof**. Proof equals twice the percentage of alcohol; for example, 100 proof liquor is 50 percent alcohol.

A serving of an alcoholic beverage, commonly called a **drink**, delivers 15 millilitres of pure ethanol. Figure C3–1 depicts servings of alcoholic beverages that are considered to be one drink. These standard measures may have little in common with the drinks served by enthusiastic bartenders, however. Many wine glasses easily hold 180 to 240 millilitres of wine; wine coolers may come packaged 360 millilitres to a bottle; a large beer stein can hold 480 millilitres, 600 millilitres, or even more; and a strong liquor drink may contain 60 to 90 millilitres of various liquors.

Servings of Alcoholic Beverages That Equal One Drink

142 mL wine (12% alcohol)

341 mL beer

300 mL wine cooler

43 mL hard liquor (80 proof whiskey, gin, brandy, rum, vodka)

© Polara Studios, Inc.

The federal, provincial, and territorial ministers of Health are promoting Canada's *Low-Risk Alcohol Drinking Guidelines*;[3] see Table C3–2 for a summary of these guidelines. It is especially important to note limiting alcohol intake in relation to pregnancy and fetal alcohol syndrome. Refer to Chapter 13 for Canada's recommendations for preventing fetal alcohol syndrome.

Unlike most states in the United States, where the legal drinking age is 21 years, in most provinces in Canada, it is 19 (exceptions are Quebec, Alberta, and Manitoba, where it is 18).[4] The blood alcohol limit is 0.08 percent.[5]

Alcohol Enters the Body

From the moment an alcoholic beverage is swallowed, the body pays special attention to it. Unlike food, which requires digestion before it can be absorbed, the tiny alcohol molecules can diffuse right through the stomach walls and reach the brain within a minute. Ethanol is a toxin, and a too-high dose of alcohol triggers one of the body's primary defences against poison—vomiting. Many times, though, alcohol arrives gradually and in a beverage dilute enough that the vomiting reflex is delayed and the alcohol is absorbed.

A person can become intoxicated almost immediately when drinking, especially if the stomach is empty.

When the stomach is full of food, molecules of alcohol have less chance of touching the stomach walls and diffusing through, so alcohol reaches the brain more gradually (see Figure C3-2). In addition, some alcohol may be metabolized by alcohol dehydrogenase enzymes in the stomach lining, further reducing the level absorbed. By the time the stomach contents are emptied into the small intestine, however, alcohol is absorbed rapidly whether food is present or not.

A person who wants to drink socially and not become intoxicated should eat the snacks provided by the host (avoid the salty ones; they make you thirstier). Other tips include adding ice or water to alcoholic drinks to dilute them and alternating alcoholic with nonalcoholic beverages to quench thirst.

Anyone who has had an alcoholic drink has experienced one of alcohol's physical effects: alcohol increases urine output (because alcohol depresses the brain's production of **antidiuretic hormone**). Loss of body water leads to thirst. The only fluid that relieves dehydration is water, so alternating alcoholic beverages with nonalcoholic ones will quench thirst. Otherwise, each drink may worsen the thirst.

Food Slows Alcohol's Absorption

The alcohol in a stomach filled with food has a low probability of touching the walls and diffusing through. Food also holds alcohol in the stomach longer, slowing its entry into the highly absorptive small intestine.

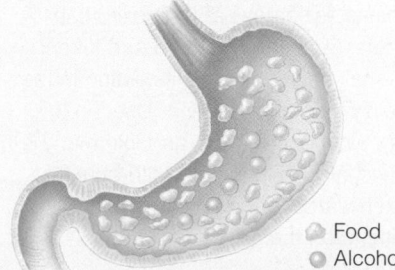

○ Food
◉ Alcohol

The water lost due to hormone depression takes with it important minerals, such as magnesium, potassium, calcium, and zinc, depleting the body's reserves. These minerals are vital to fluid balance and to nerve and muscle coordination. When drinking incurs mineral losses, the losses must be made up in subsequent meals to avoid deficiencies.

If a person drinks slowly enough, the alcohol, after absorption, will be collected by the liver and processed without much effect on other parts of the body. If a person drinks more rapidly, however, some of the alcohol bypasses the liver and flows for a while through the rest of the body and the brain.

Alcohol Arrives in the Brain

Some people use alcohol as a kind of social anaesthetic to help them relax or to relieve anxiety. One drink relieves inhibitions, which gives people the impression that alcohol is a stimulant. It gives this impression by sedating the *inhibitory* nerves, allowing excitatory nerves to take over. This effect is temporary, and, ultimately, alcohol acts as a depressant and sedates all of the nerve cells (see Figure C3–3).

It is lucky that the brain centres respond to rising blood alcohol in the order shown in the figure because a person usually passes out before drinking a lethal dose. If a person drinks fast enough, though, the alcohol continues to be absorbed, and its effects continue to accelerate after the person has gone to sleep. Every year, deaths attributed to this effect take place during drinking contests. Before passing out, the drinker drinks fast enough to receive a lethal dose. Table C3–5 shows blood alcohol levels that correspond to progressively greater intoxication, and Table C3–6 shows brain and nervous system responses that occur at these levels.

Brain cells are particularly sensitive to excessive exposure to alcohol. The brain shrinks, even in people who drink only moderately. The extent of the shrinkage

Figure C3–3

Alcohol's Effects on the Brain

When alcohol flows to the brain, it first sedates the frontal lobe of the cortex, the reasoning part. As the alcohol molecules diffuse into the cells of this lobe, they interfere with reasoning and judgment.

With continued drinking, the speech and vision centres of the brain become sedated, and the area that governs reasoning becomes more incapacitated.

Still more drinking affects the cells of the brain responsible for large-muscle control; at this point, people under the influence stagger or weave when they try to walk.

Finally, the conscious brain becomes completely subdued, and the person passes out. Now the person can drink no more. This is fortunate because a higher dose would anaesthetize the deepest brain centres, which control breathing and heartbeat, causing death.

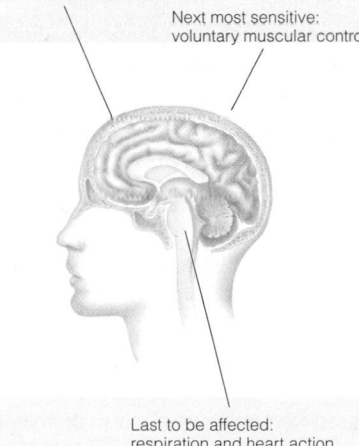

Most sensitive:
judgment and reasoning

Next most sensitive:
voluntary muscular control

Last to be affected:
respiration and heart action

is proportional to the amount drunk. Abstinence, together with good nutrition, reverses some of the brain damage, and possibly all of it, if heavy drinking has not continued for more than a few years. Prolonged drinking beyond an individual's capacity to recover, however, can do severe and irreversible harm to vision, memory, learning ability, and other brain functions.

Table C3–5

Alcohol Doses and Average Blood Levels

Number of Drinks[a]	Average Percent Blood Alcohol by Body Weight				
	45 kg	55 kg	68 kg	82 kg	90 kg
2	0.08	0.06	0.05	0.04	0.04
4	0.15	0.10	0.10	0.08	0.08
6	0.23	0.19	0.15	0.13	0.11
8	0.30	0.25	0.20	0.17	0.15
12	0.45	0.36	0.30	0.25	0.23
14	0.52	0.42	0.35	0.34	0.27

[a]Taken within an hour or so; each drink is equal to 15 mL pure ethanol.

Table C3–6

Blood Alcohol Levels and Brain Responses

Blood Alcohol Level (%)	Brain Response
0.05[a]	Judgment impaired
0.10	Emotional control impaired
0.15	Muscle coordination and reflexes impaired
0.20	Vision impaired
0.30	Drunk, lacking control
0.35	In a stupor
0.50–0.60	Loss of consciousness; death.

[a]A 0.08% level is the legal limit for intoxication in Canada; however, driving ability may be impaired at blood alcohol levels lower than 0.08%. For those in the Alberta, British Columbia, Manitoba, Ontario, New Brunswick, Nova Scotia, Prince Edward Island, and Newfoundland and Labrador Graduated Licensing Systems, blood alcohol level must be zero.

Alcohol Arrives in the Liver

The capillaries that surround the digestive tract merge into veins that carry the alcohol-laden blood to the liver. Here the veins branch and rebranch into capillaries that touch every liver cell. The liver cells make up the largest share of the body's alcohol-processing machinery. The routing of blood through the liver allows the cells to go right to work detoxifying substances before they reach other body organs such as the heart and brain.

The Liver Metabolizes Alcohol

The liver makes and maintains two sets of equipment for metabolizing alcohol. One is an enzyme that removes hydrogens from alcohol to break it down; the name, **alcohol dehydrogenase (ADH)**, almost says what it does.* This enzyme handles about 80 percent or more of the alcohol in the body. The other set

*There are actually two ADH enzymes; each performs a specific task in alcohol breakdown.

of alcohol-metabolizing equipment is a chain of enzymes, named **MEOS**, which is thought to handle about 10 percent of alcohol. The remaining 10 percent is excreted through the breath and in the urine. Because the alcohol in the breath is directly proportional to the alcohol in the blood, the breathalyzer test that law enforcement officers administer when someone may be driving under the influence of alcohol accurately reveals the person's degree of intoxication.

The amount of alcohol a person's body can process in a given time is limited by the amount of ADH enzymes residing in the liver. If more molecules of alcohol arrive at the liver cells than the enzymes can handle, the extra alcohol must wait. It circulates again and again through the brain, liver, and other organs until enzymes are available to degrade it.

Some ADH enzymes reside in the stomach and break down some alcohol before it enters the blood. Research shows that people with alcoholism make less stomach ADH than others and that women make less than men. Earlier, this Controversy warned that women should not try to keep up with male drinkers, and here is the reason why: women absorb about one-third more alcohol than men do, even when the women are the same size as the men and drink the same amount of alcohol.

The amount of ADH enzymes present is also affected by whether a person eats. Fasting for as little as a day causes degradation of body proteins, including the ADH enzymes, which can reduce the rate of alcohol metabolism by half.

The body takes about an hour and a half to metabolize one drink, depending on the person's size, the person's previous drinking experience, how recently the person has eaten, and the person's current state of health. The liver is the only organ that can dispose of significant quantities of alcohol, and its maximum rate of alcohol clearance cannot be speeded up. This explains why only time restores sobriety. Walking will not because muscles cannot metabolize alcohol. Nor will drinking a cup of coffee help. Caffeine is a stimulant, but it won't speed up the metabolism of alcohol. The police say that a cup of coffee only makes a sleepy drunk into a wide-awake drunk. Table C3–7 presents other alcohol myths.

Alcohol Affects Body Functions

Upon exposure to alcohol, the liver speeds up its synthesis of fatty acids. Fat is known to accumulate in the livers of young men after a single night of heavy drinking and to remain there for more than a day. The first stage of liver deterioration seen in heavy drinkers is therefore known as **fatty liver**; it interferes with the distribution of nutrients and oxygen to the liver cells. If the condition lasts long enough, fibrous scar tissue invades the liver. This is the second stage of liver deterioration, called **fibrosis**. Fibrosis is reversible with good nutrition and abstinence from alcohol, but the next (last) stage, **cirrhosis**, is not. In cirrhosis, the liver cells harden, turn orange, and die, losing function forever (shown in the photo on the next page).

The presence of alcohol alters amino acid metabolism in the liver cells. Synthesis of some immune system proteins slows down, weakening the body's defences against infection. Synthesis of blood lipids speeds up, increasing the concentration of triglycerides and high-density lipoproteins (see Chapter 5). In addition, excess alcohol adds to the body's acid burden and interferes with normal uric acid metabolism, causing symptoms like those of **gout**.

The reproductive system is also vulnerable to alcohol's effects. Heavy drinking in women may lead to infertility and spontaneous abortion. Alcohol may also suppress the male reproductive hormone testosterone, leading to decreases in muscle and bone tissue, altered immunity, an abnormal prostate gland, and decreased reproductive ability. All of these effects demonstrate the importance of moderation in the use of alcohol.

The Fattening Power of Alcohol

Alcohol should probably be counted as fat in the diet because metabolic interactions occur between fat and alcohol in the body. Presented with both fat and alcohol, the body stores the

---

Table C3–7

Myths and Truths Concerning Alcohol

Myth: A shot of alcohol warms you up.
Truth: Alcohol diverts blood flow to the skin, making you feel warmer, but it actually cools the body.
Myth: Wine and beer are mild; they do not lead to addiction.
Truth: Wine and beer drinkers worldwide have high rates of death from alcohol-related illnesses. It's not what you drink, but how much, that makes the difference.
Myth: Mixing drinks is what gives you a hangover.
Truth: Too much alcohol in any form produces a hangover.
Myth: Alcohol is a stimulant.
Truth: Alcohol depresses the brain's activity.
Myth: Alcohol is legal; therefore, it is not a drug.
Truth: Alcohol is legal, but it alters body functions and is medically defined as a depressant drug.

comparatively harmless fat and rids itself of the toxic alcohol by burning it off as fuel.[6] Alcohol may promote fat storage particularly in the central abdominal area—the **"beer belly"** effect seen in moderate drinkers. The risks of excess abdominal fat to the heart are described in Chapter 9.

Alcohol yields 7 Calories of energy per gram to the body, so many alcoholic drinks can be much more fattening than their nonalcoholic counterparts. A general guideline states that each ounce of ethanol in a drink represents the same number of Calories as about half an ounce of fat. An observant reader, knowing that, in the laboratory, a gram of fat and a gram of alcohol yield 9 and 7 Calories, respectively, may wonder why alcohol in a drink is worth only half the Calorie value of fat. The answer is that the body rids itself of a small but measurable amount of the alcohol by way of the breath and urine.

The Hangover

The hangover—the awful feeling of headache, pain, unpleasant sensations in the mouth, and nausea the morning after drinking too much—is a mild form of drug withdrawal. (The worst form is a delirium with severe tremors that presents a danger of death and demands medical management.) Hangovers are caused by several factors. One is the toxic effects of **congeners** that accompany the alcohol in alcoholic beverages. Mixing or switching drinks will not prevent hangover because congeners are only one factor. Dehydration of the brain is a second factor: alcohol reduces the water content of the brain cells. When they rehydrate the morning after and swell back to their normal size, nerve pain results.

Another contributor to the hangover is **formaldehyde**, the same chemical that laboratories use to preserve dead animals. Formaldehyde comes from **methanol**, an alcohol produced constantly by normal chemical processes in all of the cells. Normally, a set of liver enzymes converts this methanol to formaldehyde, and then a second set immediately converts the formaldehyde

to carbon dioxide and water, harmless waste products that can be excreted. But these same two sets of liver enzymes are the ones that process ethanol to its own intermediate (also highly toxic) waste product, **acetaldehyde**, and then to carbon dioxide and water.[7] The enzymes prefer ethanol 20 times over methanol. Both alcohols are metabolized without delay until the excess acetaldehyde monopolizes the second set of enzymes, leaving formaldehyde to wait for later detoxification. At that point, formaldehyde starts accumulating and the hangover begins.

Time alone is the cure for a hangover. Vitamins, tranquillizers, aspirin, drinking more alcohol, breathing pure oxygen, exercising, eating, and drinking something awful are all useless. Fluid replacement can help normalize the body's chemistry. The headache, unpleasantness in the mouth, and nausea of a hangover come simply from drinking too much.

Alcohol's Long-Term Effects

By far the longest-term effects of alcohol are those felt by the child of a woman who drinks during pregnancy. When a pregnant woman takes a drink, her fetus takes the same drink within minutes, and its body is defenceless against the effects. Pregnant women should not drink alcohol—this topic is so important that it has its own section in Chapter 13. For nonpregnant adults, however, what are the effects of alcohol over the long term?

A couple of drinks set in motion many destructive processes in the body. The next day's abstinence can reverse them only if the doses taken are moderate, the time between them is ample, and nutrition is adequate.

If the doses of alcohol are heavy, however, and the time between them is short, complete recovery cannot take place, and repeated onslaughts

Left, normal liver; centre, fatty liver; right, cirrhosis.

© Arthur Glauberman / Photo Researchers, Inc.

of alcohol take a toll on the body. For example, alcohol is directly toxic to skeletal and cardiac muscle, causing weakness and deterioration that is greater the larger the dose. Alcoholism makes heart disease likely, probably because chronic alcohol use raises blood pressure. At autopsy, the heart of a person with alcoholism appears bloated and weighs twice as much as a normal heart.

Alcohol attacks brain cells directly, and heavy drinking can result in dementia. Cirrhosis also develops after 10 to 20 years from the cumulative effects of frequent episodes of heavy drinking.

Alcohol abuse also leads to cancers of the breast, mouth, throat, esophagus, rectum, and lungs.[8] Daily human exposure to ethanol ranks high among carcinogenic hazards. Once cancer has started, alcohol also seems to promote its development.

A convincing body of evidence implicates alcohol intake by women in the causation of cancer of the breast—women who drink less than one drink per day elevate their risk slightly, and those who drink more increase their risk accordingly.[9] Cancer of the rectum increases with intakes of more than 15 ounces (about 450 mL) of beer each day. In the case of beer, alcohol may be acting together with other compounds formed during brewing to promote the cancer. One compound, **urethane**, often found in alcoholic beverages, is known to cause cancer in animals, but the risk to human beings is unknown.

Other long-term effects of alcohol abuse include the following:

- Bladder, kidney, pancreas, and prostate damage
- Bone deterioration and osteoporosis
- Brain disease, central nervous system damage, and strokes
- Deterioration of the testicles and adrenal glands
- Diabetes (type 2 or non-insulin-dependent)
- Disease of the muscles of the heart
- Feminization and sexual impotence in men
- Impaired immune response
- Impaired memory and balance
- Increased risks of death from all causes
- Malnutrition
- Nonviral hepatitis
- Severe psychological depression
- Skin rashes and sores
- Ulcers and inflammation of the stomach and intestines

This list is by no means all-inclusive. Alcohol abuse exerts direct toxic effects on all body organs.

Alcohol's Effect on Nutrition

Alcohol abuse also does damage indirectly via malnutrition. The more alcohol a person drinks, the less likely it is that he or she will eat enough food to obtain adequate nutrients. Like pure sugar and pure fat, alcohol provides empty Calories; it displaces nutrients. Table C3–8 shows the Calorie amounts of typical alcoholic beverages.

Alcohol abuse also disrupts every tissue's metabolism of nutrients. Stomach cells oversecrete both acid and histamine, an agent of the immune system that produces inflammation. Intestinal cells fail to absorb thiamin, folate, vitamin B_6, and other vitamins. Liver cells lose efficiency in activating vitamin D and alter their production and excretion of bile. Rod cells in the retina, which normally process vitamin A alcohol

Table C3–8
Calories in Alcoholic Beverages and Mixers

Beverage	Amount (mL)	Energy (Cal)
Beer (e.g., 5% alcohol)	360	150
Dessert wine	100	140
Fruit-flavoured soda, Tom Collins mix	240	115
Gin, rum, vodka, whiskey (86 proof)	45	105
Cola, root beer	240	100
Light beer (e.g., 4% alcohol)	360	100
Table wine	100	85
Tonic, ginger ale	240	80
Club soda, plain seltzer, diet drinks	240	1

(retinol) to the form needed in vision, find themselves processing drinking alcohol instead. Liver cells, too, suffer a reduced capacity to process and use vitamin A.[10] The kidneys excrete magnesium, calcium, potassium, and zinc.

The inadequate food intake and impaired nutrient absorption that accompany chronic alcohol abuse frequently lead to a deficiency of the B vitamin thiamin. In fact, the cluster of thiamine-deficiency symptoms commonly seen in chronic alcoholism has its own name—the **Wernicke-Korsakoff syndrome**. This syndrome is characterized by paralysis of the eye muscles, poor muscle coordination, impaired memory, and damaged nerves; the syndrome and other alcohol-related memory problems may respond to treatment with thiamin supplements.[11]

Most dramatic is alcohol's effect on folate. When an excess of alcohol is present, the body actively expels folate from all of its sites of action and storage. The liver, which normally contains enough folate to meet all needs, leaks its folate into the blood. As blood folate rises, the kidneys are deceived into excreting it, as if it were in excess. The intestine normally releases and retrieves folate continuously, but it becomes so damaged by folate deficiency and alcohol toxicity that it fails to absorb folate. Alcohol also interferes with the

action of what little folate is left, causing a buildup in the blood of a compound suspected of involvement with many diseases, including heart disease, stroke, and birth defects.*,[12] This interference inhibits the production of new cells, especially the rapidly dividing cells of the intestine and the blood.

Nutrient deficiencies are thus an inevitable consequence of alcohol abuse, not only because alcohol displaces food but also because alcohol interferes directly with the body's use of nutrients. People treated for alcohol addiction also need nutrition therapy to reverse deficiencies and even deficiency diseases rarely seen in others: night blindness, beriberi, pellagra, scurvy, and protein-energy malnutrition.

Does Moderate Alcohol Use Benefit Health?

What are the potential risks and benefits to heart health of moderate drinking? Does age matter?

Age does matter. Young people do not benefit their health by drinking; rather, they increase their risk of dying from all causes. Young nondrinkers are found to have a lower risk of dying than even light drinkers (fewer than 15 drinks per month) of the same age. Alcohol is related to car

*The compound is homocysteine; see Chapter 7.

crashes, homicides, and other violence that account for the great majority of deaths of young people each year.[13] Also, keep in mind that according to data from Transport Canada for 2010, almost 40% of fatally injured drivers had been drinking. (http://www.tc.gc.ca/eng/roadsafety/ tp-1317.htm#10). Young women in particular should not drink alcohol for the sake of their heart. For women before menopause, the risk of heart disease is low, but the risk of breast cancer is substantial. Even one drink a day, the amount providing heart benefits to older people, raises the risk of breast cancer in young women by about 10 percent.[14]

Alcohol and Heart Disease

One to two standard drinks of alcoholic beverages a day are credited with reducing the risk of death from heart disease in people over 60 years old who have an increased risk of heart disease. Increasing alcohol beyond this amount *increases* the risk of heart disease substantially.[15] Wine is often credited with aiding heart health, but research indicates that even beer may reduce heart attack risk in some populations.[16]

Although many studies support a beneficial effect of moderate alcohol intake on heart health, the matter is not yet settled. Researchers followed the alcohol intakes and health histories of almost 6,000 men for over 20 years.[17] The results showed no beneficial relationship between mortality from cardiovascular disease and *any* level of alcohol consumption. The study did show an increased risk of death from all causes with more than 22 drinks per week and that men drinking more than 35 drinks a week had double the mortality from stroke compared with nondrinkers. Strokes are associated with elevated blood pressure, and heavy alcohol intake is known to increase both of these conditions.[18]

The Health Effects of Wine

Red wine has been credited with special health-supporting properties, and recently, white wine has won attention for an antioxidant effect.[19]

The science on wine and health is mixed. For example, the high potassium content of grape juice may lower high blood pressure, and potassium persists when the grape juice is made into wine. Since alcohol in large amounts raises blood pressure, however, the grape juice may be more suitable than the wine for people with hypertension. Dealcoholized wine also facilitates the absorption of potassium, calcium, phosphorus, magnesium, and zinc. So does wine, but the alcohol in it promotes the quick *excretion* of these minerals, so the dealcoholized version is preferred.

In addition to alcohol, wine contains flavonoids that are under study as protectors against events that are thought to trigger heart disease. An antioxidant effect of flavonoids in wine has been offered as an explanation for why wine-drinking French and other Mediterranean peoples have a lower incidence of heart disease despite having many risk factors. (Controversy 5 comes back to the issue of Mediterranean diets and disease.) Compared with other food sources such as onions or other vegetables, though, wine may deliver only small amounts of antioxidant flavonoids to the body.[20] In addition, alcohol itself increases oxidation in the body.

Furthermore, recent evidence calls into question whether heart protection from antioxidants is at work. In a study of mice genetically prone to develop heart-damaging changes leading to heart disease, dealcoholized red wine effectively reduced the changes without reducing oxidation.[21] Dealcoholized wine, purple grape juice, and the grapes themselves contain phytochemicals similar to those of wine but without the potential dangers of alcohol.

Alcohol and Appetite

Alcoholic beverages affect the appetite. Usually, they reduce it, making people unaware that they are hungry. But in people who are tense and unable to eat or in the elderly who have lost interest in food, a small dose of wine taken 20 minutes before meals may improve appetite. For undernourished people and for people with severely depressed appetites, wine may facilitate eating even when psychotherapy fails to do so.

Another example of the beneficial use of alcohol comes from research showing that moderate use of wine in later life improves morale, stimulates social interaction, and promotes restful sleep. In nursing homes, improved patient and staff relations have been attributed to greater self-esteem among elderly patients who drink moderate amounts of wine. Researchers hypothesize that chronic fatigue may be responsible for some behaviours associated with old age. The positive effects of wine on sleep may alleviate fatigue.

The Final Word

This discussion has explored some of the ways in which alcohol affects health and nutrition. In contrast to some possible benefits of moderate alcohol consumption, excessive alcohol consumption presents a great potential for harm. Alcohol is guilty of contributing not only to deaths from health problems but also to most of the other needless deaths of young people each year, including car crashes, falls, suicides, homicides, drownings, and other accidents. The surest way to escape the harmful effects of alcohol is, of course, to refuse alcohol altogether. If you choose to drink, do so with care and strictly in moderation.

Self-Check

1. All of the following are correct concerning ulcers *except*
   a. they usually occur in the large intestine
   b. some are caused by a bacterium
   c. if not treated correctly, they can lead to stomach cancer
   d. their symptoms can be masked by using antacids regularly

2. Which of the following increases the production of intestinal gas?
   a. chewing gum
   b. drinking carbonated beverages
   c. eating certain vegetables
   d. all of the above

3. Chemical digestion of all nutrients mainly occurs in which organ?
   a. mouth
   b. stomach
   c. small intestine
   d. large intestine

4. Which chemical substance released by the pancreas neutralizes stomach acid that has reached the small intestine?
   a. mucus
   b. enzymes
   c. bicarbonate
   d. bile

5. Which nutrient passes through the large intestine mostly unabsorbed?
   a. starch
   b. vitamins
   c. minerals
   d. fibre

6. T cells are immune cells that ingest and destroy antigens in a process known as phagocytosis.
   T   F

7. Bile starts the process of protein digestion in the stomach.
   T   F

8. To digest food efficiently, people should not combine certain foods, such as meat and fruit, at the same meal.
   T   F

9. The gallbladder stores bile until it is needed to emulsify fat.
   T   F

10. Absorption of the majority of nutrients takes place across the mucus-coated lining of the stomach.
    T   F

Endnotes

1. L. L. Birch, Development of food preferences, *Annual Reviews of Nutrition* 19 (1999): 41–62.
2. R. J. Laheij and coauthors, Risk of community-acquired pneumonia and use of gastric acid-suppressing drugs, *Journal of the American Medical Association* 292 (2004): 1955–1960.
3. J. L. Smith, The role of gastric acid in preventing foodborne disease and how bacteria overcome acid conditions, *Journal of Food Protection* 66 (2003): 1310–1325.
4. FDA approves an implant for gastroesophageal reflux disease, *FDA Talk Paper*, 2003, available at http://www.spinics.net/lists/fda/msg00050.html.
5. N. Uemura and coauthors, *Helicobacter pylori* infection and the development of gastric cancer, *New England Journal of Medicine* 345 (2001): 784–789; J. G. Fox and T. C. Wang, *Helicobacter pylori*—Not a good bug after all, *New England Journal of Medicine* 345 (2001): 829–832.
6. S. T. Mayne and S. A. Navarro, Diet, obesity, and reflux in the etiology of adenocarcinomas of the esophagus and gastric cardia in humans, *Journal of Nutrition* 132 (2002): 3467S–3470S; T. Gislason and coauthors, Respiratory symptoms

and nocturnal gastroesophageal reflux: A population-based study of young adults in three European countries, *Chest* 121 (2002): 158–163.
7. M. C. Roberts and coauthors, Constipation, laxative use, and colon cancer in a North Carolina population, *American Journal of Gastroenterology* 98 (2003): 857–864.
8. M. Watford and A. G. Goodridge, Regulation of fuel utilization, in M. A. Stipanuk, ed., *Biochemical and Physiological Aspects of Human Nutrition* (Philadelphia, PA: W. B. Saunders, 2000), p. 387.

Controversy 3

1. Centre for Addiction and Mental Health—Alcohol, available at http://www.camh.ca/en/hospital/health_information/a_z_mental_health_and_addiction_information/alcohol/Pages/alcohol.aspx.
2. Canadian Public Health Association—Binge drinking and alcohol poisoning: Straight talk for parents, available at http://www.cpha.ca/en/portals/substance/article02.aspx.
3. Canadian Centre on Substance Abuse—Canada's Low-Risk Drinking Guidelines,

available at http://www.ccsa.ca/eng/priorities/alcohol/canada-low-risk-alcohol-drinking-guidelines/Pages/default.aspx.
4. Canadian Centre on Substance Abuse, *Legal Drinking Age by Province, in Canada*, available at http://www.ccsa.ca/Eng/Topics/Legislation/LegalDrinkingAge/Pages/default.aspx.
5. Transport Canada, Chapter 8—Alcohol http://www.tc.gc.ca/eng/civilaviation/publications/page-6083.htm.
6. Standing Committee on the Scientific Evaluation of Dietary Reference Intakes, Food and Nutrition Board, Institute of Medicine, *Dietary Reference Intakes for Energy, Carbohydrate, Fiber, Fat, Fatty Acids, Cholesterol, Protein, and Amino Acids* (Washington, D.C.: National Academies Press, 2005); Y. Schutz, Role of substrate utilization and thermogenesis on body-weight control with particular reference to alcohol, *Proceedings of the Nutrition Society* 59 (2000): 511–517.
7. C. S. Leiber, Alcohol: Its metabolism and interaction with nutrients, *Annual Review of Nutrition* 20 (2000): 395–430.
8. X.-D. Wang, Mechanisms of cancer chemoprevention: Retinoids and alcohol-related

carcinogenesis, *Journal of Nutrition* 133 (2003): 287S–290S.

9. K. W. Singletary and S. M. Gapstur, Alcohol and breast cancer: Review of epidemiologic and experimental evidence and potential mechanisms, *Journal of the American Medical Association* 286 (2001): 2143–2151.

10. X. Wang, Chronic alcohol intake interferes with retinoid metabolism and signaling, *Nutrition Reviews* 57 (1999): 51–59.

11. M. L. Ambrose, S. C. Bowden, and G. Whelan, Thiamin treatment and working memory function of alcohol-dependent people: Preliminary findings, *Alcoholism: Clinical and Experimental Research* 25 (2001): 112–116.

12. J. W. Miller, Does lowering plasma homocysteine reduce vascular disease risk? *Nutrition Reviews* 59 (2001): 242–244; N. M. van der Put and coauthors, Folate, homocysteine and neural tube defects: An overview, *Experimental Biology and Medicine* 226 (2001): 243–270.

13. Centers for Disease Control and Prevention, Alcohol-attributable deaths and years of potential life lost—United States, 2001, *Morbidity and Mortality Weekly Reports* 53 (2004): 866–870.

14. U.S. Department of Agriculture and U.S. Department of Health and Human Services, *Dietary Guidelines for Americans 2010*, 7th ed., available at http://www.cnpp.usda .gov/Publications/DietaryGuidelines/2010/ PolicyDoc/PolicyDoc.pdf.

15. H. D. Sesso and coauthors, Seven-year changes in alcohol consumption and subsequent risk of cardiovascular disease in men, *Archives of Internal Medicine* 160 (2000): 2605–2612.

16. M. Bobak, A. Skodova, and M. Marmot, Effect of beer drinking on risk of myocardial infarction: Population based case-control study, *British Medical Journal* 320 (2000): 1378–1379.

17. C. L. Hart and coauthors, Alcohol consumption and mortality from all causes, coronary heart disease, and stroke: Results from a prospective cohort study of Scottish men with 21 years of follow up, *British Medical Journal* 318 (1999): 1725–1729.

18. S. Stranges and coauthors, Relationship of alcohol drinking pattern to risk of hypertension: A population-based study, *Hypertension* 44 (2004): 813–819; K. Reynolds and coauthors, Alcohol consumption and risk of stroke: A metaanalysis, *Journal of the American Medical Association* 289 (2003): 579–588.

19. A. A. Bertelli and coauthors, Oxidative stress and inflammatory reaction modulation by white wine, *Annals of the New York Academy of Science* 957 (2002): 295–301.

20. J. H. M. de Vries and coauthors, Red wine is a poor source of bioavailable flavonols in men, *Journal of Nutrition* 131 (2001): 745–748.

21. E. Waddington, I. B. Puddey, and K. D. Croft, Red wine polyphenolic compounds inhibit atherosclerosis in apolipoprotein E-deficient mice independently of effects on lipid peroxidation, *American Journal of Clinical Nutrition* 79 (2004): 54–61.

4 The Carbohydrates: Sugar, Starch, Glycogen, and Fibre

Do You Ever . . .

Think of carbohydrates as providing nothing but Calories to the body?

Wonder why nutrition authorities unanimously recommend foods high in fibre?

Have trouble choosing among breads at the grocery store?

Try to reduce your sugar intake by choosing foods sweetened with purified fruit concentrates?

Keep Reading . . .

Learning Objectives

After completing this chapter, you should be able to

LO 4.1 Describe the major types of carbohydrates, and identify foods that are sources of carbohydrates.

LO 4.2 Describe the various roles of carbohydrates in the body, and explain why avoiding dietary carbohydrates may be ill-advised.

LO 4.3 Summarize how fibre differs from other carbohydrates and how fibre may contribute to health.

LO 4.4 Explain how complex carbohydrates are broken down and absorbed in the body.

LO 4.5 Explain the term *glycemic index* and how it may relate to diet planning.

LO 4.6 Justify this statement: "There is no such thing as a *bad* carbohydrate."

LO 4.7 Educate someone about the long- and short-term effects of untreated diabetes and suggest a lifestyle plan to help that person effectively manage type 2 diabetes.

LO 4.8 Describe what happens to glucose during fasting and feasting.

Contents

Carbohydrates are the ideal nutrients to meet your body's energy needs, feed your brain and nervous system, keep your digestive system fit, and, within Calorie limits, help keep your body lean. Digestible carbohydrates, together with fats and proteins, add bulk to foods and provide energy and other benefits for the body. Indigestible carbohydrates, which include most of the fibres in foods, yield little or no energy but provide other important benefits.

All **carbohydrates** are not equal in terms of nutrition. This chapter invites you to learn to distinguish between foods containing the **complex carbohydrates** (starch and fibre) and those made of the **simple carbohydrates** (sugars) and to consider the effects of both on the body. This chapter's Controversy feature asks whether sugar harms health and whether alternative sweeteners are preferable.

This chapter on the carbohydrates is the first of three on the energy-yielding nutrients. Chapter 5 deals with the fats and Chapter 6 with protein. The Controversy feature in Chapter 3 addressed one other contributor of energy, alcohol.

A Close Look at Carbohydrates

Carbohydrates contain the sun's radiant energy, captured in a form that living things can use to drive the processes of life. Green plants make carbohydrate through **photosynthesis** in the presence of **chlorophyll** and sunlight. In this process, water (H_2O), absorbed by the plant's roots, donates hydrogen and oxygen. Carbon dioxide gas (CO_2), absorbed into its leaves, donates carbon and oxygen. Water and carbon dioxide combine to yield the most common of the **sugars**, the single sugar **glucose**. Scientists know the reaction in the minutest detail but have never been able to reproduce it—green plants are required to make it happen (see Figure 4–1).

Light energy from the sun drives the photosynthesis reaction. The light energy becomes the chemical energy of the bonds that hold six atoms of carbon together in

carbohydrates compounds composed of single or multiple sugars. The name means "carbon and water," and a chemical shorthand for carbohydrate in CH_2O, signifying carbon (C), hydrogen (H), and oxygen (O).

complex carbohydrates long chains of sugar units arranged to form starch or fibre; also called *polysaccharides*.

simple carbohydrates sugars, including both single sugar units and linked pairs of sugar units. The basic sugar unit is a molecule containing six carbon atoms, together with oxygen and hydrogen atoms.

photosynthesis the process by which green plants make carbohydrates from carbon dioxide and water using the green pigment chlorophyll to capture the sun's energy (*photo* means "light"; *synthesis* means "making").

chlorophyll the green pigment of plants that captures energy from sunlight for use in photosynthesis.

sugars simple carbohydrates, that is, molecules of either single sugar units or pairs of those sugar units bonded together. By common usage, *sugar* most often refers to sucrose.

glucose (GLOO-cose) a single sugar used in both plant and animal tissues for energy, sometimes known as blood sugar or *dextrose*.

Figure 4–1

Carbohydrate—Mainly Glucose—Is Made by Photosynthesis

The sun's energy becomes part of the glucose molecule—its Calories, in a sense. In the molecule of glucose on the leaf here, black dots represent the carbon atoms; bars represent the chemical bonds that contain energy.

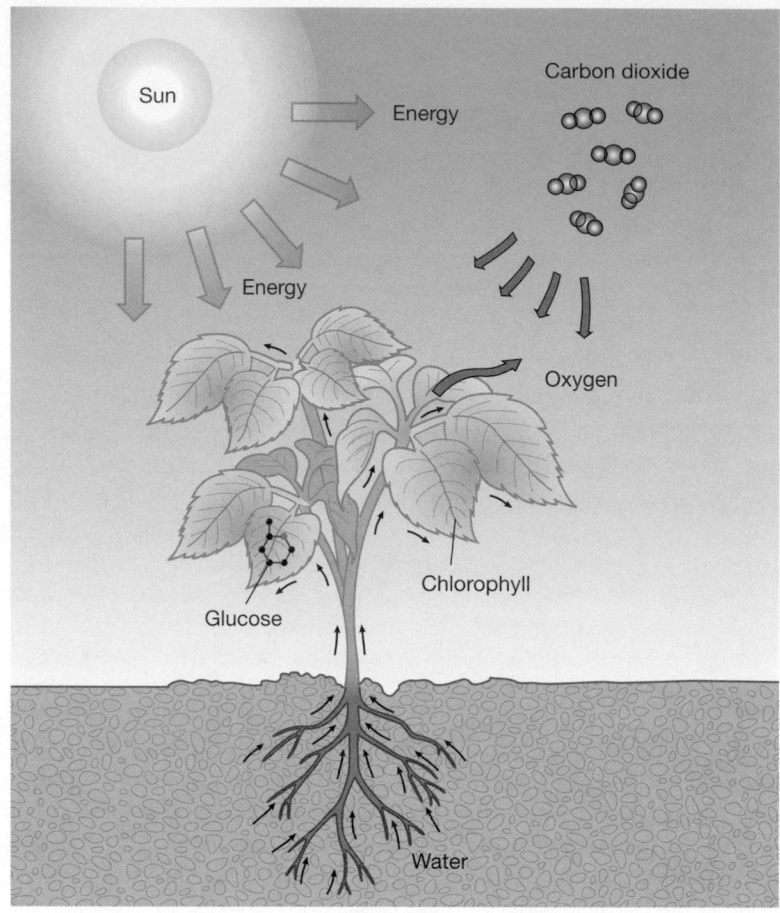

the sugar glucose. Glucose provides energy for the work of all cells of the stem, roots, flowers, and fruits of the plant. For example, in the roots, far from the energy-giving rays of the sun, each cell draws upon some of the glucose made in the leaves, breaks it down (to carbon dioxide and water), and uses the energy thus released to fuel its own growth and water-gathering activities.

Plants do not use all of the energy stored in their sugars, so it remains available for use by the animal or human being that consumes the plant. Thus, carbohydrates form the first link in the food chain that supports all life on the earth. Carbohydrate-rich foods come almost exclusively from plants; milk is the only animal-derived food that contains significant amounts of carbohydrate. The next few sections describe the forms assumed by carbohydrates: sugars, starch, glycogen, and fibre.

KEY POINT

- Through photosynthesis, plants combine carbon dioxide, water, and the sun's energy to form glucose. Carbohydrates are made of carbon, hydrogen, and oxygen held together by energy-containing bonds: *carbo* means "carbon"; *hydrate* means "water."

Sugars

Six sugar molecules are important in nutrition. Three are single sugars or **monosaccharides**. The other three are double sugars or **disaccharides**. All of their chemical

monosaccharides (mon-oh-SACK-ah-rides) single sugar units (*mono* means "one"; *saccharide* means "sugar unit").

disaccharides pairs of single sugars linked together (*di* means "two").

Figure 4–2

How Monosaccharides Join to Form Disaccharides

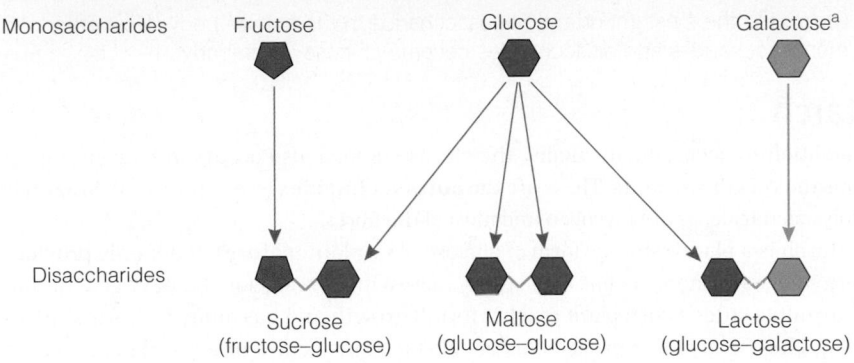

Monosaccharides   Fructose   Glucose   Galactose[a]

Disaccharides

Sucrose
(fructose–glucose)

Maltose
(glucose–glucose)

Lactose
(glucose–galactose)

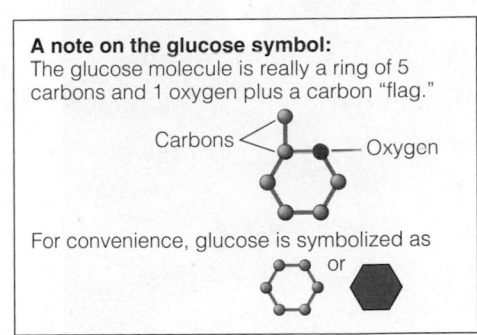

A note on the glucose symbol:
The glucose molecule is really a ring of 5 carbons and 1 oxygen plus a carbon "flag."

Carbons   Oxygen

For convenience, glucose is symbolized as

or

[a]*Milk is a major source of galactose.*

names end in *ose*, which means "sugar." Although they all sound alike at first, they exhibit distinct characteristics once you get to know them as individuals. Figure 4–2 shows the relationships among the sugars.

The three monosaccharides are glucose, **fructose**, and **galactose**. Fructose, or fruit sugar, the intensely sweet sugar of fruit, is made by rearranging the atoms in glucose molecules. Fructose occurs mostly in fruits, in honey, and as part of table sugar. Other sources include soft drinks, ready-to-eat cereals, and other products sweetened with high-fructose corn syrup (defined in Table 4-9 on page 143). Glucose and fructose are the most common monosaccharides in nature.

The other monosaccharide, galactose, has the same number and kind of atoms as glucose and fructose but in another arrangement. Galactose is one of two single sugars that are bound together to make up the sugar of milk. It rarely occurs free in nature but is tied up in milk sugar until it is freed during digestion.

The three other sugars important in nutrition are disaccharides, which are linked pairs of single sugars. All three contain glucose. In **lactose**, the milk sugar just mentioned, glucose is linked to galactose.

Malt sugar, or **maltose**, has two glucose units. Maltose appears wherever starch is being broken down. It occurs in germinating seeds and arises during the digestion of starch in the human body.

The last of the six sugars, **sucrose**, is familiar table sugar, the product most people think of when they refer to *sugar*. In sucrose, fructose and glucose are bonded together. Table sugar is obtained by refining the juice from sugar beets or sugarcane, but sucrose also occurs naturally in many vegetables and fruits. It tastes sweet because it contains the sweetest of the monosaccharides, fructose.

When you eat a food containing single sugars, you can absorb them directly into your blood. When you eat disaccharides, though, you must digest them first. Enzymes in your intestinal cells must split the disaccharides into separate monosaccharides so that they can enter the bloodstream. The blood delivers all products of digestion first to the liver, which possesses enzymes to modify nutrients, making them useful to the body. Glucose is the most-used monosaccharide inside the body, so the liver quickly converts fructose or galactose to glucose or to smaller pieces that can serve as building blocks for glucose, fat, or other needed molecules.

Although it is true that the energy of fruits and many vegetables comes from sugars, this doesn't mean that eating them is the same as eating concentrated sweets such as candy or cola beverages. From

Digestive enzymes were introduced in Chapter 3.

- Single sugars are monosaccharides.
- Pairs of sugars are disaccharides.

fructose (FROOK-tose) a monosaccharide, sometimes known as fruit sugar (*fruct* means "fruit"; *ose* means "sugar").

galactose (ga-LACK-tose) a monosaccharide, part of the disaccharide lactose (milk sugar).

lactose a disaccharide composed of glucose and galactose; sometimes known as milk sugar (*lact* means "milk"; *ose* means "sugar").

maltose a disaccharide composed of two glucose units, sometimes known as malt *sugar*.

sucrose (SOO-crose) a disaccharide composed of glucose and fructose; sometimes known as table, beet, or cane sugar or, often, simply *sugar*.

A Close Look at Carbohydrates

Foods such as these apples provide carbohydrates and other nutrients to the body.

● Strands of many sugar units are polysaccharides.

the body's point of view, fruits are vastly different from purified sugars, as a later section makes clear, except that both provide glucose in abundance.

KEY POINT

■ Glucose is the most important monosaccharide in the human body. Most other monosaccharides and disaccharides become glucose in the body.

Starch

In addition to occurring in sugars, the glucose in food also occurs in long strands of thousands of glucose units. These are the **polysaccharides** (see Figure 4–3). **Starch** is a polysaccharide, as are glycogen and most of the fibres.

Starch is a plant's storage form of glucose. As a plant matures, it not only provides energy for its own needs but also stores energy in its seeds for the next generation. For example, after a corn plant reaches its full growth and has many leaves manufacturing glucose, it stores packed clusters of starch molecules in **granules** and packs the granules into its seeds. These giant starch clusters are packed side by side in the kernels of corn. For the plant, starch is useful because it is an insoluble substance that will stay with the seed in the ground and nourish it until it forms shoots with leaves that can catch the sun's rays. Glucose, in contrast, is soluble in water and would be washed away by the rain while the seed lay in the soil. The starch of corn and other plant foods is nutritive for people as well because they can digest the starch to glucose and extract the sun's energy stored in its chemical bonds. A later section describes starch digestion in greater detail.

KEY POINT

■ Starch is the storage form of glucose in plants and is also nutritive for human beings.

Glycogen

Just as plants store glucose in long chains of starch, animal bodies store glucose in long chains of **glycogen**. Glycogen resembles starch in that it consists of glucose molecules linked together to form chains, but its chains are longer and more highly branched (see Figure 4–3). Unlike starch, which is abundant in grains, potatoes, and other foods from plants, glycogen is nearly undetectable in meats because glycogen breaks down rapidly when the animal is slaughtered. A later section describes how the human body handles its own packages of stored glucose.

KEY POINT

■ Glycogen is the storage form of glucose in animals and human beings.

Fibre

Some of the **fibres** of a plant form the supporting structures of its leaves, stems, and seeds. Other fibres play other roles, for example, to retain water and thus protect seeds from drying out. Like starch, most fibres are polysaccharides—chains of sugars—but they differ from starch in that the sugar units are held together by bonds that human digestive enzymes cannot break. Most fibres therefore pass through the human body without providing energy for its use.*

Billions of bacteria residing within the human large intestine, however, do possess enzymes that can digest fibres to varying degrees by fermenting them. Through this process, the fibres are broken down to waste products, mainly small fatlike fragments that the large intestine (colon) absorbs.

Many animals, such as cattle, depend heavily on their digestive system's bacteria to make the energy of glucose available from the abundant cellulose, a form of fibre, in their fodder. Thus, when we eat beef, we indirectly receive some of the sun's energy that was originally stored in the fibre of the plants. Beef itself contains no fibre, however; no meats or dairy products contain fibre.

polysaccharides another term for complex carbohydrates; compounds composed of long strands of glucose units linked together (*poly* means "many"). Also called *complex carbohydrates*.

starch a plant polysaccharide composed of glucose. After cooking, starch is highly digestible by human beings; raw starch often resists digestion.

granules small grains. Starch granules are packages of starch molecules. Various plant species make starch granules of varying shapes.

glycogen (GLY-co-gen) a highly branched polysaccharide composed of glucose that is made and stored by liver and muscle tissues of human beings and animals as a storage form of glucose. Glycogen is not a significant food source of carbohydrate and is not counted as one of the complex carbohydrates in foods.

fibres the indigestible parts of plant foods, largely nonstarch polysaccharides that are not digested by human digestive enzymes, although some are digested by resident bacteria of the colon. Fibres include cellulose, hemicelluloses, pectins, gums, mucilages, and the nonpolysaccharide lignin.

---

*Recently, the committee on Dietary Reference Intakes (DRI) proposed these fibre definitions: total fibre refers to the sum of fibres from two sources: naturally occurring fibres in intact foods (dietary fibres) and added fibres that have health benefits (functional fibres).

Figure 4–3

How Glucose Molecules Join to Form Polysaccharides

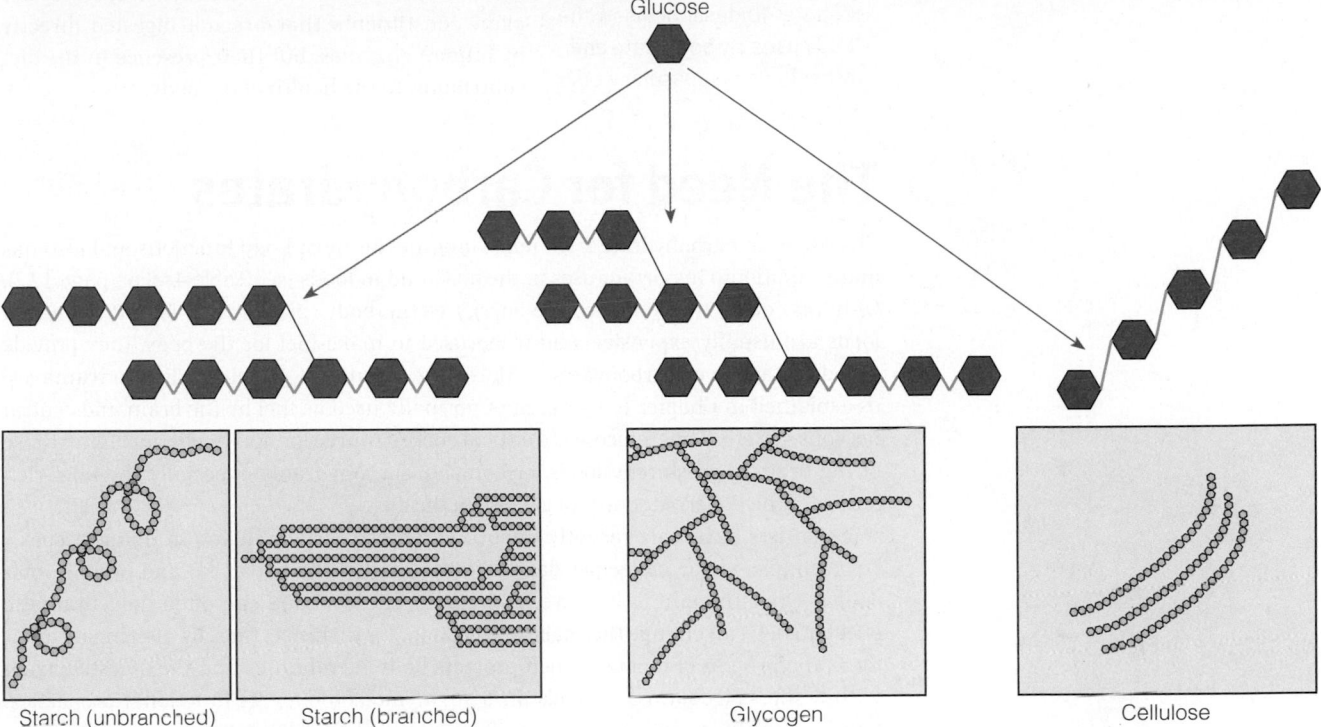

Starch Glucose units are linked in long, occasionally branched chains to make starch. Human digestive enzymes can digest these bonds, retrieving glucose. Real glucose units are so tiny that you can't see them, even with the highest-power light microscope.

Glycogen Glycogen resembles starch in that the bonds between its glucose units can be broken by human enzymes, but the chains of glycogen are more highly branched.

Cellulose (fibre) The bonds that link glucose units together in cellulose are different from the bonds in starch or glycogen. Human enzymes cannot digest them.

Fibres are often divided into two general groups by their chemical and physical properties. In the first group are fibres that dissolve in water (**soluble fibres**). These form gels (are **viscous**) and are easily digested by bacteria in the human colon (are easily fermented). Commonly found in barley, legumes, fruits, oats, and vegetables, these fibres are often associated with lower risks of chronic diseases (as discussed in a later section). In foods, soluble fibres add pleasing consistency, such as the pectin that puts the gel in jams and jellies and the gums that are added to salad dressings and other foods to thicken them.

Other fibres do not dissolve in water (**insoluble fibres**), do not form gels (are not viscous), and are less readily fermented. Insoluble fibres, such as cellulose and hemicellulose, are found in the outer layers of whole grains (bran), the strings of celery, the hulls of seeds, and the skins of corn kernels. These fibres retain their structure and rough texture even after hours of cooking. In the body, they aid the digestive system by easing elimination.[1]

KEY POINT

- Human digestive enzymes cannot break the bonds in fibre, so most of it passes through the digestive tract unchanged. Some fibre, however, is susceptible to fermentation by bacteria in the colon.

In summary, plants combine carbon dioxide, water, and the sun's energy to form glucose, which may be stored in the polysaccharide starch. Then animals or people eat the plants and retrieve the glucose. In the body, the liver and muscles may store the glucose as the polysaccharide glycogen, but, ultimately, it becomes glucose again. The glucose delivers the sun's energy to fuel the body's activities. In the

- Soluble, viscous, fermentable fibres are often gummy or add thickness to foods.

- Insoluble, nonviscous, less fermentable fibres are often tough, stringy, or gritty in foods.

soluble fibres food components that readily dissolve in water and often impart gummy or gel-like characteristics to foods. An example is pectin from fruit, which is used to thicken jellies and jams. Soluble fibres are indigestible by human enzymes but may be broken down to absorbable products by bacteria in the digestive tract.

viscous (VISS-cuss) having a sticky, gummy, or gel-like consistency that flows relatively slowly.

insoluble fibres the tough, fibrous structures of fruits, vegetables, and grains; indigestible food components that do not dissolve in water.

Chapter 15 revisits humankind's relationship with the earth's food chain.

Chapter 10 describes how the body uses carbohydrate and other fuels in muscular work.

process, glucose breaks down to the waste products carbon dioxide and water, which are excreted. Later, these compounds are used again by plants as raw materials to make carbohydrate. Fibres are plant constituents that are not digested directly by human enzymes, but their presence in the diet contributes to the health of the body.

The Need for Carbohydrates

Glucose from carbohydrate is an important fuel for most body functions and also has many additional important uses in the body and in foods (see Table 4–6 on page 127). Only two other nutrients provide energy to the body: protein and fats. Protein-rich foods are usually expensive, and when used to make fuel for the body, they provide no advantage over carbohydrates. Moreover, overuse of proteins has disadvantages, as explained in Chapter 6. Fats are not normally used as fuel by the brain and central nervous system. Thus, glucose is a critical energy source for nerve cells, including those of the brain. And starchy foods, or complex carbohydrates, especially the fibre-rich ones, are the preferred source of glucose in the diet.

Scientists have only recently uncovered other roles for sugars in living tissues.[2] For example, sugar molecules dangle from many of the body's fat and protein molecules. Once thought to be mere hitchhikers, these sugars can often have dramatic effects. They can change the shape of a protein, for instance, thereby altering its function. The protein of mucus, which protects body membranes and the digestive tract with a slippery coating, depends on a sugar molecule for its functional properties. Sugars also bind to cell membranes, affecting cellular interactions that may play roles in disease processes.

If I Want to Lose Weight and Stay Healthy, Should I Avoid Carbohydrates?

Popular books and magazines often wrongly accuse complex carbohydrates of being the "fattening" ingredient of foods, thereby misleading millions of weight-conscious people into avoiding all kinds of carbohydrate-rich foods.[3] Despite intense marketing of diet books and low-carbohydrate foods, the truth remains that people who wish to lose fat and to maintain lean tissue and the health of the body can do no better than to attend closely to portion sizes, control total Calories, and design their diets around foods that supply carbohydrates in balance with other energy nutrients.[4]

The DRI committee recommends that 45 to 65 percent of daily Calories come from carbohydrate. Details about controlling body fatness are in Chapter 9.

Gram for gram, carbohydrates donate fewer Calories than do dietary fats, and converting glucose into fat for storage is metabolically costly. Hence, bite for bite, a moderate balanced diet based on foods high in complex carbohydrates is likely to be lower in total Calories than a diet based on high-fat foods.

Recommendations to select complex carbohydrates do not extend to refined sugars. Whereas complex carbohydrates contribute needed nutrients, pure sugars displace nutrient-dense foods from the diet. Purified, refined sugars (mostly sucrose or fructose) contain no other nutrients—proteins, vitamins, minerals, or fibre—and thus qualify as foods of low nutrient density. A person choosing 400 Calories of sugar in place of 400 Calories of whole-grain bread loses the protein, vitamins, minerals, phytochemicals, and fibre of the bread. You can afford to do this only if you have already met all of your nutrient needs for the day and still have Calories to spend.

Overuse of sugars may have other effects as well. Some evidence suggests that, for many obese people, a diet too high in added sugars may alter blood lipids in ways that may worsen their heart disease risk (see this chapter's Controversy feature for details).[5]

• 1 g carbohydrate = 4 Calories
1 g fat = 9 Calories

For these people, weight loss on a Calorie-controlled diet high in whole grains, fruit, and vegetables reduces the blood lipid response to sugars and lowers their heart disease risk.

For health's sake, then, most people should increase their intakes of fibre-rich sources of carbohydrates such as whole grains, fruit, and vegetables and use moderation in choosing refined foods such as white flour and foods containing added sugars, for example, sweetened beverages (especially since added sugars make up an estimated half of our carbohydrate intake or about 10% to 13% of total energy) and the kinds of fats associated with heart disease (see Chapter 5).[6] Table 4–1 presents carbohydrate recommendations and guidelines from several authorities. This chapter's Consumer Corner (pages 124–126) describes various breads, and the Food Feature comes back to the sugars in foods.

- The primary source of energy in the diet of adult Canadians comes from carbohydrates, at 50% of total energy. (See Statistics Canada's Appendix Table C at http://www.statcan.gc.ca/pub/82-003-x/2006004/article/habit/4148989-eng.htm#11.)

Table 4–1

Recommendations Concerning Intakes of Carbohydrates

1. Recommendations for total carbohydrates

World Health Organization
- 55% to 75% of total Calories from carbohydrates

Canada's Food Guide[a]
- Good sources of carbohydrates can be found in all four Food Groups.
- "Eat at least one dark green and one orange vegetable each day."
- "Make at least half your grain products whole grain each day."
- "Drink skim, 1%, or 2% milk each day."
- "Have meat and alternatives such as beans, lentils, and tofu often."

Dietary Reference Intakes (DRI)
- At a minimum, 130 g per day for adults and children, to provide glucose to the brain.
- For health, most people should consume between 45% and 65% of total Calories from carbohydrate.

2. Recommendations for added sugars

World Health Organization
- Less than 10% of total Calories from sugars[b]

Canada's Food Guide
- Limit foods and beverages high in sugar, such as fruit-flavoured drinks, soft drinks, sports and energy drinks, and sweetened hot and cold drinks.

Dietary Reference Intakes (DRI)
- Insufficient evidence exists to set an upper limit for added sugars; however, the DRI committee suggests a high maximum of 25% or less of Calories for people who otherwise meet their nutrient needs, maintain a healthy body weight, and need additional energy.[c]

American Heart Association
- Women—no more than 100 Calories per day (~6 tsp); men—no more than 150 Calories per day (~9 tsp)

3. Recommendations for fibre

World Health Organization
- More than 25 g of fibre from whole grains, fruits, and vegetables

Canada's Food Guide
- Have vegetables and fruit more often than juice, make at least half of your grain products whole grains each day, and have meat alternatives such as beans and lentils often.

Dietary Reference Intakes (DRI)
- Adequate intake is 38 g of total fibre per day for men through age 50 and 30 g for men 51 and older.
- Adequate intake is 25 g of total fibre per day for women through age 50 and 21 g for women 51 and older.

Canada's Food Guide is presented in Figure 2–4 on pages 38–43.

[a]Serving sizes were presented in Chapter 2.

[b]The World Health Organization uses the term free sugars to mean all monosaccharides and disaccharides added to foods by the manufacturer, cook, or consumer, plus sugars naturally present in honey, syrups, and fruit juices.

[c]An example might be an athlete in training whose high energy need allows greater amounts of added sugars from sports drinks without compromising nutrient intakes; for most sedentary people, maximums of 3 to 12 tsp per day are suggested.

The Need for Carbohydrates

- The body tissues use carbohydrates for energy and other functions; the brain and nerve tissues prefer carbohydrate as fuel. Nutrition authorities recommend a diet based on foods rich in complex carbohydrates and fibre.

Why Do Nutrition Experts Recommend Fibre-Rich Foods?

As mentioned, carbohydrate-rich foods offer additional benefits if they are also rich in fibre. Foods such as whole grains, vegetables, legumes, and fruit supply valuable vitamins, minerals, and phytochemicals, along with a healthy dose of fibre, and with little or no fat. Apples, barley, carrots, legumes, and oats are rich in viscous fibres that have a significant cholesterol-lowering effect. Cooked legumes can also help regulate the blood glucose following a carbohydrate-rich meal. Wheat bran, composed mostly of insoluble nonviscous fibre, is one of the most effective stool-softening fibre-rich foods. These benefits of fibre are the best known: promotion of normal blood cholesterol concentrations, modulation of blood glucose concentrations, and maintenance of healthy bowel function.[7] Add one other benefit of a fibre-rich diet to the list—help in maintaining a healthy body weight—and the obvious choice for anyone placing a value on health is to obtain fibres from a variety of sources each day.[8]

Table 4–2 shows the diverse effects of different fibres, and Figure 4–4 provides a brief guide to finding these fibres in foods. Most unrefined plant foods contain a mix of fibre types. The following paragraphs describe health benefits associated with daily intakes of these foods.

Fibre's Best-Known Health Benefits Include:

1. Promotion of normal blood cholesterol concentrations (reduced risk of heart disease)

2. Modulation of blood glucose concentrations (reduced risk of diabetes)

3. Maintenance of healthy bowel function (reduced risk of bowel diseases)

4. Promotion of a healthy body weight

Visit http://www.hc-sc.gc.ca/fn-an/nutrition/fiche-nutri-data/cnf_downloads-telechargement_fcen-eng. php and search Canadian Nutrient File 2010 to check the fibre content of any food.

- Fibre-rich diets benefit the body by helping to normalize blood cholesterol and blood glucose and by maintaining healthy bowel function. They are also associated with healthy body weight.

Lower Cholesterol and Heart Disease Risk Diets rich in legumes, vegetables, and whole grains and therefore rich in complex carbohydrates may protect against heart

Table 4–2

Characteristics, Sources, and Health Effects of Fibres

Fibre Characteristics	Major Food Sources	Actions in the Body	Health Benefits
Viscous, soluble, more fermentable			
- Gums - Pectins - Psyllium - Some hemicelluloses	Barley, oats, oat bran, rye, fruit (apples, citrus), legumes (especially young green peas and black-eyed peas), seaweeds, seeds and husks, vegetables; fibres used as food additives	- Lower blood cholesterol by binding bile - Slow glucose absorption - Slow transit of food through small intestine, lending satiety - Hold moisture in stools, softening them - Yield small fatlike molecules after fermentation that the colon can use for energy	- Lower risk of heart disease - Lower risk of diabetes - May help with weight management
Nonviscous, insoluble, less fermentable			
- Cellulose - Lignin - Resistant starch - Many hemicelluloses - Inulin (fructose polymers)	Brown rice, fruit, legumes, seeds, vegetables (cabbage, carrots, Brussels sprouts), wheat bran, whole grains; extracted fibres used as food additives, asparagus, onions, garlic, bananas, wheat, dandelion root, chicory root; added to some pastas	- Increase fecal weight and speed fecal passage though colon - Provide bulk and feelings of fullness - Plant-based source of dietary fibre	- Alleviate constipation - Lower risks of diverticulosis, hemorrhoids, and appendicitis - May help with weight management - May be beneficial as a prebiotic (e.g., support the growth of beneficial bacteria)

Figure 4–4

Fibre Composition of Common Foods

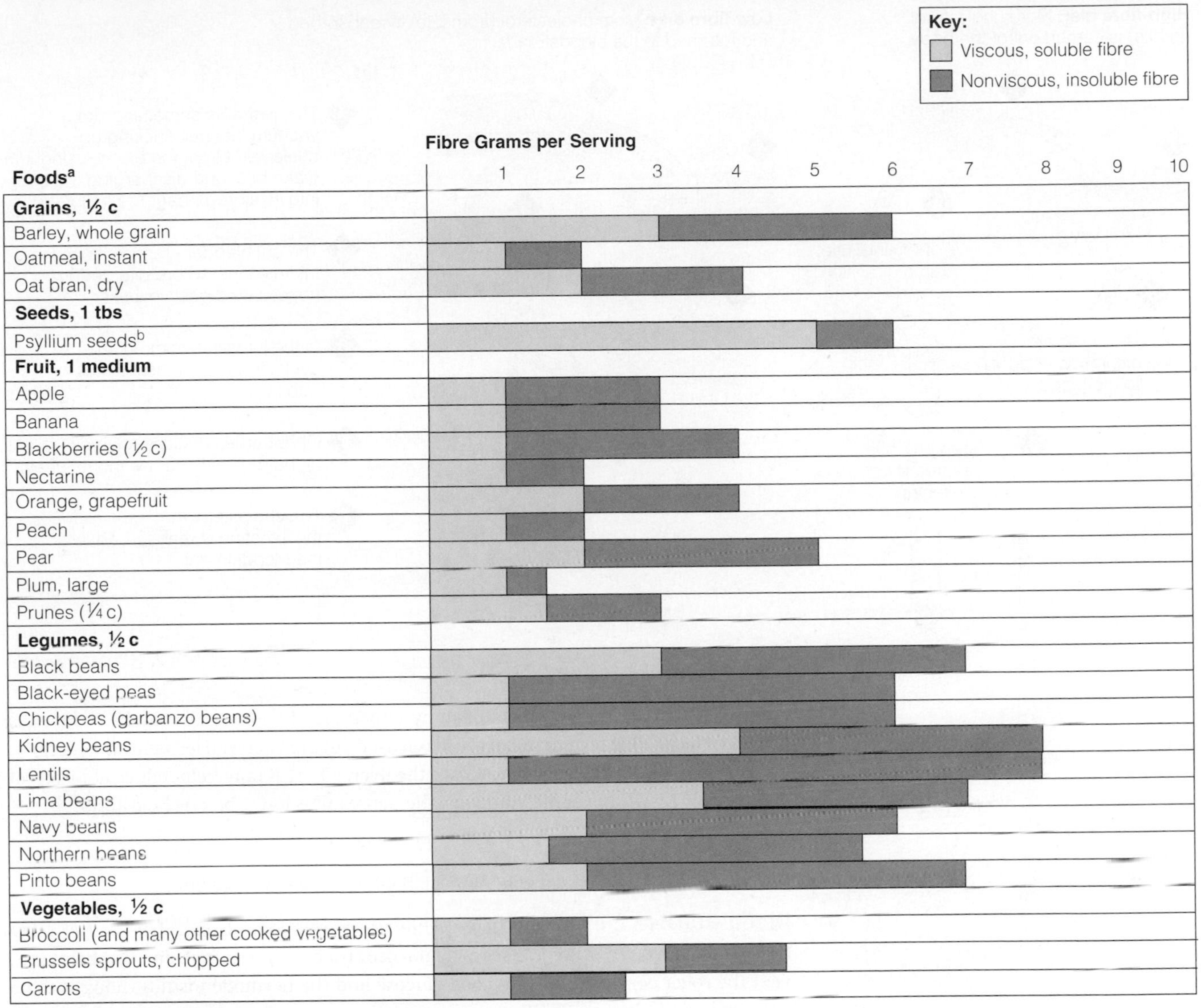

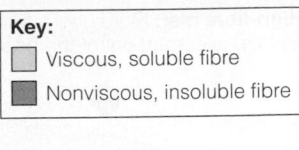

Key:
- Viscous, soluble fibre
- Nonviscous, insoluble fibre

Fibre Grams per Serving

Foods[a]	1	2	3	4	5	6	7	8	9	10
Grains, ½ c										
Barley, whole grain										
Oatmeal, instant										
Oat bran, dry										
Seeds, 1 tbs										
Psyllium seeds[b]										
Fruit, 1 medium										
Apple										
Banana										
Blackberries (½ c)										
Nectarine										
Orange, grapefruit										
Peach										
Pear										
Plum, large										
Prunes (¼ c)										
Legumes, ½ c										
Black beans										
Black-eyed peas										
Chickpeas (garbanzo beans)										
Kidney beans										
Lentils										
Lima beans										
Navy beans										
Northern beans										
Pinto beans										
Vegetables, ½ c										
Broccoli (and many other cooked vegetables)										
Brussels sprouts, chopped										
Carrots										

[a]Values are for cooked or ready-to-serve foods unless specified.

[b]Psyllium is used as a fibre laxative and fibre-rich food additive.

Source: Data from the National Heart, Lung and Blood Institute. Third Report of the National Cholesterol Education Program (NCEP) Expert Panel on Detection, Evaluation and Treatment of High Blood Cholesterol in Adults *(Adult Treatment Panel 10, NIH publication no. 02-5215(2002); V-6; ESHA Research, 2004.*

The roles of saturated fat, trans fat, cholesterol, and other lipids in heart disease are discussed in Chapters 5 and 11. The role of vegetable proteins in heart disease is presented in Chapter 6. The benefits of phytochemicals in disease prevention are featured in Controversy 2 in Chapter 2.

disease and stroke, although sorting out the reasons why has proven difficult.[9] Such diets are generally low in saturated fat, *trans* fat, and cholesterol and high in fibres, vegetable proteins, and phytochemicals—all factors associated with a lower risk of heart disease (see sidebar).

It is relatively certain that foods rich in viscous fibres lower blood cholesterol by binding with cholesterol-containing bile in the intestine and carrying it out with the feces (see Figure 4–5).[10] Bile is needed in digestion, so the liver responds to its loss by drawing on the body's cholesterol to

Figure 4–5

One-Way Fibre in Food May Lower Cholesterol in the Blood

High-fibre diet: More cholesterol (in bile) is carried out of the body.

Low-fibre diet: More cholesterol (from bile) is reabsorbed and returned to the bloodstream.

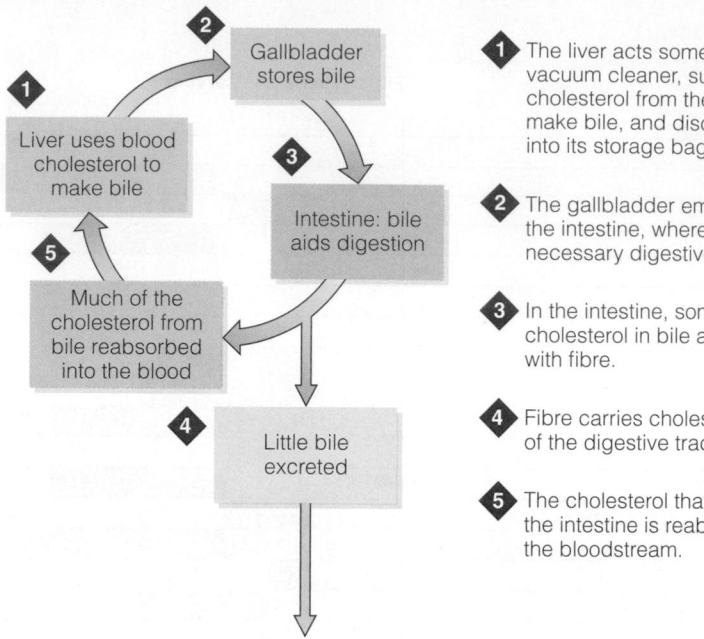

1 The liver acts something like a vacuum cleaner, sucking up cholesterol from the blood, using it to make bile, and discharging the bile into its storage bag, the gallbladder.

2 The gallbladder empties its bile into the intestine, where bile performs necessary digestive tasks.

3 In the intestine, some of the cholesterol in bile associates with fibre.

4 Fibre carries cholesterol in bile out of the digestive tract with the feces.

5 The cholesterol that remains in the intestine is reabsorbed into the bloodstream.

synthesize more. Another mechanism by which blood cholesterol may be reduced is through the actions of a small fatty acid released during bacterial fermentation of fibre. This fatty acid is absorbed and travels to the liver, where it may help reduce cholesterol synthesis.[11] By whatever mechanisms, the net result is lower blood cholesterol.[12]

KEY POINT

- Foods rich in soluble viscous fibres help control blood cholesterol.

Blood Glucose Control   When viscous fibres from foods trap nutrients and delay their transit through the digestive tract, glucose absorption is slowed, and this helps prevent the roller coaster surges in blood glucose and the hormone insulin thought to be associated with the onset of the most common form of diabetes.[13] In people with established diabetes, high-fibre foods (many of which have a low glycemic index; see page 134) may play a role in modulating blood glucose and insulin levels, thus lowering the likelihood of medical complications. A later section comes back to diabetes and its control.

KEY POINT

- Foods rich in viscous fibres help modulate blood glucose concentrations.

Maintenance of Digestive Tract Health   All kinds of fibres, along with an ample fluid intake, probably play roles in maintaining proper colon function. Fibres such as cellulose (as in cereal brans, fruit, and vegetables) enlarge and soften the stools, easing their passage out of the body and speeding up their transit time through the intestine. Thus, foods rich in these fibres help alleviate or prevent **constipation**.

Large, soft stools ease the task of elimination for the rectal muscles. Pressure is then reduced in the lower bowel (colon), making it less likely that rectal veins will swell (**hemorrhoids**). Fibre prevents compaction of the intestinal contents, which could obstruct the appendix and permit bacteria to invade and infect it (**appendicitis**). In addition, fibre stimulates the gastrointestinal tract muscles so that they retain their strength and resist bulging out into pouches known as **diverticula** (illustrated in Figure 4–6).[14]

constipation difficult, incomplete, or infrequent bowel movements, associated with discomfort in passing dry, hardened feces from the body.

hemorrhoids (HEM-or-oids) swollen, hardened (varicose) veins in the rectum, usually caused by the pressure resulting from constipation.

appendicitis inflammation and/or infection of the appendix, a sac protruding from the intestine.

diverticula (dye-ver-TIC-you-la) sacs or pouches that balloon out of the intestinal wall, caused by weakening of the muscle layers that encase the intestine. The painful inflammation of one or more of these diverticula is known as *diverticulitis*.

Populations consuming high-fibre diets generally have lower rates of colon cancer than similar populations consuming low-fibre diets.[15] Most research also suggests that increasing dietary fibre protects against colon cancer.[16] On completing a study of almost 520,000 people, researchers concluded that doubling the naturally occurring fibre in diets of populations with low fibre intakes could reduce the risks of colon and rectal cancers by 40 percent.[17] They caution, though, that they studied only fibre in foods, not supplements, and so suggest food as a fibre source. Fibre-rich foods also contain important nutrients and phytochemicals that supplements lack, and these substances may reduce the risk of colon cancer.

How fibre may help prevent colon cancer is under investigation. One focus of research is fibre's ability to dilute and speed removal of potential cancer-causing agents from the colon. Other possibilities involve the intestine's resident bacteria. In fibre-rich intestinal contents, feasting bacteria reproduce rapidly, and in so doing, they bind nitrogen and carry it out of the body in the feces. Nitrogen is under study as a potential factor in cancer causation.

As mentioned earlier, soluble fibres yield small fatlike molecules when fermented by bacteria in the colon. The cells of the colon prefer one of these little fats, **butyrate**, to provide energy.[18] A colon well supplied with butyrate from a diet high in soluble fibres may resist chemical injury that could otherwise lead to cancer formation.[19] Another possible link: a well-fed colon frequently replaces its own lining, sloughing damaged cells before they can initiate the cancer process.

Other processes may also be at work. As research progresses, cancer experts recommend a high-fibre diet that includes five to nine half-cup (125 mL) servings of vegetables and fruits each day and generous portions of whole grains and legumes.[20]

KEY POINT

- Fibres in foods help maintain digestive tract health.

Healthy Weight Management   It bears repeating that foods rich in complex carbohydrates tend to be low in fats and added sugars and can therefore promote weight loss by delivering less energy per bite. Fibres also create feelings of fullness and delay hunger because they swell as they absorb water from the digestive juices.[21]

Some weight-loss products on the market today contain bulk-inducing fibres, but buying pure fibre compounds like this is neither necessary nor advisable.* To use fibre in a weight-loss plan, select fresh fruits, vegetables, legumes, and whole grain foods. High-fibre foods not only add bulk to the diet but are also economical and nutritious, bringing many benefits to the eater.[22]

KEY POINT

- Diets that are adequate in fibre assist the eater in maintaining a healthy body weight.

Recommendations and Intakes

Few people in Canada or the United States eat a diet providing all of their needed fibre. Compare the average intake of about 14 to 15 grams of fibre with the DRI fibre recommendations in the margin, which are based on energy needs and so vary widely among gender and age groups.[23]

An effective way to add fibre while lowering fat is to substitute plant sources of proteins (legumes) for some of the animal sources of protein (meats and cheeses) in the diet. Another way is to focus on consuming the recommended amounts of fruit and vegetables each day. People choosing high-fibre foods are wise to seek out a variety of fibre sources and to drink extra fluids to help the fibre do its job.

Fibre recommendations are given in terms of total fibre without distinction between fibre types. This makes sense because most fibre-rich foods supply a mixture of fibres (recall Figure 4–4, page 121). The Consumer Corner provides detailed information about choosing wisely among grain foods.

---

*An example is methylcellulose, a fibre that swells up and fills the stomach.

Figure 4–6

Diverticula

Diverticula are abnormal bulging pockets formed in the colon wall. These pockets can entrap feces and become painfully infected and inflamed, requiring hospitalization, antibiotic therapy, or surgery.

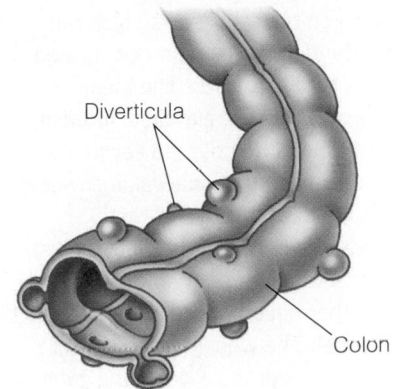

Diverticula

Colon

DRI Recommendations for Fibre

- Men, age 19–50   38 g/day
- Men, age 51 and up   30 g/day
- Women, age 19–50   25 g/day
- Women, age 51 and up 21 g/day

butyrate (BYOO-tier-ate) a small fat fragment produced by the fermenting action of bacteria on viscous, soluble fibres; the preferred energy source for the colon cells.

use it! Consumer Corner

Refined, Enriched, and Whole-Grain Bread

For many people, bread supplies much of the carbohydrate, or at least most of the starch, in a day's meals. Any food used in such abundance in the diet should be scrutinized closely, and if it doesn't measure up to high nutrition standards, it should be replaced with a food that does. The meanings of the words **refined**, **enriched**, **fortified**, and **whole grain** hold the key to understanding the nutritional value of wheat breads (see Table 4–3).

The part of the wheat plant that is made into flour and then into bread and other baked goods is the seed or kernel. The wheat kernel (a whole grain) has four main parts: the **germ**, the **endosperm**, the **bran**, and the **husk**, as shown in Figure 4–7. The germ is the part that grows into a wheat plant and therefore contains concentrated food to support the new life—it is especially rich in vitamins and minerals. The endosperm is the soft, white, inside portion of the kernel, containing starch and proteins that help nourish the seed as it sprouts. The kernel is encased in the bran, a protective coating that is similar in function to the shell of a nut; the bran is also rich in nutrients and fibre. The husk, commonly called chaff, is the dry outermost layer and is inedible for human beings but can be used in animal feed.

In earlier times, people milled wheat by grinding it between two stones, blowing or sifting out the chaff, and retaining the nutrient-rich bran and germ as well as the endosperm. Then milling machinery was "improved," and it became possible to remove the dark, heavy germ and bran as well, leaving a whiter, smoother-textured flour with a higher starch content and far less fibre.[*,1] People looked on this flour as more desirable than the crunchy, dark brown, "old-fashioned" flour.

In turning to white bread, bread eaters suffered a tragic loss of needed nutrients. Many people developed

*Consumer Corner references are listed separately at the end of the chapter.

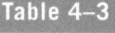

Table 4–3

Terms That Describe Grain Foods

- **bran** the protective fibrous coating around a grain; the chief fibre donator of a grain.
- **brown bread** bread containing ingredients such as molasses that lend a brown colour; may be made with any kind of flour, including white flour.
- **endosperm** the bulk of the edible part of a grain, the starchy part.
- **enriched** the addition of nutrients back to a food that may have been lost during processing, for example, the addition of thiamin, riboflavin, niacin, and iron to bleached wheat flour. Thus, you may see the term *enriched* on certain types of breads or cereals.
- **fortified** the addition of nutrients to foods that did not contain them initially, for example, orange juice to which calcium was added. Thus, you may see the term *fortified* on such beverages.
- **germ** the nutrient-rich inner part of a grain.
- **husk** the outer, inedible part of a grain.
- **refined** refers to the process by which the coarse parts of food products are removed. For example, the refining of wheat into flour involves removing three of the four parts of the kernel—the chaff, the bran, and the germ—leaving only the endosperm, composed mainly of starch and a little protein.
- **stone ground** refers to a milling process using limestone to grind any grain, including refined grains, into flour.
- **unbleached flour** a beige-coloured endosperm flour with texture and nutritive qualities that approximate those of regular white flour.
- **wheat flour** any flour made from wheat, including white flour.
- **white flour** an endosperm flour that has been refined and bleached for maximum softness and whiteness.
- **whole grain** refers to a grain milled in its entirety (all but the husk), not refined.
- **whole-wheat flour** flour made from whole-wheat kernels; a whole-grain flour.

Figure 4–7

A Wheat Plant and a Single Kernel of Wheat

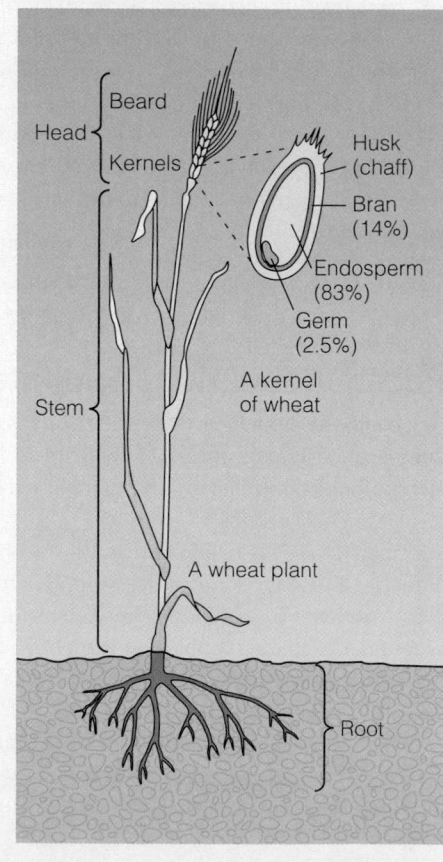

Head
Beard
Kernels
Stem

Husk (chaff)
Bran (14%)
Endosperm (83%)
Germ (2.5%)
A kernel of wheat

A wheat plant

Root

In Western societies, bread is the staff of life.

Figure 4–8

Nutrients in Whole-Grain, Enriched White, and Unenriched White Bread

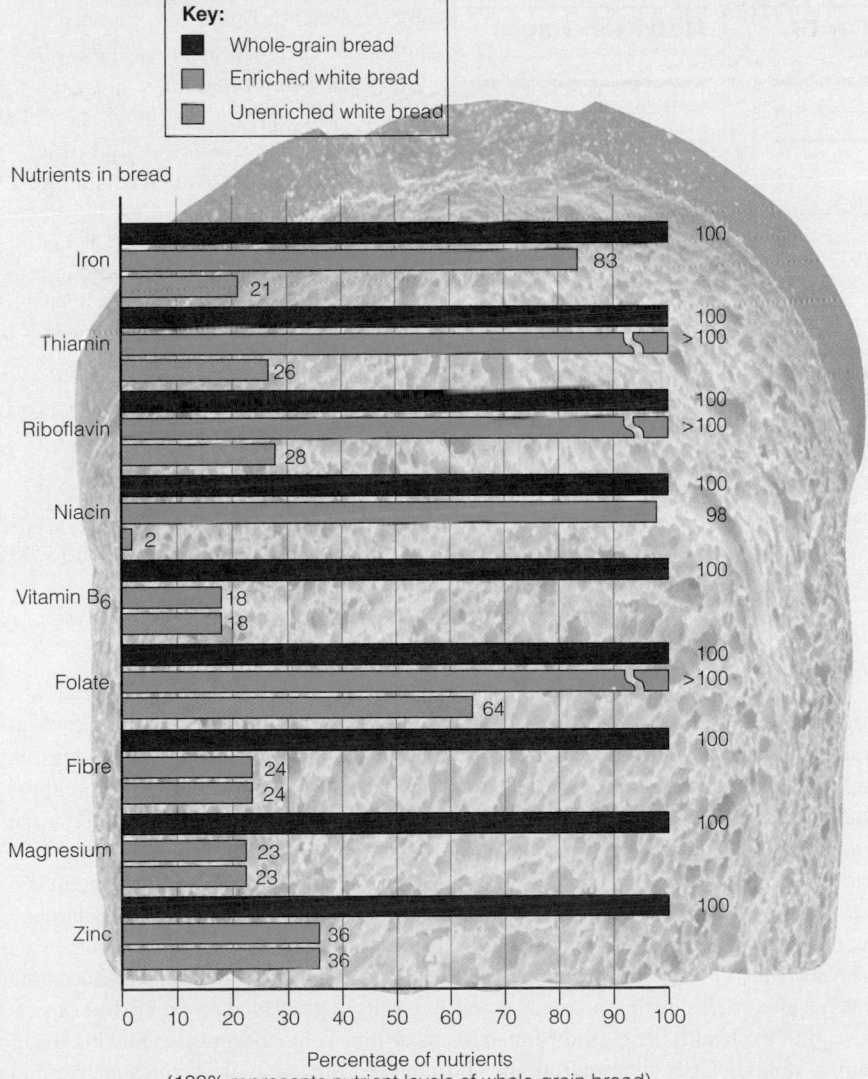

Key:
- ■ Whole-grain bread
- ■ Enriched white bread
- ■ Unenriched white bread

Nutrients in bread

Iron	Whole-grain: 100, Enriched: 83, Unenriched: 21
Thiamin	100, >100, 26
Riboflavin	100, >100, 28
Niacin	100, 98, 2
Vitamin B₆	100, 18, 18
Folate	100, >100, 64
Fibre	100, 24, 24
Magnesium	100, 23, 23
Zinc	100, 36, 36

Percentage of nutrients
(100% represents nutrient levels of whole-grain bread)

deficiencies of iron, thiamin, riboflavin, and niacin—nutrients formerly received from whole-grain bread. In the early 1950s, Health and Welfare Canada allowed optional enrichment of white wheat flour with B vitamins; in the mid-1970s, it became mandatory to add riboflavin, thiamin, niacin, and iron to bleached wheat flour; and in the late 1990s it also became mandatory to add folic acid and optional to add yet other nutrients.[2]

A single slice of refined bread is not "rich" in the enrichment nutrients, but people who eat several slices of bread a day obtain significantly more of the nutrients than they would from unenriched white bread, as Figure 4–8 shows. Today, breads, wheat-based grain products such as macaroni and spaghetti, and most types of wheat-based cereals have been enriched with at least the mandatory nutrients (four vitamins and iron) mentioned in the paragraph above.

To a great extent, the enrichment of grain products eliminated known deficiency problems, but other deficiencies went undetected for many more years. The trouble with enriched flour is that it is comparable to whole grain only with respect to the added nutrients and not with respect to others. Enriched products still contain less magnesium, zinc, vitamin B₆, vitamin E, and chromium than whole-grain products do. When a grain is refined, fibre is lost, too (see Table 4–4).

Only *whole-grain* flour contains all of the nutritive portions of the grain. Notice the distinctions between **wheat**

Table 4–4

Grams of Fibre in One Cup (250 mL) of Canadian Flour

Dark rye, 15.7
Whole grain, 16
Light rye, 14
Buckwheat, 4.4
Cornmeal, 3.8
Enriched white, 4.1

Figure 4–9

Bread Labels Compared

Although breads may appear similar, their ingredients vary widely. Breads made mostly from whole-grain flours provide more benefits to the body than breads made of enriched refined wheat flour. Some "high-fibre" breads may contain purified cellulose or more nutritious whole grains. "Low-carbohydrate" breads may be regular white bread, thinly sliced to reduce carbohydrates per serving, or may contain lower-starch soy flour, barley flour, or flaxseed.

A trick for estimating a bread's content of a nutritious ingredient, such as whole-grain flour, is to read the ingredients list (ingredients are listed in order of predominance). Bread recipes generally include one teaspoon of salt per loaf. Therefore, when a bulky nutritious ingredient, such as whole grain, is listed after the salt, you'll know that less than a teaspoonful of the nutritious ingredient was added to the loaf—not enough to significantly change the nutrient value per slice.

flour, **whole-wheat flour**, **white flour**, and **unbleached flour** among the terms that describe grain foods; also notice that the terms *wheat bread*, **brown bread**, *multi-grain*, *organic*, and **stone ground** on a label do not guarantee that the bread has been made with whole-grain flour (see Figure 4–9). Also, a product that indicates it is made with whole wheat or is multi-grain or organic isn't necessarily made with the whole grain. Until Health Canada legally defines "whole grain," look for "whole grain" on food labels, including the ingredient list. To help better understand this issue, see "Whole Grain—Get the Facts" at http://www.hc-sc.gc.ca/fn-an/nutrition/whole-grain-entiers-eng.php. Also, inulin (oligofructose) is being added to some foods such as pasta as a source of plant-based fibre; look for it in the ingredients list. Bread sold for weight-reduction dieting may be fortified with pure cellulose, but adding cellulose alone is not enough; the bread still lacks other beneficial substances that occur in whole wheat. If bread is a staple food in your diet—that is, if you eat it every day—you are well advised to learn to like the hearty flavour of whole-grain bread.

Whole Grain
WHOLE WHEAT

Nutrition Facts

Serving size 1 slice (30 g)
Servings per Container 18

Amount per serving

Calories 90

	Daily Value (%)
Total Fat 1.5 g	2
Trans Fat 0 g	
Sodium 135 mg	6
Total Carbohydrate 15 g	5
Dietary fibre 2 g	8
Sugars 2 g	
Protein 4 g	

MADE FROM: UNBROMATED STONE GROUND 100% WHOLE-WHEAT FLOUR, WATER, CRUSHED WHEAT, HIGH-FRUCTOSE CORN SYRUP, PARTIALLY HYDROGENATED VEGETABLE SHORTENING (SOYBEAN AND COTTONSEED OILS), RAISIN JUICE CONCENTRATE, WHEAT GLUTEN, YEAST, WHOLE-WHEAT FLAKES, UNSULPHURED MOLASSES, SALT, HONEY, VINEGAR, ENZYME MODIFIED SOY LECITHIN, CULTURED WHEY, UNBLEACHED WHEAT FLOUR, SOY LECITHIN.

Natural
Wheat Bread

Nutrition Facts

Serving size 1 slice (30 g)
Servings per Container 15

Amount per serving

Calories 90

	Daily Value (%)
Total Fat 1.5 g	2
Trans Fat 0 g	
Sodium 220 mg	9
Total Carbohydrate 15 g	5
Dietary fibre less than 1 g	2
Sugars 2 g	
Protein 4 g	

INGREDIENTS: UNBLEACHED ENRICHED WHEAT FLOUR [MALTED BARLEY FLOUR, NIACIN, REDUCED IRON, THIAMIN MONONITRATE (VITAMIN B_1), RIBOFLAVIN (VITAMIN B_2), FOLIC ACID], WATER, HIGH-FRUCTOSE CORN SYRUP, MOLASSES, PARTIALLY HYDROGENATED SOYBEAN OIL, YEAST, CORN FLOUR, SALT, GROUND CARAWAY, WHEAT GLUTEN, CALCIUM PROPIONATE (PRESERVATIVE), MONOGLYCERIDES, SOY LECITHIN.

Multi-fibre
Low carb

Nutrition Facts

Serving size 1 slice (30 g)
Servings per Container 21

Amount per serving

Calories 60

	Daily Value (%)
Total Fat 1.5 g	2
Trans Fat 0 g	
Sodium 135 mg	6
Total Carbohydrate 9 g	3
Dietary fibre 3 g	12
Sugars 0 g	
Protein 5 g	

INGREDIENTS: UNBLEACHED ENRICHED WHEAT FLOUR, WATER, WHEAT GLUTEN, CELLULOSE, YEAST, SOYBEAN OIL, CRACKED WHEAT, SALT, BARLEY, NATURAL FLAVOUR PRESERVATIVES, MONOCALCIUM PHOSPHATE, MILLET, CORN, OATS, SOYBEANS, BROWN RICE, FLAXSEED, SUCRALOSE.

• Chelating agents are often sold by supplement vendors to "remove poisons" from the body. Some valid medical uses, such as treatment of lead poisoning, exist, but most of the chelating agents sold over the counter are based on unproven claims.

chelating (KEE-late-ing) **agents** molecules that attract or bind with other molecules and are therefore useful in either preventing or promoting movement of substances from place to place.

Can My Diet Have Too Much Fibre?   Adding purified fibres, such as oat or wheat bran, to foods can be taken to extremes. One enthusiastic eater of purified oat bran in muffins required emergency surgery for a blocked intestine; too much oat bran and too little fluid overwhelmed his digestive system. This doesn't mean that you should avoid bran-containing foods, of course, but that you should use bran with moderation and drink an extra beverage with it. Less extreme concerns are that purified fibre might displace nutrients from the diet or cause them to be lost from the digestive tract by binding the nutrients and speeding up transit. Purified fibres are like refined sugars in one way: the nutrients that originally accompanied the fibres have been lost. Also, a purified fibre may not affect the body the same way as the fibre in its original food product. Most experts agree that the health benefits attributed to a fibre may come from other constituents of fibre-containing foods and not from the fibre alone.[24] You can make a quick approximation of a day's fibre intake by following the instructions in Table 4–5.

Table 4–5

A Quick Method for Estimating Fibre Intake

To quickly estimate fibre in a day's meals:

1. Multiply serving equivalents[a] of fruit and vegetables (excluding juice) by 1.5 g.[b]
   Example: 5 servings of fruit and vegetables $\times$ 1.5 g = 7.5 g fibre

2. Multiply serving equivalents of refined grains by 1.0 g.
   Example: 4 servings of refined grains $\times$ 1.0 g = 4.0 g fibre

3. Multiply serving equivalents of whole grains by 2.5 g.
   Example: 3 servings of whole grains $\times$ 2.5 g = 7.5 g fibre

4. Add fibre values for serving equivalents of legumes, nuts, seeds, and high-fibre cereals
   and breads; look these up in the online version of the Canadian Nutrient File.
   Example: ½ c (125 mL) navy beans = 6.0 g fibre

5. Add up the grams of fibre from the previous lines.
   Example: 7.5 g + 4.0 g + 7.5 g + 6.0 g = 25 g fibre

Day's total: 25 g fibre

[a]Use standard serving equivalents presented in Figure 2–4 in Chapter 2.
[b]Most cooked and canned fruit and vegetables contain about this amount, while whole raw fruit and some
vegetables contain more.

Binders in Fibre   Binders in some fibres act as **chelating agents**. This means that they link chemically with important nutrient minerals (iron, zinc, calcium, and others) and then carry them out of the body. The mineral iron is mostly absorbed at the beginning of the intestinal tract, and excess insoluble fibres may limit its absorption by speeding foods through the upper part of the digestive tract. Too much bulk in the diet can also limit the total amount of food consumed and cause deficiencies of both nutrients and energy. People with marginal intakes, such as the malnourished, the elderly, and children who consume no animal products, are particularly vulnerable to this chain of events. Fibres also carry water out of the body and can cause dehydration. Add an extra glass or two of water to go along with the fibre added to your diet.

The next section focuses on the handling of carbohydrates by the digestive system. Table 4–6 sums up the points made so far concerning the functions of carbohydrates in the body and in foods.

Table 4–6

Usefulness of Carbohydrates

Carbohydrates in the Body	Carbohydrates in Foods
Energy source. Sugars and starch from the diet provide energy for many body functions; they provide glucose, the preferred fuel for the brain and nerves.	**Flavour.** Sugars provide sweetness.
Glucose storage. Muscle and liver glycogen store glucose.	**Browning.** When exposed to heat, sugars undergo browning reactions, lending appealing colour, aroma, and taste to foods.
Raw material. Sugars are converted into other compounds, such as amino acids (the building blocks of proteins), as needed.	**Texture.** Sugars help make foods tender. Cooked starch lends a smooth, pleasing texture.
Structures and functions. Sugars interact with fat and protein molecules, affecting their structures and functions.	**Gel formation.** Starch molecules expand when heated and trap water molecules, forming gels. The fibre pectin forms the gel of jellies when cooked with sugar and acid from fruit.
Digestive tract health. Fibres help maintain healthy bowel function (reduce risk of bowel diseases).	**Bulk and viscosity (thickness).** Carbohydrates lend bulk and increased viscosity to foods. Soluble, viscous fibres lend thickness to foods such as salad dressings.
Blood cholesterol. Fibres promote normal blood cholesterol concentrations (reduce risk of heart disease).	**Moisture.** Sugars attract water and keep foods moist.
Blood glucose. Fibres modulate blood glucose concentrations (help control diabetes).	**Preservative.** Sugar in high concentrations dehydrates bacteria and preserves the food.
Satiety. Fibres and sugars contribute to feelings of fullness.	**Fermentation.** Carbohydrates are fermented by yeast, a process that causes bread dough to rise and beer to brew, among other uses.
Body weight. A fibre-rich diet may promote a healthy body weight.	

- Most adults need between 21 and 38 grams of total fibre each day, but few consume this amount. Fibre needs are best met with whole foods. Purified fibre in large doses can have undesirable effects. Fluid intake should increase with fibre intake.

From Carbohydrates to Glucose

You may eat bread or a baked potato, but the body's cells cannot use foods or even whole molecules of lactose, sucrose, or starch for energy. They need the glucose in those molecules, and they need it continuously. The various body systems must make glucose available to the cells not all at once when it is eaten but at a steady rate all day.

Digestion and Absorption of Carbohydrate

To obtain glucose from newly eaten food, the digestive system must first render the starch and disaccharides from the food into monosaccharides that can be absorbed through the cells that line the small intestine. The largest of the digestible carbohydrate molecules, starch, requires the most extensive breakdown. Disaccharides, in contrast, need be split only once before they can be absorbed.

Starch   Digestion of most starch begins in the mouth, where an enzyme in saliva mixes with food and begins to split starch into maltose. While chewing a bite of bread, you may notice that a slightly sweet taste develops—maltose is being liberated from starch by the enzyme. The salivary enzyme continues to act on the starch in the bite of bread while it remains tucked in the stomach's upper storage area. As each chewed lump is pushed downward and mixed with the stomach's acid and other juices, the salivary enzyme (made of protein) is deactivated by the stomach's protein-digesting acid. Not all digestive enzymes are susceptible to digestion in the stomach. For example, a protein-digesting enzyme is designed to work best in the stomach—its structure protects it from the stomach's acid. With the breakdown of the salivary enzyme, starch digestion ceases in the stomach, but it resumes at full speed in the small intestine, where another starch-splitting enzyme is delivered by the pancreas. This enzyme breaks starch down into disaccharides and small polysaccharides. Other enzymes liberate monosaccharides for absorption.

Some forms of starch are easily digested. The starch in bread made of refined white flour, for example, breaks down rapidly to glucose that is absorbed high up in the small intestine.[25] Some starch, such as that of cooked beans, digests more slowly and releases its glucose later in the digestion process. Less digestible starch, called **resistant starch**, is technically a kind of fibre and may behave similarly in the body.[26] The starch of raw potatoes, for example, resists digestion; so does the resistant starch that forms during overheating of foods and the starch tucked inside the unbroken hulls of swallowed seeds.[27] Some resistant starch may be digested, but slowly, and most remains intact until the bacteria of the colon eventually break it down. The rate of starch digestion may affect the body's handling of its glucose, as a later section explains.

Sugars   Sucrose and lactose from food, along with maltose and small polysaccharides freed from starch, undergo one more split to yield free monosaccharides before they are absorbed. This split is accomplished by enzymes attached to the cells of the lining of the small intestine. The conversion of a bite of bread to nutrients for the body is completed when monosaccharides cross these cells and are washed away in a rush of circulating blood that carries them to the waiting liver. Figure 4–10 presents a quick review of carbohydrate digestion.

The absorbed carbohydrates (glucose, galactose, and fructose) travel to the liver, which converts fructose and galactose to glucose or related products. The circulatory system transports the glucose and other products to the cells. Liver and muscle cells may store circulating glucose as glycogen; all cells may split glucose for energy.

resistant starch the fraction of starch in a food that is digested slowly, or not at all, by human enzymes.

Figure 4–10

How Carbohydrate in Food Becomes Glucose in the Body

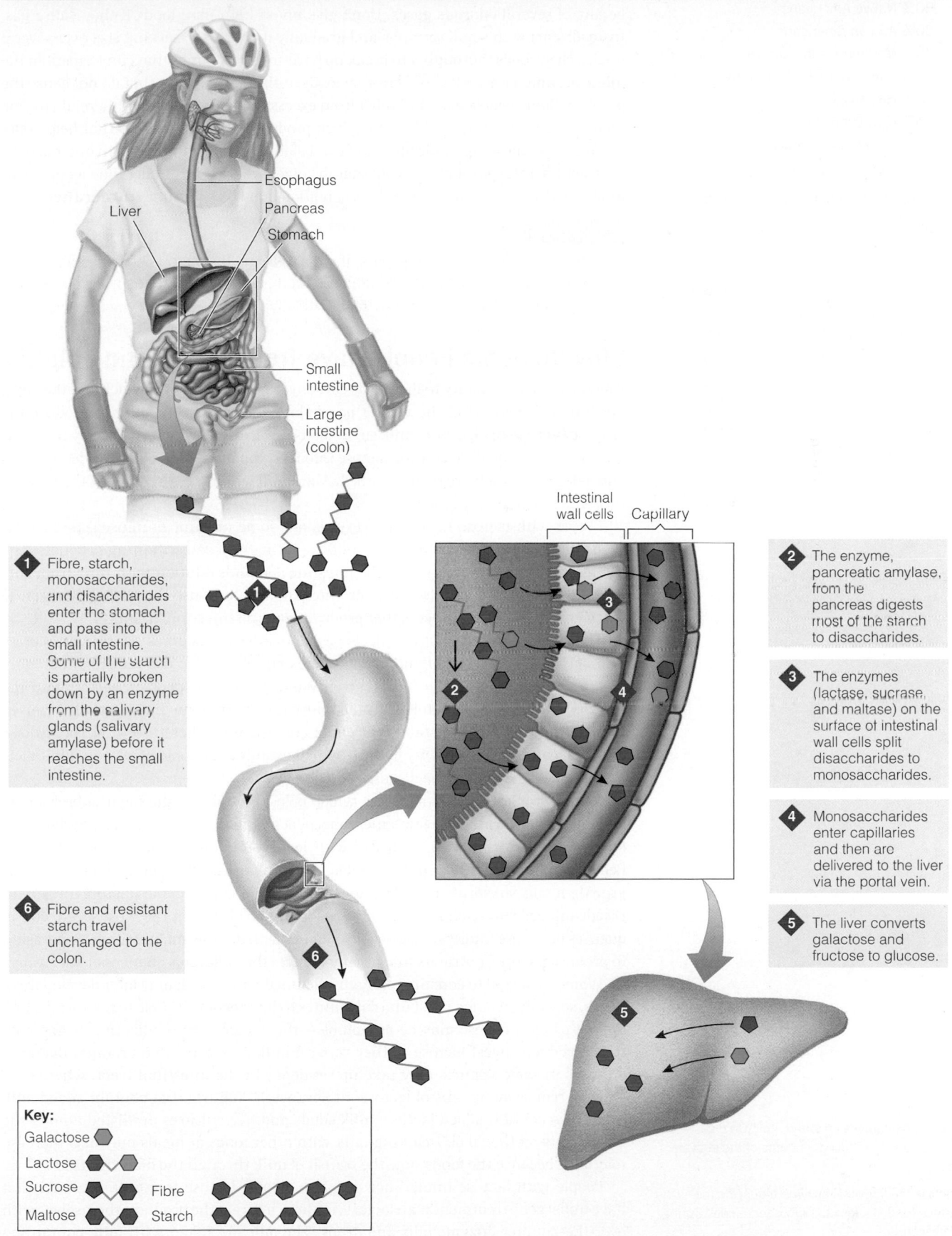

Esophagus

Liver

Pancreas

Stomach

Small intestine

Large intestine (colon)

Intestinal wall cells

Capillary

1 Fibre, starch, monosaccharides, and disaccharides enter the stomach and pass into the small intestine. Some of the starch is partially broken down by an enzyme from the salivary glands (salivary amylase) before it reaches the small intestine.

6 Fibre and resistant starch travel unchanged to the colon.

2 The enzyme, pancreatic amylase, from the pancreas digests most of the starch to disaccharides.

3 The enzymes (lactase, sucrase, and maltase) on the surface of intestinal wall cells split disaccharides to monosaccharides.

4 Monosaccharides enter capillaries and then are delivered to the liver via the portal vein.

5 The liver converts galactose and fructose to glucose.

Key:

Galactose

Lactose

Sucrose   Fibre

Maltose   Starch

Approximate Percentages of U.S. Adults with Lactose Intolerance:

- 90% Asian Americans
- 80% Native Americans
- 80% African Americans
- 70% Mediterranean peoples
- 60% Inuits (most Alaskan natives)
- 50% Hispanics
- 25% U.S. population
- <15% Northern Europeans

Lactose in Selected Foods:

Whole-wheat bread, 1 slice	0.5 g
Dinner roll, 1	0.5 g
Cheese, 30 g	
• Cheddar	0.5 g
• Parmesan or cream	0.8 g
Doughnut (cake type), 1	1.2 g
Chocolate candy, 30 g	2.3 g
Sherbet, 1 c (250 mL)	4.0 g
Cottage cheese (low fat), 1 c	7.5 g
Ice cream, 1 c	9.0 g
Milk, 1 c	12.0 g
Yogurt (low fat, 1 c with added milk solids)	15.0 g

lactose intolerance impaired ability to digest lactose due to reduced amounts of the enzyme lactase.

lactase the intestinal enzyme that splits the disaccharide lactose to monosaccharides during digestion.

Fibre Although molecules of many fibres are not changed by human digestive enzymes, many of them can be digested (fermented) by the bacterial inhabitants of the human digestive tract. A by-product of metabolism by the bacteria in the colon can be any of several odorous gases. Don't give up on high-fibre foods if they cause gas. Instead, start with small servings and gradually increase the serving size over several weeks, chew foods thoroughly to break up hard-to-digest lumps that can ferment in the intestine, and try a variety of fibre-rich foods until you find some that do not cause the problem. Some people also find relief from excessive gas by using commercial enzyme preparations sold for use with beans. Such products contain enzymes that help break down some of the indigestible fibres in foods before they reach the colon. In other people, persistent painful gas may indicate that the digestive tract has undergone a change in its ability to digest the sugar in milk, a condition known as **lactose intolerance**.

KEY POINT

- With respect to starch and sugars, the main task of the various body systems is to convert them to glucose to fuel the cells' work. Fermentable fibres may release gas as they are broken down by bacteria in the intestine.

Why Do Some People Have Trouble Digesting Milk?

Among adults, the ability to digest the carbohydrate of milk varies widely. As they age, upward of 75 percent of the world's people lose much of their ability to produce the enzyme **lactase** to digest the milk sugar lactose.[28] Lactase, which is made by the small intestine, splits the disaccharide lactose into its component monosaccharides, glucose and galactose, which are then absorbed. Almost all mammals lose some of their ability to produce lactase as they age.

People with lactose intolerance experience some amount of nausea, pain, diarrhea, and excessive gas on drinking milk or eating lactose-containing products. The undigested lactose remaining in the intestine demands dilution with fluid from surrounding tissue and the bloodstream. Intestinal bacteria use the undigested lactose for their own energy, a process that produces gas and intestinal irritants.

The failure to digest lactose affects people to differing degrees. Many can tolerate as much as a cup or two of milk a day; some can tolerate lactose-reduced milk; only a rare few cannot tolerate lactose in any amount. Often people overestimate the severity of their lactose intolerance, blaming it for symptoms most probably caused by something else—a mistake that could cost them the health of their bones (see Chapter 8 and its Controversy feature, which examine the topic of milk in adult diets in relation to the adult bone disease osteoporosis).[29]

Infants produce abundant lactase, which helps them absorb the sugar of breast milk and milk-based formulas; a few suffer inborn lactose intolerance and must be fed solely on lactose-free formulas or provided with lactose-free milk or lactose supplements. Because milk is an almost indispensable source of the calcium every child needs for growth, a milk substitute must be found for any child who becomes lactose intolerant. Disadvantaged young children in the developing world sustain the most severe consequences of lactose intolerance when it combines with disease, malnutrition, or parasites to produce a loss of nutrients that greatly reduces the children's chances of survival.

Women who fail to consume enough calcium during youth may later develop weak bones, so young women must find substitutes if they become unable to tolerate milk.[30] Yogurt or aged cheese may be acceptable—the bacteria or moulds that help create these products digest lactose as they convert milk to a fermented product. Bacterial cultures in some yogurts may take up residence in the intestinal tract, where they seem to reduce symptoms of lactose intolerance.[31] Yogurts that contain added milk solids also contain added lactose; milk solids and live cultures are listed among the ingredients on the label. Drinking milk with other foods at meals may also increase tolerance because the foods slow the transit of milk through the digestive tract.[32]

People with lactose intolerance can also choose lactose-free milk products that have undergone treatment with lactase, or they can treat the products themselves with over-the-counter enzyme pills and drops. The pills are taken with milk-containing

Chapter 4 The Carbohydrates: Sugar, Starch, Glycogen, and Fibre   NEL meals, and the drops are added to milk-based foods; both products help digest lactose by replacing the missing natural enzyme. In all cases, the trick is to find ways of splitting lactose to glucose and galactose so that the body can absorb the products, rather than leaving the lactose undigested to feed the bacteria of the colon.

Sometimes sensitivity to milk is not due to lactose intolerance but to an allergic reaction to the protein in milk. Milk allergy arises the same way other allergies do—from sensitization of the immune system to a substance. In this case, the immune system overreacts when it encounters the protein of milk. Children and adults with milk allergy often cannot tolerate cheese or yogurt, and finding nondairy calcium sources becomes imperative. Good choices are calcium-fortified orange juice, calcium- and vitamin-fortified soy drink, and canned sardines or salmon with the bones.

> Milk allergy is a serious problem unrelated to lactose intolerance; see Chapter 14.

KEY POINT

- Lactose intolerance is a common condition in which the body fails to produce sufficient amounts of the enzyme needed to digest the sugar of milk. Uncomfortable symptoms result and can lead to milk avoidance. Lactose-intolerant people and those allergic to milk need milk alternatives that contain the calcium and vitamins of milk.

The Body's Use of Glucose

Glucose is the basic carbohydrate unit that each cell of the body uses for energy. The body handles its glucose judiciously—maintaining an internal supply for use in case of need and tightly controlling its blood glucose concentration to ensure that glucose remains available for ongoing use. As mentioned, carbohydrates serve structural roles in the body, too, such as forming part of the mucus that protects the body's linings and organs, but they are best known for their role in providing energy.

Splitting Glucose for Energy

Glucose fuels the work of most of the body's cells. When a cell splits glucose for energy, it performs an intricate sequence of manoeuvres that are of great interest to the biochemist—and of no interest whatever to most people who eat bread and potatoes. What everybody needs to understand, though, is that there is no good substitute for carbohydrate. Carbohydrate is *essential*, as the following details illustrate.

The Point of No Return   At a certain point, glucose is forever lost to the body. Inside a cell, glucose is broken in half, or lysed, during a process called **glycolysis**, releasing some energy. Two pathways are then open to these glucose halves. They can be put back together to make glucose again, or they can be broken into smaller fragments. If they are broken further, they cannot be reassembled to form glucose. The smaller fragments can yield still more energy and in the process break down completely to carbon dioxide in the **Krebs cycle**, and water via the electron transport chain; they can be formed into building blocks of protein, or they can be hitched together into units of body fat. Figure 4–11 shows how glucose is broken down to yield energy and carbon dioxide.

Below a Healthy Minimum   Although glucose can be converted into body fat, body fat cannot be converted into glucose to feed the brain adequately. When the body faces a severe carbohydrate deficit, it has two problems. Having no glucose, it must turn to protein to make some (the body has this ability), diverting protein from critical functions of its own, such as maintaining the body's immune defences. Protein's functions in the body are so indispensable that carbohydrate should be kept available precisely to prevent the use of protein for energy. This is called the **protein-sparing action** of carbohydrate.

The second problem arises because fat fragments normally combine with a compound derived from glucose before being used by the cells to supply energy. Without the help of this compound, fat fragments combine with each other instead, producing

glycolysis an important metabolic pathway in the cytoplasm of our cells that releases a small amount of energy by splitting glucose in half.

Krebs cycle an important metabolic pathway in the mitochondria of our cells from which we derive most of the energy from molecules like glucose and fatty acids.

protein-sparing action the action of carbohydrate and fat in providing energy that allows protein to be used for purposes it alone can serve.

Figure 4–11

The Breakdown of Glucose Yields Energy and Carbon Dioxide

Cell enzymes split the bonds between the carbon atoms in glucose, liberating the energy stored there for the cell's use.

❶ The first split yields two 3-carbon fragments. The two-way arrows mean that these fragments can also be rejoined to make glucose again. ❷ Once they are broken down further into 2-carbon fragments, however, they cannot rejoin to make glucose. ❸ The carbon atoms liberated when the bonds split are combined with oxygen and released into the air, via the lungs, as carbon dioxide. Although not shown here, water is also produced at each split.

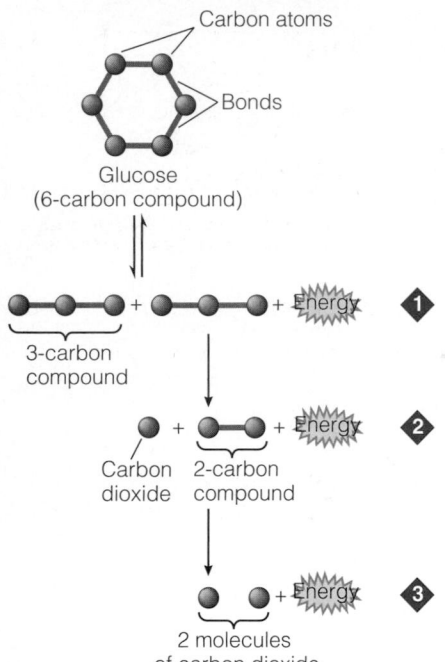

Carbon atoms

Bonds

Glucose
(6-carbon compound)

3-carbon
compound

+ Energy ❶

Carbon   2-carbon
dioxide   compound

+ Energy ❷

+ Energy ❸

2 molecules
of carbon dioxide

ketone (kee-tone) **bodies** acidic, fat-related compounds that can arise from the incomplete breakdown of fat when carbohydrate is not available.

ketosis (kee-TOE-sis) an undesirable high concentration of ketone bodies, such as acetone, in the blood or urine.

insulin a hormone secreted by the pancreas in response to a high blood glucose concentration. It assists cells in drawing glucose from the blood.

glucagon (GLOO-cah-gon) a hormone secreted by the pancreas that stimulates the liver to release glucose into the blood when blood glucose concentration dips.

increased amounts of the normally scarce acidic products called **ketone bodies**. Ketone bodies can accumulate in the blood (**ketosis**) to reach levels high enough to disturb the normal acid–base balance.[33] Adults consuming a diet that produces chronic ketosis may also face deficiencies of vitamins and minerals, loss of bone minerals, altered blood lipids, increased risk of kidney stones, an impaired mood and sense of well-being, and glycogen stores that are too scanty to meet a metabolic emergency or to support maximal high-intensity muscular work.[34] Ketosis isn't all bad, however. A therapeutic ketosis-inducing diet has long been used along with medication to reduce the occurrence of seizures in children with severe epilepsy.[35]

The minimum amount of digestible carbohydrate set by the DRI committee to adequately feed the brain and reduce ketosis has been set at 130 grams a day for an average-sized person.[36] Several times this minimum is recommended to maintain health and glycogen stores (see the next section). The amounts of vegetables, fruit, legumes, grains, and milk recommended in Canada's Food Guide (see Figure 2–4, pages 38–43) deliver abundant carbohydrates.

KEY POINT

- Without glucose, the body is forced to alter its uses of protein and fats. To help supply the brain with glucose, the body breaks down protein to make glucose and converts its fats into ketone bodies, incurring ketosis.

Storing Glucose as Glycogen

After a meal, as blood glucose rises, the pancreas is the first organ to respond. It releases the hormone **insulin**, which signals the body's tissues to take up surplus glucose (see Figure 4–12). Muscle and liver cells use some of this excess glucose to build the polysaccharide glycogen. The muscles hoard two-thirds of the body's total glycogen and use it just for themselves. The brain stores a tiny fraction of the total, thought to provide an emergency glucose reserve sufficient to fuel the brain for an hour or two in severe glucose deprivation.[37] The liver stores the remainder and is generous with its glycogen, making it available as blood glucose for the brain or other tissues when the supply runs low.

Unlike starch, which has long chains with only occasional branches that are cleaved linearly during digestion, glycogen is highly branched, with hundreds of ends extending from each molecule's surface (review this structure in Figure 4–3 on page 117). When the blood glucose concentration drops and cells need energy, a pancreatic hormone, **glucagon**, floods the bloodstream. Then enzymes within the liver cells respond by attacking a multitude of glycogen ends simultaneously to release a surge of glucose into the blood for use by all of the body's other cells. Thus, the branched structure of glycogen uniquely suits the purpose of releasing glucose on demand.

KEY POINT

- Glycogen is the body's storage form of glucose. The liver stores glycogen for use by the whole body. Muscles have their own glycogen stock for their exclusive use. The hormone glucagon acts to liberate stored glucose from liver glycogen.

Returning Glucose to the Blood

Should your glucose supplies ever fall too low, you would feel dizzy and weak. Should your blood glucose ever climb abnormally high, you might become confused or have difficulty breathing. The healthy body guards against both conditions.

Regulation of Blood Glucose   Maintaining normal blood glucose concentration depends on two safeguards: replenishment from liver glycogen stores and siphoning off of excess glucose into the liver (to be converted to glycogen or fat) and into the muscles (to be converted to glycogen).

When blood glucose starts to fall too low, the hormone glucagon triggers the breakdown of liver glycogen to free glucose. Hormones that promote the conversion of protein to glucose are also released, but only a little protein can be spared. When body protein is used, it is taken from blood, organ, or muscle proteins; no surplus of protein

Figure 4–12

Blood Glucose Regulation—Overview

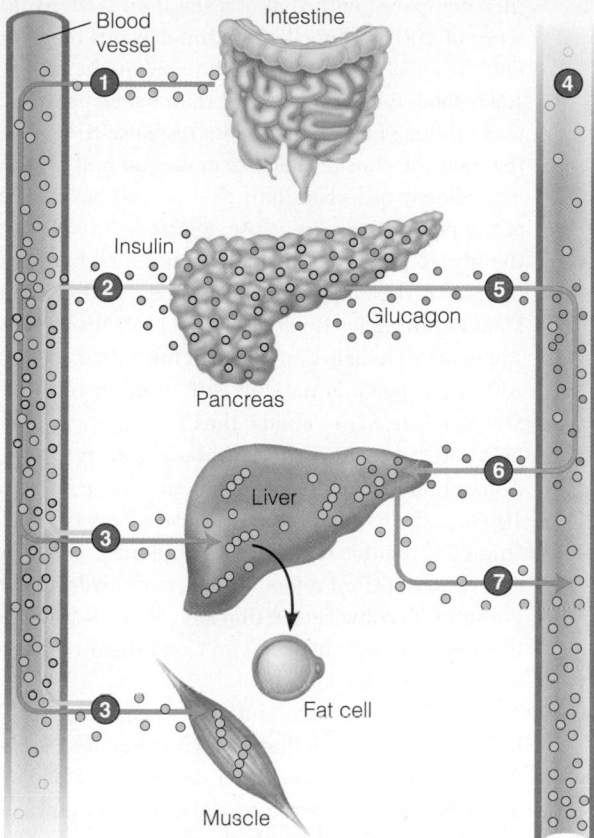

1. When a person eats, blood glucose rises.

2. High blood glucose stimulates the pancreas to release insulin into the bloodstream.

3. Insulin stimulates the uptake of glucose into cells and storage as glycogen in the liver and muscles. Insulin also stimulates the conversion of excess glucose into fat for storage.

4. As the body's cells use glucose, blood levels decline.

5. Low blood glucose stimulates the pancreas to release glucagon into the bloodstream.

6. Glucagon stimulates liver cells to break down glycogen and release glucose into the blood.[a]

7. Blood glucose begins to rise.

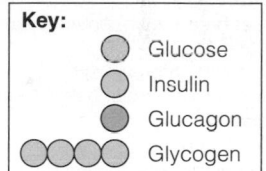

Key:
○ Glucose
○ Insulin
● Glucagon
○○○○ Glycogen

[a]The stress hormone epinephrine and other hormones also bring glucose out of storage.

is stored specifically for emergencies. As for fat, it cannot regenerate enough glucose to feed the brain and prevent ketosis.

Another hormone, epinephrine, also breaks down liver glycogen as part of the body's defence mechanism in times of danger.* To a person living in the Stone Age, this internal source of quick energy was indispensable. Life was filled with physical peril, and the person who stopped and ate before running from a sabre-toothed tiger did not survive to produce our ancestors. The quick-energy response in a stress situation works to our advantage today as well. For example, it accounts for the energy you suddenly have to clean up your room when you learn that a special person is coming to visit. To meet such emergencies, we are advised to eat and store carbohydrate at regularly timed meals throughout the day because the liver's glycogen stores can be depleted within half a waking day.

You may be asking, "What kind of carbohydrate?" Candy, "energy bars," and sugary beverages supply sugar energy quickly but are not the best choices. Balanced meals, eaten on a regular schedule, help the body maintain its blood glucose. Meals containing starch and fibre along with some protein and a little fat slow digestion so that glucose enters the blood gradually in an ongoing steady supply.

KEY POINT

- Blood glucose regulation depends mainly on the hormones insulin and glucagon. Most people have no problem regulating their blood glucose when they consume mixed meals at regular intervals.

---

*Epinephrine is also called *adrenaline*.

Figure 4–13

Glycemic Index* of Selected Foods

HIGH

Glucose

Baked potato

Cornflakes

Sports drinks, jelly beans
Pumpkin, doughnut

Watermelon, popcorn, bagel
White bread

Couscous
Raisins, white rice
Ice cream

Cola, pineapple
Brown rice
Wheat bread, corn, pound cake
Banana
Rye bread, orange juice
Green peas, carrots, baked beans, pasta
Grapes
Chocolate pudding
Bran cereals, black-eyed peas, peaches
Apple juice
Tomato juice, navy beans, apples, pears
Yogurt

Butter beans

Milk, kidney beans, garbanzo beans
Barley

Cashews, cherries

Soybeans

Peanuts

LOW

*The original research on this index was carried out at the University of Toronto by Drs. Jenkins, Wolever, and others in the early 1980s.

glycemic index (GI) a ranking of foods according to their potential for raising blood glucose relative to a standard such as glucose or white bread.

glycemic load a mathematical expression of both the glycemic index and the carbohydrate content of a food, meal, or diet (glycemic index multiplied by grams of carbohydrate).

The Glycemic Response Some carbohydrate-rich foods elevate blood glucose and insulin concentrations more than others. When this effect is measured, each food's score can be ranked on a scale known as the **glycemic index (GI)**. Scores are then compared with that of a standard food, usually white bread or glucose (given a score of 100).[38] A food's ranking depends on a number of factors working together, and the effect is not always what one might expect. Ice cream, for example, is a high-sugar food, but it ranks lower than baked potatoes, a high-starch food. Mashed potatoes produce more of a glucose response than pure sugar (sucrose), perhaps because the monosaccharide fructose makes up half of each sucrose molecule, and fructose is more slowly absorbed than glucose and has little effect on blood glucose. The starch of the potatoes is all glucose. Figure 4–13 shows generally where some foods fall on the glycemic index scale, although individuals' responses often vary.[39] As noted in Chapter 2, the Canadian Diabetes Association (CDA) produces the "Beyond the Basics: Meal Planning for Healthy Eating, Diabetes Prevention and Management" poster (see Appendix C) to help Canadians living with diabetes manage their carbohydrate intake. Although the GI is not currently used to counsel those with diabetes in the United States, it is used in Canada: the CDA advocates its use during counselling. It is used to help patients identify foods that are known to raise blood sugar to a lesser or greater degree than the reference food items, white bread or glucose, that are given a score of 100 (e.g., fruits such as apples have a "low GI" and grains such as instant rice have a "high GI" relative to reference standards). The concept of *glycemic load* (mathematical expression of GI of a food and its carbohydrate content, i.e., GI of food multiplied by grams of carbohydrate in that food or meal) is also being explored in studies examining the effects of carbohydrates on blood sugar response (see Figure 4–13 for the glycemic indices of selected foods).

The glycemic index, and its mathematical offshoot **glycemic load**, may be meaningful to people with diabetes who must take steps to regulate their blood glucose.[40] A theory states that the lower the glycemic load of the diet, the less glucose builds up in the blood, and, therefore, the less insulin is needed to maintain normal blood glucose concentrations. Evidence also suggests that a low glycemic load may even help control body weight by ensuring a steady flow of glucose into the bloodstream and extending feelings of fullness.[41] In contrast, a rapid rise in blood glucose seems to promote overeating in some overweight people and may lead to the increased presence of a marker of cardiovascular disease risk.[42] New research is focusing on differences in the rate of blood glucose clearance by the tissues rather than absorption as a key factor in glycemic load.[43]

The concept of glycemic load offers an accounting of both a food's glycemic index and its carbohydrate content. Take carrots, for example. In laboratory tests, 50 grams of carbohydrate from boiled carrots ranks in the middle of the glycemic index scale, indicating a moderate capacity for elevating blood glucose. However, the glycemic index fails to reveal that a typical half-cup serving of carrots presents the body with only 8 grams of absorbable carbohydrate—to receive a test portion of 50 grams requires eating more than 3 cups of boiled carrots at a sitting. Therefore, the *glycemic load* of a serving of carrots is low, a point often overlooked. In addition, nutritional scientists are concerned about access to recent glycemic index and glycemic load values for all the new food products pouring onto the market and the possibility of manufacturers adjusting the carbohydrate content of or reformulating familiar foods, thus necessitating their re-evaluation in terms of glycemic index or glycemic load.

Today, the utility of the glycemic index or glycemic load for reducing weight or risks of diseases remains uncertain.[44] One problem is that many factors can affect glycemic index test results, including the time of day of the test, body size and weight, blood volume, and metabolic rate.[45] Another problem is that a food's glycemic effect may vary from person to person and also depends on how the food is prepared, its ripeness, and which *other* foods accompany it in a meal.[46] Even a cup of coffee can alter glucose absorption.[47] Research is evolving to address these issues, but, meanwhile, dietary guidelines already suggest choosing foods ranking fairly low on the glycemic index scale—whole grains, legumes, vegetables, fruits, and milk products.[48]

You had better play the game if you are going to eat the food.

Handling Excess Glucose

Suppose you have eaten dinner and are now sitting on the couch, munching pretzels and drinking cola as you watch a hockey game on television. Your digestive tract is delivering molecules of glucose to your bloodstream, and your blood is carrying these molecules to your liver and other body cells. The body cells use as much glucose as they can for their energy needs of the moment. Excess glucose is linked together and stored as glycogen until the muscles and liver are full to capacity with glycogen. Still, the glucose keeps coming. To handle the excess glucose, body tissues shift to burning more glucose for energy instead of fat. As a result, more fat is left to circulate in the bloodstream until it is picked up by the fatty tissues and stored there.

If these measures still do not accommodate all of the incoming glucose, the liver has no choice but to handle the excess. The liver breaks the extra glucose into small fragments and puts them together into its durable energy-storage compounds—fats.[49] These newly made fats are then released into the blood, carried to the fat tissues, and deposited. The fat cells may also take up glucose and convert it to fat directly.[50] Unlike the liver cells, which can store only about four to six hours' worth of glycogen, the fat cells can store practically unlimited quantities of fats.

Human beings possess enzymes to convert excess glucose to fat, but the process requires many enzymatic steps, costing a great deal of energy. The body is thrifty by nature, so when presented with both glucose and fat from a mixed meal, it prefers to store the fat and use the glucose to meet immediate energy needs. In this way, the maximum available food energy is retained because the dietary fat slips easily into storage with few conversions—its energy is conserved.[51] Moral: You had better play the game if you are going to eat the food. (The Think Fitness feature offers tips to help you play.)

A balanced diet that is high in complex carbohydrates helps control body weight and maintain lean tissue. Chapter 5 presents a few more details, but the main point is that, bite for bite, carbohydrate-rich foods contribute less to the body's available

Think Fitness  What Can I Eat to Make Workouts Easier?

A working body needs carbohydrate fuel to replenish glycogen, and when it runs low, physical activity can seem more difficult. If your workouts seem to drag and never get easier, take a look at your diet. Are your meals regularly timed? Do they provide abundant carbohydrate to fill up glycogen stores so they last through a workout?

Here's a trick: about two hours before you work out, eat a small snack of about 300 Calories of foods rich in complex carbohydrates and drink some extra fluid (see Chapter 10 for ideas). The snack provides glucose at a steady rate to spare glycogen, and the fluid helps maintain hydration. Also, after exercise is a good time to replenish glycogen stores. A Food Guide serving of low-fat 1 percent milk (even chocolate milk) or fruit yogurt may be enough.

energy than do fat-rich foods. Thus, if you want to stay healthy and remain lean, you should make every effort to choose a Calorie-appropriate diet providing 45 to 65 percent of its Calories from mostly unrefined sources of complex carbohydrates and less than 35 percent from the right kind of fats.[52] This chapter's Food Feature provides the first set of tools required for the job of designing such a diet. Once you have learned to identify the carbohydrates in foods, you must then learn which fats are which (Chapter 5) and how to obtain adequate protein without overdoing it (Chapter 6). Chapter 9 puts it all together with regard to a healthy body weight.

KEY POINT

- The liver has the ability to convert glucose into fat; under normal conditions, most excess glucose is stored as glycogen or used to meet the body's immediate needs for fuel.

Diabetes and Hypoglycemia

What happens if the body cannot handle carbohydrates normally? One result is **diabetes**, which is common in developed nations and can be detected by a blood test. Another is hypoglycemia, which is rare as a true disease condition, but many people believe they experience its symptoms at times.

What Is Diabetes?

The mission of the Canadian Diabetes Association is to lead the fight against diabetes by helping people with diabetes live healthy lives while we work to find a cure. diabetes.ca
Source: Courtesy of the Canadian Diabetes Association

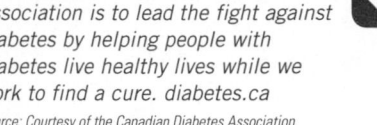

- "The Canadian Diabetes Association releases 2013 Clinical Practice Guidelines"; see http://www.diabetes.ca/get-involved/news/the-canadian-diabetes-association-releases-2013-clinical-practice-guideline.

Diabetes is a chronic disease characterized by elevated blood glucose concentrations that often leads to or contributes to a number of other serious diseases. Diabetes is one of the top 10 killers of adults, and its prevalence is rising both here and worldwide.[53] Diabetes not only causes blindness; other possible complications are amputations, complications in pregnancy, heart disease, kidney disease, and premature death. People with diabetes are three times as likely to die of flu or pneumonia as people without diabetes.[54] It has recently been estimated that the number of cases of diabetes in Canada will rise from 1.4 million to 2.4 million between 2000 and 2016. The projected health-care cost during this period is estimated to increase from $4.7 billion to $8.1 billion.[55]

Fully half of those suffering from diabetes are unaware of their condition and so fail to take action to prevent its damage. The early stage of the most common form of diabetes often presents few or no warning signs typically associated with diabetes (see Table 4–7). Therefore, the Canadian and U.S. diabetes associations are calling for everyone over 40 and 45 years old, respectively, and younger people with risk factors such as overweight to be tested regularly for diabetes.[56]

Table 4–7
Warning Signs of Diabetes

These signs appear reliably in type 1 diabetes and often in the later stages of type 2 diabetes:

- Excessive urination and thirst
- Glucose in the urine
- Weight loss with nausea, easy tiring, weakness, or irritability
- Cravings for food, especially for sweets
- Frequent infections of the skin, gums, vagina, or urinary tract
- Vision disturbances; blurred vision
- Pain in the legs, feet, or fingers
- Slow healing of cuts and bruises
- Itching
- Drowsiness
- Abnormally high glucose in the blood

diabetes (dye-uh-BEET-eez) a disease (technically termed *diabetes mellitus*) characterized by elevated blood glucose and inadequate or ineffective insulin, which impairs a person's ability to regulate blood glucose normally.

Table 4–8

Diabetes Types 1 and 2 Compared

	Type 1 Diabetes	Type 2 Diabetes
Age at onset	Childhood or midlife	Adulthood or, increasingly, childhood
Body cells	Responsive to insulin action	Resistant to insulin action
Body fatness	Generally low to average	Generally high
Insulin shots required	Yes	Yes
Insulin-stimulating drugs or other drugs may be effective	No	Yes
Natural insulin	Pancreas makes too little or none	Pancreas may make enough or too much
Pancreatic function	Insulin-producing cells impaired or nonfunctional	Insulin-producing cells may be normal
Severity of symptoms	Relatively severe; many are apparent on diagnosis	Relatively mild; few or none may be present on diagnosis

[a] People past age 40 who suffer from type 2 diabetes may lose pancreatic function and become dependent on insulin.

The common forms of diabetes are type 1 and type 2. Both are disorders of blood glucose regulation. Their characteristics are summarized in Table 4–8.

Type 1 Diabetes **Type 1 diabetes** is less common overall (about 10 percent of cases) but seems to be on the rise and is currently the leading chronic disease among children and adolescents.[57] In type 1 diabetes, the person's own immune system attacks the cells of the pancreas that synthesize the hormone insulin. Soon the pancreas can no longer produce insulin, and after each meal, blood glucose remains elevated, even though body tissues are simultaneously starving for glucose. The person must receive insulin from an external source to assist the cells in taking up the needed glucose from the blood; therefore, an older name for this type of diabetes is *insulin-dependent diabetes mellitus (IDDM)*. Researchers concur that genetics, viral infection, other diseases, toxins, allergens, and a disordered immune system are all probable culprits in provoking an immune system attack on the pancreas.[58]

Insulin is a protein, and if it were taken orally, the digestive system would digest it. Insulin must therefore be injected, either by daily shots or by a small insulin pump, about the size of a personal pager; the pump is worn next to the abdomen and delivers insulin through an implanted needle or tube. New fast-acting and long-lasting forms of insulin and other drugs allow more flexibility in managing meals and treatments, but users must still plan ahead to balance blood insulin and glucose concentrations. Medical advances may one day eliminate the need for insulin shots—an insulin nasal spray and an inhaler that delivers insulin to the lungs are proving useful in clinical studies.[59] Surgery to transplant insulin-producing cells can eliminate the need for insulin and normalize blood indicators of the disease for more than three years, although the technique is rarely employed because of the scarcity of human insulin-producing cells.[60] A more abundant supply is under development in genetic laboratories.[61] Also on the horizon is a vaccine to prevent type 1 diabetes.

Type 2 Diabetes The predominant type of diabetes mellitus is **type 2 diabetes**, and according to the latest recommendation for the management of cardiovascular disease in Canada, adults with diabetes are considered at high risk for developing cardiovascular disease.[62] **Insulin resistance** of the body's cells is the telling characteristic of type 2 diabetes. Insulin may be present in varying amounts, but it is not effective in moving glucose from the bloodstream into the cells. Blood glucose rises too high, as in type 1, but, in this case, blood insulin also rises. Eventually, the pancreas may become less able to make insulin. At some point, as people with type 2 diabetes age, they may require insulin to supplement their own supply. If drugs are necessary, a preferred therapy is to take a drug that stimulates the person's own pancreas to secrete insulin sufficient to overwhelm the cells' resistance or one that improves the uptake of glucose by the tissues.

type 1 diabetes the type of diabetes in which the pancreas produces no or very little insulin; often diagnosed in childhood, although some cases arise in adulthood. Formerly called *juvenile-onset* or *insulin-dependent diabetes*.

type 2 diabetes the type of diabetes in which the pancreas makes plenty of insulin, but the body's cells resist insulin's action; often diagnosed in adulthood. Formerly called *adult-onset* or *non-insulin-dependent diabetes*.

insulin resistance a condition in which a normal or high level of insulin produces a less-than-normal response by the tissues; thought to be a metabolic consequence of obesity.

- The first use of genetic engineering was to alter the DNA of a bacterium to produce insulin for treatment of diabetes. Read more on genetic engineering in Controversy 12.

- The recently announced "new" meal planning guide, "Beyond the Basics: Meal Planning Guide for Healthy Eating, Diabetes Prevention and Management," by the Canadian Diabetes Association, which was introduced in Chapter 2 and reproduced in Appendix C, is designed to help people with diabetes control carbohydrate and sugar intakes (http://www.diabetes.ca/for-professionals/resources/nutrition/beyond-basics).

Figure 4–14

An Obesity–Diabetes Cycle

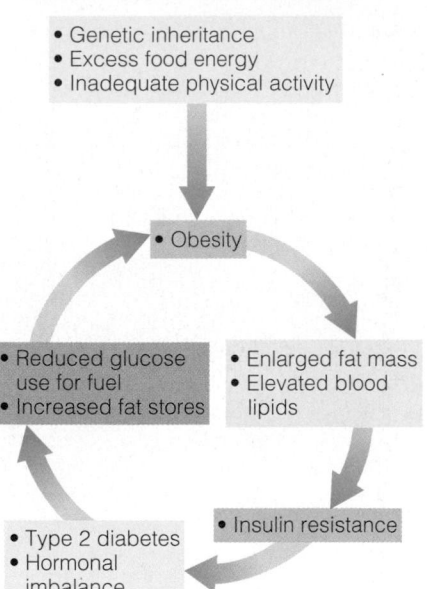

- Genetic inheritance
- Excess food energy
- Inadequate physical activity

- Obesity

- Reduced glucose use for fuel
- Increased fat stores

- Enlarged fat mass
- Elevated blood lipids

- Type 2 diabetes
- Hormonal imbalance

- Insulin resistance

Source: Reprinted from Medical Hypotheses, *Vol. 60, issue 4, John P. Girod, Daniel J. Brotman, "The metabolic syndrome as a vicious cycle: does obesity beget obesity?," pp. 584–589, Copyright (2003), with permission from Elsevier.*

impaired glucose tolerance blood glucose levels higher than normal but not high enough to be diagnosed as diabetes; sometimes called *prediabetes.*

dialysis (die-AL-ih-sis) in kidney disease, treatment of the blood to remove toxic substances or metabolic wastes; more properly, hemodialysis, meaning "dialysis of the blood."

Type 2 Diabetes and Obesity Type 2 diabetes tends to occur late in life, but overweight children and adolescents are now being diagnosed with the condition, and no one really knows why (see Controversy 13).[63] People with the disease often tend to be obese, and obesity often brings on insulin resistance. Compared with normal-weight people with diabetes, obese people require much more insulin to maintain normal blood glucose. The greater the accumulation of body fat, the more insulin resistant the cells become, and the higher the blood glucose rises.[64] Even moderate overweight often brings a foreshadowing of diabetes with the slightly elevated blood glucose known as **impaired glucose tolerance**.

One theory of how obesity and type 2 diabetes may worsen each other is depicted in Figure 4–14.[65] Many factors may contribute to obesity (see Chapter 9), but according to the theory, once obesity sets in, metabolic changes trigger the tissues to resist insulin. As insulin resistance develops, glucose builds up in the blood, while the tissues are deprived of glucose (type 2 diabetes). Meanwhile, blood lipid levels rise to meet the energy demands of the glucose-starved tissues, resulting in an overabundance of circulating fuels available to be stored as fat in the fat cells. As a result, fat mass increases, insulin resistance worsens, and obesity is perpetuated. Even moderate weight gain in adults has been observed to predict diabetes. Given this series of events, is it any wonder that obese people with type 2 diabetes have trouble losing weight?

Type 2 Diabetes and the Genes Type 2 diabetes tends to run in families. Particularly, people of African, Hispanic, Canadian Aboriginal,* Asian, or Pacific Island descent may inherit certain genetic variations that make them susceptible to developing type 2 diabetes.[66] Not every person with these genetic variations suffers from the disease, however. Having the genes may increase the risk for diabetes by about 30 percent, but other factors, such as diet and exercise, strongly affect its development.[67]

In the great majority of cases, prevention is not only possible but is also likely to occur when individuals take action to control their lifestyle choices. Recent research findings indicate that North American men and women who maintain a healthy body weight and who also choose a diet high in vegetables, fruit, fish, poultry, and whole grains; exercise regularly; restrict alcohol; and abstain from smoking have a greatly reduced incidence of type 2 diabetes compared with those with less healthy lifestyles.[68]

Diagnosis and Perils of Diabetes Diabetes can be diagnosed when two or more fasting blood glucose tests register positive. In this test, a clinician draws blood after a night of fasting and measures an indicator of blood glucose to determine whether it falls within the normal range.

The effects of diabetes can be severe, but, in general, the tighter the control over blood glucose, the milder those effects tend to be. In diabetes, blockage or destruction of capillaries that feed the body organs and tissues causes these tissues to die from lack of nourishment.[69] Problems include impaired circulation leading to disease of the feet and legs, often necessitating amputation; kidney disease, sometimes requiring a machine to assist the failing kidney in cleansing the blood (**dialysis**) or kidney transplant; impaired vision or blindness due to cataracts and damaged retinas; nerve damage; skin damage; disease of the gums and tooth loss; and strokes and heart attacks. Some of this damage may result from oxidation that accompanies elevated blood glucose.[70] A diet high in antioxidant-containing vegetables and fruit may be protective, but much more research is needed to confirm the oxidation theory. Meanwhile, a person with diabetes is advised to control not only weight but also all possible lifestyle risk factors that might contribute to heart and blood vessel disease

*Age-adjusted rates may be as high as 26%, which is three to five times the national average (see 2008 Clinical Practice Guidelines for Health Professionals—Type 2 Diabetes in Aboriginal Peoples at http://www.diabetes.ca/files/cpg2008/cpg-2008.pdf).

(atherosclerosis and hypertension, discussed in Chapter 11). In addition, aggressive medical treatment of risk factors that can lead to heart attacks and strokes may reduce the occurrence of these killers by as much as half.[71]

Prediabetes   According to the Canadian Diabetes Association's 2013 Clinical Practice Guidelines, "Elevated blood glucose levels below the threshold for diabetes also have clinical consequences. The term *prediabetes* is a practical and convenient term for impaired fasting glucose (IFG) and impaired glucose tolerance (IGT) . . . conditions that place individuals at risk for developing diabetes and its complications" (http://guidelines.diabetes.ca/Browse/Chapter3).

Preventing Type 2 Diabetes   In the great majority of cases today, prevention is not only possible, but is also likely when individuals take action to control their lifestyle choices.[72] Men and women who maintain a healthy body weight; choose a diet high in vegetables, fruit, fish, poultry, and whole grains; and exercise regularly, restrict alcohol, and abstain from smoking have a greatly reduced incidence of type 2 diabetes compared to those who live less healthy lifestyles.[73]

Managing Diabetes   Nutrition intervention plays a central role in managing diabetes, with a focus on weight control in type 2 diabetes.[74] Often weight loss alone in overweight people with type 2 diabetes helps control the disease. Constructed of a balanced pattern of foods, the same diet that best controls diabetes can also help control body weight and support physical activity. This diet

- Is adequate in nutrients (to avoid deficiencies).
- Is adequate in fibre (from whole grains, fruit, legumes, and vegetables).
- Is moderate in added sugars (must be counted among the day's carbohydrates).
- Is controlled in total carbohydrate (to regulate glucose concentration).[75]
- Is low in saturated fat (thought to worsen insulin response and cardiovascular disease) and should provide some unsaturated oils (to provide essential nutrients).[76]
- Is adequate but not too high in protein (protein may help modulate blood glucose, but too much may damage kidneys weakened by diabetes).[77]

Such a diet also has all of the characteristics important to prevention of chronic diseases and meets most of the recommendations of Canada and the United States. The diet can vary, depending on personal tastes and on how much restriction is required to control an individual's blood glucose and lipid values. A person at risk for diabetes can do no better than to adopt such a diet long before symptoms appear.

The role of regular physical activity in preventing and controlling diabetes cannot be overstated.[78] Not only does exercise help achieve and maintain a healthy body weight, but it also heightens tissue sensitivity to insulin. With even modest weight loss, increasing physical activity in overweight people seems to delay diabetes onset, and in those with the disease, increased activity, even without weight loss, often helps control it.[79] Like a juggler who keeps three balls in motion, the person with diabetes must constantly balance three lifestyle

Chapter 13 discusses a form of diabetes seen only in pregnancy—*gestational diabetes.*

● Prediabetes is a condition in which blood glucose levels are higher than normal but not high enough to be diagnosed as diabetes. It is considered a major risk factor for future diabetes and cardiovascular diseases. It was formerly called *impaired glucose tolerance.*

Physical activity: a key player in controlling diabetes.

© iofoto/iStock/Thinkstock

Regularly timed, balanced meals help hold blood glucose steady.

factors—diet, exercise, and medication—to control the blood glucose level.

If I Feel Dizzy between Meals, Do I Have Hypoglycemia?

The term **hypoglycemia** refers to abnormally low blood glucose. People with the condition **postprandial hypoglycemia**, literally, "low blood glucose after a meal," may experience fatigue, weakness, dizziness, irritability, a rapid heartbeat, anxiety, sweating, trembling, hunger, or headaches. Mental symptoms, such as confusion and impairment of intellectual tasks, are also evident.[80] These symptoms are so general and common to many conditions that people can easily misdiagnose themselves as having postprandial hypoglycemia. The condition is rare, however, except among very lean people or those who have recently lost a great deal of weight, often due to an exaggerated sensitivity to insulin.[81] A true diagnosis requires a test to detect low blood glucose while the symptoms are present to confirm that both occur simultaneously.

A person who has symptoms while fasting (e.g., overnight) has a different kind of hypoglycemia—**fasting hypoglycemia**. Its symptoms are headache, mental dullness, fatigue, confusion, amnesia, and even seizures and unconsciousness. Serious diseases and conditions, such as cancer, pancreatic damage, uncontrolled diabetes, infection of the liver accompanied with damage (hepatitis), and advanced alcohol-induced liver disease, can all produce true hypoglycemia.

To bring on even mild hypoglycemia with symptoms in normal, healthy people requires extreme measures—administering drugs that overwhelm the body's glucose-controlling hormones, insulin and glucagon. Without such intervention, those hormones hardly ever fail to keep blood glucose within normal limits. Symptoms that people ascribe to hypoglycemia rarely correlate with low blood glucose in blood tests, and such conditions may best be classified as *non*hypoglycemia. Still, people who feel such symptoms may benefit from eating regularly timed, balanced, protein-containing meals; they should especially avoid oscillating between low-carbohydrate dieting and sudden, large, refined carbohydrate doses.[82] It may also help to minimize alcoholic beverages because a high alcohol intake can injure an otherwise healthy pancreas.[83]

Part of eating right is choosing wisely among the many foods available. The previous section explained that largely without your awareness, the body responds to the carbohydrates supplied by your diet. Now you can take the controls by learning how to integrate carbohydrate-rich foods into a diet that meets your body's needs.

hypoglycemia (HIGH-poh-gly-SEE-mee-uh) a blood glucose concentration below normal, a symptom that may indicate any of several diseases, including impending diabetes.

postprandial hypoglycemia an unusual drop in blood glucose that follows a meal and is accompanied by symptoms such as anxiety, rapid heartbeat, and sweating; also called *reactive hypoglycemia*.

fasting hypoglycemia hypoglycemia that occurs after 8 to 14 hours of fasting.

Finding the Carbohydrates in Foods

To support health, a diet must supply enough of the right kinds of carbohydrate-rich foods. According to the DRI committee, a health-promoting 2,000-Calorie diet delivers between 225 and 325 grams of carbohydrate each day. The World Health Organization recommends even more: between 275 and 375 grams per 2,000 Calories. People needing more or less energy need proportionately more or less carbohydrate. To find your own DRI range, use your DRI estimated energy requirement (inside front cover) and multiply first by 45 percent and then by 65 percent; then divide both answers by 4 Calories per gram (see the example below).

DRI example for a 2,700-Calorie diet:

$$2{,}700 \text{ kcal} \times 0.45 = 1{,}215 \text{ kcal}$$
$$1{,}215 \text{ kcal} \div 4 \text{ kcal/g} = 304 \text{ g}$$
$$2{,}700 \text{ kcal} \times 0.65 = 1{,}755 \text{ kcal}$$
$$1{,}755 \text{ kcal} : 4 \text{ kcal/g} = 439 \text{ g}$$

The DRI recommended carbohydrate intake for a 2,700-Calorie diet is approximately 300 to 440 grams per day.

This Food Feature illustrates how you can obtain the carbohydrate-rich foods you need. Breads, cereals, starchy vegetables, fruits, and milk are all good contributors of starches and dilute sugars, both valuable energy-yielding carbohydrates. Many foods also provide fibre in varying amounts, as Figure 4–15 demonstrates. Concentrated sweets contain sugars but little else, as the last section demonstrates.

Grain Products

Breads and other starchy foods are famous for their carbohydrates. Nutrition authorities encourage people to eat grains often and recommend that half of the grain choices should be whole grains. A slice of bread, half an English muffin, a 6-inch tortilla, a third-cup of rice or pasta, or a half-cup of cooked cereal provides about 15 grams of carbohydrate, mostly as starch.

Do not mistake all high-fibre foods for whole grains. One hundred percent bran cereal and bran muffins may be high-fibre foods, but their added bran doesn't qualify them as whole grains. These foods provide beneficial fibre, but they do not contribute to the day's need for whole-grain foods. Conversely, puffed wheat cereal, a whole-grain food, registers low in fibre per cup because the air that puffs up the grains takes up space in the measuring cup.

Most grain choices should be low in fat and sugar. When extra Calories are required to meet energy needs, some selections higher in fat (unsaturated fat—see Chapter 5) and sugar can supply discretionary Calories. These choices include biscuits, croissants, muffins, and snack crackers.

Vegetables

Starchy vegetables are major contributors of starch in the diet. Just one small white or sweet potato or a half-cup of cooked dry beans, corn, peas, plantain, or winter squash provides 15 grams of carbohydrate, as much as in a slice of bread, although as a mixture of sugars and starch. A half cup of carrots, okra, onions, tomatoes, cooked greens, or most other non-starchy vegetables or a cup of salad greens provides about 5 grams as a mixture of starch and sugars.

Fruit

A typical fruit serving—one half-cup of juice; a small banana, apple, or orange; a half-cup of most canned or fresh fruit; or a quarter-cup of dried fruit—contains an average of about 15 grams of carbohydrate, mostly as sugars, including the fruit sugar fructose. Fruits vary greatly in their water and fibre contents and in their sugar concentrations. No more than a third of a day's fruit should be from juice. With the exception of

- Visit http://www.hc-sc.gc.ca/fn-an/nutrition/fiche-nutri-data/index-eng.php and search the Canadian Nutrient File 2010 to check the carbohydrate content of any food.

- Fibre recommendations are listed in the margin on page 119.

- Recall from Chapter 2 that discretionary Calories are the balance of Calories remaining in a person's energy allowance after consuming the nutrient-dense foods sufficient to meet the day's nutrient needs. See Appendix F.

avocado, which is high in fat, fruits contain insignificant amounts of fat and protein.

Meat and Alternatives

With two exceptions, foods of this group provide almost no carbohydrate to the diet. The exceptions are nuts, which provide a little starch and fibre along with their abundant fat, and dry beans, revered by diet watchers as low-fat sources of both starch and fibre. Just a half-cup of beans provides 15 grams of carbohydrate, an amount equalling the richest carbohydrate sources. Among sources of fibre, beans and other legumes are peerless, providing as much as 8 grams in a half-cup.

Milk and Alternatives

A cup of milk or yogurt is a generous contributor of carbohydrate, donating about 12 grams. Cottage cheese provides about 6 grams of carbohydrate per cup, but most other cheeses contain little, if any, carbohydrate. These foods also contribute high-quality protein (a point in their favour), as well as several important vitamins and minerals. Calcium-fortified soy beverages are options for providing calcium and 14 grams of carbohydrate. Milk products

Figure 4–15

Fibre in the Food Groups

Grain Products

Food	Fibreᵃ (g)	Food	Fibre (g)
100% bran cereal, 30 g	10	Pumpernickel bread, 1 slice	2
Barley, pearled, ½ c	3	Shredded wheat, 1 large biscuit	2
Cheerios, 30 g	3	Cornflakes, 30 g	1
Whole-wheat bread, 1 slice	3	Muffin, blueberry, 1	1
Wheat flakes, 30 g	3	Pasta,ᵇ ½ c	1
Brown rice, ½ c	2	Puffed wheat, 1½ c	1
Light rye bread, 1 slice	2	Cream of wheat, 1½ c	<1
Muffin, bran, 1 small	2	White bread, 1 slice	<1
Oatmeal, ½ c	2	White rice, ½ c	<1
Popcorn, 2 c	2		

Vegetables

Food	Fibre (g)	Food	Fibre (g)
Baked potato with skin, 1	4	Mashed potatoes, home recipe, ½ c	2
Broccoli, chopped, ½ c	3	Bell peppers, ½ c	1
Brussels sprouts, ½ c	3	Broccoli, raw, chopped, ½ c	1
Spinach, ½ c	3	Carrot juice, ½ c	1
Asparagus, ½ c	2	Celery, ½ c	1
Baked potato, no skin, 1	2	Dill pickle, 1 whole	1
Cabbage, red, ½ c	2	Eggplant, ½ c	1
Carrots, ½ c	2	Lettuce, romaine, 1 c	1
Cauliflower, ½ c	2	Onions, ½ c	1
Corn, ½ c	2	Tomato, raw, 1 medium	1
Green beans, ½ c	2	Tomato juice, canned, ¾ c	1

Fruit

Food	Fibre (g)	Food	Fibre (g)
Pear, raw, 1 medium	5	Other berries, raw, ½ c	2
Blackberries/raspberries, raw, ½ c	4	Peach, raw, 1 medium	2
Prunes, cooked, ¼ c	3	Strawberries, sliced, ½ c	1
Figs, dried, 3	3	Cantaloupe, raw, ½ c	1
Apple, 1 medium	3	Cherries, raw, ½ c	1
Apricots, raw, 4 each	3	Fruit cocktail, canned, ½ c	1
Banana, raw, 1	3	Peach half, canned	1
Orange, 1 medium	3	Raisins, dry, ¼ c	1
		Orange juice, ¾ c	< 1

Meat and Alternatives

Food	Fibre (g)	Food	Fibre (g)
Lentils, ½ c	8	Soybeans, ½ c	5
Kidney beans, ½ c	8	Almonds or mixed nuts, ¼ c	4
Pinto beans, ½ c	8	Peanuts, ¼ c	3
Black beans, ½ c	7	Peanut butter, 2 tbs	2
Black-eyed peas, ½ c	6	Cashew nuts, ¼ c	1
Lima beans, ½ c	5	Meat, poultry, fish, and eggs	0

ᵃAll values are for ready-to-eat or cooked foods, unless otherwise noted. Fruit values include edible skins. All values are rounded values.

ᵇPasta includes spaghetti noodles, lasagna, and other noodles made from enriched white flour. Whole-wheat pastas have significantly more fibre.

Table 4–9

Terms That Describe Sugar

Note: The term *sugars* in this table refers to all of the monosaccharides and disaccharides. On a label's ingredients list, the term *sugar* means sucrose. See Controversy 4 for terms related to artificial sweeteners and sugar alcohols.

- **brown sugar** white sugar with molasses added; 95% pure sucrose.
- **concentrated fruit juice sweetener** a concentrated sugar syrup made from dehydrated, deflavoured fruit juice, commonly grape juice; used to sweeten products that can then claim to be "all fruit."
- **confectioner's sugar** or **icing sugar** finely powdered sucrose; 99.9% pure.
- **corn sweeteners** corn syrup and sugar solutions derived from corn.
- **corn syrup** a syrup, mostly glucose, partly maltose, produced by the action of enzymes on cornstarch. *High-fructose corn syrup (HFCS)* is a mixture of fructose, glucose (dextrose), and maltose.
- **dextrose** an older name for glucose.
- **evaporated cane juice** raw sugar from which impurities have been removed.
- **fructose, galactose, glucose** the monosaccharides.
- **granulated sugar** common table sugar, crystalline sucrose, 99.9% pure.
- **honey** a concentrated solution primarily composed of glucose and fructose, produced by enzymatic digestion of the sucrose in nectar by bees.
- **invert sugar** a mixture of glucose and fructose formed by the splitting of sucrose in an industrial process. Sold only in liquid form and sweeter than sucrose, invert sugar forms during certain cooking procedures and works to prevent crystallization of sucrose in soft candies and sweets.

- **lactose, maltose, sucrose** the disaccharides.
- **levulose** an older name for fructose.
- **maple sugar** a concentrated solution of sucrose derived from the sap of the sugar maple tree, mostly sucrose. This sugar was once common but is now usually replaced by sucrose and artificial maple flavouring.
- **molasses** a syrup left over from the refining of sucrose from sugar cane; a thick, brown syrup. The major nutrient in molasses is iron, a contaminant from the machinery used in processing it.
- **raw sugar** the first crop of crystals harvested during sugar processing. Raw sugar cannot be sold in Canada or the United States because it contains too much filth (dirt, insect fragments, and the like). Sugar sold as "raw sugar" is actually evaporated cane juice.
- **turbinado** (ter-bih-NOD-oh) **sugar** raw sugar from which the filth has been washed; legal to sell in Canada and the United States.
- **white sugar** pure sucrose, produced by dissolving, concentrating, and recrystallizing raw sugar.

vary in fat content, an important consideration in choosing among them; Chapter 5 provides the details.

Butter and cream cheese, although dairy products, are not equivalent to milk because they contain little or no carbohydrate and insignificant amounts of the other nutrients important in milk. They are appropriately associated with the solid fats.

Oils and Fats

While oils and fats are devoid of carbohydrate, added sugars supply carbohydrate. Most people enjoy sweets, so it is important to learn something of their nature. First, the definition of "sugar" comes into play. (Table 4–9 defines sugar terms.) A sugar molecule arising in a grape by way of photosynthesis, one of the **naturally occurring sugars**, is chemically indistinguishable from one added at the jam factory to sweeten grape jam. The term **added sugars**

refers to all sugars added to foods, regardless of their origin. The combined total of naturally occurring and added sugars appears on food labels in the line reading "sugars." The body handles all sugars in the same way, whatever their source.

However, in the United States, the *Dietary Guidelines for Americans, 2010*, distinguishes between naturally occurring and added sugars, designating the Calories from added sugars as discretionary Calories.[84] Concentrated sugars add Calories but no other nutrients and therefore contribute discretionary Calories to the diet. Because the law requires manufacturers to list only total sugars on food labels, consumers are hard-pressed to determine how much added sugar, and therefore how many discretionary Calories, their foods contain.

Whether they come from beets, corn, grapes, honey, or sugar cane, the carbohydrate sweeteners are all alike. All arise naturally and, through processing, are purified of most or all of the original

plant material—bees process honey, and machines process the other types. Nutrition authorities recommend that we limit the use of added sugars (see Controversy 4 in this chapter).

The Nature of Sugar

Each teaspoonful of any sweet can be assumed to supply about 16 Calories and 4 grams of carbohydrate. You may not think of candy or molasses in terms of teaspoons, but this helps emphasize that all sugary items are like white sugar—in spite of many people's belief

naturally occurring sugars sugars that are not added to a food but are present as its original constituents, such as the sugars of fruit or milk.

added sugars sugars and syrups added to a food for any purpose, such as to add sweetness or bulk or to aid in browning (baked goods). Also called *carbohydrate sweeteners*, they include glucose, fructose, corn syrup, concentrated fruit juice, and other sweet carbohydrates.

Figure 4–16

Sugar in Processed Foods

½ c canned corn = 3 tsp sugar[a]

355 mL cola = 8 tsp sugar

1 tbs ketchup = 1 tsp sugar

1 tbs creamer = 2 tsp sugar

230 g sweetened yogurt = 7 tsp sugar

55 g chocolate = 8 tsp sugar

Dick Hemingway

[a]Values based on 1 tsp or 4 grams of sugar (16 Calories).

that some are different or "better." If you use ketchup liberally, remember that a tablespoon of it contains a teaspoon of sugar. And for the soft drink user, a 355-millilitre can of sugar-sweetened cola contains 8 or more teaspoons of sugar. Figure 4–16 shows that processed foods contain surprisingly large

Figure 4–17

Jam and Fruit Spread Labels Compared

Notice that a product claiming to contain "100% fruit" can contain concentrated purified fruit juice sweeteners that contribute sweet flavour but few nutrients, just as ordinary sugar does. Also, of particular interest to people with diabetes, the Canadian Food Inspection Agency and Health Canada recently clarified the requirements under the Food and Drug Regulations that pertain to the nutrient content descriptor "No Added Sugars" (see http://www.inspection.gc.ca/english/fssa/labeti/inform/sugsuce.shtml); for example, if fruit juice/fruit juice concentrate is added to foods that otherwise would not contain them, then this descriptor is not permitted.

Strawberry Jam

Nutrition Facts

Serving size 1 Tbsp (20 g)
Servings Per Container About 14

Amount per serving

Calories 40

	Daily Value (%)*
Total Fat 0 g	0
Sodium 1 mg	1
Total Carbohydrate 10 g	4
Sugars 7 g	
Protein 0 g	

*Percent Daily Values are based on a 2,000 Calorie diet.

INGREDIENTS: Strawberries, Corn Syrup, Sugar, High-Fructose Corn Syrup, Citric Acid, Fruit Pectin.

Strawberry 100% Fruit Spread

Nutrition Facts

Serving size 1 Tbsp (18 g)
Servings Per Container About 16

Amount per serving

Calories 40

	Daily Value (%)*
Total Fat 0 g	0
Sodium 0 mg	0
Total Carbohydrate 10 g	3
Sugars 8 g	
Protein 0 g	

*Percent Daily Values are based on a 2,000 Calorie diet.

INGREDIENTS: Clarified Grape Juice Concentrate, Strawberries, Clarified Pear Juice Concentrate, Pectin, Natural Flavour, Citric Acid.

amounts of sugar. Figure 4–17 shows that strawberry spread claiming to be "100% fruit" can contain even more

sugars per tablespoon than regular sucrose-sweetened jam.

What about the nutritional value of a product such as molasses, honey,

Table 4–10

The Empty Calories of Sugar

At first glance, honey, jelly, and brown sugar look more nutritious than plain sugar, but when compared with a person's nutrient needs, none contribute anything to speak of. The cola beverage is clearly an empty-Calorie item, too.

Food	Energy (Cal)	Protein (g)	Fibre (g)	Calcium (mg)	Iron (mg)	Magnesium (mg)	Potassium (mg)
Sugar (1 tbs)	46	0	0	0	0.0	0	0
Honey (1 tbs)	64	0	0	1	0.1	0	11
Molasses (1 tbs)	55	0	0	42	1.0	50	300
Concentrated grape or fruit juice sweetener (1 tbs)	30	0	0	0	0	0	0
Jelly (1 tbs)	49	0	0	1	0.0	1	12
Brown sugar (1 tbs)	34	0	0	8	0.2	3	31
Cola beverage (355 mL)	153	0	0	11	0.1	4	4
Daily Values	2,000	56	25	1,000	18.0	400	3,500

or concentrated fruit juice sweetener compared with white sugar? Molasses contains 1 milligram of iron per tablespoon, so, if used frequently, it can contribute some of this important nutrient. Molasses is less sweet than the other sweeteners, however, so more molasses is needed to provide the same sweetness as sugar. Also, the iron comes from the iron machinery in which the molasses is made and is in the form of an iron salt that is not easily absorbed by the body.

Honey is no better for health than sugars by virtue of being "natural"—honey is chemically almost indistinguishable from sucrose. Honey contains the two monosaccharides glucose and fructose in approximately equal amounts. Sucrose contains the same monosaccharides but joined together in the disaccharide form. Spoon for spoon, however, sugar contains fewer Calories than honey because the dry crystals of sugar take up more space than the sugars of honey dissolved in its water.

As for concentrated juice sweeteners, these are highly refined and have lost virtually all of the beneficial nutrients and nonnutrients of the original fruit. No form of sugar is "more healthy" than white sugar, as Table 4–10 shows.

It would be absurd to rely on any sugar for nutrient contributions. A tablespoon of honey (64 Calories) does offer 1 milligram of iron, but it would take 180 tablespoons of honey—11,500 Calories—to provide 100 percent of a young woman's DRI value of 18 milligrams of iron. The nutrients of honey just don't add up as fast as its Calories. Thus, if you choose molasses, brown sugar, or honey, choose them not for their nutrient contributions but for the pleasure they give. These tricks can help magnify the sweetness of foods without boosting their Calories:

- Serve sweet food warm (heat enhances sweet tastes).
- Add sweet spices such as cinnamon, nutmeg, allspice, or clove.
- Add a tiny pinch of salt; it will make food taste sweeter.
- Try reducing the sugar added to recipes by one-third.
- Select fresh fruits or fruit juice or those prepared without added sugar.
- Use small amounts of sugar substitutes in place of sucrose.
- Read food labels for clues on sugar content.

Finally, enjoy whatever sugar you do eat. Sweetness is one of life's great sensations, so enjoy it in moderation.

- *Sugars* on the nutrition facts panel of a food label reflect both added and naturally occurring sugars in foods. Sugars listed among the ingredients are all added. Products listing sugars among the first few ingredients contain substantial amounts of added sugars.

- Sugar alcohols, discussed in this chapter's Controversy feature, help protect against tooth decay.

Zinc (mg)	Vitamin A (µg)	Thiamin (mg)	Riboflavin (mg)	Niacin (mg)	Vitamin B$_6$ (mg)	Folate (µg)	Vitamin C (mg)
0.0	0	0	0	0.0	0	0	0
0.0	0	0	0	0.0	0	<1	0
0.1	0	0	0	0.2	0.1	0	0
0	0	0	0	0	0	0	
0.0	0	0	0	0.0	0	0	<1
0.0	0	0	0	0.0	0	0	0
0	0	0	0	0.0	0	0	0
15.0	1,000	1.5	1.7	20.0	2.0	400	60

Sugar and Alternative Sweeteners: Are They Bad for You?

Almost everyone finds sweet tastes pleasing—after all, the preference for sweets is inborn.[*,1] To a child's taste, the sweeter the food, the better. In adults, the preference for sweets is somewhat diminished, but adult consumption of sugars and sweeteners remains high in Canada.

Statistics Canada estimates that, per capita, Canadians consumed 23.82 kilograms of sugar and syrup combined in 2009.[†,2] That would be like pouring more than 12 teaspoons of sugar onto/into your foods and beverages every day. Such numbers are useful for approximating average Canadian sugar consumption and for tracking changes from year to year (see Figure C4–1).

A steady upward trend in U.S. sugar consumption parallels a dramatic increase in purchases of commercially prepared foods and beverages that contain added sugars. By one account, consumption of regular soft drinks and sugar-sweetened fruit drinks is responsible for 80 percent of this increase; however, in Canada the consumption of sugars and syrups has declined since 2001 and remained about the same until 2009.[3] Desserts and jams and jellies make up most of the remainder. In contrast, people are adding less sugar to foods from the sugar bowl at home.

In addition to increasing their intake of sugars, people are also consuming more artificial sweeteners, such as aspartame and saccharine. These substances are intended to reduce sugar

intakes, but instead of substituting artificial sweeteners for sugar, people seem to be choosing more of both.

Carbohydrates remain the main source of Calories for Canadians, and while intake was steady from the mid-1970s to 1990, their level paralleled an increase in both total Calories and fat from 1990 to 2000. How such increases relate to the rise in weight gain of both adults and children during this period remains to be fully explained (see Chapter 9). Recall from Chapter 2 that the DRI reports recommend a carbohydrate intake of 45–65 percent of total Calories but also that a maximum of 25 percent of our Calories come from added sugars. Note also that the Canadian Diabetes Association 2013 Clinical Practice Guidelines allow up

to 10 percent of total energy as sugar (approximately 50 g of sucrose per day in a 2,000-Calorie diet).

In response to a worldwide trend toward increasing sugar consumption, the World Health Organization also took a stand on sugar intake echoing the advice of more than 23 countries: consume no more than 10 percent of total Calories from added sugar.[*,4]

Does sugar harm people's health? And if it does, are sugar substitutes a better choice? This Controversy addresses these questions and, in the process, demonstrates how nutrition

The World Health Organization uses the term free sugars to mean all monosaccharides and disaccharides added to foods by the manufacturer, cook, or consumer plus the naturally occurring sugars in honey, syrups, and fruit juices.

*References for this Controversy feature are listed separately at the end of the chapter.

†Food Statistics 2009, Table 4–2, Statistics Canada Cat. no. 21-020-X http://www.statcan.gc.ca/pub/21-020-x/21-020-x2009001-eng.pdf.

Figure C4–1

Sugar and Syrup Intake in Canada (in kilograms), 1981–2009

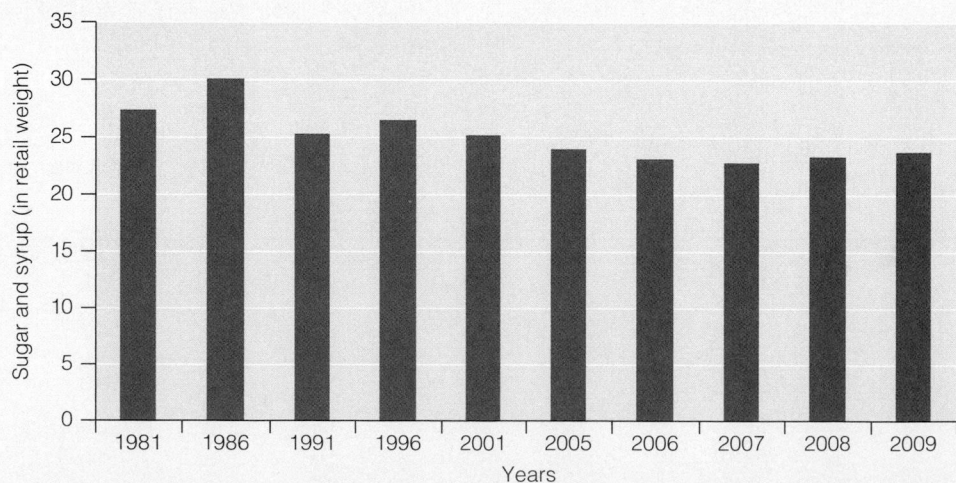

Source: Statistics Canada, Food Statistics 2009, Table 4–2, Statistics Canada Cat. no. 21-020-X, 2010. Reproduced and distributed on an "as is" basis with the permission of Statistics Canada.

researchers pursue their answers, step by step, via scientific inquiry.

Evidence Concerning Sugar

Sugar has been accused of these nutrition problems: (1) promoting and maintaining obesity, (2) causing and aggravating diabetes, (3) increasing the risk of heart disease, (4) disrupting behaviour in children and adults, and (5) causing dental decay and gum disease. Is sugar guilty or innocent of these charges?

Does Sugar Cause Obesity?

Over the past two decades, obesity rates have risen sharply in Canada; just prior to this (1986), sugar consumption had reached an all-time high, remained fairly steady during the 1990s, and fell slightly since then. Does this mean that sugar intakes are responsible for the increase in obesity? Human studies are in conflict on this question. When eaten in excess of need, Calories from sugar contribute to body fat stores, just as Calories from other sources do. From available research reviews, on the one hand, it seems unlikely that moderate amounts of sugar would cause obesity when total Calories are controlled, while on the other hand, the intake of sugar-sweetened beverages has been shown to be positively associated with weight gain and obesity.[5]

People with diets high in added sugars do often consume more Calories each day than people with lower sugar intakes.[6] For example, adolescents who drink upward of 26 ounces (about two cans) of sugar-sweetened soft drinks daily consume 400 more Calories a day than teens who abstain from such drinks.[7] Soft drinks have been the focus of particular attention because the increase in intake of added sugars is accounted for largely by a dramatic rise in high-fructose corn syrup intake, mostly in soft drinks. The trend toward greater use of this sweetener parallels unprecedented gains in body fatness in the population.[8] Overweight children and adolescents increase their risk of becoming obese by 60 percent with each additional syrup-sweetened drink they add to the daily diet.[9] Researchers theorize that sugar in liquid form may go unnoticed by the body, in the sense that the body does not compensate by reducing food energy intakes later in the day.[10] Between 1990 and 2000, as people grew fatter, their intake of Calories from carbohydrates and fat also increased.[11] Investigators are evaluating these and other possible links between weight gain and fructose in the syrupy sweeteners of soft drinks.[12]

Such findings appear to be a smoking gun implicating added sugars as the culprit in the rise of obesity, but before concluding that sugar is guilty, consider that some population studies have found a *negative* correlation between intakes of added sugar and degree of body fatness.[13] These reports have been questioned, however, because people are notoriously poor at recalling their actual food intakes, and overweight people often underestimate their intakes of sugary treats.[14]

Findings from populations of many developing nations seem to strengthen the case against sugar: the prevalence of obesity often increases as sugar consumption rises, but this evidence is still insufficient to name sugar as the cause. Often a rise in a nation's sugar intake mirrors a rise in income and, with it, greater consumption of Calories, processed foods, meats, and fats.[15] Another confounding factor: as people begin to gain weight, their physical activity often declines, making it impossible to tell whether the sugar, excess Calories from other sources, or too little physical activity is at fault.

Research is easier with laboratory rats—they are fed controlled diets and need not remember what they ate. In laboratory studies, rats fed a sucrose-rich diet do not become fatter than rats eating the same number of Calories of other foods, although their fat distribution may change toward a greater percentage of abdominal fat (see Chapter 9 for the dangers of abdominal obesity).[16] When rats are offered *unlimited* amounts of sucrose-sweetened chow, however, they consume more Calories than from plain chow, and weight gain follows. Sugar itself may not induce obesity in rats when it replaces other energy sources Calorie for Calorie, but sugar stimulates overeating when food is unlimited, and the excess Calories cause weight gain—at least in rats.

Sugar acts on areas of the brain responsible for pleasure and reward. When stimulated, this area of the brain releases chemicals that produce a pleasurable sensation that, in animals, causes repetition of the behaviour producing the sensation. When animals are given sugar-sweetened chow, they increase their intake compared with regular chow because the sweet taste rewards them with a pleasure sensation.[17] If the same holds true for people, this mechanism could explain why some people crave sweets, even though they rarely sit down to bowlfuls of plain sugar Instead, they seek out sweet-flavoured high-fat treats, such as cakes, candies, chocolate bars, cookies, doughnuts, ice cream, and muffins. Sugar added to foods high in fat may be what produces sufficient rewards to trigger overconsumption. More research is needed to determine connections between human brain chemistry, the sweetness of sugar, and obesity.

© gwolters/Shutterstock

Some recent studies show that sugary soft drinks are the leading source of added sugars; cakes, cookies, pies, and other baked goods come next; and sweetened fruit drinks and punches follow closely behind.

Controversy 4 Sugar and Alternative Sweeteners

Does Sugar Cause Type 2 Diabetes?

Recall from the chapter that in diabetes, insulin secretion or tissue responsiveness to it becomes abnormal, affecting the body's ability to manage sugar. At one time, people thought that eating sugar caused diabetes by "overstraining the pancreas," but now we know that this is not the case. Body fatness is more closely related to diabetes than diet is; high rates of diabetes have not been reported in any society where obesity is rare.

Still, in some populations around the world, and especially among Canada's Aboriginal peoples, a profound increase in the prevalence of diabetes has occurred simultaneously with an increase in sugar consumption. Also, a recent meta-analysis of over a dozen studies on sugar-sweetened beverages revealed that higher consumption (1–2 servings/d) of such beverages increases the risk of developing type 2 diabetes by over 25 percent.[18]

Wherever starch and the fibre that accompanies it are the major carbohydrates in the diet, diabetes is rare.[19] But this does not prove that sugar causes diabetes or that starch prevents it. The apparent protective effect of starch might be due, for example, to the fibre or the mineral chromium that comes with it. Likewise, the apparent causative effect of sugar may reflect a sudden availability of Calorie-rich foods in societies gaining in both disposable income and body fatness.

Recent popular books have claimed links among sugar intake, the glycemic index, and type 2 diabetes, but science in this area is inconclusive. A decade ago, a study tracking the dietary habits of over 65,000 women and almost 43,000 men seemed to indicate that consuming a diet with a high glycemic load (based on mashed potatoes, white rice, highly refined cold breakfast cereals, and white bread) was associated with diabetes, while a diet with a low glycemic load (more whole grains, legumes, and fruit and vegetables) was protective. In contrast, no effect on diabetes risk from glycemic load or glycemic index

was reported in a subsequent study of almost 36,000 women in Iowa.[20] In this study, a diet high in whole-grain foods and dietary fibre predicted a reduced risk of type 2 diabetes, but the mechanism is not known. As for sugar itself, remember from the chapter that sucrose elicits only a moderate glycemic effect, so the fairest conclusion is that sugar alone is not culpable in type 2 diabetes causation. If a high energy intake from added sugars causes gains of excess body fat, however, then sugar does indeed elevate the risk for type 2 diabetes.[21] And both obesity and diabetes increase the risk of heart disease.

Does Eating Sugar Increase the Risk of Heart Disease?

Several years ago, results from research on rats launched investigations into the relationship between sugar and heart disease. When researchers fed rats a diet with sucrose as the only carbohydrate source, the rats sustained microscopic damage to their arteries, and their blood tested high for saturated fat. Rats fed starch instead of sugar did not develop the damage or the highly altered blood lipids. When researchers applied similar study conditions to human beings, they confirmed that some people, too, respond to diets high in sugars, particularly sugars that contain fructose, by releasing saturated fat (probably made from the sugar) into the blood.[22] Studies have also found that with a high-sugar diet, the level of a *protective* blood lipid (high-density lipoprotein, the "good cholesterol"; see Chapter 5) falls in some people.[23] The amount of sugar required to evoke these changes is about double the nation's *average* intake, so, for most people, moderate sugar intakes pose little risk of altering their blood lipids by much.[24] Throughout many years of research, no one has conclusively shown that an average intake of sugar adversely affects heart health in otherwise healthy human beings.[25]

Saturated fat, however, clearly remains the major *dietary* culprit in heart disease susceptibility, but there is a *genetic* culprit, too: some people seem genetically prone to increasing the

production of saturated fat in the body in response to dietary sugar. This is especially true of obese people who secrete abnormal amounts of insulin in response to sugar intake because one of insulin's actions is to increase the liver's synthesis of saturated fat, which then enters the bloodstream.[26] In the same people, insulin's other action on saturated fat, that is, to clear it from the blood into storage in the fat tissue, is diminished.

We cannot say with certainty whether the blood lipid changes observed with high sugar intakes are benign or whether they indeed predict heart disease until more research reveals the needed evidence.[27] However, recently, one large prospective study in women revealed that regular consumption of sugar-sweetened beverages is associated with an increased risk of cardiovascular disease.[28] Furthermore, the World Health Organization, Canada's Food Guide, DRI, and the American Heart Association recently provided recommendations to reduce the amount of added sugar intake for both adult females and males (see Table 4–1 on page 119).

What about Sugar and Behaviour?

Many years ago, claims began appearing that eating sugary foods caused children to become unruly and adolescents and adults to exhibit antisocial and even criminal behaviour. Science has put the "sugar-behaviour" theory to rest, but many teachers, parents, grandparents, and others still believe that some children react behaviourally to sugar.[29] Sugar might influence behaviour in many ways: by altering the levels of chemicals in the brain that affect mood, by inducing nutrient deficiencies, by stimulating the release of the series of hormones the body secretes after consuming sugar, or by providing pure energy (the Halloween effect). Children allowed to load up on colas and chocolate candies may become overstimulated by the action of the stimulant caffeine found in these treats (see Chapter 14 and its Controversy feature).

Research results do not suggest that sugar itself negatively affects behaviour.[30] Indeed, in several well-controlled studies, sugar administered to normal children calmed them down, a finding consistent with biochemical evidence. In adults, carbohydrate-rich foods seem to improve mood and memory.[31] In the end, the most rational conclusion seems to be that while occasional behavioural reactions to sugar may be possible, studies have failed to demonstrate any consistent effects of sucrose on behaviour in either normal or hyperactive children.

Does Sugar Cause Dental Caries?

Dental caries are a serious public health problem afflicting the majority of people in Canada (i.e., 96% of adults have a history of cavities, see http://www.hc-sc.gc.ca/hl-vs/pubs/oral-bucco/fact-fiche-oral-bucco-stat-eng.php) (see Figure C4–2). A very lucky few *never* get dental caries because they have an inherited resistance; others have sealant applied to teeth

during childhood that stops caries before they can begin. Table C4–1 defines some terms related to caries.

Another successful measure taken to reduce the incidence of dental decay is fluoridation of community water. But sugar has something to do with dental caries, too.

Caries develop as acids produced by bacterial growth in the mouth eat into tooth enamel. Bacteria form colonies known as **plaque** whenever they can get established on tooth surfaces. Once established, they multiply and affix themselves more and more firmly unless they are brushed, flossed, or scraped away. Eventually, the acid of plaque creates pits that deepen into cavities. Below the gum line, plaque works its way down until the acid erodes the roots of teeth and the jawbone in which they are embedded, loosening the teeth and leading to infections of the gums. Gum (periodontal) disease severe enough to threaten tooth loss afflicts about 25 percent of our population by their later years (see http://www.fptdwg.ca/assets/PDF/CHMS/CHMS-E-summ.pdf).

Bacteria thrive on carbohydrate. Carbohydrate as sugar has been named as the main causative factor in the formation of caries, but starch also supports bacterial growth if the bacteria are allowed sufficient time to work on it. Of prime importance is the length of time the food stays in your mouth, and this depends on the food's composition, how sticky it is, how often you eat it, and especially on whether you brush your teeth soon afterward.[32]

Bacteria produce acid for 20 to 30 minutes after exposure to sugar. Thus, when you eat three pieces of candy, one right after the other, your teeth are exposed to approximately 30 minutes of acid demineralization; when you eat the candy pieces at half-hour intervals, the acid exposure time is 90 minutes. Likewise, slowly sipping a sugary soft drink may be more harmful than drinking quickly and emptying the mouth of sugar. Foods such as milk and cheese may be particularly helpful in minimizing the effects of the acids and in restoring the damaged enamel.[33]

Some forms of candy, such as milk chocolate and caramels, may be less harmful because the sugar dissolves completely and is washed away in saliva. Breads, granola bars, sugary cereals, oatmeal cookies, raisins, salted crackers, and chips, however, may be worse because particles get stuck in the teeth and do not dissolve. These particles may remain in contact with tooth surfaces for hours, providing a feast for bacteria and greatly increasing the likelihood of caries. Table 14–5 in Chapter 14 (page 614) lists foods of both high and low caries potential. The best advice seems to be as follows: Brush your teeth after eating. Regular brushing (twice a day, with a fluoride toothpaste) and flossing (once a day) may be more effective in preventing dental caries and gum disease than restricting sugary foods. The nutrition labelling regulations permit a health claim for the role of sugar alcohols related to dental caries. The following examples of claims would be acceptable: "Won't cause cavities" and "Does not promote tooth decay" on items such as gum that contain sugar alcohols (http://www.inspection.gc.ca/english/fssa/labeti/guide/ch8e.shtml).

Total sugar intake does play a major role in the prevalence of dental caries. Populations whose diets provide no more than 10 percent of Calories from sugar have a low prevalence of dental caries.[34] Worldwide, many governing agencies urge their citizens to consume no more than 10 percent of Calories from sugar because of sugar's link with dental caries. Sugar is an energy source for

Figure C4–2

Dental Caries

Caries begin when acid dissolves the enamel that covers the tooth. If not repaired, the decay may penetrate the dentin and spread into the pulp of the tooth, causing inflammation and an abscess.

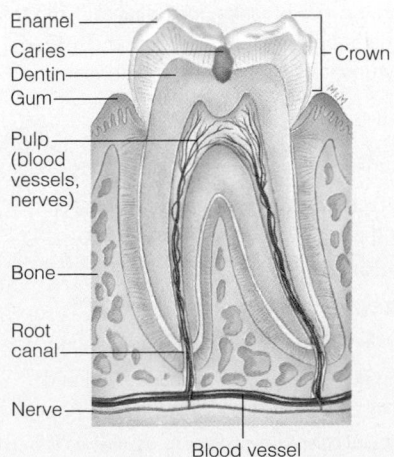

Enamel
Caries
Dentin
Gum
Crown
Pulp (blood vessels, nerves)
Bone
Root canal
Nerve
Blood vessel

the bacteria that cause tooth decay, and thus it is clearly implicated in this major public health problem.[35]

Personal Strategy for Using Sugar

Based on research, no guilty verdict can yet be issued for any of the first four accusations against sugar, but of the fifth, it is guilty as charged—sugar does cause dental caries. Should you avoid sugar or reduce your intakes? The DRI reports suggest that you limit the Calories from added sugars, not avoid them altogether. As mentioned, authorities agree that added sugars should contribute no more than 10 percent of the total Calorie intake.[36] Thus, a person who eats 2,000 Calories of energy a day is allowed 200 Calories from sugar. Those 200 Calories of sugar, about 13 teaspoons (50 grams), sound like quite a lot. But when you add up all of the teaspoons of sugars added to common foods, 200 Calories may seem restrictive.

To meet these sugar intake recommendations, many people should reduce their intakes. One option is to replace sugar's sweetness by choosing from two sets of alternative sweeteners: the sugar alcohols, which are energy-yielding sweeteners sometimes referred to as *nutritive sweeteners*, and the artificial sweeteners, which provide virtually no energy and are thus sometimes referred to as *nonnutritive sweeteners*. These options do provide sweetness without sucrose, but what about their safety?

Evidence Concerning Sugar Alcohols

The sugar alcohols are familiar to people who use special dietary products. Many new low-sugar food products depend on sugar alcohols for their bulking and sweetening powers. Contrary to the meaning implied by the name *sugar alcohols*, these sweeteners do not contain ethanol (the alcohol of alcoholic beverages) or any other intoxicant. They are members of the chemical family *alcohol* by virtue of their structures.

Many people are familiar with **isomalt, lactitol, maltitol, mannitol, sorbitol,** and **xylitol**, sugar alcohols that provide sweetness and bulk to cookies, sugarless gum and hard candies, and jams and jellies. Their sweetness relative to sugar is shown in Table C4–2. Sugar alcohols can be metabolized by human beings, and most provide a little less energy than sucrose.[37] In 2004, Health Canada approved a new sweetener, erythritol, a sugar alcohol similar to xylitol, for use in food items such as dietetic beverages and chewing gum.*

Sugar alcohols evoke a low glycemic response. The body absorbs sugar alcohols slowly; consequently, they are slower to enter the bloodstream than other sugars. Side effects such as gas, abdominal discomfort, and diarrhea arise from ingesting large quantities, however. For this reason, regulations require that if a food is likely to present more than 50 grams of sugar alcohols in a day, its label must state that "Excess consumption may have a laxative effect."

The real benefit of using sugar alcohols is that they do not contribute to dental caries. Bacteria in the mouth cannot metabolize sugar alcohols as rapidly as sugar. They are therefore valuable in chewing gums, breath

*http://publications.gc.ca/gazette/archives/p2/2004/2004-12-15/pdf/g2-13825.pdf.

mints, toothpaste, and other products that people keep in their mouths for a while.

If you want to reduce energy intake, remember that the sugar alcohols do provide energy. The body handles them differently from sugar, but unlike artificial sweeteners, they are not Calorie free.

Evidence Concerning Artificial Sweeteners

Like the sugar alcohols, artificial sweeteners make foods taste sweet without promoting dental decay. Unlike sugar alcohols, they are practically Calorie-free, and the human taste buds perceive them as supersweet. But how do we know they are safe?

All substances are toxic if high enough doses are consumed. Artificial sweeteners, their components, and their metabolic by-products are not exceptions. The questions to ask are whether artificial sweeteners are harmful to human beings at the levels normally used and how much is too much. Table C4–3 defines some sugar substitute terms. **Acceptable daily intake (ADI)** levels for some of the artificial sweeteners are provided in Table C4–4. The major synthetic sweeteners on the market today are **saccharin, aspartame, acesulfame-potassium, sucralose, cyclamate,** and **tagatose**.

Table C4–2

Sugar Alcohols

Sugar Alcohols	Relative Sweetness[a]	Energy (Cal/g)	Approved Uses
Erythritol	0.6–0.7	0.24	Seven categories of foods, including tabletop sweeteners, breakfast cereals, unstandardized table syrups, and coating mixtures for snack foods
Isomalt	0.5	0.5	Candies, chewing gum, ice cream, jams and jellies, frostings, beverages, baked goods
Lactitol	0.4	2.0	Candies, chewing gum, frozen dairy desserts, jams and jellies, frostings, baked goods
Maltitol	0.9	2.1	Candy coating
Mannitol	0.7	1.6	Bulking agent, chewing gum
Sorbitol	0.5	2.6	Special dietary foods, candies, gums
Xylitol	1.0	2.4	Chewing gum, candies, pharmaceutical and oral health products

[a]*The relative sweetness depends on the temperature, acidity, and other flavours of the foods in which the substance occurs. The sweetness of pure sucrose is the standard with which the approximate sweetness of sugar substitutes is compared.*

Table C4–3
Sugar Substitute Terms

- **acceptable daily intake (ADI)** the estimated amount of sweetener that can be consumed daily over a person's lifetime without any adverse effects.
- **acesulfame-** (AY-sul-fame) **potassium**, also called **acesulfame-K** a zero-Calorie sweetener approved by Health Canada and the U.S. Food and Drug Administration (FDA).
- **aspartame** a compound of phenylalanine and aspartic acid that tastes like the sugar sucrose but is much sweeter. It is used in both Canada and the United States.
- **cyclamate** a zero-Calorie sweetener used with restrictions in Canada and under consideration for use in the United States.
- **erythritol, isomalt, lactitol, maltitol, mannitol, sorbitol, xylitol** sugar alcohols that can be derived from fruit or commercially produced from a sugar; absorbed more slowly and metabolized differently from other sugars in the human body and not readily used by ordinary mouth bacteria.
- **saccharin** a zero-Calorie sweetener restricted in Canada but used freely in the United States.
- **stevia** (STEEV-ee-uh) the sweet-tasting leaves of a shrub sold as a dietary supplement but lacking U.S. FDA approval as a sweetener. However, small amounts of Steviol Glycosides (a purified Stevia extract) are allowed to be added to foods in Canada and may also be found in some natural health products.
- **sucralose** a noncaloric sweetener derived from a chlorinated form of sugar that travels through the digestive tract unabsorbed. Approved for use in Canada and the United States.
- **tagatose** an incompletely absorbed monosaccharide sweetener derived from lactose with a caloric value of 1.5 Calories per gram. About 80% of the ingested tagatose travels to the large intestine, where bacterial colonies ferment it. Tagatose is not readily used by mouth bacteria and so does not promote dental caries.

Saccharin

Saccharin has had a rocky history of acceptance, although it is now consumed by millions of people in the United States, primarily in prepared foods and beverages and secondarily as a tabletop sweetener. Questions about its safety surfaced in the late 1970s, when experiments suggested that it caused bladder tumours in rats. As a result, the U.S. Food and Drug Administration (FDA) proposed banning it. The public outcry in favour of retaining it was so loud, however, that Congress imposed a moratorium on any action, and the ban proposal was eventually withdrawn. For 25 years, saccharin was widely used but remained on the government's roster of "anticipated carcinogens." Products containing it carried a warning label about saccharin as a cancer hazard. In the year 2000, government officials reviewed the research and reversed their opinion, removing saccharin from the carcinogen list and freeing it from the labelling requirement.[38] Opponents to these changes,

however, maintain that saccharin causes cancer in mice and rats and so should be avoided.

Does saccharin cause cancer? The evidence in animals is as follows. Rats fed diets high in saccharin from the time of weaning to adulthood were mated. The offspring of those rats were then fed high-saccharin diets throughout their lives and were found to have a higher incidence of bladder tumours than comparable animals not fed saccharin. In Canada, on the basis of these findings, saccharin was banned except for use as a tabletop sweetener to be sold in pharmacies with a warning label.

Some years ago, the U.S. National Cancer Institute released results from a large-scale population study involving 9,000 people. The results seemed to show that women who drank two or more saccharin-sweetened diet sodas a day and men and women who both smoked heavily and used artificial sweeteners had a slightly elevated risk of some cancers.[39] Other studies involving more

than 5,000 people showed no excess risk of bladder cancers.

A solid clue from the laboratory is based on some physiological differences between the urinary systems of rats and human beings. Proportionally, rats excrete far less water in their urine than people do. As a result, rats can make highly concentrated solutions of substances in just small amounts of water in their urine. Dissolved substances in such high concentrations are likely to crystallize.[40] In safety tests, saccharin overdoses caused crystals to form in the rats' bladders, and the crystals probably caused the tumours. Human beings cannot concentrate urinary substances to such a degree, so they would never form saccharin crystals, even if they consumed larger-than-normal doses of saccharin. They would, however, lose large amounts of water as the kidneys struggled to free the blood of the overload.

Overloading on huge saccharin doses is probably not safe, but consuming moderate amounts almost certainly does not cause bladder cancer in human beings. An ADI has been set for saccharin in the amount of 5 milligrams per kilogram of body weight (see Table C4–4). The amount of saccharin that can be commercially added to foods or drinks in the United States is limited to about 30 milligrams per serving.

Aspartame

Aspartame is one of the most thoroughly studied substances ever to be approved for use in foods, and Health Canada recently affirmed its safety but is still examining data from a European study from 2005.[41] Manufacturers use aspartame under the name *NutraSweet* to sweeten foods that require sweetness but are not exposed to cooking temperatures, because aspartame is not heat stable. A gram of aspartame provides 4 Calories, as does a gram of protein, but because so little is needed, Calories are negligible. Under various brand names, such as *Equal* or *NutraSweet*, aspartame is also available as a powder to use at home in place of sugar. In powdered form, it is mixed with lactose, so a 1-gram packet contains 4 Calories.

Approved Artificial Sweeteners and Sugar-Based Sweeteners

Artificial Sweetener	Energy (Cal/g)	Acceptable Daily Intake (ADI)	Average Amount to Replace 1 tsp Sucrose[a]	Approved Uses
Cyclamate (SugarTwin, Sweet 'N Low, others)	0	11 mg/kg body weight (341 mg for a 68-kg person)	12 mg	Tabletop sweeteners, wide range of foods, beverages, cosmetics, and pharmaceutical products
Aspartame (NutraSweet, Equal, others)	4	40 mg/kg body weight (3,409 mg for a 68-kg person)	18 mg	General-purpose sweetener in all foods and beverages; warning to population with PKU, e.g., contains phenylalanine
Acesulfame-potassium (Sunette, Sweet One)	0	15 mg/kg body weight (1,023 mg for a 68-kg person)	25 mg	Alcoholic beverages, baked goods, candies, chewing gum, desserts, gelatins, puddings, tabletop sweeteners
Sucralose (Splenda)	0	8.8 mg/kg body weight (600 mg for a 68-kg person)	6 mg	Baked goods, carbonated beverages, chewing gum, coffee and tea, dairy products, frozen desserts, fruit spreads, salad dressing, syrups, tabletop sweeteners
Saccharin		5 mg/kg body weight (341 mg for a 68-kg person)		Tabletop sweeteners
Tagatose[b]		80 mg/kg body weight (5,456 mg for a 68-kg person)	1 tsp	Bakery products, beverages, cereals, chewing gum, confections, dairy products, dietary supplements, health bars, tabletop sweeteners
Neotame	0	2 mg/kg body weight (136 mg for a 68-kg person)	<1 mg	Beverages, breakfast cereals, chewing gum
Erythritol	0	1000 mg/kg body weight (68,200 mg for a 68-kg person)	¾ tsp	Tabletop sweeteners, candies, dietetic cookies and beverages
Thaumatin		0.9 mg/kg body weight (61 mg for a 68-kg person)	2,000–3,000 times as sweet as sugar	
Steviol Glycosides		4 mg/kg body weight (272 mg for a 68-kg person)		Seven categories of foods, including tabletop sweeteners, breakfast cereals, unstandardized table syrups, and coating mixtures for snack foods

[a]Rounded values.

[b]Not approved as a food additive in Canada.

The amazing popularity of aspartame is mostly due to its flavour, which is almost identical to that of sugar. Furthermore, aspartame is touted as safe for children, so families wishing to limit their children's sugar intakes are offering them NutraSweet products instead.

Aspartame is a simple chemical compound: two protein fragments (the amino acids phenylalanine and aspartic acid) joined together. In the digestive tract, the two fragments are split apart, absorbed, and metabolized just as they would be if they had come from protein in food. The flavours of the components give no clue to the combined effect; one of them tastes bitter, and the other is tasteless. Yet aspartame is 200 times as sweet as sucrose.

With its phenylalanine base, aspartame poses problems for people with an inherited metabolic disease known as phenylketonuria (PKU). People with PKU have the hereditary inability to dispose of phenylalanine eaten in excess of need. Unusual products made from phenylalanine build up and damage the tissues. PKU causes irreversible, progressive brain damage if left untreated in early life. Newborns are tested for PKU; if they have it, the treatment is to limit dietary intake of phenylalanine.

Children with PKU should not get their phenylalanine from aspartame.

Phenylalanine occurs in such protein-rich and nutrient-rich foods as milk and meat, and the PKU child is allowed only a limited amount of these foods. The child has difficulty obtaining the many essential nutrients, such as calcium, iron, and the B vitamins, found along with phenylalanine in these foods. To suggest that such a child squander any of the limited phenylalanine allowance on the purified phenylalanine of aspartame, with none of the associated nutrients to support normal growth, would be to invite nutritional disaster. Product labels carry special warnings for people with PKU.

Other concerns about aspartame's safety have had to do with compounds that arise briefly during its metabolism. These compounds (methyl alcohol, formaldehyde, and diketopiperazine) are not toxic at the levels generated from the ADI amount of aspartame, and concerns about them have been laid to rest.

Urban legends circulating on the Internet accuse aspartame of causing everything from Alzheimer's disease and brain cancer to nerve disorders and skin warts. Orderly scientific investigations into these issues find no relationship between aspartame intake and brain tumours, behaviour, mood, or brain chemistry. Nor are any other physical symptoms evident from research. No experimental evidence has shown a connection between headaches and aspartame, but the U.S. Centers for Disease Control and Prevention (CDC) has received many thousands of individual complaints. Every day, millions of people use aspartame. Every day, millions of people have headaches. Anyone who claims, on this basis, that aspartame causes headaches is using personal experience to jump to conclusions. Some of the headache sufferers might indeed be reacting to the artificial sweetener, but they might also be reacting to another substance, such as caffeine, in aspartame-sweetened beverages or to factors in their lives unrelated to foods. People who believe aspartame gives them headaches should use a different sweetener.

On approving aspartame for U.S. consumers, the U.S. FDA set the ADI at 50 milligrams per kilogram of body weight in a day. In Canada, the acceptable level is set at 40 milligrams per kilogram. These are reasonable numbers. For a 60-kilogram person, 50 milligrams equals 80 packets of aspartame sweetener or 15 soft drinks sweetened only with aspartame. It is possible to exceed the ADI amount, however: a child who drinks a quart of Kool-Aid on a hot day and who also has pudding, chewing gum, cereal, and other products sweetened with aspartame can pack in more than the daily ADI limit. Infants or toddlers under two years old should not be fed artificially sweetened foods and drinks.

Acesulfame-Potassium

During 15 years of testing and use, the artificial sweetener acesulfame-potassium (or acesulfame-K) has been used without reported health problems. An ADI of 15 milligrams per kilogram of body weight was set for acesulfame-potassium on its approval. Marketed under the trade names *Sunette* and *Sweet One*, this sweetener is about as sweet as aspartame and is used in chewing gum, beverages, instant coffee and tea, gelatins, and puddings, as well as for table use. Acesulfame-potassium holds up well during cooking.

Acesulfame-potassium is 200 times as sweet as sucrose, but, to some, it leaves a slight aftertaste. Blending it with other sweeteners solves the problem. Acesulfame-potassium is not recognized by the body's metabolic equipment and therefore is excreted unchanged by the kidneys.

Sucralose

Approved for use as a sweetener in Canada and the United States, sucralose (trade name *Splenda*) is the only artificial sweetener made from sucrose. Three chlorine atoms substitute for three hydrogen and oxygen groups on the structure of sucrose, making a product that provides 600 times the sweetness of sugar. Many years of testing have deemed sucralose safe to use and, specifically, not a cause of cancer. Sucralose is not recognized by the body as sugar and therefore passes through unchanged. The ADI for sucralose has been set at 5 milligrams per kilogram of body weight per day for all ages, including pregnant and lactating women. Sucralose is heat stable and so is useful for cooking and baking; it is used in commercially prepared products and as a tabletop sweetener.

Tagatose

The U.S. FDA has granted tagatose, a relative of fructose, the status of "generally recognized as safe," making it available as a lower-Calorie sweetener for foods, beverages, confections, dietary supplements, and other uses.[42]

Tagatose is derived from lactose, but unlike fructose or lactose, 80 percent of tagatose remains unabsorbed until it reaches the large intestine. There the normal bacterial colonies of the colon ferment tagatose, releasing gases and small products that are absorbed. At high doses, tagatose causes flatulence, rumbling, and loose stools. Otherwise, no adverse side effects have been noted by the maker.

Other Sweeteners

In Canada, cyclamate is restricted to use as a tabletop sweetener on the advice of a physician and as a sweetening additive in medicines and should be avoided during pregnancy.

A naturally sweet herb called stevia is gaining in popularity as a sugar substitute, especially in beverages. Food additives must provide evidence of their safety and effectiveness before receiving Health Canada approval, and for stevia little is known about its effects on human health, save that it can be absorbed by the human digestive tract.[43] But stevia, as steviol glycosides, can be sold in Canada and added to table-top sweeteners, various foods and beverages, and breath fresheners (see http://www.hc-sc.gc.ca/fn-an/consult/steviol/document-consultation-eng.php) and can be sold in the United States as a dietary supplement. However, because dietary supplements in the United States need not present any supporting evidence of safety or effectiveness, this highlights a problem in the U.S. FDA's regulation of supplements. Stevia may be harmful, safe, or even beneficial in some way, but no one can say for sure until science reveals more about this sweetener.[44] However, stevia can also be added to natural health products in Canada as a sweetener (http://www.hc-sc.gc.ca/dhp-mps/prodnatur/legislation/docs/notice-avis-stevia-eng.php).

Do Artificial Sweeteners Help with Weight Control?

Many people eat and drink products sweetened with artificial sweeteners in the belief that the products help control weight. Do they work? Ironically, some studies of rats report that intense sweeteners, such as saccharin, stimulate appetite and lead to weight *gain* instead of loss. Many studies on *people*, however, find either no change or a decline in feelings of hunger. Food energy intake has also been reported to be lower when artificial sweeteners replace sugar, resulting in greater weight losses when obese people eat or drink artificially sweetened products instead of their sugar-sweetened counterparts.[45]

In studying the effects of artificial sweeteners on food intake and body weight, researchers ask different questions and take different approaches. It matters, for example, whether the people used in a study are of a healthy weight and whether they are following a weight-loss diet. Motivations for using sweeteners can affect total Calorie intakes, too. For example, a person wishing to eat a high-Calorie food might try to compensate for its Calories by drinking an artificially sweetened beverage. This person's energy intake might stay the same or increase. In contrast, another person who wants to cut total Calorie intake might choose the artificial sweetener in the context of a whole diet of low-Calorie foods. This person's Calorie intake might well be lower than it otherwise would have been.

Researchers must also distinguish between the effects of the experience of tasting something sweet and the physiological effects of a particular substance on the body. If a person experiences hunger or feels full shortly after eating an artificially sweetened snack, is that because tasting something sweet

stimulates or depresses the appetite? Or is it because the artificial sweetener itself somehow affects the appetite through nervous, hormonal, or other means? Furthermore, if appetite is stimulated, does that actually lead to increased food intake?

A recent study reports sizable weight losses when artificial sweeteners replace sizable amounts of sugar in the diet.[46] Researchers supplemented the diets of overweight men and women with snacks, mostly beverages, containing either sucrose (snacks totalling about 600 Calories) or artificial sweeteners (snacks totalling about 200 Calories) and then allowed free choice to determine the rest of the diet. After 10 weeks, the sucrose group had gained about 1.7 kilograms, while the artificial sweetener group had lost about 10 kilograms. As a side benefit to weight loss, blood pressure dropped in the artificial sweetener group, too. The researchers speculate that sugars in the form of fluids may be less satisfying than those in solid foods, making it easier to overconsume Calories later in the day. To say with any certainty whether artificial sweeteners reduce energy intakes or body fatness requires more evidence, however, because many other studies report no weight differences between people fed sugar and those fed artificial sweeteners.[47]

In contrast to the findings for the overweight subjects just described, sugar consumed before a meal by normal-weight people reliably damps

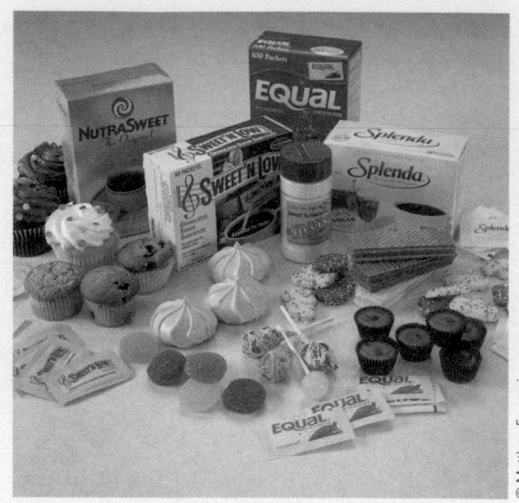

Can artificial sweeteners help people lose weight?

the appetite.[48] The common belief that sugar "spoils the appetite" proves true for most people and especially for children.

Personal Strategies for Using Artificial Sweeteners

Current evidence indicates that moderate intakes of artificial sweeteners pose no health risks. For those who choose to include artificial sweeteners in their diets, moderation is the key. Using artificial sweeteners does not automatically lower energy intake; controlling energy intake successfully requires informed diet and activity decisions throughout the day (as Chapter 9 explains). Although not magic bullets in fighting overweight, artificial sweeteners probably do not hinder weight-loss efforts either, and they are safer for the teeth than carbohydrate sweeteners.

Self-Check

Answers to these Self-Check questions are in Appendix D.

1. The dietary monosaccharides include
   a. sucrose, glucose, and lactose
   b. fructose, glucose, and galactose
   c. galactose, maltose, and glucose
   d. glycogen, starch, and fibre

2. The polysaccharide that helps form the supporting structures of plants is
   a. cellulose
   b. maltose
   c. glycogen
   d. sucrose

Chapter 4 The Carbohydrates: Sugar, Starch, Glycogen, and Fibre

3. Digestible carbohydrates are absorbed as _____ through the small intestinal wall and are delivered to the liver, where they are converted to _____.

   a. disaccharides; sucrose

   b. glucose; glycogen

   c. monosaccharides; glucose

   d. galactose; cellulose

4. When blood glucose concentration rises, the pancreas secretes _____, and when blood glucose levels fall, the pancreas secretes _____.

   a. glycogen; insulin

   b. insulin; glucagon

   c. glucagon; glycogen

   d. insulin; fructose

5. When the body uses fat for fuel without the help of carbohydrate, this results in the production of

   a. ketone bodies

   b. glucose

   c. starch

   d. galactose

6. Foods rich in fibre lower blood cholesterol.

   T   F

7. Type 1 diabetes is most often controlled by successful weight-loss management.

   T   F

8. Around the world, most people are lactose intolerant.

   T   F

9. By law, enriched white bread must equal whole-grain bread in nutrient content.

   T   F

10. The fibre-rich portion of the wheat kernel is the bran layer.

   T   F

track it! Diet Analysis PLUS ✚   Concepts in Action

start now! ┄┄┊ Choose a one-week period and on those days that you exercise have a healthy carbohydrate-rich snack of about 300 Calories, along with a bottle of water, about an hour before you exercise. Be sure to also track your diet in Diet Analysis Plus during this period so that you can accurately track your total Calorie intake. Did you *feel* more energetic? Have more energy for exercise after you changed your eating plan?

Analyze Your Carbohydrate Intake

The purpose of this chapter's exercise is to help you examine the carbohydrate-rich foods in your diet, compare your intakes with recommendations, and help you obtain the recommended daily intake of carbohydrates and soluble and insoluble fibre.

1. In the DA+ program, select the Reports tab, and under the Nutrients column, select the Macronutrient Ranges. Using your 3-day diet records, choose Day Two and choose all meals. Did your intake meet the recommendation to consume between 45 and 65 percent of total Calories as carbohydrate?

2. Determine the distribution of carbohydrate among the day's foods. Select Reports, then under the Advanced heading, select Source Analysis, and then Carbohydrate from the drop-down box. Generate a separate report for each meal: breakfast, lunch, and dinner. At which meal did you consume the most carbohydrate? Which foods were the greatest contributors?

3. From the dropdown box, select Dietary Fibre, Total. Select all meals for Day 2. Did your fibre intake fall within the recommended range (25–38 grams per day)? In other words, did you meet your fibre need?

4. From the Reports tab, under the Advanced heading, select Source Analysis. Using Day Three, choose all meals, and use the drop-down box to select Dietary Fibre, Total. Which foods provided the greatest amounts of fibre for the day's intake? If you are short on fibre, take a look at Figure 4–4 (page 121) and Table 4–2 (page 120), and suggest fibre-rich foods to increase your intake of both soluble and insoluble fibre.

5. Whole-grain foods add more than just fibre to the diet. From Track Diet, create a new day (do not alter your 3-day record), and enter two food items as a snack: 2.5 cups Froot Loops cereal and 0.5 cup granola (these amounts are equal in Calories). Select Reports, Source Analysis, and the mineral magnesium from the drop-down box. Generate a report for the new snack. Which was the better magnesium source, the refined cereal (Froot Loops) or the whole grain cereal (granola)?

Endnotes

1. B. V. McCleary, Dietary fibre analysis, *Proceedings of the Nutrition Society* 62 (2003): 3–9.

2. T. Maeder, Sweet medicines, *Scientific American* 287 (2002): 40–47; J. Travis, The true sweet science—Researchers develop a taste for the study of sugars, *Science News* 161 (2002): 232–233; Multiple articles in Carbohydrates and glycobiology—Searching for medicine's sweet spot, *Science* 291 (2001): 2338–2378.

3. R. O. Bonow and R. H. Eckel, Diet, obesity and cardiovascular risk, *New England Journal of Medicine* 348 (2003): 2057–2058; D. M. Bravata and coauthors, Efficacy and safety of low-carbohydrate diets, *Journal of the American Medical Association* 289 (2003): 1837–1850.

4. U.S. Food and Drug Administration, *Counting Calories: Report of the Working Group on Obesity*, 2004, available at http://www.fda.gov/ohrms/dockets/ac/04/briefing/4039b1_01_calories%20count.pdf; Standing Committee on the Scientific Evaluation of Dietary Reference Intakes, Food and Nutrition Board, Institute of Medicine, *Dietary Reference Intakes for Energy, Carbohydrate, Fiber, Fat, Fatty Acids, Cholesterol, Protein, and Amino Acids* (Washington, D.C.: National Academies Press, 2002): pp. 13–17; A. Trichopoulou and coauthors, Lipid, protein and carbohydrate intake in relation to body mass index, *European Journal of Clinical Nutrition* 56 (2002): 37–43.

5. S. K. Fried and S. P. Rao, Sugars, hypertriglyceridemia, and cardiovascular disease, *American Journal of Clinical Nutrition* 78 (2003): 873S–880S; D. R. Lineback and J. M. Jones, Sugars and health workshop: Summary and conclusions, *American Journal of Clinical Nutrition* 78 (2003): 893S–897S; M. K. Hellerstein, Carbohydrate-induced hypertriglyceridemia: Modifying factors and implications for cardiovascular risk, *Current Opinion in Lipidology* 13 (2002): 33–40; E. J. Parks, Changes in fat synthesis influenced by dietary macronutrient content, *Proceedings of the Nutrition Society* 61 (2002): 281–286.

6. Joint WHO/FAO Expert Consultation, *Diet, Nutrition and the Prevention of Chronic Diseases* (Geneva, Switzerland: World Health Organization, 2003), pp. 57–58; S. H. F. Vermunt and coauthors, Effects of sugar intake on body weight: A review, *Obesity Reviews* 4 (2003): 91–99; National Heart, Lung, and Blood Institute, Facts about the Dash Eating Plan, NIH publication no. 03-4082, 2003; Standing Committee on the Scientific Evaluation of Dietary Reference Intakes, 2002 [see reference 4]; Third Report of the National Cholesterol Education Program (NCEP) Expert Panel on Detection, Evaluation, and Treatment of High Blood Cholesterol in Adults (Adult Treatment Panel III), 2002, NIH publication no. 02-5215, pp. V-1-V-4; Nutrition Committee of the American Heart Association, AHA dietary guidelines revision 2000: A statement for healthcare professionals from the nutrition committee of the American Heart Association, *Circulation* 102 (2000): 2284–2299; Health Canada. Eating Well with Canada's Food Guide. Cat: H164-38/1-2011E. http://www.hc-sc.gc.ca/fn-an/food-guide-aliment/index-eng.php; American Heart Association. Sugars 101, Need to reduce added sugars. http://www.heart.org/HEARTORG/GettingHealthy/NutritionCenter/Sugars-101_UCM_306024_Article.jsp; Canadian Sugar Institute. Sugars Consumption. http://www.sugar.ca/english/healthprofessionals/sugarsconsumption.cfm.

7. Standing Committee on the Scientific Evaluation of Dietary Reference Intakes, 2002, pp. 7–9 [see reference 4].

8. S. Liu and coauthors, Relation between changes in intakes of dietary fiber and grain products and changes in weight and development of obesity among middle-aged women, *American Journal of Clinical Nutrition* 78 (2003): 920–927.

9. F. B. Hu and W. C. Willett, Optimal diets for prevention of coronary heart disease, *Journal of the American Medical Association* 288 (2002): 2569–2578; N. M. McKeown and coauthors, Whole-grain intake is favorably associated with metabolic risk factors for type 2 diabetes and cardiovascular disease in the Framingham Offspring Study, *American Journal of Clinical Nutrition* 76 (2002): 390–398; S. Liu and coauthors, Whole-grain consumption and risk of coronary heart disease: Results from the Nurses' Health Study, *American Journal of Clinical Nutrition* 70 (1999): 412–419.

10. Position of the American Dietetic Association, Health implications of dietary fiber, *Journal of the American Dietetic Association* 102 (2002): 993–999; L. Brown and coauthors, Cholesterol-lowering effects of dietary fiber: A meta-analysis, *American Journal of Clinical Nutrition* 69 (1999): 30–42.

11. M. L. Fernandez, Soluble fiber and nondigestible carbohydrate effects on plasma lipids and cardiovascular risk, *Current Opinion in Lipidology* 12 (2001): 35–40; Brown and coauthors, 1999 [see reference 10].

12. B. M. Davy and coauthors, High-fiber oat cereal compared with wheat cereal consumption favorably alters LDL-cholesterol subclass and particle numbers in middle-aged and older men, *American Journal of Clinical Nutrition* 76 (2002): 351–358; D. J. A. Jenkins and coauthors, Soluble fiber intake at a dose approved by the US Food and Drug Administration for a claim of health benefits: Serum lipid risk factors for cardiovascular disease assessed in a randomized controlled crossover trial, *American Journal of Clinical Nutrition* 75 (2002): 834–839.

13. T. T. Fund and coauthors, Whole-grain intake and the risk of type 2 diabetes: A prospective study in men, *American Journal of Clinical Nutrition* 76 (2002): 535–540.

14. W. Aldoori and M. Ryan-Harshman, Preventing diverticular disease: Review of recent evidence on high-fibre diets, *Canadian Family Physician* 48 (2002): 1632–1637.

15. U. Peters and coauthors, Dietary fibre and colorectal adenoma in a colorectal cancer early detection programme, *Lancet* 361 (2003): 1491–1495; S. A. Bingham and coauthors, Dietary fibre in food and protection against colorectal cancer in the European Prospective Investigation into Cancer and Nutrition (EPIC): An observational study, *Lancet* 361 (2003): 1496–1501; T. Honda, I. Kai, and G. Ohi, Fat and dietary fiber intake and colon cancer mortality: A chronological comparison between Japan and the United States, *Nutrition and Cancer* 33 (1999): 95–99; B. S. Reddy, Role of dietary fiber in colon cancer: An overview, *American Journal of Medicine* 106 (1999): S16–S19.

16. A. Schatzkin and coauthors, Lack of effect of a low-fat, high-fiber diet on the recurrence of colorectal adenomas, *New England Journal of Medicine* 342 (2000): 1149–1155; D. S. Alberts and coauthors, Lack of effect of a high-fiber cereal supplement on the recurrence of colorectal adenomas, *New England Journal of Medicine* 342 (2000): 1156–1162; F. Macrae, Wheat bran fiber and development of adenomatous polyps: Evidence from randomized, controlled clinical trials, *American Journal of Medicine* 106 (1999): 38S–42S; D. Kritchevsky, Protective role of wheat bran fiber: Preclinical data, *American Journal of Medicine* 106 (1999): 28S–31S; C. S. Fuchs and coauthors, Dietary fiber and risk of colorectal cancer and adenoma in women, *New England Journal of Medicine* 340 (1999): 169–176.

17. Bingham and coauthors, 2003 [see reference 15].

18. Standing Committee on the Scientific Evaluation of Dietary Reference Intakes, 2002, pp. 7–8 [see reference 4].

19. A. Andoh, T. Tsujikawa, and Y. Fujiyama, Role of dietary fiber and short-chain fatty acids in the colon, *Current Pharmaceutical Design* 9 (2003): 347–358; L. McMillan and coauthors, Opposing effects of butyrate and bile acids on apoptosis of human colon adenoma cells: Differential activation of PKC and MAP kinases, *British Journal of Cancer* 88 (2003): 748–753; M. E. Rodriguez-Cabezas and coauthors, Dietary fiber down-regulates colonic tumor necrosis factor alpha and nitric oxide production in trinitrobenzenesulfonic acid-induced colitic rats, *Journal of Nutrition* 132 (2002): 3263–3271; J. L. Slavin, Mechanisms for the impact of whole grain foods on cancer risk, *Journal of the American College of Nutrition* 19 (2000): 300S–307S.

20. American Gastroenterological Association medical position statement: Impact of dietary fiber on colon cancer occurrence, *Gastroenterology* 118 (2000): 1233–1234.

21. N. C. Howarth, E. Saltzman, and S. B. Roberts, Dietary fiber and weight regulation, *Nutrition Reviews* 59 (2001): 129–139; A. Sparti and coauthors, Effect of diets high or low in unavailable and slowly digestible carbohydrates on the pattern of 24-h substrate oxidation and feelings of hunger in humans, *American Journal of Clinical Nutrition* 72 (2000): 1461–1468.

22. Standing Committee on the Scientific Evaluation of Dietary Reference Intakes, 2005 [see reference 4].

23. Institute of Medicine, *Dietary Reference Intakes for Energy, Carbohydrate, Fiber, Fat, Fatty Acids, Cholesterol, Protein, and Amino Acid* (Washington, D.C.: National Academies Press, 2002/2005).

24. Standing Committee on the Scientific Evaluation of Dietary Reference Intakes, 2005 [see reference 4].

25. K. N. Englyst and coauthors, Rapidly available glucose in foods: An in vitro measurement that reflects the glycemic response, *American Journal of Clinical Nutrition* 69 (1999): 448–454.

26. J. G. Muir and coauthors, Combining wheat bran with resistant starch has more beneficial effects on fecal indexes than does wheat bran alone, *American Journal of Clinical Nutrition* 79 (2004): 1020–1028.

27. B. V. McCleary, Dietary fiber analysis, *Proceedings of the Nutrition Society* 62 (2003): 3–9; S. Kimura, Glycemic carbohydrate and health: Background and synopsis of the symposium, *Nutrition Reviews* 61 (2003): S1–S4.

28. D. L. Swagerty, A. D. Walling, and R. M. Klein, Lactose intolerance, *American Family Physician* 65 (2002): 1845–1850.

29. D. Savaiano, Lactose intolerance: A self-fulfilling prophecy leading to osteoporosis? *Nutrition Reviews* 61 (2003): 221–223.

30. H. J. Kalkwarf, J. C. Khoury, and B. P. Lanphear, Milk intake during childhood and adolescence, adult bone density, and osteoporotic fractures in US women, *American Journal of Clinical Nutrition* 77 (2003): 257–265.

31. P. Marteau and M. C. Boutron-Ruault, Nutritional advantages of probiotics and prebiotics, *British Journal of Nutrition* 87 (2002): S153–S157; M. de Vrese and coauthors, Probiotics—Compensation for lactase insufficiency, *American Journal of Clinical Nutrition* 73 (2001): 421S–429S; L. Kopp-Hoolihan, Prophylactic and therapeutic uses of probiotics: A review, *Journal of the American Dietetic Association* 101 (2001): 229–238, 241; J. M. Saavedra, Clinical applications of probiotic agents, *American Journal of Clinical Nutrition* 73 (2001): 1147S–1151S.

32. M. Levitt, as quoted in Who ya gonna call? Gas busters, *Nutrition Action Healthletter*, May 2003, pp. 3–5.

33. T. B. VanItallie and T. H. Nufert, Ketones: Metabolism's ugly duckling, *Nutrition Reviews* 61 (2003): 327–341.

34. J. Achten and coauthors, Higher dietary carbohydrate content during intensified running training results in better maintenance of performance and mood state, *Journal of Applied Physiology* 96 (2004): 1331–1340; Standing Committee on the Scientific Evaluation of Dietary Reference Intakes, 2005 [see Reference 4]; S. T. Reddy and coauthors, Effect of low-carbohydrate high-protein diet on acid-base balance, stone-forming propensity, and calcium metabolism, *American Journal of Kidney Disease* 40 (2002): 265–274; H. R. Lieberman, C. M. Falco, and S. S. Slade, Carbohydrate administration during a day of sustained aerobic activity improves vigilance, as assessed by a novel ambulatory monitoring device, and mood, *American Journal of Clinical Nutrition* 76 (2002): 120–127.

35. J. L. Dorman, Pediatric ketogenic diets for intractable seizures, *Today's Dietitian* 5 (2003): 16–20.

36. Standing Committee on the Scientific Evaluation of Dietary Reference Intakes, 2002, pp. 6–9 [see reference 4].

37. R. Gruetter, Glycogen: The forgotten cerebral energy store, *Journal of Neuroscience Research* 74 (2003): 179–183; I.Y. Choi, E. R. Seaquist, and R. Gruetter, Effect of hypoglycemia on brain glycogen metabolism in vivo, *Journal of Neuroscience Research* 72 (2003): 25–32.

38. K. Foster-Powell, S. A. H. Holt, and J. C. Brand-Miller, International table of glycemic index and glycemic load values: 2002, *American Journal of Clinical Nutrition* 76 (2002): 5–56; G. Nantel, Glycemic carbohydrate: An international perspective, *Nutrition Reviews* 61 (2003): S34–S39; T. M. S. Wolever, Carbohydrate and the regulation of blood glucose and metabolism, *Nutrition Reviews* 61 (2003): S40–S48; D. J. A. Jenkins and coauthors, Glycemic index: Overview of implications in health and disease, *American Journal of Clinical Nutrition* 76 (2002): 266S–273S.

39. J. C. Brand-Miller, Glycemic load and chronic disease, *Nutrition Reviews* 61 (2003): S49–S55.

40. J. C. Brand-Miller, Physiological validation of the concept of glycemic load in lean young adults, *Journal of Nutrition* 133 (2003): 2728–2732; Jenkins and coauthors, 2002 [see reference 38]; S. Liu and coauthors, Dietary glycemic load assessed by food-frequency questionnaire in relation to plasma high-density lipoprotein cholesterol and fasting plasma triacylglycerols in postmenopausal women, *American Journal of Clinical Nutrition* 73 (2001): 560–566; S. Liu and coauthors, A prospective study of dietary glycemic load, carbohydrate intake, and risk of coronary heart disease in US women, *American Journal of Clinical Nutrition* 71 (2000): 1455–1461.

41. Brand-Miller, 2003 [see reference 40]; D. S. Ludwig, The glycemic index: Physiological mechanisms relating to obesity, diabetes, and cardiovascular disease, *Journal of the American Medical Association* 287 (2002): 2414–2423; L. E. Spieth and coauthors, A low-glycemic index diet in the treatment of pediatric obesity, *Archives of Pediatrics & Adolescent Medicine* 154 (2000): 947–951; D. S. Ludwig and coauthors, Dietary fiber, weight gain, and cardiovascular disease risk factors in young adults, *Journal of the American Medical Association* 282 (1999): 1539–1546.

42. S. Liu and coauthors, Relation between a diet with a high glycemic load and plasma concentrations of high-sensitivity C-reactive protein in middle-aged women, *American Journal of Clinical Nutrition* 75 (2002): 492–498; D. S. Ludwig and coauthors, High glycemic index foods, overeating, and obesity, *Pediatrics* 103 (1999): e26 (http://pediatrics.aappublications.org/).

43. S. Schenk and coauthors, Different glycemic indexes of breakfast cereals are not due to glucose entry into blood but to glucose removal by tissue, *American Journal of Clinical Nutrition* 77 (2003): 742–748.

44. Ludwig, 2002 [see reference 41]; F. X. Pi-Sunyer, Glycemic index and disease, *American Journal of Clinical Nutrition* 76 (2002): 290S–298S; A. E. Buyken and coauthors, Glycemic index in the diet of European outpatients with type 1 diabetes: Relations to glycated hemoglobin and serum lipids, *American Journal of Clinical Nutrition* 73 (2001): 574–581.

45. Wolever, 2003 [see reference 38].

46. W. Willett, J. Manson, and S. Liu, Glycemic index, glycemic load, and risk of type 2 diabetes, *American Journal of Clinical Nutrition* 76 (2002): 274S–280S.

47. International Food Information Council, Glycemic index: The ups and downs of indexing blood sugar, *Food Insight*, May/June 2003, available at http://www.foodinsight.org/Portals/0/pdf/May-June-2003-PDF.pdf; K. L. Johnson, M. N. Clifford, and L. M. Morgan, Coffee acutely modifies gastrointestinal hormone secretion and glucose tolerance in humans: Glycemic effects of chlorogenic acid and caffeine, *American Journal of Clinical Nutrition* 78 (2003): 728–733.

48. C. Beebe, Diets with a low glycemic index: Not ready for practice yet! *Nutrition Today* 34 (1999): 82–86.

49. O. Lammert and coauthors, Effects of isoenergetic overfeeding of either carbohydrate or fat in young men, *British Journal of Nutrition* 88 (2002): 331–332.

50. W. H. M. Saris, Sugars, energy metabolism, and body weight control, *American Journal of Clinical Nutrition* 78 (2003): 850S–857S.

51. J. M. Schwartz and coauthors, Hepatic de novo lipogenesis in normoinsulinemic and hyperinsulinemic subjects consuming high-fat, low-carbohydrate and low-fat, high carbohydrate isoenergetic diets, *American Journal of Clinical Nutrition* 77 (2003): 43–50.

52. Standing Committee on the Scientific Evaluation of Dietary Reference Intakes, 2005 [see reference 4].

53. Canadian Diabetes Association and Diabetes Quebec. Diabetes: Canada at the Tipping Point—Charting a New Path, April 2011, available at http://www.diabetes.ca/documents/get-involved/web_eng.cda_report_.pdf; A. H. Mokdad and coauthors, Diabetes trends in the U.S.: 1990–1998, *Diabetes Care* 23 (2000): 1278–1283; K. M.V. Narayan and coauthors, Diabetes—A common, growing, serious, costly, and potentially preventable public health problem, *Diabetes Research and Clinical Practice* 50 (2000): S77–S84.

54. Public Health Agency of Canada—Diabetes in Canada: Facts and Figures from a Public Health Prespective, 2011, available at http://www.phac-aspc.gc.ca/cd-mc/publications/diabetes-diabete/facts-figures-faits-chiffres-2011/; National Center for Chronic Disease Prevention and Health Promotion, Diabetes: National Diabetes Factsheet 2011, available at http://www.cdc.gov/diabetes/pubs/pdf/ndfs_2011.pdf.

55. A. Ohinmaa and coauthors, The projection of prevalence and cost of diabetes in Canada: 2000–2016, *Canadian Journal of Diabetes* 28 (2004): 116–123.

56. Canadian Diabetes Association Clinical Practice Guidelines Expert Committee. Canadian Diabetes Association 2013 Clinical Practice Guidelines for the Prevention and Management of Diabetes in Canada. *Canadian Journal of Diabetes* 37 (2013): S1–S212, available at http://guidelines.diabetes.ca/App_Themes/CDACPG/resources/cpg_2013_full_en.pdf.

57. National Centers for Chronic Disease Prevention and Health Promotion, 2003 [see reference 54]; E. A. Gale, The rise of childhood type 1 diabetes in the 20th century, *Diabetes* 51 (2003): 3353–3361.

58. K. Sadeharju and coauthors, Enterovirus infections as a risk factor for type 1 diabetes: Virus analyses in a dietary intervention trial, *Clinical and Experimental Immunology* 132 (2003): 271–277; C. D. Berdanier, Mitochondrial gene expression in diabetes mellitus: Effect of nutrition, *Nutrition Reviews* 59 (2001): 61–70; F. A. Darlsson and coauthors, Beta-cell activity and destruction in type 1 diabetes, *Upsala Journal of Medical Sciences* 105 (2000): 85–95.

59. J. Hopkins, Treating diabetes with aerosolized insulin, *Chest* 120 (2001): 99S–106S.

60. D. B. Kaufman and W. L. Lowe, Clinical islet transplantation, *Current Diabetes Reports* 3 (2003): 344–350; M. Atkinson and G. Eisenbarth, Type 1 diabetes: New perspectives on disease pathogenesis and treatment, *Lancet* 358 (2001): 221–229.

61. E. Roche and coauthors, Bio-engineering insulin-secreting cells from embryonic stem cells: A review of progress, *Medical and Biological Engineering and Computing* 41 (2003): 384–391.

62. T. J. Anderson and coauthors, 2012 Update of the Canadian Cardiovascular Society Guidelines for the Diagnosis and Treatment of Dyslipidemia for the Prevention of Cardiovascular Disease in the Adult, *Canadian Journal of Cardiology* 29 (2013): 151–167.

63. D. H. Amschler, The alarming increase of type 2 diabetes in children, *Journal of School Health* 72 (2002): 39–41; A. Fagot-Campagna, K.M. Narayan, and G. Imperatore, Type 2 diabetes in children exemplifies the growing problem of chronic diseases, *British Medical Journal* 322 (2001): 377–378; American Diabetes Association Consensus Statement, Type 2 diabetes in children and adolescents, *Diabetes Care* 23 (2000): 381–389, available at http://care.diabetesjournals.org/content/23/3/381.full.pdf; American Diabetes Association, Type 2 diabetes in children and adolescents, *Pediatrics* 105 (2000): 671–680.

64. U. B. Pajvani and P. E. Scherer, Adiponectin: Systemic contributor to insulin sensitivity, *Current Diabetes Reports* 3 (2003): 207–213; M. Li and coauthors, Small molecule insulin receptor activators potentiate insulin action in insulin-resistant cells, *Diabetes* 50 (2001): 2323–2328; I. D. Goldfine, Unraveling the riddle of insulin resistance (editorial), *Journal of Laboratory and Clinical Medicine* 134 (1999): 100–102.

65. J. P. Girod and D. J. Brotman, The metabolic syndrome as a vicious cycle: Does obesity beget obesity? *Medical Hypotheses* 60 (2003): 584–589.

66. S. Klein and coauthors, Weight management through lifestyle modification for the prevention and management of type 2 diabetes: rationale and strategies. A statement of the American Diabetes Association, the North American Association for the Study of Obesity, and the American Society for Clinical Nutrition, *American Journal of Clinical Nutrition* 80 (2004): 257–263; K. Silander and coauthors, A large set of Finnish affected sibling pair families with type 2 diabetes suggests susceptibility loci on chromosomes 6, 11, and

14, *Diabetes* 53 (2004): 821–829; C. N. Rotimi and coauthors, A genome-wide search for type 2 diabetes susceptibility genes in West Africans: The Africa America Diabetes Mellitus (AADM) Study, *Diabetes* 53 (2004): 838–841.

67. K. L. Cox and coauthors, Independent and additive effects of energy restriction and exercise on glucose and insulin concentrations in sedentary overweight men, *American Journal of Clinical Nutrition* 80 (2004): 308–316; Researchers find potential gene link to diabetes, *Newsday.Com*, March 12, 2004, available at http://www.bionews.org.uk/page.asp?obj_id=5937&ASTemp=38738.

68. National Center for Chronic Disease Prevention and Health Promotion, 2003 [see reference 57]; R.M. van Dam and coauthors, Dietary patterns and risk for type 2 diabetes mellitus in U.S. men, *Annals of Internal Medicine* 136 (2002): 201–209; B. Hu and coauthors, Diet, lifestyle, and the risk of type 2 diabetes mellitus in women, *New England Journal of Medicine* 345 (2001): 790–797.

69. R. Kikkawa, Chronic complications in diabetes mellitus, *British Journal of Nutrition* 84 (2000): S183–S185.

70. J. L. Evans and coauthors, Are oxidative stress-activated signaling pathways mediators of insulin resistance and beta-cell dysfunction? *Diabetes* 52 (2003): 1–8; I. G. Obrosova, How does glucose generate oxidative stress in peripheral nerve? *International Review of Neurobiology* 50 (2002): 3–35.

71. P. Gaude and coauthors, Multifactorial interventions and cardiovascular disease in patients with type 2 diabetes, *New England Journal of Medicine* 348 (2003): 383–393.

72. K. L. Cox and coauthors, Independent and additive effects of energy restriction and exercise on glucose and insulin concentrations in sedentary overweight men, *American Journal of Clinical Nutrition* 80 (2004): 308–316; F. Collins, as quoted by E. Lane [see reference 67].

73. National Center for Chronic Disease Prevention and Health Promotion, 2003 [see reference 57].

74. S. Tesfaye and coauthors, Vascular risk factors and diabetic neuropathy, *New England Journal of Medicine* 352 (2005): 341–350; J. G. Pastors, How effective is medical nutrition therapy in diabetes care? *Journal of the American Dietetic Association* 103 (2003): 827–831.

75. Position of the American Dietetic Association: Total diet approach to communicating food and nutrition information, *Journal of the American Dietetic Association* 102 (2002): 100–108.

76. American Diabetes Association, Evidence-based nutrition principles and recommendations for the treatment and prevention of diabetes and related complications, *Diabetes Care* 26 (2003): S51–S61.

77. M. C. Gannon and coauthors, An increase in dietary protein improves the blood glucose response in persons with type 2 diabetes, *American Journal of Clinical Nutrition* 78 (2003): 734–741; M. J. Franz and M. L. Wheeler, Nutrition therapy for diabetic nephropathy, *Current Diabetes Reports* 3 (2003): 412–417; E. M. Wrone and coauthors, Association of dietary protein intake with microalbuminuria in healthy adults: Third National Health and Nutrition Examination Survey, *American Journal of Kidney Diseases* 41 (2003): 580–587.

78. H. T. Pigman, D. X. Gan, and M. A. Krousel-Wood, Role of exercise for type 2 diabetic patient management, *Southern Medical Journal* 95 (2002): 72–77.

79. N.F. Sheard, Moderate changes in weight and physical activity can prevent or delay the development of type 2 diabetes mellitus in susceptible individuals, *Nutrition Reviews* 61 (2003): 76–79; A. M. Swartz and coauthors, Increasing daily walking improves glucose tolerance in overweight women, *Preventive Medicine* 37 (2003): 356–362.

80. L. Dye, A. Lluch, and J. E. Blundell, Macronutrients and mental performance, *Nutrition* 16 (2000): 1021–1034.

81. J. F. Brun, C. Fedou, and J. Mercier, Postprandial reactive hypoglycemia, *Diabetes and Metabolism* 26 (2000): 337–351.

82. G. Pourmotabbed and A. E. Kitabchi, Hypoglycemia, *Obstetrics and Gynecology Clinics of North America* 28 (2001): 383–400.

83. M. V. Apte and J. S. Wilson, Alcohol-induced pancreatic injury, *Best Practice and Research: Clinical Gastroenterology* 17 (2003): 593–612.

84. U.S. Department of Agriculture and U.S. Department of Health and Human Services, *Dietary Guidelines for Americans, 2010*, available at http://www.health.gov/dietaryguidelines/2010.asp.

Consumer Corner 4

1. S. Liu, Intake of refined carbohydrates and whole grain foods in relation to risk of type 2 diabetes mellitus and coronary heart disease, *Journal of the American College of Nutrition* 21 (2002): 298–306.

2. T. Nathoo, C. P. Holmes, and A. Ostry, An analysis of Canadian food fortification policies: The case of B vitamins, *Health Promotion International* 20 (2005): 375–382.

Controversy 4

1. A. S. Levine, C. M. Kotz, and B. A. Gosnell, Sugars and fats: The neurobiology of preference, *Journal of Nutrition* 133 (2003): 831S–834S.

2. Economic Research Service, Estimating consumption of caloric sweeteners, *Amber Waves*, April 2003, available at http://webarchives.cdlib.org/sw1vh5dg3r/http://ers.usda.gov/Amberwaves/April03/Indicators/BehindData.htm.

3. B. M. Popkin and S. J. Nielsen, The sweetening of the world's diet, *Obesity Research* 11 (2003): 1325–1332; Statistics Canada – Food Statistics. Table 4.2 Sugars and Syrups http://www.statcan.gc.ca/pub/21-020-x/2009001/tablesectlist-listetableauxsect-eng.htm.

4. M. Nestle, as quoted by O. Dyer, U.S. government rejects WHO's attempts to improve diet, *British Medical Journal* 328 (2004): 185.

5. V. S. Malik, M. B. Schulze, and F. B. Hu, Intake of sugar-sweetened beverages and weight gain: A systematic review, *American Journal of Clinical Nutrition* 84 (2006): 274–288; Joint WHO/FAO Expert Consultation, *Diet, Nutrition and the Prevention of Chronic Diseases* (Geneva, Switzerland: Word Health Organization, 2003), pp. 57–58; S. H. F. Vermunt and coauthors, Effects of sugar intake on body weight: A review, *Obesity Reviews* 4 (2003):91–99.

6. A. K. Kant, Consumption of energy-dense, nutrient-poor foods by adult Americans: Nutrition and health implications, The Third National Health and Nutrition Examination Survey, 1988–1994, *American Journal of Clinical Nutrition* 72 (2000): 929–936.

7. L. Harnack, J. Stang, and M. Story, Soft drink consumption among U.S. children and adolescents: Nutritional consequences, *Journal of the American Dietetic Association* 99 (1999): 436–441.

8. A. M. Coulston and R. K. Johnson, Sugar and sugars: Myths and realities, *Journal of the American Dietetic Association* 102 (2002): 351–353; J. F. Guthrie and J.F. Morton, Food sources of added sweeteners in the diets of Americans, *Journal of the American Dietetic Association* 100 (2000): 43–48.

9. D. S. Ludwig, K. E. Peterson, and L. S. Gortmaker, Relation between consumption of sugar-sweetened drinks and childhood obesity: A prospective, observational analysis, *Lancet* 357 (2001): 505–508; R. P. Troiano and coauthors, Energy and fat intakes of children and adolescents in the United States: Data from the National Health and Nutrition Examination Surveys, *American Journal of Clinical Nutrition* 72 (2000): 1343S–1353S.

10. D. P. DiMeglio and R. D. Mattes, Liquid versus solid carbohydrate: Effects of food intake and body weight, *International Journal of Obesity* 24 (2000): 794–800.

11. G. A. Bray, S. J. Nielsen, and B. M. Popkin, Consumption of high-fructose corn syrup in beverages may play a role in the epidemic of obesity, *American Journal of Clinical Nutrition* 79 (2004): 537–543; S. J. Nielsen and B. M. Popkin, Changes in beverage intake between 1977 and 2001, *American Journal of Preventive Medicine* 27 (2004): 205–210.

12. Bray, Nielsen, and Popkin, 2004 [see reference 11], S. S. Elliott and coauthors, Fructose, weight gain, and the insulin resistance syndrome, *American Journal of Clinical Nutrition* 76 (2002): 911–922.

13. Standing Committee on the Scientific Evaluation of Dietary Reference Intakes, Food and Nutrition Board, Institute of Medicine, *Dietary Reference Intakes for Energy, Carbohydrate, Fiber, Fat, Fatty Acids, Cholesterol, Protein, and Amino Acids* (Washington, D.C.: National Academies Press, 2002), pp. 6–35.

14. L. Lissner, B. L. Heitmann, and C. Bengtsson, Population studies of diet and obesity, *British Journal of Nutrition* 83 (2000): S21–S24.

15. Popkin and Nielsen, 2003 [see reference 3].

16. A. S. Levine, C. M. Kotz, and B. A. Gosnell, Sugars: Hedonic aspects, neuroregulation, and energy balance, *American Journal of Clinical Nutrition* 78 (2003): 834S–842S; M. Kanazawa and coauthors, Effects of a high-sucrose diet on body weight, plasma triglycerides, and stress tolerance, *Nutrition Reviews* 61 (2003): S27–S33.

17. Levine, Kotz, and Gosnell, 2003 [see reference 16].

18. Joint WHO/FOA Expert Consultation, 2003, pp. 72–80 [see reference 5].

19. Joint WHO/FOA Expert Consultation, 2003, pp. 72–80 [see reference 5].

20. K. A. Meyer and coauthors, Carbohydrates, dietary fiber, and incident type 2 diabetes in older women, *American Journal of Clinical Nutrition* 71 (2000): 921–930.

21. M. B. Schulze and coauthors, Sugar-sweetened beverages, weight gain, and incidence of type 2 diabetes in young and middle-aged women, *Journal of the American Medical Association* 292 (2004): 927–934; Centers for Disease Control and Prevention, Prevalence of overweight and obesity among adults with diagnosed diabetes—United States, 1988–1994 and 1999–2002, *Morbidity and Mortality Weekly Report* 53 (2004): 1066–1068.

22. M. K. Hellerstein, Carbohydrate-induced hypertriglyceridemia: Modifying factors and implications for cardiovascular risk, *Current Opinion in Lipidology* 13 (2002): 33–40; E. J. Parks, Changes in fat synthesis influenced by dietary macronutrient content, *Proceedings of the Nutrition Society* 61 (2002): 281–286.

23. Kanazawa and coauthors, 2003 [see reference 16]; A. Raben and A. Astrup, Ad libitum intake of low-fat diets rich in either starchy foods or sucrose: Effects on blood lipids, factor VII coagulant activity, and fibrinogen, *Metabolism: Clinical and Experimental* 49 (2000): 731–735; J. P. Bantle and coauthors, Effects of dietary fructose on plasma lipids in healthy subjects, *American Journal of Clinical Nutrition* 72 (2000): 1128–1134; F. Abbasi and coauthors, High carbohydrate diets, triglyceride-rich lipoproteins, and coronary heart disease risk, *American Journal of Cardiology* 85 (2000): 45–48.

24. E. J. Parks and M. K. Hellerstein, Carbohydrate-induced hypertriacylglycerolemia: Historical perspective and review of biological mechanisms, *American Journal of Clinical Nutrition* 71 (2000): 412–433.

25. Standing Committee on the Scientific Evaluation of Dietary Reference Intakes, 2002, pp. 6–29 [see reference 13].

26. J. M. Schwarz and coauthors, Hepatic de novo lipogenesis in normoinsulinemic and hyperinsulinemic subjects consuming high-fat, low-carbohydrate and low-fat, high-carbohydrate isoenergetic diets, *American Journal of Clinical Nutrition* 77 (2003): 43–50; A. T. Erkkila and coauthors, *APOE* polymorphism and the hypertriglyceridemic effect of dietary sucrose, *American Journal of Clinical Nutrition* 73 (2001): 746–752.

27. S. Dosreis and coauthors, Parental perceptions and satisfaction with stimulant medication for attention-deficit hyperactivity disorder, *Journal of Developmental and Behavioral Pediatrics* 24 (2003): 155–162.

28. Meyer and coauthors, 2000 [see reference 20].

29. Dosreis and coauthors, 2003 [see reference 26].

30. Standing Committee on the Scientific Evaluation of Dietary Reference Intakes, 2002, pp. 6–24 [see reference 13].

31. D. Benton and S. Nabb, Carbohydrate, memory, and mood, *Nutrition Reviews* 61 (2003): S61–S67; C. E. Greenwood, Dietary carbohydrate, glucose regulation, and cognitive performance in elderly persons, *Nutrition Reviews* 61 (2003): S68–S74.

32. S. Gibson and S. Williams, Dental caries in pre-school children: Associations with social class, toothbrushing habit and consumption of sugars and sugar-containing foods. Further analysis of data from the National Diet and Nutrition Survey of children aged 1.5–4.5 years, *Caries Research* 33 (1999): 101–113.

33. S. Kashket and D. P. DePaola, Cheese consumption and the development and progression of dental caries, *Nutrition Reviews* 60 (2002): 97–103; Department of Health and Human Services, *Oral Health in America: A Report of the Surgeon General* (Rockville, MD: National Institutes of Health, 2000), pp. 250–251.

34. Joint WHO/FAO Expert Consultation, 2003, p. 119 [see reference 5].

35. Position of the American Dietetic Association: Oral health and nutrition, *Journal of the American Dietetic Association* 103 (2003): 615–625.

36. Joint WHO/FAO Expert Consultation, 2003, p. 119 [see reference 5].

37. K. McNutt, What clients need to know about sugar replacers, *Journal of the American Dietetic Association* 100 (2000): 466–469.

38. Fact Sheet: The report on carcinogens, 9th ed., National Institutes of Health News Release, available at http://www.nih.gov/news/pr/may2000/niehs-15.htm.

39. National Cancer Institute, Artificial sweeteners and cancer, 2009, available at http://www.cancer.gov/cancertopics/factsheet/Risk/artificial-sweeteners.

40. S. M. Cohen and coauthors, Calcium phosphate-containing precipitate and the carcinogenicity of sodium salt in rats, *Carcinogenesis* 21 (2000): 783–792.

41. Health Canada comments on the recent study relating to the safety of aspartame, available at http://www.hc-sc.gc.ca/fn-an/securit/addit/sweeten-edulcor/aspartame_statement-eng.php; a bibliography of 167 research articles on aspartame can be found in J. Van de Kamp, Adverse effects of aspartame, *Current Bibliographies in Medicine* (Washington, D.C.: Government Printing Office, 1991).

42. Food and Drug Administration, Agency response letter GRAS Notice no. GRN 000078, October 25, 2001, available at http://www.fda.gov/Food/IngredientsPackagingLabeling/GRAS/NoticeInventory/ucm154191.htm.

43. E. Koyama and coauthors, Absorption and metabolism of glycosidic sweeteners of stevia mixture and their alglycone, steviol in rats and humans, *Food and Chemical Toxicology* 41 (2003): 875–883.

44. P. Chan and coauthors, A double-blind placebo-controlled study of the effectiveness and tolerability of oral stevioside in human hypertension, *British Journal of Clinical Pharmacology* 50 (2000): 215–220.

45. A. Raben and coauthors, Sucrose compared with artificial sweeteners: Different effects on ad libitum food intake and body weight after 10 wk of supplementation in overweight subjects, *American Journal of Clinical Nutrition* 76 (2002): 721–729.

46. Raben and coauthors, 2002 [see reference 45].

47. M.-P. St-Onge and S. B. Heymsfield, Usefulness of artificial sweeteners for body weight control, *Nutrition Reviews* 61 (2003): 219–220.

48. G. H. Anderson and D. Woodend, Effect of glycemic carbohydrates on short-term satiety and food intake, *Nutrition Reviews* 61 (2003): S17–S26.

5 The Lipids: Fats, Oils, Phospholipids, and Sterols

Do You Ever . . .

Think of fats as unhealthy food constituents that are best eliminated from the diet?

Wonder about the differences between "bad" and "good" cholesterol?

Choose fish for health's sake without fully knowing why?

Recognize the invisible fats in your foods?

Keep Reading . . .

Learning Objectives

After completing this chapter, you should be able to

LO 5.1 Discuss why a moderate intake of lipids is an essential part of a healthy diet.

LO 5.2 Compare and contrast the physical properties and food sources of saturated and monounsaturated fats.

LO 5.3 Generally describe how and where lipids are broken down, absorbed, and transported throughout the body, used to make the phospholipids of all of our cell membranes and to make hormones and numerous bioactive compounds.

LO 5.4 Describe the significance of the blood tests for HDL and LDL cholesterol.

LO 5.5 Describe the roles of omega-3 and omega-6 fatty acids in the body and the importance of achieving a balanced intake.

LO 5.6 Justify the recommendation to eat fatty fish instead of relying on fish oil supplements.

LO 5.7 Describe the formation and structure of *trans* fatty acids, and discuss the possibility of eliminating them from the diet.

LO 5.8 Develop a diet plan that provides enough of the right kinds of fats within Calorie limits.

Contents

A health-care provider reports, "Your blood **cholesterol** is high." Your physician advises, "You must cut down on the saturated **fats** in your diet and replace them with **oils** to lower your risk of **cardiovascular disease (CVD)**." Blood cholesterol, saturated fats, and oils—what are they, and how do they relate to health?

No doubt you are expecting to hear that fat-related compounds can harm your health, but **lipids** are also valuable. In fact, lipids are absolutely necessary. The diet recommended for health is moderate in fats, but it is by no means a "no-fat" diet. Luckily, at least traces of fats and oils are present in almost all foods, so you needn't make an effort to eat any extra as long as your diet is balanced among nutritious foods.

Introducing the Lipids

The lipids in foods and in the human body fall into three classes. About 95 percent are **triglycerides**. The other classes of the lipid family are the **phospholipids** (of which **lecithin** is one) and the **sterols** (cholesterol is the best known of these). Some of these names may sound unfamiliar, but most people will recognize at least a few functions of lipids in the body and in food that are listed in Table 5–1. More details on each of the lipid classes follow later.

Usefulness of Fats in the Body

When people speak of fat, they are usually talking about triglycerides. The term *fat* is more familiar, though, and we will use it in this discussion. Fat is the body's chief storage form for the energy from food eaten in excess of need. The storage of fat is a valuable survival mechanism for people who live a feast-or-famine existence: stored during times of plenty, fat enables them to remain alive during times of famine. Fats also provide most of the energy needed to perform much of the body's work, especially muscular work.

cholesterol (koh-LESS-ter-all) a member of the group of lipids known as sterols; a soft, waxy substance made in the body for a variety of purposes and also found in animal-derived foods.

fats lipids that are solid at room temperature (20°C or 68°F).

oils lipids that are liquid at room temperature (20°C or 68°F).

cardiovascular disease (CVD) disease of the heart and blood vessels; disease of the arteries of the heart is called *coronary heart disease* (CHD).

lipids (LIP-ids) a family of organic (carbon-containing) compounds soluble in organic solvents but not in water. Lipids include triglycerides (fats and oils), phospholipids, and sterols.

triglycerides (try-GLISS-er-ides) one of the three main classes of dietary lipids and the chief form of fat in foods and in the human body. A triglyceride is made up of three units of fatty acids and one unit of glycerol (fatty acids and glycerol are defined later). Triglycerides are also called *triacylglycerols*.

Table 5–1

The Usefulness of Fats

Fats in the Body	Fats in Food
■ **Energy stores** Fats are the body's chief form of stored energy. ■ **Muscle fuel** Fats provide most of the energy to fuel muscular work. ■ **Emergency reserve** Fats serve as an emergency fuel supply in times of illness and diminished food intake. ■ **Padding** Fats protect the internal organs from shock through fat pads inside the body cavity. ■ **Insulation** Fats insulate against temperature extremes through a fat layer under the skin. ■ **Cell membranes** Fats form the major material of cell membranes. ■ **Raw materials** Fats are converted to other compounds, such as hormones, bile, numerous bioactive compounds, and vitamin D, as needed.	■ **Nutrient** Fats provide essential fatty acids. ■ **Energy** Fats provide a concentrated energy source in foods. ■ **Transport** Fats carry the fat-soluble vitamins A, D, E, and K along with some phytochemicals and assist in their absorption. ■ **Raw materials** Fats provide raw material for making needed products. ■ **Sensory appeal** Fats contribute to the taste and smell of foods. ■ **Appetite** Fats stimulate the appetite. ■ **Satiety** Fats contribute to feelings of fullness. ■ **Texture** Fats help make foods tender.

Thanks to internal fat pads, vital organs are cushioned from shock.

phospholipids (FOSS-foh-LIP-ids) one of the three main classes of dietary lipids. These lipids are similar to triglycerides, but each has a phosphorus-containing acid in place of one of the fatty acids. Phospholipids are present in *all* cell membranes.

lecithin (LESS-ih-thin) a phospholipid manufactured by the liver and also found in many foods; a major constituent of cell membranes.

sterols (STEER-alls) one of the three main classes of dietary lipids. Sterols have a structure similar to that of cholesterol.

essential fatty acids fatty acids that the body needs but cannot make in amounts sufficient to meet physiological needs.

Most body cells can store only limited fat, but some cells are specialized for fat storage. These fat cells seem able to expand almost indefinitely—the more fat they store, the larger they grow. An obese person's fat cells may be many times the size of a thin person's. Far from being a collection of inert sacks of fat, however, adipose (fat) tissue secretes hormones that help regulate the appetite and influence other body functions.*,[1] A fat cell is shown in Figure 5–1.

You may be wondering why the carbohydrate glucose is not the body's major form of stored energy. As mentioned in Chapter 4, glucose is stored in the form of glycogen. Because glycogen holds a great deal of water, it is quite bulky and heavy, and the body cannot store enough to provide energy for very long. Fats, however, pack tightly together without water and can store much more energy in a small space. Gram for gram, fats provide more than twice the energy of carbohydrates, making fats an efficient storage form of energy. The body fat found on a normal-weight, healthy person contains more than sufficient energy to fuel an entire marathon run or to battle disease should the person become ill and stop eating for a while.

Fat serves many other purposes in the body, too. Pads of fat surrounding the vital internal organs serve as shock absorbers. Thanks to these fat pads, you can ride a mountain bike or a motorcycle for many hours with no serious internal injuries. The fat blanket under the skin also insulates the body from extremes of temperature, thus assisting with internal climate control. Lipids are also important to all of the body's cells as part of their surrounding envelopes, the cell membranes.

Some essential nutrients are soluble in fat. They are therefore found mainly in foods that contain fat and are absorbed most efficiently from them. These nutrients are the fat-soluble vitamins: A, D, E, and K. Other essential nutrients, the **essential fatty acids**, constitute parts of the fats themselves. As a later section explains, the essential fatty acids serve as raw materials from which the body makes molecules it requires. Fat also aids in the absorption of some phytochemicals, plant constituents believed to benefit health (see Controversy 2).

KEY POINT

■ Lipids not only serve as energy reserves but also cushion the vital organs, protect the body from temperature extremes, carry the fat-soluble nutrients and phytochemicals, serve as raw materials, and provide the major component, that is, the fatty acids of phospholipids, of which *all* cell membranes are made.

Usefulness of Fats in Food

The energy density of fats makes foods rich in fat valuable in many situations. A gram of fat or oil delivers more than twice as many Calories as a gram of carbohydrate or

---

*Reference notes are found at the end of this chapter.

Figure 5–1
A Fat Cell

Within the fat cell, lipid is stored in a droplet. This droplet can greatly enlarge, and the fat cell membrane will grow to accommodate its swollen contents. More about fat tissue (also called *adipose tissue*) and body functions can be found in Chapter 9.

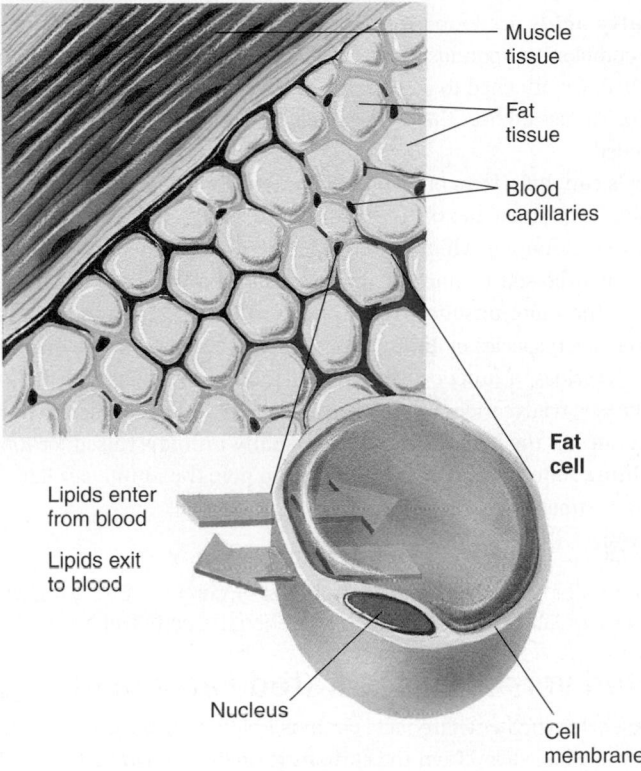

Muscle tissue

Fat tissue

Blood capillaries

Fat cell

Lipids enter from blood

Lipids exit to blood

Nucleus

Cell membrane

Figure 5–2
Two Lunches

Both lunches contain the same number of Calories, but the fat-rich lunch takes up less space and weighs less.

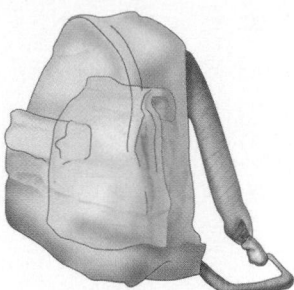

Carbohydrate-rich lunch
1 low-fat muffin
1 banana
60 g carrot sticks
250 mL fruit yogurt

Calories   = 550
Weight (g) = 500

Fat-rich lunch
6 butter-style crackers
45 g cheddar cheese
60 g trail mix with candy

Calories   = 550
Weight (g) = 115

- A reminder from Chapter 1:
  1 g carbohydrate = 4 Cal
  1 g fat = 9 Cal
  1 g protein = 4 Cal

protein. A hunter or hiker needs to consume a large amount of food energy to travel long distances or to survive in intensely cold weather. As Figure 5–2 shows, such a person can carry energy most efficiently in fat-rich foods. But for a person who is not expending much energy in physical work, those same high-fat foods may deliver many unneeded Calories in only a few bites.

People naturally like high-fat foods. Around the world, as fat becomes less expensive and more available in a given food supply, people seem to choose diets providing greatly increased amounts of fat. Fat carries with it many dissolved compounds that give foods enticing aromas and flavours, such as the aroma of frying bacon or French fries. In fact, when a sick person refuses food, dietitians offer foods flavoured with some fat to tempt that person to eat again. Fat also lends tenderness to foods such as meat and baked goods.

Fat also contributes to **satiety**, the satisfaction of feeling full after a meal. The fat of swallowed food triggers a series of physiological events that slow down the emptying of the stomach and promote satiety. Even so, before the sensation of fullness stops them,

Chapter 9 revisits the topic of appetite and its control.

people can easily overeat on fat-rich foods because the delicious taste of fat stimulates eating and each bite of a fat-rich food delivers many Calories.

KEY POINT

- Lipids provide more energy per gram than carbohydrate and protein, enhance the aromas and flavours of foods, and contribute to satiety, or a feeling of fullness, after a meal.

satiety (sat-EYE-uh-tee) the feeling of fullness or satisfaction that people experience after meals.

A Close Look at Lipids

Each class of lipids—triglycerides, phospholipids, and sterols—possesses unique characteristics. As mentioned, the term *fat* refers to triglycerides, the major form of lipid found in the body and in foods. Triglycerides, in turn, are made of fatty acids and glycerol.

Triglycerides: Fatty Acids and Glycerol

Very few **fatty acids** are found free in the body or in foods; most are incorporated into large, complex compounds: triglycerides. The name almost explains itself: three fatty acids (*tri*) are attached to a molecule of **glycerol** to form a triglyceride molecule (Figure 5–3). Tissues all over the body can easily assemble triglycerides or disassemble them as needed.

Fatty acids can differ from one another in two ways: in chain length and in degree of saturation (explained next). Triglycerides usually include mixtures of various fatty acids. Depending on which fatty acids are incorporated into a triglyceride, the resulting fat will be soft or hard. Triglycerides containing mostly the shorter-chain fatty acids or the more unsaturated ones are softer and melt more readily at lower temperatures. Each species of animal (including people) makes its own characteristic kinds of triglycerides, a function governed by genetics. Fats in the diet, though, can affect the types of triglycerides made because dietary fatty acids are often incorporated into triglycerides in the body.[2] For example, many animals raised for food can be fed diets containing softer or harder triglycerides to give the animals softer or harder fat, whichever consumers demand.

KEY POINT

- The body combines three fatty acids with one glycerol to make a triglyceride, its storage form of fat. Fatty acids in food influence the composition of fats in the body.

Saturated versus Unsaturated Fatty Acids

Saturation refers to whether a fatty acid chain is holding all of the hydrogen atoms it can hold. If every available bond from the carbons is holding a hydrogen, the chain forms a **saturated fatty acid**, sometimes abbreviated **SAFA**; it is filled to capacity with hydrogen. The zigzag structure on the left in Figure 5–4a represents a saturated fatty acid.

- There are three types of fatty acids: saturated, monounsaturated, and polyunsaturated.

fatty acids organic acids composed of carbon chains of various lengths. Each fatty acid has an acid end and hydrogens attached to all of the carbon atoms of the chain.

glycerol (GLISS-er-all) an organic compound, three carbons long, of interest here because it serves as the backbone for triglycerides.

saturated fatty acid (SAFA) a fatty acid carrying the maximum possible number of hydrogen atoms (having no points of unsaturation).

Figure 5–3

Triglyceride Formation

Glycerol, a small, water-soluble carbohydrate derivative, plus three fatty acids, equals a triglyceride.

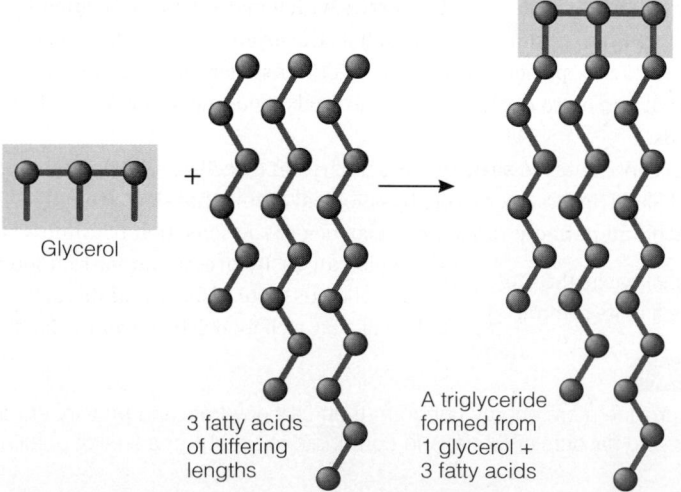

Glycerol

3 fatty acids of differing lengths

A triglyceride formed from 1 glycerol + 3 fatty acids

Sometimes, especially in the fatty acids of plants and fish, the chain has a place where hydrogens are missing: an "empty spot" or **point of unsaturation**. A fatty acid carbon chain that possesses one or more points of unsaturation is an **unsaturated fatty acid**. With one point of unsaturation, the fatty acid is a **monounsaturated fatty acid**, sometimes abbreviated **MUFA** (see the second structure in Figure 5–4a). With two or more points of unsaturation, it is a **polyunsaturated fatty acid**, sometimes abbreviated **PUFA** (see the third structure in Figure 5–4a; other examples are given later in the chapter). Figure 5–4b illustrates why we name certain families

When people add fat or oil to foods, they are adding triglycerides.

Figure 5–4a

Three Types of Fatty Acids

The more carbon atoms in a fatty acid, the longer it is. The more hydrogen atoms attached to those carbons, the more saturated the fatty acid is.

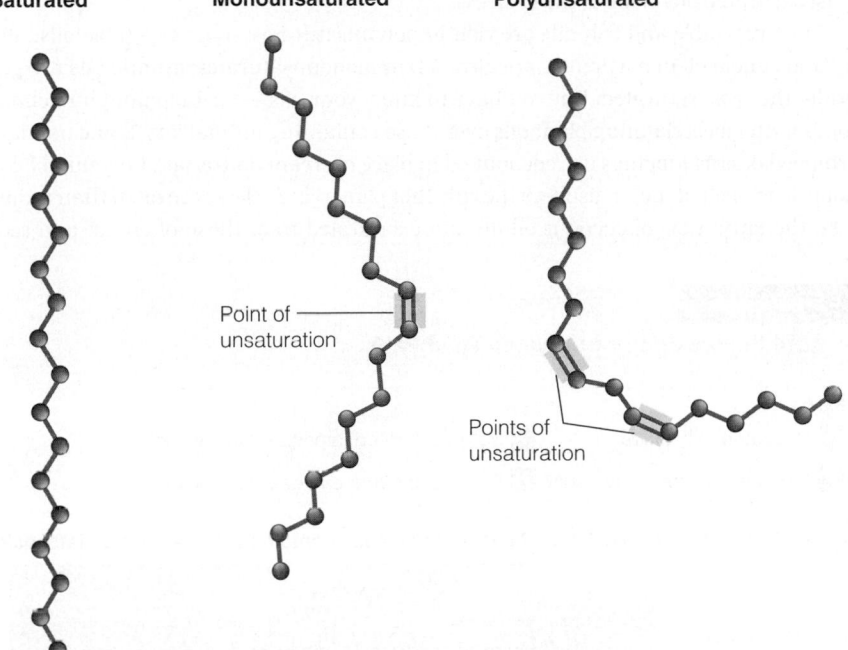

Saturated   Monounsaturated   Polyunsaturated

Point of unsaturation

Points of unsaturation

Figure 5–4b

Omega-3 and Omega-6 Fatty Acids Compared

Linolenic acid, an omega-3 fatty acid

Omega carbon

Methyl end

3

Acid end

Linoleic acid, an omega-6 fatty acid

Omega carbon

Methyl end

6

Acid end

point of unsaturation a site in a molecule where the bonding is such that additional hydrogen atoms can easily be attached.

unsaturated fatty acid a fatty acid that lacks some hydrogen atoms and has one or more points of unsaturation. An unsaturated fat is a triglyceride that contains one or more unsaturated fatty acids.

monounsaturated fatty acid (MUFA) a fatty acid containing one point of unsaturation.

polyunsaturated fatty acid (PUFA) a fatty acid with two or more points of unsaturation

of fatty acids the way we do: we count from the end of the molecule that has the methyl group and assign the family name based on where the first unsaturated/double bond occurs. For example, omega-3 fatty acids differ from omega-6 or omega-9 fatty acids due to the placement of the first unsaturated/double bond.

The degree of saturation of the fatty acids in a fat affects the temperature at which the fat melts. Generally, the more unsaturated the fatty acids, the more liquid the fat is at room temperature. In contrast, the more saturated the fatty acids, the firmer the fat. Thus, looking at three fats—beef tallow (a type of beef fat), chicken fat, and safflower oil—beef tallow is the most saturated and the hardest; chicken fat is less saturated and somewhat soft; and safflower oil, which is the most unsaturated, is a liquid at room temperature. If a health-care provider recommends limiting **saturated fats** or *trans* **fats** and using **monounsaturated fats** or **polyunsaturated fats** instead, you can generally judge by the hardness of the fats which ones to choose. Figure 5–5 compares the percentages of saturated, monounsaturated, and polyunsaturated fatty acids in various fats and oils. To determine whether an oil you use contains saturated fats, place the oil in a clear container in the refrigerator and watch for cloudiness. The least saturated oils remain the clearest.

Most vegetable and fish oils are rich in polyunsaturates; some vegetable oils, olive oil and canola oil in particular, are also rich in monounsaturates; animal fats are generally the most saturated. But you have to know your oils—it is not enough to choose foods with labels claiming plant oils over those containing animal fats. Some nondairy whipped dessert toppings use coconut oil in place of cream (butterfat). Coconut oil does come from a plant, but it disobeys the rule that plant oils are less saturated than animal fats; the fatty acids of coconut oil are more saturated than those of cream and seem

---

Figure 5–5

Acid Composition of Common Food Fats

Key:

- ▮ Saturated fatty acids
- ▒ Monounsaturated fatty acids
- ▨ Polyunsaturated, omega-6 fatty acids[a]
- ▤ Polyunsaturated, omega-3 fatty acids[a]

Animal fats and the tropical oils of coconut and palm contain mostly saturated fatty acids.

Coconut oil
Butter
Beef tallow (beef fat)
Palm oil
Lard (pork fat)
Chicken fat

Some vegetable oils, such as olive and canola, are rich in monounsaturated fatty acids.

Olive oil
Canola oil
Peanut oil

Many vegetable oils are rich in omega-6 polyunsaturated fatty acids.[a]

Safflower oil[b]
Sunflower oil
Corn oil
Soybean oil
Walnut oil
Cottonseed oil

Only a few oils provide significant omega-3 polyunsaturated fatty acids.[a]

Flaxseed oil
Fish oil[c]

[a]These families of polyunsaturated fatty acids are explained in a later section.
[b]Salad or cooking type over 70% linoleic acid.
[c]Fish oil average values derived from USDA data for salmon, sardine, and herring oils.

---

saturated fats triglycerides in which most of the fatty acids are saturated.

trans **fats** fats that contain unusual fatty acids; *trans* fatty acids are largely formed during processing; a later section provides details.

monounsaturated fats triglycerides in which most of the fatty acids have one point of unsaturation (are monounsaturated).

polyunsaturated fats triglycerides in which most of the fatty acids have two or more points of unsaturation (are polyunsaturated).

to add to heart disease risk.[3] Palm oil, a vegetable oil used in food processing, is also highly saturated and has been shown to elevate blood cholesterol.[4] Likewise, shortenings, stick margarine, and commercially fried or baked products may claim to be "all vegetable fat," but much of their fat may be of the harmful saturated or *trans* kind.

Researchers report a benefit to heart health when monounsaturated or polyunsaturated fats replace saturated fat and *trans* fat in the diet. When olive oil, rich in monounsaturated fatty acids, replaces other fats in the diet, it may even offer a degree of protection against heart disease, as evidence from Mediterranean regions suggests. In addition to abundant monounsaturated fatty acids, dark-coloured olive oils deliver valuable phytochemicals as well.[5] Canola oil, rich in both monounsaturated and polyunsaturated fatty acids, also supports heart health when replacing saturated fats in the diet. Dietitians of Canada (DC) and the American Dietetic Association (ADA) have released their joint position statement on dietary fatty acids (see http://www.dietitians.ca/downloadable-content/public/dietaryfats-position-paper.aspx). It provides an excellent overview of the current recommendations for fat intake and reinforces the point that unsaturated fatty acids should be the predominant source of fats in our diet.

Fats melt at different temperatures. The more unsaturated a fat, the more liquid it is at room temperature. The more saturated a fat, the higher the temperature at which it melts.

KEY POINT

- Fatty acids are energy-rich carbon chains that can be saturated (filled with hydrogens), monounsaturated (with one point of unsaturation), or polyunsaturated (with more than one point of unsaturation). The degree of saturation of the fatty acids in a fat determines the fat's softness or hardness.

Phospholipids and Sterols

Thus far, we have dealt with the largest of the three classes of lipids—the triglycerides and their component fatty acids. The other two classes—phospholipids and sterols—also play important roles in the body.

Phospholipids   A phospholipid, like a triglyceride, consists of a molecule of glycerol with fatty acids attached, but it contains two, rather than three, fatty acids. In place of the third is a molecule containing phosphorus, which makes the phospholipid soluble in water, while its fatty acids make it soluble in fat. This versatility permits any phospholipid to play a role in keeping fats dispersed in water—it can serve as an **emulsifier**.

Food processors blend fat with watery ingredients by way of **emulsification**. Some salad dressings separate to form two layers—vinegar on the bottom, oil on the top. Other dressings, such as mayonnaise, are also made from vinegar and oil but never separate. The difference lies in a special ingredient of mayonnaise, the emulsifier lecithin in egg yolks. Lecithin, a phospholipid, blends the vinegar with the oil to form the stable, spreadable mayonnaise.

Lecithin and other phospholipids also play key roles in the structure of cell membranes. Because phospholipids are emulsifiers, they have both water-loving and fat-loving characteristics, which enable them to help fats travel back and forth across the lipid-containing membranes of cells into the watery fluids on both sides. Health-promoting properties, such as the ability to lower blood cholesterol, are sometimes attributed to lecithin, but the people making the claims profit from selling supplements. Lecithin supplements have no special ability to promote health—the body can make all of the lecithin it needs.

Sterols   Sterols such as cholesterol are large, complicated molecules consisting of interconnected *rings* of carbon atoms with side chains of carbon, hydrogen, and oxygen attached. Cholesterol serves as the raw material for making another emulsifier, **bile**, which is important to digestion (see the next section for details). Other sterols include vitamin D, which is made from cholesterol, and the familiar steroid hormones, including the sex hormones.

Cholesterol is important in the structure of cell membranes and so is a part of every cell and necessary to the body's functioning. Like lecithin, cholesterol can be made by the body, so it is not an essential nutrient. Cholesterol is also a major component of the plaques that narrow the arteries in atherosclerosis, the underlying cause of heart attacks and strokes.

Chapter 3 first described the action of bile and gave details of the digestive system.

- *Trans* fats are the topic of a later section.

- The Controversy section explores the effects of fats in foods on the health of the heart.

emulsifier a substance that mixes with both fat and water and permanently disperses the fat in the water, forming an emulsion.

emulsification the process of mixing lipid with water by adding an emulsifier.

bile an emulsifier made by the liver from cholesterol and stored in the gallbladder. Bile does not digest fat as enzymes do but emulsifies it so that enzymes in the watery fluids may contact it and split the fatty acids from their glycerol for absorption.

- Phospholipids, including lecithin, play key roles in cell membranes; sterols play roles as part of bile, vitamin D, the sex hormones, and other important compounds.

Lipids in the Body

From the moment they enter the body, lipids affect the body's functioning and condition. They also demand special handling because fat separates from water, and body fluids consist largely of water.

Digestion and Absorption of Fats

A bite of food in the mouth first encounters the enzymes of saliva. One enzyme, produced by the tongue, plays a major role in digesting milk fat in infants but is of little importance to digestion in adults.[6]

After being chewed and swallowed, the food travels to the stomach, where the fat separates from the watery components and floats as a layer on the top. Fat does not mix well with the stomach fluids; however, some fat digestion is initiated in the stomach by gastric lipase.

As the stomach contents empty into the small intestine, the digestive system faces a problem: how to thoroughly mix fats, which are now separated and floating, with its own watery fluids. The solution is bile. A bile molecule, made from cholesterol, works because one of its ends attracts and holds fat, while the other end is attracted to and held by water.

When fat enters the small intestine, the gallbladder, which stores the liver's output of bile, contracts (due in part to the action of the hormone cholecystokinin produced by the small intestine) and squirts its bile into the intestine. Bile mixes fat particles with watery fluid by emulsifying them (see Figure 5–6), suspending them in the fluid until the fat-digesting enzymes contributed by the pancreas (e.g., pancreatic lipase) can split them into smaller particles for absorption. To review: first, the digestive system mixes fats with bile-containing digestive juices to emulsify the fats; then fat-digesting enzymes can break the fats down.

People sometimes wonder how a person without a gallbladder can digest food. The gallbladder is just a storage organ. Without it, the liver still produces bile but delivers it continuously into the small intestine. People who have had their gallbladders removed must initially reduce their fat intakes because they can no longer store bile and release it at mealtimes. As a result, their systems can handle only a little fat at a time.

Figure 5–6

The Action of Bile in Fat Digestion

Detergents are emulsifiers and work the same way, which is why they are effective in removing grease spots from clothes. Molecule by molecule, the grease is dissolved out of the spot and suspended in the water, where it can be rinsed away.

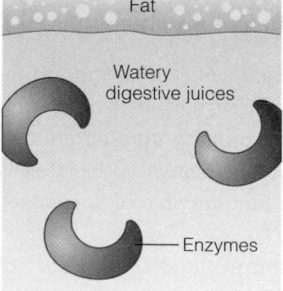

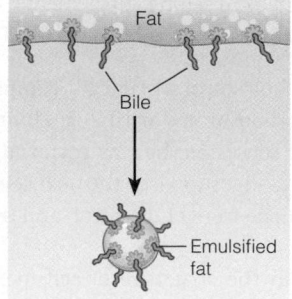

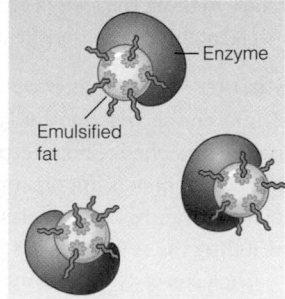

In the stomach, the fat and watery digestive juices tend to separate. Enzymes are in the water and can't get at the fat.

When fat enters the small intestine, the gallbladder secretes bile. Bile compounds have an affinity for both fat and water, so bile can mix the fat into the water.

After emulsification, more fat is exposed to the enzymes, and fat digestion proceeds efficiently.

monoglycerides (mon-oh-GLISS-er-ides) products of the digestion of lipids; consist of glycerol molecules with one fatty acid attached (*mono* means "one"; *glyceride* means "a compound of glycerol").

micelles spheres of lipids that form in the aqueous medium of the small intestine; with the help of bile, lipids become emulsified.

Once the intestine's contents are emulsified, fat-splitting enzymes act on triglycerides to split fatty acids from their glycerol backbones. Free fatty acids, glycerol, and **monoglycerides** cling together in spherical particles called **micelles**, which are surrounded by bile. At this point, the fats face another watery barrier, the watery layer of mucus that coats the absorptive lining of the digestive tract. Fats must traverse this layer to enter the cells of the digestive tract lining. The solution again depends on bile, this time in the balls of digested lipids. The bile shuttles the lipids across the watery mucus layer to the waiting absorptive cells of the intestinal villi. The cells then extract the lipids. The bile may be absorbed and reused by the body, or it may exit with the feces, as was shown in Figure 4–5 on page 122 in Chapter 4.

The digestive tract absorbs triglycerides from a meal with up to 98 percent efficiency. In other words, little fat is excreted by a healthy system. The process of fat digestion takes time, though, so the more fat taken in at a meal, the slower the digestive system action becomes. The efficient series of events just described is depicted in Figure 5–7.

Figure 5–7

The Process of Lipid Digestion and Absorption

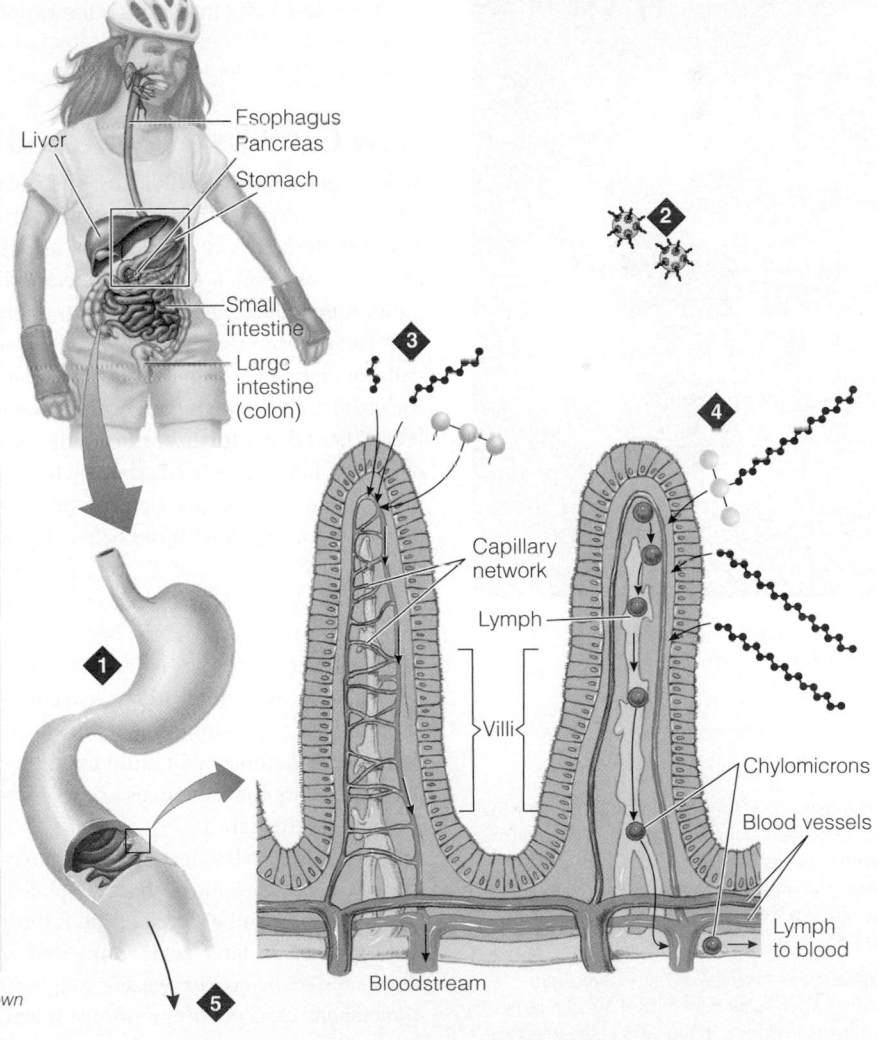

1 In the mouth and stomach:

Little fat digestion takes place.

2 In the small intestine:

Digestive enzymes accomplish most fat digestion in the small intestine. There, bile emulsifies fat, making it available for enzyme action. The enzymes cleave triglycerides into free fatty acids, glycerol, and monoglycerides.

3 At the intestinal lining:

The parts are absorbed by intestinal villi. Glycerol and short-chain fatty acids enter directly into the bloodstream.

4 The cells of the intestinal lining convert large lipid fragments, such as monoglycerides and long-chain fatty acids, back into triglycerides and combine them with protein, forming chylomicrons (a type of lipoprotein) that travel in the lymph vessels to the bloodstream.

5 In the large intestine:

A small amount of cholesterol trapped in fibre exits with the feces.

Liver
Esophagus
Pancreas
Stomach
Small intestine
Large intestine (colon)

Capillary network
Lymph
Villi
Chylomicrons
Blood vessels
Lymph to blood
Bloodstream

NOTE: In this diagram, molecules of fatty acids are shown as large objects, but, in reality, molecules of fatty acids are too small to see even with a powerful microscope, while villi are visible to the naked eye.

Source: P. A. Cotton and coauthors, "Dietary sources of nutrients among U.S. adults, 1994–1996." Journal of the American Dietetic Association *104 (2004): 921–930.*

- In the stomach, fats separate from other food components. In the small intestine, bile emulsifies the fats, enzymes digest them, and the intestinal cells absorb them.

Transport of Fats

The smaller products of lipid digestion, glycerol and shorter-chain fatty acids, pass directly through the cells of the intestinal lining into the bloodstream, where they travel unassisted to the liver. The larger lipids, however, present a problem for the body. As mentioned, fat floats in water. Without some mechanism to keep it dispersed, large lipid globules would separate out of the watery blood as it circulates around the body, disrupting the blood's normal functions. The solution to this problem lies in an ingenious use of proteins: many fats travel from place to place in the watery blood as passengers in **lipoproteins**, assembled packages of lipid and protein molecules.

The larger digested lipids, monoglycerides and long-chain fatty acids, must form lipoproteins before they can be released into the lymph that leads to the blood. Inside the intestinal cells, they are re-formed into triglycerides and clustered together with proteins and phospholipids to form **chylomicrons** that can safely travel in the watery blood. Chylomicrons form one type of lipoprotein (shown in Figure 5–7); other types receive attention later with regard to their profound effects on health.

- Small lipids travel in the bloodstream unassisted. Large lipids are incorporated into chylomicrons for transport in the lymph and blood. Blood and other body fluids are watery, so fats need special transport vehicles for the lipoproteins in order to carry them in these fluids.

How Can I Use My Stored Fat for Energy?

Many triglycerides eaten in foods are transported by the chylomicrons to the fat depots—muscles, breasts, the insulating fat layer under the skin, and others—where they are stored by the body's fat cells for later use. When a person's body starts to run out of available fuel from food, it begins to retrieve this stored fat to use for energy. (It also draws on its stored glycogen in the liver and muscles, as Chapter 4 described.) While muscle cells can draw on their own internal fat stores for energy, fat cells respond to additional calls for energy by dismantling stored fat molecules and releasing free fatty acids into the blood. Upon receiving these components, the energy-hungry cells (e.g., muscle cells) break them down further into small 2-carbon fragments using a process called beta-oxidation. Finally, each 2-carbon fat fragment is combined with a fragment derived from glucose, and the energy-releasing process continues as these combined fragments are further metabolized with the help of the Krebs cycle and the electron transport chain, liberating energy, carbon dioxide, and water. The way to use more of the energy stored as body fat, then, is to create a greater demand for it in the tissues by decreasing intake of food energy, by increasing the body's expenditure of energy, or both.

Whenever body fat is broken down to provide energy, carbohydrate must be available as well. Without carbohydrate, as described in Chapter 4 or under conditions of a very-low-carbohydrate diet or in starvation, products of incomplete fat breakdown (ketones) will build up in the blood and urine. Because the fat breakdown process and its consequences are so important in weight control, Chapter 9 describes them in greater detail.

The body can also store excess carbohydrate as fat, but this conversion is not energy efficient. Figure 5–8 illustrates a simplified series of steps from carbohydrate to fat. Before excess glucose can be stored as fat, it must first be broken into tiny fragments and then reassembled into fatty acids, steps that require energy to perform. Fat requires fewer chemical steps before storage. For weight-loss dieters, however, knowing these differences in metabolic costs of energy storage is less important than remembering what common sense tells us: successful weight loss depends on a low energy intake—not the proportion of energy nutrients.[7] Still, the proportions of certain lipids in the diet matter greatly, particularly to the health of the heart, as the next section makes clear.

Body fat supplies much of the fuel that muscles need to do their work.

© Sergey Peterman/Shutterstock

lipoproteins (LYE-poh-PRO-teens, LIH-poh-PRO-teens) clusters of lipids associated with protein, which serve as transport vehicles for lipids in blood and lymph. Major lipoprotein classes are the chylomicrons, the VLDL, the LDL, and the HDL.

chylomicrons (KYE-low-MY-krons) clusters formed when lipids from a meal are combined with carrier proteins in the cells of the intestinal lining. Chylomicrons transport food fats through the watery body fluids to the liver and other tissues.

Figure 5–8

Glucose to Fat

Glucose can be used for energy, or it can be changed into fat and stored.

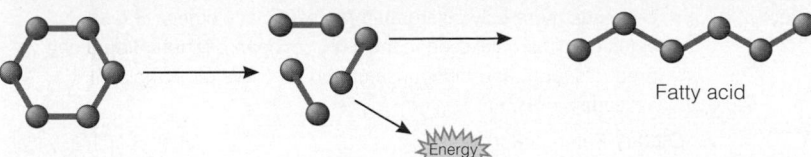

Fatty acid

| Glucose is broken down into fragments. | The fragments can provide immediate energy for the tissues. | Or, if the tissues need no more energy, the fragments can be reassembled, not back to glucose but into fatty acid chains. |

KEY POINT

- When low on fuel, the body draws on its stored fat for energy. Carbohydrate is necessary for the complete breakdown of fat.

Dietary Fat, Cholesterol, and Health

High intakes of certain dietary fats are associated with serious diseases. The person who chooses a diet too high in saturated fats or *trans* fats invites the risk of heart and artery disease [cardiovascular disease (CVD)], and heart disease is the number one killer of adults in Canada and the United States. As for cancer, research is mixed, but some studies suggest that a person who eats a high-fat diet may also incur a greater than average risk of developing some forms of cancer.[8] Obesity carries serious risks to health, and the high energy density of fatty foods makes it easy for people to exceed their energy needs and so gain unneeded weight. Much research has focused on the links between diet and disease, and Chapter 11 is devoted to these connections. Some points about fats and heart health are presented here because they underlie dietary recommendations concerning fats (see Table 5–2). More specifically, concerns surround the lipoproteins, their functions, and their roles in heart health.

Lipoproteins and Heart Disease Risk

As previously mentioned, the monoglycerides and long-chain fatty acids liberated from digested food fat must travel in the bloodstream as chylomicrons. These protein and phospholipid clusters act as emulsifiers, attracting both water and fat, to enable their large lipid passengers to travel dispersed in the watery body fluids. The tissues of the body can extract whatever fat they need from chylomicrons passing by in the bloodstream. The remnants are then picked up by the liver, which dismantles them and reuses their parts.

Major Lipoproteins: VLDL, LDL, HDL   In addition to the chylomicrons, the body uses three other types of lipoproteins to carry fats:

- **Very low-density lipoproteins (VLDL)**, which carry triglycerides and other lipids made in the liver to the body cells for their use.
- **Low-density lipoproteins (LDL)**, which transport cholesterol and other lipids to the tissues. LDL are made from VLDL after they have donated many of their triglycerides to body cells.
- **High-density lipoproteins (HDL)**, which are critical in the process of carrying cholesterol away from body cells to the liver for disposal.[9]

The last of two of these lipoproteins, LDL and HDL, play major roles with regard to heart health and are the focus of most recommendations made for reducing the risk

very low-density lipoproteins (VLDL) lipoproteins that transport triglycerides and other lipids from the liver to various tissues in the body.

low-density lipoproteins (LDL) lipoproteins that transport lipids from the liver to other tissues such as muscle and fat; contain a large proportion of cholesterol.

high-density lipoproteins (HDL) lipoproteins that return cholesterol from the tissues to the liver for dismantling and disposal; contain a large proportion of protein.

Table 5–2

Recommendations Concerning Intakes of Fats for Healthy People

1. Total fat[a]

Heart and Stroke Foundation of Canada[b]

- 45–75 g/day for a woman and about 60–105 g/day for a man).

American Heart Association

- Limit fat to 30% or less of total energy.

Dietary Reference Intakes[c]

- An acceptable range of fat intake is estimated at 20 to 35% of total Calories.

World Health Organization

- 15 to 30% of total Calories from fat

2. Saturated fat

Heart and Stroke Foundation of Canada

- Consume lower amounts of saturated fat.

Dietary Reference Intakes,[c] Dietary Guidelines for Americans, 2010

- Keep saturated fat intake to less than 10% of Calories by replacing them with monounsaturated and polyunsaturated fatty acids.

World Health Organization

- Less than 10% of total Calories from saturated fat

3. *Trans* fat

Heart and Stroke Foundation of Canada

- Consume a healthy balanced diet that includes lower amounts of *trans* fat.

World Health Organization

- Less than 1% of total Calories from *trans* fatty acids

4. Polyunsaturated fatty acids

Heart and Stroke Foundation of Canada[b]

- Consume more polyunsaturated fat, especially omega-3 fatty acids (fatty fish, flaxseed, canola oil, soybean oil, nuts, liquid egg products, etc.) and monounsaturated fat (olive oil, canola oil, avocados, nuts, etc.).

Dietary Reference Intakes

- Linoleic acid (5 to 10% of total Calories):
  17 g per day for young men
  12 g per day for young women
- Linolenic acid (0.6 to 1.2% of total Calories):
  1.6 g per day for men
  1.1 g per day for women

World Health Organization

- 6 to 10% of total Calories from omega-6 polyunsaturated fatty acid[d]
- 1 to 2% of total Calories from omega-3 polyunsaturated fatty acid[e]

5. Cholesterol

Dietary Reference Intakes[c]

- The consumption of saturated fat, *trans* fat, and cholesterol should be as low as possible while consuming a nutritionally adequate diet.

[a]*Includes monounsaturated fatty acids.*

[b]*Heart & Stroke Foundation of Canada Position Statement—Trans Fatty Acids ("Trans Fat") and Heart Disease and Stroke, http://www.heartandstroke.com/site/c .ikIQLcMWJtE/b.3799313/k.C112/Position_Statements__Trans_fatty_acids_position_statement.htm.*

[c]*For DRI values set for other life stages, see the inside front cover. Linoleic and linolenic acids are defined in Table 5-3 on page 177.*

[d]*The fatty acid family that includes linoleic acid (page 176).*

[e]*The fatty acid family that includes linolenic acid (page 176).*

- Here's a trick: Remember HDL is Healthy. LDL is Less healthy.

of heart disease. Figure 5–9 depicts typical lipoproteins and demonstrates how a lipoprotein's density changes with its lipid and protein contents.

The LDL and HDL Difference   The separate functions of LDL and HDL are worth a moment's attention because they carry important implications for the health of the heart and blood vessels. Both LDL and HDL carry lipids in the blood, but LDL are larger, lighter, and richer in cholesterol; HDL are smaller, denser, and packaged with more protein. To repeat: LDL deliver triglycerides and cholesterol from the liver to the tissues; HDL scavenge excess cholesterol and phospholipids from the tissues for disposal.

Both LDL and HDL carry cholesterol, but elevated LDL concentrations in the blood are a sign of high risk of heart attack, whereas elevated HDL concentrations are usually associated with a low risk. Thus, some people refer to LDL as "bad" cholesterol and HDL as "good" cholesterol—yet they carry the same kind of cholesterol. The difference to health between LDL and HDL lies in the proportions of lipids they contain and the tasks they perform, not in the *type* of cholesterol they carry.

The Importance of LDL and HDL Cholesterol   The importance of blood cholesterol to heart health cannot be overstated.* A blood lipid profile tells much about a

---

Blood, plasma, and *serum* all refer to about the same thing; this book uses the term *blood* cholesterol. Plasma is blood with the cells removed; in serum, the clotting factors are also removed. The concentration of cholesterol is not altered much by these treatments.

Figure 5–9

Lipoproteins

As the graph shows, the density of a lipoprotein is determined by its lipid-to-protein ratio. All lipoproteins contain protein, cholesterol, phospholipids, and triglycerides in varying amounts. An LDL has a high ratio of lipid to protein (about 80% lipid to 20% protein) and is especially high in cholesterol. An HDL has more protein relative to its lipid content (about equal parts lipid and protein).

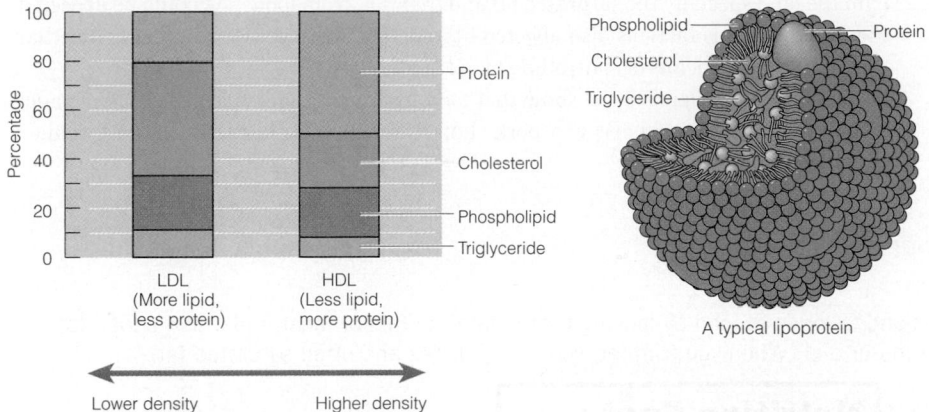

A typical lipoprotein

person's blood concentrations of cholesterol and the lipoproteins that carry it.[10] Blood LDL and HDL cholesterol account for two major risk factors for CVD (listed in the margin). A high blood LDL cholesterol concentration is a predictor of the likelihood of suffering a fatal heart attack or stroke, and the higher the LDL, the earlier the episode is expected to occur. Conversely, high HDL cholesterol signifies a *lower* disease risk.

KEY POINT

- The chief lipoproteins are chylomicrons, VLDL, LDL, and HDL. Blood LDL and HDL concentrations are among the major risk factors for heart disease.

⚡ What Does Food Cholesterol Have to Do with Blood Cholesterol?

The answer may be, "Not as much as most people think." Most saturated food fats (and *trans* fats; see later section) raise blood cholesterol more than food *cholesterol* does. When told that cholesterol doesn't matter as much as saturated fat, people may then jump to the wrong conclusion—that blood cholesterol doesn't matter. It does matter. High *blood* cholesterol is an indicator of risk for CVD. The main dietary factors associated with elevated blood cholesterol are high saturated fat and *trans* fat intakes. LDL cholesterol indicates a risk of heart disease because the LDL are carrying cholesterol, made mostly from saturated fat in the diet, to the body tissues to be deposited there.

Dietary cholesterol makes a smaller but still significant contribution to elevated blood cholesterol.[11] The margin lists the top five contributors to dietary cholesterol in the North American diet. Genetic inheritance modifies everyone's ability to handle dietary cholesterol somewhat. Many people (about 60%) exhibit little increase in their blood cholesterol even with a high dietary intake.[12] A smaller percentage responds to the same diet with greatly increased blood cholesterol. A few individuals have inherited a total inability to clear from their blood the cholesterol they have eaten and absorbed.

People with a genetic tendency toward high blood cholesterol must strictly limit fats and refrain from eating foods rich in cholesterol. For most others, a limited amount of eggs, liver, and other cholesterol-containing foods poses no threat of incurring high blood cholesterol because the body slows its cholesterol synthesis when the diet provides greater amounts. Moderation, not elimination, is key for most people as far as cholesterol-containing foods are concerned.

Standards for blood lipids are found in Figure 11–6 on page 467 in Chapter 11.

The More of These Factors Present in a Person's Life, the More Urgent the Need for Changes in Diet and Other Controllable Factors to Reduce Heart Disease Risk

- High blood LDL cholesterol
- Low blood HDL cholesterol
- High blood pressure (hypertension)
- Diabetes (insulin resistance)
- Obesity
- Physical inactivity
- Cigarette smoking
- An "atherogenic" diet (high in saturated fats, including *trans* fats, and low in vegetables, legumes, fruit, and whole grains)

● Family history, older age, and male gender are risk factors that cannot be changed.

These Five Foods Contribute about 70% of the Food Cholesterol in the North American Diet

- Eggs, 30%
- Beef, 16%
- Poultry, 12%
- Cheese, 6%
- Milk, 5%

Source: P. A. Cotton and coauthors, "Dietary sources of nutrients among U.S. adults, 1994–1996," Journal of the American Dietetic Association 104 (2004): 921–930.

■ Elevated blood cholesterol is a risk factor for cardiovascular disease. Among major dietary factors that raise blood cholesterol, saturated fat and *trans* fat intakes are the most influential. Dietary cholesterol raises blood cholesterol to a lesser degree.

Lowering LDL Cholesterol

To repeat, dietary saturated fat and *trans* fat are potent in triggering a rise in LDL cholesterol in the blood.[13] A dietary tactic often effective against high blood cholesterol is to trim the fat, especially the saturated fat and *trans* fat, from foods. As could be expected, the success of this tactic is also affected by genetics; some people respond better than others to dietary means of controlling blood lipids.[14]

The photos in Figure 5–10 show that food trimmed of fat is also trimmed of much of its saturated fat and energy. A pork chop trimmed of its border of fat loses almost

● Canadian reference standard for saturated fat and *trans* fat on food labels: 2,000-Cal diet: 20 g.

Figure 5–10

Food Fat, Saturated Fat, and Calories

You can find much of the saturated fat and Calories in food by looking for the fat. The fats of meat, milk, and added fats are major contributors of saturated fat in our diet. When you trim fat, you trim Calories and often saturated fat.

Nutrition Facts

Amount per Serving

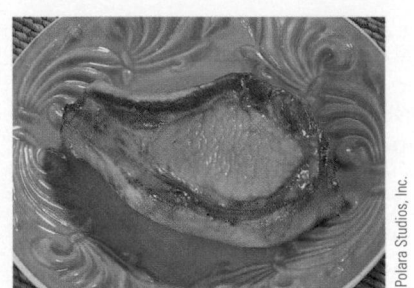

Pork chop (150 g) with ½ inch of fat

Calories 300	
	Daily (%)
Total Fat 20 g	**33**
Saturated Fat 7 g	**35**

Potato (180 g) with 1 tbs butter and 1 tbs sour cream

Calories 400 Calories from Fat 250	
	Daily (%)
Total Fat 28 g	**43**
Saturated Fat 18 g	**90**

Whole (3.25%)

Calories 150 Calories from Fat 70	
	Daily (%)
Total Fat 8 g	**12**
Saturated Fat 5 g	**25**

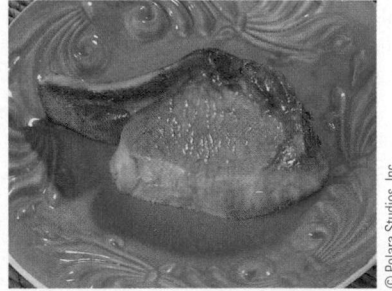

Pork chop (120 g) with fat trimmed off

Calories 240	
	Daily (%)
Total Fat 9.5 g	**16**
Saturated Fat 3.5 g	**17.5**

Plain potato (180 g)

Calories 150 Calories from Fat 0	
	Daily (%)
Total Fat 0 g	**0**
Saturated Fat 0 g	**0**

Skim milk (1 cup)

Calories 90 Calories from Fat 0	
	Daily (%)
Total Fat 0 g	**0**
Saturated Fat 0 g	**0**

Source: Data from ESHA Research, The Food Processor Nutrition and Fitness Software, version 8.3, 2004.

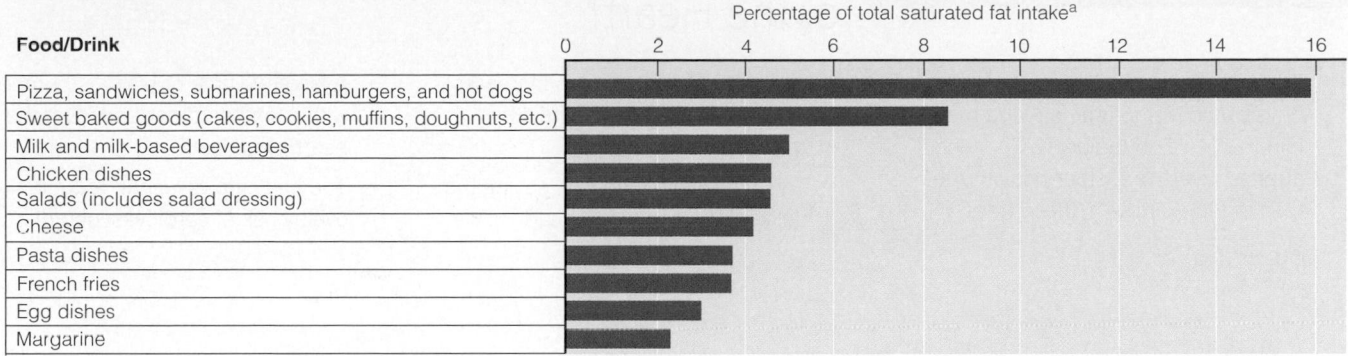

Figure 5–11

Top Contributors of Saturated Fats to the Canadian Diet

Percentage of total saturated fat intake[a]

Food/Drink	
Pizza, sandwiches, submarines, hamburgers, and hot dogs	
Sweet baked goods (cakes, cookies, muffins, doughnuts, etc.)	
Milk and milk-based beverages	
Chicken dishes	
Salads (includes salad dressing)	
Cheese	
Pasta dishes	
French fries	
Egg dishes	
Margarine	

[a]*Rounded values*

NOTE: Includes basic food and main recipes. Excludes women who were pregnant or breast-feeding.

Source: Data from Table 7 of the 2004 Canadian Community Health Survey 2.2 Nutrition, *"Foods and drinks accounting for most fat consumed, household population aged 4 or older, Canada excluding territories, 2004": www.statcan.ca/english/research/82-620 MIE/82-620-MIE2006002.pdf.*

Antioxidant nutrients are topics of Chapters 7 and 8; phytochemicals are discussed in Controversy 2; Chapter 11 provides perspective on the role of diet in heart disease prevention.

Chapter 11 presents many details about lowering LDL cholesterol, and the Controversy feature in this chapter helps distinguish between fats that may be harmful and those compatible with good health.

70 percent of its saturated fat and 220 Calories. A plain baked potato has no saturated fat and about 40 percent of the Calories of one with butter and sour cream. Choosing skim (fat-free), 1 percent, or 2 percent milk over whole milk provides large savings of fat, saturated fat, and Calories. The single most effective step you can take to reduce a food's potential for elevating blood cholesterol is to eliminate as much of its saturated fat and *trans* fat as possible. Figure 5–11 identifies top sources of fat in the Canadian diet. *Trans* fat sources are identified in a later figure.

As for HDL cholesterol, dietary measures are generally ineffective at significantly raising its concentrations.[15] Instead, regular physical activity defends against heart disease partly because it effectively raises HDL, as the Think Fitness feature points out.

An important detail about LDL concerns its susceptibility to damage by **oxidation**. Evidence points to oxidation of the lipid part of LDL as injurious to the arteries of the heart. Adequate intakes of **dietary antioxidants**, such as vitamin C, vitamin E, the mineral selenium, and antioxidant phytochemicals, may slow LDL oxidation.

KEY POINT

- Trimming fat from food trims Calories and often saturated fat and *trans* fat as well.

Recommendations Applied

Some health authorities recommend that all adults take steps to reduce their LDL cholesterol; others say that only those medically identified as having an elevated risk for heart disease should do so. In any case, most people are wise to choose a diet that provides 20 to 35 percent of its Calories from fat and that keeps saturated fat and *trans* fat as low as possible (less than 10% and 1% of Calories, respectively).[16] Controversy 5 in this chapter suggests substituting monounsaturated or polyunsaturated fats for artery-clogging saturated fats. No beneficial change in blood lipids occurs when monounsaturated or polyunsaturated fat is *added* to a diet rich in saturated or *trans* fat, however. A heart-healthy diet is also rich in fruit, vegetables, nuts, and whole grains that offer many health advantages by supplying abundant nutrients and antioxidants along with beneficial fibre.

What about cholesterol intake? The best course is to proceed with caution. Eggs, shellfish, liver, and other cholesterol-containing foods are nutritious. Cholesterol

oxidation interaction of a compound with oxygen; in this case, a damaging effect by a chemically reactive form of oxygen (Chapter 7 provides details).

dietary antioxidant (anti-OX-ih-dant) a substance in food that significantly decreases the damaging effects of reactive compounds, such as reactive forms of oxygen and nitrogen on tissue functioning (*anti* means "against"; oxy means "oxygen").

Dietary Fat, Cholesterol, and Health

Every leading authority recommends physical activity to promote and maintain the health of the heart. The blood, arteries, heart, and other body tissues respond to exercise in these ways:

- Blood HDL concentration increases, shifting blood lipids in a healthy direction.
- The circulation improves, easing the delivery of blood to the heart.

- A larger volume of blood is pumped with each heartbeat, reducing the heart's workload.
- The body grows leaner, reducing overall risk of cardiovascular disease.

---

differs from salt and added fats and sugar in this respect: it cannot be omitted from the diet without omitting nutritious foods. As mentioned, cholesterol is not an essential nutrient—the body makes plenty for itself—but the foods rich in cholesterol are often also rich in nutrients. A caution is in order, however: many high-cholesterol foods, such as cheeseburgers, are also high in saturated fat.

KEY POINT

- Dietary measures to lower LDL in the blood involve reducing saturated fat and *trans* fat and substituting monounsaturated and polyunsaturated fats. Cholesterol-containing foods are nutritious and are best used in moderation by most people.

Essential Polyunsaturated Fatty Acids

Although saturated, *trans*, and monounsaturated fatty acids are not essential, the human body needs certain essential fatty acids. Two of these are **linoleic acid** and **linolenic acid**. Body cells cannot make these two polyunsaturated fatty acids from scratch, nor can the cells convert one to the other. Linoleic and linolenic acids must be supplied by the diet and are therefore essential nutrients.

The essential fatty acids serve many functions in the body. They serve as raw materials from which the body makes substances known as **eicosanoids** that act somewhat like hormones, affecting a wide range of diverse body functions, such as muscle relaxation and contraction; blood vessel dilation and constriction; blood clot formation; blood lipid regulation; and immune response to injury and infection including fever, inflammation, and pain.[17] A familiar drug, Aspirin, relieves fever, inflammation, and pain by slowing the synthesis of these eicosanoids.

Table 5–3 summarizes the many roles of the essential polyunsaturated fatty acids, and new functions continue to emerge. So important are these two fatty acids that the DRI committee has set recommended intake levels for them (see the margin).

Deficiencies of Essential Fatty Acids

A deficiency of an essential fatty acid in the diet leads to observable changes in cells, some more subtle than others. When the diet is deficient in *all* of the polyunsaturated fatty acids, symptoms of reproductive failure, skin abnormalities, and kidney and liver disorders appear. In infants, growth is retarded and vision is impaired. The body stores some essential fatty acids, so extreme deficiency disorders are seldom seen except when intentionally induced in research or on rare occasions when inadequate diets have been provided to infants or hospital patients by mistake.

The DRI-recommended intakes reflect average intakes of healthy people in Canada and the United States because deficiencies of essential polyunsaturated fatty acids severe enough to cause symptoms among healthy adults in these countries are unknown. The story doesn't end there, however. Research has established that a higher

---

- Dietary Reference Intakes for young adults (19–30 years old):

Linoleic Acid (5 to 10% of Total Calories)

- 17 g per day for young men (current intake ~14 g/day)
- 12 g per day for young women (current intake ~9.5 g/day)

Linolenic Acid (0.6 to 1.2% of Total Calories)

- 1.6 g per day for men (current intake ~2.5 g/day)
- 1.1 g per day for women (current intake ~1.5 g/day)

For other life stages, see inside the front cover.

linoleic (lin-oh-LAY-ic) **acid** (an omega-6 fatty acid) and **linolenic** (lin-oh-LEN-ic) **acid** (an omega-3 fatty acid) polyunsaturated fatty acids that are essential nutrients for human beings. The full name of linolenic acid is *alphalinolenic acid*.

eicosanoids (eye-COSS-ah-noyds) biologically active compounds that regulate body functions.

intake of certain fatty acids, the omega-3 fatty acids, can often improve the health of the heart. Note: The upper end of the AMDR for polyunsaturated fatty acids is 10 percent of total Calories.

Omega-6 and Omega-3 Fatty Acid Families

Linoleic acid is the "parent" member of the **omega-6 fatty acid** family, so named for the chemical structure of these compounds. Given dietary linoleic acid, the body can produce other needed members of the omega-6 family. One of these is **arachidonic acid**, notable for its role as a starting material from which a number of eicosanoids are made.

Linolenic acid is the parent member of the **omega-3 fatty acid** family. Given dietary linolenic acid, the body can make other members of the omega-3 series. Two family members of great interest to researchers in the field of heart health are **EPA** and **DHA**.[18] The body makes only limited amounts of these omega-3 fatty acids, but they are found abundantly in the oils of certain fish. Those interested in the effects and developments regarding of these fatty acids and health can remain up to date by visiting the DHA·EPA Omega 3 Institute at http://dhaomega3.org/index.php on a regular basis.

Years ago, someone thought to ask why the Native peoples of Greenland and Alaska, who eat a diet very high in fat, have such low rates of death from heart disease.[19] The trail led to the abundant fish and other marine life in their diets, then to the oils in fish, and finally to EPA and DHA in fish oils.[20] Furthermore, as younger generations of Native peoples of the north abandon traditional marine-based diets for more modern foodways, their rates of high blood pressure, elevated blood lipids, diabetes, and obesity soar.[21]

Although not every study supports a benefit from fish and fish oil, results from many population studies and controlled clinical trials support a recommendation to eat fish.[22] It seems safe to say that a diet that includes two meals of fatty fish each week can reduce deaths and illness from heart disease, especially in people who have already suffered a heart attack. It also seems clear that fish is more beneficial than supplements of fish oil.[23]

Current research suggests that linolenic acid, the chemical parent of the omega-3 family, may benefit heart health as well.[24] Evidence is also mounting to suggest that omega-3 fatty acids may support immunity and inhibit development of certain cancers.[25] Potential mechanisms for beneficial effects of these remarkable lipids are listed in Table 5–4.

Recommendations for Omega-3 Fatty Acid Intake

For healthy people, a normal balanced diet that includes grains, seeds, nuts, leafy vegetables, oils, and fish supplies all of the needed forms of fatty acids in abundance and prevents deficiencies. Including fatty fish in a meal two or three times a week, for a total of about 350 to 425 grams of fish per week, can help achieve a healthy balance between omega-3 and omega-6 fatty acid intakes needed for health.[26] To improve the balance further, foods high in omega-6 fatty acids, such as most vegetable oils and other fats, should be consumed in moderation.

Greater heart benefits can be expected when fish is grilled, baked, or broiled, partly because the varieties prepared this way often contain more EPA and DHA than species used for fried fish in fast-food restaurants and frozen products. Additionally, benefits result from avoiding commercial frying fats, which are often laden with saturated fat and *trans* fat. Further benefits arise when fish displaces high-fat meats or other foods rich in saturated fats in several meals each week.[27] Table 5–5 lists sources of both omega-6 and omega-3 fatty acids.

Fish Oil Supplements

Taking fish oil supplements is not recommended, although many claims are made for their power to cure diseases. The Natural Health Products Directorate (NHPD) of Health Canada

---

Table 5–3

Functions of the Essential Fatty Acids

These roles for the essential fatty acids are known, but others are under investigation.

Linoleic and linolenic acid:
- Provide raw material for eicosanoids.
- Serve as structural and functional parts of cell membranes.
- Contribute lipids to the brain and nerves.
- Promote normal growth and vision.
- Assist in gene regulation.
- Maintain outer structures of the skin, thus protecting against water loss.
- Help regulate genetic activities affecting metabolism.
- Support immune cell functions.

Canada's Food Guide—Oils and Fats
- Include a small amount—30 to 45 mL (2 to 3 tbs)—of unsaturated fat each day. This includes oil used for cooking, salad dressings, margarine, and mayonnaise

---

omega-6 fatty acid a polyunsaturated fatty acid with its endmost double bond six carbons from the end of the carbon chain. Linoleic acid is an example.

arachidonic (ah-RACK-ih-DON-ik) **acid** an omega-6 fatty acid derived from linoleic acid.

omega-3 fatty acid a polyunsaturated fatty acid with its endmost double bond three carbons from the end of the carbon chain. Linolenic acid is an example.

EPA, DHA eicosapentaenoic (EYE-cossa-PENTA-ee-NO-ick) acid, docosahexaenoic (DOE-cossa-HEXA-ee-NO-ick) acid; omega-3 fatty acids made from linolenic acid in the tissues of fish.

Table 5–4

Potential Health Benefits of Fish Oils

Research suggests these benefits from fish or fish oil as part of a healthy diet:

Against heart disease (supported by most studies):

- A shift toward omega-3 eicosanoids by reducing production of omega-6 eicosanoids. This shift may reduce abnormal blood clotting, help sustain more regular heartbeats, and reduce inflammation of many body tissues, including the arteries of the heart.[a]
- Reduced blood triglycerides (in some studies, fish oil supplements elevated blood LDL cholesterol, an opposing, detrimental outcome).[b]
- Retarded hardening of the arteries (atherosclerosis).[c]
- Relaxation of blood vessels, mildly reducing blood pressure.[d]

In infant growth and development (well researched and accepted):

- Normal brain development in infants. DHA concentrates in the brain's cortex, the conscious thinking part.[e]
- Normal vision development in infants. DHA helps form the eye's retina, the seat of normal vision.

Against cancer (early research promising but requires further investigation):

- Eicosanoid shift that may oppose cancer.[f]
- Altered genetic activities that affect cell metabolism, possibly inhibiting cancer development.
- Other potential effects that inhibit certain cancers.[g]

[a]J. N. Din, D. E. Newby, and A. D. Flapan, Omega 3 fatty acids and cardiovascular disease—Fishing for a natural treatment, British Medical Journal 328 (2004): 30–35; H. Tapiero and coauthors, Polyunsaturated acids (PUFA) and eicosanoids in human health and pathologies, Biomedicine and Pharmacotherapy 56 (2002): 215–222; I. Hiroyasu and coauthors, Intake of fish and omega-3 fatty acids and risk of stroke in women, Journal of the American Medical Association 285 (2001): 304–312; R. De Caterina, J. K. Liao, and P. Libby, Fatty acid modulation of endothelial activation, American Journal of Clinical Nutrition 71 (2002): 213S–223S.

[b]M. Laidlaw and F. J. Holub, Effects of supplementation with fish oil–derived n-3 fatty acids and gamma-linolenic acid on circulating plasma lipids and fatty acid profiles in women, American Journal of Clinical Nutrition 77 (2003): 37–42; T. A. Mori and L. J. Beilin, Long-chain omega 3 fatty acids, blood lipids and cardiovascular risk reduction, Current Opinions in Lipidology 12 (2001): 11–17.

[c]R. A. Christon, Mechanisms of action of dietary fatty acids in regulating the activation of vascular endothelial cells during atherogenesis, Nutrition Reviews 61 (2003): 272–279.

[d]M. M. Engler and coauthors, Effects of docosahexaenoic acid on vascular pathology and reactivity in hypertension, Experimental Biology and Medicine 228 (2003): 229–307; T. A. Mori and coauthors, Differential effects of eisosapentanoic acid and docosahexaenoic acid on vascular reactivity of the forearm microcirculation in hyperlipidemic, overweight men, Circulation 102 (2002): 1264–1269.

[e]R. Uauy and P. Mena, Lipids and neurodevelopment, Nutrition Reviews 59 (2001): S34–S48.

[f]S. C. Larsson and coauthors, Dietary long-chain n-3 fatty acids for the prevention of cancer: A review of potential mechanisms, American Journal of Clinical Nutrition 79 (2004): 935–945.

[g]M. F. Leitzman and coauthors, Dietary intake of n-3 and n-6 fatty acids and the risk of prostate cancer, American Journal of Clinical Nutrition 80 (2004): 204–216.

Table 5–5

Food Sources of Omega-6 and Omega-3 Fatty Acids

Omega-6	
Linoleic acid	Leafy vegetables, seeds, nuts, grains, vegetable oils (corn, cottonseed, safflower, sesame, soybean, sunflower), poultry fat
Omega-3	
Linolenic acid[a]	Oils (canola, flaxseed, soybean, walnut, wheat germ; liquid or soft margarine made from canola or soybean oil)
	Nuts and seeds (butternuts, fresh ground flaxseeds, walnuts, soybeans) Vegetables (soybeans)
EPA and DHA	Human milk (levels depend on mother's status and intake)
	Omega-3 milk beverage
	Fatty cold-water fish[b] (mackerel, salmon, bluefish, mullet, sablefish, menhaden, anchovy, herring, lake trout, sardines, tuna)
	Omega-3 eggs

[a]Gamma-linolenic acid is found, for example, in the seed oil of the herb evening primrose.

[b]All of these fish except tuna provide at least 1 g of omega-3 fatty acids in 100 g of fish (3.5 oz); the fish oil content of each species varies with the season and site of harvest. Tuna provides fewer omega-3 fatty acids, but because it is commonly consumed, its contribution can be significant.

allows claims on approved fish oil products such as "Source of omega-3 fatty acids for the maintenance of good health" (see http://webprod.hc-sc.gc.ca/nhpid-bdipsn/monoReq .do?id=88&lang=eng). But keep in mind that the high levels of vitamin A in some fish oil products available in Canadian jurisdictions (e.g., in cod liver or halibut liver oil) may not be safe for females planning a family.

Fish is a good source of omega-3 fatty acids.

Chapter 12 provides more information on the contaminants from human activities that end up in the earth's oceans and lakes.

Supplements of fish oil may raise LDL cholesterol and may not be the best choice for a number of reasons. Most important among them, high intakes of omega-3 polyunsaturated fatty acids may increase bleeding time, interfere with wound healing, and suppress immune function.[28] Excessive amounts of either omega-6 or omega-3 fatty acids can interfere with normal functions that depend on a proper balance between the two.[29] Supplements also lack the other beneficial nutrients that fish provides, such as the minerals iodine and selenium and fish protein.

Yet another drawback is that fish oil supplements are made from fish skins and livers, which may have accumulated toxic concentrations of pesticides, heavy metals such as mercury, and other industrial contaminants. Unless the oils are refined to eliminate them, such contaminants can become further concentrated in the pills.[30]

In addition to contamination, fish oil naturally contains high levels of the two most potentially toxic vitamins, A and D. Lastly, supplements of fish oil are expensive. Considering these known drawbacks and that so little is known about the long-term effects of fish oil supplements, only one reasonable conclusion can be drawn: taking them is risky.

Also, those who may be concerned about the safety of fish oil consumption during pregnancy should read Health Canada's latest prenatal nutrition guidelines at http:// www.hc-sc.gc.ca/fn-an/nutrition/prenatal/qa-prenatal-qr-eng.php; these guidelines note that fish oil supplements (regarded as natural health products) are tested for heavy metals (including mercury) and pesticides, and so on.

Is Fish Safe to Eat?

On learning of the contamination of fish oils, consumers may wonder whether fish is safe to eat. The answer is a qualified yes. For most healthy people, most ocean fish is safe to consume several times a week; for freshwater species in some areas, consumption should be held to government limits. Also, choosing from a variety of fish is a good idea to minimize exposure to any single toxin that may accumulate in a favoured species. With regard to mercury, the margin lists the most heavily contaminated species and those that are lower in mercury.

Some people face greater risks. Pregnant women and children are more sensitive to contaminants than others, but even they can benefit from safer fish varieties within recommended limits (see Chapter 13 for details). People with existing heart disease are a special concern because mercury may worsen heart disease.[31] While researchers work to establish precisely how much mercury poses a hazard, consumers with heart disease should choose the fish varieties lowest in mercury to receive fish benefits while minimizing risk to health.

Government limits on freshwater fish intakes are in Chapter 12, page 503.

Most people can safely consume fish to receive its benefits, but no such claim can be made for fish oil supplements. It is better to go to the source for fish oils: eat safer varieties of fish.

• Species most heavily contaminated with mercury: shark, swordfish, king mackerel, fresh tuna steaks, and tilefish.

• Lower in mercury: shrimp, canned light tuna, salmon, pollock, and catfish. Canned albacore ("white") tuna contains more mercury than light tuna.

Baked goods often contain hydrogenated fats.

For the levels of mercury retained in fish and those permitted in these fish, see Health Canada's March 2007 document on this issue, "Human Health Risk Assessment of Mercury in Fish and Health Benefits of Fish Consumption," at http://www.hc-sc.gc.ca/fn-an/pubs/mercur/merc_fish_poisson-eng.php.

KEY POINT

■ Two polyunsaturated fatty acids, linoleic acid (an omega-6 fatty acid) and linolenic acid (an omega-3 fatty acid), are essential nutrients used to make substances that perform many important functions. The omega-6 family includes linoleic acid and arachidonic acid. The omega-3 family includes linolenic acid, EPA, and DHA. The principal food source of EPA and DHA is fish, but some species have become contaminated with environmental pollutants.

The Effects of Processing on Unsaturated Fats

Vegetable oils contribute a significant amount of fat to our diet because fast-food chains use them for frying, food manufacturers add them to processed foods, and consumers tend to choose margarine over butter.[32] Consumers of vegetable oils may feel safe in choosing them because they are generally less saturated than animal fats. If consumers choose a liquid oil, they may be justified in feeling secure. If the choice is a processed food, however, their security may be questionable, especially if the word *hydrogenated* appears on the label's ingredient list.

What Is "Hydrogenated Vegetable Oil," and What's It Doing in My Chocolate Chip Cookies?

When manufacturers process foods, they often alter the fatty acids in the fat (triglycerides) the foods contain through a process called **hydrogenation**. Hydrogenation of fats makes them stay fresher longer and also changes their physical properties.

Points of unsaturation in fatty acids are weak spots that are vulnerable to attack by oxygen. Oxidative damage is not confined to fats within body tissues but occurs anywhere oxygen mixes with fats. When the unsaturated points in the oils of food are oxidized, the oils become rancid and the food tastes "off." This is why cooking oils should be stored in tightly covered containers that exclude air. If stored for long periods, they need refrigeration to retard oxidation.

One way to prevent spoilage of unsaturated fats and make them harder and more stable when heated to high temperatures is to change their fatty acids chemically by hydrogenation, as shown on the left side of Figure 5–12. When food producers want to use a polyunsaturated oil such as corn oil to make a spreadable margarine, for example, they hydrogenate it by forcing hydrogen into the liquid oil. Some of the unsaturated fatty acids become more saturated as they accept the hydrogen, and the oil hardens. The resulting product is more saturated and more spreadable than the original oil. It is also more resistant to damage from oxidation or breakdown from high cooking temperatures. Hydrogenated oil has a high **smoking point**, so it is suitable for purposes such as frying.

Hydrogenated oils thus are easy to handle, are easy to spread, and store well. Makers of peanut butter often replace a small quantity of the liquid oil from the ground peanuts with hydrogenated vegetable oils to create a creamy paste that does not separate into layers of oil and peanuts as the "old-fashioned" types do. Neither type of peanut butter is high in saturated fat, however.

hydrogenation (high-dro-gen-AY-shun) the process of adding hydrogen to unsaturated fatty acids to make fat more solid and resistant to the chemical change of oxidation.

smoking point the temperature at which fat gives off an acrid blue gas.

Figure 5–12

Hydrogenation Yields Both Saturated and *Trans* Fatty Acids

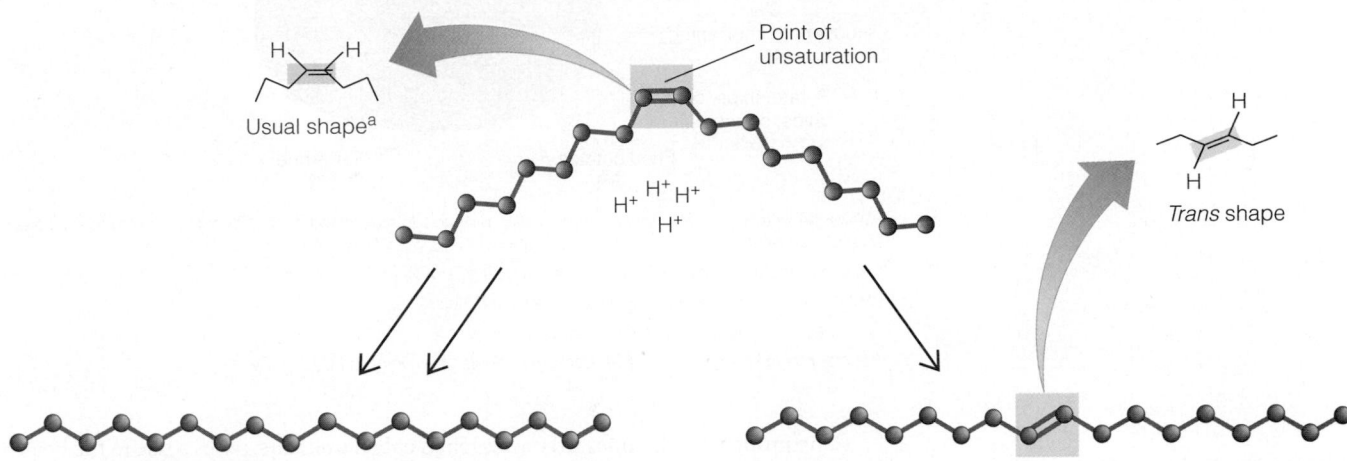

Unsaturated fatty acid
Points of unsaturation are places on fatty acid chains where hydrogen is missing. The bonds that would normally be occupied by hydrogen in a saturated fatty acid are shared, reluctantly, as a double bond between two carbons that both carry a slightly negative charge.

Usual shape[a]

Point of unsaturation

H⁺ H⁺ H⁺ H⁺

Trans shape

Hydrogenated fatty acid (now fully saturated)
When a positively charged hydrogen is made available to an unsaturated bond, it readily accepts the hydrogen and, in the process, becomes saturated. The fatty acid no longer has a point of unsaturation.

Trans fatty acid
The hydrogenation process also produces some *trans* fatty acids. The *trans* fatty acid retains its double bond but takes a twist instead of becoming fully saturated. It resembles a saturated fatty acid both in shape and in its effects on health.

[a] The usual shape of the double-bond structure is known as a *cis* (pronounced sis) formation.

> A famous antioxidant, vitamin E, occurs naturally in foods; see Chapter 7.

Once fully hydrogenated, oils lose their unsaturated character and the health benefits that go with it. Hydrogenation may affect not only the fatty acids in oils but also vitamins, such as vitamin K, decreasing their activity in the body.[33] If you, the consumer, are looking for health benefits from polyunsaturated oils, hydrogenated oils such as those in shortening or stick margarine will not meet your need.

An alternative to hydrogenation is to add a chemical preservative that will compete for oxygen and thus protect the oil. The additives are antioxidants, and they work by reacting with oxygen before it can do damage. Examples are the additives BHA and BHT* listed on snack food labels. The blending of different vegetable oils is also used to make some soft nonhydrogenated margarines. Another alternative, already mentioned, is to keep the product refrigerated.

KEY POINT

- Vegetable oils become more saturated when they are hydrogenated. Hydrogenated fats resist rancidity better, are firmer textured, and have a higher smoking point than unsaturated oils, but they also lose the health benefits of unsaturated oils.

What Are *Trans* Fatty Acids, and Are They Harmful?

When polyunsaturated oils are hardened by hydrogenation, some of the unsaturated fatty acids end up changing their shapes instead of becoming saturated (look at the right side of Figure 5–12). This change in chemical structure creates unusual unsaturated fatty acids that are similar in shape to saturated fatty acids. They are not made by the body but occur naturally in tiny amounts, mainly in dairy foods and beef. These changed fatty acids, or **trans fatty acids**, affect the body's health.

trans fatty acids fatty acids with unusual shapes that can arise when polyunsaturated oils are hydrogenated.

*BHA and BHT are butylated hydroxyanisole and butylated hydroxytoluene, respectively.

Figure 5–13

Major Sources of *Trans* Fat in the North American Diet[a]

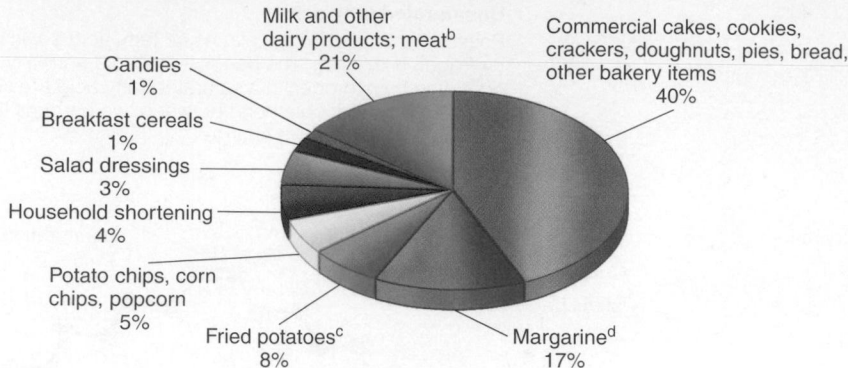

Candies
1%

Breakfast cereals
1%

Salad dressings
3%

Household shortening
4%

Milk and other
dairy products; meat[b]
21%

Commercial cakes, cookies,
crackers, doughnuts, pies, bread,
other bakery items
40%

Potato chips, corn
chips, popcorn
5%

Fried potatoes[c]
8%

Margarine[d]
17%

[a]*Many manufacturers are currently reformulating products to reduce* trans *fats. Other fats used to replace them may be saturated or unsaturated—read the labels.*

[b]*Mostly from commercial fried chicken or fried fish products.*

[c]*Mostly commercial French fries, hash browns, and "tots."*

[d]*Except liquids, sprays, and some soft margarines.*

Source: *"Revealing trans fats,"* FDA Consumer, *September/October 2003, p. 24.*

Disease Risk Reduction Claims

• Provided foods meet strict criteria set out by Health Canada, manufacturers may make health claims such as "A healthy diet low in saturated and *trans* fats may reduce the risk of heart disease."

• This chapter's Controversy feature takes up the issue of whether butter or margarine is better for heart health.

• The words *hydrogenated vegetable oil* and *shortening* in an ingredients list indicate that *trans* fatty acids are present in the product.

Consuming fats with *trans* fatty acids, often called *trans* fats, poses a risk to the health of the heart and arteries by raising LDL and lowering HDL cholesterol and by producing inflammation.[34] When processing changes essential fatty acids into their *trans* counterparts, the consumer derives none of the original health benefits of the oil and runs risks similar to those posed by saturated fats. The DRI committee concludes that people should consume as little trans fat as possible while consuming a nutritionally adequate diet.

A diet high in *total* fat and especially in saturated fat may be associated with cancer susceptibility, and *trans* fats contribute to the total fat intake.[35] To date, no evidence suggests that *trans* fatty acids by themselves play a specific role in promoting or causing cancer.

Popular reports have alerted consumers to the *trans* fat in margarine. While some margarines, especially the solid stick varieties, can contain almost half of their fat as *trans* fat, many other popular foods contribute a greater percentage of *trans* fat to the diet (see Figure 5–13). However, in 2007 Health Canada called upon the food industry to voluntarily reduce the *trans* fats in foods and since that time our *trans* fat intake has fallen to just under 1.5 percent.[36] Fast foods, chips, baked goods, and other commercially prepared foods are high in fats and may still contain appreciable amounts of *trans* fats, so it is important to continue to read food labels. Many fast-food chains currently fry foods in nonhydrogenated vegetable oils that contain little or no *trans* fatty acids, while healthier commercial fats are under development.

As of 2006, all food labels must list grams of *trans* fat in foods to help consumers make informed choices.[37] Replacing both saturated and *trans* fats with monounsaturated and polyunsaturated fats may be the wisest strategy in preventing heart disease.[38] To this end, many manufacturers are reformulating foods to reduce their contents of harmful *trans* fats (also see *"Trans* Fats in Canadian Foods" in the Controversy section of this chapter). At the same time, food scientists are perfecting fat replacers intended to eliminate added fats altogether (described in this chapter's Consumer Corner, pages 184–186).

Although *trans* fat intake has begun to decrease as a result of efforts by the Canadian food industry to meet the recommendation set out by Canada's Trans Fat Task Force (a multistakeholder task force spearheaded by Health Canada and the Heart and Stroke Foundation of Canada), the limits of 2 percent for vegetable oils and spreadable margarines and 5 percent for all other foods have not yet been achieved. To view recent changes to *trans* fats in the Canadian food supply, see the Trans Fat Monitoring Program at http://www.hc-sc.gc.ca/fn-an/nutrition/gras-trans-fats/tfa-age_tc-tm-eng.php. Note: Thus far, two provinces have brought in legislation to limit the amount of *trans* fat: Ontario limits *trans* fat in foods and beverages available in schools (http://www.edu.gov.on.ca/eng/document/nr/08.04/nr0416 .html), and British Columbia limits the amount of *trans* fat in foods available in restaurants, schools, and vending machines (http://www.health.gov.bc.ca/healthyeating/transfats.html).

KEY POINT

■ The process of hydrogenation also creates *trans* fatty acids. *Trans* fats act somewhat like saturated fats in the body.

Fat in the Diet

Canada's Food Guide is reproduced in Figure 2–4 on pages 38–43.

Table 2–3, on page 47 in Chapter 2 specifies how much oil is required to meet nutrient needs at several Calorie levels.

The concept of discretionary Calories was also addressed in Chapter 2.

The remainder of this chapter and its Controversy feature show you how to choose fats wisely with the goals of providing optimal health and pleasure in eating. As you read, notice which foods offer unsaturated fat and which offer saturated fat and *trans* fat. Also, always remember that fat delivers many Calories per bite of food, and limiting energy intake may be important to maintaining good health.[39] Your choices can make a difference in the unseen condition of your arteries.

Remember, too, that some fat is necessary for health. People who take fat recommendations to an extreme and try to eliminate all traces of fat from food do so at their peril. Most people need about 20 percent of their daily energy in the form of unsaturated fat.

In the Canadian diet, fat provides, on average, just over 31 percent of total daily Calories, down from 40 percent in the early 1970s. At first glance, this appears to be a healthy trend—until the actual grams of fat and carbohydrate are inspected. The total number of fat grams people take in has actually increased, rather than decreased, but the number of carbohydrate grams has increased even more. The net result is a higher total Calorie intake and a misleading relative drop in the percentage of fat Calories. Bottom line: people should learn to recognize the fats in foods and to distinguish harmful saturated fats and *trans* fats, which should be kept to a minimum, from more beneficial unsaturated fats that provide the needed essential fatty acids. Perhaps most important for many people is learning to control portion sizes, particularly of fatty foods that can pack hundreds of Calories into just a few bites.

Beyond a healthy minimum, people should limit their intakes of saturated fat, *trans* fat, and Calories. To do this requires consistently making nutrient-dense choices such as skim milk, fat-free cheese, the leanest meats, and so forth, and refraining from adding solid fats, such as butter, hard margarines, or shortening, to foods during preparation or at the table. Higher-fat foods may be included in the diet, but the fat Calories they provide must fit within a person's discretionary Calorie allowance. Exceptions are the fats of fatty fish, nuts, and vegetable oils: they provide beneficial EPA and DHA, linoleic acid and linolenic acid, and vitamin E, which are needed for a healthful diet, and so, within Calorie limits, the Calories these fats provide are necessary, not discretionary. Many people, especially sedentary people, have few or no discretionary Calories to spend on high-fat foods.

Keep in mind that the fat of some foods, such as the rim of fat on a steak, is visible (and therefore removable); other fats are invisible, such as the fats in the marbling of meat, the fat ground into lunch meat and hamburger, the fats blended into sauces of mixed dishes, and the fats in avocados, biscuits, cheese, coconuts, other nuts, olives, and fried foods. Invisible fats are on the rise in North American diets.[40]

Added Fats

A dollop of dessert topping, a spread of butter on bread, oil or shortening in a recipe, dressing on a salad—all of these are examples of *added* fats. All sorts of fats can be added to foods during commercial or home preparation or at the table. The following amounts

Ten small olives or a sixth of an avocado each provide about 5 grams of mostly monounsaturated fat.

Fat in the Diet

of these fats contain about 5 grams of pure fat, providing 45 Calories and negligible protein and carbohydrate:

- 1 teaspoon (5 mL) oil or shortening
- 1½ teaspoon (7.5 mL) mayonnaise, butter, or margarine
- 1 tablespoon (15 mL) regular salad dressing, cream cheese, or heavy cream
- 1½ tablespoon (23 mL) sour cream

The majority of added fats in the diet are invisible. They are the hidden fats in fried foods and baked goods, sauces and mixed dishes, and dips and spreads.

The Canadian diet provides approximately 31 percent of Calories from fat for young adults. Sources of fat in the Canadian diet come mainly from meat and alternatives, followed closely by "other foods"; indeed, close to 30 percent of adults 31–50 years old exceed the upper end of the AMDR range of 35 percent (see CCHS 2.2 report at http://www.statcan.gc.ca/pub/82-620-m/82-620-m2006002-eng.pdf).

KEY POINT

- Fats added to foods during preparation or at the table are a major source of fat in the diet.

Fat Replacers

Today, consumers can choose from thousands of fat-reduced products. Many bakery goods, lunch meats, cheeses, spreads, frozen desserts, and other products made with **fat replacers** (see Table 5–6) offer less than half a gram of fat, saturated fat, and *trans* fat in a serving. Some of these products contain **artificial fats**, and others use conventional ingredients in unconventional ways to reduce fats and Calories. Among the latter, manufacturers can

- Add water or whip air into foods.
- Add skim fat-free milk to creamy foods.

- Use lean meat and soy protein to replace high-fat meat.
- Bake foods instead of frying them.

Common food ingredients, such as fibres, sugars, or proteins, can also take the place of fats in some foods. In particular, fat replacers made from oats or barley not only cut down on fats in foods but also introduce beneficial viscous fibres, while imparting desirable tastes and textures associated with real fats.[1] Products made from sugars or proteins still provide Calories, but far fewer Calories than if they were made from fats.

Figure 5–14

Olestra and Triglyceride Compared

Human digestive enzymes easily break apart triglycerides but cannot digest olestra.

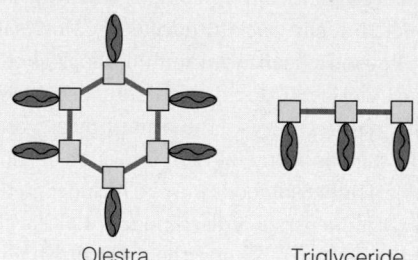

Olestra   Triglyceride

Manufactured fat replacers consist of chemical derivatives of carbohydrate, protein, or fat or modified versions of foods rich in those constituents (see Table 5–7). To gain the U.S. FDA's consent for the use of a new fat replacer, U.S. manufacturers must prove that their fat replacer contributes little food energy, is nontoxic, is not stored in body tissues, and does not rob the body of needed nutrients. Olestra serves as an example of an artificial fat that has won the FDA's approval.

Table 5–6

Terms Related to Fat Replacers

- **Artificial fats** zero-energy fat replacers that are chemically synthesized to mimic the sensory and cooking qualities of naturally occurring fats but are totally or partially resistant to digestion. Also called *fat analogues*.
- **Fat replacers** ingredients that replace some or all of the functions of fat and may or may not provide energy. Often used interchangeably with *fat substitutes*, but the latter technically applies only to ingredients that replace all of the functions of fat and provide no energy.
- **Olestra** a noncaloric artificial fat made from sucrose and fatty acids; formerly called *sucrose polyester*.
- **Sucrose polyester** any of a family of compounds in which fatty acids are bonded with sugars or sugar alcohols. Olestra is an example.

Chapter 5 The Lipids: Fats, Oils, Phospholipids, and Sterols

Table 5–7

A Sampling of Fat Replacers

Fat replacers can dramatically reduce the saturated fat, *trans* fats, and Calories in processed foods. Further, fibre-based replacers may provide some of the health benefits of viscous fibres (see Chapter 4). For comparison, remember that fat has 9 Calories per gram.

Fat Replacer	Energy (Cal/g)	Uses in Foods
Carbohydrate-Based Fat Replacers		
■ *Fruit*: purees and pastes of apples, bananas, cherries, plums, or prunes; add bulk and tenderness to baked goods.	1–4	*Foods*: Baked goods, candy, dairy products. *Uses*: Replace bulk of fat; add moisture and tenderness.
■ *Maltodextrins*: made from corn; powdered and flavoured to resemble the taste of butter.	1–4	*Foods*: Butter-flavoured "sprinkles" for melting on hot foods. *Uses*: Add "buttery" flavour.
Fibre-Based Fat Replacers		
■ *Gels*: derived from cellulose or starch to mimic the texture of fats in regular margarine and other products.	0–4	*Foods*: Fat-free margarine, salad dressing, frozen desserts. *Uses*: Replace bulk; lend thickness.
■ *Gums*: extracted from beans, sea vegetables, or other sources.	0–4[a]	*Foods*: Salad dressing, processed meat, desserts. *Uses*: Replace bulk; thicken salad dressings.
■ *Oatrim*: derived from oat fibre; has the added advantage of providing satiety.	4	*Foods*: Dips, dressings, baked goods, cereal bars, beverages, meat. *Uses*: Lends creaminess; replaces bulk of fat; can be used in baking but not frying.
■ *Z-trim*: a modified form of insoluble fibre; is powdered and feels like fat in the mouth.	0	*Foods*: Cheese, meat, sauces, dips, baked goods, dressings, spreads, desserts, ice cream. *Uses*: Lends creaminess; replaces bulk of fat; can be used in baking but not frying.
Fat-Based Replacers		
■ *Olestra*:[b] a noncaloric artificial fat made from sucrose and fatty acids; formerly called *sucrose polyester*.	0	*Foods*: Potato chips, tortilla chips, snack crackers. *Uses*: Same properties as fats; heat stable in frying, cooking, and baking. Not available for home use.
■ *Salatrim*:[c] derived from fat and contains short- and long-chain fatty acids.	5	*Foods*: Confections, dairy products, bakery products. *Uses*: Same properties as fats; can be used in baking but not frying.
Protein-Based Fat Replacers		
■ *Microparticulated protein*:[d] processed from the proteins of milk or egg white into mistlike particles that feel and taste like fat when they roll over the tongue.	4	*Foods*: Ice cream, dairy products, mayonnaise, salad dressing, baked goods, spreads. *Uses*: Lends creaminess; heat stable in some cooking and baking but not frying.

[a]Energy made available by action of colonic bacteria.
[b]Trade name: Olean. Not available in Canada.
[c]Trade name: Benefat.
[d]Trade names: Simplesse and K-Blazer.

An Artificial Fat: Olestra

Olestra, brand name Olean, is a member of the **sucrose polyester** chemical family and is *currently not allowed to be added to foods in Canada*. Chemically, olestra bears some resemblance to ordinary fat; it consists of a core molecule of the carbohydrate sucrose to which up to eight fatty acid molecules are bonded (see Figure 5-14). Human enzymes of the digestive tract do not recognize molecules of olestra and so cannot split its fatty acids from its sucrose. All of the olestra eaten in a food passes through the digestive tract and exits intact.

Olestra's properties are identical to those of fats and oils when used in frying, cooking, and baking. It can be heated to frying temperatures without breaking down. Aside from a slight aftertaste, to many people it tastes like fat.

More than two decades of research have revealed that olestra is safe in most regards, but when consumed in large quantities, it can cause digestive distress, nutrient losses, and losses of phytochemicals. The presence of indigestible olestra in the large intestine can theoretically cause diarrhea, gas, cramping, and an urgent need for defecation. Oily olestra can creep through the feces and leak uncontrollably from the anus, producing smelly, dark yellow stains on underwear.

No significant increase in digestive distress was detected in an experiment with some 3,000 volunteers who ate olestra-containing snacks.[2] In ordinary consumers, however, about 10 percent of olestra users calling a toll-free number reported digestive disturbances after consuming olestra-containing foods.[3] These effects are not considered serious or dangerous, so the U.S. FDA no longer requires olestra-containing foods to carry a warning on their labels.[4] But, as stated before, olestra is not allowed to be added to foods in Canada.

Olestra acts as a potent solvent for some of the fat-soluble substances in foods, such as the vitamins that dissolve in fat (vitamins A, D, E, and K). The absorption of these vitamins from a meal that includes olestra is reduced because olestra dissolves them and carries them out of the digestive tract unabsorbed. To compensate for this effect, olestra is fortified with vitamins A, D, E, and K.

Olestra also causes the loss of health-promoting phytochemicals from foods. One study showed that just 3 grams of olestra a day strongly reduced (by about 40%) the blood concentrations of lycopene, a phytochemical believed to defend the body against some forms of cancer (see Controversy 2). To date, no studies exist to predict the effects, if any, of lifelong olestra exposure or the effects of olestra on growing children, which is important because children often favour the foods in which olestra is allowed. Olestra's pros and cons are summed up in Figure 5–15.

Fat Replacers and Weight Control

People choosing reduced-fat foods, but not necessarily foods made with fat replacers, generally consume fewer Calories, less saturated fat, and more nutrients than nonusers of such foods.[5] Whether using fat replacers assists in weight control, however, seems to depend on whether people compensate for the resulting energy and fat deficit by eating more food later on. In two small studies, researchers secretly replaced one-third of young men's and women's regular intake of daily fat with olestra.[6] The subjects seemed not to notice the energy shortfall as the study progressed—they didn't fully compensate for the shortfall and so lost weight. As for blood lipids, people who used olestra heavily, consuming more than 2 grams each day for a year, significantly lowered their blood cholesterol. These subjects did not lose significant weight.[7]

A natural thought seems to be, "If my food has less fat, then I can eat more and remain lean." Labels reveal, however, that many reduced-fat foods deliver appreciable fat and about as many Calories as a comparable regular product. If the U.S. experience with artificial sweeteners, described in Controversy 4, is any guide, consumers are likely to eat fat-replacer products *in addition* to other high-fat foods they prefer, negating the potential benefits of the fat replacers. Used wisely, though, fat replacers can help consumers achieve some of their dietary goals, especially when the user learns to cut Calories and saturated fat from the diet in other ways as well (see this chapter's Food Feature).

Figure 5–15

Olestra's Pros and Cons

Pros of Olestra

- Zero Calories
- Zero fat, saturated fat, and *trans* fat
- Zero cholesterol
- Withstands frying
- Withstands baking
- Tastes like fat

Cons of Olestra

- Vitamin losses
- Phytochemical losses
- Possible digestive upset
- Possible anal leakage
- Slight aftertaste
- Expensive
- No long-term studies in children

© PhotoLink/PhotoDisc/Getty Images

Meat, Poultry, Fish, Dried Peas and Beans, Eggs, and Nuts

Meat conceals a good deal of the fat—and much of the saturated fat—that people consume. To help "see" the fat in meat, it is useful to think of it in four categories according to fat content: extra lean, lean, medium, and regular meat, as shown in Figure 5–16. Meats in all four categories contain about equal amounts of protein, but their fat contents differ and the saturated fat and Calorie amounts vary significantly. Figure 5–16 shows fat and Calorie data for some ground meats. Table 2–7 on pages 57–58 in Chapter 2 provided some definitions concerning the fat contents of foods including meat.

Canada's Food Guide suggests that most adults consume two to three Food Guide servings of meat and alternatives per day or about 150 to 225 grams. For comparison, the smallest fast-food hamburger weighs about 90 grams. A steak served in a restaurant often runs to 150, 350, or 450 grams, more than a whole day's meat allowance. You may have to weigh a serving or two of meat to see how much you are eating.

People think of meat as protein food, but calculation of its nutrient contents reveals a surprising fact. A big 120-gram (4-ounce) fast-food hamburger sandwich contains 23 grams of protein and 20 grams of fat. Because protein offers 4 Calories per gram and fat offers 9, the sandwich provides 92 Calories from protein and about twice that amount from fat. The Calorie total, counting carbohydrates from the bun and condiments, is over 400 Calories, with more than 50 percent of them

---

Figure 5–16

Calories, Fat, and Saturated Fat in Cooked Ground Meat Patties

Only the ground round, at 10 percent fat by raw weight, qualifies to bear the term *extra lean* on its label. To be called *extra lean*, products must contain less than 10 grams of fat, 4 grams of saturated fat, and 95 milligrams of cholesterol per 100 grams of food. The white labels with red type on these packages list rules for safe meat handling, explained in Chapter 12.

Higher in fat → Lower in fat

Regular ground beef
25% fat (Regular)
260 Cal/90 g — 4½ tsp fat, 8 g saturated fat

Ground chuck
18% fat (Medium)
220 Cal/90 g — 3 tsp fat, 6 g saturated fat

Commercial ground turkey[a]
(with skin ground in)
13% fat (Lean)
200 Cal/90 g — 2¼ tsp fat, 3 g saturated fat

Ground round
10% fat (Extra Lean)
180 Cal/90 g — 1½ tsp fat, 4 g saturated fat

[a]Values for 90 g of cooked turkey breast ground without skin are 108 Calories, ½ teaspoon fat, and 1 g saturated fat. Larger servings will, of course, provide more fat, saturated fat, and Calories than the values listed here.

Source: Data from ESHA Research, The Food Processor Nutrition and Fitness Software, version 8.3, 2004.

from fat. Hot dogs, fried chicken sandwiches, and fried fish sandwiches are also high-fat choices. Because so much of the energy in a meat eater's diet is hidden from view, people can easily overeat on high-fat food, making weight control difficult.

When choosing beef or pork, look for lean cuts named *loin* or *round* from which the fat can be trimmed. Eat small portions, too. As for chicken and turkey, these meats are naturally lean, but commercial processing and frying add fats, especially in "patties," "nuggets," "fingers," and "wings." Chicken wings are mostly skin, and a chicken stores most of its fat just under its skin. The tastiest wing snacks have also been fried in cooking fat (often a hydrogenated saturated type with *trans* fatty acids); smothered with a buttery, spicy sauce; and then dipped in blue cheese dressing, making wings an extraordinarily high-fat snack. If you snack on wings, plan on eating low-fat foods at several other meals to balance them out.

Watch out for ground turkey or chicken products. The skin is often ground in to add moisture when cooked, and these products can be much higher in fat than even lean beef—see Figure 5–16. The regulations about the fat in ground meat are different in Canada from the information in Figure 5–16. The Canadian Food Inspection Agency's *2003 Guide to Food Labelling and Advertising* presents the following Canadian standards.

For ground (naming the species) meat including poultry meat:

a) Composition

"Extra lean ground (naming the species)" and "lean ground (naming the species)" are prescribed common names that may be used for ground meat, including poultry meat, containing no more than 10 percent fat and 17 percent fat, respectively.

b) Labelling

The terms "extra lean" (no more than 10% fat), "lean" (no more than 17% fat), "medium" (no more than 23% fat), and "regular" (no more than 30% fat) are part of the prescribed common names for "ground (naming the species)" meat including poultry meat (S.94(4) and Schedule I, *Meat Inspection Regulations*).

Some people (even famous chefs) misinterpret Figure 5–5 on page 166, believing that because the fats of poultry and pork are less saturated than beef fat they are harmless to the heart. Nutrition authorities, however, emphatically state that all sources of saturated fat pose a risk to the heart and that even poultry with skin should be limited for heart health.

KEY POINT

- Meat accounts for a large proportion of the hidden fat and saturated fat in many people's diets. Most people consume meat in larger amounts than recommended.

Milk, Yogurt, and Cheese

Milk's Names
- Milk, whole/homo/homogenized milk (3.25% milk)
- Reduced-fat, less-fat milk (2% milk)
- Low-fat milk (1% milk)
- Fat-free, zero-fat, or no-fat milk (skim or nonfat milk)

Some milk products contain fat, as Figure 5–17 shows. In homogenizing whole milk, milk processors blend in the cream, which otherwise would float and could be removed by skimming. A cup of whole milk contains the protein and carbohydrate of skim (fat-free) milk, but in addition it contains about 60 extra Calories from fat. A cup of reduced-fat (2% fat) milk falls between whole and skim milk, with 45 Calories of fat. The fat of whole milk occupies only a teaspoon or two of the volume but nearly doubles the Calories in the milk. Depending on its fat content, milk bears one of the names listed in the margin.

Milk and yogurt appear in the milk group, but cream and butter do not. Milk and yogurt are rich in calcium and protein, but cream and butter are not. Cream and butter are fats, as are whipped cream, sour cream, and cream cheese, so they are

Figure 5-17

Lipids in Milk and Alternatives

Red boxes below indicate foods with higher lipid contents that warrant moderation in their use. Green indicates lower-fat choices.

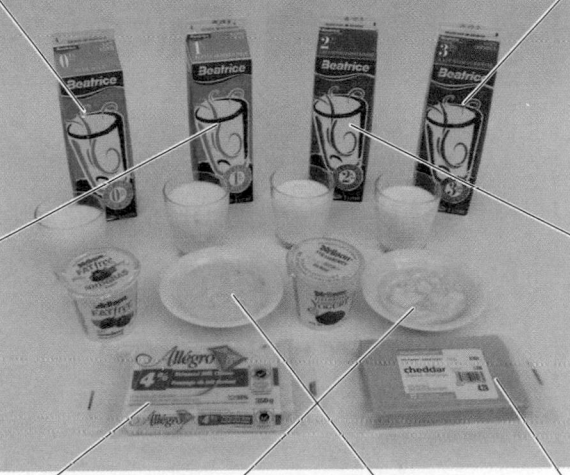

Fat-free, skim, zero-fat, no-fat, or nonfat milk, 250 mL (<0.5% fat by weight)

Calories 80	Calories from Fat 0
	Daily Value (%)*
Total Fat 0 g	0
Saturated Fat 0 g	0
Cholesterol 5 mg	2

Low-fat milk, 250 mL (1% fat by weight)

Calories 105	Calories from Fat 20
	Daily Value (%)*
Total Fat 2 g	3
Saturated Fat 1.5 g	8
Cholesterol 10 mg	3

Low-fat cheddar cheese, 45 g

Calories 70	Calories from Fat 30
	Daily Value (%)*
Total Fat 3 g	5
Saturated Fat 2 g	10
Cholesterol 10 mg	3

Nutrition Facts

Amount per Serving

Strawberry yogurt, 250 mL

Calories 250	Calories from Fat 45
	Daily Value (%)*
Total Fat 5 g	8
Saturated Fat 3 g	15
Cholesterol 15 mg	5

Whole milk, 250 mL (3.3% fat by weight)

Calories 150	Calories from Fat 70
	Daily Value (%)*
Total Fat 8 g	12
Saturated Fat 5 g	25
Cholesterol 24 mg	8

Reduced fat, less-fat milk, 250 mL (2% fat by weight)

Calories 120	Calories from Fat 45
	Daily Value (%)*
Total Fat 5 g	8
Saturated Fat 2 g	10
Cholesterol 20 mg	7

Cheddar cheese, 45 g

Calories 165	Calories from Fat 130
	Daily Value (%)*
Total Fat 14 g	22
Saturated Fat 9 g	45
Cholesterol 40 mg	13

Low-fat strawberry yogurt, 250 mL

Calories 240	Calories from Fat 20
	Daily Value (%)*
Total Fat 2.5 g	4
Saturated Fat 2 g	10
Cholesterol 15 mg	5

Dick Hemingway

grouped together with the solid fats. Cheeses are the single greatest contributor of saturated fat in the diet.[41] Among food fats, only the lipids of palm oil and coconut oil rank higher for saturation than the butterfat in fatty dairy products (review Figure 5–5 on page 166).

Grains

Grain foods in their natural state are very low in fat, but fat, including saturated fat and *trans* fat, may be added during manufacturing, processing, or cooking (see Figure 5–18). The fats in these foods can be particularly hard to detect, so diners must remember which foods stand out as being high in fat. Notable are granola and certain other ready-to-eat cereals, croissants, biscuits, cornbread, fried rice, pasta with creamy or oily sauces, quick breads, snack and party crackers, muffins, pancakes, and

Figure 5–18

Lipids in Grain Products

Red boxes below indicate foods with higher lipid contents that warrant moderation in their use. Green indicates lower-fat choices.

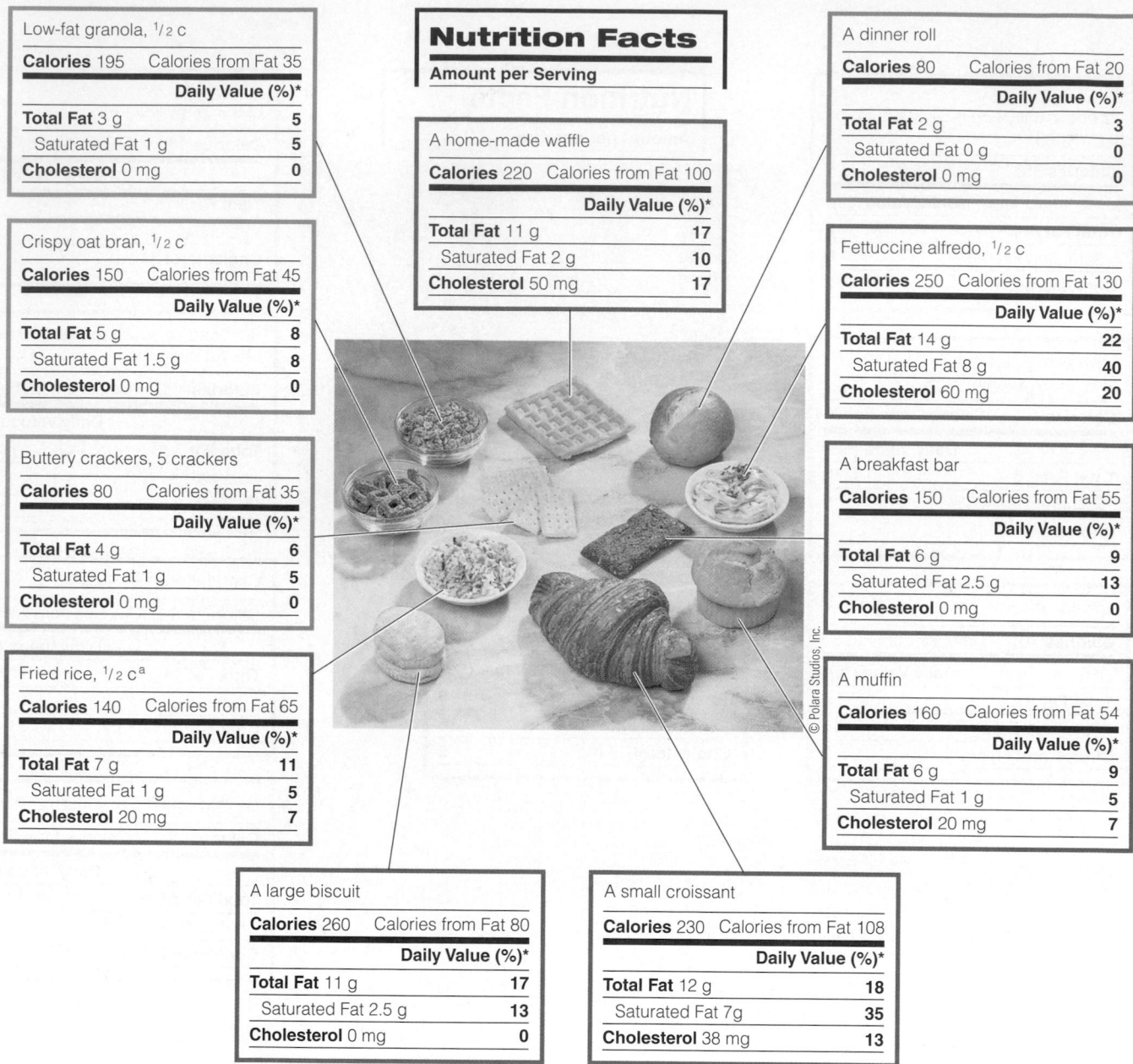

Low-fat granola, ¹/₂ c

Calories 195	Calories from Fat 35
	Daily Value (%)*
Total Fat 3 g	5
Saturated Fat 1 g	5
Cholesterol 0 mg	0

Crispy oat bran, ¹/₂ c

Calories 150	Calories from Fat 45
	Daily Value (%)*
Total Fat 5 g	8
Saturated Fat 1.5 g	8
Cholesterol 0 mg	0

Buttery crackers, 5 crackers

Calories 80	Calories from Fat 35
	Daily Value (%)*
Total Fat 4 g	6
Saturated Fat 1 g	5
Cholesterol 0 mg	0

Fried rice, ¹/₂ c ᵃ

Calories 140	Calories from Fat 65
	Daily Value (%)*
Total Fat 7 g	11
Saturated Fat 1 g	5
Cholesterol 20 mg	7

Nutrition Facts

Amount per Serving

A home-made waffle

Calories 220	Calories from Fat 100
	Daily Value (%)*
Total Fat 11 g	17
Saturated Fat 2 g	10
Cholesterol 50 mg	17

A dinner roll

Calories 80	Calories from Fat 20
	Daily Value (%)*
Total Fat 2 g	3
Saturated Fat 0 g	0
Cholesterol 0 mg	0

Fettuccine alfredo, ¹/₂ c

Calories 250	Calories from Fat 130
	Daily Value (%)*
Total Fat 14 g	22
Saturated Fat 8 g	40
Cholesterol 60 mg	20

A breakfast bar

Calories 150	Calories from Fat 55
	Daily Value (%)*
Total Fat 6 g	9
Saturated Fat 2.5 g	13
Cholesterol 0 mg	0

A muffin

Calories 160	Calories from Fat 54
	Daily Value (%)*
Total Fat 6 g	9
Saturated Fat 1 g	5
Cholesterol 20 mg	7

A large biscuit

Calories 260	Calories from Fat 80
	Daily Value (%)*
Total Fat 11 g	17
Saturated Fat 2.5 g	13
Cholesterol 0 mg	0

A small croissant

Calories 230	Calories from Fat 108
	Daily Value (%)*
Total Fat 12 g	18
Saturated Fat 7g	35
Cholesterol 38 mg	13

© Polara Studios, Inc.

ᵃThe Calorie and fat contents of fried rice vary by preparation method.

homemade waffles. Packaged breakfast bars often resemble vitamin-fortified chocolate bars in their fat and sugar contents.

KEY POINT

- Fat in breads and cereals can be well hidden. Consumers must learn which foods of this group contain fats.

Now that you know where the fats in foods are found, how can you reduce or eliminate the harmful ones from your diet? The Food Feature provides some pointers.

Defensive Dining

To meet today's dietary recommendations concerning fats requires not only identifying total fat in foods but learning to recognize and limit saturated and *trans* fats, too. People with diseases such as heart disease or obesity are advised to reduce their intakes of total fat to help them minimize illness. Even healthy people, if they are consuming diets that supply over 35 percent of Calories as fat, should cut back to prevent health and nutrition problems.

The recommendation to limit daily intakes of saturated and *trans* fats for the health of the heart applies to all people. To repeat: no amount of these fats is needed for health, and to stay healthy, intakes should be minimized in a balanced, adequate diet. Although this advice is easy to dispense, following it may not be so easy because even the unsaturated vegetable oils, needed for their essential fatty acids, contain some saturated fat.[42] The first step in achieving low intakes of saturated and *trans* fats while obtaining necessary fatty acids is to learn which foods contain heavy doses of the heart clogging fats. Then keep these foods to a minimum. This Food Feature can help.

The first arena is the grocery store. The right choices here can save you many grams of fat, saturated fat, and *trans* fats, while the wrong ones can undermine your efforts. Food labels can reveal much about a processed food's fat contents. With that knowledge, you can decide whether to use a food as a staple item in your diet or as an occasional treat. Choose foods lowest in harmful fats for everyday use; limit others to occasional use only. For example, choose frozen vegetables (a staple food) without butter or other high-fat sauces, which are often highly saturated and generally drive up the Calorie content of the vegetables, as well as the price; add your own flavouring, such as a touch of herbs, olive oil, garlic, or lemon pepper, at home. If you choose precooked meats, avoid those that are coated and fried or prepared in fatty sauces. Try rotisserie chicken from the deli—rotisserie cooking lets much of the fat and saturated fat drain away. Look for new innovations aimed at reducing saturated fats: these appear all the time.

Once at home, one of the most effective steps is to eliminate solid saturated fats used as seasonings. This means eating cooked vegetables without butter, bacon, or stick margarine; replacing shortening with oils such as olive or canola oil; omitting high-fat meat gravies and cheese or cream sauces; and leaving off most other last-minute fatty additions. As for Calories, butter and regular margarine contain the same number of Calories (about 35 per teaspoon); diet margarine contains fewer Calories because water, air, or fillers have been added. Imitation butter-flavoured sprinkles contain no fat and few Calories.

For snacks, make it a habit to choose lower-fat microwave popcorn and then sprinkle on butter or cheese flavouring, if you like it. Keep that flavouring on hand together with other substitutes such as diet, soft, or liquid margarine (generally low in saturated and *trans* fats), reduced-fat sauce mixes or recipes, and nonstick spray or olive oil for frying. Table 5–8 provides a list of possible substitutes for high-fat ingredients in recipes. These replacements will not change the taste or appearance of the finished product very much, but they will dramatically lower the Calories and saturated fat.

When you add fats to foods, be sure that they are detectable and that you enjoy them. For example, if you use strongly flavoured fat, a little goes a long way. Sesame oil, peanut butter, nut oils, and the fats of strong cheeses are equal in Calories to others, but they are so strongly flavoured that you can use much less. Try small amounts of grated Parmesan, Romano, or other hard cheeses to replace larger amounts of less flavourful cheeses.

When choosing oils, trade off among different types to obtain the benefits different oils offer. Peanut and safflower oils are especially rich in vitamin E. Olive oil presents the heart with health benefits (see the Controversy section for details), and canola oil is rich with monounsaturates and the essential fatty acids. High temperatures, such as those used in frying, destroy some omega-3 acids and other beneficial constituents, so treat your oils gently. Especially important: take care to *substitute* oils for saturated fats in the diet; do not add oils to an already fat-rich diet. No benefits are expected unless oils replace other, more saturated fats.

Here are some other tips to revise high-fat recipes that contribute excess Calories and saturated fats:

- Grill, roast, broil, boil, bake, stir-fry, microwave, or poach foods. Don't fry in solid fats, such as shortening or butter. If you must fry, use a little liquid oil for pan frying.

- Choose large portions of salad greens and other vegetables and dress lightly. Reduce or eliminate "add-ons" such as butter, creamy sauces, cheese, sour cream, and bacon that drive up the Calories and saturated fat.

- Cut recipe amounts of meat in half; use only lean meats. Fill in the lost bulk with soy meat replacers, shredded vegetables, legumes, pasta, grains, or other low-fat items.

- Replace a thick slice of ham with two or three wafer-thin slices. The serving will be smaller and thus provide less fat, but the taste will be the same because the surface area that imparts flavour to the taste buds is greater.[43]

Table 5–8

Substitutes for High-Fat Ingredients

Use	Instead of
Fat-free milk products	Whole-milk products
Evaporated fat-free (skim) milk (canned)	Cream
Yogurt[a] or fat-free sour cream replacer	Sour cream
Reduced-Calorie margarine; butter replacers	Butter
Wine, lemon juice, or broth	Butter
Fruit butters	Butter
Part-skim or fat-free ricotta; low-fat or fat-free cottage cheese[a]	Whole-milk ricotta
Part-skim or reduced-fat cheeses; "filled" cheeses in which vegetable oil has replaced saturated fat	Regular cheeses
1 tbs cornstarch (for thickening sauces)	1 egg yolk
Low-fat or fat-free mayonnaise	Regular mayonnaise
Low-fat or fat-free salad dressing (for salads and marinades)	Regular salad dressing
Water-packed canned fish and meat	Oil-packed fish and meat
Lean ground meat and grain mixture	Ground beef
Low-fat frozen yogurt or sherbet	Ice cream
Herbs, lemons, spices, fruit, liquid smoke flavouring, or ham-flavoured bouillon cubes	Butter, bacon, bacon fat
Baked tortilla or potato chips; pretzels	Regular chips

[a]If the recipe calls for the food to be boiled, the yogurt or cottage cheese must be stabilized with a small amount of cornstarch or flour.

- Refrigerate meat pan drippings and broth and lift off the fat when it solidifies. Then add the defatted broth to a recipe.

- Make prepared mixes, such as rice or potato mixtures, without the fats called for on the label, or substitute liquid oils for solid fats in preparing them.

All of these suggestions work well when a person plans and prepares each meal at home. But in the real world, people fall behind schedule and don't have time to cook, so they eat fast food. Figure 5–19 compares some fast-food choices and offers tips to reduce the Calories and saturated fat to make fast-food meals healthier.

Keep these facts about fast food in mind:

- Salads are a good choice, but beware of toppings such as fried noodles, bacon bits, greasy croutons, sour cream, or shredded cheese that can drive up the Calorie, saturated fat, and *trans* fat contents. To reduce Calories, avoid mixed salad bar items, such as macaroni salad. Use only about a quarter of the dressing provided with fast-food salads or use low-fat dressing.

- If you are really hungry, order a small hamburger or "veggie burger" and a side salad. Hold the cheese; use mustard or ketchup as condiments.

- A small bowl of chilli (hold the cheese and sour cream) poured over a plain baked potato can also satisfy a bigger appetite. Top with chopped raw onions or hot sauce for spice.

- Tacos and other Mexican treats can often be ordered with salsa instead of cheese and sour cream.

- Fast-food fried fish or chicken sandwiches provide at least as much fat as hamburgers—and more *trans* fat. Broiled sandwiches are far less fatty if you order them made without spreads, dressings, cheese, bacon, or mayonnaise.

Because fast foods are short on variety, let them be part of a lifestyle in which they complement the other parts. Eat differently, often, elsewhere.

By this time you may be wondering if you can realistically make all of the changes recommended for your diet. In truth, even small changes yield big dividends in terms of reducing harmful fats in the diet (see Table 5–9). Be assured that most such changes can become habits after a few repetitions. You do not have to give up all high-fat treats, nor should you strive to eliminate all fats; you need only learn to exercise moderation. You decide what the treats should be and then choose them judiciously, just for pure pleasure. Meanwhile, make sure that your everyday, ordinary choices are those whole, nutrient-dense foods suggested throughout this book. That way you'll meet all of your body's needs for nutrients and never feel deprived.

Figure 5–19

Compare the Calories and Saturated Fat in Fast-Food Choices

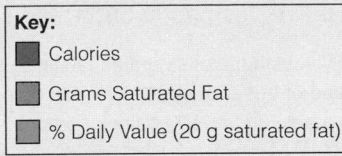

Key:
- ◼ Calories
- ◼ Grams Saturated Fat
- ◼ % Daily Value (20 g saturated fat)

Higher in saturated fat   **Lower in saturated fat**

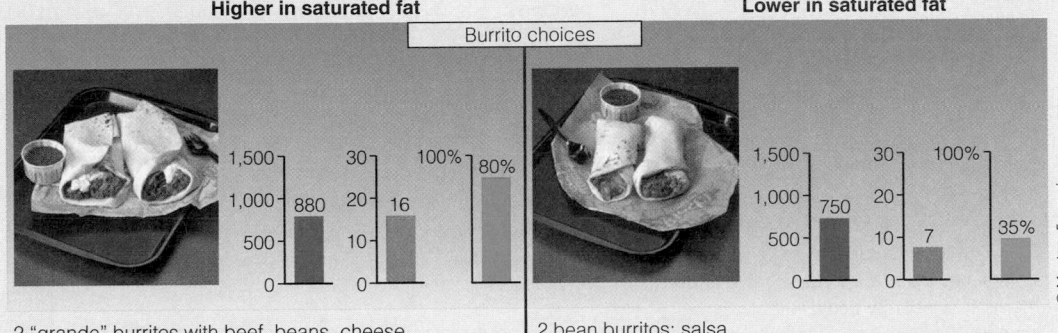

When ordering Mexican-style fast food, you can reduce both Calories and saturated fat by limiting cheese, meat, and sour cream.

Burrito choices

880   16   80%

750   7   35%

2 "grande" burritos with beef, beans, cheese, and sour cream; salsa

2 bean burritos; salsa

A broiled chicken breast sandwich with spicy mustard is just as tasty as a burger but delivers far less saturated fat and fewer Calories. Beware of fried chicken sandwiches or "patties"—these can be as fatty as the hamburger choice.

Sandwich choices

1,610   27   135%

560   2   10%

Big double bacon cheeseburger, large fries, regular milkshake

Big broiled chicken breast sandwich, pickle, side salad with low-Calorie dressing, vegetable or fruit juice

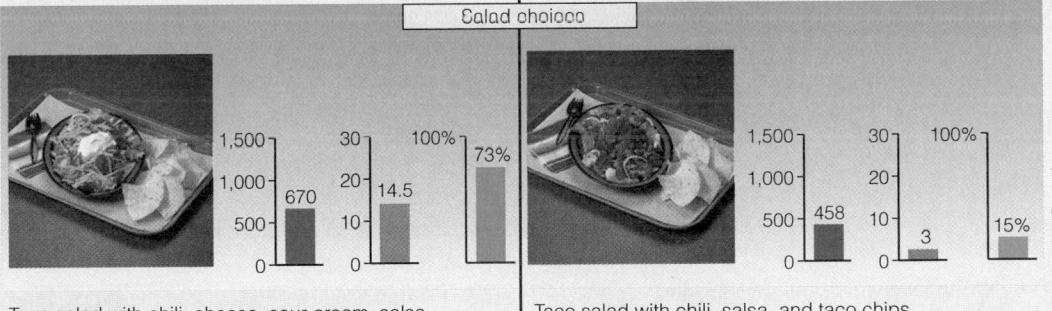

Don't let add-ons such as greasy croutons, chips, bacon bits, full-fat cheese, and sour cream pile the Calories and saturated fat onto your otherwise healthy fast-food salad. To cut fats and Calories, leave off most of the toppings and use just half the dressing.

Salad choices

670   14.5   73%

458   3   15%

Taco salad with chili, cheese, sour cream, salsa, and taco chips

Taco salad with chili, salsa, and taco chips

Reduce Calories and saturated fat even further: try ordering your veggie pizza with half the regular melted cheese and sprinkle it with parmesan cheese, herbs, or hot peppers for flavour.

Pizza choices

1,246   34   170%

560   6   30%

Two slices extra cheese pizza with sausage and pepperoni

Two slices cheese pizza with mushrooms, olives, onions, and peppers

Four reasons to keep intakes of fats low:

- Diets lower in fat are generally lower in Calories and thereby help achieve and maintain a healthy body weight.
- Diets low in saturated and *trans* fats may reduce the risk of heart disease.
- Diets lower in fat, particularly saturated fat, may lower the risks of some cancers.
- Diets with fewer Calories from fat have more room for health-promoting foods such as fruit, fish, legumes, low-fat milk products, nuts, vegetables, and whole grains.

Table 5–9

Choosing Unsaturated Fats Instead of Saturated Fats

Unsaturated fats can easily substitute for saturated fats in everyday foods, for example, cooking with olive oil instead of butter or slicing avocado on a salad instead of cheese. The fat grams listed in this table are for 100 Calorie portions.

Foods (100 Cal portions)	Saturated Fat (g/100 Cal)	Unsaturated Fat (g/100 Cal)	Total Fat (g/100 Cal)
Olive oil (1 tbs) vs. butter (1 tbs)	2 vs. 7	9 vs. 4	11 vs. 11
Sunflower seeds (2 tbs) vs. bacon (2 slices)	1 vs. 3	7 vs. 6	8 vs. 9
Mixed nuts (2 tbs) vs. potato chips (10 chips)	1 vs. 2	8 vs. 5	9 vs. 7
Avocado (6 small slices) vs. cheese (1 slice)	2 vs. 4	8 vs. 4	10 vs. 8
Salmon (55 g) vs. steak (42 g)	1 vs. 2	3 vs. 3	4 vs. 5

CONTROVERSY 5

High-Fat Foods: Which to Choose for Good Health

To consumers, advice about dietary fats appears to change almost daily. "Eat less fat—buy more fatty fish." "Give up butter—use margarine instead." "Give up margarine—replace it with olive oil." "Avoid saturated fat—increase omega-3 fat." To researchers, however, the evolution of such advice reflects many decades of following leads and testing theories about the health effects of dietary fats. As scientific understanding has grown, dietary guidelines have become more specific and therefore more meaningful.

This Controversy begins with a look at the latest guidelines for lipid intakes from a scientific point of view. It also singles out the Mediterranean diet as an eating style famous for supporting the health of the heart while including foods high in fat. It concludes with strategies for choosing the right amounts of the right kinds of fats within the context of a heart-healthy diet and lifestyle.

The Changing Fat Guidelines

For years, consumers were urged to cut their fat intakes in everything from hot dogs to salad dressings. This advice was straightforward—cut the fat, improve your health. Saturated fat was a well-established culprit behind elevated blood cholesterol, but the guideline makers focused on total fat in the diet, limiting intake to 30 percent or less of Calories because when total fat is reduced, saturated fat intake also falls. Did this strategy work to cut saturated fat intake? Yes, but only in people who applied the advice consistently. Many who tried failed, finding it impossible to maintain a low-fat diet over the long run.[1]

Low-fat diets present several other problems.[2] For example, low-fat diets are not necessarily low-Calorie diets, and many people with heart disease are overweight and need to reduce body fatness. In fact, many "fat-reduced" foods, especially snack foods, may contain only 10 percent less energy than the regular product, owing in part to the addition of carbohydrate-based fat replacers. Also, diets high in carbohydrates but low in fibre, especially those high in refined sugars, cause blood triglycerides to rise with unknown effects on heart health.[3] Finally, taken to an extreme, a low-fat diet may exclude nutritious foods, such as fatty fish, nuts, seeds, and vegetable oils, that provide the essential fatty acids along with many phytochemicals, vitamins, and minerals.

Low-Fat Diet Questions

Low-fat diets remain a centrepiece of treatment plans for people with elevated blood lipids or heart disease and are therefore important in nutrition.[4] But what about healthy people? Evidence from around the world has led researchers to question whether a low-fat diet is the only way, or even the best way, for healthy people to stay healthy. In a classic study of the effects of diet on the world's people, the Seven Countries Study, death rates from heart disease were strongly associated with diets high in saturated fats but only weakly linked with total fat.[5] In fact, the two places with the highest fat intakes were Finland and the Greek island of Crete, yet Finland had the highest rate of death from heart disease in the study, while Crete had the lowest.

In both places, the people consumed 40 percent or more of their Calories from fat. These findings indicated that total fat was clearly not to blame for a high rate of heart disease—something else was affecting the risk. When researchers examined the diets of these fat-loving peoples, they found that diets high in olive oil but low in saturated fat (less than 10% of Calories) were consistently associated with relatively low disease risks. These results have since been supported by many other studies.

Today's Fat Guidelines

On reviewing the evidence, the DRI committee concluded that a diet containing a slightly greater percentage of fat—up to 35 percent of total Calories—but reduced in saturated fat and trans fat and controlled in energy (Calories) is compatible with low rates of heart disease, diabetes, obesity, and cancer. Canada's Food Guide also has numerous recommendations regarding fat intake, for example, that we limit fat intake, select leaner meats, use cooking methods that require little or no added fat, limit *trans* fat, and choose lower-fat milk products.[6] The human body has no need of dietary saturated fat or *trans* fat, so the less consumed the better, as long as the diet is adequate in nutrients, including the essential fatty acids.[7] Following this advice requires that consumers first learn which foods contain which fats and then make appropriate selections among them.

Trans Fats in Canadian Foods

According to Canadian nutrition labelling regulations, the amount of *trans* fats in packaged foods is included together with saturated fats on the core list in the "Nutrition Facts" table on food labels. The amount is stated in grams and is included with saturated fat when calculating the %DV.

Most of the *trans* fats in the Canadian diet arise from the partially hydrogenated vegetable oils used to cook or make food items such as baked and fried foods. *Trans* fat not only raises plasma LDL cholesterol (bad cholesterol), it also reduces HDL cholesterol (good cholesterol). In the June 2006 final report of the *Trans* Fat Task Force (co-chaired by Health Canada and the Heart and Stroke Foundation of Canada) that was submitted to the minister of Health, the task force agreed "to a regulatory approach to effectively eliminate trans fats in all processed foods or reduce it to the lowest possible level" (http://www.hc-sc.gc.ca/fn-an/nutrition/gras-trans-fats/tf-ge/tf-gt_rep-rap-eng.php). They also projected that if such an action were taken, then "the average daily intake of trans fats for all age groups would represent less than 1% of energy intake," a level consistent with recommendations from the World Health Organization and American Heart Association.

High-Fat Foods and Heart Health

Avocados, bacon, walnuts, potato chips, and mackerel are all high-fat foods, yet the fats of these foods differ markedly in their effects on health. The following evidence can help clarify why some high-fat foods rightly belong in a heart-healthy diet and why others are best left on the shelf.

Olive Oil: The Potential Connection

The traditional diets of Greece and the Mediterranean region are exemplary in their use of "good" fats, especially olives and their oil. In population and laboratory studies, use of dark green olive oil instead of other cooking fats, especially butter, stick margarine, and meat fats, has been linked with numerous potential health benefits.[8] When olive oil replaces saturated fats, such as those of butter, coconut or palm oil, hydrogenated stick margarine, lard, or shortening, it may help protect against heart disease by some of these mechanisms:

- Lowering total and LDL cholesterol and not lowering HDL cholesterol or raising triglycerides[9]

- Reducing LDL cholesterol's vulnerability to oxidation[10]
- Lowering blood-clotting factors[11]
- Providing phytochemicals that act as antioxidants (see Controversy 2)[12]
- Lowering blood pressure[13]

Although such findings are promising, controlled human studies are too scarce to support population-wide recommendations to switch to a high-fat diet rich in olive oil.[14] Other vegetable oils, in their liquid unhydrogenated states, are also generally low in saturated fats and high in unsaturated fats, but they lack the phytochemicals that olive oil provides. When choosing olive oils, go for the darker "extra virgin" kind because it contains the highest levels of potentially beneficial phytochemicals.

People who hope that olive oil will be a magic potion against heart disease are bound to be disappointed. Drizzling olive oil on a food high in saturated fat, such as a cheese and sausage pizza, does not make such foods healthier. Also, like other fats, olive oil delivers 9 Calories per gram, which can contribute to weight gain in people who fail to balance their energy intake with their energy output.

The Mediterranean Diet: Beyond Olive Oil

Factors other than olive oil probably deserve some of the credit for the low rates of heart disease among people

Olives and their oil may benefit heart health.

consuming a traditional Mediterranean diet.[15] Such factors as amounts and types of meat, nuts, vegetables, fruit, and sweets differ widely between the traditional Mediterranean diets of the past century and modern North American diets.

Although each of the countries bordering the Mediterranean Sea has its own culture and dietary traditions, researchers have identified some common characteristics. Most traditional Mediterranean people focus their diets on crusty breads, whole grains, nuts, potatoes, and pastas; a variety of vegetables (including wild greens) and legumes; feta and mozzarella cheeses and yogurt; nuts; and fruit (especially grapes and figs). They eat some fish, other seafood, poultry, a few eggs, and a little meat. Along with olives and olive oil, their principal sources of fat are nuts and fish; they rarely use butter or encounter hydrogenated fats. Consequently, traditional Mediterranean diets are

- Low in saturated fat
- Very low in *trans* fat
- Rich in unsaturated fat
- Rich in starch and fibre
- Rich in nutrients and phytochemicals that support good health

These characteristics are consistent with many indicators of heart health.[16]

In addition, because the animals graze in fields, their meat, dairy products, and eggs are richer in omega-3 fatty acids than those from animals kept in feedlots and fed grain, as they are elsewhere. Omega-3 fatty acids in the Mediterranean diet also derive from other typical foods, such as wild plants and snails, that are unavailable to North American consumers. Apparently, each of the foods in Mediterranean diets contributes some small benefit that harmonizes with others to produce substantial cumulative or synergistic benefits.[17]

Nuts are extraordinarily popular in Mediterranean cuisines and show up in everything from sauces to desserts. Recent scientific findings have fostered

a turnabout in the attitude toward these high-fat foods.

Nuts: More Than a High-Calorie Snack Food

Nuts and peanuts traditionally have no place in a low-fat diet, with good reason. Nuts provide up to 80 percent of their Calories from fat, and a quarter-cup (30 grams) of mixed nuts provides over 200 Calories.

Nevertheless, scientists are finding links between nuts and heart health. A recent review of the literature suggests that people who eat a one-ounce serving of nuts on five or more days a week have lower heart disease risks than those consuming no nuts.[18] Even as little as two servings of nuts per week provide a positive, if smaller, benefit. The nuts under study are common varieties: almonds, Brazil nuts, cashews, hazelnuts, macadamia nuts, pecans, pistachios, walnuts, and even peanuts. On average, such nut varieties contain mostly monounsaturated fat (59%), some polyunsaturated fat (27%), and just a small amount of saturated fat (14%).[19]

Walnuts and almonds in particular may prove beneficial. In study after study, walnuts, when substituted for other fats in the diet, produce favourable effects on blood lipids—even in people whose total and LDL cholesterol were elevated at the outset.[20] The results are similar for almonds. Researchers gave men and women one of three kinds of snacks, all of equal Calories: whole-wheat muffins, almonds (75 grams), or half muffins and half almonds.[21] At the end of a month, people receiving the full almond snack had the greatest drop in blood LDL cholesterol; those eating the half almond snack had a lesser, but still significant, drop in blood lipids; and those eating the muffin-only snack demonstrated no change in blood lipids.

Studies on peanuts, macadamia nuts, pecans, and pistachios also indicate that consuming a variety of nuts may be a

Chapter 5 The Lipids: Fats, Oils, Phospholipids, and Sterols

NEL

Stay mindful of Calories when snacking on nuts.

wise choice. Nuts may lower heart disease risk because they are

- Low in saturated fats
- High in fibre, vegetable protein, and other valuable nutrients, including the antioxidant vitamin E
- High in phytochemicals that act as antioxidants

Walnuts also supply the essential fatty acid linolenic acid, which may quell blood vessel inflammation associated with heart disease.[22]

In addition to their heart benefits, nuts may also benefit other body organs—people who frequently consume nuts and other healthy fats suffer fewer gallbladder problems.[23]

Before deciding to include nuts in your diet, remember that a snack of nuts delivers substantially more Calories per bite than, say, a snack of whole-grain pretzels and many more still than crunchy raw vegetables. For people who struggle to maintain enough body weight for health, the Calories of nuts are a welcome addition. For the majority, however, caution is in order. In studying the effects of nuts on heart disease, researchers carefully adjust the Calories of experimental diets to make room for the nuts—that is, they use nuts instead of, not in addition to, other fat sources (such as meats, potato chips, oils, margarine, and butter) to keep Calories constant. People who decide to start eating nuts are urged to do likewise to prevent unneeded weight gain because weight gain elevates blood lipids and raises the risk of heart disease.

Butter or Margarine: Which to Choose

When news of the possible effects of *trans* fatty acids on heart health first emerged, some people stopped using margarine and switched back to butter, believing oversimplified reports that margarine provides no heart health advantage over butter.

Admittedly, hardened margarines and virtually all shortenings are made largely from hydrogenated fats and are therefore saturated and contain substantial *trans* fatty acids—up to 40 percent by weight. Some margarines, however, especially the soft or liquid varieties, are made from unhydrogenated oils, which are mostly unsaturated and so are less likely to elevate blood cholesterol than the saturated fats of butter.

When oils (but not hydrogenated oils) are the first ingredient listed on a margarine label, the margarine is, in all probability, low in saturated fat and *trans* fat and therefore a good choice for a healthy heart. On average, margarine contributes less *trans* fat to the diet than do other contributors (see Figure 5–13 on page 182).

In addition to soft and liquid margarine choices, some stick margarines are now specially formulated to contain few or no *trans* fatty acids. Popular in the United States and Europe, but not yet available in Canada, are other types, containing an added phytochemical ingredient, sterol esters, which reduce blood cholesterol when consumed as part of a low-fat diet.* These compounds belong to the sterol family of lipids and so are chemical relatives of cholesterol. Unlike cholesterol, though, sterol esters come from plants and are not recognized by the intestine and not absorbed. They may also block the absorption of cholesterol itself.[24]

Simply adding sterol ester–containing margarine to a diet high in

saturated fat is unlikely to bring health benefits. Sterol esters lower blood cholesterol only when people cut their fat intakes as well. Drawbacks to the sterol ester margarine include the price (three or four times as high as regular margarine); a high fat and Calorie content (the full-fat kind equals the fat and Calories in regular margarine); and an unproven record of safety for use by certain populations, such as growing children. Recently, sterol esters have also been added to some kinds of orange juice and candies, which may make these compounds more accessible to more people who may or may not need them. But these are not available in Canada.

Fish: Benefits and Cautions

This chapter made clear that fish oils hold the potential to improve health, particularly the health of the heart. Research studies have provided strong evidence that increasing omega-3 fatty acids in the diet supports heart health and lowers the risk of death from heart disease.[25] People who eat some fish each week lower their risks of heart attack and stroke.[26] For this reason, Canada's Food Guide and other authorities recommend including two fatty fish servings a week in a heart-healthy diet. Table 5–5 on page 178 identified fish varieties that supply at least 1 gram of omega-3 fatty acids per serving.

Fish is the best source of EPA and DHA in the diet, but fish is also a major source of mercury and other potentially toxic environmental contaminants, as mentioned in the chapter. Most fish have at least trace amounts of mercury, but tilefish, swordfish, king mackerel, marlin, shark, and tuna have especially high levels of contamination. Freshwater fish may contain PCBs and other pollutants, so local advisories warn sport fishers of species that can pose problems. The chapter listed safer species of fish. To minimize risks while obtaining fish benefits, vary your choices among fatty fish species often.

*The term sterol esters *includes related stanol esters. Controversy 2 defined these terms.*

Fish is the only good food source of EPA and DHA.

Fats to Avoid: Saturated Fats and *Trans* Fats

The number one dietary determinant of LDL cholesterol is saturated fat. Figure C5–1 shows that each 1 percent increase in energy from saturated fatty acids in the diet produces an estimated 2 percent jump in heart disease risk by way of elevating blood LDL cholesterol. Conversely, reducing saturated fat intake by 1 percent is estimated to produce a 2 percent drop in heart disease risk by the same mechanism.

Even a 2 percent drop in LDL represents a significant improvement for the health of the heart.[27] Similarly, *trans* fats also raise heart disease risk by elevating LDL cholesterol. A heart-healthy diet limits foods rich in these two types of fat. In this regard, Health Canada allows food manufacturers to use disease risk reduction claims on foods. One such claim links a diet low in saturated fat and *trans* fat and the reduction of risk of heart disease. As mentioned before, the wording of these claims is prescribed, for example, "A healthy diet low in saturated and trans fats may reduce the risk of heart disease."

To limit saturated fat intake, consumers must choose carefully among high-fat foods. The major sources of saturated fats in the diet are fatty meats, whole-milk products, coconut and palm oils, and products made from any of these foods. Over a third of the fat in most meats is saturated (review Figure 5–5). Over half of the fat in whole milk and other high-fat dairy products, such as cheese, butter, cream, half-and-half, cream cheese, sour cream, and ice cream, is saturated. The saturated fats of palm and coconut oils are rarely used by consumers in the kitchen, but their stability and other properties make them useful to food manufacturers, so commercially prepared foods provide these fats in abundance.

To restate the message of the chapter, when choosing meats, milk products, and commercially prepared foods, read labels and choose foods lowest in saturated fat and *trans* fat. To check the saturated fat content of foods that do not bear labels, go to http://www.hc-sc.gc.ca/fn-an/nutrition/fiche-nutri-data/index-eng.php and search the Canadian Nutrient File 2010.

Keeping total fat within the recommended level of 35 percent of total Calories is essential for controlling saturated fat intake. Even with careful selections, a nutritionally adequate diet will necessarily provide some saturated fat because oils that provide the essential polyunsaturated fatty acids also supply a mixture of other fatty acids, including saturated fatty acids.[28] Designing an adequate diet with zero saturated fat is not possible, even for experts.[29] Diets based on fruit, greens, legumes, nuts, soy products, vegetables, and whole grains can, and often do, deliver less saturated fat than diets that depend heavily on animal-derived foods, however.

Finally, keeping *trans* fat intake low requires restricting foods known

Figure C5–1

Impact of Change in Saturated Fatty Acid Intake on Blood LDL Cholesterol and Heart Disease Risk

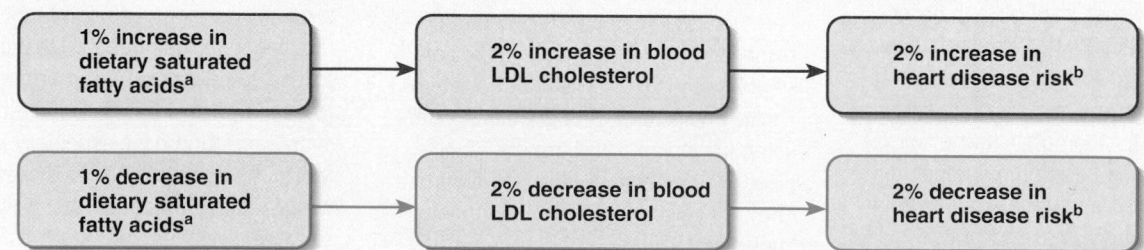

1% increase in dietary saturated fatty acids[a] → 2% increase in blood LDL cholesterol → 2% increase in heart disease risk[b]

1% decrease in dietary saturated fatty acids[a] → 2% decrease in blood LDL cholesterol → 2% decrease in heart disease risk[b]

[a] Percentage of change in total energy intake from saturated fatty acids.

[b] The change in an individual's risk may compound when blood lipid changes are sustained over time.

Source: Third Report of the National Cholesterol Education Program (NCEP) Expert Panel on Detection, Evaluation, and Treatment of High Blood Cholesterol in Adults (Adult Treatment Panel III), *NIH publication no. 02-5215 (Bethesda, MD: National Heart, Lung and Blood Institute, 2002), pp. II-4 and V-8.*

Food Sources of Fatty Acids

Healthful Fatty Acids		
Monounsaturated	Omega-6 Polyunsaturated	Omega-3 Polyunsaturated
Avocado	Margarine (nonhydrogenated)	Fatty fish (herring, mackerel, salmon, tuna)
Nuts (almonds, cashews, filberts, hazelnuts, macadamia nuts, peanuts, pecans, pistachios)	Mayonnaise	Flaxseed
	Nuts (walnuts)	Nuts
	Oil (corn, cottonseed safflower, soybean)	
Oils (canola, olive, peanut, sesame) or margarines made from canola or olive oil	Salad dressing	
	Seeds (pumpkin, sunflower)	
Olives		
Peanut butter (old-fashioned)		
Seeds (sesame)		

Harmful Fatty Acids	
Saturated	*Trans*
Bacon	Commercial baked goods, including cookies, cakes, pies, or other goodies made with margarine or vegetable shortening
Butter	Fried foods, particularly restaurant and fast foods
Cheese	
Chocolate	Many fried or processed snack foods, including microwave popcorn, chips, and crackers
Coconut	
Cream. half-and-half	Margarine (hydrogenated or partially hydrogenated)
Cream cheese	Nondairy creamers
Lard	Shortening
Meat	
Milk fat (whole-milk products)	
Oils (coconut, palm, palm kernel)	
Shortening	
Sour cream	

NOTE: Keep in mind that foods contain a mixture of fatty acids; see Figure 5–5, page 166.

to contain it. Table C5–1 summarizes which foods provide which fats. Substituting unsaturated fats for saturated fats at each meal and snack can help protect against heart disease. Table 5–9 in this chapter's Food Feature showed how such substitutions can lower saturated fat even when total fat and Calories remain unchanged.

Conclusion

Are some fats "good" and others "bad" from the body's point of view? Certainly, the saturated and *trans* fats seem mostly bad for the health of the heart. Aside from providing energy, which unsaturated fats can do equally well, saturated and *trans* fats bring no indispensable benefits to the body. Furthermore, no harm can come from consuming diets low in saturated fats and *trans* fats.

In contrast, unsaturated fats are mostly good for the health of the heart when consumed in moderation and within a sensible Calorie total. To date, their one proven fault seems to be that they, like all fats, provide abundant energy and so may promote obesity if they drive Calorie intakes higher than energy needs.[30] Obesity, in turn, often begets many body ills (see Chapter 9).

When judging foods by their fatty acids, keep in mind that food fats present the body with a mixture, providing both saturated and unsaturated fatty acids. Even olive oil and other vegetable oils deliver some saturated fat. Consequently, even when a person chooses foods with mostly unsaturated fats, saturated fat can still add up if total fat is high.

Food manufacturers may soon come to the assistance of consumers wishing to avoid the health threats from saturated and *trans* fats. Most major snack manufacturers are reducing the saturated and *trans* fats in some of their products and offering snack foods in single-serving packages.

Adopting some of the Mediterranean eating habits may serve the needs of those who enjoy somewhat more fat in the diet. Figure C5–2 presents a Mediterranean food pyramid for guidance. Basing the diet on vegetables, fruit, whole grains, and legumes as part of a balanced daily diet is a good idea, as is *replacing* saturated fats such as butter, shortening, and meat fat with unsaturated fats like olive oil and the oils from nuts and fish. These foods also provide vitamins, minerals, and phytochemicals—all valuable in protecting the body's health.

The authors of this book would not stop there, however. They would urge you to reduce fats from convenience foods and fast foods; choose small portions of meats, fish, and poultry; and select portion sizes that do not exceed your energy requirement. Also, Mediterranean peoples lead physically active lifestyles, and physical activity reduces disease risks. Therefore, if you want to include olive oil and generally eat like a Greek, you'd better walk, garden, bicycle, and swim like one, too.[31]

Figure C5–2
A Mediterranean Diet Pyramid

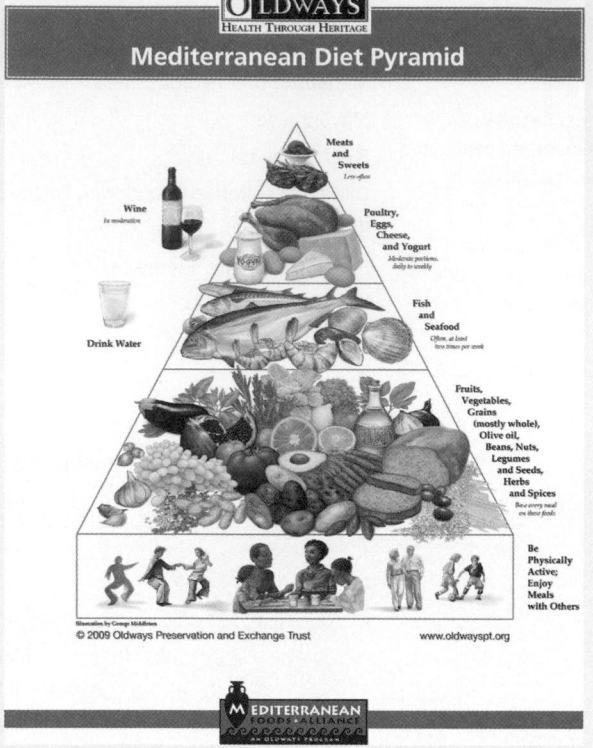

[a] The authors of this pyramid also recommend regular physical exercise and moderate consumption of wine.

[b] Other oils rich in monounsaturated fats, such as canola or peanut oil, can be substituted for olive oil. People who are watching their weight should limit their oil consumption.

Source: © 2009 Oldways Preservation & Exchange Trust. www.oldwayspt.org.

Self-Check

Answers to these Self-Check questions are in Appendix D.

1. Which of the following is *not* one of the ways fats are useful in foods?
    a. Fats contribute to the taste and smell of foods.
    b. Fats carry fat-soluble vitamins.
    c. Fats provide a low-Calorie source of energy compared to carbohydrates.
    d. Fats provide essential fatty acids.

2. Generally speaking, vegetable and fish oils are rich in which of these?
    a. polyunsaturated fat
    b. saturated fat
    c. cholesterol
    d. *trans* fatty acids

3. A benefit to health is seen when _____ is used in place of _____ in the diet.
    a. saturated fat; monounsaturated fat
    b. saturated fat; polyunsaturated fat
    c. monounsaturated fat; saturated fat
    d. polyunsaturated fat; cholesterol

4. Chylomicrons, a class of lipoproteins, are produced in the
    a. gallbladder
    b. small intestinal cells
    c. large intestinal cells
    d. liver

5. The roles of the essential fatty acids include

   a. form parts of cell membranes

   b. support infant growth and vision development

   c. support immune function

   d. all of the above

6. LDL deliver triglycerides and cholesterol from the liver to the body's tissues.

   T   F

7. Taking supplements of fish oil is recommended for those who don't like fish.

   T   F

8. Consuming large amounts of *trans* fatty acids lowers LDL cholesterol and thus lowers the risk of heart disease and heart attack.

   T   F

9. When the fat replacer olestra is present in the digestive tract, it enhances the absorption of vitamin E.

   T   F

10. Fried fish from fast-food restaurants and frozen fried fish products are often low in omega-3 and high in *trans* and saturated fatty acids.

    T   F

Concepts in Action

start now! ····> Ready to make a change?

Analyze Your Lipid Intake

The purpose of this exercise is to help you identify fatty foods in your diet, as well as sources of essential fatty acids, as well as saturated and *trans* fats. The Diet Analysis Plus (DA+) program will help you learn which foods contain which fats and help you to choose food sources of unsaturated fats.

1. The Macronutrient Ranges report compares your intakes to the DRI recommended intake ranges. From the Reports tab select Day 2 (choose all meals), click on the Macronutrient Ranges report, and then generate a report. What percentage of your calories came from fat? Did your intake for fats fall within the recommended range?

2. No amount of dietary saturated or *trans* fat is required for health. Open the DA+ Home page. From the Reports tab, under the Nutrients heading select Fat Breakdown. Choose Day 3 (choose all meals), and then generate a report. Your

report will show a breakdown of your fatty acid intake for that day as a percentage of total calories from the various types of fatty acids in the foods/beverages you consumed that day. What are the percentages for saturated, monounsaturated, poly-unsaturated, and *trans* fatty acids in your day's intake? Are they in line with the DRI recommendations for each type of fatty acid? To find out, check Table 5–2 on page 172 and the margin note on page 176.

3. Which foods provide not only the most fat but also the different types of fatty acids to your diet? From the Reports tab, under the Advanced heading select Source Analysis, and select Day 1 (choose all meals). From the pick-list choose saturated fat and select Create PDF. Do the same for monounsaturated, polyunsaturated, and *trans* fatty acids. What three foods contributed the most saturated and monounsaturated fats? Polyunsaturated and *trans* fats? Are any of your foods listed as saturated fat contributors as shown in Figure 5–5 (page 166) or Figure 5–10 (page 174)?

4. To study your intake of essential fatty acids, from the Reports tab, under the Nutrients heading select Intake vs. Goals, and then select

Day One (all meals) and generate a report. Look for the Essential Fatty Acids heading. Compared with the DRI goal, how did your intake stack up? From this same Reports tab under the Advanced heading select Source Analysis and then use the pick-list "down" arrow to find the sources of omega-3 and omega-6 essential fatty acids in your meals. What foods might you change to improve your intake [see Figure 5–5 on page 166, Table 5–5 (page 178), and Table C5–1 (page 199)].

5. Toppings and sauces added to nutritious foods drive up Calorie and saturated fat intakes. The Food Feature in this chapter on page 191 gives suggestions for reducing these add-ons. From the Track Diet tab, under the Create or Edit Foods and Recipes heading select the Recipes button, Create New Recipe, to create an appealing heart-healthy salad with little saturated/ *trans* fats. Save and close your recipe. Select a new day (not from your 3-day record) and select only your salad. Click on View: Favourites and then click the "*i*" *icon* next to the recipe name to display the nutrients in the salad. How did you do?

Endnotes

1. E. Faloia and coauthors, Adipose tissue as an endocrine organ? A review of some recent data, *Eating and Weight Disorders* 5 (2000): 116–123; S.S. Gropper and J.L. Smith, Chapter 5 Lipids in Advanced Nutrition and Human Metabolism (6th ed). Wadsworth Cengage Learning. USA. 2013.

2. A. Baylin and coauthors, Adipose tissue biomarkers of fatty acid intake, *American Journal of Clinical Nutrition* 76 (2002): 750–757.

3. J. Zhang and H. Kesteloot, Differences in all-cause, cardiovascular and cancer mortality between Hong Kong and Singapore: Role of nutrition, *European Journal of Epidemiology* 17 (2001): 469–477.

4. F. J. Sanchez-Muniz and coauthors, Dietary fat saturation affects apolipoprotein AII levels and HDL composition in postmenopausal women, *Journal of Nutrition* 132 (2002): 50–54; D. O. Edem, Palm oil: Biochemical, physiological, nutritional, hematological, and toxicological aspects: A review, *Plant Foods for Human Nutrition* 57 (2002): 319–341.

5. A. H. Stark and Z. Madar, Olive oil as a functional food: Epidemiology and nutritional approaches, *Nutrition Reviews* 60 (2002): 170–176.

6. C. T. Phan and P. Tso, Intestinal lipid absorption and transport, *Frontiers in Bioscience* 6 (2001): D299–D319.

7. U.S. Department of Agriculture and U.S. Department of Health and Human Services, *Dietary Guidelines for Americans*, 2010, available at http://www.health.gov/dietaryguidelines/2010.asp

8. S. A. Bingham and coauthors, Are imprecise methods obscuring a relation between fat and breast cancer? *Lancet* 362 (2003): 212–214; C. E. Spiegelman and coauthors, Premenopausal fat intake and risk of breast cancer, *Journal of the National Cancer Institute* 95 (2003): 1079–1085; P. L. Zock, Dietary fats and cancer, *Current Opinion in Lipidology* 12 (2001): 5–10.

9. A. L. Lichtenstein and P. J. H. Jones, Lipids: Absorption and transport, in *Present Knowledge in Nutrition*, eds. B. A. Bowman and R. M. Russell (Washington, D.C.: ILSI Press, 2001), p. 99; C. F. L. Semenkovich, Nutrient and genetic regulation of lipoprotein metabolism, in *Modern Nutrition in Health and Disease*, eds. M. E. Shils and coeditors (Baltimore, MD: Williams & Wilkins, 1999), p. 1196.

10. Executive Summary of the Third Report of the National Cholesterol Education Program (NCEP) Expert Panel on Detection, Evaluation, and Treatment of High Blood Cholesterol in Adults (Adult Treatment Panel III), *Journal of the American Medical Association* 285 (2001): 2486–2497.

11. U.S. Department of Agriculture and U.S. Department of Health and Human Services, 2010 [see reference 7].

12. K. L. Herron and coauthors, Men classified as hypo- or hyperresponders to dietary cholesterol feeding exhibit differences in lipoprotein metabolism, *Journal of Nutrition* 133 (2003): 1036–1042; K. L. Herron and coauthors, Premenopausal women, classified as hypo- or hyperresponding, do not alter their LDL/HDL ratio following a high dietary cholesterol challenge, *Journal of the American College of Nutrition* 21 (2002): 250–258.

13. J. F. Mauger and coauthors, Effect of different forms of dietary hydrogenated fats on LDL particle size, *American Journal of Clinical Nutrition* 78 (2003): 370–375; J. T. Judd and coauthors, Dietary cis and trans monounsaturated and saturated FA and plasma lipids and lipoproteins in men, *Lipids* 37 (2002): 123–131; Standing Committee on the Scientific Evaluation of Dietary Reference Intakes, Food and Nutrition Board, Institute of Medicine, *Dietary Reference Intakes for Energy, Carbohydrate, Fiber, Fat, Fatty Acids, Cholesterol, Protein, and Amino Acids* (Washington, D.C.: National Academies Press, 2002), pp. 9-1–9-32.

14. M. Rantala and coauthors, Apolipoprotein B gene polymorphisms and serum lipids: Meta-analysis of the role of genetic variation in responsiveness to diet, *American Journal of Clinical Nutrition* 71 (2000): 713–724.

15. Executive Summary of the Third Report of the National Cholesterol Education Program (NCEP) Expert Panel on Detection, Evaluation, and Treatment of High Blood Cholesterol in Adults (Adult Treatment Panel III), 2001 [see reference 10].

16. Joint WHO/FAO Expert Consultation, *Diet, Nutrition and the Prevention of Chronic Diseases* (Geneva, Switzerland: World Health Organization, 2003), p. 56.

17. D. Hwang, Fatty acids and immune responses—A new perspective in searching for clues to mechanism, *Annual Review of Nutrition* 20 (2000): 431–456.

18. H. Tapiero and coauthors, Polyunsaturated fatty acids (PUFA) and eicosanoids in human health and pathologies, *Biomedicine and Pharmacotherapy* 56 (2002): 215–222.

19. J. P. Middaugh, Cardiovascular deaths among Alaskan Natives, 1980–1986, *American Journal of Public Health* 80 (1990): 282–285; J. Dyerberg, Linolenate-derived polyunsaturated fatty acids and prevention of atherosclerosis, *Nutrition Reviews* 44 (1986): 125–134.

20. J. N. Din, D. E. Newby, and A. D. Flapan, Omega 3 fatty acids and cardiovascular disease—Fishing for a natural treatment, *British Medical Journal* 328 (2004): 30–35; E. Dewailly and coauthors, n-3 fatty acids and cardiovascular disease risk factors among the Inuit of Nunavik, *American Journal of Clinical Nutrition* 74 (2001): 464–473.

21. Dewailly and coauthors, 2001 [see reference 20].

22. Health Canada, *Eating Well with Canada's Food Guide* (Ottawa, 2011), available at http://www.hc-sc.gc.ca/fn-an/food-guide-aliment/index_e.html. T. A. Mori and L. J. Beilin, Long-chain omega 3 fatty acids, blood lipids and cardiovascular risk reduction, *Current Opinion in Lipidology* 12 (2001): 11–17.

23. P. Marckmann, Fishing for heart protection, *American Journal of Clinical Nutrition* 78 (2003): 781–782.

24. P. M. Kris-Etherton, W. S. Harris, and L. J. Appel, Fish consumption, fish oil, omega-3 fatty acids, and cardiovascular disease, *Circulation* 106 (2002): 2747–2757.

25. V. Wijendran and K. C. Hayes, Dietary n-6 and n-3 fatty acid balance and cardiovascular health, *Annual Review of Nutrition* 24 (2004): 597–615; G. Zhao and coauthors, Dietary a-linolenic acid reduces inflammatory and lipid cardiovascular risk factors in hypercholesterolemic men and women, *Journal of Nutrition* 134 (2004): 2991–2997; S. C. Larsson and coauthors, Dietary long-chain n-3 fatty acids for the prevention of cancer: A review of potential mechanisms, *American Journal of Clinical Nutrition* 79 (2004): 935–945; S. Kew and coauthors, Lack of effect of foods enriched with plant- or marine-derived n-3 fatty acids on human immune function, *American Journal of Clinical Nutrition* 77 (2003): 1287–1295.

26. Fish oil, American Heart Association Recommendation, 2002, available at http://circ.ahajournals.org/content/106/21/2747.full ; S. L. Connor and W. E. Connor, Are fish oils beneficial in the prevention and treatment of coronary artery disease? *American Journal of Clinical Nutrition* 66 (1997): S1031–S1020.

27. Standing Committee on the Scientific Evaluation of Dietary Reference Intakes, Food and Nutrition Board, Institute of Medicine, 2002, pp. 8–26 [see reference 13].

28. F. Thies and coauthors, Dietary supplementation with eicosapentaenoic acid, but not with other long-chain n-3 or n-6 polyunsaturated fatty acids, decreases natural killer cell activity in healthy subjects aged >55 y, *American Journal of Clinical Nutrition* 73 (2001): 539–548; V. M. Montori and coauthors, Fish oil supplementation in type 2 diabetes: A quantitative systematic review, *Diabetes Care* 23 (2000): 1407–1415.

29. M. T. Nakamura and coauthors, Metabolism and functions of highly unsaturated fatty acids: An update, *Lipids* 36 (2001): 961–964.

30. Backgrounder for the 2004 FDA/EPA Consumer Advisory: What you need to know about mercury in fish and shellfish, 2004, available at http://www.fda.gov/downloads/Food/FoodborneIllnessContaminants/UCM182158.pdf; S. L. Schantz and coauthors, Impairment of memory and learning in older adults exposed to polychlorinated biphenyls via consumption of Great Lakes fish, *Environmental Health Perspectives* 110 (2002): A70–A72; Health Canada, Human health risk assessment of mercury in fish and health benefits of fish consumption, March 2007, available at http://www.hc-sc.gc.ca/fn-an/pubs/mercur/merc_fish_poisson-eng.php.

31. H. M. Chan and G. M. Egeland, Fish consumption, mercury exposure, and heart diseases, *Nutrition Reviews* 62 (2004): 68–72.

32. B. M. Popkin and coauthors, Where's the fat? Trends in U.S. diets 1965–1996, *Preventive Medicine* 32 (2001): 245–254.

33. S. L. Booth and coauthors, Effects of a hydrogenated form of vitamin K on bone formation and resorption, *American Journal of Clinical Nutrition* 74 (2001): 783–790.

34. D. J. Baer and coauthors, Dietary fatty acids affect plasma markers of inflammation in healthy men fed controlled diets: A randomized crossover study, *American Journal of Clinical Nutrition* 79 (2004): 969–973; M. B. Katan, Trans fatty acids and plasma lipoproteins, *Nutrition Reviews* 58 (2000): 188–191.

35. Bingham and coauthors, 2003 [see reference 8].

36. Standing Committee on the Scientific Evaluation of Dietary Reference Intakes, Food and Nutrition Board, Institute of Medicine, 2002, pp. 8–46 [see reference 13]; W. M. N. Ratnayake and coauthors, Trans fatty acids: current contents in Canadian foods and estimated intake levels for the Canadian population, *Journal of AOAC International* 92 (2009): 1258–1276.

37. Revealing *trans* fats, *FDA Consumer*, September/October 2003, pp. 20–26.

38. A. H. Lichtenstein and coauthors, Effects of different forms of dietary hydrogenated fats on serum lipoprotein cholesterol levels, *New England Journal of Medicine* 340 (1999): 1933–1940.

39. E. A. Bell and B. J. Rolls, Energy density of foods affects energy intake across multiple levels of fat content in lean and obese women, *American Journal of Clinical Nutrition* 73 (2001): 1010–1018; M. Raeini-Sarjaz and coauthors, Comparison of the effect of dietary fat restriction with that of energy on human lipid metabolism, *American Journal of Clinical Nutrition* 73 (2001): 262–267.

40. Popkin and coauthors, 2001 [see reference 32].

41. P. A. Cotton and coauthors, Dietary sources of nutrients among U.S. adults, 1994–1996, *Journal of the American Dietetic Association* 104 (2004): 921–930.

42. Committee on the Scientific Evaluation of Dietary Reference Intakes, Food and Nutrition Board, Institute of Medicine, 2002, pp. 11–46 [see reference 13].

43. T. Zind, Out to lunch, *Prepared Foods*, May 2003, pp. 21–22.

Consumer Corner 5

1. Position of the American Dietetic Association: Fat replacers, *Journal of the American Dietetic Association* 105 (2005): 266–275; G. Inglett, Food ingredients from cereals with nutraceutical properties, ARS online publications, October 1, 2002, from the USDA Agricultural Research Service research project: *Heart Healthy Foods: Enzymatic and Physical Modifications of Carbohydrates*, available at http://www.ars.usda.gov/research/publications/publications.htm?SEQ_NO_115=140228.

2. R. S. Sandler and coauthors, Gastrointestinal symptoms in 3181 volunteers ingesting snack foods containing olestra or triglycerides: A 6-week randomized, placebo-controlled trial, *Annals of Internal Medicine* 130 (1999): 253–261.

3. G. S. Allgood and coauthors, Postmarketing surveillance of new food ingredients: Results from the program with the fat replacer olestra, *Regulatory Toxicology and Pharmacology* 33 (2001): 224–233.

4. FDA changes labeling requirement for olestra, *FDA Talk Paper* #T03-59, August 2003.

5. E. Kennedy and S. Bowman, Assessment of the effect of fat-modified foods on diet quality in adults, 19 to 50 years, using data from the Continuing Survey of Food Intake by Individuals, *Journal of the American Dietetic Association* 101 (2001): 455–460.

6. H. J. Roy and coauthors, Effect on body weight of replacing dietary fat with olestra for two or ten weeks in healthy men and women, *Journal of the American College of Nutrition* 21 (2002): 259–267.

7. R. E. Patterson and coauthors, Changes in diet, weight, and serum lipid levels associated with olestra consumption, *Archives of Internal Medicine* 160 (2000): 2600–2604.

Controversy 5

1. M. de Lorgeril and coauthors, Mediterranean diet, traditional risk factors, and the rate of cardiovascular complications after myocardial infarction: Final report of the Lyon Diet Heart Study, *Circulation* 99 (1999): 779–785.

2. F. B. Hu, J. E. Manson, and W. C. Willett, Types of dietary fat and risk of coronary heart disease: A critical review, *Journal of the American College of Nutrition* 20 (2001): 5–19.

3. L. A. Piché and E. Bright-See, Energy and fat content of fat-modified and comparable regular food products available in supermarkets, Dietetic Research Event by the Canadian Foundation for Dietetic Research, Montreal, PQ, July 1997, *Journal of the Canadian Dietetic Association* 58 (1997): 19, abstract; M. Kanazawa and coauthors, Effects of a high-sucrose diet on body weight, plasma triglycerides, and stress tolerance, Nutrition Reviews 61 (2003): S27–S33; E. J. Parks, Changes in fat synthesis influenced by dietary macronutrient content, *Proceedings of the Nutrition Society* 61 (2002): 281–286.

4. *Third Report of the National Cholesterol Education Program (NCEP) Expert Panel on Detection, Evaluation, and Treatment of High Blood Cholesterol in Adults (Adult Treatment Panel III)*, 2002, NIH publication no. 02-1205.

5. A. Keys, *Seven Countries: A Multivariate Analysis of Death and Coronary Heart Disease* (Cambridge, MA: Harvard University Press, 1980).

6. Committee on the Scientific Evaluation of Dietary Reference Intakes, Food and Nutrition Board, Institute of Medicine, *Dietary Reference Intakes for Energy, Carbohydrate, Fiber, Fat, Fatty Acids, Cholesterol, Protein, and Amino Acids* (Washington, D.C.: National Academies Press, 2002); Health Canada, Food and Nutrition: *Eating Well with Canada's Food Guide*, available at http://www.hc-sc.gc.ca/fn-an/food-guide-aliment/index-eng.php.

7. Committee on the Scientific Evaluation of Dietary Reference Intakes, Food and Nutrition Board, Institute of Medicine, 2005 [see reference 6].

8. A. H. Stark and Z. Madar, Olive oil as a functional food: Epidemiology and nutritional approaches, *Nutrition Reviews* 60 (2002): 170–176.

9. P. M. Kris-Etherton and coauthors, High-monounsaturated fatty acid diets lower both plasma cholesterol and triacylglycerol concentrations, *American Journal of Clinical Nutrition* 70 (1999): 1009–1015.

10. R. L. Hargrove and coauthors, Low fat and high monounsaturated fat diets decrease human low density lipoprotein oxidative susceptibility in vitro, *Journal of Nutrition* 131 (2001): 1758–1763.

11. C. M. Williams, Beneficial nutritional properties of olive oil: Implications for postprandial lipoproteins and factor VII, *Nutrition, Metabolism, and Cardiovascular Diseases* 11 (2001): 51–56; J. P. De La Cruz and coauthors, Antithrombotic potential of olive oil administration in rabbits with elevated cholesterol, *Thrombosis Research* 100 (2000): 305–315.

12. F. Visioli and coauthors, Virgin Olive Oil Study (VOLOS): Vasoprotective potential of extra virgin olive oil in mildly dyslipidemic patients, *European Journal of Nutrition* 44 (2005): 121–117.

13. L. A. Ferrara and coauthors, Olive oil and reduced need for antihypertensive medications, *Archives of Internal Medicine* 160 (2000): 837–842.

14. L. Van Horn and N. Ernst, A summary of the science supporting the new National Cholesterol Education program dietary recommendations: What dietitians should know, *Journal of the American Dietetic Association* 101 (2001): 1148–1154.

15. A. Trichopoulou and coauthors, Adherence to a Mediterranean diet and survival in a Greek population, *New England Journal of Medicine* 348 (2003): 2599–2608; A. T. Lada and L. L. Rudel, Dietary monounsaturated versus polyunsaturated fatty acids: Which is really better for protection from coronary heart disease? *Current Opinion in Lipidology* 14 (2003): 41–46.

16. D. B. Panageotakos, as quoted in Greek diet reduces inflammatory protein, *Science News* 164 (2003): 164.

17. D. R. Jacobs Jr. and L. M. Steffen, Nutrients, foods, and dietary patterns as exposures in research: A framework for food synergy, *American Journal of Clinical Nutrition* 78 (2003): 508S–513S.

18. P. M. Kris-Etherton and coauthors, The effects of nuts on coronary heart disease risk, *Nutrition Reviews* 59 (2001): 103–111.

19. F. B. Hu and M. J. Stampfer, Nut consumption and risk of coronary heart disease: A review of epidemiologic evidence, *Current Atherosclerosis Reports* 1 (1999): 204–209.

20. E. B. Feldman, The scientific evidence for a beneficial health relationship between walnuts and coronary heart disease, *Journal of Nutrition* 132 (2002): 1062S–1101S; D. Zambon and coauthors,

Substituting walnuts for monounsaturated fat improves the serum lipid profile of hypercholesterolemic men and women: A randomized crossover trial, *Annals of Internal Medicine* 132 (2000): 538–546.

21. D. J. Jenkins and coauthors, Dose response of almonds on coronary heart disease risk factors: blood lipids, oxidized low-density lipoproteins, lipoprotein (a), homocysteine, and pulmonary nitric oxide: a randomized, controlled, crossover trial, *Circulation* 106 (2002): 1327–1332.

22. G. Zhao and coauthors, Dietary a-linolenic acid reduces inflammatory and lipid cardiovascular risk factors in hypercholesterolemic men and women, *Journal of Nutrition* 134 (2004): 2991–2997.

23. C.-J. Tsai and coauthors, Frequent nut consumption and decreased risk of cholecystectomy in women, *American Journal of Clinical Nutrition* 80 (2004): 76–81.

24. M. A. Hallikainen and M. I. Uusitupa, Effects of 2 low-fat stanol ester-containing margarines on serum cholesterol concentrations as part of a low-fat diet in hypercholesterolemic subjects, *American Journal of Clinical Nutrition* 69 (1999): 403–410.

25. F. B. Hu and coauthors, Fish and omega-3 fatty acid intake and risk of coronary heart disease in women, *Journal of the American Medical Association* 287 (2002): 1815–1821; C. M. Albert and coauthors, Blood levels of long-chain n-3 fatty acids and the risk of sudden death, *New England Journal of Medicine* 346 (2002): 1113–1118.

26. H. Iso and coauthors, Intake of fish and omega-3 acids and risk of stroke in women, *Journal of the American Medical Association* 285 (2001): 304–312.

27. *Third Report of the National Cholesterol Education Program (NCEP) Expert Panel on Detection, Evaluation, and Treatment of High Blood Cholesterol in Adults (Adult Treatment Panel III)*, 2002, p. V-8 [see reference 4].

28. Committee on the Scientific Evaluation of Dietary Reference Intakes, Food and Nutrition Board, Institute of Medicine, 2002, pp. 11–22 [see reference 6].

29. Committee on the Scientific Evaluation of Dietary Reference Intakes, Food and Nutrition Board, Institute of Medicine, 2002, pp. 11–46 and G-1 [see reference 6].

30. Committee on the Scientific Evaluation of Dietary Reference Intakes, Food and Nutrition Board, Institute of Medicine, 2002, pp. 11–19 [see reference 6].

31. K. T. B. Knoops and coauthors, Mediterranean diet, lifestyle factors, and 10-year mortality in elderly European men and women, *Journal of the American Medical Association* 292 (2004): 1433–1439.

6 The Proteins and Amino Acids

Do You Ever . . .

Wonder why protein is important to the health of the body?

Find it curious that heating an egg changes it from a liquid to a solid?

Take protein or amino acid supplements to bulk up muscles or lose weight?

Fear that your diet will lack protein unless you eat at least some meat?

Keep Reading . . .

Learning Objectives

After completing this chapter, you should be able to

LO 6.1 Discuss why some amino acids are essential, non-essential, or conditionally essential to the human body, and state what happens when essential amino acids are lacking.

LO 6.2 Compare the digestion of protein and transport of amino acids in the body with that of lipids.

LO 6.3 Discuss the various roles of proteins and amino acids in the body.

LO 6.4 Describe the fate of amino acids that are taken in with a balanced diet versus a carbohydrate-poor diet.

LO 6.5 Discuss the concept of nitrogen balance, and compute the amount of protein needed for a healthy college or university student.

LO 6.6 Compare the major forms of protein malnutrition, and discuss why consuming excess protein is not recommended.

LO 6.7 Summarize the health advantages and disadvantages of various vegetarian diets, and develop a day's meal plan for a nutritious vegetarian diet.

Contents

First named 150 years ago after the Greek word *proteios* ("of prime importance"), the proteins are versatile and vital cellular working molecules. Without them, life would not exist. Research on **proteins** has revealed countless secrets of the processes of life and has helped to answer many questions about nutrition. How do we grow? How do our bodies replace the materials they lose? How does blood clot? What gives us immunity? What makes one person different from another? Understanding the nature of the proteins in the body helps solve these mysteries.

Some of the body's proteins are working proteins; others form structures. Working proteins include the body's enzymes, antibodies, transport vehicles, hormones, cellular "pumps," and oxygen carriers. Structural proteins include tendons and ligaments, scars, the fibres of muscles, the cores of bones and teeth, the filaments of hair, the materials of nails, and more. Yet, however different their functions, all protein molecules have much in common.

The Structure of Proteins

proteins compounds composed of carbon, hydrogen, oxygen, and nitrogen and arranged as strands of amino acids. Some amino acids also contain the element sulphur.

amino (a-MEEN-o) **acids** the building blocks of protein. Each has an amine group at one end, an acid group at the other, and a distinctive side chain.

The structure of proteins enables them to perform many vital functions. One key difference from carbohydrates and fats is that proteins contain nitrogen atoms in addition to the carbon, hydrogen, and oxygen atoms that all three energy-yielding nutrients contain. These nitrogen atoms give the name *amino* ("nitrogen containing") to the **amino acids**, the building blocks of proteins. Another key difference is that in contrast to the carbohydrates, whose repeating units, glucose molecules, are identical, the amino acids in a strand of protein are different from one another. A strand of amino acids that makes up a protein may contain 20 *different* kinds of amino acids.

Chapter 6 The Proteins and Amino Acids

Amino Acids

All amino acids have the same simple chemical backbone consisting of a single carbon atom with both an **amine group** (the nitrogen-containing part) and an acid group attached to it. Each amino acid also has a distinctive chemical **side chain** attached to the centre carbon of the backbone (see Figure 6–1). It is this side chain that gives identity and chemical nature to each amino acid. About 20 amino acids, each with its own different side chain, make up most of the proteins of living tissue.[*,1] Other rare amino acids, such as seleno-cysteine, appear in a few proteins.

The side chains make the amino acids differ in size, shape, and electrical charge. Some are negative, some are positive, and some have no charge (are neutral). The first part of Figure 6–2 is a diagram of three amino acids, each with a different side chain attached to its backbone. The rest of the figure shows how amino acids link to form protein strands. Long strands of amino acids form large protein molecules, and the side chains of the amino acids ultimately help determine the molecules' shapes and behaviours.

Indispensable/Essential Amino Acids
The body can make about half of the 20 amino acids for itself, given the needed parts: fragments derived from carbohydrate or other amino acids to form the backbones and nitrogen from other amino acids and other sources to form the amine groups. The healthy human body cannot make some amino acids or makes them too slowly to meet its needs. These are the **indispensable/essential amino acids** (listed in Table 6–1). Without these essential nutrients in the amounts indicated along with adequate total energy intake from other sources, the body cannot make the proteins it needs to grow and do its work. Because the essential amino acids can be replenished only from foods, a person must frequently eat the foods that provide them.

Under special circumstances, a nonessential amino acid can become essential. For example, the body normally makes tyrosine (a nonessential amino acid) from the essential amino acid phenylalanine. If the diet fails to supply enough phenylalanine, or if the body cannot make the conversion for some reason (as happens in the inherited disease phenylketonuria; see Controversy 4 in Chapter 4), then tyrosine becomes a **conditionally indispensable/essential amino acid**.

Recycling Amino Acids
The body not only makes some amino acids but also breaks protein molecules apart and reuses those amino acids. Both food proteins, after digestion, and body proteins, when they have finished their cellular work, are dismantled to liberate their component amino acids. Amino acids from both sources provide the cells with a tiny pool (of about 150 g) of raw materials from which they can build the protein molecules they need. Cells can also use the amino acids for energy and discard the nitrogen atoms as wastes. By reusing amino acids to build proteins, however, the body recycles and conserves (protein turnover is about 300–400 g/day) a valuable commodity while easing its nitrogen disposal burden.

This recycling system also provides access to an emergency fund of amino acids in times of fuel, glucose, or protein deprivation. At such times, tissues can break down their own proteins, sacrificing working molecules before the ends of their normal lifetimes, to supply energy and amino acids to the body's cells. The body employs a priority system in selecting the tissue proteins to dismantle—it uses the most dispensable ones first, such as the small proteins of the blood and muscles.[2] It guards the structural proteins of the heart and other organs until forced, by dire need, such as starvation, to relinquish them.

---

*Reference notes are found at the end of this chapter.

Figure 6–1

An Amino Acid

The "backbone" is the same for all amino acids. The side chain differs from one amino acid to the next. The nitrogen is in the amine group.

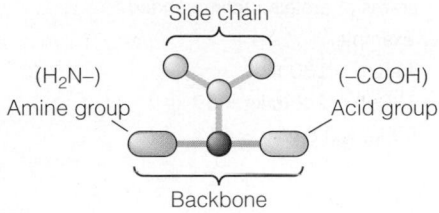

Figure 6–2

Different Amino Acids Join Together

This is the basic process by which proteins are assembled.

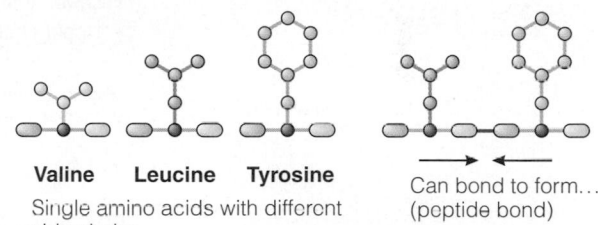

Valine Leucine Tyrosine
Single amino acids with different side chains...

Can bond to form... (peptide bond)

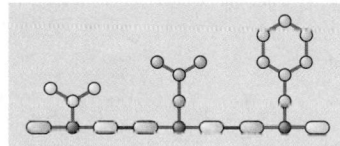

A strand of amino acids, part of a protein.

---

amine (a-MEEN) **group** the nitrogen-containing portion of an amino acid.

side chain the unique chemical structure attached to the backbone of each amino acid that differentiates one amino acid from another.

indispensable/essential amino acids amino acids that either cannot be synthesized at all by the body or cannot be synthesized in amounts sufficient to meet physiological need.

conditionally indispensable/essential amino acid an amino acid that is normally nonessential but must be supplied by the diet in special circumstances when the need for it exceeds the body's ability to produce it.

The DRI recommended intake for protein (adult) is o.8 g/kg.

To figure your protein need:

1. Find your body weight in pounds.

2. Convert pounds to kilograms (by dividing pounds by 2.2).

3. Multiply kilograms by 0.8 to find total grams of protein recommended.

For example:

- Weight = 130 lb
- 130 lb ÷ 2.2 lb/kg = 59 kg
- 59 kg × 0.8 g/kg = 47 g

Table 6–1

Recommendations Concerning Intakes of Protein for Adults

Part A

DRI recommended intakes:[a]

- Acceptable Macronutrient Distribution Range (AMDR) is 10–35% of total energy
- 0.8 g protein per kilogram of body weight per day
- Women: 46 g/day; men: 56 g/day

Canada's Food Guide servings per day:

- Meat and alternatives: children, 1–2; teens, 2–3; adults, 2–3, e.g., one Food Guide serving is 75 g of meat, poultry, or fish; 2 eggs; 150 g of tofu; 30 mL peanut butter
  - Have meat alternatives such as beans, lentils, and tofu often.
  - Eat at least two Food Guide servings of fish each week.
  - Select lean meat and alternatives prepared with little or no fat or salt.
- Milk and alternatives: children, 2–4; teens, 3–4; adults, 2–3, e.g., 1 cup of milk or fortified soy beverage; 175 g of yogurt; 50 g of cheese
  - Drink skim, 1%, or 2% milk each day.
  - Select lower-fat milk alternatives.

World Health Organization

- Lower limit: 10% of total Calories from protein
- Upper limit: 15% of total Calories from protein

[a]*Protein recommendations for infants, children, and pregnant and lactating women are higher; see inside front cover, page A.*

Part B

RDA (mg/kg body weight/day) for indispensable [+ conditionally indispensable[a]] amino acids for adults 19 years and older

Histidine	14
Isoleusine	19
Leucine	42
Lysine	38
Methionine (+ cysteine[a])	19
Phenylalanine (+ tyrosine[a])	33
Threonine	20
Tryptophan	5
Valine	24

Dispensable/Nonessential Amino Acids

Alanine
Aspartic Acid
Asparagine
Glutamic Acid
Serine

[a]*Conditionally Indispensable Amino Acids*
Arginine
Cysteine
Glutamine
Glycine
Proline
Tyrosine

- Proteins are unique among the energy nutrients in that they possess nitrogen-containing amine groups and may be composed of as many as 20 different amino acid units. Of the 20 amino acids, some are indispensable/essential and some are dispensable, while others may be conditionally indispensable/essential only in special circumstances.

How Do Amino Acids Build Proteins?

In the first step of making a protein, each amino acid is hooked to the next (as shown in Figure 6–2). A chemical bond, called a **peptide bond**, is formed between the amine group end of one amino acid and the acid group end of the next. The side chains bristle out from the backbone of the structure, giving the protein molecule its unique character.

The strand of protein does not remain a straight chain. Figure 6–2 shows only the first step in making proteins—the linking of amino acid units with peptide bonds until the strand contains from several dozen to as many as 300 amino acids. Amino acids at different places along the strand are chemically attracted to each other, and this attraction causes some segments of the strand to coil, somewhat like a metal spring (see Figure 6–3a). Also, each spot along the coiled strand is attracted to, or repelled from, other spots along its length. These interactions cause the entire coil to fold this way and that, forming either a globular structure (e.g., hemoglobin) (see Figure 6–3b) or a fibrous structure (e.g., collagen; not shown).

The amino acids whose side chains are electrically charged are attracted to water. Therefore, in the body's watery fluids, they orient themselves on the outside of the protein structure. The amino acids whose side chains are neutral are repelled by water and are attracted to one another; these tuck themselves in the centre, away from the body fluids. All of these interactions among the amino acids and the surrounding fluids give each protein a unique architecture, a form to suit its function.

One final detail may be needed for the protein to become functional. Several strands may cluster together into a functioning unit (see Figure 6–4), or a metal ion (mineral) or a vitamin may join to the unit and activate it.

- Amino acids link into long strands that coil and fold to make a wide variety of different proteins.

The Variety of Proteins

The particular shapes of proteins enable them to perform different tasks in the body. Those of globular shape, such as some proteins of blood, are water soluble. Some form hollow balls, which can carry and store materials in their interiors. Some proteins, such as those of tendons, are more than 10 times as long as they are wide, forming stiff, rod-like structures that are somewhat insoluble in water and very strong. A form of the protein **collagen** acts somewhat like glue between cells. The hormone insulin, a protein, helps regulate blood glucose levels. Among the most fascinating proteins are the **enzymes**, which act on other substances to change them chemically.

Some protein strands function alone, while others must associate with others to become functional. One molecule of **hemoglobin**—the large, globular protein molecule that, by the millions, packs the red blood cells and carries oxygen—is made of four associated protein strands, each holding the mineral iron (see Figure 6–4 on page 211).

The great variety of proteins in the world is possible because an essentially infinite number of sequences of amino acids can be found. To understand how so many different proteins can be designed from only 20 or so amino acids, think of how many words are in an unabridged dictionary—all of them constructed from just 26 letters. If you had only the letter "G," all you could write would be a string of Gs: G–G–G–G–G–G–G. But with 26 different letters available, you can create poems, songs, or novels. Similarly, the 20 amino acids can be linked together in a huge variety of sequences—many more than are possible for letters in a word, which must alternate

peptide bond a bond that connects one amino acid with another, forming a link in a protein chain.

collagen (KAHL-ah-jen) a type of body protein from which connective tissues such as tendons, ligaments, scars, and the foundations of bones and teeth are made.

enzymes (EN-zimes) protein catalysts. A catalyst is a compound that facilitates a chemical reaction without itself being altered in the process.

hemoglobin the globular protein of red blood cells, whose iron atoms carry oxygen around the body via the bloodstream (more about hemoglobin in Chapter 8).

Figure 6–3

The Coiling and Folding of a Protein Molecule

1. The first shape of a strand of amino acids is a chain, which can be very long. This shows just a portion of the strand.

2. Coiling the strand. The strand of amino acids takes on a springlike shape as their side chains variously attract and repel each other.

3. Folding the coil. The coil then folds and flops over on itself to take a functional shape.

4. Once coiled and folded, the protein may be functional as is, or it may need to join with other proteins, or add a carbohydrate molecule or a vitamin or mineral, as the iron of the protein hemoglobin demonstrates in Figure 6–4 (page 211).

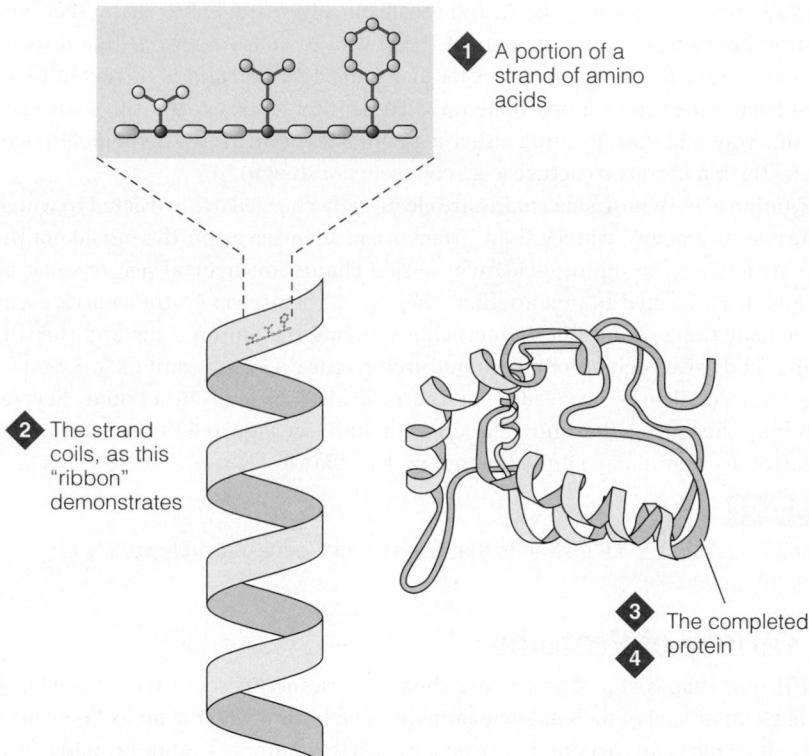

1. A portion of a strand of amino acids

2. The strand coils, as this "ribbon" demonstrates

3.
4. The completed protein

a) Coiling the strand. The strand of amino acids takes on a springlike shape as their side chains variously attract and repel each other.

b) Folding the coil. Once coiled and folded, the protein may be functional as is, or it may need to join with other proteins or add vitamins or minerals to become active.

consonant and vowel sounds. Thus, the variety of possible sequences for amino acid strands is tremendous. A single human cell may contain as many as 10,000 different proteins, each one present in thousands of copies.

Inherited Amino Acid Sequences For each protein, there exists a standard amino acid sequence, and that sequence is specified by heredity. Often, if a wrong amino acid is inserted, the result can be disastrous to health.

Sickle cell anemia, in which hemoglobin, the oxygen-carrying protein of the red blood cells, is abnormal, is an example of an inherited variation in the amino acid sequence. Normal hemoglobin contains two kinds of protein strands. In sickle cell anemia, one of the strands is an exact copy of that in normal hemoglobin, but in the

Figure 6–4

The Structure of Hemoglobin

Four highly folded protein strands form the globular hemoglobin protein.

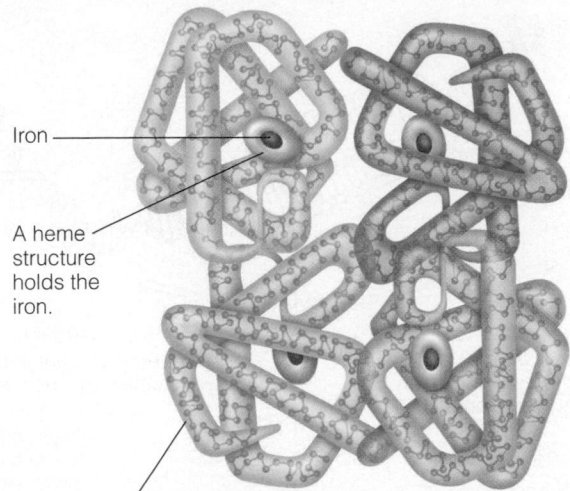

Iron

A heme structure holds the iron.

The amino acid sequence causes the strands to coil and loop, forming the globular protein structure.

Hair, skin, eyesight, and the health of the whole body depend on protein from food.

other strand, one amino acid in a critical position has been replaced by a different one. This replacement of one amino acid so alters the protein that it is unable to properly carry and release oxygen. As a result, some of the red blood cells collapse from the normal disk shape into crescent shapes (see Figure 6–5). If too many crescent-shaped cells appear in the blood, the result is abnormal blood clotting, strokes, bouts of severe pain, susceptibility to infection, and early death.[3]

You are unique among human beings because of minute differences in your body proteins. These differences are determined by the amino acid sequences of your proteins, which are written into the genetic code you inherited from your parents and they from theirs. Your unique combination of genes directs the making of all of your body's proteins, as shown in Figure 6–6. Ultimately, the genes determine the sequence of amino acids in each finished protein, and some genes are involved in making more than one protein. As scientists completed the Human Genome Project, they recognized that a still greater task lies ahead: the identification of every protein made by the human body.*

DNA was defined in Chapter 1.

Nutrients and Gene Expression
When a cell makes a protein as shown in Figure 6–6, scientists say that the gene for that protein has been "expressed." Every cell nucleus contains the DNA for making every human protein, but cells do not make them all. Instead, cells specialize in making certain proteins typical of their cell types. For example, cells of the pancreas express the gene for the protein hormone insulin; in other cells, that gene is idle.

Nutrients influence genetic expression and the resulting protein synthesis, and scientists are working out the details of these

FIGURE 6–5

Normal Red Blood Cells and Sickle Cells

Normal red blood cells are disk shaped. In sickle cell anemia, one amino acid in the protein strands of hemoglobin takes the place of another, causing some of the red blood cells to change shape and lose function.

Sickle-shaped blood cells   Normal red blood cells

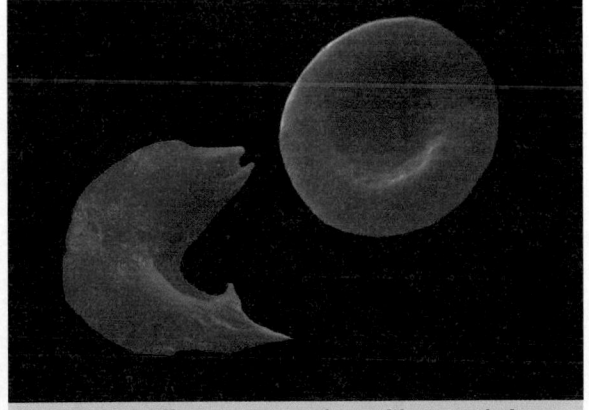

What a difference one amino acid can make!

Amino acid sequence of normal hemoglobin:

Val — His — Leu — Thr — Pro — Glu — Glu

Amino acid sequence of sickle cell hemoglobin:

Val — His — Leu — Thr — Pro — Val — Glu

---

*The identification of the entire collection of human proteins, the *human proteome* (PRO-tee-ome), is a work in progress.

Figure 6–6
Protein Synthesis

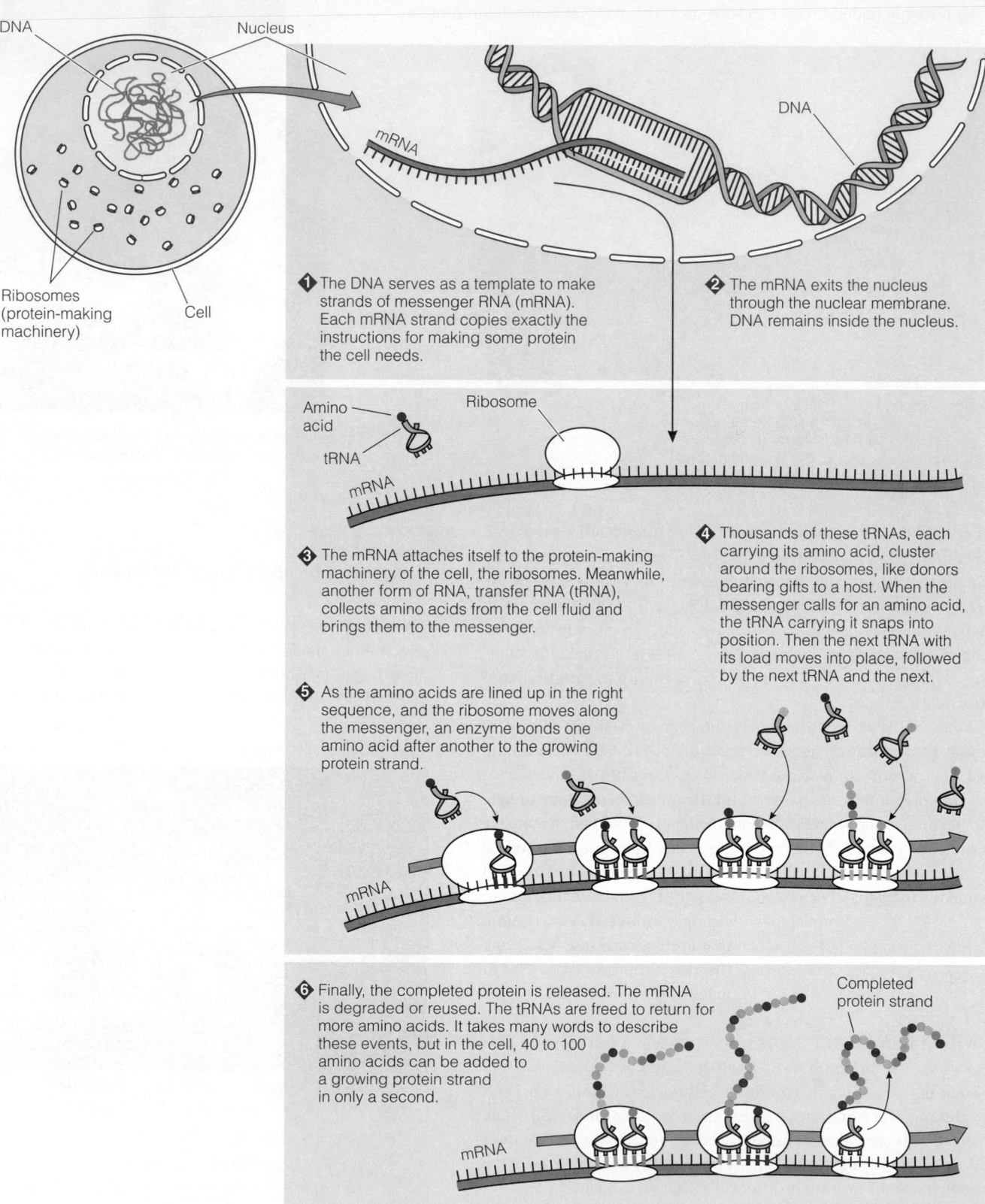

DNA

Nucleus

DNA

mRNA

Ribosomes (protein-making machinery)

Cell

❶ The DNA serves as a template to make strands of messenger RNA (mRNA). Each mRNA strand copies exactly the instructions for making some protein the cell needs.

❷ The mRNA exits the nucleus through the nuclear membrane. DNA remains inside the nucleus.

Amino acid

Ribosome

tRNA

mRNA

❸ The mRNA attaches itself to the protein-making machinery of the cell, the ribosomes. Meanwhile, another form of RNA, transfer RNA (tRNA), collects amino acids from the cell fluid and brings them to the messenger.

❹ Thousands of these tRNAs, each carrying its amino acid, cluster around the ribosomes, like donors bearing gifts to a host. When the messenger calls for an amino acid, the tRNA carrying it snaps into position. Then the next tRNA with its load moves into place, followed by the next tRNA and the next.

❺ As the amino acids are lined up in the right sequence, and the ribosome moves along the messenger, an enzyme bonds one amino acid after another to the growing protein strand.

mRNA

❻ Finally, the completed protein is released. The mRNA is degraded or reused. The tRNAs are freed to return for more amino acids. It takes many words to describe these events, but in the cell, 40 to 100 amino acids can be added to a growing protein strand in only a second.

Completed protein strand

mRNA

fascinating interactions.[4] Living cells, including the cells of the body, continuously monitor nutrient concentrations in the fluids circulating around them. A nutrient lack or overabundance triggers a cascade of molecular events inside the cell that ultimately leads to expression or suppression of certain genes. The cell's genetic material speeds up or slows down its synthesis of certain proteins to cope with the nutrient imbalance.

Two examples may clarify this relationship. The genes of specialized cells of the pancreas, just mentioned, respond to molecular messages generated when blood glucose is overabundant. The cells' genetic material steps up synthesis of the protein insulin, whose job it is to help bring the glucose level down. The mineral iron also plays roles in regulating protein synthesis. Normally, immature red blood cells pack their interiors with hemoglobin, but when the body's iron stores run low, the cells respond by suppressing hemoglobin synthesis.[*,5] Conversely, iron abundance stimulates hemoglobin synthesis. Later chapters come back to topics of nutrient–gene interactions. The Think Fitness feature (page 214) addresses a related concern of athletes: Can more dietary protein trigger the synthesis of muscle tissue?

KEY POINT

- Each type of protein has a distinctive sequence of amino acids and so has great specificity. Often cells specialize in synthesizing particular types of proteins in addition to the proteins necessary to all cells. Nutrients act as environmental signals affecting genetic activities.

Denaturation of Proteins

Proteins can be denatured (distorted in shape) by heat, alcohol, acids, bases, or the salts of heavy metals. The **denaturation** of a protein is the first step in its destruction; thus, these agents are dangerous because they damage the body's proteins. In digestion, however, denaturation is useful to the body. During the digestion of a food protein, the stomach acid opens up the protein's structure, permitting digestive enzymes to make contact with the peptide bonds, irreversibly beginning to dismantle the protein. Denaturation also occurs during the cooking of foods. Cooking an egg irreversibly denatures the proteins of the egg, and makes it firm, as the margin photo demonstrates. More important for nutrition is that heat denatures two proteins in raw eggs: one binds the B vitamin biotin and the mineral iron, and the other slows protein digestion. Thus, cooking eggs liberates biotin and iron and aids digestion.

Heat denatures egg protein, making it firm.

Chapter 10 discusses the nutrient needs of athletes in detail.

Chapter 3 discussed the use of medicines to control the stomach's acidity (page 96) and also defined pH as a measure of acidity (page 90).

Many well-known poisons are salts of heavy metals like mercury and silver; these denature protein strands wherever they touch them. The common first-aid antidote for swallowing a heavy-metal poison is to drink milk. The poison then acts on the protein of the milk rather than on the protein tissues of the mouth, esophagus, and stomach. Later, vomiting can be induced to expel the poison that has combined with the milk.

KEY POINT

- Proteins can be denatured by heat, acids, bases, alcohol, or the salts of heavy metals. Denaturation begins the process of digesting food protein and can also destroy body proteins.

Digestion and Absorption of Protein

Each protein performs a special task in a particular tissue of a specific kind of animal or plant. When a person eats food proteins, whether from cereals, vegetables, beef, fish, or cheese, the body must first alter them by breaking them down into amino acids;

denaturation the irreversible change in a protein's shape brought about by heat, acids, bases, alcohol, salts of heavy metals, or other agents.

---

*Mature red blood cells in the bloodstream have lost their nuclei and DNA and so lack the ability to make hemoglobin or other proteins.

Can Eating Extra Protein Make Muscles Grow Larger?

Although about 15 to 20 grams of protein per meal is needed to stimulate protein synthesis, can athletes and fitness seekers stimulate their muscles to grow larger simply by consuming more protein or amino acids? No. Hard work, not excess dietary protein, is the trigger for the genes to build more muscle tissue. Exercise generates cellular messages that stimulate DNA to begin the process of building up muscle fibres (muscle fibres are made of protein). Nevertheless, a snack rich in both protein and carbohydrate (half a turkey sandwich, for example) eaten directly *after* exercise may be of some help in this regard (more on this in Chapter 10). The path to bigger muscles is rigorous physical training with adequate energy and nutrients, including proteins, from balanced, well-timed meals, not simply consuming excess protein.

only then can it rearrange them into specific human body proteins. See Chapter 14 regarding allergies to some of these proteins.

The whole process of digestion is an ingenious solution to a complex problem. Certain acid-tolerant proteins (many of which are enzymes), when activated by acid, digest proteins from food, which have been denatured by acid. The coating of mucus secreted by the stomach wall protects its proteins from attack by either acid or enzymes. The normal acid in the stomach is so strong (pH 1.5) that no food is acidic enough to make it stronger; for comparison, the pH of vinegar is about 3.

Protein Digestion

Other than being crushed by chewing and moistened with saliva in the mouth, nothing happens to protein until the strong acid of the stomach denatures it. The acid helps uncoil the protein's tangled strands so that molecules of the stomach's protein-digesting enzyme can attack the peptide bonds. You might expect that the stomach enzyme, being a protein, would be denatured by the stomach's acid. Unlike most enzymes, though, the stomach enzyme functions best in an acid environment. The job of one of these enzymes is to break other protein strands into smaller pieces. The stomach lining, which is also made partly of protein, is protected against attack by acid and enzymes by its coat of mucus, secreted by its cells.

By the time most proteins are released from the stomach into the small intestine, they are denatured and broken into smaller pieces. A few are single amino acids, but the majority remain in large strands called **polypeptides**. In the small intestine, alkaline juice from the pancreas neutralizes the acid digesta released by the stomach. The pH rises to about 7 (neutral), enabling the next enzyme team to accomplish the final breakdown of the strands. Protein-digesting enzymes from the pancreas and intestine continue working until almost all pieces of protein are broken into strands of two or three amino acids, **dipeptides** and **tripeptides**, respectively (see Figure 6–7), or single amino acids. Figure 6–8 summarizes the whole process.

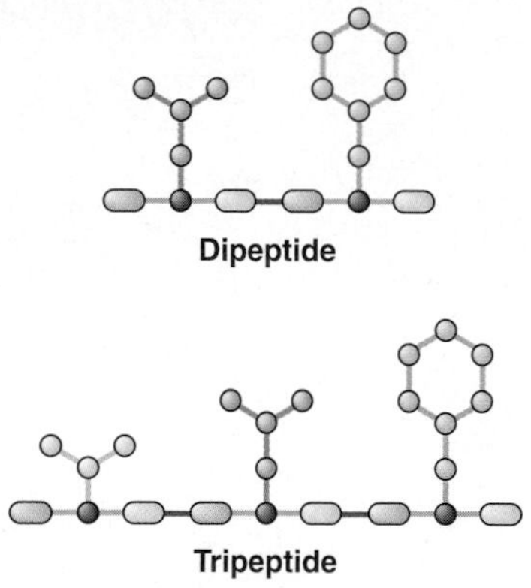

Consumers who fail to understand the basic mechanism of protein digestion are easily misled by advertisers of products and books urging, "Take enzyme A to help digest your food" or "Don't eat foods containing enzyme C, which will digest cells in your body." The writers of such statements fail to realize that ingested enzymes (proteins) are digested before they are absorbed, just as all proteins are, unless they are protected in some way. Even the stomach's digestive enzymes are denatured and digested when their jobs are through. Similar false claims are made that predigested proteins (amino acid supplements) are "easy to digest" and can therefore protect the digestive system from "overworking." Of course, the healthy digestive system is superbly designed to digest whole proteins with ease. In fact, it handles whole

Figure 6–7

A Dipeptide and a Tripeptide

Dipeptide

Tripeptide

polypeptides (POL-ee-PEP-tides) protein fragments of many (more than 10) amino acids bonded together (*poly* means "many"). A peptide is a strand of amino acids. A strand of between 4 and 10 amino acids is called an *oligopeptide*.

dipeptides (dye-PEP-tides) protein fragments that are two amino acids long (*di* means "two").

tripeptides (try-PEP-tides) protein fragments that are three amino acids long (*tri* means "three").

Figure 6–8

How Protein in Food Becomes Amino Acids in the Body

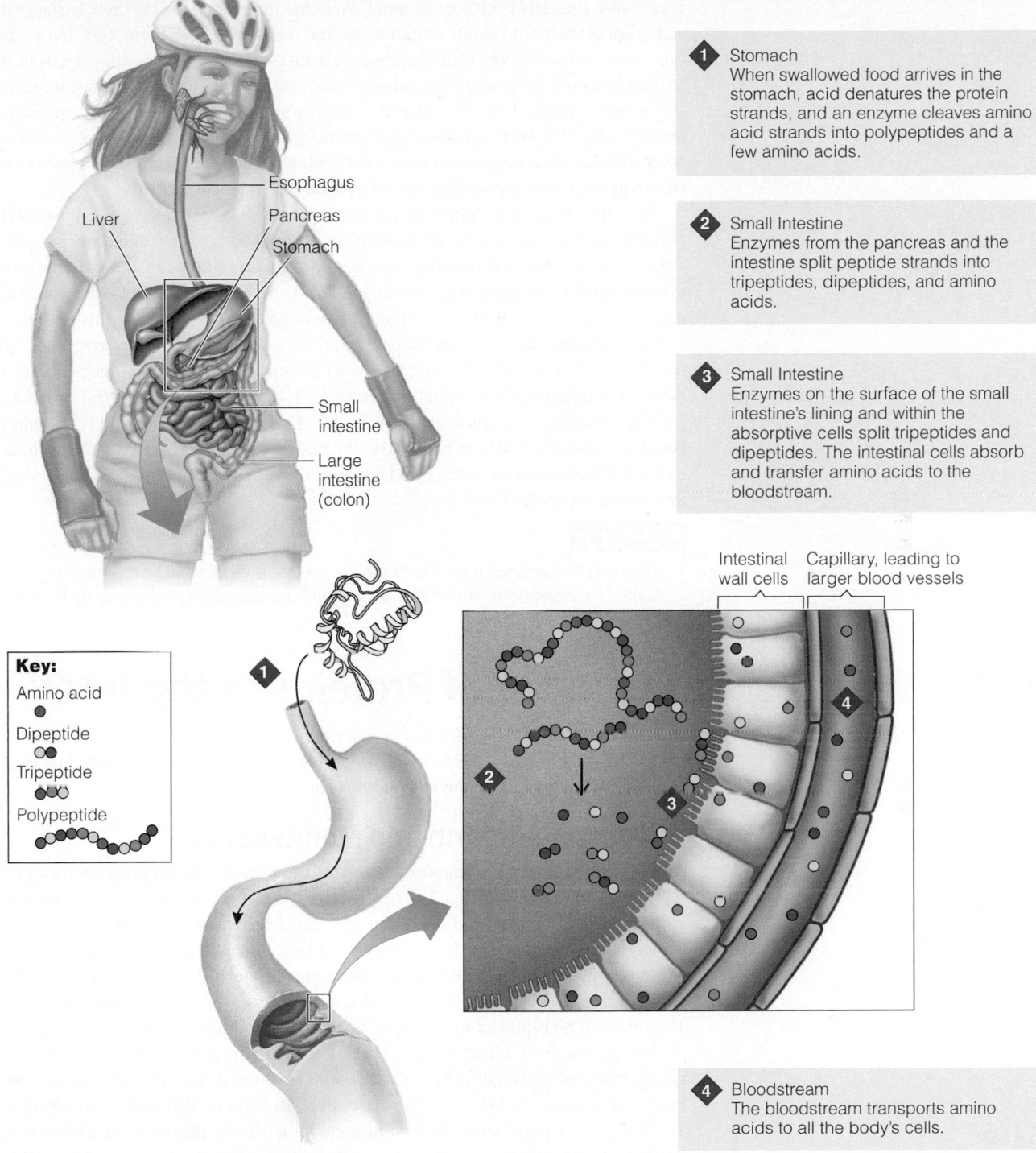

1 Stomach
When swallowed food arrives in the stomach, acid denatures the protein strands, and an enzyme cleaves amino acid strands into polypeptides and a few amino acids.

2 Small Intestine
Enzymes from the pancreas and the intestine split peptide strands into tripeptides, dipeptides, and amino acids.

3 Small Intestine
Enzymes on the surface of the small intestine's lining and within the absorptive cells split tripeptides and dipeptides. The intestinal cells absorb and transfer amino acids to the bloodstream.

Esophagus
Liver
Pancreas
Stomach
Small intestine
Large intestine (colon)

Intestinal wall cells   Capillary, leading to larger blood vessels

Key:
Amino acid
Dipeptide
Tripeptide
Polypeptide

4 Bloodstream
The bloodstream transports amino acids to all the body's cells.

proteins *better* than predigested ones because it dismantles and absorbs the amino acids at rates that are optimal for the body's use.

KEY POINT

- Digestion of protein involves denaturation by stomach acid and then enzymatic digestion in the stomach and small intestine to amino acids, dipeptides, and tripeptides.

After Protein Is Digested, What Happens to Amino Acids?

The cells all along the small intestine absorb single amino acids. As for dipeptides and tripeptides, the cells that line the small intestine have enzymes on their surfaces that split most of them into single amino acids, and the cells absorb them, too. Some dipeptides and tripeptides are also absorbed as is into the cells, where they are split into individual amino acids and released with others into the bloodstream. A few larger peptide molecules can escape the digestive process altogether and enter the bloodstream intact.[6] Scientists believe these larger particles may act as triggers that provide the body with information about the external environment. The larger molecules may also stimulate an immune response and thus play a role in food allergy.

The cells of the small intestine possess separate sites for absorbing different types of amino acids. Amino acids of the same type compete for the same absorption sites. Consequently, when a person ingests a large dose of any single amino acid, that amino acid may limit absorption of others of its general type. The Consumer Corner (page 222) cautions against taking single amino acids as supplements, partly for this reason.

Once amino acids enter the bloodstream, they are carried to the liver, where they may be used in protein synthesis, used as a source of energy, or released into the blood to be taken up by other cells of the body. The cells can then link the amino acids together to make proteins that they keep for their own use or liberate into lymph or blood for other uses. When necessary, the body's cells can also use the carbon skeletons of amino acids for energy; in fact, both the intestines and liver use amino acids as a primary source of energy.

KEY POINT

- The cells of the small intestine complete protein digestion, absorb amino acids and some larger peptides, and release them into the bloodstream for use by the body's cells.

The Roles of Proteins in the Body

Only a sampling of the many roles proteins play can be described here, but these illustrate their versatility, uniqueness, and importance in the body. No wonder their discoverers called proteins the primary material of life.

Supporting Growth and Maintenance

Amino acids must be continuously available to maintain tissue proteins as they are replaced or build new proteins. The new tissue may be in an embryo; in the muscles of an athlete in training; in a growing child; in new blood needed to replace blood lost in burns, hemorrhage, or surgery; in the scar tissue that heals wounds; or in new hair and nails.

Less obvious is the protein that helps replace worn-out cells and internal cell structures. Each of your millions of red blood cells lives for only three or four months. Then it must be replaced by a new cell produced by the bone marrow. The millions of cells lining your intestinal tract live for only three days; they are constantly being shed and replaced.[7] The cells of your skin die and rub off, and new ones grow from underneath. Nearly all cells arise, live, and die in this way, and while they are living, they constantly make and break down their proteins. In addition, cells must continuously replace their own internal working proteins as old ones wear out. Amino acids conserved from these processes provide a great deal of the required raw material from which new structures are built. The entire process of breakdown, recovery, and synthesis is called **protein turnover** (e.g., in adults, about 300–400 g of protein turns over each day, accounting for about 20% of our resting energy needs). Each day, about a quarter of available amino acids are irretrievably diverted to other uses, such as fuel (e.g., by the intestines and liver). For this reason, amino acids from food are needed each day to support any new growth that occurs and maintenance of all cells.

protein turnover the continuous breakdown and synthesis of body proteins involving the recycling of 300–400 g of amino acids each day.

Chapter 6 The Proteins and Amino Acids

Figure 6–9

Enzyme Action

Enzymes are catalysts: they speed up reactions that would happen anyway, but much more slowly. This enzyme works by positioning two compounds, A and B, so that the reaction between them will be especially likely to take place.

Compounds A and B (the substrates) are attracted to the enzyme's active site and park there for a moment in the exact position that makes the reaction between them most likely to occur. They react by bonding together and leave the enzyme as the new compound, AB (the product).

A single enzyme can facilitate several hundred such synthetic reactions in a second. Other enzymes break compounds apart into two or more products or rearrange the atoms in one compound to make another one.

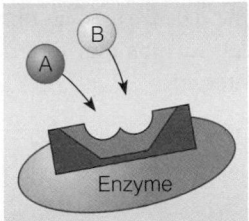

Enzyme plus two compounds A and B

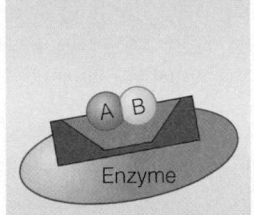

Enzyme complex with A and B

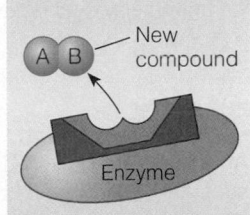

Enzyme plus new compound AB

KEY POINT

- The body needs dietary amino acids to grow new cells and to replace worn-out ones.

Building Enzymes, Hormones, and Other Compounds

Enzymes are among the most important of the proteins formed in living cells. Thousands of enzymes reside inside a single cell, each one a catalyst that facilitates a specific chemical reaction. Figure 6–9 shows how a hypothetical enzyme works.

The body's many **hormones** are messenger molecules, and some are made from amino acids. (Recall from Chapter 5 that some "local" hormones are made from lipids.) Various body glands release hormones in response to changes in the internal environment; the hormones then elicit the responses necessary to restore normal conditions. Among the hormones made of amino acids is the thyroid hormone, which regulates the body's metabolism. An opposing pair of hormones, insulin and glucagon, help maintain blood glucose levels, as described in Chapter 4. For interest, Figure 6–10 shows how many amino acids are linked in sequence to form human insulin. It also shows how certain side groups are linked together, while others attract one another to complete the insulin molecule and make it functional.

In addition to serving as building blocks for proteins, amino acids also perform other tasks in the body. For example, the amino acid tyrosine is used to synthesize the chemical messengers epinephrine and norepinephrine, which relay messages throughout the nervous system and affect the activity of numerous enzymes involved in carbohydrate and fat metabolism. The body also uses tyrosine to make the brown pigment melanin, which is responsible for skin, hair, and eye colour. Tyrosine is also converted into the hormone thyroxine, which helps regulate the body's metabolic rate. The amino acid tryptophan serves as starting material for the neurotransmitter **serotonin** and the vitamin niacin.

Neurotransmitters were introduced in Chapter 3; the vitamin niacin is discussed in Chapter 7.

Figure 6–10

Amino Acid Sequence of Human Insulin

This picture shows a refinement of protein structure not mentioned in the text. The amino acid cysteine (cys) has a sulphur-containing side group. The sulphur groups on two cysteine molecules can bond together, creating a bridge between two protein strands or two parts of the same strand. Insulin contains three such bridges.

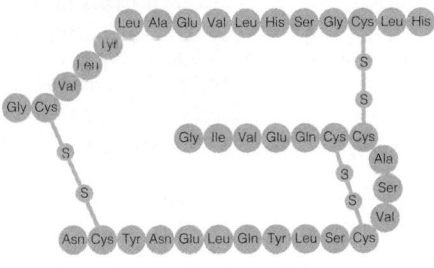

hormones chemical messengers secreted by a number of body organs in response to conditions that require regulation. Each hormone affects a specific organ or tissue and elicits a specific response. Also defined in Chapter 3.

serotonin (SARE-oh-TONE-in) a compound related in structure to (and made from) the amino acid tryptophan. It serves as one of the brain's principal neurotransmitters.

Building Antibodies

Of all of the proteins in living organisms, the **antibodies** best demonstrate that proteins are specific to one organism. Antibodies recognize every protein that belongs in "their" body and leave it alone, but they attack foreign particles (usually proteins) that invade that body. The foreign protein may be part of a bacterium, a virus, or a toxin, or it may be present in a food that causes allergy. The body, upon recognizing that it has been invaded, manufactures antibodies specially designed to inactivate the foreign protein.

Each antibody is designed to destroy one specific invader. An antibody active against one strain of influenza is of no help to a person ill with another strain. Once the body has learned how to make a particular antibody, it remembers. The next time the body encounters that same invader, it destroys the invader even more rapidly. In other words, the body develops **immunity** to the invader. This molecular memory underlies the principle of immunizations, injections of drugs made from destroyed and

> The immune system is a topic of Chapter 3.

inactivated microbes or their products that activate the body's immune defences. Some immunities are lifelong; others, such as that to tetanus, must be "boosted" at intervals.

KEY POINT

- Antibodies are proteins that defend against foreign proteins and other foreign substances within the body.

Maintaining Fluid and Electrolyte Balance

Proteins help maintain the **fluid and electrolyte balance** by regulating the quantity of fluids in the compartments of the body. To remain alive, cells must contain a constant amount of fluid. Too much can cause them to rupture; too little makes them unable to function. Although water can diffuse freely into and out of cells, proteins cannot, and proteins attract water. By maintaining stores of internal proteins and also of some minerals, cells retain the fluid they need. By the same mechanism, fluid is kept inside the blood vessels by proteins too large to move freely across the capillary walls. The proteins attract water and hold it within the vessels, preventing it from freely flowing into

> The control of water's location by electrolytes is discussed further in Chapter 8.

the spaces between the cells. Should any part of this system begin to fail, too much fluid will soon collect in the spaces between the cells of tissues, causing **edema**.

Not only is the quantity of body fluids vital to life, but so also is their composition. Transport proteins in the membranes of cells maintain this composition by continuously transferring substances into and out of cells (see Figure 6–11). For example, sodium is concentrated outside the cells, and potassium is concentrated inside. A disturbance of this balance can impair the action of the heart, lungs, and brain, trig-

> Chapter 3 provides a discussion of pH.

gering a major medical emergency. Cell proteins avert such a disaster by holding fluids and electrolytes in their proper chambers.

KEY POINT

- Proteins help regulate the body's electrolytes and fluids.

Maintaining Acid–Base Balance

Normal processes of the body continually produce **acids** and their opposite, **bases**, which must be carried by the blood to the organs of excretion. The blood must do this without allowing its own **acid–base balance** to be affected. This feat is another trick of the blood proteins, which act as **buffers** to maintain the blood's normal pH. The protein buffers pick up hydrogens (acid) when there are too many in the bloodstream and release them again when there are too few. The secret is that negatively charged side chains of amino acids can accommodate additional hydrogens, which are positively charged.

antibodies (AN-te-bod-ees) large proteins of the blood, produced by the immune system in response to an invasion of the body by foreign substances (antigens). Antibodies combine with and inactivate the antigens. Also defined in Chapter 3.

immunity protection from or resistance to a disease or infection by development of antibodies and by the actions of cells and tissues in response to a threat.

fluid and electrolyte balance the distribution of fluid and dissolved particles among body compartments (see also Chapter 8).

edema (eh-DEEM-uh) swelling of body tissue caused by leakage of fluid from the blood vessels; seen in protein deficiency (among other conditions).

acids compounds that release hydrogens in a watery solution.

bases compounds that accept hydrogens from solutions.

acid–base balance equilibrium between acid and base concentrations in the body fluids.

buffers compounds that help keep a solution's acidity or alkalinity constant.

Figure 6–11

Proteins Transport Substances into and out of Cells

The transport protein within the cell membrane acts as a sort of two-door passageway—substances enter on one side and are released on the other, but the protein never leaves the membrane. The protein differs from a simple passageway in that it actively escorts the substances in and out of cells; therefore, this form of transport is often called active transport.

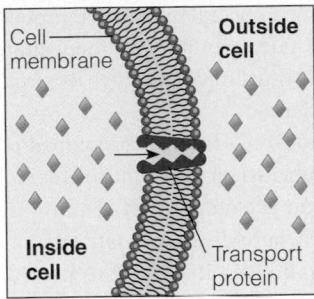
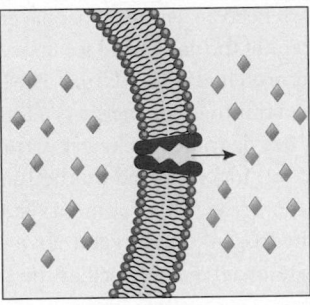
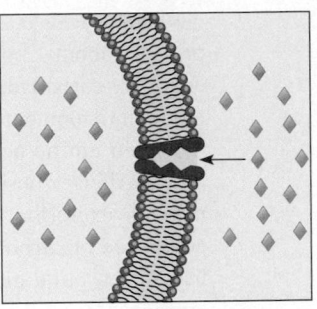
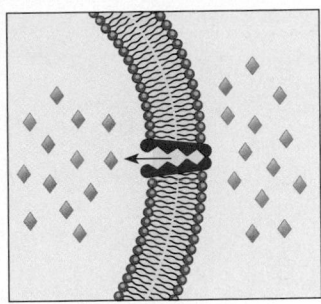

| Molecule enters protein from inside cell. | Protein changes shape; molecule exits protein outside the cell. | Molecule enters protein from outside cell. | Molecule exits protein; proper balance restored. |

Blood pH is one of the most rigidly controlled conditions in the body. If blood pH changes too much, **acidosis** or the opposite basic condition, **alkalosis**, can cause coma or death. These conditions constitute medical emergencies because of their effect on proteins. When the proteins' buffering capacity is filled—that is, when they have taken on all of the acid hydrogens they can accommodate—additional acid pulls them out of shape, denaturing them and disrupting many body processes. Table 6–2 sums up the functions of protein.

KEY POINT
- Proteins buffer the blood against excess acidity or alkalinity.

Clotting of Blood

To prevent dangerous blood loss, special blood proteins respond to an injury by clotting the blood. In an amazing series of chemical events, these proteins form a stringy net that traps platelets to form a clot. The clot acts as a plug to stem blood flow from the

Table 6–2

Summary of Functions of Proteins

- **Acid–base balance.** Proteins help maintain the acid–base balance of various body fluids by acting as buffers.
- **Antibodies.** Proteins form the immune system molecules that fight diseases.
- **Blood clotting.** Proteins provide the netting on which blood clots are built.
- **Energy.** Proteins provide some fuel for the body's energy needs.
- **Enzymes.** Proteins facilitate needed chemical reactions.
- **Fluid and electrolyte balance.** Proteins help maintain the water and mineral composition of various body fluids.
- **Growth and maintenance.** Proteins form integral parts of most body tissues and serve as building materials for growth and repair of body tissues, such as skin, connective tissues, muscles, organs, and bone.
- **Hormones.** Proteins regulate body processes. Some hormones are proteins or are made from amino acids.
- **Transportation.** Proteins help transport needed substances, such as lipids, minerals, and oxygen, around the body.
- **Vision.** Various proteins called opsins are important for both colour and night vision.

acidosis (acid-DOH-sis) the condition of excess acid in the blood, indicated by a below-normal pH (*osis* means "too much in the blood").

alkalosis (al-kah-LOH-sis) the condition of excess base in the blood, indicated by an above-normal blood pH (alkalinity—*alka* means "base"; *osis* means "too much in the blood").

The Roles of Proteins in the Body

wound. Later, as the wound heals, the protein collagen finishes the job by replacing the clot with scar tissue.

- Proteins are important for blood clotting and wound healing.

Providing Energy and Glucose

Only protein can perform all of the functions just described, but protein will be surrendered to provide energy if need be. For most people eating a normal mixed diet, protein provides about 15 percent of the daily need for energy. Under conditions of inadequate energy or carbohydrate, protein use speeds up.[8] The body must have energy to live from moment to moment, so obtaining that energy is a top priority.

When amino acids are degraded for energy, their amine groups are stripped off and used elsewhere or are incorporated by the liver into **urea** and sent to the kidneys for excretion in the urine. The fragments (carbon skeletons) that remain are composed of carbon, hydrogen, and oxygen, as are carbohydrate and fat, and can be used to build glucose or fatty acids or can be metabolized like them to provide energy.

Not only can amino acids supply energy, but many of them can be converted to glucose, as fatty acids can never be. Thus, if the need arises, protein can help maintain a steady blood glucose level and serve the glucose need of the brain.

The similarities and differences of the three energy-yielding nutrients should now be clear. Carbohydrate offers energy; fat offers concentrated energy; and protein can offer energy plus nitrogen (see Figure 6–12).

Glucose is stored as glycogen and fat as triglycerides, but there is no specialized protein energy–storage compound. Body protein is available only as the active working molecular and structural components of the tissues. When protein-sparing energy from carbohydrate and fat is lacking and the need becomes urgent, as in starvation, prolonged fasting, severe Calorie restriction, or extended high-intensity physical activity, the body must dismantle its tissue proteins to obtain amino acids for energy. As mentioned, each protein is taken in its own time: first, small proteins from the blood and then proteins from the muscles, liver, and other organs. Thus, energy deficiency (starvation)

Figure 6–12

Three Different Energy Sources

Carbohydrate offers energy; fat offers concentrated energy; and protein, if necessary, can offer energy plus nitrogen. The compounds at the left yield the 2-carbon fragments shown at the right. These fragments oxidize quickly in the presence of oxygen to yield carbon dioxide, water, and energy.

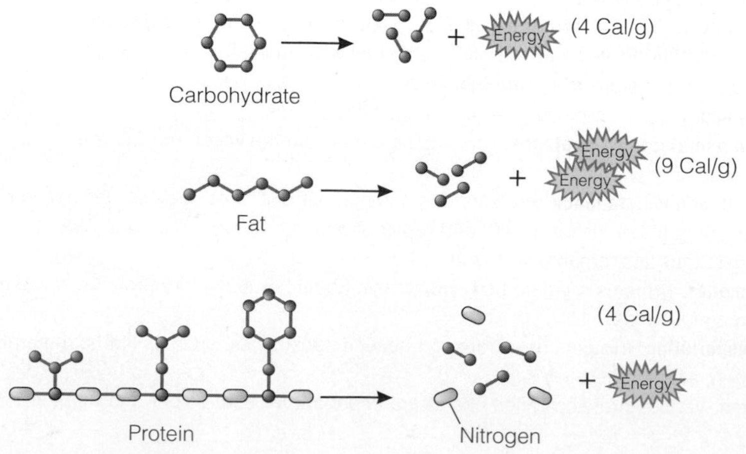

Carbohydrate → + Energy (4 Cal/g)

Fat → + Energy Energy (9 Cal/g)

Protein → Nitrogen + Energy (4 Cal/g)

urea (yoo-REE-uh) the principal nitrogen-excretion product of protein metabolism; generated mostly by removal of amine groups from unneeded amino acids or from amino acids being sacrificed to a need for energy.

Chapter 6 The Proteins and Amino Acids

Read more about the effects of fasting in Chapter 9.

always incurs wasting of lean body tissue as well as loss of fat.

If amino acids are oversupplied, the body cannot store them. It has no choice but to remove and excrete their amine groups and then use the residues to meet ongoing energy needs, convert them to glucose for storage as glycogen, or convert them to fat for energy storage. The body readily converts amino acids to glucose. As for converting them to fat, the body possesses enzymes to do so and can produce fatty acids for storage as triglycerides in the fat tissue.

KEY POINT

■ When insufficient carbohydrate and fat are consumed to meet the body's energy need, food protein and body protein are sacrificed to supply energy. The nitrogen part is removed from each amino acid, and the resulting fragment is oxidized for energy. No storage form of amino acids exists in the body.

The Fate of an Amino Acid

To review the body's handling of amino acids, let us follow the fate of an amino acid that was originally part of a protein-containing food. When the amino acid arrives in a cell, it can be used in one of several ways, depending on the cell's needs at the time:

■ The amino acid can be used as is to build part of a growing protein.

■ The amino acid can be altered somewhat to make another needed compound, such as the vitamin niacin.

■ The cell can dismantle the amino acid in order to use its amine group to build a different amino acid. The remainder can be used for fuel or, if fuel is abundant, converted to glucose or fat.

In a cell that is starved for energy but has no glucose or fatty acids, the cell strips the amino acid of its amine group (the nitrogen part) and uses the remainder of its structure for energy. To do this, some of these carbon skeletons may enter metabolic pathways such as glycolysis or the Krebs cycle or be further metabolized to compounds that can enter these pathways. The amine group is excreted from the cell and then from the body in the urine. When the body has a surplus of amino acids and energy, the cell takes the amino acid apart, excretes the amine group, and uses the rest for energy or converts it to glucose or fat for storage.[9]

When not used to build protein or make other nitrogen-containing compounds, amino acids are "wasted" in a sense. This wasting occurs under any of four conditions:

1. When the body does not have enough energy from other sources.

2. When the diet provides more protein than the body needs.

3. When the body has too much of any single amino acid, such as from a supplement.

4. When the diet supplies protein of low quality, with too few essential amino acids, as described in the next section.

To prevent the wasting of dietary protein and permit the synthesis of needed body protein, the dietary protein must be adequate in quantity, it must supply all essential amino acids in the proper amounts, and it must be accompanied by enough energy-yielding carbohydrate and fat to permit the dietary protein to be used as such.

KEY POINT

■ Amino acids can be metabolized to protein, nitrogen plus energy, glucose, or fat. They will be metabolized to protein only if sufficient energy is present from other sources. The diet should supply all essential amino acids and a full measure of protein according to guidelines.

Amino acids in a cell can be
- Used to build protein.
- Converted to other amino acids or small nitrogen-containing compounds.

Stripped of their nitrogen, amino acids can be
- Burned as fuel.
- Converted to glucose or fat.

Amino acids are wasted when
- Energy is lacking.
- Protein is overabundant.
- An amino acid is oversupplied in supplement form.
- The quality of the diet's protein is too low (too few essential amino acids).

The Roles of Proteins in the Body

Amino Acid Supplements

Why do people take amino acid supplements? Athletes often take them when trying to build muscle. Dieters may take them in the hope of speeding the process of weight loss. Some consumers believe the products will cure herpes virus infections, induce restful sleep, or relieve pain or depression. Do protein and amino acid supplements really do any of these things? Probably not. Are they safe? Not always.

In the skilled hands of clinical dietitians, formulas with supplemental amino acids may help reverse malnutrition in some critically ill patients.*,[1] Not every patient is a candidate for such therapy, though, because supplemental amino acids may also stimulate inflammation and so worsen some illnesses.[2]

Enthusiastic popular reports have led to widespread use of certain amino acids. One is lysine, touted to prevent or relieve the infections that cause herpes sores on the mouth or genital organs. Lysine does not cure herpes infections. Whether it reduces outbreaks or even whether it is safe is unknown because scientific studies are lacking. Blends of the branched-chain amino acids leucine, isoleucine, and valine have become popular with athletes hoping for a competitive edge, but the value of these potions also remains unclear (see Controversy 10).

Tryptophan supplements are advertised to relieve pain, depression, and insomnia. Tryptophan plays a role as a precursor for the brain neurotransmitter serotonin, which makes it an important regulator of sleep, appetite, mood, and sensory perception.[3] In the case of tryptophan supplements, however, advertising and popular reports have long preceded careful scientific experiments. The DRI committee concludes that high doses of tryptophan may induce sleepiness, but they may also have side effects such as severe nausea and skin disorders.[4]

In the not-too-distant past, people who elected to take supplements of the amino acid tryptophan developed a blood disorder (EMS, short for *eosinophilia-myalgia syndrome*), and at least 15 of the supplement takers died. Contaminants in the supplement were blamed for the disease, and the U.S. Food and Drug Administration (FDA) recalled tryptophan supplements and formulas to which it was added. Impurities of the same sort are still detected in some tryptophan-containing products currently on the market.[5] The body is designed to handle whole proteins best. It breaks them into manageable pieces (dipeptides and tripeptides) and then splits these a few at a time, simultaneously releasing them into the blood. This slow, bit-by-bit assimilation is ideal because groups of chemically similar amino acids compete for the carriers when absorbed from the blood by tissues such as the brain. An excess of one amino acid can tie up a carrier and disturb amino acid absorption, at least temporarily. Digestive disturbances, excess water in the digestive tract, and an increased need for the vitamin thiamin also pose potential problems from amino acid supplements.[6]

The DRI committee reviewed the available research on amino acids, but with next to no safety research in existence, the committee was unable to set tolerable upper intake levels for supplemental doses. Until research becomes available, no level of amino acid supplementation can be assumed safe for all people. Growth or altered metabolism makes the following groups of people especially likely to suffer harm from self-prescribed amino acid supplements:

- All women of childbearing age
- Pregnant or lactating women
- Infants, children, and adolescents
- Elderly people

*Consumer Corner references are listed separately at the end of the chapter.

- People with inborn errors of metabolism that affect their bodies' handling of amino acids
- Smokers
- People on low-protein diets
- People with compromised kidney function
- People with chronic or acute mental or physical illnesses

A careful review of the literature concluded that not enough research exists to support recommending long-term consumption of amino acid supplements by healthy people and that more research into adverse effects is needed.[7] Amino acid supplements are regulated as natural health products in Canada (although small amounts of certain amino acids are allowed to be added to caffeinated energy drinks that have recently been classified as foods), and those approved for sale, such as arginine and lysine, carry a Natural Product Number (NPN). The warning is this: much is still unknown, and the taker of amino acid supplements cannot be certain of their safety or effectiveness. See the following URL for a list of natural health products approved by Canada's Natural Health Products Directorate, which includes amino acids such as arginine and lysine: Licensed Natural Health Products at http://webprod .hc-sc.gc.ca/lnhpd-bdpsnh/start-debuter .do?language-langage=english.

Many chapters of this book present evidence on purified nutrients added to foods or taken singly. The Consumer Corner in Chapter 4 showed that a nutritionally inferior food (refined bread) enriched with a few added nutrients is still inadequate in many others. The Consumer Corner in Chapter 5 showed that artificial fats can have side effects. The same is true of amino acids. Even with all that we know about science, it is hard to improve on nature.

Food Protein: Quality, Use, and Need

The body's response to protein depends on many factors: the body's state of health, the other nutrients and energy taken with the protein, and the protein's quality. To know whether, say, 60 grams of a particular protein is enough to meet a person's daily needs, one must consider the effects of these other factors on the body's use of the protein.

Regarding a person's state of health, malnutrition or infection may greatly increase the need for protein while making it hard to eat even normal amounts of food. In malnutrition, secretion of digestive enzymes slows as the tract's lining degenerates, impairing protein digestion and absorption. When infection is present, extra protein is needed for enhanced immune functions.

Regarding the other nutrients taken with protein, the need for ample energy, carbohydrate, and fat has already been emphasized. To be used efficiently by the cells, protein must also be accompanied by the full array of vitamins and minerals.

The remaining factor, protein quality, helps determine how well a diet supports the growth of children and the health of adults. Two factors influence protein quality: a protein's digestibility and its amino acid composition.

Which Kinds of Protein-Rich Foods Are Easiest to Digest?

The digestibility of protein varies from food to food and bears profoundly on protein quality. The protein of oats, for example, is less digestible than that of eggs. In general, amino acids from animal proteins are most easily digested and absorbed (over 90%). Those from **legumes** are next (about 80 to 90%). Those from grains and other plant foods vary (from 70 to 90%). Cooking with moist heat improves protein digestibility, whereas dry heat methods can impair it.

In measuring a protein's quality, digestibility is important. Simple measures of the total protein in foods are not useful by themselves—even animal hair and hooves would receive a top score by those measures alone. They are made of protein, but not in a form that people can use.

KEY POINT

- The body's use of a protein depends in part on the user's health, the protein quality, and the other nutrients and energy taken with it. Digestibility of protein varies from food to food, and cooking can improve or impair it.

Amino Acid Composition

Put simply, **high-quality proteins** provide enough of all of the essential amino acids needed by the body to create its own working proteins, whereas low-quality proteins don't. In making their required proteins, the cells need a full array of amino acids from food, from their own **amino acid pools**, or from both. If a dispensable/nonessential amino acid (that is, one the cell *can* make) is unavailable from food, the cell synthesizes it and continues attaching amino acids to the protein strands being manufactured. If the diet fails to provide enough of an indispensable/essential amino acid (one the cell *cannot* make), the cells begin to adjust their activities. Within a single day of restricted intake of an essential amino acid, the cells begin to conserve it by limiting the breakdown of their working proteins and by reducing their use of amino acids for fuel.

Limiting Amino Acids Can Limit Protein Synthesis The measures just described help the cells channel the available **limiting amino acid** to its wisest use: making new proteins. Even so, the normally fast rate of protein synthesis slows to a crawl as the cells make do with the proteins on hand. When the limiting amino acid once again becomes available in abundance, the cells resume their normal protein-related activities. If the shortage becomes chronic, however, the cells begin to break down their protein-making machinery. Consequently, when protein intakes become

Cooking with moist heat improves protein digestibility, whereas frying makes protein harder to digest.

© Hongqu Zhang/Dreamstime.com

- Isolated casein protein is more slowly absorbed than isolated whey protein; however, manufacturers are now producing blends of both whey and casein. Also, those with allergies to milk protein need to be mindful of the fact that these proteins are isolated from milk.

legumes (leg-GOOMS, LEG-yooms) plants of the bean, pea, and lentil family that have roots with nodules containing special bacteria. These bacteria can trap nitrogen from the air in the soil and make it into compounds that become part of the plant's seeds. The seeds are rich in protein compared with those of most other plant foods. Also defined in Chapter 1.

high-quality proteins dietary proteins containing all of the essential amino acids in relatively the same amounts that human beings require. They may also contain dispensable/nonessential amino acids.

amino acid pools amino acids dissolved in the body's fluids that provide cells with ready raw materials from which to build new proteins or other molecules.

limiting amino acid an essential amino acid that is present in dietary protein in an insufficient amount, thereby limiting the body's ability to build protein.

Just as each letter of the alphabet is important in forming whole words, each amino acid must be available to build finished proteins.

adequate again, protein synthesis lags behind until the needed machinery can be rebuilt. Meanwhile, the cells function less and less effectively as their proteins wear out and are only partially replaced.

Thus, a diet that is short in any of the indispensable/essential amino acids limits protein synthesis. An earlier analogy likened amino acids to letters of the alphabet. To be meaningful, words must contain all of the right letters. For example, a print shop that has no letter "N" cannot make personalized stationery for Jana Johnson. No matter how many Js, As, Os, Hs, and Ss are in the printer's possession, they cannot replace the missing Ns. Likewise, in building a protein molecule, no amino acid can fill another's spot. If a cell that is building a protein cannot find a needed amino acid, synthesis stops, and the partial protein is released.

Partially completed proteins are not held for completion at a later time when the diet may improve. Rather, they are dismantled, and the component amino acids are returned to the circulation to be made available to other cells. If they are not soon inserted into protein, their amine groups are removed and excreted, and the residues are used for other purposes. The need that prompted the call for that particular protein will not be met. Since the other amino acids are wasted, the amine groups are excreted, and the body cannot resynthesize the amino acids later.

Complementary Proteins   It follows that if a person does not consume all of the essential amino acids in proportion to the body's needs, the body's pools of essential amino acids will dwindle until body organs are compromised. Consuming the essential amino acids presents no problem to people who regularly eat proteins containing ample amounts of all of the essential amino acids, such as meat, fish, poultry, cheese, eggs, milk, and most soybean products. An equally sound choice is to eat a combination of foods from plants so that amino acids that are low in some foods will be supplied by the others. The protein-rich foods are combined to yield **complementary proteins** (see Figure 6–13), or proteins containing all of the essential amino acids in amounts sufficient to support health.[10] This concept, called **mutual supplementation**, is illustrated in Figure 6–14. The complementary proteins need not even be eaten together as long as the day's meals supply them all and the diet provides enough energy and total protein from a variety of sources.

Concern about the quality of individual food proteins is of only theoretical interest in settings where food is abundant. Most people in Canada and the United States eat a variety of nutritious foods to meet their energy needs. Healthy adults would find it next to impossible *not* to meet their protein requirements, even if they were to eat no meat, fish, poultry, eggs, cheese, or soy products. They need not pay attention to

---

FIGURE 6–13
Complementary Protein Combinations

Healthful foods like these contribute substantial protein (42 grams total) to this day's meals without meat. Additional servings of nutritious foods, such as milk, bread, and eggs, can easily supply the remainder of the day's need for protein (14 additional grams for men and 4 for women).

¾ c oatmeal =	5 g
Protein total	5 g

| 1 c rice | = | 4 g |
1 c beans	=	16 g
Protein total		20 g

| 1½ c pasta | = 11 g |
| 1 c vegetables | = 2 g |
2 tbs parmesan cheese =	4 g
Protein total	17 g

Chapter 6 The Proteins and Amino Acids

Figure 6–14

Proteins That Complement Each Other Work Together

In general, legumes provide plenty of the amino acids isoleucine (Ile) and lysine (Lys), but fall short in methionine (Met) and tryptophan (Trp). Grains have the opposite strengths and weaknesses, making them a perfect match for legumes.

	Ile	Lys	Met	Trp
Legumes	✓	✓		
Grains			✓	✓
Together	✓	✓	✓	✓

mutual supplementation as long as the diet is varied, nutritious, and adequate in energy and other nutrients—not made up just of, say, cookies, potato chips, and alcoholic beverages. Protein sufficiency follows effortlessly behind.

For people in areas where food sources are less reliable, protein quality can make the difference between health and disease. When food energy intake is limited (where malnutrition is widespread) or when the selection of foods available is severely limited (where a single food such as potatoes provides 90% of the Calories), the primary food source of protein must be checked because its quality is crucial.

KEY POINT

- A protein's amino acid assortment greatly influences its usefulness to the body. Proteins lacking essential amino acids can be used only if those amino acids are present from other sources.

Measuring Protein Quality

Researchers have developed many methods of evaluating the quality of food protein. The most important one for consumers is the **protein digestibility–corrected amino acid score**, or **PDCAAS**, which is used by the DRI committee to evaluate people's protein intakes.

On the PDCAAS scale of 100 to 0, with 100 representing protein sources that are most readily digested and most perfectly balanced for meeting human needs, egg white, ground beef, chicken products, skim (fat-free) milk, and tuna all score 100. Soybean protein isn't far behind at 94, due in part to a limited amount of certain amino acids (see Figure 6–14). Most legumes rank in the 60s and 50s. The wheat protein gluten, formed during bread making, ranks 25. Something interesting happens when pea flour (67) and whole-wheat flour (40) are combined: the score for the resulting flour is 82. Why? They are complementary proteins.

In trying to choose between peanut butter and chilli in the grocery store, you may think you have no use for the PDCAAS. Although Canada does not currently have a value for %DV on our food labels, when you read the "% Daily Value" for protein listed on U.S. labels, you are using it indirectly. Manufacturers that list values for protein on food labels must use the PDCAAS to determine the protein quality of their products. Thus, protein values on labels reflect both the digestibility and the amino acid composition of the foods. Another measure relevant to the average well-fed North American is the DRI recommended intake for protein, discussed next.

KEY POINT

- The quality of a protein is measured by its amino acids, by its digestibility, and by how well it meets human needs. The protein value listed on a U.S. food label reflects the PDCAAS of the protein in the food.

How Much Protein Do People Really Need?

The DRI recommendation for protein intake is designed to cover the need to replace protein-containing tissue that healthy adults lose and wear out every day. Therefore,

complementary proteins two or more proteins whose amino acid assortments complement each other in such a way that the essential amino acids missing from one are supplied by the other.

mutual supplementation the strategy of combining two incomplete protein sources so that the amino acids in one food make up for those lacking in the other food. Such protein combinations are sometimes called *complementary proteins*.

protein digestibility–corrected amino acid score (PDCAAS) a measuring tool used to determine protein quality. The PDCAAS reflects a protein's digestibility as well as the proportions of amino acids that it provides.

Food Protein: Quality, Use, and Need

it depends on body size: larger people have a higher protein need. For adults, the DRI recommended intake is set at 0.8 gram for each kilogram (or 2.2 pounds) of body weight (see inside the front cover, page A). The minimum amount is set at 10 percent of total Calories. Athletes may need slightly more according to authorities other than the DRI committee, but the increased need is well covered by a regular diet. For infants and growing children, the protein recommendation, like all nutrient recommendations, is higher per unit of body weight. The DRI committee set an upper limit for protein intake of no more than 35 percent of total Calories, an amount significantly higher than average intakes of Canadians of ~17%. Table 6–1 (on page 208) reviews recommendations for protein intakes, and the item in the margin beside it provides a method for determining your own protein need.

Recommendations for protein intake assume a normal mixed diet, that is, a diet that includes a combination of animal and plant protein. Because not all proteins are used with 100 percent efficiency, the recommendation is quite generous. Many healthy people can consume less than this amount and still meet their bodies' protein needs. What this means in terms of food selections is presented in this chapter's Food Feature.

Underlying the protein recommendation are **nitrogen balance** studies, which compare nitrogen lost by excretion with nitrogen eaten in food. In healthy adults, nitrogen-in (consumed) must equal nitrogen-out (excreted). Scientists measure the body's daily nitrogen losses in urine, feces, sweat, and skin under controlled conditions and then estimate the amount of protein needed to replace these losses.*[11]

Under normal circumstances, healthy adults are in nitrogen equilibrium, or zero balance; that is, they have the same amount of total protein in their bodies at all times. When nitrogen-in exceeds nitrogen-out, people are said to be in *positive nitrogen balance*; somewhere in their bodies more proteins are being built than are being broken down and lost. When nitrogen-in is less than nitrogen-out, people are said to be in *negative nitrogen balance*; they are losing protein. Figure 6–15 illustrates these different states.

Growing children add new blood, bone, and muscle cells to their bodies every day, so children must have more protein, and therefore more nitrogen, in their bodies

Figure 6–15
Nitrogen Balance

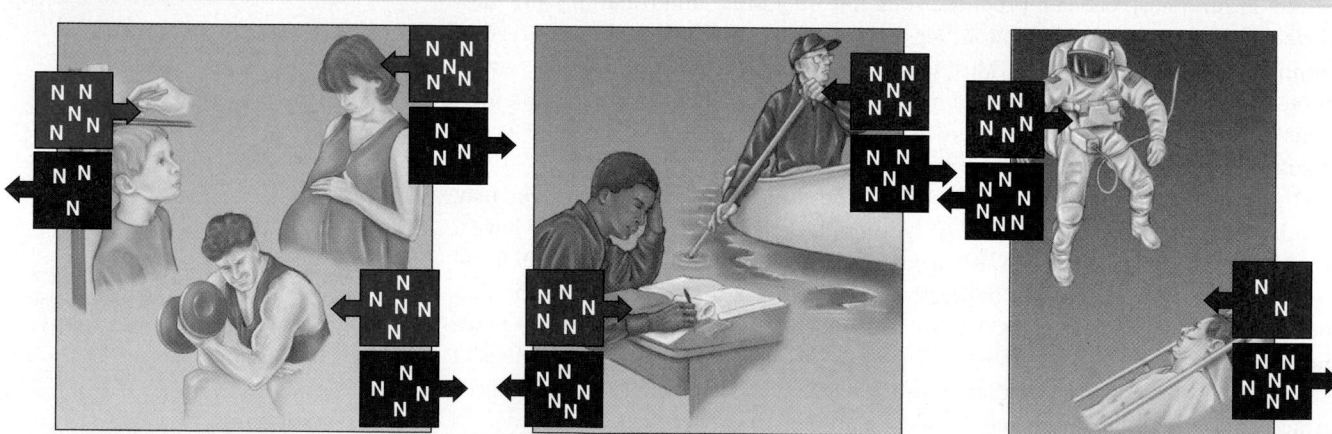

Positive Nitrogen Balance
These people, a growing child, a person building muscle, and a pregnant woman, are all retaining more nitrogen than they are excreting.

Nitrogen Equilibrium
These people, a healthy college student and a young retiree, are in nitrogen equilibrium.

Negative Nitrogen Balance
These people, an astronaut and a surgery patient, are losing more nitrogen than they are taking in.

nitrogen balance the amount of nitrogen consumed compared with the amount excreted in a given time period.

*The average protein is 16% nitrogen by weight; that is, each 100 grams of protein contains 16 grams of nitrogen. As a rule of thumb, multiply the nitrogen's weight by 6.25 to estimate the protein's weight.

at the end of each day than they had at the beginning. A growing child is therefore in positive nitrogen balance. Similarly, when a woman is pregnant, she must be in positive nitrogen balance until after the birth, when she once again reaches equilibrium.

Negative nitrogen balance occurs when muscle or other protein tissue is broken down and lost. Illness or injury triggers the release of powerful messengers* that signal the body to break down some of the less vital proteins, such as those of the skin and even muscle.[12] This action floods the blood with the amino acids and energy needed to fuel the body's defences and fight the illness. The result is negative nitrogen balance. Astronauts, too, may experience negative nitrogen balance. In the stress of space flight and with no need to support the body's weight against gravity, the astronauts' muscles waste and weaken. To minimize the inevitable loss of muscle tissue, the astronauts must do special exercises in space.[13] Also, check out "The Hadfield Shake" on YouTube (http://www.youtube.com/watch?v=Wam7poPzG1w) to see how Commander Chris Hadfield exercised in space.

Growing children end each day with more bone, blood, muscle, and skin cells than they had at the beginning of the day.

KEY POINT

■ The amount of protein needed daily depends on body size and stage of growth. The DRI recommended intake for adults is 0.8 gram of protein per kilogram of body weight. Protein recommendations are based on nitrogen balance studies, which compare nitrogen ingested in food with nitrogen excreted from the body.

Protein Deficiency and Excess

Protein deficiencies are well known because, together with energy deficiencies, they are the world's leading form of malnutrition. The health effects of too much protein are far less well known. Both deficiency and excess are of concern.

What Happens When People Consume Too Little Protein?

Protein deficiency and energy deficiency go hand in hand. This combination—**protein-energy malnutrition (PEM)**—is the most widespread form of malnutrition in the world today. Over 500 million children face imminent starvation and suffer the effects of severe malnutrition and **hunger**. Most of the 33,000 children who die each day are malnourished. PEM is prevalent in Africa, Central America, South America, the Middle East, and East and Southeast Asia, but developed countries, including those in North America, are not immune to it.

PEM strikes early in childhood, but it endangers many adults as well. Inadequate food intake leads to poor growth in children and to weight loss and wasting in adults. Stunted growth due to PEM is easy to overlook because a small child can look normal. The small stature of children in impoverished nations was once thought to be a normal adaptation to the limited availability of food; now it is known to be an avoidable failure of growth due to a lack of food during the growing years.

PEM takes two different forms, with some cases exhibiting a combination of the two. In one form, the person is shrivelled and lean all over—this disease is called **marasmus**. In the second, a swollen belly and skin rash are present, and the disease is named **kwashiorkor**.**,[14] In the combination, some features of each type are present. Marasmus reflects a chronic inadequate food intake and therefore inadequate energy, vitamins, and minerals, as well as too little protein. Kwashiorkor may result from severe acute malnutrition, with too little protein to support body functions.

Scant supplies of donated food save some from starvation, but many others go hungry.

protein-energy malnutrition (PEM) the world's most widespread malnutrition problem, including both *marasmus* and *kwashiorkor* and states in which they overlap; also called *protein-Calorie malnutrition (PCM)*.

hunger the physiological craving for food; the progressive discomfort, illness, and pain resulting from the lack of food. (See also Chapters 9 and 15.)

marasmus (ma-RAZ-mus) the Calorie-deficiency disease; starvation.

kwashiorkor (kwash-ee-OR-core, kwashee-or-CORE) a disease related to protein malnutrition, with a set of recognizable symptoms, such as edema.

---

*The messengers are cytokines.
**A term gaining acceptance for use in place of kwashiorkor is *hypoalbuminemic-type PEM*.

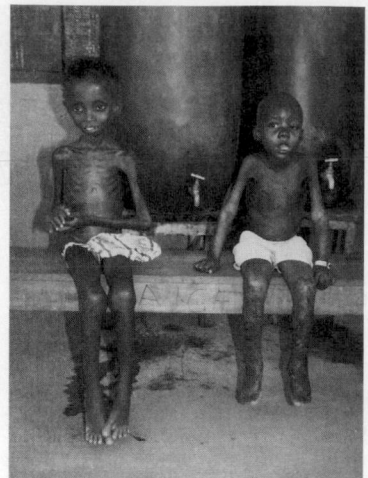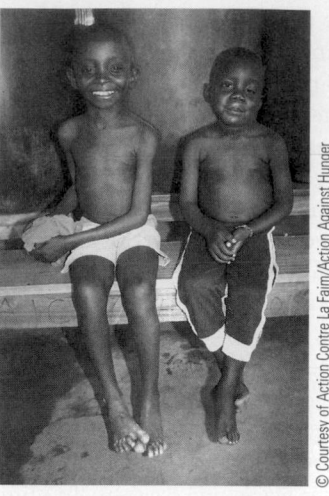

© Courtesy of Action Contre La Faim/Action Against Hunger

The extreme loss of muscle and fat characteristic of marasmus is apparent in these children's arms in the photo on the left. The photo on the right shows the children after they have recovered.

Marasmus   Marasmus occurs most commonly in children from 6 to 18 months of age in overpopulated city slums. Children in impoverished nations subsist on a weak cereal drink with scant energy and protein of low quality; such food can barely sustain life, much less support growth. A starving child often looks like a wizened little old person—just skin and bones.

Without adequate nutrition, muscles, including the heart muscles, waste and weaken.[15] Brain development is stunted, and learning is impaired. Metabolism is so slow that body temperature is subnormal. There is little or no fat under the skin to insulate against cold, and hospital workers have found that children with marasmus need to be wrapped up and kept warm. They also need love because they have often been deprived of parental attention as well as food.

The starving child faces this threat to life by engaging in as little activity as possible—not even crying for food. The body collects all of its forces to meet the crisis and so cuts down on any expenditure of protein not needed for the heart, lungs, and brain to function. Growth ceases; the child is no larger at age four than at age two. The skin loses its elasticity and moisture, so it tends to crack; when sores develop, they fail to heal. Digestive enzymes are in short supply, the digestive tract lining deteriorates, and absorption fails. The child can't assimilate what little food is eaten.

Blood proteins, including hemoglobin, are no longer produced, so the child becomes anemic and weak. If a bone breaks, healing is delayed because the protein needed to heal it is lacking.[16] Antibodies to fight off invading bacteria are degraded to provide amino acids for other uses, leaving the child an easy target for infection. Then **dysentery**, an infection of the digestive tract, causes diarrhea, further depleting the body of nutrients, especially minerals. Measles, which might make a healthy child sick for a week or two, kills a child with PEM within two or three days. In the marasmic child, once infection sets in, kwashiorkor often follows, and the immune response weakens further.[17] Infections that occur with malnutrition are responsible for two-thirds of the deaths of young children in developing countries.

Ultimately, marasmus progresses to the point of no return when the body's machinery for protein synthesis, itself made of protein, has been degraded. At this point, attempts to correct the situation by giving food or protein fail to prevent death. If caught before this time, however, the starvation of a child can be reversed by careful nutrition therapy.[18] The fluid balances are most critical. Diarrhea will have depleted the body's potassium and upset other electrolyte balances. The combination of electrolyte imbalances, anemia, fever, and infections often leads to heart failure and sudden death. Careful correction of fluid and electrolyte balances usually raises the blood pressure and strengthens the heartbeat within a few days. Later, skim (fat-free)

dysentery (DISS-en-terry) an infection of the digestive tract that causes diarrhea.

The edema and enlarged liver characteristic of kwashiorkor are apparent in this child's swollen belly.

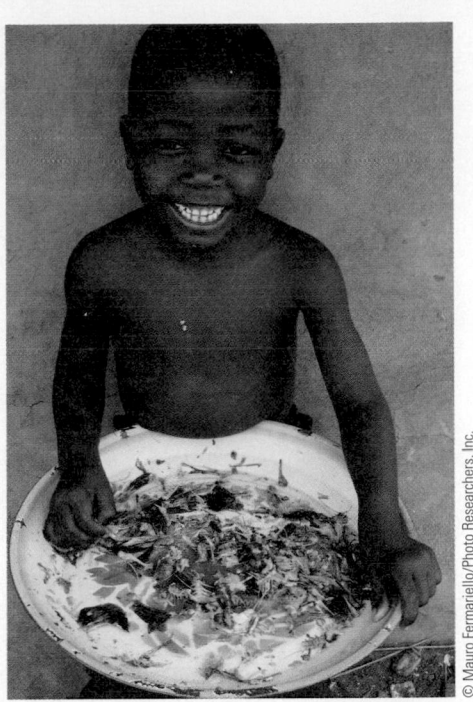

Given appropriate nutrition and care, this child has successfully recovered from kwashiorkor.

milk, providing protein and carbohydrate, can safely be given; fat is introduced still later, when body protein is sufficient to provide carriers to remove the fat from the liver. Years after PEM is corrected, a child may experience deficits in thinking and school achievement compared with well-nourished peers.[19]

Kwashiorkor Kwashiorkor is the Ghanaian name for "the evil spirit that infects the first child when the second child is born." In countries where kwashiorkor is prevalent, each baby is weaned from breast milk as soon as the next one comes along. The older baby no longer receives breast milk, which contains high-quality protein designed perfectly to support growth, but is given a watery cereal with scant protein of low quality—small wonder the just-weaned child sickens when the new baby arrives. Although rare in Canada and the United States, kwashiorkor is not entirely unknown, usually occurring when fad diets replace sound nutrition in children.

Some kwashiorkor symptoms resemble those of marasmus (see Table 6–3) but often without severe wasting of body fat. Proteins and hormones that previously maintained fluid balance are now diminished, so fluid leaks out of the blood and accumulates in the belly and legs, causing edema, a distinguishing feature of kwashiorkor. The kwashiorkor victim's belly often bulges with a fatty liver, caused by lack of the protein carriers that transport fat out of the liver. The fatty liver loses some of its ability to clear poisons from the body, prolonging their toxic effects. Without sufficient tyrosine to make melanin, the child's hair loses its normal colour; inadequate protein synthesis leaves the skin patchy and scaly; sores fail to heal.

PEM at Home PEM occurs among some groups in Canada: the poor living in inner cities and in rural areas; many elderly people; hungry and homeless children; and those suffering from the eating disorder anorexia nervosa. Some well-meaning but misinformed parents have inflicted PEM and other deficiency diseases on their toddlers by replacing their milk with unenriched, protein-poor "health food" soy or rice drinks.[20] Also at risk for PEM are those with wasting diseases such as cancer or AIDS and those addicted to drugs and alcohol. In a downward spiral, PEM and serious illness worsen each other, so treating the PEM often reduces medical complications and suffering even when an underlying disease exists.[21]

● Melanin, a brown pigment of hair, skin, and eyes, was mentioned earlier as a product made from tyrosine.

Turn to Chapter 15 for details concerning the causes of hunger at home and abroad.

Protein Deficiency and Excess

Table 6–3

Features of Marasmus and Kwashiorkor in Children

Separating PEM into two classifications oversimplifies the condition, but at the extremes, marasmus and kwashiorkor exhibit marked differences. Marasmus–kwashiorkor mix presents symptoms common to both marasmus and kwashiorkor. In all cases, children are likely to develop diarrhea, infections, and multiple nutrient deficiencies.

Marasmus	Kwashiorkor
Infants and toddlers (less than 2 yr)	Older infants and young children (1 to 3 yr)
Severe deprivation or impaired absorption of protein, energy, vitamins, and minerals	Inadequate protein intake or, more commonly, infections
Develops slowly; chronic PEM	Rapid onset; acute PEM
Severe weight loss	Some weight loss
Severe muscle wasting with fat loss	Some muscle wasting, with retention of some body fat
Growth: <60% weight-for-age	Growth: 60 to 80% weight-for-age
No detectable edema	Edema
No fatty liver	Enlarged, fatty liver
Anxiety, apathy	Apathy, misery, irritability, sadness
Appetite may be normal or impaired	Loss of appetite
Hair is sparse, thin, and dry; easily pulled out	Hair is dry and brittle; easily pulled out; changes colour; becomes straight
Skin is dry, thin, and wrinkled	Skin develops lesions

Today, many people who work to support their children earn so little that they cannot afford nutritious food—over 880,000 Canadians, 38 percent or close to 340,000 of whom were children, "needed emergency food assistance in March, 2012" according to the 2012 Hunger Count.[22] Hunger, especially in children, threatens everyone's future. Hungry children do not learn as well as fed children, nor are they as competitive. They are ill more often, they have higher absentee rates from school, and when they attend, they cannot concentrate for long. The forces driving poverty and hunger will require many great minds working together to find solutions. In fighting hunger, programs that tailor interventions to the local people and involve them in the process of identifying problems and devising solutions report the most success.[23]

KEY POINT

- Protein-deficiency symptoms are always observed when either protein or energy is deficient. Extreme food energy deficiency results in marasmus; extreme protein deficiency results in kwashiorkor. The two diseases overlap most of the time and together are called PEM.

Is It Possible to Consume Too Much Protein?

The DRI committee recommends that the diet contain no more than 35 percent of Calories from protein to decrease risks of chronic diseases. Overconsumption of protein offers no benefits and may pose health risks for the heart, for weakened kidneys, and for the bones. Diets high in protein-rich foods are often associated with obesity and its many accompanying health risks.[24] Animal protein sources in particular can be high in saturated fat, a known contributor to atherosclerosis and heart disease. The effect of animal protein itself on heart health is uncertain. Conversely, substituting plant protein for animal protein improves indicators of heart disease risk, as this chapter's Controversy feature explains.[25]

Animals fed experimentally on high-protein diets often develop enlarged kidneys or livers. In human beings, a high-protein diet worsens existing kidney problems and may accelerate a decline in only mildly impaired kidneys.[26] One of the most effective treatments for people with established kidney problems is to reduce protein intakes to slow down the progression of their disease.

Evidence is mixed about whether high intakes of protein from animal sources, especially when accompanied by low calcium and low fruit and vegetable intakes, can accelerate adult bone loss. No doubt exists about the effect of feeding purified protein to human subjects—purified protein causes calcium to be spilled from the urine. Also, eating diets high in protein, particularly animal protein, correlates with a greater incidence of hip fractures in some populations. In one population, however, the reverse may be true—in malnourished elderly individuals, protein deficiency and hip fractures often occur together, and restoring dietary protein and giving calcium and vitamin D supplements can improve bone status.[*,27] In establishing protein recommendations, the DRI committee considered the effect of excess protein on the bones but found the evidence insufficient to set a tolerable upper intake level.

A balance between protein and at least one other energy nutrient seems necessary for survival. Inuit survive for long periods on a diet constructed almost entirely of meats; they choose fatty meats and obtain a significant percentage of their Calories from fat to balance their high intake of protein from meat. No one yet knows exactly what percentage of dietary protein is hazardous, but the meat-eating Inuit typically consume less than 50 percent of Calories from protein. The Canadian Community Health Survey revealed that adults are obtaining about 17 percent of their total Calories from protein.[28] Health recommendations typically advise a protein intake between 10 and 35 percent of energy intake. Popular low-carbohydrate, high-protein weight-loss diets often suggest up to 65 percent of energy from protein, an amount that may border on being too high for health.[29]

Read more about high-protein diets for weight loss in Chapter 9.

KEY POINT

■ Health risks may follow the overconsumption of a protein-rich diet.

---

*The calcium supplement is citrate malate.

---

try it!

···> Food Feature

Getting Enough but Not Too Much Protein

People in developed nations usually eat more than ample protein. The DRI recommendation for protein is generous and more than adequately covers the estimated needs of most people, even those with unusually high requirements. Most foods contribute at least some protein to the diet.

Protein-Rich Foods

Foods in the meat and alternatives group and in the milk and alternatives group contribute an abundance of high-quality protein. Two others, the vegetables and fruit group (mostly the vegetables) and the grain products group, contribute smaller amounts of protein, but they can add up to significant quantities.

Figure 6–16 shows that a wide variety of foods contribute protein to the diet. Figure 6–17 (page 233) shows some of the major sources of protein in the Canadian diet.

Protein is critical in nutrition, but too many protein-rich foods can displace other important foods from the diet. Foods richest in protein carry with them a characteristic array of vitamins and minerals, including vitamin B_{12} and iron, but they lack others—vitamin C and folate, for example. In addition, many protein-rich foods, such as meat, are high in Calories, and to overconsume them is to invite obesity. Because Canadian consumption of protein is ample, you can plan meatless or

reduced-meat meals with pleasure. Of the many interesting protein-rich meat equivalents available, one has already been mentioned: legumes.

The Advantages of Legumes

The protein of some legumes is of a quality almost comparable to that of meat, an unusual trait in a fibre-rich vegetable. For practical purposes, the quality of soy protein can be considered equivalent to that of meat. Figure 6–18 shows a legume plant's special root system, which enables it to make abundant protein. Legumes are also excellent sources of many B vitamins, iron, calcium, and other minerals,

---

Protein Deficiency and Excess

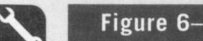

Figure 6–16

Finding the Protein in Food

Grain Products

Food		Protein (g)
Pancakes	2 small	6
Bagel	½	4
Brown rice	½ c	3
Grain bread	1 slice	3
Noodles, pasta	½ c	3
Oatmeal	½ c	3
Barley	½ c	2
Cereal flakes	30 g	2

© Polara Studios, Inc.

Vegetables and Fruit

Food		Protein (g)
Corn	½ c	3
Broccoli	½ c	2
Collard greens	½ c	2
Sweet potato	½ c	2
Baked potato	½ c	1
Bean sprouts	½ c	1
Winter squash	½ c	1

© Polara Studios, Inc.

Food		Protein (g)
Avocado	½ c	2
Cantaloupe	½ c	1
Orange sections	½ c	1
Strawberries	½ c	1

© Polara Studios, Inc.

Meat and Alternatives

Food		Protein (g)
Roast beef	60 g	19
Turkey leg	60 g	16
Chicken breast	60 g	15
Pork meat	60 g	15
Tuna	60 g	14
Lentils, beans, peas	½ c	9
Peanut butter	2 tbs	8
Almonds	¼ c	8
Hot dog	1 regular	7
Lunch meat	60 g	6
Egg	1 large	6
Cashew nuts	¼ c	5

© Polara Studios, Inc.

Milk and Alternatives

Food		Protein (g)
Cheese, processed	60 g	13
Milk, yogurt	1 c	10
Pudding	1 c	5

© Polara Studios, Inc.

Oils and Fats

Not a significant source of protein

© Dusan Zildar/Shutterstock

Source: Data from ESHA Research, The Food Processor Nutrition and Fitness Software, *version 10.6, 2004.*

Figure 6-17

Major Sources of Protein in the Canadian Diet

Sample of the quantities (in kilograms) of protein sources (adjusted for losses/waste) available to Canadians in 2009.

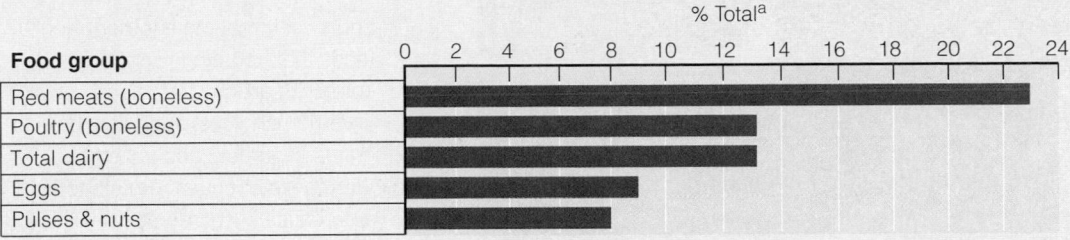

% Total[a]

Food group	
Red meats (boneless)	
Poultry (boneless)	
Total dairy	
Eggs	
Pulses & nuts	

[a]Rounded values.

Source: Data from Statistics Canada, Food statistics, 2009, catalogue no. 21--020-X, http://www.statcan.gc.ca/pub/21-020-x/21-020-x2009001-eng.pdf. Reproduced and distributed on an "as is" basis with the permission of Statistics Canada.

Figure 6-18

A Legume

The legumes include such plants as the kidney bean, soybean, garden pea, lentil, black-eyed pea, and lima bean. Bacteria in the root nodules can "fix" nitrogen from the air, contributing it to the beans. Ultimately, thanks to these bacteria, the plant accumulates more nitrogen than it can get from the soil and also leaves more nitrogen in the soil than it takes out. The legumes are so efficient at trapping nitrogen that farmers often grow them in rotation with other crops to fertilize fields. Legumes are included with the meat and alternatives group in Figure 6-16.

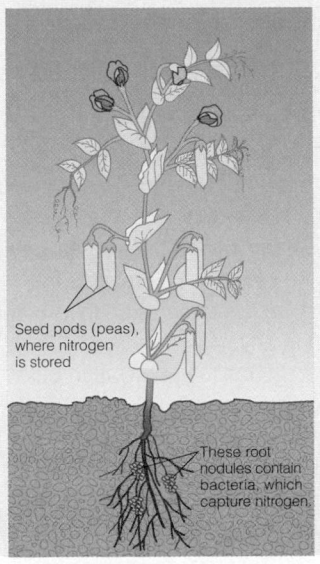

Seed pods (peas), where nitrogen is stored

These root nodules contain bacteria, which capture nitrogen.

making them exceptionally nutritious. On average, a cup (250 mL) of cooked legumes contains almost 20 grams of protein and 30 percent of the Daily Values for iron.* Like meats, though, legumes do not offer every nutrient, and they do not make a complete meal by themselves. They contain no vitamin A, vitamin C, or vitamin B_{12}, and their balance of amino acids can be much improved by using grains and other vegetables with them.

Soybeans are versatile legumes, and many nutritious products are made from them. Heavy use of soy products in place of meat, however, inhibits iron absorption. The effect can be alleviated by using small amounts of meat and/ or foods rich in vitamin C in the same meal with soy products. Vegetarians sometimes use convenience foods made from **textured vegetable protein** (soy protein) formulated to look and taste like hamburgers or breakfast sausages. Many of these are intended to match the known nutrient contents of animal protein foods, but they often fall short.* A wise vegetarian uses such

foods sparingly and learns to use combinations of whole foods to supply the needed nutrients.

The nutrients of soybeans are also available as bean curd, or **tofu**, a staple used in many Asian dishes. Thanks to the use of calcium salts when some tofu is made, it can be high in calcium. Check the Nutrition Facts panel on the label.

The Food Features presented so far show that the recommendations for the three energy-yielding nutrients occur in balance with each other. The diets of most people, however, supply too little fibre, too much fat, too many Calories, and abundant protein. To bring their diets into line with recommendations, then, requires changing the bulk of intake from Calorie-rich fried foods, fatty meats,

In Canada, regulations govern the nutrient contents of such products, many of which are fortified to provide higher-quality protein and vitamins such as vitamin B_{12}.

textured vegetable protein processed soybean protein used in products formulated to look and taste like meat, fish, or poultry.

tofu (TOE-foo) a curd made from soybeans that is rich in protein, often rich in calcium, and variable in fat content; used in many Asian and vegetarian dishes in place of meat.

Data from The Food Processor Plus, ESHA research, version 10.5.

Legumes: Protein-rich and exceptionally nutritious.

This chapter's Controversy section describes the benefits and pitfalls of vegetarian and meat-containing diets.

and sweet treats to "nutrient-rich" foods that contain lower-Calorie complex carbohydrates and fibre-rich choices, such as whole grains, legumes, and vegetables. With these changes, protein totals automatically come into line with the requirements.

CONTROVERSY 6

Vegetarian and Meat-Containing Diets: What Are the Benefits and Pitfalls?

In recent years, obesity, heart disease, high blood pressure, and cancer have taken a great toll on the health of Canadians and others living in developed nations. The scientific community has observed that, in affluent countries, people who eat well-planned **vegetarian** diets often have reduced rates of these killers and may even live longer lives.*,[1] Should people consider eating a vegetarian diet? If so, is it beneficial to simply stop eating meat, or is more demanded of the vegetarian diet planner? And what positive contributions do animal products make to the diet?

This Controversy feature looks first at the positive health aspects of vegetarian

*Controversy references are listed separately at the end of the chapter.

diets and then at the positive aspects of meat eaters' diets. It lends practical assistance to both vegetarians and meat eaters in making beneficial choices that minimize their risks.

Vegetarianism is often mistakenly associated with a particular culture or belief system, but individuals choose it for many different reasons. Some omit meat to reduce their intakes of Calories or saturated fat. Some believe that we should not kill animals to eat their meat. Some believe that we should not partake of animal products such as milk, cheese, eggs, or honey or use items made from leather, wool, or silk. Many people object to inhumane treatment of livestock in pens, feedlots, and slaughterhouses. Some believe

we should eat less meat for health reasons or for environmental reasons—production of meat protein requires a much greater input of resources than does an equal amount of vegetable protein. Some fear contracting diseases, such as food poisoning or "mad cow disease" from meat. (The effects of food choices on the earth's resources are topics of Chapter 15 and its Controversy feature, and Chapter 12 provides the whole story on the threat from food-borne illnesses.) In any case, vegetarian diets are not categorized by motivation but by the foods they exclude, and even the experts struggle to agree on the terms to describe them (see Table C6–1) Four percent of adult Canadians reportedly follow a vegetarian diet.[2]

Terms Used to Describe Omnivores, Vegetarians, and Their Diets

Some of the terms below are in common usage, but others are useful only to researchers.

- **omnivore** includes food of both plant and animal origin, including animal flesh.
- **fruitarian** includes only raw or dried fruit, seeds, and nuts in the diet.
- **lacto-ovo vegetarian** includes dairy products, eggs, vegetables, grains, legumes, fruit, and nuts; excludes flesh and seafood.
- **lacto-vegetarian** includes dairy products, vegetables, grains, legumes, fruit, and nuts; excludes flesh, seafood, and eggs.
- **macrobiotic diet** a vegan diet composed mostly of whole grains, beans, and certain vegetables; taken to extremes, macrobiotic diets have resulted in malnutrition and even death.
- **ovo-vegetarian** includes eggs, vegetables, grains, legumes, fruit, and nuts; excludes flesh, seafood, and milk products.
- **partial vegetarian** a term sometimes used to mean an eating style that includes seafood, poultry, eggs, dairy products, vegetables, grains, legumes, fruit, and nuts; excludes or strictly limits certain meats, such as red meats.
- **pesco-vegetarian** same as partial vegetarian but eliminates poultry.
- **vegan** includes only food from plant sources: vegetables, grains, legumes, fruit, seeds, and nuts; also called strict vegetarian.
- **vegetarian** includes plant-based foods and eliminates some or all animal-derived foods.

People who eat meat (**omnivores**) also do so for a variety of reasons. Some find that a hamburger makes a convenient lunch while providing a concentrated source of energy and nutrients. Others enjoy the taste of roast chicken or beef stew. Others wouldn't know what to eat without meat; they are accustomed to seeing it on the plate. Still others mistakenly think that eating meats instead of grains, potatoes, and breads will help them lose weight (Chapter 9 takes up the issues of weight-loss dieting). Whatever your diet or reasons for choosing it, the foods most important to your health are the foods that you choose regularly.

Positive Health Aspects of Vegetarian Diets

Strong evidence linking vegetarian diets with reduced incidences of chronic diseases has prompted several nutrition authorities to state with confidence that a well-chosen vegetarian diet can meet nutrient needs while supporting health.[3] Such evidence, though abundant, is not easily obtained. It would be easy if vegetarians differed from others only in not consuming meat, but they often have *increased* intakes of fruits and vegetables

as well. These foods are the primary contributors of nutrients and phytochemicals believed to reduce disease risks. Vegetarian diets often contain more fibre, potassium, and several vitamins associated with reduced disease risks. Also, though there are exceptions, vegetarians typically use no tobacco, use alcohol in moderation if at all, and may be more physically active than other adults. Researchers must account for the effects of a total health-conscious lifestyle on disease development before they can

see how diet alone correlates with health. Despite these limitations, much evidence weighs in favour of vegetarian diets, as the next sections make clear.

Weight Control

In general, vegetarians maintain a healthier body weight than nonvegetarians.[4] Studies report that body weights for height are higher for some people eating a mixed diet than for vegetarians and that weight increases as frequency of meat consumption increases.[5] Lower body weights also correlate with high intakes of fibre and low intakes of fat. Obesity impairs health in a number of ways, and vegetarians who maintain a healthy weight are at an advantage.

Heart Disease

People consuming plant-based diets have less risk of dying from heart disease and related illnesses than do meat-eating people.[6] In general, plant-based diets, such as vegetarian diets, are lower in saturated fat and cholesterol than are diets based on fatty meat, and dietary saturated fat intake and to a lesser extent cholesterol intake are directly linked with heart disease. Plant-based diets contain fats, but they are generally the unsaturated fats of soybean products, seeds, nuts, and vegetable oils that are associated with a lower risk of heart disease.[7]

A balanced meal need not include meat to be nutritious.

Furthermore, such diets are generally higher in dietary fibres, a bonus to blood lipids and the condition of the heart. Vegetarians who eat fish and milk products have blood lipids between the low blood lipids of **vegans** and the higher blood lipids of people eating typical Western diets high in meat.[8]

Vegetables may also lower disease risks by virtue of their phytochemicals (see Controversy 2). For example, vegetarians often seek tofu (the curd of soybeans) for its protein value, but its heart health benefits may exceed protein alone in some groups of individuals.[9] The phytochemicals of soy products help lower cholesterol, and when tofu replaces red meat in the diet, blood cholesterol and triglyceride levels drop even when intakes of energy, protein, carbohydrate, total fat, saturated fat, unsaturated fat, alcohol, and fibre are held constant.[10] Tofu may have a reputation as a high-fat food, but tofu contains just slightly less fat than an equal portion of skinless chicken thigh meat. Furthermore, the fat of tofu is far less saturated than the fat of chicken.

Heart Benefits from Plant Proteins

Over 60 years of experimentation have revealed that when soy protein *replaces* animal protein in the diet, total blood cholesterol concentration is reduced along with LDL cholesterol, triglycerides, blood pressure, and other indicators of heart disease risk.[11] At the same time, blood HDL cholesterol rises or stays the same. The question remains, however, whether these potentially beneficial effects are attributable to soy protein itself or to the phytochemicals that accompany it.

Weighing in on this issue are results from a study on a breed of mice that develop the hardening of the arteries associated with heart disease. The mice were divided into three groups: one group was fed chow made of regular soy protein, another group was fed soy protein from which the active phytochemicals had been washed away,

and a control group was fed soy-free chow. When the groups were compared at the end of the study, both soy-fed groups had lower blood lipids and had developed less hardening of the arteries than the controls. The mice fed regular soy chow developed significantly less artery damage than did the washed-soy group, suggesting an extra benefit from soy's phytochemicals.[12] Similar findings from similar experiments with other species confirm this idea, but here's a puzzle: when researchers extract the soy phytochemicals and feed them to animals, the benefits of whole soy foods do not occur.[13]

Human studies tip the scale in favour of replacing some of the animal protein in the diet with whole soy foods.[14] Many of the beneficial blood lipid changes mentioned earlier often occur among people who regularly consume soy foods.[15] A firm base of such findings prompted the U.S. FDA to approve the food label claim that "25 grams of soy protein a day, as part of a diet low in saturated fat and cholesterol, may reduce the risk of heart disease," a claim not currently allowed on Canadian foods.

The benefits of vegetable proteins may also reach beyond just soy foods. Even the protein gluten, formed in wheat bread, may reduce oxidation and other indicators of heart disease risk when it replaces animal protein in the diet.[16] Likewise, in people, skim (fat-free) milk *lowers* blood cholesterol when it replaces other animal proteins, and meals of fish consumed for its protein provide benefits to heart health in other ways, as Chapter 5 described.[17] These developments have led researchers to look beyond dietary protein for answers about the benefits to vegetarians with regard to heart disease risk.

Defence against Blood Pressure

Vegetarians tend to have lower blood pressure and lower rates of hypertension than nonvegetarians. Appropriate body weight helps maintain a healthy blood pressure, as does a diet low in total fat

and saturated fat and high in fibre, fruit, and vegetables. Lifestyle factors also influence blood pressure: smoking and alcohol intake raise blood pressure, and physical activity lowers it.

Defence against Cancer

Vegetarians have significantly lower rates of certain cancers than the general population. Again, though, low rates of cancer may be associated more with the abundance of fruit and vegetables in vegetarian diets than with the exclusion of all animal products. Colon cancer appears to correlate with moderate-to-high intakes of

- Alcohol[18]
- Total food energy[19]
- Fatty red meats and processed meats (but not poultry or fish)[20] (a diet high in red meat and processed meat may be positively associated with stomach cancer as well[21])

Possible correlations with colon cancer have been found with

- High intakes of refined grain products
- Low intakes of whole grains in the United States[22]
- Low intakes of vitamin D[23]

Certain cancers appear to occur less frequently among people who eat mostly plant-based diets that are rich in vegetables, fruit, whole grains, and legumes (soybeans in particular). The protective effect may be related to the activities of phytochemicals in those foods, activities that occur whether or not the diet also contains some meat.[24]

Positive Health Aspects of the Meat Eater's Diet

Meat eaters generally consume other foods in addition to meat. The healthiest meat eaters base their diets on abundant fruit, vegetables, whole grains, and milk products with the addition of small servings of fish, meat, and poultry. True meat lovers and misguided weight-loss dieters who shun all green and yellow vegetables, fruit, and grains place themselves in immediate peril of malnutrition and chronic diseases.

Unlike vegetarians, who can find suitable replacements for meat in a healthy

This 5-ounce steak provides almost all of the meat recommended for a day's intake in a 2,000-Calorie diet.

diet, those who would exclude fruit and vegetables have no adequate substitutes for these foods (not even antioxidant supplement pills, as the next chapter points out). The following sections consider a *balanced, adequate* diet whether or not meats, eggs, and milk products play a part.

What Diet Offers the Best Support during Critical Times?

Both meat eaters and **lacto-ovo vegetarians** can generally rely on their diets during critical times of life. In contrast, a vegan diet can pose challenges. The chapter made clear that protein from animal sources, such as meat, milk, and eggs, is the clear winner in tests of digestibility and indispensable amino acid availability to the body, with soy protein a close second. In addition to providing protein, meat provides the abundant iron, zinc, and vitamin B_{12} needed by everyone, but in particular by pregnant women, infants, children, and adolescents.

In Pregnancy and Infancy

Unlike vegans, women who eat meat, eggs, and milk products can be sure of receiving enough vitamin B_{12}, vitamin D, calcium, iron, and zinc, as well as protein, to support pregnancy and breast-feeding. A woman following a well-planned lacto-ovo vegetarian diet can also relax in the knowledge that she is supplied with all necessary nutrients.

If she also habitually consumes more folate in the form of vegetables and fruit, she can relax further, knowing that her developing fetus is at lower risk from birth defects associated with low folate intakes.

A too-low body weight is generally not a problem faced by meat-eating women. A vegan woman who doesn't meet her nutrient needs, however, may enter pregnancy too thin; have inadequate stores of iron, zinc, and vitamin B_{12}; and fail to consume the omega-3 fatty acids needed to support normal fetal development. She may then find it difficult to gain enough weight to support a normal pregnancy.

Obtaining enough vitamin B_{12}, abundant in foods of animal origin but absent from vegetables, poses a challenge to vegans of all ages, and deficiencies of this vitamin are on the rise.[25] The need for vitamin B_{12} is critical for pregnant and lactating women.[26] A severe disorder that is often irreversible and sometimes fatal is reported among breast-fed infants of vegan mothers who fail to obtain sufficient vitamin B_{12}.[27] The infants exhibit a syndrome of body tremors and facial twitches involving the tongue and throat that combine to make nursing or eating difficult. After some months, deprivation of vitamin B_{12} leads to infant growth failure, psychomotor retardation, and shrinkage of the brain. In some cases, the retardation from the deficiency lingers long after treatment with the missing vitamin begins.

In Childhood

Children who eat small servings of meat, poultry, and fish receive abundant protein, iron, vitamin B_{12}, and food energy, making these foods reliable, convenient sources of these key nutrients needed for growth. Likewise, children eating well-planned vegetarian diets that

include eggs, milk, and milk products also receive adequate nutrients and grow as well as their meat-eating peers.[28]

Compared with meat-eating children, well-fed vegan children tend to be shorter and lighter in weight but not excessively so. Most studies find that their growth falls within normal ranges as long as they consume ample energy from food.

Child-sized servings of vegan foods can fail to provide sufficient energy or several key nutrients to support normal growth. A child's small stomach can hold only so much food, and the vegan child may feel full before eating enough to meet his or her nutrient needs. Frequent meals of fortified breads, cereals, or pastas with legumes, nuts, nut butters, and sources of unsaturated fats can help meet protein and energy needs in a smaller volume at each sitting.[29]

Because vegan children derive protein only from plant foods, their daily protein requirement may be somewhat higher than the DRI indicates for the general meat-eating population.[30] Specific recommendations to support the growth of vegan children have not been established.

There is some evidence that children reared on vegan diets and then switched to more liberal diets may have difficulty achieving an adequate vitamin B_{12} status, even with moderate consumption of animal products.[31] Other nutrients of concern for vegan children include vitamin D, calcium, iron, and zinc. Numerous fortified animal-free foods are now available, but supplements may also help meet these nutrient needs.[32]

In Adolescence

Like the diets of meat-eating adolescents, adolescent vegetarian diets range from healthy eating plans to those causing health-destroying deficiencies. On the positive side, some vegetarian adolescents choose diets with more fruit and vegetables and fewer sweets, fast foods, and salty snacks than is common among their meat-eating peers. As a result, these teens enjoy robust growth and health.[33]

Other adolescent vegans, however, adopt poorly planned diets lacking not only vitamin B_{12} but calcium and vitamin D as well. Omissions of calcium and vitamin D lead to weak bone development at precisely the time when bones must develop strength to protect them through later life.[34] As Controversy 8 makes clear, bone density is a now-or-never proposition for adolescents—bone density rarely increases in adulthood.

Urban legends may convince vegan adolescents that a lack of vitamin B_{12} poses no problems, but they are far off the mark. The well-known threat to a developing infant was already described, but vitamin B_{12} deficiency in older children and adolescents also causes problems such as impaired reasoning and memory.[35] In fact, even grown men are vulnerable, as evidenced by a report of a vegan man suffering permanent blindness apparently brought on by vitamin B_{12} deficiency.[36]

Some teens may adopt a vegetarian identity to serve as a sort of camouflage to hide an eating disorder.[37] Even university-age women may disguise their eating disorders as vegetarianism.[38] By doing so, these individuals can greatly limit their food choices while distracting their families and peers from an eating disorder that threatens their health and, in the case of adolescents, their growth and bone strength.

In the Elderly and in Illness

For elderly people with diminished appetites or for people recovering from illnesses, soft or ground meat can provide a well-liked, well-tolerated concentrated source of nutrients. Variety is key to nutritional adequacy in any diet, of course. People battling life-threatening diseases may encounter testimonial stories of cures attributed to restrictive eating plans, such as **macrobiotic diets**, but these diets limit food selections to a few grains and vegetables and cannot possibly deliver the full array of nutrients needed for recovery.

A Few Nutrients of Interest

The quality of a vegetarian or meat-containing diet depends not on whether it includes meat but on whether the other food choices are nutritionally sound. Both vegetarian and meat-containing diets, if not properly balanced, can lack nutrients. Poorly planned vegetarian diets typically lack iron, zinc, calcium, vitamin B_{12}, and vitamin D; without planning, the meat eater's diet may lack vitamin A, vitamin C, folate, and fibre, among others. Quite simply, the negative health aspects of any diet, including vegetarian diets, reflect poor diet planning—the diet omits foods that supply important nutrients.

Protein

The DRI recommended intake for protein is the same for vegetarians as for others, although some have suggested that it should be higher because of the lower digestibility of plant proteins.[39] Vegetarians who use animal-derived foods such as milk and eggs receive high-quality protein and are likely to meet their protein needs. Even those who adopt only plant-based diets are likely to meet protein needs provided that energy intakes are adequate and the protein sources varied.[40]

As mentioned earlier, vegetarians sometimes use foods made from textured vegetable protein, which is formulated to look and taste like meat. Though fortified, these foods often fall short of the nutrients in meats and may also be high in salt, sugar, or other additives. A wise vegetarian learns to use a variety of whole, unrefined foods often and commercially prepared foods less frequently. Vegetarians may also use soybeans in the form of plain tofu (bean curd) to bolster protein intake without consuming unwanted salt, sugar, or other additives.

Iron

Getting enough iron can be a problem even for meat eaters, and vegetarians must be especially vigilant about obtaining iron. The iron in plant foods such as legumes, dark green leafy vegetables, iron-fortified cereals, and whole-grain breads and cereals is poorly absorbed.[41] Such foods contain inhibitors of iron absorption, so the DRI committee recommended that iron intake for vegetarians be adjusted upward (see Chapter 8 for more details). The committee suggests that vegetarians need 1.8 times the amount of iron recommended for the general population.

At some point, the body may adapt to a vegetarian diet by absorbing iron more efficiently.[42] Also, the absorption of iron obtained from plants (nonheme iron) is enhanced by vitamin C consumed with iron-rich foods, and vegetarians typically eat many vitamin C–rich fruits and vegetables.[43] Consequently, vegetarians may suffer no more iron deficiency than other people do.[44]

Zinc

Zinc is similar to iron in that meat is its richest food source, and zinc from plant sources is not well absorbed.[45] In addition, soy, which is commonly used as a meat alternative in vegetarian meals, interferes with zinc absorption. Zinc can be a problem for growing children, but few vegetarian adults are zinc-deficient. Perhaps the best advice to vegetarians regarding zinc is to eat a variety of nutrient-dense foods; include whole grains, nuts, and legumes such as black-eyed peas, pinto beans, and kidney beans; and maintain an adequate energy intake.

Calcium

The calcium intakes of vegetarians who use milk and milk products are similar to those of the general population, but those who do not use milk products risk inadequacy. Careful planners select calcium-rich foods, such as calcium-fortified juices, soy milk, and yogurt products (some of which may also be fortified with vitamin D), in ample quantities regularly. This is especially important for children and adolescents. Soy formulas for infants are fortified with calcium and can be used in cooking, even for adults. Other good sources of absorbable calcium include figs; calcium-set tofu;* some legumes; some green vegetables (broccoli, kale,

*Calcium salts are often added during processing to set/coagulate the tofu.

and turnip greens, but not spinach—see Chapter 8); some nuts, such as almonds; and certain seeds, such as sesame seeds. The choices should be varied because calcium absorption from some plant foods is limited.

Vitamin B$_{12}$

The requirement for vitamin B$_{12}$ is small, but this vitamin is found only in animal-derived foods, such as meats, milk, and eggs. Those who consume these foods are rarely deficient in the vitamin. For vegans, fermented soy products may contain some vitamin B$_{12}$ from the bacteria that did the fermenting, but, unfortunately, much of the vitamin B$_{12}$ found in these products may be an inactive form. Seaweeds such as nori and chlorella supply some vitamin B$_{12}$, but not much, and excessive intakes of these foods can lead to iodine toxicity. To defend against vitamin B$_{12}$ deficiency, vegans must rely on vitamin B$_{12}$-fortified foods (such as soy milk and meat analogue products, or fortified cereal-type meal replacement products) or pills that contain it. As described earlier, without vitamin B$_{12}$, the nerves suffer damage, leading to such health consequences as loss of vision.[46]

Vitamin D

People who do not use vitamin D-fortified foods and do not receive enough exposure to sunlight to synthesize adequate vitamin D (from mid-October to mid-March in Canada) may need supplements to defend against bone loss.[47] This is particularly important for infants, children, and older adults. In northern climates during winter months, young children on vegan diets can readily develop rickets, the vitamin D-deficiency disease.

Omega-3 Fatty Acids

Vegetarian diets typically provide enough omega-6 fatty acids but lack animal-derived longer-chain omega-3 fatty acids. This imbalance slows production of EPA and DHA in the body, and without fish, eggs, or sea vegetables

(certain marine algae) in the diet, intake of EPA and DHA falls short as well.[48] Other sources to consider include omega-3 eggs and omega-3 milk beverages. A vegetarian's daily diet should include good sources of linolenic acid, such as canola oil and flaxseed, walnuts, soybeans, and their oils, because linolenic acid is an essential nutrient.[49]

Planning a Vegetarian Diet

Vegetarians are often advised to follow the Daily Food Guide presented in Chapter 2 with a few modifications. Those who include milk products and eggs can follow the regular plan, using legumes, nuts, and seeds and products made from them, such as peanut butter and tofu, in place of meat. Soy milk and tofu fortified with calcium, vitamin D, and vitamin B$_{12}$ can substitute for

cow's-milk products. Dark green vegetables and legumes help meet iron and zinc needs.

Several food guides have been developed to ease the task of planning nutritious vegetarian diets.[50] Figure C6–1 presents one version to consider.[51] Notice that green leafy vegetables in the vegetable group are distinguished because some of these foods provide almost five times as much calcium per serving as other vegetables. Similarly, dried fruit receive special notice in the fruit group because some of them deliver six times as much iron as other fruit. A separate group for legumes, nuts, and other protein-rich foods was established to provide additional sources of protein, iron, zinc, and essential fatty acids. Beans and soy milk are also found in this group. A group for fats, the smallest arc, encourages the use of vegetable oils rich in unsaturated fats and omega-3 fatty acids.

Figure C6–1

Vegetarian Food Guide Rainbow

Foods and the human body are made of the same materials.

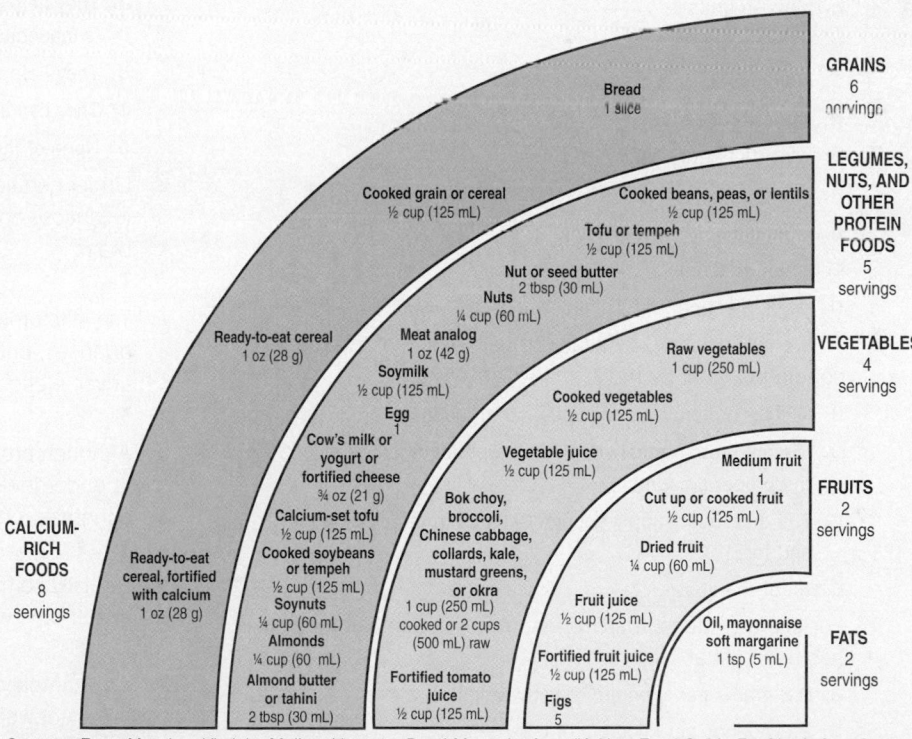

Sources: From Messina, Virginia; Melina, Vesanto; Reed Mangels, Ann. "A New Food Guide For North American Vegetarians." Journal of Dietetic Practice and Research 2003; 64:(2): pp 82–86. Copyright 2003. Dietitians of Canada. Used with permission.

A word of caution in planning a vegetarian diet: choose fresh, whole foods as often as possible and avoid heavy reliance on highly processed convenience foods that contain added sugars, saturated fats, and *trans* fats. An example clarifies this point: a snack of a medium sliced banana provides 100 Calories and practically no fat. A snack of a quarter-cup of banana chips, often sold as a "healthy" or "natural" alternative to other snack foods, provides 150 Calories with 7 grams of saturated fat. (A quarter-pound hamburger delivers only 1 gram more of saturated fat—8 grams.) Banana chips are made from regular bananas but are sweetened with sugar and fried in coconut oil, one of the most saturated fats available.

To avoid such tricks of processing, scrutinize the labels of convenience and prepared vegetarian foods just as you would those of ordinary foods and choose foods that provide needed nutrients without a lot of unneeded Calories from sugar or excess saturated fat or *trans* fat.

Finally, to ensure adequate intakes of vitamin B_{12}, vitamin D, and calcium, vegans need to select fortified foods or use supplements daily.

Conclusion

This comparison has shown that both a meat eater's diet and a vegetarian's diet are best approached scientifically. Some people make much of the distinctions between types of vegetarians (such as **lacto-vegetarian**, **ovo-vegetarian**, **pesco-vegetarian**, **partial vegetarian**, and **fruitarian**); although these distinctions are useful academically, they do not represent uncrossable lines. Some people use meat as a condiment or seasoning for vegetable or grain dishes. Some people eat meat only once a week and use plant protein foods the rest of the time. Many people rely mostly on milk products to meet their protein needs but eat fish occasionally, and so forth. To force people into the categories of "vegetarians" and "meat eaters" leaves out all of these in-between styles of eating that have much to recommend them.

If you are just beginning to study nutrition, consider adopting the attitude that the choice to make is not whether to be a meat eater or a vegetarian but where along the spectrum to locate yourself. Your preferences should be honoured with only these caveats: that you plan your own diet, and the diets of those in your care, to be adequate, balanced, and varied and that you use moderation when choosing foods high in saturated fat or Calories.

Self-Check

Answers to these Self-Check questions are in Appendix D.

1. The basic building blocks for protein are
   a. glucose units
   b. amino acids
   c. side chains
   d. saturated bonds

2. Protein digestion begins in the
   a. mouth
   b. stomach
   c. small intestine
   d. large intestine

3. To prevent wasting of dietary protein, which of the following conditions must be met?
   a. Dietary protein must be adequate in quantity.
   b. Dietary protein must supply all essential amino acids in the proper amounts.
   c. The diet must supply enough Calories from carbohydrate and fat.
   d. All of the above.

4. For healthy adults, the DRI recommended intake for protein has been set at
   a. 0.8 grams per kilogram of body weight
   b. 2.2 pounds per kilogram of body weight
   c. 12 to 15 percent of total Calories
   d. 100 grams per day

5. Which of the following statements is correct regarding protein and amino acid supplements?
   a. They help athletes build muscle even when energy intake is inadequate.
   b. They help dieters lose weight quicker.
   c. They can assist in relieving depression.
   d. None of the above.

6. Under certain circumstances, protein can be converted to glucose and so serve the energy needs of the brain.
   T   F

7. Too little protein in the diet can have severe consequences, but excess protein has not been proven to have adverse effects.
   T   F

8. Although protein-energy malnutrition (PEM) is prevalent in underdeveloped nations, it is not seen in developed countries.
   T   F

9. Partially completed proteins are not held for completion at a later time when the diet may improve.
   T   F

10. An example of a person in positive nitrogen balance is a pregnant woman.
   T   F

start now! ····⟩ Ready to make a change?

Go to Diet Analysis Plus and from the Reports tab and then under the Nutrient heading select Intake vs. Goals and choose all 3 days in your diet record. What is your protein intake level? If it is low, create an alternative Profile and substitute one 250 mL glass of skim or low-fat milk (or Milk Alternative, such as a soy beverage) at two meals (or one meal and one snack). What is the effect on your protein intake?

Analyze Your Protein Intake

The purpose of this exercise is to make you aware of the effects of choosing protein-rich foods in balancing the three energy-yielding nutrients while planning a nutritious diet.

1. Do you take in adequate protein? From the DA+ Home page, select Reports tab, then under the Nutrients heading select Macronutrient Ranges, choose Day Three (include all meals), and generate a report. What percentage of your caloric intake consists of protein? Is your intake within the recommended 10 to 35 percent of total energy intake range, as recommended by the DRI reports? If your intake is lower than 10 percent of calories, what foods would you add to your eating pattern to meet your protein need? If your protein intake is higher than 35 percent, what foods could you choose less often to bring you within range?

2. From the Reports tab, under the Nutrients heading select Intake vs. Goals, choose Day Two (include all meals) and generate a report. Did your protein gram values fall in line with your DRI recommended intake? [see Table 6–1 (page 208) and multiply your weight in kilograms by 0.8 gram as demonstrated in the Margin Note on page 208]

3. Which foods in your meals provide the greatest amounts of protein? From the Reports tab under the Advanced Analysis heading select Source Analysis, choose all meals for Day 2, select Protein from the drop-down pick-list, and then generate a report. This report will help you determine your protein sources; for example, see the food items with a silver star (Good Source) or a gold star (Excellent Source) for some high-quality protein sources.

4. Using the same report and date from the previous question, break it down further to see how many grams of protein you eat for each meal: breakfast, lunch, dinner, and snacks.

5. Using the Controversy section (especially Figure C6–1 page 239) create a vegetarian or vegan meal that provides one-third of the daily requirement for protein for a 19-year-old female vegan (~ 15 of 45g/day?). Select the Track Diet tab and input the foods in a meal for a separate day; then under the Advanced heading select Source Analysis and Protein from the drop-down pick-list. How successful were you in achieving about 15 grams of protein in the meal? If the meal fell short of the goal, what other vegetarian or vegan foods can you change or add to the meal to more closely match this person's protein need?

Endnotes

1. Standing Committee on the Scientific Evaluation of Dietary Reference Intakes, Food and Nutrition Board, Institute of Medicine, *Dietary Reference Intakes for Energy, Carbohydrate, Fiber, Fat, Fatty Acids, Cholesterol, Protein, and Amino Acids* (Washington, D.C.: National Academies Press, 2002), pp. 10-2–10-3.

2. Standing Committee on the Scientific Evaluation of Dietary Reference Intakes, Food and Nutrition Board, Institute of Medicine, 2002, pp. 10-5–10-6 [see reference 1]; M. A. McNurlan and P. J. Garlick, Protein synthesis and degradation, in M. H. Stipanuk, ed., *Biochemical and Physiological Aspects of Human Nutrition* (Philadelphia, PA: Saunders, 2000), pp. 211–232.

3. A. Tomer and coauthors, Thrombogenesis in sickle cell disease, *Journal of Laboratory and Clinical Medicine* 137 (2001): 398–407; S. T. Miller and coauthors, Prediction of adverse outcomes in children with sickle cell disease, *New England Journal of Medicine* 342 (2000): 83–89.

4. R. N. Kulkarni and C. R. Kahn, HNFs—linking the liver and pancreatic islets in diabetes, *Science* 303 (2004): 1311–1312; N. Moustaid-Moussa and C. D. Berdanier, *Nutrient-Gene Interactions in Health and Disease* (Boca Raton, FL: CRC Press, 2001).

5. M. J. Koury and P. Ponka, New insights into erythropoiesis: The roles of folate, vitamin B_{12}, and iron, *Annual Review of Nutrition* 24 (2004): 105–131.

6. B. R. Stevens, Digestion and absorption of protein, in M. H. Stipanuk, ed., *Biochemical and Physiological Aspects of Human Nutrition* (Philadelphia, PA: Saunders, 2000), pp. 121–122.

7. T. R. Ziegler and coauthors, Trophic and cytoprotective nutrition for intestinal adaptation, mucosal repair, and barrier function, *Annual Review of Nutrition* 23 (2003): 229–261.

8. Standing Committee on the Scientific Evaluation of Dietary Reference Intakes, Food and Nutrition Board, Institute of Medicine 2002, pp. 10–13 [see reference 1].

9. Standing Committee on the Scientific Evaluation of Dietary Reference Intakes, Food and Nutrition Board, Institute of Medicine 2002, pp. 10–14 [see reference 1]; M. A. McNurlan and P. J. Garlick, Protein synthesis and degradation, in M. H. Stipanuk, ed., *Biochemical and Physiological Aspects of Human Nutrition* (Philadelphia: Saunders, 2000), p. 306.

10. Position of the American Dietetic Association and Dietitians of Canada: Vegetarian diets, *Journal of the American Dietetic Association* 103 (2003): 748–765.

11. W. M. Rand, P. L. Pellett, and V. R. Young, Meta-analysis of nitrogen balance studies for estimating protein requirements in healthy adults, *American Journal of Clinical Nutrition* 77 (2003): 109–127.

12. L. D. Plank and G. L. Hill, Energy balance in critical illness, *Proceedings of the Nutrition Society* 62 (2003): 545–552.

13. J. L. McCrory and coauthors, Locomotion in simulated microgravity: Gravity replacement loads, *Aviation, Space, and Environmental Medicine* 73 (2002): 625–631.

14. B. Woodward, Protein, calories, and immune defenses, *Nutrition Reviews* 56 (1998): S84–S92.

15. L. Combaret, D. Taillandier, and D. Attaix, Nutritional and hormonal control of protein breakdown, *American Journal of Kidney Diseases* 37 (2001): S108–S111.

16. S. M. Day and D. H. DeHeer, Reversal of the detrimental effects of chronic protein malnutrition on long bone fracture healing, *Journal of Orthopaedic Trauma* 15 (2001): 47–53.

17. M. Reid and coauthors, The acute-phase protein response to infection in edematous and nonedematous protein-energy malnutrition, *American Journal Clinical Nutrition* 76 (2002): 1409–1415.

18. V. Scherbaum and P. Furst, New concepts on nutritional management of severe malnutrition: The role of protein, *Current Opinion in Clinical Nutrition and Metabolic Care* 3 (2000): 31–38.

19. S. M. Grantham-McGregor, S. P. Walker, and S. Chang, Nutritional deficiencies and later behavioral development, *Proceedings of the Nutrition Society* 59 (2000): 47–54.

20. T. Liu and coauthors, Kwashiorkor in the United States: Fad diets, perceived and true milk allergy, and nutritional ignorance, *Archives of Dermatology* 137 (2001): 630–636; N. F. Carvalho and coauthors, Severe nutritional deficiencies in toddlers resulting from health food milk alternatives (electronic article), *Pediatrics* 107 (2001): E46.

21. Position of the American Dietetic Association and Dietitians of Canada: Nutrition intervention in the care of persons with human immunodeficiency virus infection, *Journal of the American Dietetic Association* 100 (2000): 708–717.

22. Canadian Association of Food Banks, Hunger Count 2012, available at http://www .foodbankscanada.ca/getmedia/3b946e67-fbe2-490e-90dc-4a313dfb97e5/HungerCount2012. pdf.aspx.

23. B. A. Underwood and S. Smitasiri, Micronutrient malnutrition: Policies and programs for control and their implications, *Annual Review of Nutrition* 19: 303–324; C. G. Victora and coauthors, Potential interventions for the prevention of childhood pneumonia in developing countries: Improving nutrition, *American Journal of Clinical Nutrition* 70 (1999): 309–320.

24. A. Trichopoulou and coauthors, Lipid, protein and carbohydrate intake in relation to body mass index, *European Journal of Clinical Nutrition* 56 (2002): 37–43.

25. S. Tonstad, K. Smerud, and L. Hoie, A comparison of the effects of 2 doses of soy protein or casein on serum lipids, serum lipoproteins, and plasma total homocysteine in hypercholesterolemic subjects, *American Journal of Clinical Nutrition* 76: 78–84.

26. E. L. Knight and coauthors, The impact of protein intake on renal function decline in women with normal or mild renal insufficiency, *Annals of Internal Medicine* 138 (2003): 460–467.

27. B. Dawson-Hughes and S. S. Harris, Calcium intake influences the association of protein intake with rates of bone loss in elderly men and women, *American Journal of Clinical Nutrition* 75 (2002): 773–779.

28. D. Garriguet, Nutrition Findings from the Canadian Community Health Survey—Overview of Canadians' Eating Habits 2004, available at http://www.statcan.gc.ca/pub/82-620-m/82-620-m2006002-eng.pdf.

29. S. T. St. Jeor and coauthors, Dietary protein and weight reduction, *Circulation* 104 (2001): 1869–1874.

Consumer Corner 6

1. H. Moriwaki and coauthors, Branched-chain amino acids as a protein- and energy-source in liver cirrhosis, *Biochemical and Biophysical Research Communications* 313 (2004): 405–409; M. A. Choudhry and coauthors, Enteral nutritional supplementation prevents mesenteric lymph node T-cell suppression in burn injury, *Critical Care Medicine* 31 (2003): 1764–1770; G. S. Sacks, L. Genton, and K. A. Kudsk, Controversy of immunonutrition for surgical critical-illness patients, *Current Opinion in Critical Care* 9 (2003): 300–305.

2. U. Suchner, D. K. Heyland, and K. Peter, Immune-modulatory actions of arginine in the critically ill, *British Journal of Nutrition* 87 (2002): S121–S132.

3. J. Hernandez-Rodriguez and G. Manjarrez-Guitierrez, Macronutrients and neurotransmitter formation during brain development, *Nutrition Reviews* 59 (2001): S49–S59.

4. Standing Committee on the Scientific Evaluation of Dietary Reference Intakes, Food and Nutrition Board, Institute of Medicine, *Dietary Reference Intakes for Energy, Carbohydrate, Fiber, Fat, Fatty Acids, Cholesterol, Protein, and Amino Acids* (Washington, D.C.: National Academies Press, 2002), pp. 10-105–10-106.

5. Impurities confirmed in dietary supplement 5-hydroxy-L-tryptophan, FDA Talk Paper, August 1998, available from Food and Drug Administration, U.S. Department of Health and Human Services, Public Health Service, 5600 Fishers Lane, Rockville, MD 20857; Medline Plus. 5-HTP. May 2011, available at http://www .nlm.nih.gov/medlineplus/druginfo/natural/794.html.

6. T. L. Schwenk and C. D. Costley, When food becomes a drug: Nonanabolic nutritional supplement use in athletes, *American Journal of Sports Medicine* 30 (2002): 907–916.

7. P. Garlick, Assessment of the safety of glutamine and other amino acids, *Journal of Nutrition* 131 (2001): S2556–S2561.

Controversy 6

1. P. N. Singh, J. Sabate, and G. E. Fraser, Does low meat consumption increase life expectancy in humans? *American Journal of Clinical Nutrition* 78 (2003): 526S–532S.

2. S. I. Barr and G. E. Chapman, Perceptions and practices of self-defined current vegetarian, former vegetarian, and nonvegetarian women, *Journal of the American Dietetic Association* 102 (2002): 354–360; R. Weinsier, Use of the term vegetarian, *American Journal of Clinical Nutrition* 71 (2000): 1211–1212; S. I. Barr and C. A. Rideout, Nutritional considerations for vegetarian athletes, *Nutrition* 20 (2004): 696–703.

3. Position of the American Dietetic Association and Dietitians of Canada: Vegetarian diets, *Journal of the American Dietetic Association* 103 (2003): 748–765; U.S. Department of Agriculture and U.S. Department of Health and Human Services, *Dietary Guidelines for Americans*, 2010, available at http://www.health.gov/dietaryguidelines/2010.asp; W. J. Craig and A. R. Mangels, Position of the American Dietetic Association: Vegetarian diets, *Journal of the American Dietetic Association* 109 (2009): 1266–1282.

4. E. H. Haddad and J. S. Tanzman, What do vegetarians in the United States eat? *American Journal of Clinical Nutrition* 78 (2003): 626S–632S; N. Brathwaite and coauthors, Obesity, diabetes, hypertension, and vegetarian status among Seventh-Day Adventists in Barbados: Preliminary results, *Ethnicity and Disease* 13 (2003): 34–39; J. Sabante, The contribution of vegetarian diets to health and disease: A paradigm shift? *American Journal of Clinical Nutrition* 78 (2003): 502S–507S.

5. G. E. Fraser, Associations between diet and cancer, ischemic heart disease, and all-cause mortality in non-Hispanic white California Seventh-Day Adventists, *American Journal of Clinical Nutrition* 70 (1999): 532S–538S; P. N. Appleby and coauthors, The Oxford Vegetarian Study: An overview, *American Journal of Clinical Nutrition* 70 (1999): 525S–531S.

6. F. B. Hu, Plant-based foods and prevention of cardiovascular disease: An overview, *American Journal of Clinical Nutrition* 78 (2003): 544S–551S.

7. *Expert Panel on Detection, Evaluation, and Treatment of High Blood Cholesterol in Adults (Adult Treatment Panel III)*, Third Report of the National Cholesterol Education Program (NCEP) NIH publication no. 02-5215 (Bethesda, MD: National Heart, Lung, and Blood Institute, 2002).

8. Appleby and coauthors, 1999 [see reference 5].

9. C. D. Gardner and coauthors, The effect of soy protein with or without isoflavones relative to milk protein on plasma lipids in hypercholesterolemic post-menopausal women, *American Journal of Clinical Nutrition* 73 (2001): 667–668.

10. E. L. Ashton, F. S. Dalais, and M. J. Ball, Effect of meat replacement by tofu on CHD risk factors including copper induced LDL oxidation, *Journal of the American College of Nutrition* 19 (2000): 761–767.

11. L. J. Appel, The effects of protein intake on blood pressure and cardiovascular disease, *Current Opinion in Lipidology* 14 (2003): 55–59; T. B. Clarkson, Soy, soy phyto-estrogens, and cardiovascular disease, *Journal of Nutrition* 132 (2002): 566S–569S; S. Tonstad, K. Smerud, and L. Hoie, A comparison of the effects of 2 doses of soy protein or casein on serum lipids, serum lipoproteins, and plasma total homocysteine in hypercholesterolemic subjects, *American Journal of Clinical Nutrition* 76 (2002): 78–84.

12. M. R. Adams and coauthors, The inhibitory effect of soy protein isolate on atherosclerosis in mice does not require the presence of LDL receptors or alteration of plasma lipoproteins, *Journal of Nutrition* 132 (2002): 43–49.

13. Clarkson, 2002 [see reference 11].

14. M. Messina, C. Gardner, and S. Barnes, Gaining insight into the health effects of soy but a long way still to go: Commentary on the Fourth International Symposium on the Role of Soy in Preventing and Treating Chronic Disease, *Journal of Nutrition* 132 (2002): 547S–551S; S. R. Teixeira and coauthors, Effects of feeding 4 levels of soy protein for 3 and 6 wk on blood lipids and apoliproproteins in moderately hypercholesterolemic men, *American Journal of Clinical Nutrition* 71 (2000): 1077–1084.

15. Clarkson, 2002 [see reference 11].

16. D. J. Jenkins and coauthors, High-protein diets in hyperlipidemia: Effect of wheat gluten on serum lipids, uric acid, and renal function, *American Journal of Clinical Nutrition* 74 (2001): 57–63.

17. Gardner and coauthors, 2001 [see reference 9]; M. Pfeuffer and J. Schrezenmeir, Bioactive substances in milk with properties decreasing risk of cardiovascular diseases, *British Journal of Nutrition* 84 (2000): S155–S159.

18. D. A. Lieberman and coauthors, Risk factors for advanced colonic neoplasia and hyperplastic polyps in asymptomatic individuals, *Journal of the American Medical Association* 290 (2003): 2959–2967.

19. E. Giovannucci, Modifiable risk factors for colon cancer, *Gastroenterology Clinics of North America* 31 (2002): 925–943.

20. C. Van Der Meer-Van Kraaij and coauthors, Mucosal pentraxin (Mptx), a novel rat gene 10-fold down-regulated in colon by dietary heme, *The Federation of American Societies for Experimental Biology* 17 (2003): 1277–1285; A. R. Eynard and C. B. Lopez, Conjugated linoleic acid (CLA) versus saturated fats/cholesterol: Their proportion in fatty and lean meats may affect the risk of developing colon cancer, *Lipids in Health and Disease* 2 (2003): 6; F. Pierre and coauthors, Meat and cancer: Haemoglobin and haemin in a low calcium diet promote colorectal carcinogenesis at the aberrant crypt state in rats, *Carcinogenesis* 24 (2003): 1683–1690.

21. H. Chen and coauthors, Dietary patterns and adenocarcinoma of the esophagus and distal stomach, *American Journal of Clinical Nutrition* 75 (2002): 137–144.

22. Lieberman and coauthors, 2003 [see reference 18].

23. Lieberman and coauthors, 2003 [see reference 18].

24. E. Gonzalez de Mejia, T. Bradford, and C. Hasler, The anticarcinogenic potential of soybean lectin and lunasin, *Nutrition Reviews* 61 (2003): 239–246; W. H. Xu and coauthors, Soya food intake and risk of endometrial cancer among Chinese women in Shanghai: Population based case-control study, *British Medical Journal* 328 (2004): 1285–1288; E. Riboli and T. Norat, Epidemiologic evidence of the protective effect of fruit and vegetables on cancer risk, *American Journal of Clinical Nutrition* 78 (2003): 559S–569S; C. C. Yeh and coauthors, Risk factors for colorectal cancer in Taiwan: A hospital-based case control study, *Journal of the Formosan Medical Association* 102 (2003): 305–312; Giovannucci, 2002 [see reference 19].

25. S. P. Stabler and R. H. Allen, Vitamin B_{12} deficiency as a worldwide problem, *Annual Review of Nutrition* 24 (2004): 299–326.

26. A. C. Antony, Vegetarianism and vitamin B-12 (cobalamin) deficiency, *American Journal of Clinical Nutrition* 78 (2003): 3–6; W. Herrmann and coauthors, Vitamin B-12 status, particularly holotranscobalamin II and methylmalonic acid concentrations, and hyperhomocysteinemia in vegetarians, *American Journal of Clinical Nutrition* 78 (2003): 131–136.

27. Neurologic impairment in children associated with maternal dietary deficiency of cobalamin—Georgia, 2001, *Morbidity and Mortality Weekly Reports* 52 (2003): 61–64.

28. M. Hebbelinck, P. Clarys, and A. DeMalsche, Growth, development, and physical fitness of Flemish vegetarian children, adolescents, young adults, *American Journal of Clinical Nutrition* 70 (1999): 579S–585S.

29. Position of the American Dietetic Association and Dietitians of Canada, 2003 [see reference 3].

30. Position of the American Dietetic Association and Dietitians of Canada, 2003 [see reference 3].

31. M. van Dusseldorp and coauthors, Risk of persistent cobalamin deficiency in adolescents fed a macrobiotic diet in early life, *American Journal of Clinical Nutrition* 69 (1999): 664–671.

32. V. Messina and A. R. Mangels, Considerations in planning vegan diets: Children, *Journal of the American Dietetic Association* 101 (2001): 661–669.

33. C. L. Perry and coauthors, Adolescent vegetarians: How well do their dietary patterns meet the Healthy People 2010 objectives? *Archives of Pediatrics and Adolescent Medicine* 156 (2002): 431–437.

34. C. A. Venti and C. S. Johnston, Modified food guide pyramid for lactovegetarians and vegans, *Journal of Nutrition* 132 (2002): 1050–1054; Messina and Mangels, 2001 [see reference 32]; T. J. Parsons and coauthors, Are levels of bone turnover related to lower bone mass of adolescents previously fed a macrobiotic diet? *Experimental and Clinical Endocrinology and Diabetes* 109 (2001): 288–293.

35. M. W. Louwman and coauthors, Signs of impaired cognitive function in adolescents with marginal cobalamin status, *American Journal of Clinical Nutrition* 72 (2000): 762–769.

36. D. Milea, N. Cassoux, and P. LeHoang, Blindness in a strict vegan, *New England Journal of Medicine* 342 (2000): 897–898.

37. C. L. Perry and coauthors, Characteristics of vegetarian adolescents in a multiethnic urban population, *Journal of Adolescent Health* 29 (2001): 406–416; Y. Martins, P. Pliner, and R. O'Connor, Restrained eating among vegetarians: Does a vegetarian eating style mask concerns about weight? *Appetite* 32 (1999): 145–154.

38. S. A. Klopp, C. J. Heiss, and H. S. Smith, Self-reported vegetarianism may be a marker for college women at risk for disordered eating, *Journal of the American Dietetic Association* 103 (2003): 745–747.

39. Venti and Johnston, 2002 [see reference 34]; Messina and Mangels, 2001 [see reference 32].

40. Position of the American Dietetic Association and Dietitians of Canada, 2003 [see reference 3].

41. J. R. Hunt, Moving toward a plant-based diet: Are iron and zinc at risk? *Nutrition Reviews* 60 (2002): 127–134.

42. J. R. Hunt and Z. K. Roughead, Nonheme-iron absorption, fecal ferritin excretion, and blood indexes of iron status in women consuming controlled lactoovovegetarian diets for 8 wk, *American Journal of Clinical Nutrition* 69 (1999): 944–952.

43. J. Kandiah, Impact of tofu or tofu + orange juice on hematological indices of lacto-ovo vegetarian females, *Plant Foods for Human Nutrition* 57 (2002): 197–204.

44. C. L. Larsson and G. K. Johansson, Dietary intake and nutritional status of young vegans and omnivores in Sweden, *American Journal of Clinical Nutrition* 76 (2002): 100–106; M. J. Ball and M. A. Bartlett, Dietary intake and iron status of Australian vegetarian women, *American Journal of Clinical Nutrition* 70 (1999): 353–358.

45. Hunt, 2002 [see reference 41].

46. Milea, Cassoux, and LeHoang, 2000 [see reference 36].

47. T. A. Outila and coauthors, Dietary intake of vitamin D in premenopausal, healthy vegans was insufficient to maintain concentrations of serum 25-hydroxyvitamin D and intact parathyroid hormone within normal ranges during the winter in Finland, *Journal of the American Dietetic Association* 100 (2000): 434–441.

48. C. M. Oomen and coauthors, a-Linolenic acid intake is not beneficially associated with 10-y risk of coronary artery disease incidence: The Zutphen Elderly Study, *American Journal of Clinical Nutrition* 74 (2001): 457–463.

49. W. E. Connor, n-3 Fatty acids from fish and fish oil: Panacea or nostrum? (editorial), *American Journal of Clinical Nutrition* 74 (2001): 415–416.

50. V. Messina, V. Melina, and A. R. Mangels, A new food guide for North American vegetarians, *Journal of the American Dietetic Association* 103 (2003): 771–775; Venti and Johnston, 2002 [see reference 34]; E. H. Haddad, J. Sabate, and C. G. Whitten, Vegetarian food guide pyramid: A conceptual framework, *American Journal of Clinical Nutrition* 70 (1999): 615S–619S.

51. V. Messina, M. Vesanto, and A. Reed Mangels, A new food guide for North American vegetarians, *Canadian Journal of Dietetic Practice and Research* 64 (2003): 82–86.

7 The Vitamins

Do You Ever . . .

Wonder how vitamins work in the body?

Associate sunshine with good health?

Take vitamin C tablets to ward off a cold?

Eat highly fortified foods or "meal replacers," regarding them as a harmless form of vitamin insurance?

Keep Reading . . .

© sarsmis/Shutterstock

Learning Objectives

After completing this chapter, you should be able to

LO 7.1 List the fat-soluble and water-soluble vitamins, and describe how solubility affects the absorption, transport, and excretion of each type.

LO 7.2 Explain how vitamins and minerals work in combination to maintain the health of the bones.

LO 7.3 Define the term *antioxidant*, and name the vitamins that act as antioxidants in the body.

LO 7.4 Discuss the roles of B vitamins in body tissues, and explain in a general way how B vitamins assist with energy metabolism.

LO 7.5 Suggest ways that foods can be prepared and stored to minimize the loss of vitamins.

LO 7.6 Suggest foods that can help to ensure adequate vitamin intakes without providing too many Calories.

LO 7.7 Justify this statement: "It is better to get vitamins from food than from supplements."

LO 7.8 List some valid reasons why supplements may be required by some people.

Contents

At the beginning of the 20th century, the thrill of the discovery of the first **vitamins** captured the world's imagination as seemingly miraculous cures took place. In the usual scenario, a whole group of people were unable to walk (or were going blind or bleeding profusely) until an alert scientist stumbled onto the substance missing from their diets. The scientist confirmed the discovery by feeding vitamin-deficient food to laboratory animals, which responded by becoming unable to walk (or going blind or bleeding profusely). When the missing ingredient was restored to their diet, they soon recovered. People, too, were quickly cured when they received the vitamins they lacked.

In the following decades, advances in chemistry and biology allowed scientists to isolate the vitamins and define their chemical structures. More scientific advances brought an understanding of the biological roles that vitamins play in maintaining health and preventing deficiency diseases. Today, research hints that two of the major scourges of humankind, cardiovascular disease (CVD) and cancer, may be linked with low intakes of vitamins. Respected thinkers in genetics suspect that chronic deficiencies of vitamins and minerals may be major contributors to genetic damage that can lead to cancer (others suspect that some vitamin excesses may do the same thing).*,1 Can it be that foods rich in vitamins will protect us from life-threatening diseases? What about vitamin pills? For now, we can say only this with certainty: the only disease a vitamin will *cure* is the one caused by a deficiency of that vitamin. As for chronic disease *prevention*, the evidence is

The Maximum Daily Dose (MDD) specified by the Natural Health Products Directorate for single-ingredient vitamin supplements in this chapter (and minerals in the next chapter) will be shown in the margin of each section where these nutrients are discussed.

- The only disease a vitamin can cure is the one caused by a deficiency of that vitamin.

- The DRI recommended levels for vitamin intakes are found on the inside front cover.

vitamins organic compounds that are vital to life and indispensable to body functions but are needed only in minute amounts; noncaloric essential nutrients.

*References are listed at the end of the chapter.

Table 7–1

Vitamin Names[a]

Fat-Soluble Vitamins

Vitamin A
Vitamin D
Vitamin E
Vitamin K

Water-Soluble Vitamins

B vitamins
   Thiamin (B_1)
   Riboflavin (B_2)
   Niacin (B_3)
   Folate
   Vitamin B_{12}
   Vitamin B_6
   Biotin
   Pantothenic acid
Vitamin C

[a]Vitamin names established by the International Union of Nutritional Sciences Committee on Nomenclature. Other names are listed in Tables 7–3 and 7–4 (pages 281–282 and 282–285).

Vitamins fall into two classes—fat soluble and water soluble.

Definition and Classification of Vitamins

A child once defined a vitamin as "what, if you don't eat, you get sick." Although the grammar left something to be desired, the definition was accurate. Less imaginatively, a vitamin is defined as an essential, noncaloric, organic nutrient needed in tiny amounts in the diet. The role of many vitamins is to help make possible the processes by which other nutrients are digested, absorbed, and metabolized or built into body structures. Although small in size and quantity, the vitamins accomplish mighty tasks.

As they were discovered, the vitamins were named, and many were also given letters and numbers. This led to the confusing variety of vitamin names that still exists today. This chapter uses the names in Table 7–1; alternative names are given in Tables 7–3 and 7–4 (pages 281–282 and 282–285).

Certain vitamins occur in foods in a form known as **precursors**, or **provitamins**. Once inside the body, these are transformed chemically to one or more active vitamin forms. Thus, to measure the amount of a vitamin found in food, we often must count not only the amount of the true vitamin but also the vitamin activity potentially available from its precursors. Tables 7–3 and 7–4 specify which vitamins have precursors.

The vitamins fall naturally into two classes: fat soluble and water soluble (listed in Table 7–1). Solubility confers on vitamins many of their characteristics. It determines how they are absorbed into and transported around by the bloodstream, whether they can be stored in the body, and how easily they are lost from the body. In general, like other lipids, fat-soluble vitamins are absorbed into the lymph, and they travel in the blood in association with protein carriers. Fat-soluble vitamins can be stored in the liver or with other lipids in fatty tissues, and some can build up to toxic concentrations. The water-soluble vitamins are absorbed directly into the bloodstream, where they travel freely. Most are not stored in tissues to any great extent; rather, excesses are excreted in the urine. Thus, the risks of immediate toxicities are not as great as for fat-soluble vitamins. This chapter examines the fat-soluble vitamins first and then the water-soluble ones. The tables at the end of the chapter sum up the basic facts about all of them.

KEY POINT

- Vitamins are essential, noncaloric nutrients that are needed in tiny amounts in the diet and help drive cell processes in the body. The fat-soluble vitamins are vitamins A, D, E, and K; the water-soluble vitamins are vitamin C and the B vitamins.

The Fat-Soluble Vitamins

The fat-soluble vitamins—A, D, E, and K—are found in the fats and oils of foods and require bile for absorption. Once absorbed, these vitamins are stored in the liver and fatty tissues until the body needs them. The body can survive weeks of consuming foods that lack these vitamins as long as the diet as a whole provides *average* amounts that approximate the recommended intakes. This capacity to be stored also sets the stage for toxic buildup if you take in too much. Excesses of vitamins A and D from supplements can reach toxic levels especially easily.

Look back at Figure 5–6 (page 168) of Chapter 5 to see how bile acts in fat absorption.

Deficiencies of the fat-soluble vitamins are likely when the diet is consistently low in them. We also know that any disease that produces fat malabsorption (such as liver disease that prevents bile production) can cause the loss of vitamins dissolved in undigested fat and so bring about deficiencies. In the same way, a person who uses mineral oil (which the body can't absorb) as a laxative risks losing fat-soluble

Characteristics Fat-Soluble Vitamins Share

- Dissolve in lipid
- Require bile for absorption
- Are stored in tissues
- May be toxic in excess

precursors, provitamins compounds that can be converted into active vitamins.

vitamins because they dissolve in the oil and are excreted. Deficiencies are also likely when people eat diets that are extraordinarily low in fat because such diets interfere with absorption of these vitamins.

Fat-soluble vitamins play diverse roles in the body. Vitamins A and D may act somewhat like hormones, directing cells to convert one substance to another, to store this, or to release that. Many of their effects are exerted at the level of the genes, influencing protein production.[2] Vitamin E flows throughout the body, preventing oxidative destruction of tissues. Vitamin K is necessary for blood to clot. Each is worth a book in itself.

Vitamin A

Vitamin A has the distinction of being the first fat-soluble vitamin to be recognized. Today, after a century of research, preformed vitamin A (e.g., retinol) and its plant-derived precursor, **beta-carotene**, are still very much a focus of research.

Three forms of vitamin A are active in the body; one of the active forms, **retinol**, is stored in the liver. The liver makes retinol available to the bloodstream and thereby to the body's cells. The cells convert retinol to its other two active forms, retinal and retinoic acid, as needed.

A Jack of All Trades—Vitamin A   Vitamin A is a versatile vitamin, with roles in gene expression, vision, maintenance of body linings and skin, immune defences, growth of bones and of the body, and normal development of cells. It is of critical importance for reproduction.[3] In short, vitamin A is needed everywhere (its chief roles/functions in the body are listed in this chapter in Snapshot 7–1 on page 252 and in Table 7–3 on pages 281–282).

Regulation of Gene Expression   Vitamin A exerts considerable influence on body functions through its regulation of the activities of the genes.[4] Genes direct the synthesis of proteins, including enzymes, and enzymes perform the metabolic work

> Chapter 6 describes gene expression, protein synthesis, and the work of proteins within the body.

of the tissues (see Chapter 6). Hence, factors that influence gene expression also affect the metabolic activities of the tissues and the health of the body. Hundreds of genes have been suggested as regulatory targets of the retinoic acid form of vitamin A.[5]

Researchers have long known that simply possessing the genetic equipment needed to make a particular protein does not guarantee that the protein will be produced, any more than owning a car guarantees you a trip across town. To get the car rolling, you must also use the right key to trigger the events that start up its engine or turn it off at the appropriate time. Some dietary components, including the retinoic acid form of vitamin A, are now known to be such keys—they help activate or deactivate certain genes and thus affect the production of specific proteins.[6]

Eyesight   The most familiar function of vitamin A, however, is in eyesight. Vitamin A plays two indispensable roles: in the process of light perception at the **retina** and in the maintenance of a healthy, crystal-clear outer window, the **cornea** (see the margin drawing).

When light falls on the eye, it passes through the clear cornea and strikes the cells of the retina, bleaching many molecules of the pigment **rhodopsin** contained within those cells. Vitamin A is a part of the rhodopsin molecule. When bleaching occurs, the vitamin is broken off, initiating the signal that conveys the sensation of sight to the optic centre in the brain. The vitamin then reunites with the pigment, but a little vitamin A is destroyed each time this reaction takes place, and fresh vitamin A must regenerate the supply. If the supply begins to run low, a lag occurs before the eye can see again after a flash of bright light at night (see Figure 7–1). This lag in the recovery of night vision, termed **night blindness**, may indicate a vitamin A deficiency. A bright flash of light can temporarily blind even normal, well-nourished eyes, but if you experience a long recovery period before vision returns, your health-care provider may want to check your vitamin A intake.

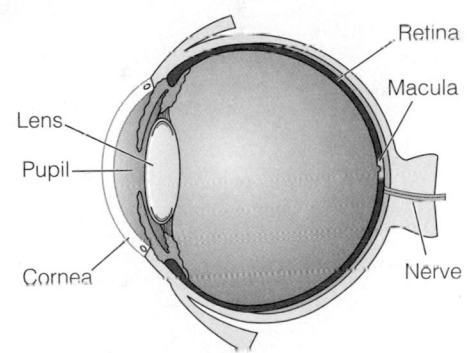

An eye (sectioned)

beta-carotene an orange pigment with antioxidant activity; a vitamin A precursor made by plants and stored in human fat tissue.

retinol one of the active forms of vitamin A made from beta-carotene in animal and human bodies; an antioxidant nutrient. Other active forms are *retinal* and *retinoic acid*.

retina (RET-in-uh) the layer of light-sensitive nerve cells lining the back of the inside of the eye.

cornea (KOR-nee-uh) the hard, transparent membrane covering the outside of the eye.

rhodopsin (roh-DOP-sin) the light-sensitive pigment of the cells in the retina; it contains vitamin A (*rod* refers to the rod-shaped cells; *opsin* means "visual protein").

night blindness slow recovery of vision after exposure to flashes of bright light at night; an early symptom of vitamin A deficiency.

Figure 7–1
Night Blindness

This is one of the earliest signs of vitamin A deficiency.

In dim light, you can make out the details of this room.

A flash of bright light momentarily blinds you as the pigment in the retina is bleached.

You quickly recover and can see the details again in a few seconds.

With inadequate vitamin A, you do not recover but remain blind for many seconds; this is night blindness.

A more profound deficiency of vitamin A is exhibited when the protein **keratin** accumulates and clouds the eye's outer vitamin A–dependent part, the cornea. The condition is known as **keratinization**, and if the deficiency of vitamin A is not corrected, it can worsen to **xerosis** (drying) and then progress to thickening and permanent blindness, **xerophthalmia**. Tragically, a half million of the world's vitamin A-deprived children become blind each year from this often preventable condition. If the deficiency is discovered early, capsules providing 60,000 micrograms of vitamin A taken twice each year can reverse it. Better still, a child fed fruit and vegetables regularly is virtually ensured of protection.

Skin and Body Linings   Vitamin A is needed by all **epithelial tissue** (external skin and internal linings), not just by the cornea.[7] The skin and all of the protective linings of the lungs, intestines, vagina, urinary tract, and bladder serve as barriers to infection or damage from other sources. An example of vitamin A's work behind the scenes at the genetic level is the process of **cell differentiation**, in which each type of cell develops to perform a specific function.[8] When goblet cells (cells found in linings of the small intestine) mature, for example, they specialize in synthesizing and releasing mucus to protect delicate tissues from toxic particles or bacteria and other microbial invaders.

If vitamin A is deficient, the cell differentiation and maturing process is impaired. Goblet cells, among others, fail to mature, then fail to make protective mucus, and eventually die off. Some of the cells in these areas are displaced by cells that secrete keratin, the protein mentioned earlier. Keratin is the same protein that provides toughness in hair and fingernails, but in the wrong place, like the skin, keratin makes the tissue surfaces dry, hard, and cracked. As dead cells accumulate on the surface, the tissue becomes vulnerable to infection (see Figure 7–2). In the cornea, keratinization leads to xerophthalmia; in the lungs, the displacement of mucus-producing cells makes respiratory infections likely; in the vagina, the same process leads to vaginal infections.

The process of cell differentiation also has links to cancer. Cancer researchers are investigating the roles of retinoic acid in regulating genes that control cell differentiation because such genes may suppress or even reverse malignant cell changes leading to cancer.[9]

Immunity   Vitamin A has gained a reputation as an "anti-infective" vitamin because so many of the body's defences against infection depend on an adequate supply. Much research supports the need for vitamin A in the regulation of the genes that produce proteins involved in immunity. Without sufficient vitamin A, these genetic interactions produce an altered response to infection that weakens the body's defences against disease.

keratin (KERR-uh-tin) the normal protein of hair and nails.

keratinization accumulation of keratin in a tissue; a sign of vitamin A deficiency.

xerosis (zeer-OH-sis) drying of the cornea; a symptom of vitamin A deficiency.

xerophthalmia (ZEER-ahf-THALL-me-uh) progressive hardening of the cornea of the eye in advanced vitamin A deficiency that can lead to blindness (*xero* means "dry"; *ophthalm* means "eye").

epithelial (ep-ith-THEE-lee-ull) **tissue** the layers of the body that serve as selective barriers to environmental factors. Examples are the cornea, the skin, the respiratory tract lining, and the lining of the digestive tract.

cell differentiation the process by which immature cells are stimulated to mature and gain the ability to perform functions characteristic of their cell type.

Figure 7-2

The Skin in Vitamin A Deficiency

The hard lumps on this person's skin indicate accumulations of keratin in the epithelial cells.

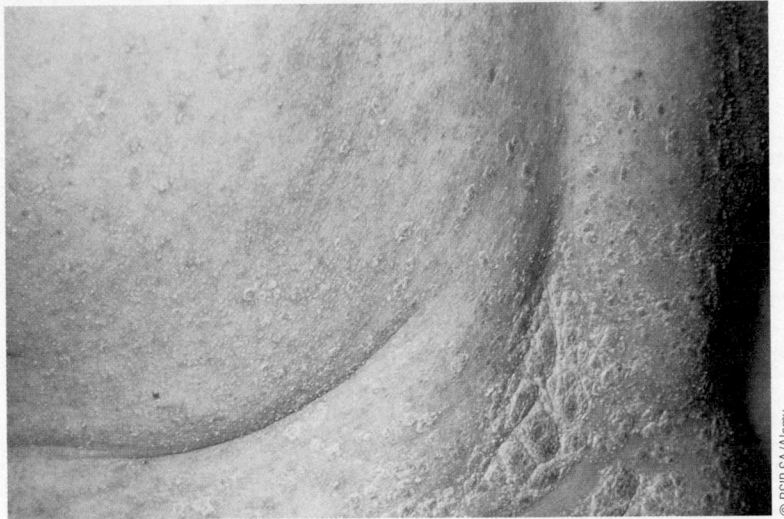

© BSIP SA/Alamy

When the defences are weak, especially in vitamin A-deficient children, an illness such as measles can become severe. A downward spiral of malnutrition and infection can set in. The child's body must devote its scanty store of vitamin A to the immune system's fight against the measles virus, but the infection causes vitamin A to be lost from the body. As vitamin A dwindles, the infection worsens. Even if the child survives the measles infection, blindness is likely. The corneas, already damaged by the chronic vitamin A shortage, degenerate rapidly as the child's meagre supply of vitamin A is diverted to the immune system.

> Using new technologies, researchers are close to developing a vitamin A-rich rice to serve as a staple food for the world's children who lack vitamin A. See the Controversy section of Chapter 12 for details.

Growth   Vitamin A also assists in the growth of bone (and teeth). Normal children's bones grow longer, and the children grow taller, by remodelling each old bone into a new, bigger version. To do so, the body dismantles the old bone structures and replaces them with new, larger bone parts. Growth cannot take place just by adding on to the original small bone; vitamin A is needed in the critical dismantling steps. In children, failure to grow is one of the first signs of poor vitamin A status. Restoring vitamin A to such children is imperative, but correcting dietary deficiencies may be more effective than giving vitamin A supplements alone because other nutrients from nutritious food are also needed for children to gain weight and grow taller.

Vitamin A Deficiency around the World   Vitamin A deficiency presents a vast problem worldwide, placing a heavy burden on society.[10] Between 3 and 10 million of the world's children suffer from signs of severe vitamin A deficiency—not only xerophthalmia and blindness but also diarrhea and reduced food intake that rapidly worsen their condition.[11] A staggering 275 million more children suffer from milder deficiency that impairs immunity and promotes infections. In some areas of the world, vitamin A and other deficiencies seem to be the rule rather than the exception among new mothers and infants.[12]

> World hunger is a topic of Chapter 15.

In countries where children receive vitamin A supplements, childhood death rates have declined by half. Even in the United States, vitamin A supplements are recommended for certain groups of infants and for children with measles. Vitamin

Figure 7–3

Vitamin A Deficiency and Toxicity

Danger lies both above and below a normal range of intakes of vitamin A.

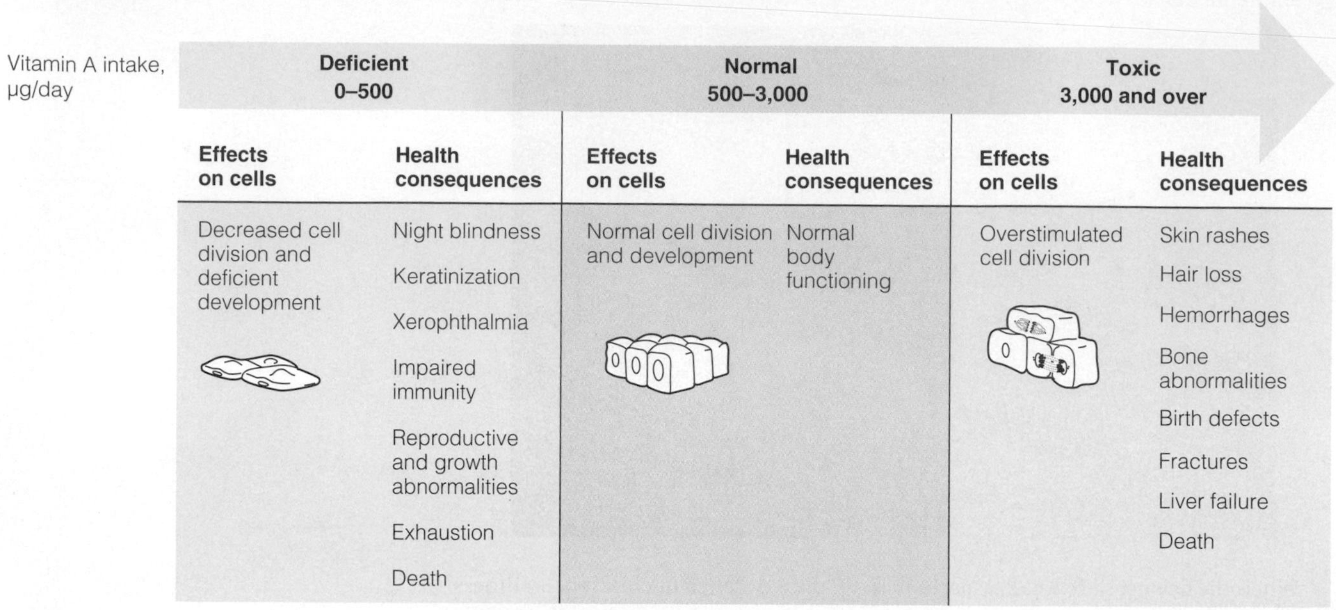

Vitamin A intake, µg/day	Deficient 0–500		Normal 500–3,000		Toxic 3,000 and over	
	Effects on cells	**Health consequences**	**Effects on cells**	**Health consequences**	**Effects on cells**	**Health consequences**
	Decreased cell division and deficient development	Night blindness	Normal cell division and development	Normal body functioning	Overstimulated cell division	Skin rashes
		Keratinization				Hair loss
		Xerophthalmia				Hemorrhages
		Impaired immunity				Bone abnormalities
		Reproductive and growth abnormalities				Birth defects
		Exhaustion				Fractures
		Death				Liver failure
						Death

A supplementation also offers some protection against the complications of other life-threatening infections, including malaria, lung diseases, and HIV.[13] The World Health Organization (WHO) and UNICEF (United Nations International Children's Emergency Fund) are working to eliminate vitamin A deficiency; achieving this goal would improve child survival throughout the developing world.

Vitamin A Toxicity Figure 7–3 shows that toxicity in people who take excess vitamin A in supplements or fortified foods compromises the tissues just as deficiency does and is equally dangerous. The many symptoms of vitamin A toxicity include abdominal pain, hair loss, joint pain, stunted growth, bone and muscle soreness, cessation of menstruation, nausea, diarrhea, rashes, damage to the liver, and enlargement of the spleen. The earliest symptoms of overdoses are loss of appetite, blurred vision, growth failure in children, headache, itching of the skin, and irritability. Over the years, even relatively small excesses may weaken the bones and contribute to hip fractures.[14] Some foods contain substantial amounts of vitamin A (see Table 7–2). Some experts suggest that vitamin A supplements be reserved for treatment of true deficiencies caused by malabsorption or malnutrition.[15]

Pregnant women, especially, should be wary—chronic use of vitamin A supplements providing three to four times the amount recommended for pregnancy and prescription levels of a popular acne medication have caused malformations of the fetus. Even a single massive vitamin A dose (100 times the need) may do so. Children, who often mistake chewable vitamin pills for candy, are also likely to be hurt by vitamin A excesses because they need less and are more sensitive to overdoses. Adolescents may take massive vitamin A doses in the mistaken belief that vitamin A can correct acne. An effective acne medicine, Accutane, is *derived* from vitamin A, but it is chemically altered and given in carefully controlled dosages—vitamin A itself has no effect on acne.

Healthy people can eat foods naturally rich in vitamin A in large amounts without risking toxicity, with the possible exception of liver. When laboratory pigs eat chow made from salmon parts, including the livers, the animals stop growing and fall ill from vitamin A toxicity. Inuit people and Arctic explorers know that polar bear livers are a dangerous food source because the bears eat fish whole with the livers and concentrate large amounts of vitamin A. One ounce of ordinary liver

Table 7–2

Fortification Sources of Vitamin A

Vitamin A from fortified foods and other rich sources can add up. The Tolerable Upper Intake Level (UL) for vitamin A is 3,000 µg/d.

High-potency vitamin pill	3,000 µg
Calf's liver, 30 g cooked	2,300 µg
Regular multivitamin pill	1,500 µg
Chicken liver, 30 g cooked	1,400 µg
"Complete" liquid supplement drink, 1 serving	350–1,500 µg
Cod-liver oil (1 tsp)	1,350 µg
Milk, 1 c	150 µg
Margarine, 1 tsp	55 µg

offers three times the Dietary Reference Intakes (DRI) committee recommended intake of preformed vitamin A along with abundant nutrients of many kinds, and eating it occasionally can boost nutrient status. Daily use invites vitamin A toxicity, however, especially in young children and pregnant women who eat other fortified foods or take supplements.[16]

The effects of excessive vitamin A intakes during pregnancy are discussed in Chapter 13.

Vitamin A Recommendations The ability of vitamin A to be stored in the tissues means that although the vitamin A intake recommendation is given as a daily amount, you need not consume the vitamin every day. An average intake that meets the daily need over several months is sufficient. The amount of vitamin A you need is proportional to your body weight. According to the DRI committee, a man needs a daily average of about 900 micrograms; a woman needs about 700 micrograms. During lactation, her need is higher. Children need less. A regular balanced diet that includes the recommended servings of vegetables and fruit each day supplies more than adequate amounts.

The Canadian and U.S. standard for vitamin A intake is the DRI recommended intake, listed on the inside front cover, page A.

- 1 IU = 0.3 µg retinol

Vitamin A recommendations are expressed in micrograms, but most food tables and supplement labels still express vitamin A contents using a different unit, the **IU (international unit)**. Be careful to notice whether food tables or supplement labels use micrograms or IU. See the Aids to Calculations (Appendix B) for help in converting many kinds of units. When comparing vitamin A in foods, make sure that the amounts are all expressed in the same units.

As for vitamin A supplements, the DRI committee and other nutrition agencies recommend that people avoid taking supplements that exceed the Tolerable Upper Intake Level of 3,000 micrograms [for adults over age 18; also see the margin note for the Maximum Daily Dose (MDD) in single-ingredient supplements sold in Canada]. The best way to ensure a safe intake of vitamin A is to steer clear of supplements and obtain it instead from foods.

- The maximum daily dose (MDD) for single-ingredient supplements for vitamin A is 3,000 µg of RAE*/d.

*Retinol activity equivalents, defined later in this chapter.

Food Sources of Vitamin A Active vitamin A is provided in foods of animal origin. The richest sources are liver and fish oil, but milk and milk products and other fortified foods such as cereals can also be good sources. Even butter and eggs provide some vitamin A to the diet. Plants contain no active vitamin A, but many vegetables and fruit contain the vitamin A precursor, beta-carotene. Snapshot 7–1 is the first of a series of figures that show the nutrient contribution of one Food Guide serving of a sample of foods (for each Food Group) in relation to the DRI Recommendations for young adults along with a few unusual sources of these nutrients in our diet.

The definitive fast-food meal—a hamburger, fries, and cola—lacks vitamin A. Many fast-food restaurants, however, now offer salads with cheese and carrots and other vitamin A–rich foods. These selections greatly improve the nutritional quality of a fast-food meal.

Vitamin A conversion factors are provided in Appendix B.

KEY POINT

- Vitamin A is essential to vision, the integrity of epithelial tissue, bone growth, reproduction, and more. Vitamin A deficiency causes blindness, sickness, and death and is a major problem worldwide. Overdoses are possible and cause many serious symptoms. Foods are preferable to supplements for supplying vitamin A.

Beta-Carotene In plants, vitamin A exists only in its precursor forms. Beta-carotene, the most abundant of these **carotenoid** precursors, has the highest vitamin A activity. The conversion of beta-carotene to retinol in the body entails losses, however, so vitamin A activity for vitamin A precursors is measured in **retinol activity equivalents (RAE)**.[17] It takes about 12 micrograms of beta-carotene from food to supply the equivalent of 1 microgram of retinol to the body.

IU (international unit) a measure of fat-soluble vitamin activity sometimes used on supplement labels.

carotenoid (CARE-oh-ten-oyd) a member of a group of pigments in foods that range in colour from light yellow to reddish orange and are chemical relatives of beta-carotene, many with a degree of vitamin A activity in the body (also defined in Controversy 2).

retinol activity equivalents (RAE) a new measure of the vitamin A activity of beta-carotene and other vitamin A precursors that reflects the amount of retinol that the body will derive from a food containing vitamin A precursor compounds.

Snapshot 7-1 ···⟩ Vitamin A and Beta-Carotene

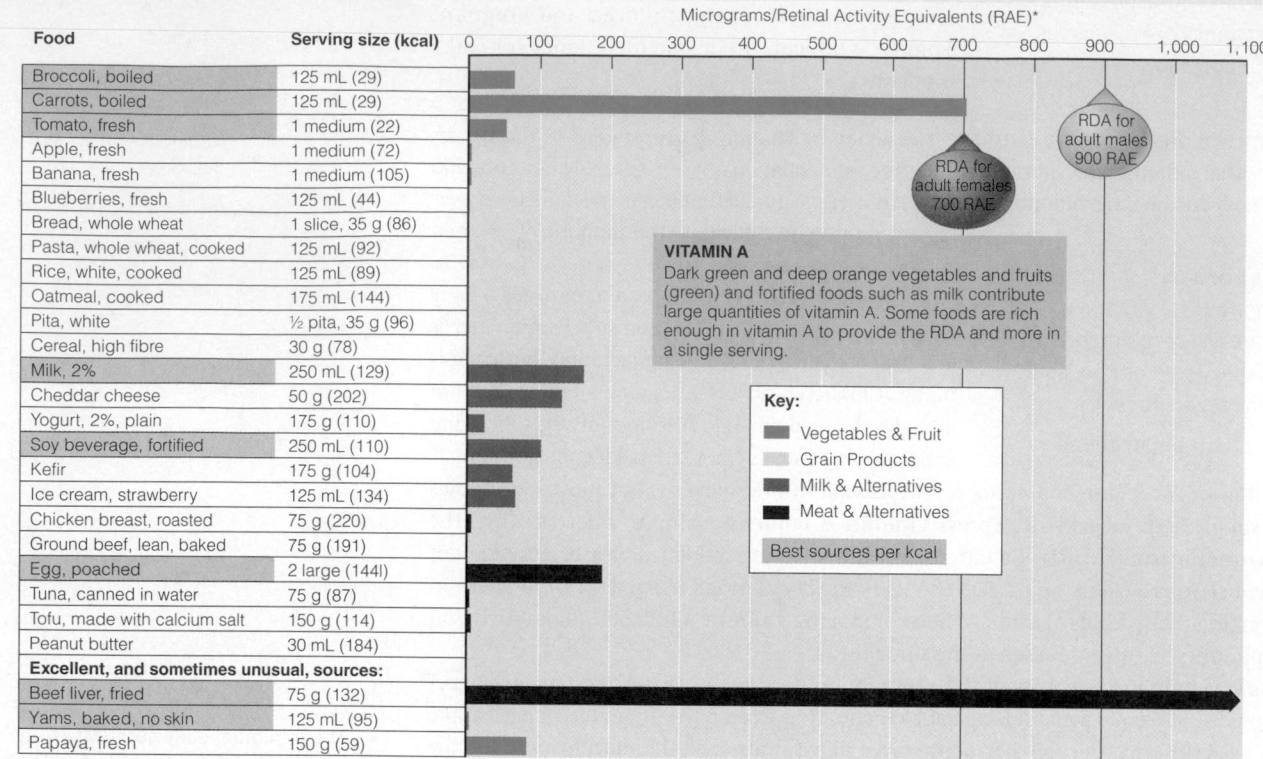

Microgram/Retinal Activity Equivalents (RAE)*

Food	Serving size (kcal)
Broccoli, boiled	125 mL (29)
Carrots, boiled	125 mL (29)
Tomato, fresh	1 medium (22)
Apple, fresh	1 medium (72)
Banana, fresh	1 medium (105)
Blueberries, fresh	125 mL (44)
Bread, whole wheat	1 slice, 35 g (86)
Pasta, whole wheat, cooked	125 mL (92)
Rice, white, cooked	125 mL (89)
Oatmeal, cooked	175 mL (144)
Pita, white	½ pita, 35 g (96)
Cereal, high fibre	30 g (78)
Milk, 2%	250 mL (129)
Cheddar cheese	50 g (202)
Yogurt, 2%, plain	175 g (110)
Soy beverage, fortified	250 mL (110)
Kefir	175 g (104)
Ice cream, strawberry	125 mL (134)
Chicken breast, roasted	75 g (220)
Ground beef, lean, baked	75 g (191)
Egg, poached	2 large (144l)
Tuna, canned in water	75 g (87)
Tofu, made with calcium salt	150 g (114)
Peanut butter	30 mL (184)
Excellent, and sometimes unusual, sources:	
Beef liver, fried	75 g (132)
Yams, baked, no skin	125 mL (95)
Papaya, fresh	150 g (59)

RDA for adult females 700 RAE

RDA for adult males 900 RAE

VITAMIN A
Dark green and deep orange vegetables and fruits (green) and fortified foods such as milk contribute large quantities of vitamin A. Some foods are rich enough in vitamin A to provide the RDA and more in a single serving.

Key:
- Vegetables & Fruit
- Grain Products
- Milk & Alternatives
- Meat & Alternatives

Best sources per kcal

* Vitamin A recommendations are expressed as Retinal Activity Equivalents (RAE).

DRI Recommended Intakes:
Men: 900 µg/d[a]
Women: 700 µg/d[a]

CCHS 2.2 Mean Intake:
Men: 590 RAE/d
Women: 703 RAE/d

Tolerable Upper Intake Level:
Adults: 3,000 µg vitamin A/d

Chief Functions:
Vision; maintenance of cornea, epithelial cells, mucous membranes, skin; bone and tooth growth; regulation of gene expression; reproduction; immunity

Deficiency:
Night blindness, corneal drying (xerosis), and blindness (xerophthalmia); impaired bone growth and easily decayed teeth; keratin lumps on the skin; impaired immunity

Toxicity:
Vitamin A:
Increased activity of bone-dismantling cells causing reduced bone density and pain; liver abnormalities; birth defects
Beta-carotene:
Harmless yellowing of skin

[a]Vitamin A recommendations are expressed in retinol activity equivalents (RAE).

Source: All nutrient and Caloric values for the food items shown are based on the 2010 version of the Canadian Nutrient File, available at http://webprod3.hc-sc .gc.ca/cnf-fce/index-eng.jsp

Retinol in excess is toxic, but beta-carotene in food is not converted to retinol efficiently enough to cause vitamin A toxicity symptoms. A steady diet of abundant pumpkin, carrots, carrot juice, and the like has been known to turn people bright yellow because beta-carotene builds up in the fat just beneath the skin and imparts a harmless yellow cast; see Figure 7–4 in the margin.[18] Concentrated beta-carotene supplements, however, may have adverse effects, as another section points out.

Does Eating Carrots Really Promote Good Vision? Bright orange fruit and vegetables derive their colour from beta-carotene and are so colourful that they decorate the plate. Carrots, sweet potatoes, pumpkins, mango, cantaloupe, and apricots are all rich sources of beta-carotene—and therefore contribute vitamin A to the eyes and to the rest of the body—so, yes, eating carrots does promote good vision. Another colourful group, *dark* green vegetables, such as spinach, other greens, and broccoli, owe their colour to the green pigment chlorophyll and to beta-carotene. The green and orange pigments together give a deep, dark green colour to the vegetables.

Other colourful vegetables, such as red cabbage, beets, and yellow corn, can fool you into thinking they contain beta-carotene, but these foods derive their colours from other pigments and are poor sources of beta-carotene. As for "white" plant foods such as grains and potatoes, they have none. Some confusion exists concerning the term *yam*. A white-fleshed Mexican root vegetable called "yam" is devoid of beta-carotene, but the orange-fleshed sweet potato called "yam" in Canada is one of the richest beta-carotene sources known. Canada's Food Guide recommendations state that a person should eat *deep* orange or *dark* green vegetables and fruit regularly.

Carotenoids and Diseases

The important roles of active vitamin A in vision have been emphasized, but another link is worth mentioning. People whose diets lack foods rich in beta-carotene have a high incidence of the most common form of untreatable age-related blindness, **macular degeneration**.[19] The macula is a yellow spot located at the focal centre of the retina (identified in the drawing on page 247). In macular degeneration, the macula loses integrity, causing impairment of the most important field of vision, the central focus. For a while, beta-carotene was credited with providing the macula's protective yellow pigment, but research soon determined that carotenoids other than beta-carotene deserve the credit.[20] These other carotenoids occur together with beta-carotene in colourful foods such as leafy green vegetables.*

Likewise, abundant beta-carotene from foods and elevated beta-carotene in the blood are associated with lower cancer incidence, but beta-carotene supplements are not. In fact, they appear to pose a cancer hazard to smokers. This seems to indicate that beta-carotene is not itself responsible for an anticancer effect but simply tags along as a marker for another unknown factor or combination of factors that occurs along with it. Beta-carotene is just one of the major **dietary antioxidants** present in foods—others are vitamin E, vitamin C, the mineral selenium, and many phytochemicals. Further, dietary antioxidants are just one class of a complex array of beneficial constituents in whole foods that seem to benefit health synergistically. In the case of beta carotene, diets rich in this antioxidant and its chemical relatives correlate with low rates of eye diseases and cancer.

> Chapter 5 introduced antioxidants as substances that protect body compounds from damage by oxidation. Controversy 2 introduced the carotene family of phytochemicals and explored more of their disease-fighting potential. This chapter's Controversy comes back to supplements and disease prevention.

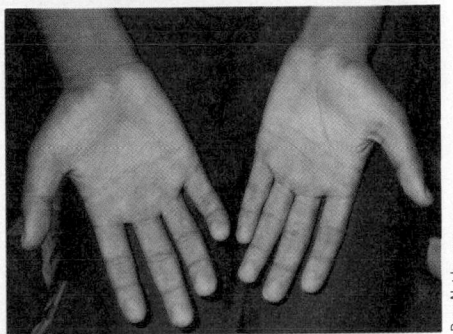

KEY POINT

- The vitamin A precursor in plants, beta-carotene, is an effective antioxidant in the body. Brightly coloured plant foods are richest in beta-carotene, and diets containing these foods are associated with eye health.

Vitamin D

Vitamin D is different from all of the other nutrients in that the body can synthesize all it needs with the help of sunlight. Therefore, in a sense, vitamin D is not an essential nutrient. Given enough sun each day, most people need consume no vitamin D at all from foods. As simple as this may sound, recent surveys indicate that many people, particularly those of African descent, may border on vitamin D insufficiency.[21]

Roles of Vitamin D

The best-known role of vitamin D is as a member of a large cast of nutrients and hormones that interact to regulate blood calcium and phosphorus levels and thereby maintain bone integrity. Many of these interactions take place at the genetic level in ways that are under investigation.[22]

One of these other carotenoids is zeaxanthin.

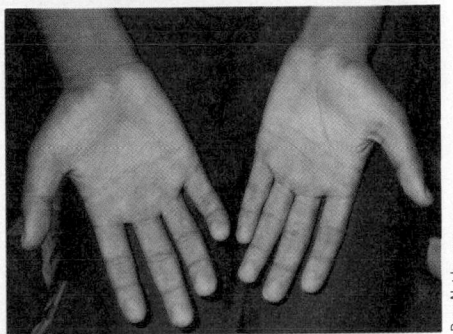

Figure 7–4

Excess Beta-Carotene Symptom— Discoloration of the Skin

The hand on the right shows skin discoloration from excess beta-carotene. Another person's normal hand (left) is shown for comparison.

DermNet Images

Colourful foods are often rich in vitamins.

© Tomo Jesenicnik/Shutterstock

macular degeneration a common, progressive loss of function of the part of the retina that is most crucial to focused vision (the macula is shown in the drawing of the eye earlier in this chapter.). This degeneration often leads to blindness.

dietary antioxidants compounds typically found in plant foods that significantly decrease the adverse effects of oxidation on living tissues. The major antioxidant vitamins are vitamin E, vitamin C, and beta-carotene.

The sunshine vitamin: vitamin D.

Calcium is indispensable to the proper functioning of cells in all tissues of the body, including muscles, nerves, and glands, which draw calcium from the blood as they need it. When more calcium is needed to replenish the supply, vitamin D acts at three body locations to raise the blood calcium level. First, the skeleton serves as a vast warehouse of stored calcium that can be tapped when blood calcium begins to fall. Only two other organs can act to raise the level of blood calcium: the digestive tract, where food brings calcium in, and the kidneys, which can recycle calcium into the body from blood filtrate destined to become urine.

Vitamin D functions as a hormone, that is, a compound manufactured by one organ of the body that acts on other organs or tissues. In addition to its actions in the bones, intestines, and kidneys, vitamin D plays roles in the workings of the brain, heart, stomach, pancreas, skin, and reproductive organs. Like vitamin A, vitamin D stimulates maturation of cells, including cells of the immune system. Research is hinting (sometimes strongly) that to incur a deficit of vitamin D is to invite problems of many kinds, including high blood pressure, some common forms of cancer (e.g., colon, prostate), type 1 diabetes, heart disease, rheumatoid arthritis, inflammatory bowel disease, and even multiple sclerosis.[23] The most recent Canadian Health Measures Survey revealed that according to current standards for plasma vitamin D, 90 percent of Canadians (6–79 years old) met or exceed the levels considered adequate for bone health. However, these standards are currently under review. Furthermore, recent research indicates that vitamin D may also play an important role in diseases other than bone health, such as some forms of cancer, CVD, multiple sclerosis, and immune function. In addition, the Institute of Medicine has been asked not only to review and update the DRIs for vitamin D and calcium but also to report on chronic and nonchronic diseases, and thus go beyond bone health. The institute's report was released in November of 2010 (http://www.nap.edu/catalog.php?record_id=13050).

The well-established problems, however, concern impaired calcium balance and the bones, especially during growth. Health Canada has allowed food manufacturers to use a diet-related heath claim on foods meeting certain criteria, linking calcium, vitamin D, and physical activity with osteoporosis, but, as with all other diet-related health claims, the exact wording is prescribed. One example of such a claim is "A healthy diet with adequate calcium and vitamin D and regular physical activity helps to achieve strong bones and may reduce the risk of osteoporosis." In addition, the Natural Health Products Directorate allows health claims on vitamin and mineral supplements, for example, vitamin D "helps in the absorption and use of calcium and phosphorus" (http://www.nap.edu/catalog.php?record_id=13050).

> Chapter 8 and Controversy 8 present more about bone minerals and their regulation and about osteoporosis, the bone-weakening disease.

Too Little Vitamin D—A Danger to Bones
The most obvious sign of vitamin D deficiency is abnormality of the bones in the disease **rickets**, shown in Figure 7–5. Children with rickets develop bowed legs because they are unable to mineralize newly forming bone material, a rubbery protein matrix. As gravity pulls their body weight against these weak bones, the legs bow. Many such children also have a protruding belly because of lax abdominal muscles. Health Canada has "recommended that all breastfed, healthy term infants in Canada receive a daily vitamin D supplement of 10 µg (400 IU)." Health Canada further suggested that this practice continue until the infant is receiving this amount from other dietary sources or until one year of age.

As early as the 1700s, rickets was known to be curable with cod-liver oil, which is rich in vitamin D. More than 100 years later, a Polish physician linked sunlight exposure to prevention and cure of rickets. Today, the bowed legs, knock-knees, beaded ribs, and protruding (pigeon) chests of children with rickets are not common sights in Canada, although rickets occasionally occurs among breast-fed black infants not supplemented with vitamin D and infants and toddlers fed unfortified soy and rice beverages instead of formula or milk.[24] Many children worldwide suffer the ravages of rickets because of inadequate food combined with a lack of sunlight.

Canada's Food Guide
- The need for vitamin D increases after the age of 50. In addition to following Canada's Food Guide, everyone over the age of 50 should take a daily vitamin D supplement of 10 µg (400 IU) (http://www.hc-sc.gc.ca/fn-an/food-guide-aliment/index-eng.php).

rickets the vitamin D-deficiency disease in children; characterized by abnormal growth of bone and manifested in bowed legs or knock-knees, outward-bowed chest, and knobs on the ribs.

Adolescents, who often abandon vitamin D–fortified milk in favour of soft drinks, may also prefer indoor pastimes such as video games to outdoor activities during daylight hours. Such teens often lack vitamin D and so fail to develop the bone density needed to prevent bone loss in later life.[25]

Even older people can suffer painful joints and muscles if their vitamin D levels are low, although the condition is easily missed during examinations and may be mistaken for arthritis or other painful conditions.[26] The adult form of rickets, **osteomalacia**, occurs most often in women who have low calcium intakes and little exposure to sun and who go through repeated pregnancies and periods of lactation. Given this combination of risk factors, bone proteins fail to mineralize normally, and the leg bones may soften to such an extent that a young woman who was tall and straight at 20 may become bent and bowlegged before she turns 30.

Too Much Vitamin D—A Danger to Soft Tissues   Vitamin D is the most potentially toxic of all vitamins. Chronic ingestion of excesses may be directly toxic to the bones, kidneys, brain, nerves, and the heart and arteries. Symptoms of toxicity include appetite loss, nausea, vomiting, and increased urination and thirst; a severe form of psychological depression can result from vitamin D's effects on the central nervous system. If overdoses continue, vitamin D raises the blood mineral level to dangerous extremes, forcing calcium to be deposited in soft tissues such as the heart, blood vessels, lungs, and kidneys. Even the soft pulp of the teeth hardens, while tooth enamel thins. Calcium deposited in critical organs may cause them to malfunction, with serious consequences to health and life.

The likeliest victims of vitamin D poisoning are infants whose well-intentioned but misguided parents think that if some is good, more is better. Also, older people who take vitamin D supplements to stem adult bone loss may also easily overdose. Two people died and others became ill after drinking milk from a dairy that had mistakenly overfortified the milk with up to 500 times the usual dosage of vitamin D. One infant survivor later developed dental problems because the vitamin D overdose disturbed the normal development of her permanent teeth. Such occurrences are rare, but the incident renewed awareness of the potential for harm from vitamin D and the need for close monitoring of those who fortify the nation's foods with vitamins. The DRI committee has set a Tolerable Upper Intake Level for vitamin D at 100 micrograms per day [current Maximum Daily Dose (MDD) on single-ingredient supplement labels is 25 µg = 1,000 IU].

How Can People Make a Vitamin from Sunlight?   Most of the world's population relies on natural exposure to sunlight to maintain adequate vitamin D nutrition. When ultraviolet light from the sun shines on a cholesterol compound in human skin, the compound is transformed into a vitamin D precursor and is absorbed directly into the blood. Slowly, over the next day and a half, the liver and kidneys finish converting the precursor to the active form of vitamin D (see Figure 7–6). Diseases that affect either the liver or the kidneys can impair the conversion of the inactive precursor to the active vitamin and therefore produce symptoms of vitamin D deficiency.

Unlike concentrated supplements, sunlight presents no risk of vitamin D toxicity; the sun itself begins breaking down excess vitamin D made in the skin. Sunbathers run *other* risks, of course, such as premature wrinkling of the skin and the increased risk of skin cancer. Sunscreens with sun protection factors (SPFs) of 8 and above can reduce these risks, but they also prevent vitamin D synthesis. Production of vitamin D doesn't demand idle hours of sunbathing, however. Between mid-March and mid-October in most locations, just being outdoors when the sun is overhead, even in lightweight clothing, is sufficient. The pigments of dark skin provide protection from ultraviolet radiation but also reduce vitamin D synthesis. Dark-skinned people require longer exposure to direct sun (up to three hours, depending on the climate) for several days' worth of vitamin D, but light-skinned people need much less time (10 or 15 minutes). Thus, a person can wait until just enough time has elapsed to make some vitamin D and then apply sunscreen. Tanning booths may or may not promote vitamin D synthesis. Health Canada has issued "Guidelines for tanning salon owners, operators and users" (http://www.hc-sc.gc.ca/ewh-semt/pubs/radiation/

Figure 7–5

Rickets

This child has the bowed legs of the vitamin D-deficiency disease rickets.

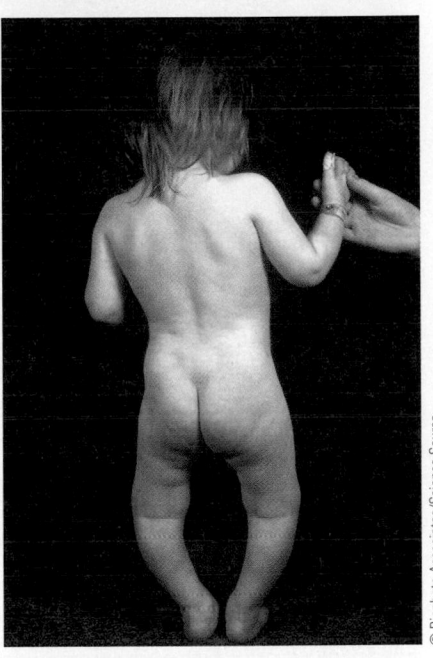

This child displays the beaded ribs common in rickets.

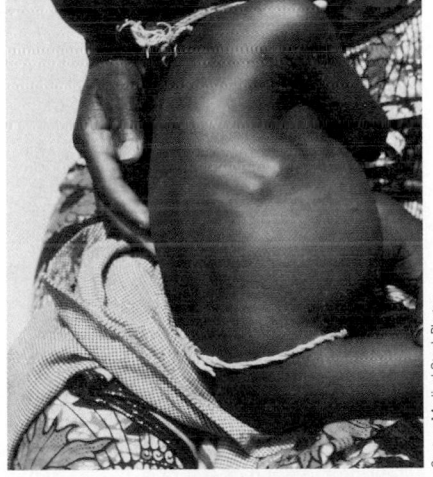

osteomalacia (OS-tee-o-mal-AY-shuh) the adult expression of vitamin D-deficiency disease, characterized by an overabundance of unmineralized bone protein (*osteo* means "bone"; *mal* means "bad"). Symptoms include bending of the spine and bowing of the legs.

Figure 7–6

Vitamin D Synthesis and Activation

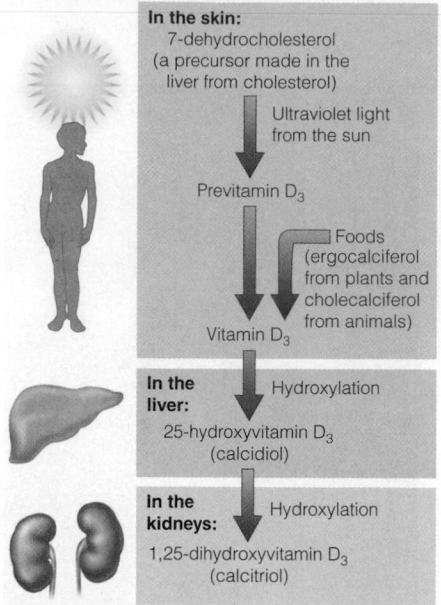

In the skin:
7-dehydrocholesterol
(a precursor made in the
liver from cholesterol)

Ultraviolet light
from the sun

Previtamin D₃

Foods
(ergocalciferol
from plants and
cholecalciferol
from animals)

Vitamin D₃

In the liver: Hydroxylation

25-hydroxyvitamin D₃
(calcidiol)

In the kidneys: Hydroxylation

1,25-dihydroxyvitamin D₃
(calcitriol)

*Factors Affecting Sun Exposure
and Vitamin D Synthesis*

- *Air pollution.* Particles in the air screen out the sun's rays.
- *City living.* Tall buildings block sunlight.
- *Clothing.* Most clothing blocks sunlight.
- *Geography.* Lack of direct sunlight prevents vitamin D synthesis:
  - September through March at latitudes above 50 degrees (most of Canada).
  - November through February at latitudes between 35 and 50 degrees (most U.S. locations).
  - In locations south of 35 degrees (northern borders of Alabama and Georgia), direct sun exposure is sufficient for vitamin D synthesis year round.
- *Homebound.* Living indoors prevents sun exposure.
- *Season.* Warmer seasons of the year bring more direct sun rays.
- *Sunscreen.* Use reduces or prevents skin exposure to sun's rays.
- *Time of day.* Midday hours provide maximum direct sun exposure.

tocopherol (tuh-KOFF-er-all) a kind of alcohol. The active form of vitamin E is alpha-tocopherol.

free radicals atoms or molecules with one or more unpaired electrons that make the atom or molecule unstable and highly reactive.

tan-bronzage/index-eng.php). Under these guidelines, operators are to advise clients of appropriate use of the facilities and about the potential for sunburn, provide protective eyewear, and so on.

The ultraviolet rays of the sun that promote vitamin D synthesis cannot penetrate clouds, smoke, smog, heavy clothing, window glass, or even window screens. In Canada and the United States, many cases of rickets show up in dark-skinned people who live in smoggy northern cities or who lack exposure to sunlight.[27] A surprisingly high number of otherwise healthy northern adults, even those drinking milk fortified with vitamin D, have recently been reported with low blood levels of vitamin D, mostly at the end of the winter season.[28] It may be that milk does not deliver enough vitamin D to prevent a drop in blood levels through the winter months. In addition, people who are housebound or institutionalized and those who work at night may incur (over years) a vitamin D deficiency, as do many elderly people, who have limited exposure to sunlight and lose efficiency in activating vitamin D as they age. For these people, dietary vitamin D is essential.[29]

Because of increased risk with age, the DRI committee set recommended intakes for vitamin D that increase over the years: 15 micrograms per day for adults 19 to 50 years, 15 micrograms for those 51 to 70 years, and 20 micrograms for those over 70.

Snapshot 7–2 shows the few significant food sources of vitamin D. Butter, cream, and fortified margarine contribute small amounts. In Canada and the United States, milk, whether fluid, dried, or evaporated, is fortified with vitamin D, as are margarines and some yogurts. Young adults who drink three cups (750 mL) a day receive half of their daily recommended intake; the other half comes from exposure to sunlight and other food sources. A daily litre of milk will supply the entire recommended amount. Children who drink two cups or more of milk a day will have a head start toward meeting their vitamin D needs for growth. Yogurt and cheese products are often not fortified, so read the labels. Strict vegetarians and their children may have low vitamin D intakes because only certain fortified plant sources exist: margarines and some plant-based beverages (e.g., soy beverage).

KEY POINT

- Vitamin D raises mineral levels in the blood, notably calcium and phosphorus, permitting bone formation and maintenance. A deficiency can cause rickets in childhood or osteomalacia in later life. Vitamin D is the most toxic of all of the vitamins, and excesses are dangerous or deadly. People exposed to the sun make vitamin D from a cholesterol-like compound in their skin; fortified milk is an important food source.

Vitamin E

More than 80 years ago, researchers discovered a compound in vegetable oils necessary for reproduction in rats. This compound was named **tocopherol**, from *tokos*, a Greek word meaning "offspring." A few years later, the compound was named vitamin E. Four tocopherol compounds have been identified, and each is designated by one of the first four letters of the Greek alphabet: alpha, beta, gamma, and delta. Of these, alpha-tocopherol is the gold standard for vitamin E activity. For this reason, DRI intake recommendations are expressed as alpha-tocopherol.

For perspectives on possible risks and benefits of vitamin E supplements, see this chapter's Controversy feature.

The Extraordinary Bodyguard   Vitamin E is an antioxidant and thus serves as one of the body's main defenders against oxidative damage. Such damage occurs when highly unstable molecules known as **free radicals**, formed during normal cell metabolism, run amok and disrupt the structures of lipids in cell membranes, molecules of DNA, or the proteins that perform cellular work. A longstanding hypothesis states that such free-radical activity, if unchecked, may lead to cancer, heart disease, or other diseases. Vitamin E, by being oxidized itself, quenches free radicals, thus protecting vulnerable cell components and membranes from destruction. Figure 7–7 provides an overview of the activity of vitamin E and its potential role in disease prevention.

Snapshot 7-2 ⋯⋯⋙ Vitamin D

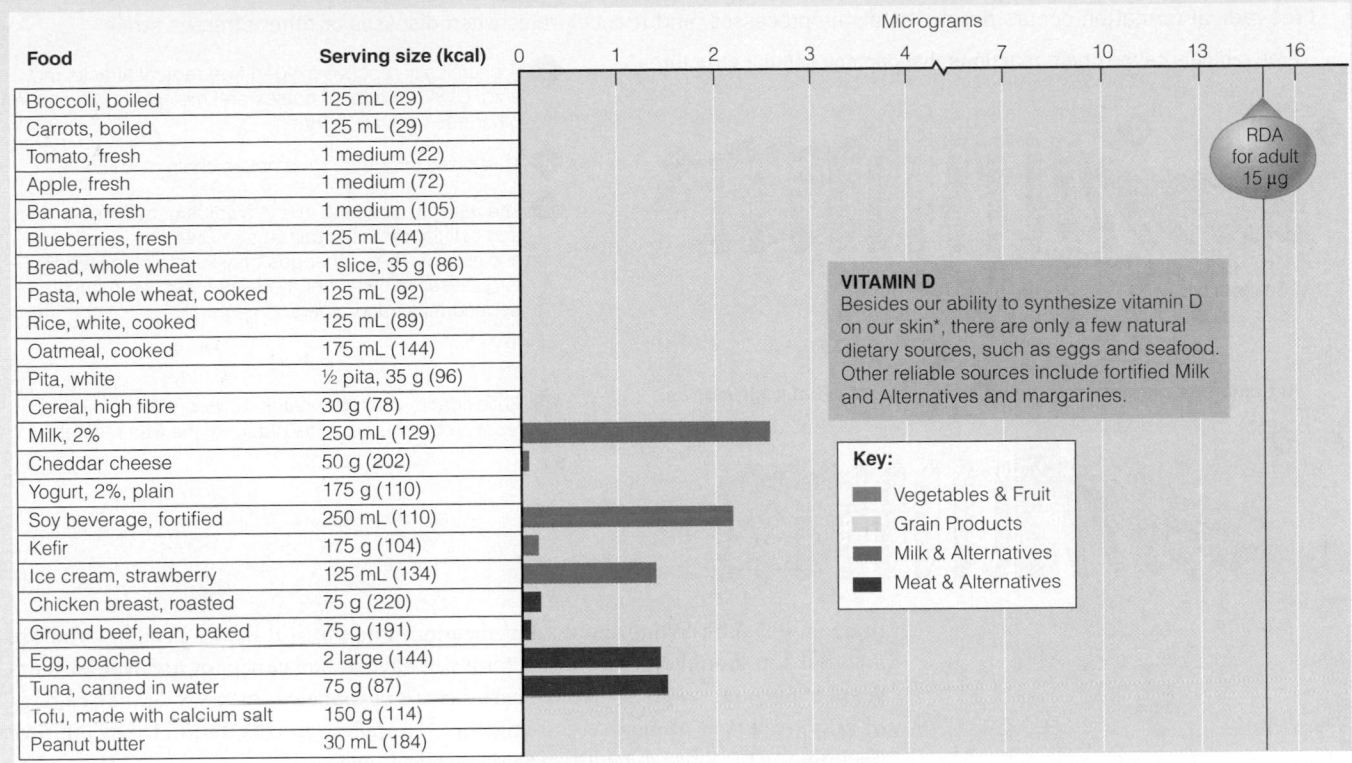

Food	Serving size (kcal)
Broccoli, boiled	125 mL (29)
Carrots, boiled	125 mL (29)
Tomato, fresh	1 medium (22)
Apple, fresh	1 medium (72)
Banana, fresh	1 medium (105)
Blueberries, fresh	125 mL (44)
Bread, whole wheat	1 slice, 35 g (86)
Pasta, whole wheat, cooked	125 mL (92)
Rice, white, cooked	125 mL (89)
Oatmeal, cooked	175 mL (144)
Pita, white	½ pita, 35 g (96)
Cereal, high fibre	30 g (78)
Milk, 2%	250 mL (129)
Cheddar cheese	50 g (202)
Yogurt, 2%, plain	175 g (110)
Soy beverage, fortified	250 mL (110)
Kefir	175 g (104)
Ice cream, strawberry	125 mL (134)
Chicken breast, roasted	75 g (220)
Ground beef, lean, baked	75 g (191)
Egg, poached	2 large (144)
Tuna, canned in water	75 g (87)
Tofu, made with calcium salt	150 g (114)
Peanut butter	30 mL (184)

RDA for adult 15 µg

VITAMIN D
Besides our ability to synthesize vitamin D on our skin*, there are only a few natural dietary sources, such as eggs and seafood. Other reliable sources include fortified Milk and Alternatives and margarines.

Key:
- Vegetables & Fruit
- Grain Products
- Milk & Alternatives
- Meat & Alternatives

DRI Recommended Intakes:
Adults: 15 µg/d (19–50 yr)
          15 µg/d (51–70 yr)
          20 µg/d (70 yr)

CCHS 2.2 Mean Intake:
Men: 5.9 µg/d
Women: 4.7 µg/d

Tolerable Upper Intake Level:
Adults: 100 µg/d

Chief Functions:
Mineralization of bones and teeth (raises blood calcium and phosphorus by increasing absorption from digestive tract, withdrawing calcium from bones, stimulating retention by kidneys)

Deficiency:
Abnormal bone growth resulting in rickets in children, osteomalacia in adults; malformed teeth, muscle spasms

Toxicity:
Elevated blood calcium; calcification of soft tissues (blood vessels, kidneys, heart, lungs, tissues of joints), excessive thirst, headache, nausea, weakness

*Avoid prolonged exposure to sun.

Vitamin E's antioxidant effect is especially crucial in the lungs, where the cells are exposed to high oxygen concentrations that can destroy molecules in their membranes. As the red blood cells carry oxygen from the lungs to other tissues, vitamin E protects their cell membranes, too. The white blood cells that defend the body against disease also depend on vitamin E, and it may play other roles in immunity. Vitamin E is also crucial for normal nerve development.

Over a decade ago, preliminary research aroused hope that supplements of vitamin E might protect against heart disease. Subsequent research, however, indicates that except for people whose blood measures indicate low vitamin E levels, people generally do not benefit from vitamin E supplements and may risk harm from high doses.[30] After a thorough investigation, Health Canada issued a report on the safety of vitamin E supplements in which it recommends ways to minimize health risks from taking high-dose vitamin E supplements on a daily basis. Some of the recommendations are

Figure 7-7

Free-Radical Damage and Antioxidant Protection

Free-radical formation occurs during metabolic processes, and it accelerates when diseases or other stresses strike.

Free radicals cause chain reactions that damage cellular structures.

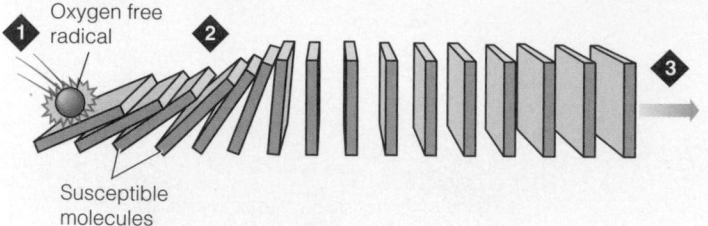

1 A chemically reactive oxygen free radical attacks fatty acid, DNA, protein, or cholesterol molecules, which form other free radicals in turn.

2 This initiates a rapid, destructive chain reaction.

3 The result is disabling injury to lipids of cell membranes and cellular proteins, damage to DNA, or oxidation of cholesterol. These changes may initiate steps leading to diseases such as heart disease, cancer, macular degeneration, and others.

Antioxidants quench free radicals and protect cellular structures.

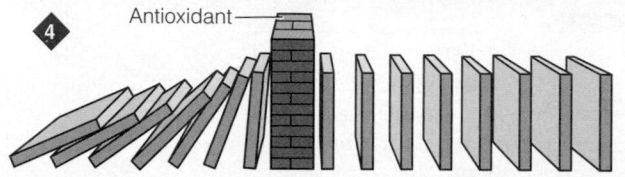

4 Antioxidants, such as vitamin E, stop the chain reaction by changing the nature of the free radical.

that you tell your doctor about all medications and natural health products you use and that you should talk to your doctor if you have or had cancer or are over 55 years years of age and diagnosed with heart disease or diabetes (http://www.hc-sc.gc.ca/hl-vs/iyh-vsv/food-aliment/vitam-eng.php).[31] Supplements of vitamin E may improve the immune response in healthy elderly people, however.

Vitamin E Deficiency A deficiency of vitamin E produces a wide variety of symptoms in laboratory animals. Most of these symptoms have not been reproduced in human beings, however, despite many attempts. Three reasons have been given: First, the vitamin is so widespread in food that it is almost impossible to create a vitamin E-deficient diet. Second, the body stores so much vitamin E in its fatty tissues that a person would find it difficult to eat a vitamin E-free diet for long enough to deplete these stores and produce a deficiency. Third, the cells recycle their working supply of vitamin E, using the same molecules over and over to ward off deficiency.

• Canada's Food Guide recommends small daily intakes of 30 to 45 mL (2 to 3 tbs) of unsaturated fat, a source of vitamin E.

The classic vitamin E-deficiency symptom in human beings occurs in premature babies who are born before the transfer of the vitamin from the mother to the infant, which takes place in the last weeks of pregnancy. Without sufficient vitamin E, the infant's red blood cells rupture (**erythrocyte hemolysis**), and the infant becomes anemic. The few symptoms of vitamin E deficiency that have been observed in adults include loss of muscle coordination and reflexes with impaired movement, vision, and speech. All of these symptoms may be caused by oxidative damage; vitamin E treatment corrects them.

In adults, vitamin E deficiency is usually associated with diseases that cause malabsorption of fat, including disease of or injury to the liver (which makes bile, necessary for digestion of fat), the gallbladder (which delivers bile into the intestine), and the pancreas (which makes fat-digesting enzymes). In people without diseases, deficiencies of vitamin E are most likely when diets extremely low in fat are consumed for years. People who rely solely on fat replacers, such as diet margarines and fat-free salad dressings, to the exclusion of all oils may have low vitamin E intakes. Those consuming diets of highly processed or "convenience" foods may lack sufficient vitamin E because vitamin E is destroyed by extensive heating in the processing of these foods.

erythrocyte (eh-REETH-ro-sight) **hemolysis** (HE-moh-LIE-sis, he-MOLL-ih-sis) rupture of the red blood cells, caused by vitamin E deficiency (*erythro* means "red"; *cyte* means "cell"; *hemo* means "blood"; *lysis* means "breaking").

Chronically low intakes of vitamin E may play other roles in diseases. One line of research suggests that when body stores of vitamin E and the mineral selenium are low, viruses respond by becoming more virulent—even normally harmless viruses appear to undergo changes that make them more likely to cause diseases.[32] No one yet knows the

Chapter 7 The Vitamins

details of these effects, but they may be related to "oxidative stress," caused when oxidative activities outstrip the capacity of the tissues' antioxidant defences.

Extravagant claims are often made for vitamin E because its deficiency affects animals' muscles and reproductive systems. Research in human beings has discredited claims that vitamin E improves athletic endurance and skill, enhances sexual performance, or cures sexual dysfunction in males, although such claims are still being used to sell supplements containing vitamin E.

Vitamin E Requirements, Toxicity, and Sources The DRI recommended intake (inside front cover) for vitamin E is 15 milligrams a day for adults. This amount seems sufficient to maintain blood values for both vitamin E and indicators of oxidation reactions within healthy normal limits. Canadian intake data on vitamin E from the Canadian Community Health Survey Cycle 2.2 have not been released, but on average, U.S. intakes of vitamin E fall substantially below the recommendation (see Figure 7–8).

The need for vitamin E rises as people consume more polyunsaturated oil because the oil requires antioxidant protection by the vitamin. Most vegetable oils contain some vitamin E, so people who eat them also receive the vitamin. As mentioned, heat processing, such as frying, destroys vitamin E, as does oxidation, so most of the processed, fast, deep-fried, and convenience foods popular among Canadian consumers retain little intact vitamin E.

> Read more about oxidative stress in Chapter 11.
>
> Vitamin E conversion factors are in Appendix B.

No adverse effects are known to arise from naturally occurring vitamin E in foods. Also, studies of vitamin E supplements in doses up to the DRI recommended intake value generally indicate safety. Larger doses may be risky, however. Vitamin E supplements increase the effects of anticoagulant medication used to oppose unwanted blood clotting, so people taking such drugs risk uncontrollable bleeding if they also take large doses of vitamin E. A decade ago, researchers reported an increase in brain hemorrhages, a form of stroke, among smokers taking just 50 milligrams of vitamin E per day. Recently, the pooled results from 19 experiments involving almost 136,000 people revealed that those taking vitamin E in doses greater than 400 IU (about a third of the Tolerable Upper Intake Level) per day were at an increased risk of death from all causes compared with people taking smaller doses.[33] To err on the safe side until more is known about the safety of vitamin E supplements, intakes should probably be kept low, and they certainly should not exceed the Tolerable Upper Intake Level of 1,000 milligrams of alpha-tocopherol per day [see the margin note; current Maximum Daily Dose (MDD) for vitamin E in single-ingredient supplements is 179 AT/d].

 Vitamin E is widespread in foods. About 20 percent of the vitamin E people consume comes from vegetable oils and products made from them, such as salad dressings and shortening (see Snapshot 7–3). Another 20 percent comes from fruit and vegetables, although none of these is a good source by itself. Fortified cereals* and other grain products contribute vitamin E in the diet, and meats, poultry, fish, eggs, milk products, nuts, and seeds contribute smaller percentages. Wheat germ is a good source of vitamin E; animal fats have almost none.

KEY POINT

- Vitamin E acts as an antioxidant in cell membranes and is especially important for the integrity of cells that are constantly exposed to high oxygen concentrations, namely, the lungs and blood cells, both red and white. Vitamin E deficiency is rare in human beings, but it does occur in newborn premature infants. The vitamin is widely distributed in plant foods; it is destroyed by high heat; toxicity is rare.

Vitamin K

Have you ever thought about how remarkable it is that blood can clot? The liquid turns solid in a lifesaving series of reactions—if blood did not clot, wounds would just keep bleeding, draining the blood from the body. The main function of vitamin K is to help

---

*Cereals fortified with vitamin E may not be available in Canada.

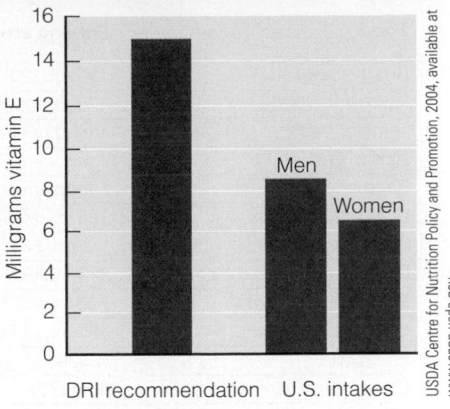

USDA Centre for Nutrition Policy and Promotion, 2004, available at www.cnpp.usda.gov

Figure 7–8

Vitamin E Recommendation and U.S. Intakes Compared

- Maximum Daily Dose (MDD) for single-ingredient supplements for vitamin E is 1,000 mg AT/d unless you have CVD.

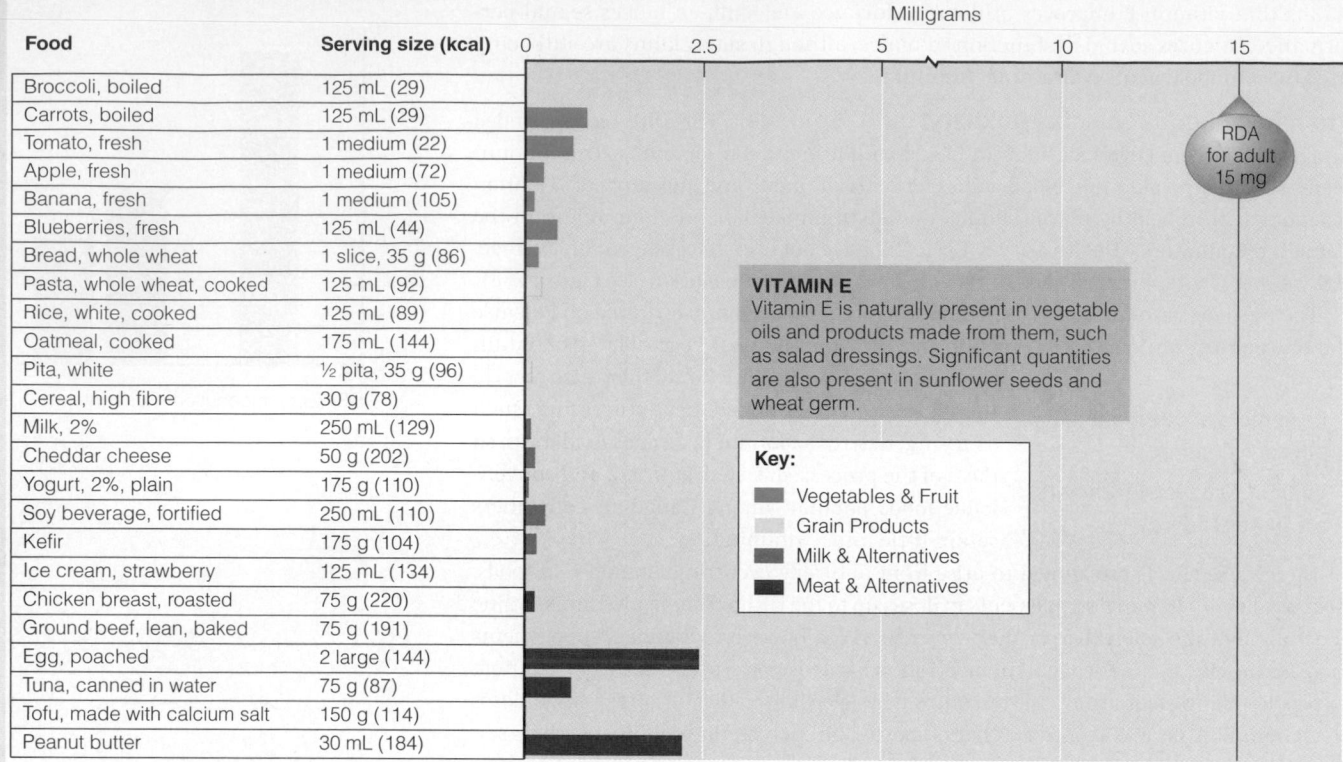

Food	Serving size (kcal)
Broccoli, boiled	125 mL (29)
Carrots, boiled	125 mL (29)
Tomato, fresh	1 medium (22)
Apple, fresh	1 medium (72)
Banana, fresh	1 medium (105)
Blueberries, fresh	125 mL (44)
Bread, whole wheat	1 slice, 35 g (86)
Pasta, whole wheat, cooked	125 mL (92)
Rice, white, cooked	125 mL (89)
Oatmeal, cooked	175 mL (144)
Pita, white	½ pita, 35 g (96)
Cereal, high fibre	30 g (78)
Milk, 2%	250 mL (129)
Cheddar cheese	50 g (202)
Yogurt, 2%, plain	175 g (110)
Soy beverage, fortified	250 mL (110)
Kefir	175 g (104)
Ice cream, strawberry	125 mL (134)
Chicken breast, roasted	75 g (220)
Ground beef, lean, baked	75 g (191)
Egg, poached	2 large (144)
Tuna, canned in water	75 g (87)
Tofu, made with calcium salt	150 g (114)
Peanut butter	30 mL (184)

VITAMIN E
Vitamin E is naturally present in vegetable oils and products made from them, such as salad dressings. Significant quantities are also present in sunflower seeds and wheat germ.

Key:
- Vegetables & Fruit
- Grain Products
- Milk & Alternatives
- Meat & Alternatives

RDA for adult 15 mg

DRI Recommended Intakes:
Adults: 15 mg/d

CCHS 2.2 Mean Intake:
Not known

Tolerable Upper Intake Level:
Adults: 1,000 mg/d

Chief Functions:
Antioxidant (protects cell membranes, regulates oxidation reactions, protects polyunsaturated fatty acids)

Deficiency:
Red blood cell breakage, nerve damage

Toxicity:
Augments the effects of anticlotting medication

---

synthesize proteins that help clot the blood. Hospitals measure the clotting time of a person's blood before surgery and sometimes administer vitamin K before operations to reduce bleeding in surgery. Vitamin K may be of value at this time, but only if a vitamin K deficiency exists. Vitamin K does not improve clotting in those with other bleeding disorders, such as the inherited disease hemophilia.

K stands for the Danish word *koagulation* (clotting). Chapter 6 describes the roles of protein in blood clotting.

Some people with heart problems need to *prevent* the formation of clots within their circulatory system—this is popularly referred to as "thinning" the blood. One of the best-known medicines for this purpose is warfarin, which interferes with the action of vitamin K in promoting clotting. Vitamin K therapy may be needed for people on warfarin if uncontrolled bleeding should occur.[34] People taking warfarin who self-prescribe vitamin K supplements or radically change their diet to include foods rich in vitamin K risk interfering with the action of the drug.

Vitamin K is also necessary for the synthesis of key bone proteins. Vitamin K, together with the more famous bone nutrient, vitamin D, ensures the health of the

• The Maximum Daily Dose (MDD) for multivitamin/mineral supplements for vitamin K is 120 µg/d.

bones. Without vitamin K, the bones produce an abnormal protein that cannot bind to the minerals that normally form bones, so bone density is low.[35] Adequate vitamin K may reduce the risk of hip fracture: people who consume abundant vitamin K, often in the form of green leafy vegetables, are reported to suffer fewer hip fractures than those with lower intakes.[36]

Like vitamin D, vitamin K can be obtained from a nonfood source—in this case, the intestinal bacteria. Billions of bacteria normally reside in the intestines, and some of them synthesize vitamin K. Newborn infants present a unique case with regard to vitamin K because they are born with a sterile intestinal tract, and the vitamin K-producing bacteria take weeks to establish themselves. To prevent hemorrhage, the newborn is given a single dose of vitamin K at birth.

 As Snapshot 7–4 shows, vitamin K's richest plant food sources include dark green leafy vegetables such as cooked spinach and collard greens, which provide an average of 300 micrograms per half-cup (125 mL) serving. Lettuces, broccoli, Brussels sprouts, and other members of the cabbage family are also good sources. There is also one rich animal food source, liver. Canola and soybean oils (unhydrogenated liquid oils) provide smaller but still significant amounts. One egg and a cup (250 mL) of milk

Snapshot 7-4 ⤏ Vitamin K

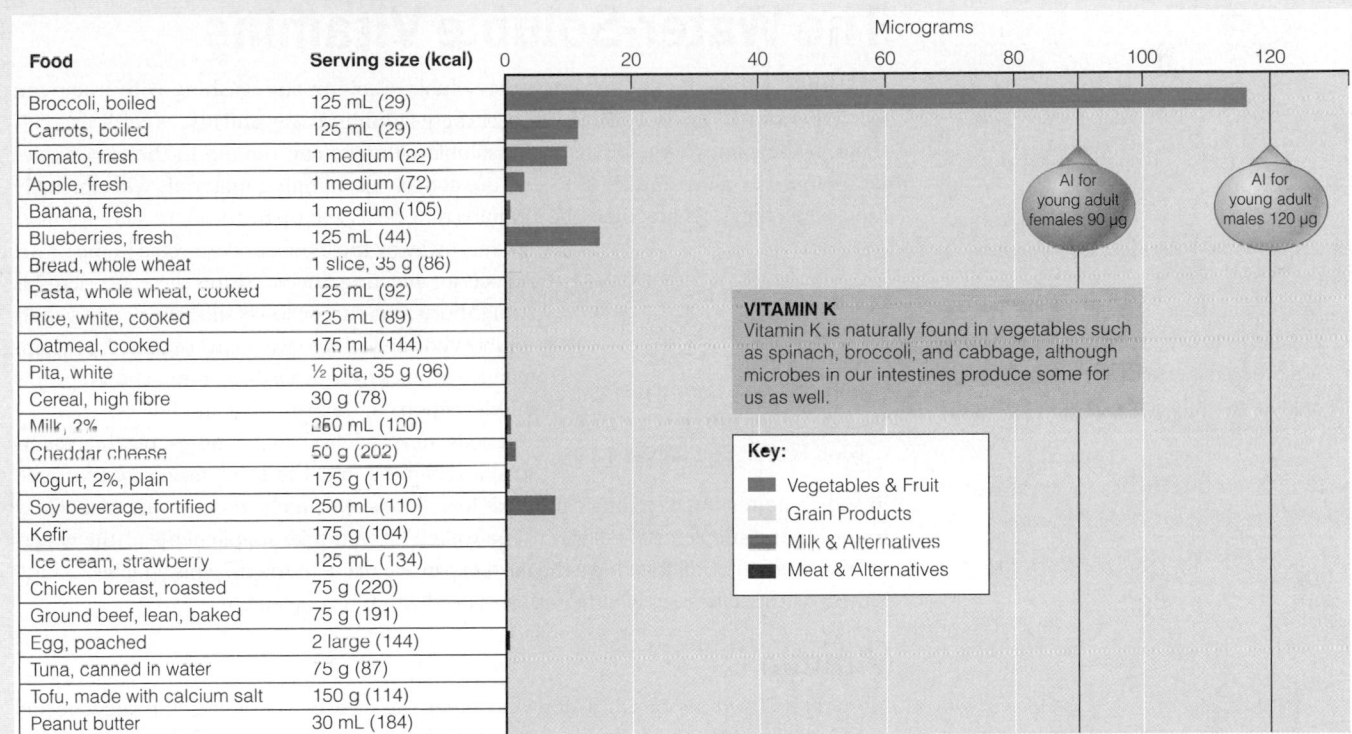

Food	Serving size (kcal)
Broccoli, boiled	125 mL (29)
Carrots, boiled	125 mL (29)
Tomato, fresh	1 medium (22)
Apple, fresh	1 medium (72)
Banana, fresh	1 medium (105)
Blueberries, fresh	125 mL (44)
Bread, whole wheat	1 slice, 35 g (86)
Pasta, whole wheat, cooked	125 mL (92)
Rice, white, cooked	125 mL (89)
Oatmeal, cooked	175 mL (144)
Pita, white	½ pita, 35 g (96)
Cereal, high fibre	30 g (78)
Milk, 2%	250 mL (120)
Cheddar cheese	50 g (202)
Yogurt, 2%, plain	175 g (110)
Soy beverage, fortified	250 mL (110)
Kefir	175 g (104)
Ice cream, strawberry	125 mL (134)
Chicken breast, roasted	75 g (220)
Ground beef, lean, baked	75 g (191)
Egg, poached	2 large (144)
Tuna, canned in water	75 g (87)
Tofu, made with calcium salt	150 g (114)
Peanut butter	30 mL (184)

VITAMIN K
Vitamin K is naturally found in vegetables such as spinach, broccoli, and cabbage, although microbes in our intestines produce some for us as well.

Key:
- Vegetables & Fruit
- Grain Products
- Milk & Alternatives
- Meat & Alternatives

AI for young adult females 90 µg

AI for young adult males 120 µg

DRI Recommended Intakes:
Men: 120 µg/d
Women: 90 µg/d

CCHS 2.2 Mean Intake:
Unknown

Chief Functions:
Synthesis of blood-clotting proteins and bone proteins

Deficiency:
Hemorrhage; abnormal bone formation

Toxicity:
Opposes the effects of anti-clotting medication

Source: Data from Standing Committee on the Scientific Evaluation of Dietary Reference Intakes, Food and Nutrition Board, Institute of Medicine, Dietary Reference Intakes for Vitamin A, Vitamin K, Arsenic, Boron, Chromium, Copper, Iodine, Iron, Manganese, Molybdenum, Nickel, Silicon, Vanadium, and Zinc (Washington, D.C.: National Academies Press, 2001), pp. 5–18.

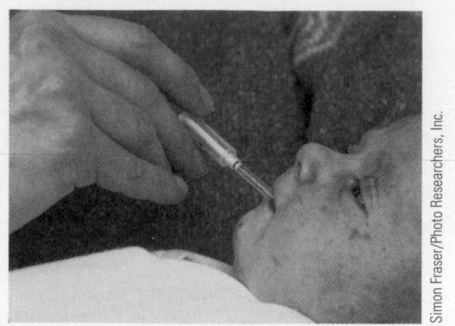

Soon after birth, newborns receive a dose of vitamin K.

Simon Fraser/Photo Researchers, Inc.

contain about equal amounts: 25 micrograms each. Tables of food composition do not include the vitamin K contents of foods because they are not well enough known.

Few adults in North America are likely to experience vitamin K deficiency, even if they seldom eat vitamin K-rich foods. Exceptions are newborns, as mentioned above, and people who have taken antibiotics that have killed both the beneficial and the harmful bacteria in their intestinal tracts. In certain medical conditions, bile production falters, making fats, including fat-soluble vitamins, unabsorbable. Supplements of the vitamin are needed in these cases because a vitamin K deficiency can be fatal.

Reports of vitamin K toxicity among healthy adults are rare, and the DRI committee has not set a Tolerable Upper Intake Level. For infants and pregnant women, however, vitamin K toxicity can result when supplements of a synthetic version of vitamin K are given too enthusiastically.* Toxicity induces breakage of the red blood cells and release of their pigment, which colours the skin yellow. A toxic dose of synthetic vitamin K causes the liver to release the blood cell pigment (bilirubin) into the blood (instead of excreting it into the bile) and leads to **jaundice**. When bilirubin invades the brain of an infant, the condition may lead to brain damage or death of the infant.

KEY POINT

- Vitamin K is necessary for blood to clot; deficiency causes uncontrolled bleeding. The bacterial inhabitants of the digestive tract produce vitamin K. Toxicity causes jaundice.

The Water-Soluble Vitamins

Vitamin C and the B vitamins are water soluble. Cooking and washing with water can leach them out of foods. The body absorbs these vitamins easily and just as easily excretes them in the urine. Some of the water-soluble vitamins can remain in the lean tissues for a month or more, but these tissues are actively exchanging materials with the body fluids at all times. At any time, the vitamins may be picked up by the extracellular fluids, washed away by the blood, and excreted in the urine. Advice for meeting the need for these nutrients is straightforward: choose foods that are rich in water-soluble vitamins to achieve an average of the recommended intakes over three days' time. The snapshots in this section can help guide your choices.

Characteristics Water-Soluble Vitamins Share

- Dissolve in water
- Are easily absorbed and excreted
- Are not stored extensively in tissues
- Seldom reach toxic levels

The water-soluble vitamins require special consideration in food preparation to avoid losing or destroying them. See the Food Feature in Chapter 12.

Foods never deliver toxic doses of the water-soluble vitamins, but the large doses concentrated in some vitamin supplements can reach toxic levels. Normally, though, the most likely hazard to the supplement taker is to the wallet: "If you take supplements of the water-soluble vitamins, you may have the most expensive urine in town." This chapter's Think Fitness feature discusses whether athletes need vitamin supplements.

Vitamin C

More than 200 years ago, any man who joined the crew of a seagoing ship knew he had only half a chance of returning alive—not because he might be slain by pirates or die in a storm but because he might contract **scurvy**, a disease that might kill as many as two-thirds of a ship's crew on a long voyage. Ships that sailed on short voyages, especially around the Mediterranean Sea, were safe from this disease. The special hazard of long ocean voyages was that the ship's cook used up the fresh fruit and vegetables early and relied on cereals and live animals for the duration of the voyage.

The first nutrition experiment to be conducted on human beings was devised nearly 250 years ago to find a cure for scurvy. A physician divided some British sailors with scurvy into groups. Each group received a different test substance: vinegar, sulphuric acid, seawater, oranges, or lemons. Those receiving the citrus fruit were

Long voyages without fresh fruit and vegetables spelled possible death by scurvy for the crew.

jaundice (JAWN-dis) yellowing of the skin due to spillover of the bile pigment bilirubin (bill-ee-ROO-bin) from the liver into the general circulation.

scurvy the vitamin C-deficiency disease.

*The version of vitamin K responsible for this effect is menadione.

Chapter 7 The Vitamins

cured within a short time. Sadly, it took 50 years for the British navy to make use of the information and require all of its vessels to provide lime juice to every sailor daily. British sailors were mocked with the term *limey* because of this requirement. The name later given to the vitamin that the fruit provided, **ascorbic acid**, literally means "no-scurvy acid." It is more commonly known today as vitamin C.

Think Fitness | Vitamins for Athletes

Do athletes who strive for top performance need more vitamins than foods can supply? Competitive athletes who choose their diets with reasonable care almost never need nutrient supplements. The reason is elegantly simple. The need for energy to fuel exercise requires that people eat extra Calories of food, and if that extra food is of the kind shown in this chapter's snapshots—fruit, vegetables, milk, eggs, whole or enriched grains, lean meats, and some oils—then the vitamins to support activity follow automatically. Chapter 10 comes back to the roles vitamins play in physical activity.

The Work of Vitamin C Vitamin C performs a variety of functions in the body, but it is best known for its work in maintaining the connective tissues and as an antioxidant. As one of its tasks, vitamin C assists several enzymes in performing their jobs. In particular, the enzymes involved in the formation and maintenance of the tissue protein **collagen** depend on vitamin C for their activity. Collagen forms the base for all connective tissues: bones, teeth, skin, and tendons. Collagen forms the scar tissue that heals wounds, the reinforcing structure that mends fractures, and the supporting material of capillaries that prevents bruises. Vitamin C also acts as a cofactor in the production of carnitine, important for transporting fatty acids within the cells.

In addition to assisting enzymes, vitamin C also acts in a more general way as an antioxidant.[37] Vitamin C protects substances from oxidation by being oxidized itself. For example, cells of the immune system maintain high levels of vitamin C to protect themselves from free radicals generated during assaults on bacteria and other invaders. While some of the oxidized vitamin C is degraded irretrievably and must be replaced by the diet, much is not lost but recycled back to the active form for reuse.

In the intestines, vitamin C protects iron from oxidation and so promotes its absorption. In the blood, vitamin C protects sensitive blood constituents from oxidation and helps protect vitamin E and recycle it to its active form. The antioxidant roles of vitamin C are the focus of extensive study, especially in relation to disease prevention. Unfortunately, research has yielded only disappointing results: vitamin C supplements seem useless against heart disease, cancer, and other diseases, unless they are prescribed to treat a deficiency.[38] In test tubes, a high concentration of vitamin C has the opposite effect of antioxidants; that is, it acts as a **prooxidant** by activating oxidizing elements, such as iron and copper. One study revealed an increase in markers of oxidation in men given 500 milligrams of vitamin C daily. The question of what, if anything, such findings may mean for human health remains unanswered.

Deficiency Symptoms Most of the symptoms of scurvy can be attributed to the breakdown of collagen in the absence of vitamin C: loss of appetite, growth cessation, tenderness to touch, weakness, bleeding gums (shown in Figure 7–9), loose teeth, swollen ankles and wrists, and tiny red spots in the skin where blood has leaked out of capillaries (also shown in the figure). One symptom, anemia, reflects an important role worth repeating—vitamin C helps the body absorb and use nonheme iron, such as that found in plants. Table 7–4 (pages 282–285) summarizes deficiency symptoms and other information about vitamin C.

ascorbic acid one of the active forms of vitamin C (the other is *dehydroascorbic* acid); an antioxidant nutrient.

collagen (COLL-a-jen) the chief protein of most connective tissues, including scars, ligaments, and tendons, and the underlying matrix on which bones and teeth are built.

prooxidant a compound that triggers reactions involving oxygen.

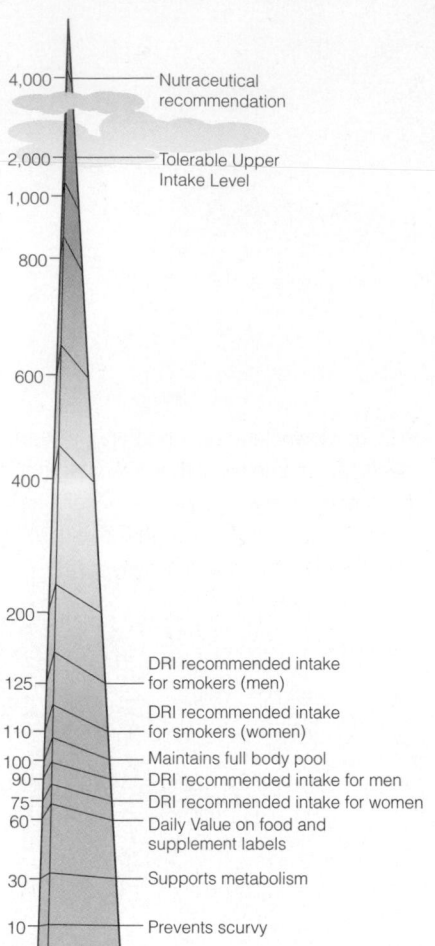

4,000 — Nutraceutical recommendation

2,000 — Tolerable Upper Intake Level
1,000 —

800 —

600 —

400 —

200 —

125 — DRI recommended intake for smokers (men)
110 — DRI recommended intake for smokers (women)
100 — Maintains full body pool
90 — DRI recommended intake for men
75 — DRI recommended intake for women
60 — Daily Value on food and supplement labels

30 — Supports metabolism

10 — Prevents scurvy
0 —

- The term *nutraceutical* is used to market nutrients with pharmacological effects.

- The Maximum Daily Dose (MDD) for single-ingredient supplements for vitamin C is 2,000 mg.

- The DRI Tolerable Upper Intake Level for vitamin C is set at 2,000 mg (2 g)/d.

Figure 7–9

Scurvy Symptoms—Gums and Skin

Vitamin C deficiency causes the breakdown of collagen, which supports the teeth.

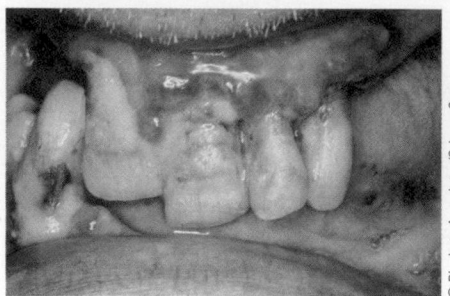

© Biophoto Associates/Science Source

Small pinpoint hemorrhages (red spots) appear in the skin indicating that invisible bleeding may also be occurring.

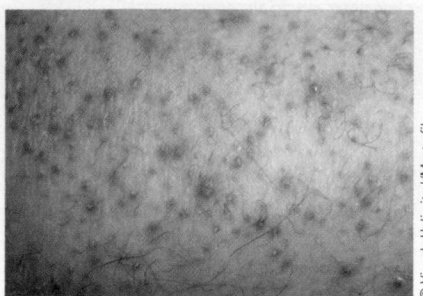

© Visuals Unlimited/Masterfile

In Canada and the United States, scurvy is seldom seen today except in a few elderly people, people addicted to alcohol or other drugs, and a few infants who are fed only cow's milk.[39] Breast milk and infant formula supply enough vitamin C, but infants who are fed cow's milk and receive no vitamin C in formula, fruit juice, or other outside sources are at risk. Low intakes of fruit and vegetables and a poor appetite overall lead to low vitamin C intakes and are not uncommon among people aged 65 and older.

Vitamin C also supports immune system functions and so protects against infection. A long-claimed relationship between vitamin C and the common cold is the topic of this chapter's Consumer Corner, on page 266.

Is Too Much Vitamin C Hazardous to Health?
The easy availability of vitamin C in pill form and the publication of books recommending vitamin C as a "nutraceutical" treatment to prevent and cure colds and cancer have led thousands of people to take huge doses of vitamin C (see the margin drawing). These "volunteer" subjects enabled researchers to study potential adverse effects of large vitamin C doses. One effect observed with a 2-gram dose is alteration of the insulin response to carbohydrate in people with otherwise normal glucose tolerances. Other adverse effects include digestive upsets, such as nausea, abdominal cramps, excessive gas, and diarrhea. Massive doses of vitamin C may interfere with medications to prevent blood clotting. Vitamin C supplements in any dosage may be dangerous for people with an overload of iron in the body because vitamin C increases iron absorption from the intestine and releases iron from storage.

The published research on large doses of vitamin C reveals few instances in which consuming more than 100 to 300 milligrams a day is beneficial, although the range of safe vitamin C intakes seems to be broad, from the absolute minimum of 10 milligrams a day to the Tolerable Upper Intake Level of 2,000 milligrams (2 g). People with kidney disorders and those with a condition of too much iron in their blood may be more susceptible to adverse effects and should avoid vitamin C supplements altogether. Doses approaching 10 grams can be expected to be unsafe. Vitamin C from food is always safe.

The Need for Vitamin C
The adult DRI intake recommendation for vitamin C is 90 milligrams for men and 75 milligrams for women. These amounts are far higher than the 10 or so milligrams per day needed to prevent the symptoms of scurvy. In fact, they are close to the amount at which the body's pool of vitamin C is full to overflowing: about 100 milligrams per day.

Tobacco use, among its many harmful effects, introduces oxidants that deplete the body's vitamin C.[40] Even "passive smokers," who live and work with smokers, and those who regularly chew tobacco need more vitamin C than others.[41] Intake recommendations for smokers are set high, at 125 milligrams for men and 110 milligrams for women, in order to maintain blood levels comparable to those of nonsmokers. Sufficient intake of vitamin C can normalize blood levels, but it cannot protect against the often serious damage caused by exposure to tobacco smoke.

 Food Sources of Vitamin C Fruit and vegetables are the foods to remember for vitamin C, as Snapshot 7–5 shows. A cup of orange juice at breakfast, a salad for lunch,

Snapshot 7-5 ⋯⋯> Vitamin C

Milligrams (scale 0 to 100)

Food	Serving size (kcal)	Vitamin C
Broccoli, boiled	125 mL (29)	~55
Carrots, boiled	125 mL (29)	~3
Tomato, fresh	1 medium (22)	~17
Apple, fresh	1 medium (72)	~8
Banana, fresh	1 medium (105)	~10
Blueberries, fresh	125 mL (44)	~9
Bread, whole wheat	1 slice, 35 g (86)	0
Pasta, whole wheat, cooked	125 mL (92)	0
Rice, white, cooked	125 mL (89)	0
Oatmeal, cooked	175 mL (144)	0
Pita, white	½ pita, 35 g (96)	0
Cereal, high fibre	30 g (78)	0
Milk, 2%	250 mL (129)	~2
Cheddar cheese	50 g (202)	0
Yogurt, 2% plain	175 g (110)	~2
Soy beverage, fortified	250 mL (110)	0
Kefir	175 g (104)	~1
Ice cream, strawberry	125 mL (134)	~5
Chicken breast, roasted	75 g (220)	0
Ground beef, lean, baked	75 g (191)	0
Egg, poached	2 large (144)	0
Tuna, canned in water	75 g (87)	0
Tofu, made with a calcium salt	150 g (114)	~1
Peanut butter	30 mL (184)	0
Excellent, and sometimes unusual, sources:		
Red bell pepper, raw	125 mL (24)	>100
Guava, fresh	125 mL (59)	>100
Kiwi, fresh	1 large (56)	~95

RDA for adult females 75 mg/day
RDA for adult males 90 mg/day

VITAMIN C
Meeting vitamin C needs without vegetables and fruit (green) is almost impossible. Many of them provide the entire RDA in one serving, and others provide at least half. Most meats, legumes, breads, and milk products are poor sources.

Key:
- Vegetables & Fruit
- Grain Products
- Milk & Alternatives
- Meat & Alternatives

Best sources per kcal

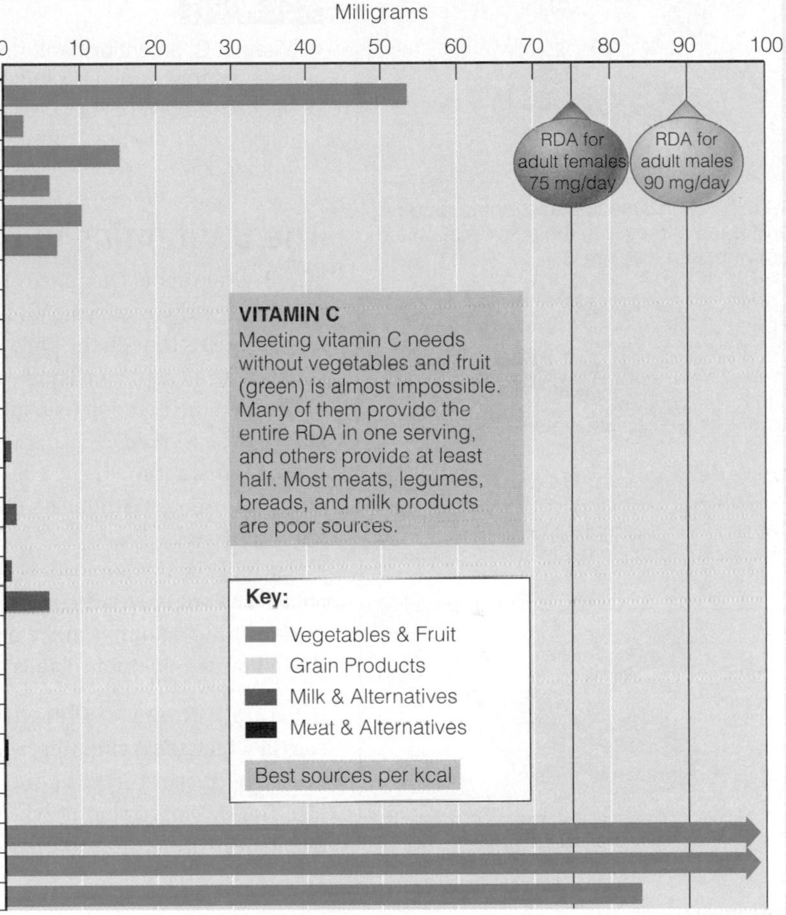

DRI Recommended Intakes:
Men:	90 mg/d
Women:	75 mg/d
Smokers:	+35 mg/d

CCHS 2.2 Mean Intake (nonsmokers):
Men: 171 mg/d
Women: 142 mg/d

Tolerable Upper Intake Level:
Adults: 2,000 mg/d

Chief Functions:
Collagen synthesis (strengthens blood vessel walls, forms scar tissue, provides matrix for bone growth), antioxidant, restores vitamin E to active form, supports immune system, boosts iron absorption

Deficiency:
Scurvy, with pinpoint hemorrhages, fatigue, bleeding gums, bruises; bone fragility, joint pain, poor wound healing, frequent infections

Toxicity:
Nausea, abdominal cramps, diarrhea; rashes; interference with medical tests and drug therapies; in susceptible people, aggravation of gout or kidney stones

Figure 7–10
Coenzyme Action

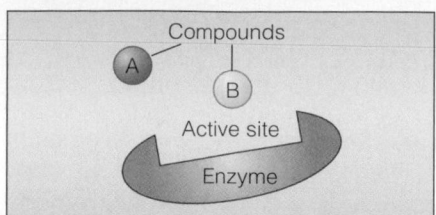

Without the coenzyme, compounds A and B don't respond to the enzyme.

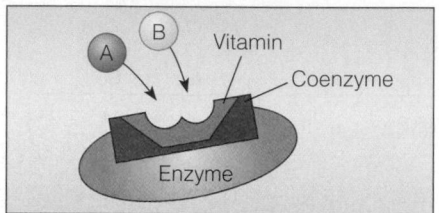

With the coenzyme in place, compounds A and B are attracted to the active site on the enzyme, and they react.

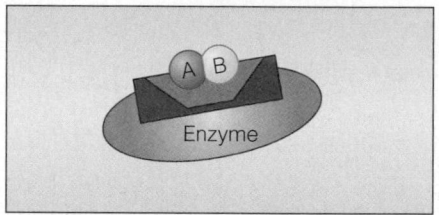

The reaction is completed with the formation of a new product. In this case the product is AB.

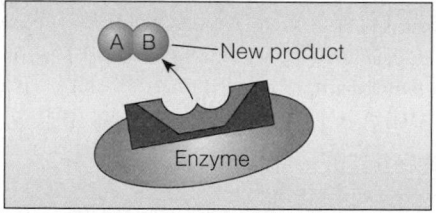

The product AB is released.

and a stalk of broccoli and a potato for dinner easily provide 300 milligrams, making pills unnecessary. People commonly identify citrus fruit as sources of vitamin C, but they often overlook other rich sources (see the photos on the next page). For maximum vitamin C, consumers should treat their fruit and vegetables gently as vitamin C is vulnerable to heat and destroyed by oxygen. Fresh, raw, and quickly cooked fruit, vegetables, and juices retain the most vitamin C, and they should be stored properly and consumed promptly after purchase.[42] The Food Feature in Chapter 12 gives tips for maximizing the vitamins in foods.

Because of their enormous popularity, white potatoes contribute significantly to vitamin C intakes, despite providing less than 10 milligrams per half-cup (125 mL) serving. The sweet potato, often ignored in favour of its paler cousin, is a gold mine of nutrients: a single half-cup serving provides about a third of many people's recommended intake for vitamin C, in addition to its lavish contribution of vitamin A.

KEY POINT

- Vitamin C, an antioxidant, helps maintain collagen, the protein of connective tissue; protects against infection; and helps in iron absorption. The theory that vitamin C prevents or cures colds or cancer is not well supported by research. Taking high vitamin C doses may be unwise. Ample vitamin C can be obtained from foods.

The B Vitamins in Unison

The B vitamins act as part of coenzymes. A **coenzyme** is a small molecule that combines with an enzyme and activates it. (Recall from Chapter 6 that enzymes are large proteins that do the body's building, dismantling, and other work.) Figure 7–10 shows how a coenzyme enables an enzyme to do its job. Sometimes the vitamin part of the enzyme is the active site, where the chemical reaction takes place. The substance to be worked on is attracted to the active site and snaps into place; the reaction proceeds instantaneously. The shape of each enzyme predestines it to accomplish just one kind of job. Without its coenzyme, however, the enzyme is as useless as a car without wheels.

Each of the B vitamins has its own special nature, and the amount of detail known about each one is overwhelming. To simplify things, this introduction describes the teamwork of the B vitamins and emphasizes the consequences of deficiencies. The sections that follow present more details about the vitamins as individuals.

B Vitamin Roles in Metabolism Figure 7–11 shows some body organs and tissues in which the B vitamins help the body metabolize carbohydrates, lipids, and amino acids. The purpose of the figure is not to present a detailed account of metabolism but to give you an impression of where the B vitamins work together with enzymes in the metabolism of energy nutrients and in the making of new cells.

Vitamin C and the Common Cold

Why do so many people take vitamin C supplements to relieve colds? Does any research support this practice? More than 30 years ago, Linus Pauling, a Nobel Prize winner, became a vocal supporter of vitamin C supplements.[*,1]

The scientific community all but discounted his claims because research comparing daily intakes of vitamin C with numbers of colds fails to support Pauling's theories.[2] No study to date has shown conclusively that vitamin C can

prevent colds. One group of researchers, however, has reached two interesting conclusions.[3] First, they confirm that daily doses of vitamin C, taken regularly, do not prevent colds. Second, they find some small therapeutic benefit from

*References for this Consumer Corner are listed separately at the end of the chapter.

vitamin C in high doses (1 g) taken at the onset of a cold. In this case, cold sufferers may shorten the duration of colds by about half a day and reduce the severity of symptoms by about 40 percent. The effect may be greater in children than in adults; in adults, doses teetering on the edge of the Tolerable Upper Intake Level (2 g/d) may be required to produce any effect at all.[4]

Vitamin C (2 g taken daily for two weeks) seems to reduce blood histamine. Anyone who has ever had a cold knows the effects of histamine: sneezing, a runny or stuffy nose, and swollen sinuses. Antihistamine medications provide relief from just those symptoms. In druglike doses, vitamin C may work like a weak antihistamine by reducing histamine levels. Alternatively, vitamin C's antioxidant or other activities may boost the body's immunity or somehow improve its defences.[5]

One other effect is hard at work with supplements of all kinds—the placebo effect.[6] Half of the experimental subjects in one study received a placebo but thought they were receiving vitamin C. These subjects reported having fewer colds than the group who had received vitamin C but thought they were receiving the placebo. At work was the powerful healing effect of faith.

Much more research is required on vitamin C and the common cold before any recommendations are possible. One thing is certain, though— no drug is risk-free, and vitamin C in large doses qualifies as a drug that may have side effects.[7]

Can vitamin C ease the suffering of a person with a cold?

When dietitians say "vitamin C," people think "oranges..."

...but these foods also supply vitamin C.

Many people mistakenly believe that B vitamins supply the body with energy. They do not, at least not directly. The B vitamins are "helpers." The energy-yielding nutrients—carbohydrate, fat, and protein—give the body fuel for energy; the B vitamins *help* the body use that fuel. More specifically, active forms of five of the B vitamins—thiamin, riboflavin, niacin, pantothenic acid, and biotin—participate in the release of energy from carbohydrate, fat, and protein. Vitamin B_6 helps the body use amino acids to make protein; the body then puts the protein to work in many ways—to build new tissues, to make hormones, to fight infections, or to serve as fuel for energy, to name only a few.

Folate and vitamin B_{12} help cells multiply, which is especially important to cells with short life spans that must replace themselves rapidly. Such cells include both the

coenzyme (co-EN-zime) a small molecule that works with an enzyme to promote the enzyme's activity. Many coenzymes have B vitamins as part of their structure (*co* means "with").

Figure 7–11

Some Roles of the B Vitamins in Metabolism: Examples

Key:

Coenzyme name*		Vitamin name
TPP	=	thiamin
FAD FMN	=	riboflavin
NAD NADP	=	niacin
PLP	=	vitamin B$_6$
THF	=	folate
CoA	=	pantothenic acid
Bio	=	biotin
B$_{12}$	=	vitamin B$_{12}$

*TPP, Thiamin pyrophosphate

FAD, Flavin adenine dinucleotide

FMN, Flavin mononucleotide

NAD, Nicotinamide adenine dinucleotide

NADP, Nicotinamide adenine dinucleotide phosphate

PLP, Pyridoxal phosphate

THF, Tetrahyrdrofolic acid

CoA, Coenzyme A

Bio, Biotin

B$_{12}$, Vitamin B$_{12}$

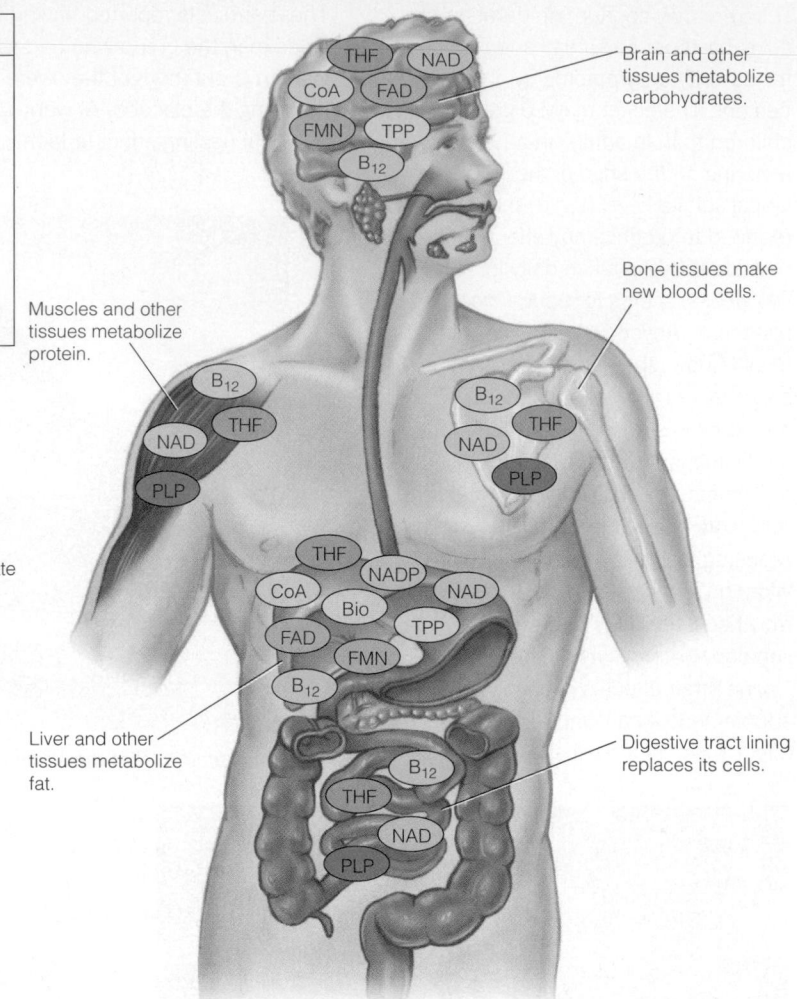

Brain and other tissues metabolize carbohydrates.

Bone tissues make new blood cells.

Muscles and other tissues metabolize protein.

Liver and other tissues metabolize fat.

Digestive tract lining replaces its cells.

To Memorize the Names of the Eight B Vitamins, Try Remembering This Sentence or Make Up One of Your Own

Tender	(thiamin)
Romance	(riboflavin)
Never	(niacin)
Fails,	(folate)
with 6 or 12	(B$_6$ and B$_{12}$)
Beautiful	(biotin)
Pearls.	(pantothenic acid)

red blood cells (which live for about 120 days) and the cells that line the digestive tract (which replace themselves every 3 days). These cells deliver energy to all of the others. In short, every B vitamin is involved, directly or indirectly, in energy metabolism.

B Vitamin Deficiencies   As long as B vitamins are present, their presence is not felt. Only when they are missing does their absence manifest itself in a lack of energy and a multitude of other symptoms, as you can imagine after looking at Figure 7–11. The reactions by which B vitamins facilitate energy release take place in every cell, and no cell can do its work without energy. Thus, in a B vitamin deficiency, every cell is affected. Among the symptoms of B vitamin deficiencies are nausea, severe exhaustion, irritability, depression, forgetfulness, loss of appetite and weight, pain in muscles, impairment of the immune response, loss of control of the limbs, abnormal heart action, severe skin problems, swollen red tongue, and teary or bloodshot eyes. Because cell renewal depends on energy and protein, which in turn depend on the B vitamins, the digestive tract and the blood are invariably damaged. In children, full recovery may be impossible. In the case of a thiamin deficiency during growth, permanent brain damage can result.

In academic discussions of the vitamins, different sets of deficiency symptoms are given for each one. Such clear-cut sets of symptoms are found only in laboratory animals that have been fed fabricated diets that lack just one nutrient.[43] In real life, a deficiency of any one B vitamin seldom shows up by itself because people don't eat nutrients singly; they eat foods that contain mixtures of nutrients. A deficiency of one B vitamin may appear to be responsible for a cluster of symptoms, but subtler, undetected deficiencies may accompany it. If treatment involves giving wholesome food rather than a single supplement, the subtler deficiencies will be corrected along with the major one. The symptoms of B vitamin deficiencies and toxicities are listed in Table 7–4 later in this chapter.

KEY POINT

■ As part of coenzymes, the B vitamins help enzymes do their jobs. The B vitamins facilitate the work of every cell. Some help generate energy; others help make protein and new cells. B vitamins work everywhere in the body tissue to metabolize carbohydrate, fat, and protein.

The B Vitamins as Individuals

Although the B vitamins all work as part of coenzymes and share other characteristics, each B vitamin has special qualities. The next sections provide details about each of the B vitamins.

Thiamin and Riboflavin   **Thiamin** plays a critical role in the energy metabolism of all cells. Thiamin also occupies a special site on nerve cell membranes. Consequently, nerve processes and their responding tissues, the muscles, depend heavily on thiamin.

The classic thiamin-deficiency disease, **beriberi**, was first observed in East Asia, where rice provided 80 to 90 percent of the total Calories most people consumed and was therefore their principal source of thiamin. When the custom of polishing rice (removing its brown coat, which contained the thiamin) became widespread, beriberi swept through the population like an epidemic. Scientists wasted years of effort hunting for a microbial cause of beriberi before they realized that the cause was not something present in the environment but something absent from it. Figure 7–12 depicts beriberi and describes its two forms.

Just before 1900, an observant physician working in a prison in East Asia discovered that beriberi could be cured with a proper diet. The physician noticed that the chickens at the prison had developed a stiffness and weakness similar to that of the prisoners who had beriberi. The chickens were being fed the rice left on prisoners' plates. When the rice bran, which had been discarded in the kitchen, was given to the chickens, their paralysis was cured. The physician met resistance when he tried to feed the rice bran, the "garbage," to the prisoners, but it worked—it produced a miracle cure like those described at the beginning of the chapter. Later, extracts of rice bran were used to prevent infantile beriberi; still later, thiamin was synthesized.

In developed countries today, alcohol abuse often leads to a severe form of thiamin deficiency, Wernicke-Korsakoff syndrome, defined in Controversy 3. Alcohol contributes energy but carries almost no nutrients with it and often displaces food. In addition, alcohol impairs absorption of thiamin from the digestive tract and hastens its excretion in the urine, tripling the risk of deficiency. The syndrome is characterized by symptoms almost indistinguishable from alcohol abuse itself: apathy, irritability, mental confusion, disorientation, loss of memory, jerky eye movements, and a staggering gait. Unlike alcohol toxicity, the syndrome responds quickly to an injection of thiamin, and some experts recommend a precautionary dose for any patients suspected of having the syndrome.

Thiamin occurs in small amounts in many nutritious foods. Ham and other pork products, sunflower seeds, enriched or whole-grain cereals, and legumes are especially rich in thiamin (see Snapshot 7–6). If you keep empty-Calorie foods to a minimum and focus your meals on nutritious foods each day, you will easily meet your thiamin needs. The DRI committee set the thiamin intake recommendation at 1.2 milligrams per day for men and at 1.1 milligrams per day for women. Pregnancy and lactation require somewhat more thiamin (see the DRI recommendations, inside front cover, page A).

Like thiamin, **riboflavin** plays a role in the energy metabolism of all cells. When thiamin is deficient, riboflavin may be lacking, too, but its deficiency symptoms may

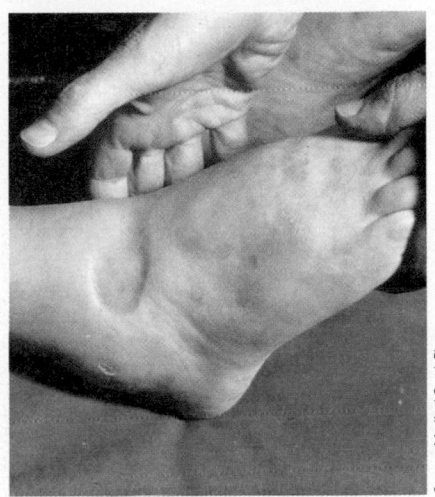

Figure 7–12
Beriberi

Beriberi takes two forms: wet beriberi, characterized by edema (fluid accumulation), and dry beriberi, without edema. This person's ankle retains the imprint of the physician's thumb, showing the edema of wet beriberi.

Custom Medical Stock Photos

● The maximum daily dose (MDD) of thiamin in single-ingredient supplements is 100 mg/d.

● The maximum daily dose (MDD) of riboflavin in single-ingredient supplements is 100 mg/d.

thiamin (THIGH-uh-min) a B vitamin involved in the body's use of fuels.

beriberi (berry-berry) the thiamin-deficiency disease; characterized by loss of sensation in the hands and feet, muscular weakness, advancing paralysis, and abnormal heart action.

riboflavin (RIBE-o-flay-vin) a B vitamin active in the body's energy-releasing mechanisms.

Milligrams

Food	Serving size (kcal)
Broccoli, boiled	125 mL (29)
Carrots, boiled	125 mL (29)
Tomato, fresh	1 medium (22)
Apple, fresh	1 medium (72)
Banana, fresh	1 medium (105)
Blueberries, fresh	125 mL (44)
Bread, whole wheat	1 slice, 35 g (86)
Pasta, whole wheat, cooked	125 mL (92)
Rice, white, cooked	125 mL (89)
Oatmeal, cooked	175 mL (144)
Pita, white	½ pita, 35 g (96)
Cereal, high fibre	30 g (78)
Milk, 2%	250 mL (129)
Cheddar cheese	50 g (202)
Yogurt, 2%, plain	175 g (110)
Soy beverage, fortified	250 mL (110)
Kefir	175 g (104)
Ice cream, strawberry	125 mL (134)
Chicken breast, roasted	75 g (220)
Ground beef, lean, baked	75 g (191)
Egg, poached	2 large (144)
Tuna, canned in water	75 g (87)
Tofu, made with calcium salt	150 g (114)
Peanut butter	30 mL (184)
Excellent, and sometimes unusual, sources:	
Veg/soy burger	150 g (266)
Pork chop, lean, fried	75 g (174)
Acorn squash, baked	125 mL (61)

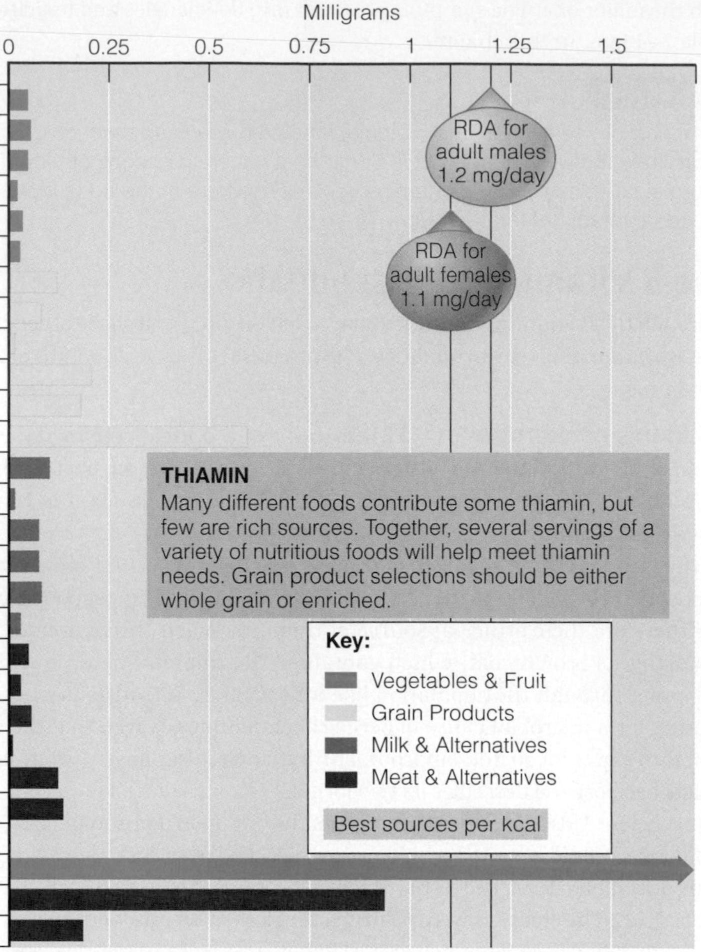

Scale: 0, 0.25, 0.5, 0.75, 1, 1.25, 1.5

RDA for adult males 1.2 mg/day

RDA for adult females 1.1 mg/day

THIAMIN
Many different foods contribute some thiamin, but few are rich sources. Together, several servings of a variety of nutritious foods will help meet thiamin needs. Grain product selections should be either whole grain or enriched.

Key:
- ■ Vegetables & Fruit
- ■ Grain Products
- ■ Milk & Alternatives
- ■ Meat & Alternatives

Best sources per kcal

DRI Recommended Intakes:
Men: 1.2 mg/d
Women: 1.1 mg/d

CCHS 2.2 Mean Intake:
Men: 2.14 mg/d
Women: 1.48 mg/d

Chief Functions:
Part of coenzyme active in energy metabolism

Deficiency:[a]
Beriberi with possible edema or muscle wasting; enlarged heart, heart failure, muscular weakness, pain, apathy, poor short-term memory, confusion, irritability, difficulty walking, paralysis, anorexia, weight loss

Toxicity:
None reported

[a]Severe thiamin deficiency is often related to heavy alcohol consumption.

go undetected because those of thiamin deficiency are more severe. Worldwide, riboflavin deficiency has been documented among children whose diets lack milk products and meats, and researchers suspect that it occurs among some U.S. elderly as well.[44] A diet that remedies riboflavin deficiency invariably contains some thiamin, and so clears up both deficiencies. People obtain over a quarter of their

riboflavin from enriched breads, cereals, pasta, and other grain products, while milk and milk products supply another 20 percent. Some vegetables, eggs, and meats contribute most of the rest (see Snapshot 7–7).[45]

Table 7–4 on pages 282–285 lists the symptoms of riboflavin deficiency.

Milligrams

Food	Serving size (kcal)	Riboflavin (mg)
Broccoli, boiled	125 mL (29)	
Carrots, boiled	125 mL (29)	
Tomato, fresh	1 medium (22)	
Apple, fresh	1 medium (72)	
Banana, fresh	1 medium (105)	
Blueberries, fresh	125 mL (44)	
Bread, whole wheat	1 slice, 35 g (86)	
Pasta, whole wheat, cooked	125 mL (92)	
Rice, white, cooked	125 mL (89)	
Oatmeal, cooked	175 mL (144)	
Pita, white	½ pita, 35 g (96)	
Cereal, high fibre	30 g (78)	
Milk, 2%	250 mL (129)	
Cheddar cheese	50 g (202)	
Yogurt, 2%, plain	175 g (110)	
Soy beverage, fortified	250 mL (110)	
Kefir	175 g (104)	
Ice cream, strawberry	125 mL (134)	
Chicken breast, roasted	75 g (220)	
Ground beef, lean, baked	75 g (191)	
Egg, poached	2 large (144)	
Tuna, canned in water	75 g (87)	
Tofu, made with a calcium salt	150 g (114)	
Peanut butter	30 mL (184)	
Excellent, and sometimes unusual, sources:		
Beef liver, fried	75 g (178)	
Mushrooms, white stirfried	125 mL (15)	
Oysters, steamed	75 g (52)	

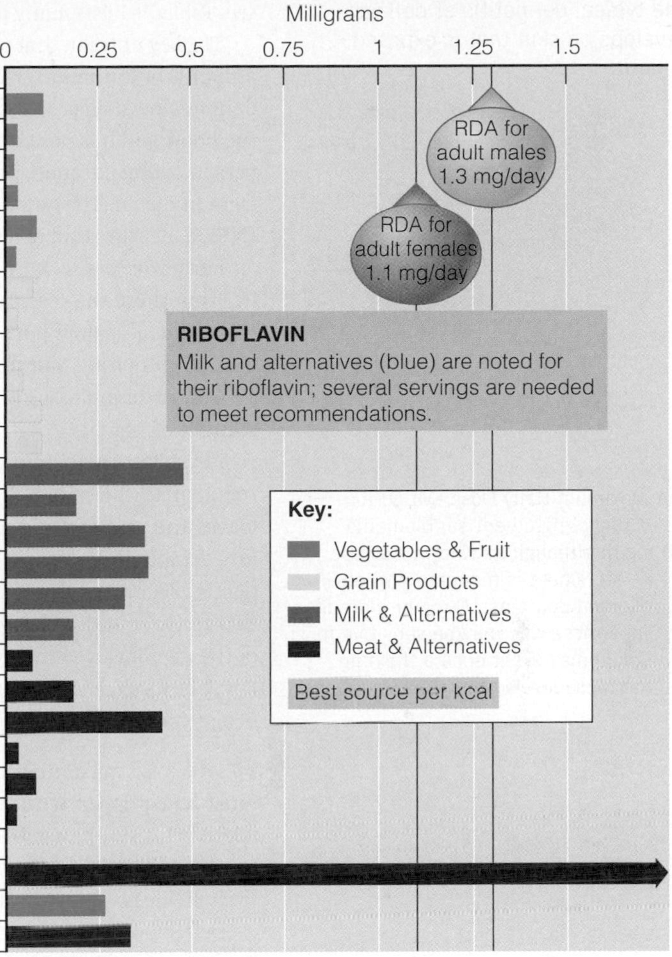

RDA for adult males 1.3 mg/day

RDA for adult females 1.1 mg/day

RIBOFLAVIN
Milk and alternatives (blue) are noted for their riboflavin; several servings are needed to meet recommendations.

Key:
- Vegetables & Fruit
- Grain Products
- Milk & Alternatives
- Meat & Alternatives

Best source per kcal

DRI Recommended Intakes:
Men: 1.3 mg/d
Women: 1.1 mg/d

CCHS 2.2 Mean Intake:
Men: 2.41 mg/d
Women: 1.72 mg/d

Chief Functions
Part of coenzymes active in energy metabolism; supports vision and skin health

Deficiency:
Cracks and redness at corners of mouth; painful, smooth, purplish red tongue; sore throat; inflamed eyes and eyelids, sensitivity to light; skin rashes

Toxicity:
None reported

Niacin The vitamin **niacin**, like thiamin and riboflavin, participates in the energy metabolism of every cell of the body. The niacin-deficiency disease, **pellagra**, appeared in Europe in the 1700s when corn from the New World became a staple food. In the early 1900s in the United States, pellagra was devastating lives throughout the South and Midwest. Hundreds of thousands of pellagra victims were thought to be suffering from a contagious disease until this dietary deficiency was identified. The disease still occurs among poorly nourished people living in urban slums and particularly in those with alcohol addiction. Pellagra is also still common in parts of Africa and Asia. Its symptoms are known as the four "Ds": diarrhea, dermatitis, dementia, and, ultimately, death.

niacin a B vitamin needed in energy metabolism. Niacin can be eaten preformed or can be made in the body from tryptophan, one of the amino acids. Other forms of niacin are *nicotinic acid*, *niacinamide*, and *nicotinamide*.

pellagra (pell-AY-gra) the niacin-deficiency disease (*pellis* means "skin"; *agra* means "rough"). Symptoms include the "4 Ds": diarrhea, dermatitis, dementia, and death.

Figure 7-13
Pellagra

The typical dermatitis of pellagra develops on skin that is exposed to light.

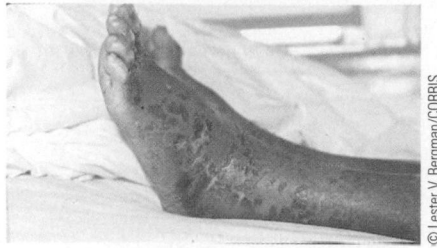

© Lester V. Bergman/CORBIS

● The Maximum Daily Dose (MDD) for niacin in single-ingredient supplements is 500 mg/d, although a "Known Adverse Reaction" statement is mandatory when the supplement contains 10 mg or more of niacin since those who may be sensitive to nicotinic acid may experience a flushing reaction at these levels of intake.

niacin equivalents (NE) the amount of niacin present in food, including the niacin that can theoretically be made from its precursor tryptophan that is present in the food.

folate (FOH-late) a B vitamin that acts as part of a coenzyme important in the manufacture of new cells. The form added to foods and supplements is *folic acid*.

neural tube defects abnormalities of the brain and spinal cord apparent at birth and believed to be related to a woman's folate intake before and during pregnancy. Also defined in Chapter 13.

Figure 7-13 shows the skin disorder associated with pellagra. For comparison, Figure 7-16 (page 278) and Figure 7-2 (page 249) show skin disorders associated with vitamin B_6 and vitamin A deficiency, respectively, a reminder that any nutrient deficiency affects the skin and all other cells. The skin just happens to be the organ you can see. Table 7-4 lists many more symptoms of niacin deficiency.

The key nutrient that prevents pellagra is niacin, but any protein containing sufficient amounts of the amino acid tryptophan will serve in its place. Tryptophan, which is abundant in almost all proteins (but is limited in the protein of corn), is converted to niacin in the body, and it is possible to cure pellagra by administering tryptophan alone. Thus, a person eating adequate protein (as most people in developed nations do) will not be deficient in niacin. The amount of niacin in a diet is stated in terms of **niacin equivalents (NE)**, a measure that takes available tryptophan into account.

Early workers seeking the cause of pellagra observed that well-fed people never got it. From there the researchers defined a diet that reliably produced the disease—one of cornmeal, salted pork fat, and molasses. Corn is not only low in protein but also lacks tryptophan. Salt pork is almost pure fat and contains too little protein to compensate, and molasses is virtually protein-free. Snapshot 7-8 shows some good food sources of niacin.

Physicians may administer large doses of a form of niacin as part of a treatment regimen to lower blood lipids associated with CVD.* When used this way, niacin leaves the realm of nutrition to become a pharmacological agent—a drug. As with any drug, self-dosing with niacin is ill-advised; large doses can injure the liver, cause peptic ulcers, or cause vision loss.[46] Certain forms of niacin supplements in amounts two to three times the DRI intake recommendation cause "niacin flush," a dilation of the capillaries of the skin with perceptible tingling that, if intense, can be painful. For safety's sake, anyone taking large doses of niacin should do so only under the care of a physician.

Folate To make new cells, tissues must have the vitamin **folate**.[47] Each new cell must be equipped with new genetic material—copies of the parent cell's DNA—and folate helps synthesize DNA. Folate is also critical to the normal metabolism of several amino acids. Because immature red and white blood cells and the cells of the digestive tract divide most rapidly, they are most vulnerable to deficiency.

Deficiencies of folate cause anemia, diminished immunity, and abnormal digestive function. In the United States, a significant number of cases of folate-deficiency anemia occur yearly. This anemia is related to the anemia of vitamin B_{12} malabsorption because the two vitamins work as teammates in producing red blood cells—see Figure 7-15 on page 276. Research suggests that a diet deficient in folate may also elevate the risk of CVD and cancer of the colon and increase a woman's risk for cervical cancer.[48] Folate deficiencies may result from an inadequate intake or from illnesses that impair folate's absorption, increase its excretion, require medication that interacts with folate, or otherwise increase the body's need.

Folate deficiency is also associated with a group of devastating birth defects known as **neural tube defects**.[49] Neural tube defects range from slight problems in the spine to mental retardation, severely diminished brain size, and death shortly after birth. These neural tube defects arise in the first days or weeks of pregnancy, long before most women suspect that they are pregnant, and most women eat too few fruits and vegetables from day to day to supply even half the folate needed to prevent them. In the late 1990s, Health Canada made it mandatory to fortify bleached wheat flour in products such as breads, cereals, and pastas with an especially absorbable synthetic

The B vitamins thiamin, riboflavin, niacin, and folate (as folic acid) are among the enrichment nutrients added to grain foods such as breads and cereals sold in Canada. Chapter 4 presented more details on enrichment of grain foods. Also see the Food Feature for this chapter.

*The form of niacin is nicotinic acid.

Milligrams/Niacin Equivalents (NE)*

Food	Serving size (kcal)	Chart value (NE)
Broccoli, boiled	125 mL (29)	~1
Carrots, boiled	125 mL (29)	~1
Tomato, fresh	1 medium (22)	~1
Apple, fresh	1 medium (72)	<1
Banana, fresh	1 medium (105)	~1
Blueberries, fresh	125 mL (44)	<1
Bread, whole wheat	1 slice, 35 g (86)	~2
Pasta, whole wheat, cooked	125 mL (92)	~2
Rice, white, cooked	125 mL (89)	~2
Oatmeal, cooked	175 mL (144)	~1
Pita, white	½ pita, 35 g (96)	~2
Cereal, high fibre	30 g (78)	~6
Milk, 2%	250 mL (129)	~2
Cheddar cheese	50 g (202)	~3
Yogurt, 2%, plain	175 g (110)	~1
Soy beverage, fortified	250 mL (110)	~2
Kefir	175 g (104)	~2
Ice cream, strawberry	125 mL (134)	~1
Chicken breast, roasted	75 g (220)	~12
Ground beef, lean, baked	75 g (191)	~6
Egg, poached	2 large (144)	~4
Tuna, canned in water	75 g (87)	~8
Tofu, made with calcium salt	150 g (114)	~4
Peanut butter	30 mL (184)	~4
Excellent, and sometimes unusual, sources:		
Beef liver, fried	75 g (52)	~17
Mushrooms, portobello, grilled	125 mL (19)	~5
Sunflower seeds, toasted	60 mL (210)	~4

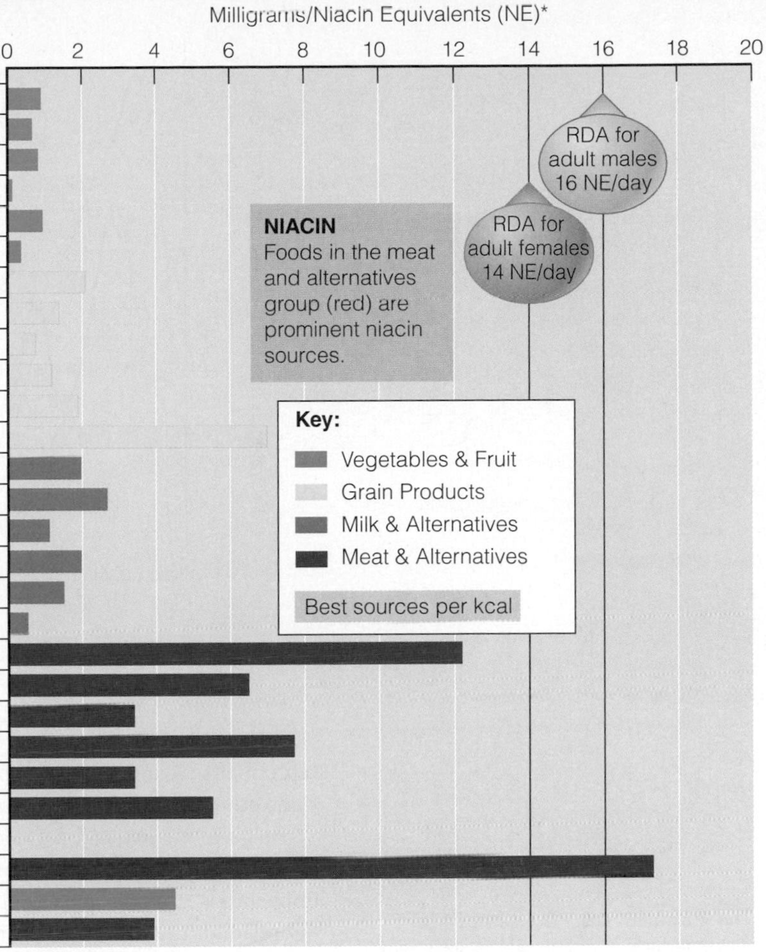

RDA for adult males 16 NE/day

RDA for adult females 14 NE/day

NIACIN
Foods in the meat and alternatives group (red) are prominent niacin sources.

Key:
- Vegetables & Fruit
- Grain Products
- Milk & Alternatives
- Meat & Alternatives

Best sources per kcal

* Niacin recommendations are expressed as Niacin Equivalents (NE)

DRI Recommended Intakes:
Men: 16 mg/d[a]
Women: 14 mg/d

CCHS 2.2 Mean Intake:
Men: 49.7 NE/d
Women: 33.1 NE/d

Tolerable Upper Intake Level:
Adults: 35 mg/d

Chief Functions:
Part of coenzymes needed in energy metabolism

Deficiency:
Pellagra, characterized by flaky skin rash (dermatitis) where exposed to sunlight; mental depression, apathy, fatigue, loss of memory, headache; diarrhea, abdominal pain, vomiting; swollen, smooth, bright red or black tongue

Toxicity:
Painful flush, hives, and rash ("niacin flush"); excessive sweating; blurred vision; liver damage, impaired glucose tolerance

[a] Niacin DRI Recommended Intakes are expressed in niacin equivalents (NE); the Tolerable Upper Intake Level refers to preformed niacin.

form of folate, folic acid. Since this fortification began, typical folate intakes from fortified foods appear to have increased dramatically, as evidenced by a decline in neural tube defects from 1.13 in 1,000 pregnancies before fortification to 0.58 in 1,000 pregnancies after fortification and an associated 41 percent increase in red cell folate in

Figure 7–14

Relationship between Neural Tube Defects and Folic Acid Food Fortification

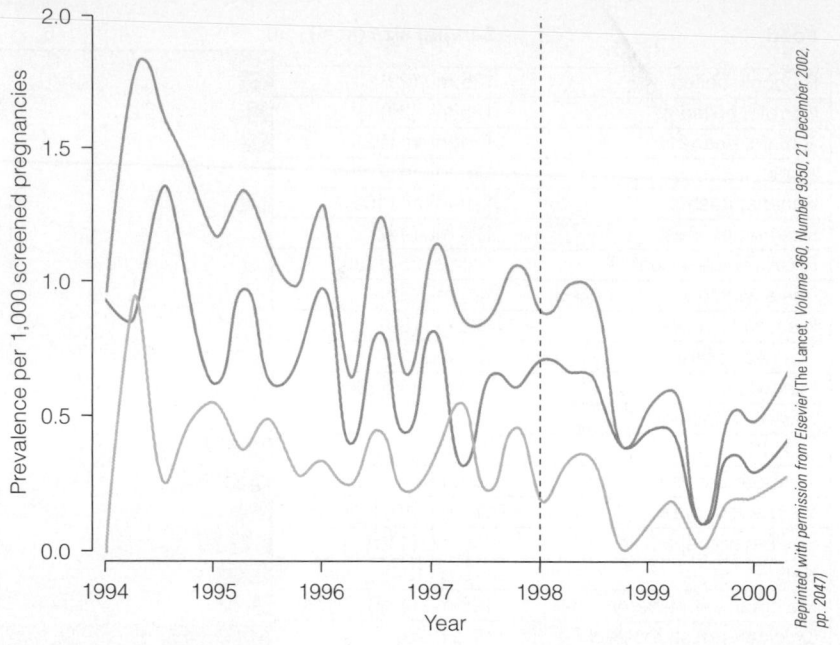

reproductive females in Ontario (Figure 7–14).[50] Researchers expect to see declines in some other birth defects and miscarriages as well.[51]

As for folate toxicity, a Tolerable Upper Intake Level for synthetic folate from supplements and enriched foods is set at 1,000 micrograms a day for adults. Of major importance are concerns about folate's ability to mask deficiencies of vitamin B$_{12}$ (more about this effect later). The possibility also exists that, once in the blood, excess folate may negate the actions of some anticancer drugs that work by blocking the activities of folate in rapidly dividing cancer cells. Time will tell whether the apparent benefits of folate enrichment outweigh the risks.

The difference in absorption between naturally occurring food folate and the synthetic folate that enriches foods and is added to supplements necessitates compensation when measuring folate. The unit of measure, **dietary folate equivalent**, or **DFE**, converts all forms of folate into micrograms that are equivalent to the folate in foods. Watch out for food and supplement labels that still express folate values in micrograms not converted to DFE; Appendix B offers a conversion factor.

 Folate's name is derived from the word *foliage*, and, sure enough, folate is naturally abundant in leafy green vegetables such as spinach and turnip greens (see Snapshot 7–9). Fresh, uncooked vegetables and fruit are good natural sources because the heat of cooking and the oxidation that occurs during storage destroy much of the folate in foods. Eggs also contain some folate. Milk included in a meal may enhance the absorption of folate.

The DRI recommendation for folate intake for healthy adults is set at 400 micrograms per day. The DRI committee also advises all women of childbearing age to consume 400 micrograms of synthetic folate, or *folic acid*, from supplements or enriched foods each day in addition to the folate that occurs naturally in their foods. Canada's Food Guide states, "All women who could become pregnant and those who are pregnant or breastfeeding need a multivitamin containing folic acid every day" (http://www.hc-sc.gc.ca/fn-an/food-guide-aliment/index-eng.php); Health Canada also has more detailed prenatal guidelines regarding folic acid (http://www.hc-sc .gc.ca/fn-an/pubs/nutrition/folate-eng.php). Of all of the vitamins, folate is most

● The Maximum Daily Dose (MDD) in single-ingredient supplements is 199 µg/d, although it may be higher for multivitamin/ mineral supplements provided specific criteria are met.

dietary folate equivalent (DFE) a unit of measure expressing the amount of folate available to the body from naturally occurring sources. The measure mathematically equalizes the difference in absorption between less absorbable food folate and highly absorbable synthetic folate added to enriched foods and found in supplements.

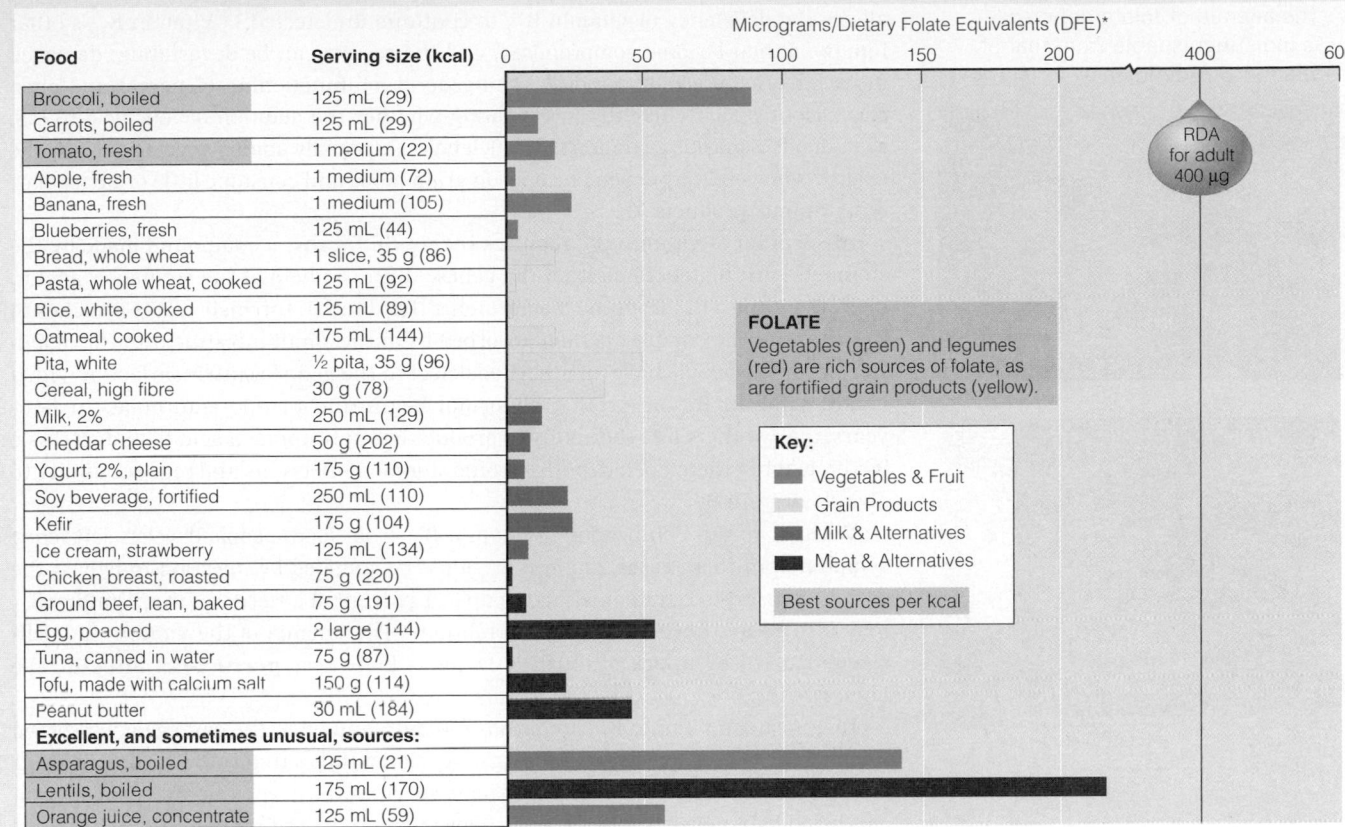

Micrograms/Dietary Folate Equivalents (DFE)*

Food	Serving size (kcal)
Broccoli, boiled	125 mL (29)
Carrots, boiled	125 mL (29)
Tomato, fresh	1 medium (22)
Apple, fresh	1 medium (72)
Banana, fresh	1 medium (105)
Blueberries, fresh	125 mL (44)
Bread, whole wheat	1 slice, 35 g (86)
Pasta, whole wheat, cooked	125 mL (92)
Rice, white, cooked	125 mL (89)
Oatmeal, cooked	175 mL (144)
Pita, white	½ pita, 35 g (96)
Cereal, high fibre	30 g (78)
Milk, 2%	250 mL (129)
Cheddar cheese	50 g (202)
Yogurt, 2%, plain	175 g (110)
Soy beverage, fortified	250 mL (110)
Kefir	175 g (104)
Ice cream, strawberry	125 mL (134)
Chicken breast, roasted	75 g (220)
Ground beef, lean, baked	75 g (191)
Egg, poached	2 large (144)
Tuna, canned in water	75 g (87)
Tofu, made with calcium salt	150 g (114)
Peanut butter	30 mL (184)
Excellent, and sometimes unusual, sources:	
Asparagus, boiled	125 mL (21)
Lentils, boiled	175 mL (170)
Orange juice, concentrate	125 mL (59)

FOLATE
Vegetables (green) and legumes (red) are rich sources of folate, as are fortified grain products (yellow).

Key:
- Vegetables & Fruit
- Grain Products
- Milk & Alternatives
- Meat & Alternatives

Best sources per kcal

RDA for adult 400 µg

* Folate recommendations are expressed as Dietary Folate Equivalents (DFE).

DRI Recommended Intake:
Adults: 400 µg/d[a]

CCHS 2.2 Mean Intake:
Men: 587 DFE/d
Women: 415 DFE/d

Tolerable Upper Intake Level:
Adults: 1,000 µg/d

Chief Functions:
Part of a coenzyme needed for new cell synthesis

Deficiency:
Anemia; smooth, red tongue; depression, mental confusion, weakness, fatigue, irritability, headache; a low intake increases the risk of neural tube birth defects

Toxicity:
Masks vitamin B_{12}–deficiency symptoms

[a]Folate recommendations are expressed in dietary folate equivalents (DFE). Note that for natural folate sources, 1 µg = 1 DFE; for enrichment sources, 1 µg = 1.7 DFE.

likely to interact with medications. Ten major groups of drugs, including antacids and aspirin and its relatives, have been shown to interfere with the body's use of folate. Occasional use of these drugs to relieve headache or upset stomach presents no concern, but frequent users may need to pay attention to their folate intakes. These include people with chronic pain or ulcers who rely heavily on aspirin or antacids as well as those who smoke or take oral contraceptives or anticonvulsant medications.

Vitamin B_{12} **Vitamin B_{12}** and folate are closely related: each depends on the other for activation. By itself, vitamin B_{12} also helps maintain the sheaths that surround and protect nerve fibres. Without sufficient vitamin B_{12}, nerves become

vitamin B_{12} a B vitamin that helps convert folate to its active form and also helps maintain the sheath around nerve cells. Vitamin B_{12}'s scientific name, not often used, is *cyanocobalamin*.

Figure 7–15

Anemic and Normal Blood Cells

The anemia of folate deficiency is indistinguishable from that of vitamin B_{12} deficiency.

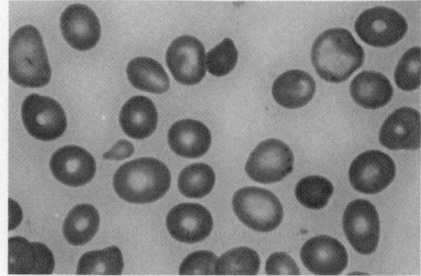

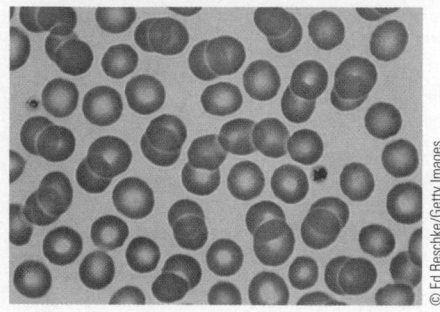

© Ed Reschke/Getty Images

● The Maximum Daily Dose (MDD) of vitamin B_{12} in single-ingredient supplements is 1,000 μg/d.

intrinsic factor a factor found inside a system. The intrinsic factor necessary to prevent pernicious anemia is now known to be a compound that helps in the absorption of vitamin B_{12}.

pernicious (per-NISH-us) **anemia** a vitamin B_{12}–deficiency disease caused by a lack of intrinsic factor and characterized by large, immature red blood cells and damage to the nervous system (*pernicious* means "highly injurious or destructive").

damaged and folate fails to do its blood-building work, so vitamin B_{12} deficiency causes an anemia identical to that caused by folate deficiency. The blood symptoms of a deficiency of either folate or vitamin B_{12} include the presence of large, immature red blood cells. Administering extra folate often clears up this blood condition but allows the deficiency of vitamin B_{12} to continue undetected.[52] Vitamin B_{12}'s other functions then become compromised, and the results can be devastating: damaged nerve sheaths, creeping paralysis, and general malfunctioning of nerves and muscles. Scientists are currently investigating whether the addition of folic acid to U.S. grain foods is masking vitamin B_{12} deficiencies, especially among vegetarians and the elderly, who generally depend heavily on grain foods and consume little or no meat or other animal products.[53]

Absorption of vitamin B_{12} requires **intrinsic factor**, a compound made by the stomach with instructions from the genes. With the help of the stomach's acid to liberate vitamin B_{12} from the food proteins that bind it, intrinsic factor attaches to the vitamin; the complex is then absorbed from the small intestine into the bloodstream. A few people have an inherited defect in the gene for intrinsic factor, which makes vitamin B_{12} absorption abnormal beginning in mid-adulthood. In later years, many others lose the ability to produce enough stomach acidity and intrinsic factor, leaving them open to both chronic stomach infections and reduced ability to absorb vitamin B_{12}.*

Without normal absorption of vitamin B_{12} from food, people develop deficiency symptoms. In these cases, vitamin B_{12} must be supplied by injection to bypass the defective absorptive system, although up to 1 percent of large doses of crystalline B_{12} may also be absorbed under these conditions. The anemia of the vitamin B_{12} deficiency caused by a lack of intrinsic factor is known as **pernicious anemia** (see Figure 7–15).

Diagnosing a vitamin B_{12} problem is difficult, and often the damage will proceed unchecked. In an effort to prevent excessive folate intakes that could mask symptoms of a vitamin B_{12} deficiency, Health Canada specifies the exact amounts of folate that can be added to enriched foods, and supplements that contain more than 200 μg of folic acid must also contain at least 2.4 μg of vitamin B_{12}.

As Snapshot 7–10 shows, vitamin B_{12} is present only in foods of animal origin, not in foods from plants. Worldwide, vitamin B_{12} deficiency among vegetarians is a growing problem.[54] The uninformed strict vegetarian is at special risk and may not show signs of deficiency right away because the body stores up to six years' worth of vitamin B_{12}.[55] A pregnant or lactating vegetarian woman who eats no foods of animal origin should be aware that her infant can develop a vitamin B_{12} deficiency, even if the mother appears healthy. A deficiency of this vitamin can cause irreversible nervous system damage in the developing fetus, which can be diagnosed only after birth when the infant displays nerve and cognitive problems that can last into childhood.[56] All strict vegetarians, and especially pregnant women, must be sure to use vitamin B_{12}–fortified products, such as vitamin B_{12}–fortified soy drink, or to take the appropriate supplements.

Controversy 6 describes the devastating effects on infants born to women who were deficient in vitamin B_{12} during pregnancy.

The way folate masks the anemia of vitamin B_{12} deficiency underscores a point worth repeating. It takes a skilled professional to correctly diagnose a nutrient deficiency or imbalance, and you take a serious risk when you diagnose yourself or listen to self-proclaimed experts. A second point: since vitamin B_{12} deficiency in the body may be caused by either a lack of the vitamin in the diet or a lack of the intrinsic factor necessary to absorb the vitamin, a change in diet alone may not correct the deficiency, another reason for seeking professional diagnosis when you have physical symptoms.

---

*This condition is atrophic gastritis (a-TRO-fik gas-TRY-tis), a chronic inflammation of the stomach accompanied by a diminished size and functioning of the stomach's mucous membrane and glands.

Snapshot 7-10 ⟶ Vitamin B₁₂

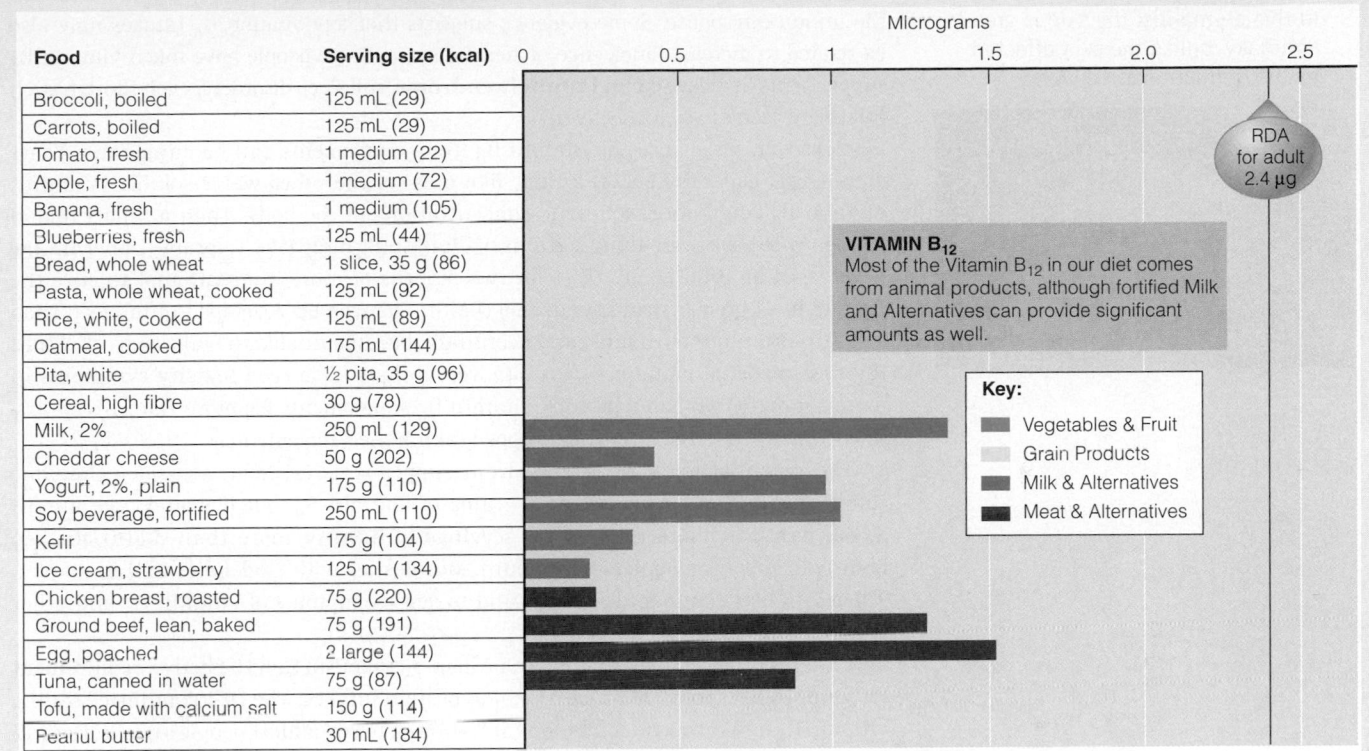

Food	Serving size (kcal)
Broccoli, boiled	125 mL (29)
Carrots, boiled	125 mL (29)
Tomato, fresh	1 medium (22)
Apple, fresh	1 medium (72)
Banana, fresh	1 medium (105)
Blueberries, fresh	125 mL (44)
Bread, whole wheat	1 slice, 35 g (86)
Pasta, whole wheat, cooked	125 mL (92)
Rice, white, cooked	125 mL (89)
Oatmeal, cooked	175 mL (144)
Pita, white	½ pita, 35 g (96)
Cereal, high fibre	30 g (78)
Milk, 2%	250 mL (129)
Cheddar cheese	50 g (202)
Yogurt, 2%, plain	175 g (110)
Soy beverage, fortified	250 mL (110)
Kefir	175 g (104)
Ice cream, strawberry	125 mL (134)
Chicken breast, roasted	75 g (220)
Ground beef, lean, baked	75 g (191)
Egg, poached	2 large (144)
Tuna, canned in water	75 g (87)
Tofu, made with calcium salt	150 g (114)
Peanut butter	30 mL (184)

VITAMIN B₁₂
Most of the Vitamin B₁₂ in our diet comes from animal products, although fortified Milk and Alternatives can provide significant amounts as well.

RDA for adult 2.4 µg

Key:
- Vegetables & Fruit
- Grain Products
- Milk & Alternatives
- Meat & Alternatives

DRI Recommended Intake:
Adults: 2.4 µg/d

Cchs 2.2 Mean Intake:
Men: 5.4 µg/d
Women: 3.4 µg/d

Chief Functions:
Part of coenzymes needed in new cell synthesis; helps maintain nerve cells

Deficiency:
Pernicious anemia;[a] anemia (large-cell type);[b] smooth tongue; tingling or numbness; fatigue, memory loss, disorientation, degeneration of nerves progressing to paralysis

Toxicity:
None reported

[a]The name pernicious anemia refers to the vitamin B₁₂ deficiency caused by a lack of stomach intrinsic factor but not to anemia from inadequate dietary intake.
[b]Large cell–type anemia is known as either macrocytic or megaloblastic anemia.

Vitamin B₆ **Vitamin B₆** participates in over 100 reactions in body tissues and is needed to help convert one kind of amino acid, which cells have in abundance, to other nonessential amino acids that the cells lack.[57] In addition, vitamin B₆ functions in these ways:

- Aids in the conversion of tryptophan to niacin
- Plays important roles in the synthesis of hemoglobin and neurotransmitters, the communication molecules of the brain; for example, vitamin B₆ assists in the conversion of the amino acid tryptophan to the neurotransmitter **serotonin**
- Assists in releasing stored glucose from glycogen and thus contributes to the regulation of blood glucose
- Has roles in immune function and steroid hormone activity
- Is critical to the developing brain and nervous system of a fetus; deficiency during this stage causes behavioural problems later

vitamin B₆ a B vitamin needed in protein metabolism. Its three active forms are *pyridoxine*, *pyridoxal*, and *pyridoxamine*.

serotonin (SER-oh-tone-in) a neurotransmitter important in sleep regulation, appetite control, and mood regulation, among other roles. Serotonin is synthesized in the body from the amino acid tryptophan with the help of vitamin B₆.

Figure 7–16

Vitamin B₆ Deficiency

In this dermatitis, the skin is greasy
and flaky, unlike the skin affected
by the dermatitis of pellagra.

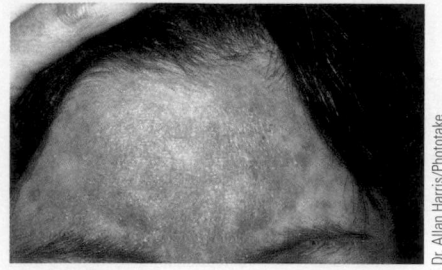

Dr. Allan Harris/Phototake

Because of these diverse functions, vitamin B_6 deficiency is expressed in general symptoms, such as weakness, psychological depression, confusion, irritability, and insomnia. Other symptoms include anemia; the greasy dermatitis depicted in Figure 7–16; and, in advanced cases of deficiency, convulsions. A shortage of vitamin B_6 may also weaken the immune response. Some evidence suggests that low vitamin B_6 intakes may also be related to increased incidence of heart disease. Some people have taken vitamin B_6 supplements to relieve **carpal tunnel syndrome** and sleep disorders, even though such treatment seems to be ineffective.[58]

Moreover, large doses of vitamin B_6 from supplements can be dangerous. Years ago, it was generally believed that, like most of the other water-soluble vitamins, vitamin B_6 could not reach toxic concentrations in the body. Then a report told of women who took more than 2 grams of vitamin B_6 daily (the Tolerable Upper Intake Level is set at 100 mg, or 0.1 g) for two months or more in an attempt to cure the symptoms of premenstrual syndrome (PMS). The women developed numb feet, then lost sensation in their hands, and eventually became unable to walk or work. Since the first report of vitamin B_6 toxicity, researchers have seen toxicity symptoms in more than 100 women who took vitamin B_6 supplements for more than five years. The women recovered after they stopped taking the supplements.

The potential for a toxic dose from supplements is great. Consider that one small capsule can easily deliver 2 grams of vitamin B_6, but it would take almost 3,000 bananas, more than 1,600 servings of liver, or more than 3,800 chicken breasts to supply an equivalent amount. Moral: stick with food. Later in this chapter, Table 7–4 lists common deficiency and toxicity symptoms of vitamin B_6 and other water-soluble vitamins.

 Vitamin B_6 plays so many roles in protein metabolism that the body's requirement for vitamin B_6 is roughly proportional to protein intakes. The DRI committee set the vitamin B_6 intake recommendation high enough to cover most people's needs, regardless of differences in protein intakes (see the inside front cover). Meats, fish, and poultry (protein-rich foods) and potatoes, leafy green vegetables, and some fruit are good sources of vitamin B_6 (that is, one serving provides at least 10 percent of the Daily Value; see Snapshot 7–11). Other foods, such as legumes and peanut butter, provide smaller amounts.

How Are B Vitamins Related to Heart Disease?

People who inherit a rare disorder that raises the level of a special amino acid, **homocysteine**, in the blood almost invariably suffer from a severe early form of CVD.* Also, some other CVD sufferers without the inherited disorder accumulate homocysteine in the blood. Some researchers suspect that elevated homocysteine may increase the risk for CVD and that a lack of some B vitamins in the diet contributes to elevating it.[59]

A deficiency of folate, vitamin B_{12}, or vitamin B_6 causes excess homocysteine to build up in the blood. When healthy men are given supplements of B vitamins (folate, vitamin B_6, and vitamin B_{12}), their homocysteine values drop significantly. Some research supports the idea that folate-fortified foods and folate supplements both raise blood folate and produce a drop in homocysteine. Whether these effects reduce a person's risk of developing CVD is unknown.[60] Higher dietary intakes of folate and vitamin B_6 also correlate with lower blood values for other substances associated with heart disease and with a lower incidence of heart disease itself.† The missing link is how, or even whether, B vitamin deficiencies or elevated homocysteine directly affects processes leading to heart disease.[61]

Emerging data indicate that blood values for folate have risen in Canada, and the United States since the folate enrichment of food started in the 1990s. Meanwhile, U.S. data also reveal that homocysteine values are dropping.[62] The missing evidence is a concurrent drop in CVD. Until more firm evidence of benefit exists, caution is in order when considering taking B vitamin supplements to improve heart health.

• The Maximum Daily Dose (MDD) for vitamin B_6 in single-ingredient supplements is 100 μg/d.

carpal tunnel syndrome a pinched nerve at the wrist, causing pain or numbness in the hand. It is often caused by repetitive motion of the wrist.

homocysteine (hoe-moe-SIS-teen) an amino acid produced as an intermediate compound during amino acid metabolism. A buildup of homocysteine in the blood is associated with deficiencies of folate and other B vitamins and may increase the risk of diseases.

---

*Although chemically an amino acid, homocysteine is not incorporated into body proteins but is metabolized to other compounds.

†One such substance is C-reactive protein.

Snapshot 7-11 ┈┈⟩ Vitamin B₆

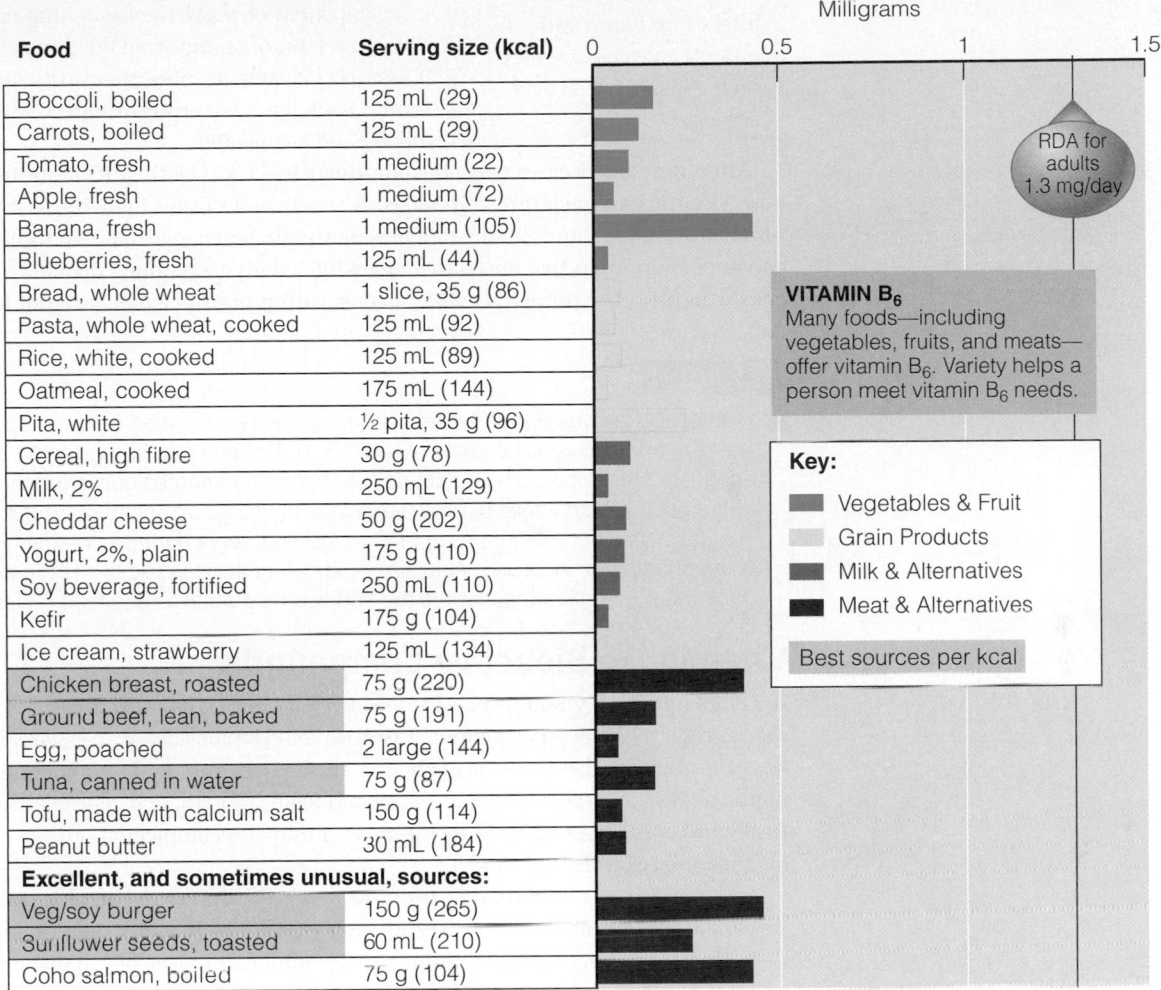

Food	Serving size (kcal)
Broccoli, boiled	125 mL (29)
Carrots, boiled	125 mL (29)
Tomato, fresh	1 medium (22)
Apple, fresh	1 medium (72)
Banana, fresh	1 medium (105)
Blueberries, fresh	125 mL (44)
Bread, whole wheat	1 slice, 35 g (86)
Pasta, whole wheat, cooked	125 mL (92)
Rice, white, cooked	125 mL (89)
Oatmeal, cooked	175 mL (144)
Pita, white	½ pita, 35 g (96)
Cereal, high fibre	30 g (78)
Milk, 2%	250 mL (129)
Cheddar cheese	50 g (202)
Yogurt, 2%, plain	175 g (110)
Soy beverage, fortified	250 mL (110)
Kefir	175 g (104)
Ice cream, strawberry	125 mL (134)
Chicken breast, roasted	75 g (220)
Ground beef, lean, baked	75 g (191)
Egg, poached	2 large (144)
Tuna, canned in water	75 g (87)
Tofu, made with calcium salt	150 g (114)
Peanut butter	30 mL (184)
Excellent, and sometimes unusual, sources:	
Veg/soy burger	150 g (265)
Sunflower seeds, toasted	60 mL (210)
Coho salmon, boiled	75 g (104)

Milligrams: 0 0.5 1 1.5

RDA for adults 1.3 mg/day

VITAMIN B₆
Many foods—including vegetables, fruits, and meats—offer vitamin B₆. Variety helps a person meet vitamin B₆ needs.

Key:
- Vegetables & Fruit
- Grain Products
- Milk & Alternatives
- Meat & Alternatives

Best sources per kcal

DRI Recommended Intake:
Adults (19–50 yr): 1.3 mg/d

Cchs 2.2 Mean Intake:
Men: 2.29 mg/d
Women: 1.59 mg/d

Tolerable Upper Intake Level:
Adults: 100 mg/d

Chief Functions:
Part of a coenzyme needed in amino acid and fatty acid metabolism; helps convert tryptophan to niacin and to serotonin; helps make hemoglobin for red blood cells

Deficiency:
Anemia, depression, confusion, abnormal brain wave pattern, convulsions; greasy, scaly dermatitis

Toxicity:
Depression, fatigue, impaired memory, irritability, headaches, nerve damage causing numbness and muscle weakness progressing to an inability to walk and convulsions; skin lesions

Biotin and Pantothenic Acid   Two other B vitamins, **biotin** and **pantothenic acid**, are, like thiamin, riboflavin, and niacin, important in energy metabolism. Biotin is a cofactor for several enzymes in the metabolism of carbohydrate, fat, and protein. Pantothenic acid is a component of a key coenzyme that makes possible the release of energy from the energy nutrients. It also participates in more than 100 steps in the synthesis of lipids, neurotransmitters, steroid hormones, and hemoglobin.

The DRI recommended intakes for biotin and pantothenic acid are listed on the inside front cover, page A.

Although rare diseases may precipitate deficiencies of biotin and pantothenic acid, both vitamins are widespread in foods. A steady diet of raw egg whites, which contain a protein that binds biotin, can produce biotin deficiency, but you would have to consume more than two dozen raw egg whites daily to produce the effect. Cooking eggs denatures the protein. Healthy people eating ordinary diets are not at risk for deficiencies.

KEY POINT

- Historically, famous B vitamin-deficiency diseases are beriberi (thiamin), pellagra (niacin), and pernicious anemia (vitamin B_{12}). Pellagra can be prevented by adequate protein because the amino acid tryptophan can be converted to niacin in the body. A high intake of folate can mask the blood symptom of vitamin B_{12} deficiency but will not prevent the associated nerve damage. Vitamin B_6 is important in amino acid metabolism and can be toxic in excess. Biotin and pantothenic acid are important to the body and are abundant in food.

Vitaminlike Bioactive Compounds

In addition to the B vitamins just discussed, a few compounds that are topics of debate among researchers deserve mention. **Choline** could be considered an essential nutrient because when the diet is devoid of choline, the body cannot make enough of the compound to meet its need. Choline is common in foods, though, and deficiencies are practically unheard of outside the laboratory. DRI intake recommendations have been set for choline (see inside front cover).

The compounds **carnitine**, **inositol**, and **lipoic acid** might appropriately be called *nonvitamins* because they are not essential nutrients for human beings. Carnitine, sometimes called vitamin B_T, is an important piece of cell machinery, but it is not a vitamin. Although deficiencies can be induced in laboratory animals for experimental purposes, these substances are abundant in ordinary foods. Even if these compounds were essential in human nutrition, supplements would be unnecessary for healthy people eating a balanced diet. Vitamin companies often include these substances to make their formulas appear more "complete," but there is no physiological reason to do so.

In addition to carnitine, inositol, and lipoic acid, other substances have been mistakenly thought to be essential in human nutrition because they are needed for growth by bacteria or other life forms. These substances include PABA (para-aminobenzoic acid), bioflavonoids ("vitamin P" or hesperidin), and ubiquinone (coenzyme Q). Other names you may hear are "vitamin B_{15}" and pangamic acid (hoaxes) or "vitamin B_{17}" (laetrile or amygdalin, not a cancer cure as claimed and not a vitamin by any stretch of the imagination).*,[63]

KEY POINT

- Choline is needed in the diet, but it is not a vitamin and deficiencies are unheard of outside the laboratory. Many other substances that people claim are B vitamins are not. Among these substances are carnitine, inositol, and lipoic acid.

This chapter has addressed all 13 of the vitamins. The basic facts about each one are summed up in Tables 7–3 and 7–4.

biotin (BY-o-tin) a B vitamin; a coenzyme necessary for fat synthesis and other metabolic reactions.

pantothenic (PAN-to-THEN-ic) **acid** a B vitamin.

choline (KOH-leen) a nonessential nutrient used to make the phospholipid lecithin and other molecules.

carnitine a nonessential nutrient that functions in cellular activities.

inositol (in-OSS-ih-tall) a nonessential nutrient found in cell membranes.

lipoic (lip-OH-ic) **acid** a nonessential nutrient.

*Read the truth about these and many other claims at the website of the U.S. National Council against Health Fraud: http://www.ncahf.org.

Table 7-3

The Fat-Soluble Vitamins—Functions, Deficiencies, and Toxicities

VITAMIN A

Other Names	Deficiency Symptoms	Toxicity Symptoms
Retinol, retinal, retinoic acid; main precursor is beta-carotene	**Blood/Circulatory System** Anemia (small-cell type)[a]	Red blood cell breakage, cessation of menstruation, nosebleeds
Chief Functions in the Body Vision; health of cornea, epithelial cells, mucous membranes, skin; bone and tooth growth; regulation of gene expression; reproduction; immunity Beta-carotene: antioxidant	**Bones/Teeth** Cessation of bone growth, painful joints; impaired enamel formation, cracks in teeth, tendency toward tooth decay	Bone pain; growth retardation; increased pressure inside skull; headaches; possible bone mineral loss
Deficiency Disease Name Hypovitaminosis A	**Digestive System** Diarrhea, changes in intestinal and other body linings	Abdominal pain, nausea, vomiting, diarrhea, weight loss
Significant Sources Retinoyl: fortified milk, cheese, cream, butter, fortified margarine, eggs, liver Beta-carotene: spinach and other dark, leafy greens; broccoli; deep orange fruit (apricots, cantaloupe) and vegetables (winter squash, carrots, sweet potatoes, pumpkin)	**Immune System** Depression; frequent respiratory, digestive, bladder, vaginal, and other infections	Overreactivity
	Nervous/Muscular Systems Night blindness (retinal)	Blurred vision, muscle weakness, fatigue, irritability, loss of appetite
	Skin and Cornea Keratinization, corneal degeneration leading to blindness,[b] rashes	Dry skin, rashes, loss of hair; cracking and bleeding lips, brittle nails; hair loss
	Other Kidney stones, impaired growth	Liver enlargement and liver damage; birth defects

VITAMIN D

Other Names	Deficiency Symptoms	Toxicity Symptoms
Calciferol, cholecalciferol, dihydroxyvitamin D; precursor is cholesterol	**Blood/Circulatory System**	Raised blood calcium; calcification of blood vessels and heart tissues
Chief Functions in the Body Mineralization of bones (raises blood calcium and phosphorus via absorption from digestive tract and by withdrawing calcium from bones and stimulating retention by kidneys)	**Bones/Teeth** Abnormal growth, misshapen bones (bowing of legs), soft bones, joint pain, malformed teeth	Calcification of tooth soft tissues; thinning of tooth enamel
Deficiency Disease Name Rickets, osteomalacia		Excessive thirst, headaches, irritability, loss of appetite, weakness, nausea
Significant Sources Self-synthesis with sunlight; fortified milk, margarine, and yogurt; liver; sardines; salmon; shrimp		**Other** Kidney stones; calcification of soft tissues (kidneys, lungs, joints); mental and physical retardation of offspring

(*continued*)

Table 7–3

The Fat-Soluble Vitamins—Functions, Deficiencies, and Toxicities (continued)

VITAMIN E

Other Names Alpha-tocopherol, tocopherol	Deficiency Symptoms	Toxicity Symptoms
Chief Functions in the Body Antioxidant (quenching of free radicals), stabilization of cell membranes, support of immune function, protection of polyunsaturated fatty acids; normal nerve development	**Blood/Circulatory System** Red blood cell breakage, anemia	Augments the effects of anticlotting medication
	Nervous/Muscular Systems Nerve degeneration, weakness, fatigue, difficulty walking, leg cramps	**Digestive System** General discomfort, nausea
Deficiency Disease Name No name		**Eyes** Blurred vision Fatigue
Significant Sources Polyunsaturated plant oils (margarine, salad dressings, shortenings), green and leafy vegetables, wheat germ, whole-grain products, nuts, seeds		

VITAMIN K

Other Names Phylloquinone, naphthoquinone	Deficiency Symptoms	Toxicity Symptoms
Chief Functions in the Body Synthesis of blood-clotting proteins and proteins important in bone mineralization	**Blood/Circulatory System** Hemorrhage	Interference with anticlotting medication
Deficiency Disease Name No name	**Bones** Poor skeletal mineralization	
Significant Sources Bacterial synthesis in the digestive tract; green leafy vegetables, cabbage-type vegetables, soybeans, vegetable oils		

[a]Small-cell anemia is termed microcytic anemia; large-cell anemia is macrocytic or megaloblastic anemia.

[b]Corneal degeneration progresses from keratinization (hardening) to xerosis (drying) to xerophthalmia (thickening, opacity, and irreversible blindness).

Table 7–4

The Water-Soluble Vitamins—Functions, Deficiencies, and Toxicities

VITAMIN C

Other Names Ascorbic acid	Deficiency Symptoms	Toxicity Symptoms
Chief Functions in the Body Collagen synthesis (strengthens blood vessel walls, forms scar tissue, matrix for bone growth), antioxidant, restores vitamin E to active form, hormone synthesis, supports immune cell functions, helps in absorption of iron	**Blood/Circulatory System** Anemia (small-cell type)[a]	**Digestive System** Nausea, abdominal cramps, diarrhea, excessive urination
	Immune System Suppression, frequent infections	
	Mouth, Gums, Tongue Bleeding gums, loosened teeth	
Deficiency Disease Name Scurvy	**Nervous/Muscular Systems** Muscle degeneration and pain, depression, disorientation	Headache, fatigue, insomnia

(continued)

Table 7–4

The Water-Soluble Vitamins—Functions, Deficiencies, and Toxicities (continued)

VITAMIN C (continued)

	Deficiency Symptoms	Toxicity Symptoms
Significant Sources Citrus fruit, cabbage-type vegetables, dark green vegetables, cantaloupe, strawberries, peppers, lettuce, tomatoes, potatoes, papayas, mangoes	**Skeletal System** Bone fragility, joint pain	Aggravation of gout
	Skin Pinpoint hemorrhages, rough skin, blotchy bruises	Rashes
	Other Failure of wounds to heal	Interference with medical tests; kidney stones in susceptible people

THIAMIN

	Deficiency Symptoms	Toxicity Symptoms
Other Names Vitamin B_1	**Blood/Circulatory System** Edema, enlarged heart, abnormal heart rhythms, heart failure	No toxicity symptoms reported
Chief Functions in the Body Part of a coenzyme needed in energy metabolism, supports normal appetite and nervous system function	**Nervous/Muscular Systems** Degeneration, wasting, weakness, pain, apathy, irritability, difficulty walking, loss of reflexes, mental confusion, paralysis	
Deficiency Disease Name Beriberi (wet and dry)	**Other** Anorexia; weight loss	
Significant Sources Occurs in all nutritious foods in moderate amounts; pork, ham, bacon, liver, whole and enriched grains, legumes, seeds		

RIBOFLAVIN

	Deficiency Symptoms	Toxicity Symptoms
Other Names Vitamin B_2	**Mouth, Gums, Tongue** Cracks at the corners of mouth;[b] smooth magenta tongue;[c] sore throat	No toxicity symptoms reported
Chief Functions in the Body Part of a coenzyme needed in energy metabolism, supports normal vision and skin health	**Nervous System and Eyes** Hypersensitivity to light, reddening of cornea	
Deficiency Disease Ariboflavinosis	**Skin** Skin rash	

NIACIN

	Deficiency Symptoms	Toxicity Symptoms
Other Names Nicotinic acid, nicotinamide, niacinamide, vitamin B_3; precursor is dietary tryptophan	**Digestive System** Diarrhea; vomiting; abdominal pain	Nausea, vomiting
Chief Functions in the Body Part of coenzymes needed in energy metabolism	**Mouth, Gums, Tongue** Black or bright red swollen smooth tongue[c]	
Deficiency Disease Name Pellagra	**Nervous System** Irritability, loss of appetite, weakness, headache, dizziness, mental confusion progressing to psychosis or delirium	
Significant Sources Synthesized from the amino acid tryptophan; milk, eggs, meat, poultry, fish, whole-grain and enriched breads and cereals, nuts, and all protein-containing foods	**Skin** Flaky skin rash on areas exposed to sun	Painful flush and rash, sweating
		Other Liver damage; impaired glucose tolerance

(continued)

Table 7–4

The Water-Soluble Vitamins—Functions, Deficiencies, and Toxicities (continued)

FOLATE

Other Names
Folic acid, folacin, pteroylglutamic acid

Chief Functions in the Body
Part of a coenzyme needed for new cell synthesis

Deficiency Disease Name
No name

Significant Sources
Asparagus, avocado, leafy green vegetables, beets, legumes, seeds, liver, enriched breads, cereal, pasta, grains

Deficiency Symptoms

Blood/Circulatory System
Anemia (large-cell type),[a] elevated homocysteine

Digestive System
Heartburn, diarrhea, constipation

Immune System
Suppression, frequent infections

Mouth, Gums, Tongue
Smooth red tongue[c]

Nervous System
Increased risk of neural tube birth defects
Depression, mental confusion, fatigue, irritability, headache

Toxicity Symptoms

Masks vitamin B_{12} deficiency

VITAMIN B_{12}

Other Names
Cyanocobalamin

Chief Functions in the Body
Part of coenzymes needed in new cell synthesis, helps maintain nerve cells

Deficiency Disease Name
No name[d]

Significant Sources
Animal products (meat, fish, poultry, milk, cheese, eggs)

Deficiency Symptoms

Blood/Circulatory System
Anemia (large-cell type)[a]

Mouth, Gums, Tongue
Smooth tongue[c]

Nervous System
Fatigue, nerve degeneration progressing to paralysis

Skin
Tingling or numbness

Toxicity Symptoms

No toxicity symptoms known

VITAMIN B_6

Other Names
Pyridoxine, pyridoxal, pyridoxamine

Chief Functions in the Body
Part of a coenzyme needed in amino acid and fatty acid metabolism, helps convert tryptophan to niacin and to serotonin, helps make red blood cells

Deficiency Disease Name
No name

Significant Sources
Meat, fish, poultry, liver, legumes, fruit, potatoes, whole grains, soy products

Deficiency Symptoms

Blood/Circulatory System
Anemia (small-cell type)[a]

Nervous/Muscular Systems
Depression, confusion, abnormal brain wave pattern, convulsions

Skin
Rashes; greasy, scaly dermatitis

Toxicity Symptoms

Bloating

Depression, fatigue, impaired memory, irritability, headaches, numbness, damage to nerves, difficulty walking, loss of reflexes, restlessness, convulsions

Lesions

(continued)

Table 7-4

The Water-Soluble Vitamins—Functions, Deficiencies, and Toxicities (continued)

PANTOTHENIC ACID

Other Names	Deficiency Symptoms	Toxicity Symptoms
Vitamin B$_5$	**Digestive System**	Water retention (infrequent)
Chief Functions in the Body	Vomiting, intestinal distress	
Part of a coenzyme needed in energy metabolism	**Nervous/Muscular Systems**	
	Insomnia, fatigue	
Deficiency Disease Name	**Other**	
No name	Hypoglycemia, increased sensitivity to insulin	
Significant Sources		
Widespread in foods		

BIOTIN

Other Names	Deficiency Symptoms	Toxicity Symptoms
Vitamin B$_7$/Vitamin H	**Blood/Circulatory System**	No toxicity symptoms reported
Chief Functions in the Body	Abnormal heart action	
A cofactor for several enzymes needed in energy metabolism, fat synthesis, amino acid metabolism, and glycogen synthesis	**Digestive System**	
	Loss of appetite, nausea	
	Nervous/Muscular Systems	
	Depression, muscle pain, weakness, fatigue, numbness of extremities	
Deficiency Disease Name		
No name	**Skin**	
Significant Sources	Dry around eyes, nose, and mouth	
Widespread in foods		

[a]Small-cell anemia is termed microcytic anemia; large-cell type is macrocytic or megaloblastic anemia.

[b]Cracks at the corners of the mouth are termed cheilosis (kee-LOH-sis).

[c]Smoothness of the tongue is caused by loss of its surface structures and is termed glossitis (gloss-EYE-tis).

[d]The name pernicious anemia refers to the vitamin B$_{12}$ deficiency caused by a lack of intrinsic factor but not to that caused by inadequate dietary intake.

 **try it!**

Food Feature

Choosing Foods Rich in Vitamins

On learning how important the vitamins are to their health, most people want to choose foods that are vitamin-rich whether they are eating at home or in restaurants. Look down the columns of vitamins and Calories in Table 7–5 to identify some vitamin-rich foods in popular restaurant meals. If you are interested in folate, for instance, you can see that cornflakes are an especially good source (folic acid is added to corn-flakes), as is orange juice (folate occurs naturally in this food).

Another way of looking at such data appears in Figure 7–17—the long bars show some foods that are rich sources of a particular vitamin, and the short or nonexistent bars indicate poor sources. The colours of the bars represent the various food groups.

Nutrient Enrichment of Foods Sold in Canada

Canadian students should be aware of the current Canadian policies about nutrient enrichment of foods. These policies differ from those in the United States; thus, the vitamin and mineral content of some Canadian foods may differ from the food sources of nutrients listed in the text. This may also affect the results of nutrient analysis of student food intakes. The Canadian Food and Drug Regulations (http://www .hc-sc.gc.ca/fn-an/legislation/acts-lois/ index-eng.php) specify the foods to which nutrients may or must be added and the amounts that may be added. Canadian regulations are sometimes more restrictive; thus, many Canadian foods have lower amounts of some vitamins and minerals. Bleached wheat flour is one of the staple foods for which it is mandatory to add back nutrients that were lost during processing and also serve as a vehicle to increase the folic acid level of the Canadian diet.

Table 7–5

Vitamin Contents of Home-Cooked Foods and Restaurant Meals

	Energy (Cal)	Vitamin A (µg)	Thiamin (mg)	Vitamin C (mg)	Folate (µg)	Vitamin B$_{12}$ (µg)
Breakfast Foods						
Pancakes with syrup and butter, scrambled egg, and sausage patty	1,140	150	0.41	0	32	1.7
Egg, ham, and cheese muffin	290	100	0.49	0	30	0.7
Oatmeal, brown sugar	107	2	0.13	0	5	0
Cornflakes	110	0	0.87	15	100	0
Hash brown potatoes	130	0	0.08	3	8	0
2 small cinnamon sweet rolls	300	50	0.25	2	20	0.1
Large blueberry muffin	400	10	0.2	2	20	0.1
English muffin	130	0	0.25	0	20	0.1
Orange juice	80	40	0.17	90	60	0
Milk (low fat 1%)	120	140	0.1	2	10	0.8
Lunch Foods						
Homemade chilli/crackers	350	150	0.26	25	40	0.5
Cold cut submarine sandwich/chips	460	80	1.0	12	55	1.1
Peanut butter and jam sandwich on whole wheat; fruit cocktail	450	30	0.3	3	62	0
Tuna sandwich on white; banana	470	40	0.32	11	49	0.6
Chef's salad with cheese, ham, turkey, and dressing/crackers	580	140	0.43	16	100	0.8
Skim (fat-free) milk	85	150	0.1	0	10	0.9
Apple juice	120	0	0.05	2	0	0
Supper Foods						
Baked ham dinner (ham, potatoes, Brussels sprouts)	440	150	0.27	80	70	1.4
Vegetable plate	400	680	0.26	53	120	0.1
Spaghetti and meatballs; small salad	600	220	0.38	25	50	1.3
Fried fish, tartar sauce, corn, and macaroni salad	510	70	0.26	6	83	1
Rolls	100	0	0.15	0	0	0
Garlic bread	190	4	0.4	0	0	0
Corn muffins	300	0	0.12	0	0	0
Lemon pie	350	60	0.16	4	11	0.2
Chocolate cake	250	20	0.02	0	5	0.1

The nutrients that must be added are thiamin, riboflavin, niacin, iron, and folic acid.

Nutrient values from food composition tables and computerized nutrient analysis programs based solely on U.S. data, such as Diet Analysis Plus software, do not accurately reflect Canadian foods and nutrient intakes. Breakfast cereals are common examples of this variation. This is especially true for vitamins A and D, which can be higher in U.S. cereal products. Vitamins A and D are currently not permitted to be added to cereals in Canada. Annex 2, Section VI in Guide to Food Labelling and Advertising (http://www.inspection .gc.ca/english/fssa/labeti/guide/toce .shtml) provides detailed information about foods to which nutrients can be added. *Nutrient Value of Some Common Foods* (NVSCF) was revised and published online by Health Canada in 2008. Go to the Health Canada website at http://www.hc-sc.gc.ca/fn-an/ nutrition/fiche-nutri-data/nutrient_value-valeurs_nutritives-eng.php. It is a quick reference to about 1,000 Canadian foods derived from Health Canada's Canadian Nutrient File (CNF). A searchable version of the CNF, which contains more than 5,000 foods, is also available electronically at http://www.hc-sc.gc.ca/ fn-an/nutrition/fiche-nutri-data/index-eng.php. As part of the search, you can also find out what constitutes one Food Guide serving according to Canada's Food Guide for food items such as milk (e.g., 250 mL of milk = 1 Food Guide serving; a medium-sized apple = 1 Food Guide serving).

The review of Canadian regulations about the addition of vitamins and minerals to foods that began in January 1998 is now complete, and Health Canada's proposed policy and implementation plans can be viewed at http:// www.agr.gc.ca/eng/industry-markets-and-trade/food-regulations/food-policy-and-regulatory-issues/current-food-policy-and-regulatory-issues/vitamin-and-mineral-addition/?id=1172254614356. Some of the reasons for this review were to maintain and improve the food supply, protect Canadians from health hazards due to nutrient excesses, and prevent misleading practices.

Which Foods Should I Choose?

After looking at Figure 7–17, don't think that you must memorize the richest sources of each vitamin and include those foods daily. That false notion would lead you to limit your variety of foods while overemphasizing the components of a few foods. Although it is reassuring to know that your carrot-raisin salad at lunch provided more

than your entire day's need for vitamin A, it is a mistake to think that you must then select equally rich sources of all of the other vitamins. Such rich sources do not exist for many vitamins—rather, foods work in harmony to provide most nutrients. For example, a baked potato, not a star performer among vitamin C providers, contributes substantially to a day's need for this nutrient and contributes some thiamin, too. By the end of the day, assuming that your food choices were made with reasonable care, the bits of thiamin, vitamin B_6, and vitamin C from each serving of food have accumulated to make a more-than-adequate total diet.

A Variety of Foods Works Best

With a few exceptions, nutritious foods provide small quantities of thiamin, as shown in Figure 7–17. Members of the pork family are an exceptionally good thiamin source, with one small pork chop (275 Cal) providing over half of the Daily Value for thiamin—but, again, this does not suggest that you eat pork every day. Legumes and grains are also good, low-fat sources, and they provide beneficial fibre and nutrients lacking in meats. Beans lack the vitamin B_{12} provided by meats, however. Peanut butter is a good source of thiamin, and of most other B vitamins as well, but its high fat and Calorie contents call for moderation in its use.

The vitamin B_6 data provide another insight to support the argument for variety. From just the few foods listed here, you can see that no one source can provide the whole day's requirement for vitamin B_6 but that many small servings of a variety of meat, fish, and poultry along

with potatoes and a few other vegetables and fruit consumed throughout the day can work together to supply it.

The last two graphs of Figure 7–17 show sources of folate and vitamin C. These nutrients are both richly supplied by fruit and vegetables. The richest source of either may be only a moderate source of the other, but the recommended amounts of fruit and vegetables in Canada's Food Guide in Chapter 2 cover both needs amply. As for vitamin E, vegetable oils and some seeds and nuts are the richest sources, and some vegetables and fruit contribute a little, too.

Canadian Daily Values for Vitamins

Some of the Canadian daily values for vitamins are different from those listed in the textbook and are based on the Recommended Daily Intake for vitamins (http://publications.gc.ca/gazette/ archives/p2/2003/2003-01-01/pdf/ g2-13701.pdf). The daily values for vitamins for persons two years of age and older are listed in Table 7–6. When you look at the Snapshots of examples of sources of the different vitamins, you might want to compare the amount in foods with the Canadian daily values. Use Table 7–7 to find out the average intake of young adult Canadians with regard to the DRI recommendations for the vitamins covered in this chapter.

Table 7–7 helps us put into context the level of vitamin intake by 19- to 30-year-old Canadians in relation to the DRI report recommendations. Notice also that while tolerable upper intake levels were not set for some of them, there are maximum daily dosages for all of those that are available as single-ingredient supplements.

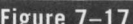

Figure 7–17

Food Sources of Vitamins Selected to Show a Range of Values

Food	Amount (Energy in cal)	

VITAMIN A — µg

Food	Amount (Energy in cal)	µg
Beef liver	3 oz fried (184)	9,092
Sweet potato	1 whole boiled (159)	1,287
Carrots	1/2 c boiled (35)	957
Cantaloupe	1/2 melon (97)	860
Spinach	1/2 c boiled (21)	369
Butternut squash	1/2 c baked (41)	361
Milk, fat-free	1 c (85)	161
Tomatoes	1/2 c boiled (33)	89
Peach	1 fresh medium (42)	26
Orange juice	1 c (fresh)	25
Summer squash	1/2 c boiled (18)	13
Apple	1 fresh medium (81)	5
Sirloin steak	3 oz lean (171)	0
Whole-wheat bread	1 slice (70)	0
Baked potato	1 whole (220)	0

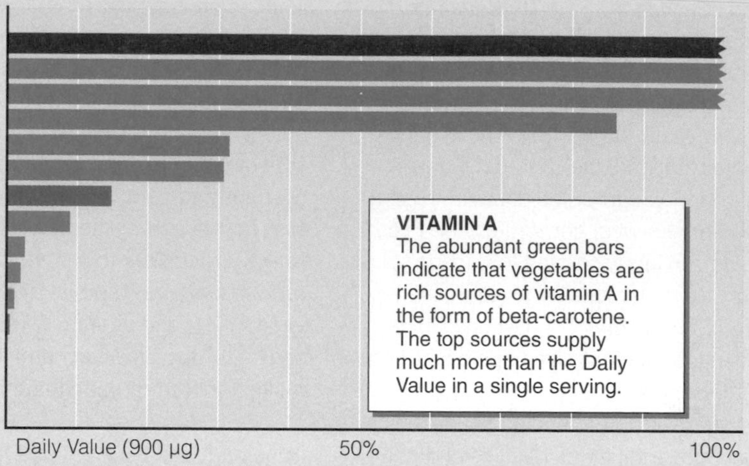

VITAMIN A
The abundant green bars indicate that vegetables are rich sources of vitamin A in the form of beta-carotene. The top sources supply much more than the Daily Value in a single serving.

Daily Value (900 µg)   50%   100%

VITAMIN E — mg

Food	Amount (Energy in cal)	mg
Sunflower seed oil	1 tbs (124)	6.5
Wheat germ	1 oz (117)	6.0
Safflower oil	1 tbs (124)	6.0
Cottonseed oil	1 tbs (124)	5.0
Sunflower seeds	2 tbs dry roasted (93)	4.2
Peanuts	1 oz dry roasted (166)	3.0
Corn oil	1 tbs (124)	3.0
Peanut butter	2 tbs (190)	3.0
Canola oil	1 tbs (124)	2.9
Shrimp	3 oz boiled (84)	1.0
Parsley	1/2 c fresh chopped (11)	1.0
Apple	1 fresh medium (81)	0.4
Sweet potato	1 baked (117)	0.3
Cheddar cheese	11/2 oz (170)	0.2
Whole-wheat bread	1 slice (70)	0.0

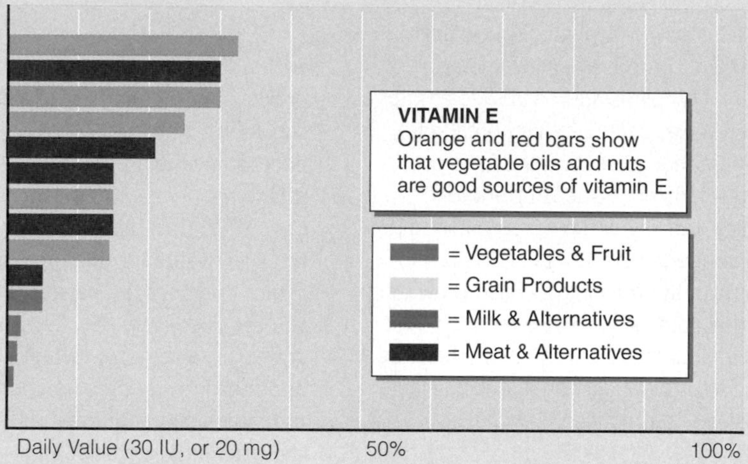

VITAMIN E
Orange and red bars show that vegetable oils and nuts are good sources of vitamin E.

- ▬ = Vegetables & Fruit
- ▬ = Grain Products
- ▬ = Milk & Alternatives
- ▬ = Meat & Alternatives

Daily Value (30 IU, or 20 mg)   50%   100%

THIAMIN — mg

Food	Amount (Energy in cal)	mg
Pork chop	3 oz broiled (275)	0.56
Black beans	1 c cooked (228)	0.42
Sunflower seeds	2 tbs dry (103)	0.41
Watermelon	1 slice (91)	0.23
Green peas	1/2 c cooked (67)	0.23
Orange juice	3/4 c fresh (84)	0.17
Oysters	5 oysters simmered (125)	0.16
Oatmeal	1/2 c cooked (73)	0.13
Sirloin steak	3 oz lean (171)	0.11
Whole-wheat bread	1 slice (70)	0.10
Milk, fat-free	1 c (85)	0.09
Cabbage	1/2 c cooked (33)	0.09
Summer squash	1/2 c cooked (18)	0.04
Apple	1 fresh medium (81)	0.02
Cheddar cheese	11/2 oz (170)	0.02

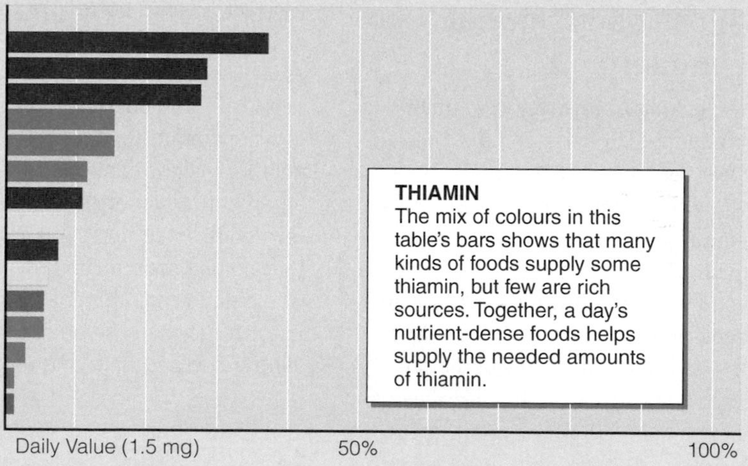

THIAMIN
The mix of colours in this table's bars shows that many kinds of foods supply some thiamin, but few are rich sources. Together, a day's nutrient-dense foods helps supply the needed amounts of thiamin.

Daily Value (1.5 mg)   50%   100%

(*continued*)

Figure 7–17

Food Sources of Vitamins Selected to Show a Range of Values (continued)

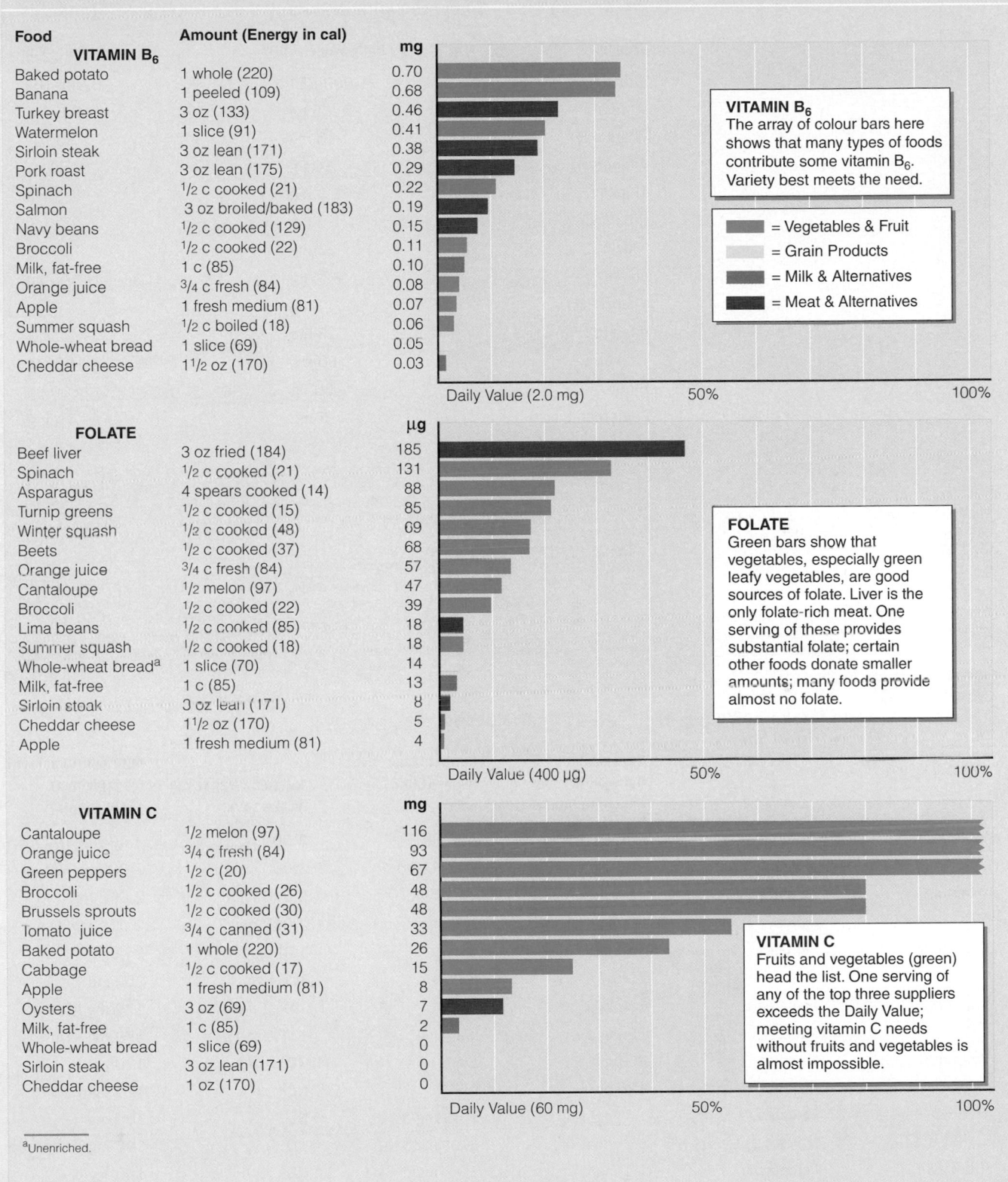

Food | **Amount (Energy in cal)**

VITAMIN B₆ | mg

Food	Amount (Energy in cal)	mg
Baked potato	1 whole (220)	0.70
Banana	1 peeled (109)	0.68
Turkey breast	3 oz (133)	0.46
Watermelon	1 slice (91)	0.41
Sirloin steak	3 oz lean (171)	0.38
Pork roast	3 oz lean (175)	0.29
Spinach	1/2 c cooked (21)	0.22
Salmon	3 oz broiled/baked (183)	0.19
Navy beans	1/2 c cooked (129)	0.15
Broccoli	1/2 c cooked (22)	0.11
Milk, fat-free	1 c (85)	0.10
Orange juice	3/4 c fresh (84)	0.08
Apple	1 fresh medium (81)	0.07
Summer squash	1/2 c boiled (18)	0.06
Whole-wheat bread	1 slice (69)	0.05
Cheddar cheese	1 1/2 oz (170)	0.03

Daily Value (2.0 mg)   50%   100%

VITAMIN B₆
The array of colour bars here shows that many types of foods contribute some vitamin B₆. Variety best meets the need.

◼ = Vegetables & Fruit
◼ = Grain Products
◼ = Milk & Alternatives
◼ = Meat & Alternatives

FOLATE | µg

Food	Amount (Energy in cal)	µg
Beef liver	3 oz fried (184)	185
Spinach	1/2 c cooked (21)	131
Asparagus	4 spears cooked (14)	88
Turnip greens	1/2 c cooked (15)	85
Winter squash	1/2 c cooked (48)	69
Beets	1/2 c cooked (37)	68
Orange juice	3/4 c fresh (84)	57
Cantaloupe	1/2 melon (97)	47
Broccoli	1/2 c cooked (22)	39
Lima beans	1/2 c cooked (85)	18
Summer squash	1/2 c cooked (18)	18
Whole-wheat bread[a]	1 slice (70)	14
Milk, fat-free	1 c (85)	13
Sirloin steak	3 oz lean (171)	8
Cheddar cheese	1 1/2 oz (170)	5
Apple	1 fresh medium (81)	4

Daily Value (400 µg)   50%   100%

FOLATE
Green bars show that vegetables, especially green leafy vegetables, are good sources of folate. Liver is the only folate-rich meat. One serving of these provides substantial folate; certain other foods donate smaller amounts; many foods provide almost no folate.

VITAMIN C | mg

Food	Amount (Energy in cal)	mg
Cantaloupe	1/2 melon (97)	116
Orange juice	3/4 c fresh (84)	93
Green peppers	1/2 c (20)	67
Broccoli	1/2 c cooked (26)	48
Brussels sprouts	1/2 c cooked (30)	48
Tomato juice	3/4 c canned (31)	33
Baked potato	1 whole (220)	26
Cabbage	1/2 c cooked (17)	15
Apple	1 fresh medium (81)	8
Oysters	3 oz (69)	7
Milk, fat-free	1 c (85)	2
Whole-wheat bread	1 slice (69)	0
Sirloin steak	3 oz lean (171)	0
Cheddar cheese	1 oz (170)	0

Daily Value (60 mg)   50%   100%

VITAMIN C
Fruits and vegetables (green) head the list. One serving of any of the top three suppliers exceeds the Daily Value; meeting vitamin C needs without fruits and vegetables is almost impossible.

[a]Unenriched.

Table 7–6

Daily Value Reference Standards for Vitamins in Canada for Persons 2 Years and Older, Compared with U.S. Daily Value Reference Standards

Vitamin	Daily Value (RDI)[a]	U.S. Daily Value
Vitamin A	1,000 RE*	5,000 IU[b]
Vitamin D	5 µg	400 IU[c]
Vitamin E	10 mg	30 IU[d]
Vitamin K	80 µg	80 µg
Thiamin	1.3 mg	1.5 mg
Riboflavin	1.6 mg	1.7 mg
Niacin	23 mg	20 mg
Folate	220 µg	400 µg
Vitamin B_{12}	2 µg	6 µg
Vitamin B_6	1.8 mg	2 mg
Vitamin C	60 mg	60 mg
Biotin	30 µg	300 µg
Pantothenic acid	7 mg	10 mg

*1 µg retinol.

[a]Data from Regulations Amending the Food and Drug Regulations (Nutrition Labelling, Nutrient Content Claims and Health Claims) P.C. 2002-2200 12 December, 2002, Canada Gazette, available at http://publications.gc.ca/gazette/archives/p2/2003/2003-01-01/pdf/g2-13701.pdf; 2003 Guide to Food Labelling and Advertising, available at http://www.inspection.gc.ca/english/fssa/labeti/guide/ch6e.shtml#6.3.2.
[b]Multiply by 0.3 to convert to retinol.
[c]Divide by 40 to convert to micrograms.
[d]Divide by 1.5 to convert to milligrams.

Sources: Modified from Health Canada and Statistics Canada. 2009. Canadian Community Health Survey, Cycle 2.2, Nutrition (2004): Nutrient Intakes from Food – Provincial, Regional and National Summary Data Tables (Vol 1-3). Cat No. 978-0-662-06542-5; Health Canada – Dietary Reference Intakes Report List http://www.hc-sc.gc.ca/fn-an/nutrition/reference/dri_rep-rap_anref-list-eng.php; Health Canada – Natural Health Products Ingredients Database http://webprod.hc-sc.gc.ca/nhpid-bdipsn/monosReq.do?lang=eng.

Table 7–7

Average Vitamin Intake by Young-Adult (19–30 Years) Canadians

		Recommended Daily Allowance/ Adequate Intake	Current Mean Intake (CCHS data)	Tolerable Upper Intake Level	MDD (NHPD values for individual supplements)[1]
Vitamin A	Females	700 µg/d	590 RAE/d[2]	3,000 µg/d	3,000 µg RAE/d
	Males	900 µg/d	703 RAE/d[2]	3,000 µg/d	3,000 µg RAE/d
Vitamin C	Females	75 mg/d	142 mg/d[2]	2,000 mg/d	2,000 mg/d
	Males	90 mg/d	171 mg/d[2]	2,000 mg/d	2,000 mg/d
Vitamin D	Females	15 µg/d	4.7 µg/d[3]	100 µg/d	25 µg/d
	Males	15 µg/d	5.9 µg/d[3]	100 µg/d	25 µg/d
Vitamin E	Females	15 mg/d	n/a	1,000 mg/d	179 mg AT/d
	Males	15 mg/d	n/a	1,000 mg/d	179 mg AT/d
Vitamin K	Females	90 µg/d	n/a	ND	120 µg/d
	Males	120 µg/d	n/a	ND	120 µg/d
Thiamin	Females	1.1 mg/d	1.48 mg/d[3]	ND	100 mg/d
	Males	1.2 mg/d	2.14 mg/d[3]	ND	100 mg/d
Riboflavin	Females	1.1 mg/d	1.72 mg/d[3]	ND	100 mg/d
	Males	1.3 mg/d	2.41 mg/d[3]	ND	100 mg/d
Niacin	Females	14 mg/d	33.1 NE/d[3]	35 mg/d	500 mg/d
	Males	16 mg/d	49.7 NE/d[3]	35 mg/d	500 mg/d

(continued)

Chapter 7 The Vitamins

Table 7–7

Average Vitamin Intake by Young-Adult (19–30 Years) Canadians (continued)

		Recommended Daily Allowance/ Adequate Intake	Current Mean Intake (CCHS data)	Tolerable Upper Intake Level	MDD (NHPD values for individual supplements)[1]
Vitamin B$_6$	Females	1.5 mg/d	1.59 mg/d[3]	100 mg/d	100 mg/d
	Males	1.3 mg/d	2.29 mg/d[3]	100 mg/d	100 mg/d
Folate	Females	400 µg/d	415 DFE/d[3]	1,000 µg/d	199 µg/d
	Males	400 µg/d	587 DFE/d[3]	1,000 µg/d	199 µg/d
Vitamin B$_{12}$	Females	2.4 µg/d	3.4 µg/d[3]	ND	1,000 µg/d
	Males	2.4 µg/d	5.4 µg/d[3]	ND	1,000 µg/d
Pantothenic Acid	Females	5 mg/d	n/a	ND	500 mg/d(mg/d)
	Males	5 mg/d	n/a	ND	500 mg/d
Biotin[4]	Females	30 µg/d	n/a	ND	500 µg/d
	Males	30 µg/d	n/a	ND	500 µg/d

ND = Not Determinable

n/a = Not Available

[1]Health Canada, Natural Health Products—Compendium of Monographs, available at http://www.hc-sc.gc.ca/dhp-mps/prodnatur/applications/licen-prod/monograph/index-eng.php.

[2]Data from CCHS 2.2, Volume 2, non-smoker.

[3]Data from CCHS 2.2, Volume 2.

[4]Health Canada—Dietary Reference Intakes Report List, available at http://www.hc-sc.gc.ca/fn-an/nutrition/reference/dri_rep-rap anref-list/index-eng.php.

Sources: Sources: Modified from Health Canada and Statistics Canada. 2009. Canadian Community Health Survey, Cycle 2.2, Nutrition (2004): Nutrient Intakes from Food—Provincial, Regional and National Summary Data Tables (Vol 1-3). Cat No. 978-0-662-06542-5; Health Canada—Dietary Reference Intakes Report List, available at http://www.hc-sc.gc.ca/fn-an/nutrition/reference/dri_rep-rap_anref-list/index-eng.php; Health Canada—Natural Health Products Ingredients Database, available at http://webprod.hc-sc.gc.ca/nhpid-bdipsn/monosReq.do?lang=eng.

CONTROVERSY 7

Vitamin Supplements: Who Benefits?

Fifty-three percent of the Canadian population dose themselves with vitamin supplements. Some take a single pill containing a multitude of nutrients; others take huge doses of single nutrients in an attempt to ward off diseases. Do most people need these supplements? What about the safety of today's supplements? Can taking a daily vitamin pill prevent chronic diseases? And who is looking out for the consumer? This Controversy examines evidence surrounding these questions and concludes with some advice for those choosing to take a supplement.

What the Experts Are Saying

On reviewing the evidence concerning supplements, researchers come to different conclusions. Several have concluded that all healthy people might benefit from a multiple vitamin tablet or two every day as a sort of nutritional insurance.*,[1] They judge that the risks of deficiencies outweigh those of any potential for overload from moderate daily doses.

Other experts vigorously disagree. They argue that the risks incurred by taking supplements are considerable and often unpredictable. Too little evidence of true benefit exists, they say, to support taking supplements except in cases where an established risk of deficiency exists or where there are demonstrated benefits for

*The references for this Controversy are listed separately at the end of the chapter.

the treatment of disease and that levels of intake otherwise remain between the RDA/AI and UL.[2] Additionally, for those who may need supplements, these scientists recommend a thorough assessment of the individual's vitamin status to determine which nutrients need attention, and, even then, they recommend dietary changes as well as supplementation to correct immediate deficiencies.[3]

Indisputably, certain people derive benefits from supplements, and these people are listed in Table C7–1. For them, nutrient supplements have been shown with certainty to prevent or reverse illnesses. Consider a woman who loses a lot of blood and therefore a lot of iron and other blood-building nutrients in menstruation each month. This woman may be able to eat in such a way as to make up all nutrient losses except that of iron; we can say with certainty that for iron, she needs an assessment of her iron status and a supplement prescribed by a health-care provider. Similarly, few women of childbearing age obtain the folic acid they need for healthy pregnancies without enriched foods or supplements in addition to folate from food.

Experts also almost always agree on these points:

- People who eat diets that omit any major food group probably need

Which is the best source of vitamins to support good health: supplements or foods?

certain supplements to ensure adequate intakes of vitamins and minerals. For example, vegetarians who eat no animal products most likely need vitamin B_{12}, calcium, and vitamin D.

- Beta-carotene supplements are probably hazardous, especially to those who smoke and consume alcoholic beverages, and are not recommended either alone or in combination with other nutrients.[4]

Many experts also agree that people who take multinutrient supplements should limit their intakes of preformed vitamin A for the sake of their bones—elevated blood vitamin A predicts a significant increase in hip fractures.[5] Vitamin A also reliably and quickly produces liver injury at doses greater than 10,000 micrograms, but liver problems

can appear with much lower doses taken regularly over many years.

The experts part company regarding who should *not* take a routine supplement. The remainder of this Controversy presents evidence on both sides of the argument, starting with an issue of paramount importance—supplement safety.

Canadian Regulation of Supplements

Vitamin and mineral supplements that are considered drugs are regulated in Canada under Part D of the Food and Drugs Act and Regulations (http://www.hc-sc.gc.ca/fn-an/legislation/acts-lois/act-loi_reg-eng.php). The regulations set minimum and maximum levels for vitamins in supplements. At higher doses, some, such as vitamin K, can be sold only by prescription. Regulations control advertising of supplements, preventing recommendations of high doses of nutrients.

Nonprescription single and multiple vitamin mineral supplements (including those from natural sources) are regulated under the Natural Health Products Directorate of Health Canada. The new regulations for natural health products are in effect. Fifty-three percent of Canadians recently reported taking vitamins (http://epe.lac-bac.gc.ca/100/200/301/pwgsc-tpsgc/por-ef/health/2011/135-09/report.pdf). Check for updates from the Natural Health Products Directorate at http://www.hc-sc.gc.ca/ahc-asc/branch-dirgen/hpfb-dgpsa/nhpd-dpsn/index-eng.php. The Natural Health Product Regulations can be found at http://www.hc-sc.gc.ca/dhp-mps/prodnatur/legislation/acts-lois/prodnatur/index-eng.php.

Table C7–1

Some Valid Reasons for Taking Supplements

These people may need supplements:
- People with nutrient deficiencies
- Women in their childbearing years (supplemental or enrichment sources of folic acid are recommended to reduce risk of neural tube defects in infants)
- Pregnant or lactating women (they may need iron and folate)
- Newborns (they are routinely given a vitamin K dose)
- Infants (they may need various supplements; see Chapter 13)
- Those who are lactose intolerant (they need calcium to forestall osteoporosis)
- Habitual dieters (they may eat insufficient food)
- Elderly people, who often benefit from some of the vitamins and minerals in a balanced supplement (they may choose poor diets, have trouble chewing, or absorb or metabolize less efficiently; see Chapter 14)
- Victims of AIDS or other wasting illnesses (they lose nutrients faster than foods can supply them)
- Those addicted to drugs or alcohol (they absorb fewer and excrete more nutrients; nutrients cannot undo damage from drugs or alcohol)
- Those recovering from surgery, burns, injury, or illness (they need extra nutrients to help regenerate tissues)
- Strict vegetarians (they may need vitamin B_{12}, vitamin D, iron, and zinc)
- People taking medications that interfere with the body's use of nutrients

If you are a Canadian student living near the U.S. border, you may find it interesting to compare the cost and the content of vitamin and mineral supplements from each country. You will also notice that U.S. vitamin/mineral supplements have a Supplement Facts panel on them that includes the quantity of each nutrient listed in the supplement along with its respective %DV (see Figure C7–1 on page 294), whereas Canadian supplements do not provide a %DV for each nutrient.

Also see Controversy 1 in Chapter 1 for resources regarding fraud and marketing of supplements.

U.S. Information about Supplements

Since the majority of Canadians live within 200 kilometres of the U.S. border and might shop there or order supplements from the U.S. online, those who do might find this section of particular interest.

Supplements Must Be Safe, or the Government Would Not Allow Their Sale, Right?

Many consumers believe that government scientists, in particular those of the U.S. Food and Drug Administration (FDA), test supplements to ensure their safety and effectiveness. This belief is false. The FDA has no mandate to test consumer products; instead, under federal law, the FDA is charged with ensuring that supplements do not pose a "significant or unreasonable risk" of illness or injury to consumers. To do this, the FDA needs scientific evidence of supplement safety from manufacturers and the records of adverse health effects reported by consumers, but just a few

ethical companies provide this information voluntarily. Consumers can report adverse reactions from supplements directly to Health Canada via their hotline or website, but most people are unaware of these options.*

Recent documented cases of serious illness and death from supplements, particularly from **ephedrine** (see Table C7–2 for definitions) sold for weight loss and as an "energy booster," have raised an alarm, and many scientists are calling for greater FDA regulation of the supplement industry. The FDA's task would be easier if makers of supplements were required to provide scientific evidence of safety, as is true for prescription drugs. Laws governing supplements, however, assume them to be safe until proven otherwise.

*Consumers should report suspected harm from dietary supplements to their health providers or to Health Canada by calling a Canada Vigilance Regional Office at 1-866-234-2345 toll-free or reporting it online at http://www.hc-sc.gc.ca/dhp-mps/medeff/report-declaration/index-eng.php#a1.

Table C7–2

Dietary Supplement Terms

- **aristolochic acid** a Chinese herb ingredient known to attack the kidneys and to cause cancer; U.S. consumers have required kidney transplants and must take lifelong antirejection medication after use. Banned by the FDA but available in supplements sold on the Internet.
- **coenzyme Q10** an enzyme made by cells and important for its role in energy metabolism. With diminished coenzyme Q10 function, oxidative stress increases, as may occur in aging. Preliminary research suggests that it may be of value for treating certain conditions; toxicity in animals appears to be low. No safe intake levels for human beings have been established.
- **DHEA**[a] a hormone secretion of the adrenal gland whose level falls with advancing age. DHEA may protect antioxidant nutrients. Real DHEA is available only by prescription; the herbal DHEA imitator for sale in health-food stores is not active in the body. No safety information exists for either.
- **dietary supplement** a product, other than tobacco, that is added to the diet and contains one of the following ingredients: a vitamin, mineral, herb, botanical (plant extract), amino acid, metabolite, constituent, or extract or a combination of any of these ingredients.
- **ephedrine** one of a group of compounds with dangerous amphetaminelike stimulant effects; extracted from the herb ma huang and recently banned by the FDA but still available from Internet sources. The most severe reported side effects of ephedrine are heart attack, stroke, and sudden death. Not allowed to add it to foods in Canada.

- **garlic oil** an extract of garlic; may or may not contain the chemicals associated with garlic; claims for health benefits unproven.
- **green pills, fruit pills** pills containing dehydrated, crushed vegetable or fruit matter. An advertisement may claim that each pill equals a pound of fresh produce, but, in reality, a pill may equal one small forkful—minus nutrient losses incurred in processing.
- **kelp tablets** tablets made from dehydrated kelp, a kind of seaweed used by the Japanese as a foodstuff.
- **ma huang** an evergreen plant that supposedly boosts energy and helps with weight control. Ma huang, also called Ephedra, contains ephedrine (see first column) and is especially dangerous in combination with kola nut or other caffeine-containing substances.
- **melatonin** a hormone of the pineal gland believed to help regulate the body's daily rhythms, to reverse the effects of jet lag, and to promote sleep. Claims for life extension or enhancement of sexual prowess are without merit.
- **nutritional yeast** a preparation of yeast cells, often praised for its high nutrient content. Yeast is a source of B vitamins, as are many other foods. Also called brewer's yeast; not the yeast used in baking.
- **organ and glandular extracts** dried or extracted material from brain, adrenal, pituitary, or other glands or tissues providing few nutrients but posing a theoretical risk of "mad cow disease." See Chapter 12.
- **SAM-e** an amino acid derivative that may have an antidepressant effect on the brain in some people but is not recommended as a substitute for standard antidepressant therapy.
- Thousands of others.

[a]Dehydroepiandrosterone.

NOTE: According to legal definitions, all of the substances listed qualify as dietary supplements, even though some appear to have the effects of drugs, not nutrients. Table 11–8 on page 481 describes many more medicinal herbs, including their effects and their hazards.

In truth, many vitamin supplements, but not all, are probably safe when used as directed.[6] The trouble is, consumers have no way of knowing which may be harmful before purchasing them.

Dietary Supplement Health and Education Act

In 1994, the U.S. Congress passed the Dietary Supplement Health and Education Act (DSHEA, often pronounced *dee-SHAY*), which specifies the FDA's roles with regard to supplements. Under DSHEA, supplements:

- Must provide a Supplement Facts panel of nutrient information (see Figure C7–1).

- Must not be adulterated; that is, they should contain the ingredients stated on the labels (although few products conformed to this standard during recent testing).

- Must not make label claims for the diagnosis, prevention, treatment, or cure of illness.

- May bear "structure/function" claims (described in a following section).[7]

DSHEA also defined the term **dietary supplement** (see Table C7–2), but the definition is too broad to be meaningful.

The stated intent of DSHEA was to enable consumers to make informed choices about nutrient supplements without too much government interference. Its effect, however, was to deregulate the supplement industry. In 1994, when DSHEA was passed, about 4,000 supplements, mostly vitamins and minerals, were on the market. Today, over 29,000 supplements are available for sale.[8] More than 1,000 new products enter the market every year. Nutrients, herbs, amino acids, dried organ tissues of animals, microorganisms, and even hormones are sold for human consumption freely over the counter. (Consult Table C7–2 for descriptions of many other supplement products.)

Unable to require credible scientific evidence to support supplement safety prior to marketing, the FDA has identified hazardous supplements only after actual harm has come to consumers. In addition to ephedrine, the dangerous weight-loss

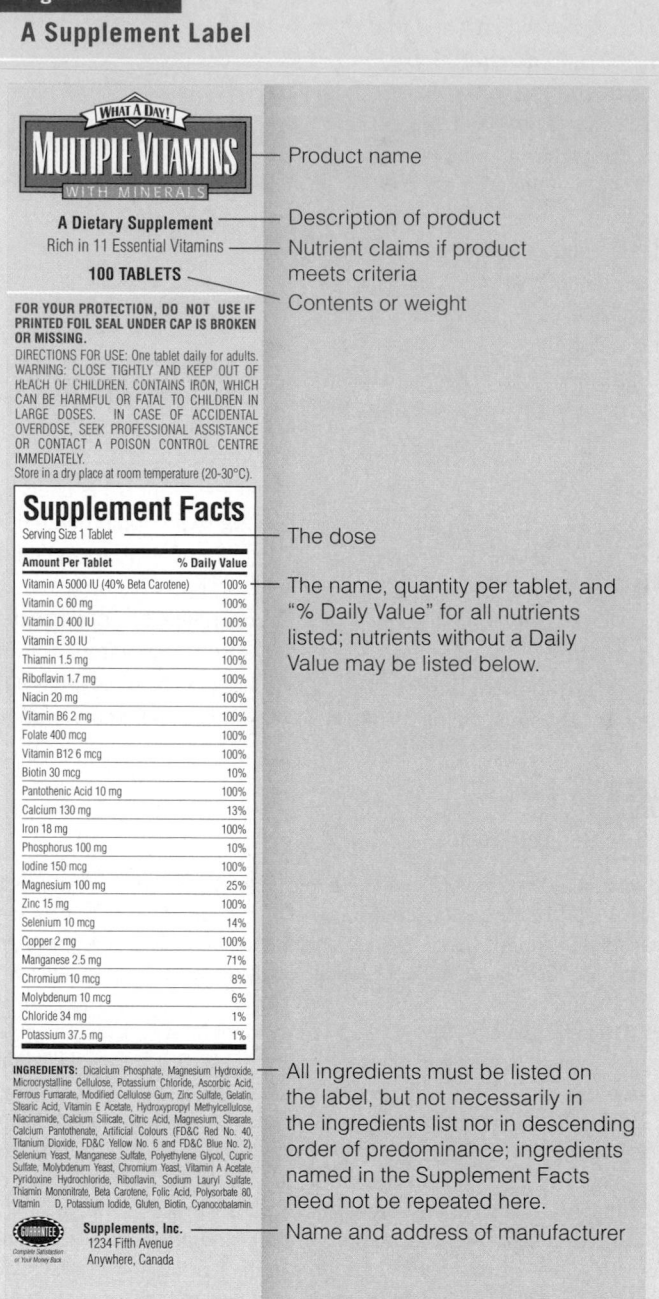

Figure C7–1
A Supplement Label

Product name

Description of product

Nutrient claims if product meets criteria

Contents or weight

The dose

The name, quantity per tablet, and "% Daily Value" for all nutrients listed; nutrients without a Daily Value may be listed below.

All ingredients must be listed on the label, but not necessarily in the ingredients list nor in descending order of predominance; ingredients named in the Supplement Facts need not be repeated here.

Name and address of manufacturer

supplement mentioned earlier, the FDA is currently taking action against usnic acid supplements now known to cause liver damage in dieters; kava, a herb sold to improve mood, is also under FDA scrutiny for causing liver failure; others are also being investigated.[9]

The FDA is currently striving to improve its ability to take action on a suspected supplement hazard before serious illnesses or deaths occur, but it still faces the problems listed in Table C7–3.

A new plan for a science-based approach to protecting consumers from unsafe supplements is under development. In the first half of 2004, the FDA sent warning letters to over a hundred U.S. makers of dietary supplements, refused entry of over a thousand foreign supplement shipments, and supervised destruction of almost $20 million worth of mislabelled or adulterated products. These efforts address some problems in the supplement industry, but they do not eliminate all potential dangers to consumers. Additionally, consumers face a confusing array of label claims made for the health effects of supplements.

Structure/Function Claims

A consumer attempting to select a nutrient or other supplement is likely to encounter claims on labels resembling the FDA's most reliable, Grade A *health* claims (described in Chapter 2's Consumer Corner). The claims found on supplement labels, however, are likely to be the less regulated structure/function claims. Before printing a Grade A health claim on a label, a food manufacturer must submit scientific evidence and petition the FDA for permission in advance, at much effort and expense. If the same manufacturer elects to print a similar-appearing structure/function claim instead, it need not obtain prior approval and must comply with only a few regulations, most importantly the requirement to include a disclaimer stating that the FDA has not evaluated the claim.[10] Our consumer, however, might reasonably assume that the following claims are identical:

- "Lowers cholesterol."

- "Helps maintain normal cholesterol levels."

Yet the first requires full FDA process and approval before printing—it is a Grade A health claim. The second is a structure/function claim, so its accuracy is uncertain.

What, then, is a consumer to do? To make a rational choice concerning whether to take a supplement, the consumer must weigh potential benefits against the potential for harm. Doing so requires studying all available scientific evidence about the supplement ingredients while ignoring marketing claims. For most supplements, unfortunately, no or few scientific studies exist. Others have been well researched, including the antioxidant vitamins often sold with promises of disease prevention. The next sections present the known evidence both for and against the theory that taking these nutrients may enhance the health of the body.

Arguments in Favour of Supplements for Chronic Disease Prevention

There is considerable scientific interest in identifying which nutrient deficiencies may be linked with diseases other than classic deficiency syndromes. The idea that subclinical, or marginal, deficiencies may compound risks for chronic diseases is currently fostering much research (definitions are in Table C7–4). In exploring these links, scientists are asking two questions important in nutrition:

- Do subclinical deficiencies of nutrients increase the risks for chronic diseases, and can supplements reverse these risks?

- Do well-nourished people gain extra protection against chronic diseases by taking supplements of nutrients?

Marginal Deficiencies and Oxidative Stress

Subclinical deficiencies present no or only subtle symptoms easily overlooked by physicians during regular examinations. For example, persons consuming a diet lacking in vitamin C silently incur an increase in **oxidative stress** in the tissues long before the symptoms of scurvy appear, but no symptoms warn the individual or alert health-care providers.[11] People lacking vitamin C in the diet often suffer greater rates of cancer and other diseases possibly due to increased oxidative stress, but perhaps due to other causes.[12] A diet low in vitamin C probably also lacks other nutrients, making it difficult to determine exactly which nutrient deficiency may be causing the problem.

The link between suboptimal intakes of **antioxidant nutrients** and chronic diseases follows from a theory linking chronic diseases, such as heart disease, with oxidative stress in the body. As body cells use oxygen to produce energy, they produce free radicals (highly unstable molecules of oxygen). Radiation, pollution, tobacco smoke, and other environmental factors can also cause free-radical formation. When free-radical activity in the body exceeds antioxidant defences, the theory goes, a destructive chain reaction of oxidation increases oxidative stress in the tissues, triggering the onset of diseases.

Today, the world's laboratories have put forth an extensive, but largely inconclusive, body of evidence on antioxidant nutrients, oxidative stress, and chronic diseases. Clearly, diets rich in fruit, vegetables, and whole grains with their abundant antioxidant nutrients, such as vitamin C, vitamin E, beta-carotene and other carotenoids, and the mineral selenium, provide benefits. Those eating such diets have low disease rates. Additionally, people whose blood tests below normal for these nutrients often have elevated rates of chronic diseases, and restoring these nutrients with foods or supplements reliably produces a drop in chronic disease incidence.[13] Such research results support an affirmative answer to the first question asked above: people whose blood tests reveal low concentrations of antioxidant nutrients benefit in terms of reduced chronic disease risks when the missing nutrients are restored through either food or supplements.

Marginal Deficiencies, Cancer, and Other Diseases

In agreement is a leading geneticist who observes that subclinical deficiencies of vitamin B_{12}, vitamin B_6, folate, vitamin C, vitamin E, or the minerals zinc and iron, common among low-income groups in the United States, appear to cause extensive breaks in DNA strands. The DNA damage from marginal deficiencies is said to mimic the well-known cancer-causing damage from radiation.[14] Not only do more breaks in DNA occur when nutrients are lacking, but they are also more slowly repaired than damage arising in well-nourished cells. Consequently, metabolic damage to the cell builds up in ways that could cause disease.

Many forms of cancer, which can arise from breaks in DNA, occur more often among poorly nourished low-income populations. The hope is that by reversing slight nutrient deficits with balanced supplements in this group, the excess burden of cancer, among other diseases, could be partially relieved. Other groups, such as menstruating women, young children, and the elderly, may suffer from the effects of low vitamin and mineral status in many other ways. Presumably, resolving their slight deficiencies might relieve a variety of illnesses, from minor complaints to premature loss of cognition in aging.[15]

Arguments against Supplements for Chronic Disease Prevention

While no one doubts the benefit from nutrient supplements for preventing deficiencies in people with suboptimal intakes, the second question posed earlier with regard to potential benefits of supplements in well-nourished people arouses considerable controversy. The argument concerns some theoretical benefits of supplements with regard to the prevention of chronic diseases. The scientists recommending supplements believe strongly that vitamins and certain minerals in amounts greater than those available from food are very likely to protect against chronic diseases, particularly heart disease, in ways explained in the following sections.[16] If the risks are low, they seem to imply, why not take supplements now to be ahead of the game in case research one day reveals a benefit?

More conservative voices point out critical gaps in the current body of evidence. Studies of the health and nutrient intakes of populations support the theory that higher intakes of vitamins and minerals correlate with lower rates of diseases—people with high intakes of fruit and vegetables that supply the antioxidant nutrients generally enjoy better health than others. Also supporting the theory are results from cell and animal studies that demonstrate the physiology of the nutrients in disease prevention—they lend biological plausibility to the argument.

Mixed or negative results, however, emerge from the gold standard for evaluating the effectiveness of a medical treatment for human beings—the controlled clinical human trial.[17] The general finding of five years of research is that routinely providing supplements of nutrients to well-nourished populations produces few, if any, observed benefits. Death rates from heart disease and other chronic diseases remain unchanged whether or not well-nourished people are given supplements.[18] One exception may involve the healthy elderly: two preliminary studies have revealed a slight reduction in the advance of common causes of vision loss in those taking a combined antioxidant supplement, and these findings warrant further investigation.[19] The following paragraphs illustrate the problems surrounding research on the potential effects of two antioxidant nutrients, beta-carotene and vitamin E, with regard to chronic disease.

Beta-Carotene and Cancer: A Disappointing Story

Low rates of many cancers are reported in people whose diets include abundant vegetables and fruit, the richest sources of antioxidants.[20] In particular, intakes of vegetables and fruit rich in beta-carotene are linked with low rates of cancers (see Figure C7–2).[21] For a time, all evidence seemed to point to beta-carotene as "the" anticancer substance in these foods, and consumers eagerly bought and took beta-carotene supplements. In a sudden reversal, support for beta-carotene crumbled as studies of supplements of beta-carotene revealed no benefit and a possibility of serious harm.[22] Major clinical trials of beta-carotene supplements were immediately ceased upon finding a 28 percent *increase* in lung cancer among smokers taking beta-carotene compared with placebos.

Were the original findings wrong? No. Intake of fruit and vegetables is undoubtedly linked with lower cancer risks, but beta-carotene itself is clearly not the agent of this effect. Fruit and

Figure C7–2

Vegetable and Fruit Intakes and Cancer in Population Studies

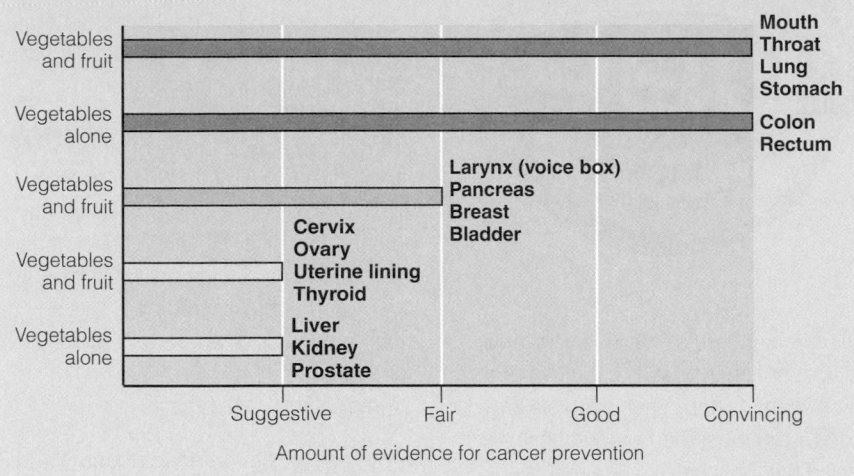

Amount of evidence for cancer prevention

vegetables contain hundreds of potentially beneficial phytochemicals, such as the other carotenoids described in Controversy 2. Such foods are also rich in fibres, and they are generally low in Calories and so may assist in weight control—diet characteristics linked with low cancer rates. In truth, perhaps the difference in cancer development should be attributed to the entire *diet* chosen by eaters of fruit and vegetables or even to their entire lifestyle. People choosing foods they perceive to be good for them probably also do not smoke, may exercise regularly, and generally take better care of themselves than other people do. In other words, the beta-carotene story provides an illustration of why population evidence alone is insufficient to establish causal relationships. The entire picture emerges only when controlled clinical trials confirm population findings. In the end, supplements of beta-carotene provide no benefits and may cause harm to certain people, especially smokers.

Vitamin E and Heart Disease: Unconvincing Evidence

High blood cholesterol carried in low-density lipoproteins (LDL) is a major risk factor for CVD, but how does LDL exert its damage? One scenario is that free radicals within the blood vessel walls oxidize LDL, changing its structure and activities. The oxidized LDL then speeds the formation of artery-clogging plaques that impede the flow of blood to the heart muscle. Factors such as a diet high in saturated fat and toxins from tobacco smoke heighten this oxidative damage within the artery walls. In contrast, a diet high in fruit and vegetables, especially when fat is kept low, strengthens antioxidant defences against LDL oxidation.[23] The question, then, is do antioxidant nutrients taken as supplements also slow the onset of heart disease?

Population studies demonstrate that people who eat foods rich in vitamin E have low rates of death from heart disease.[24] In the laboratory, vitamin E has been shown to defend against LDL oxidation, inflammation, arterial injuries, and blood clotting.[25] Yet, despite the many talents of vitamin E, supplements of the vitamin have generally proven useless against CVD in people at risk for the disease.[26] Some trials of vitamin E in healthy people are still ongoing and may reveal other findings, but so far no convincing evidence exists indicating benefits from antioxidant supplements in well-nourished people. Likewise, vitamin C exhibits potential in the laboratory for protecting lipids from oxidation, but the majority of studies indicate that vitamin C supplements offer no protection against heart disease.[27]

Should We Take Supplements to Ensure Adequate Nutrients?

A scientific approach clearly identifies foods, not supplements, as overwhelmingly the best source of nutrients. Opponents of supplements energetically oppose them on the grounds that side effects, which may not be immediately evident, might endanger supplement takers' health in these ways:

- High doses of vitamin E may interfere with vitamin K functions, delay blood clotting, increase the risk of brain hemorrhage (a form of stroke) over time, or even increase the risk of death from all causes.[28]

- Vitamin C supplements enhance iron absorption, making iron overload likely in some people.

- Vitamin C supplements in high doses *increase* markers of oxidation in the blood.

- High doses of vitamin C taken by women who have diabetes may increase their likelihood of dying of CVD.[29]

- Biotin-supplemented cell cultures suffer DNA damage of a type related to cancer formation.[30]

- Daily supplements of beta-carotene may increase lung cancer in smokers.

- Supplements of vitamin D, vitamin A, and many minerals can be toxic in large doses.

Besides, while an orange and a pill may both contain vitamin C, the orange presents a balanced array of chemicals and fibre that modulate vitamin C's effects. The pill provides only vitamin C, a lone chemical.

Still, supplements are sometimes appropriate and necessary to health. For those who need supplements, the next section provides some guidance to making a selection.

Selection of a Multinutrient Supplement

If you fall into one of the categories listed earlier in Table C7–1 (page 292) and if you absolutely cannot meet your nutrient needs from foods, a supplement containing *nutrients only* can prevent serious problems. In these cases, the benefits probably outweigh the risks.

Which supplement to choose? The first step is to remain aware that sales of vitamin supplements often approach the realm of quackery because the profits are high and the industry is largely free of oversight. To escape the clutches of the health hustlers, use your imagination and delete the picture on the label of sexy people on the beach and the meaningless, glittering generalities stating "Advanced formula," "Maximum power," and the like. Don't be misled into buying and taking unneeded supplements (Table C7–5 provides some invalid reasons for taking supplements).

When shopping online or in the United States, if you see a USP symbol on the label, it means that a manufacturer has voluntarily paid an independent laboratory to test the product and affirm that it contains the ingredients listed and that it will dissolve or disintegrate in the digestive tract to make the ingredients available for absorption. The symbol does not imply that the supplement has been tested for safety or effectiveness with regard to health, however.

Now all you have left is the list of ingredients, the form they are in, and the price—the plain facts. You have two basic questions to answer. The first question: What form do you want—chewable, liquid, or pills? If you'd rather drink your vitamins and minerals than chew them,

fine. If you choose a fortified liquid meal replacer or "energy bar" (a candy bar to which vitamins and other nutrients are added), you must then proportionately reduce the Calories you consume as food, or you may gain unwanted weight. If you choose chewable pills, be aware that vitamin C can erode tooth enamel. Swallow promptly and flush the teeth with a drink of water. Avoid vitamin-fortified bubble gum to protect both the teeth and gum-loving children who may chew a whole box and receive too large a dose for their small bodies.

The second question: Who are you? What vitamins and minerals do you need? The DRI nutrient intake recommendations listed in the tables on the inside front cover are the standards appropriate for all reasonably healthy people.

For most people, an appropriate supplement provides all of the vitamins and minerals in amounts smaller than, equal to, or very close to the intake

recommendations. Those who require a higher dose, such as young women who need supplemental folate in the childbearing years, should choose a supplement with just the needed nutrient or in combination with a reasonable dose of others. Avoid any preparation that, in a daily dose, provides more than the DRI recommended intake of vitamin A, vitamin D, or any mineral or more than the Tolerable Upper Intake Level for any nutrient. Warning: Expect to reject about 80 percent of available preparations when you choose according to these criteria; be choosy where your health is concerned.

In addition, avoid these:

- High doses of iron (more than 10 mg/d) except for menstruating women. People who menstruate need more iron, but people who don't, don't.

- "For low-carb diets." Preparations containing extra biotin are claimed to better metabolize the excess protein in such diets, but no evidence supports these claims.

- "Organic" or "natural" preparations with added substances. They are no better than standard types, but they cost much more.

- "High-potency" or "therapeutic dose" supplements. More is not better.

- Items not needed in human nutrition, such as carnitine and inositol. These particular items won't harm you, but they reveal a marketing strategy that makes the whole mix suspect. The manufacturer wants you to believe that its pills contain the latest "new" nutrient that other brands omit, but, in fact, for every valid discovery of this kind, there are 999,999 frauds.

- "Time release." Medications such as some antibiotics or pain relievers often must be sustained at a steady concentration in the blood to be effective, but nutrients are incorporated into the tissues where they are needed whenever they arrive.

- "Stress formulas." Although the stress response depends on certain B vitamins and vitamin C, the recommended amount provides all that is needed of these nutrients. If you are under stress (and who isn't?),

---

Table C7–5

Some Invalid Reasons for Taking Supplements

Watch out for plausible-sounding but false reasons given by marketers trying to convince you, the consumer, that you need supplements. The invalid reasons listed below have gained strength by repetition among friends, on the Internet, and by the media:

- You fear that foods grown on today's soils lack nutrients (a common false statement made by sellers of supplements).
- You feel tired and falsely believe that supplements can provide energy.
- You hope that supplements can help you cope with stress.
- You wish to build up your muscles faster or without physical exercise.
- You want to prevent or cure self-diagnosed illnesses.
- You hope excess nutrients will produce unnamed mysterious beneficial reactions in your body.

People who should never take supplements without a physician's approval include those with kidney or liver ailments (they are susceptible to toxicities), those taking medications (nutrients can interfere with their actions), and smokers (who should avoid products with beta-carotene).

Chapter 7 The Vitamins   NEL

generous servings of fruit and vegetables will more than cover your need.

- Pills containing extracts of parsley, alfalfa, and other vegetable components.

- Geriatric "tonics." They are generally poor in vitamins and minerals and yet may be so high in alcohol as to threaten inebriation.

- Any supplement sold with claims that today's foods lack the nutrients they once contained. Plants make vitamins for their own needs, not ours. A plant lacking a mineral or failing to make a needed vitamin dies before it can bear food for our consumption.

As for price, be aware that local or store brands may be just as good or better than nationally advertised brands.[31] If they are less expensive, it may be because the price does not have to cover the cost of national advertising. To get the most from a supplement of vitamins and minerals, take it with food. A full stomach retains and dissolves the pill with its churning action. Also, if you take an iron supplement, choose foods that will assist in its absorption, such as meats, fish, poultry, or foods containing vitamin C.

Choosing Doses

When people choose supplements, they choose doses of nutrients that can vary fivefold or more, a fact revealed by a comparison of the back panels of the products. The higher the dose, the greater the risk of toxicity, of course, and studies bear out the logic that supplement users can teeter on the edge of toxicity for nutrients.[32] Although tolerance for high doses of nutrients varies, and no one can say with certainty what level may be safe for an individual person, some guidance is offered in the DRI Tolerable Upper Intake Levels (see page C at the front of the book).

Even more worrisome than the possibility of short-term, acute overdoses is the potential for chronic, low-level nutrient toxicity whose subtle effects develop slowly and go unrecognized. Because of the potential hazards that supplements may present, some authorities believe supplements and highly fortified foods, particularly those high in vitamin A or vitamin D, should be required to bear warning labels, but such labels have not been seriously considered.

One final problem with supplements is that they may lull their takers into a false sense of security. A person may eat irresponsibly, thinking, "My supplement will cover my needs." More often, supplements supply precisely the nutrients people need least—those they consume in food—while failing to provide those missing from the diet. Further, if a person's diet is inadequate in vitamins, it probably lacks minerals, phytochemicals, and fibre as well.

Conclusion

People in developed nations are far more likely to suffer from *overnutrition* and poor lifestyle choices than from nutrient deficiencies. People wish that swallowing vitamin pills will boost their health. The truth—that they need to improve their eating and exercise habits—is harder to swallow.

Don't waste time and money trying to single out a few nutrients to take as supplements. Invest energy in eating a wide variety of fruit and vegetables in generous quantities, along with the recommended daily amounts of whole grains, lean meats, and milk products every day, and take supplements only when they are truly needed.

Self-Check

Answers to these Self-Check Questions are in Appendix D.

1. Which of the following vitamins are classified as fat soluble?
   a. vitamins B_{12}, D
   b. vitamins A, D, E, and K
   c. vitamins B_6, E, D, and C
   d. vitamins B_1 and C

2. Night blindness and xerophthalmia are the result of a deficiency of which vitamin?
   a. niacin
   b. vitamin C
   c. vitamin A
   d. vitamin K

3. Which of the following foods is (are) rich in beta-carotene?
   a. sweet potatoes
   b. pumpkin
   c. spinach
   d. all of the above

4. A deficiency of niacin may result in which disease?
   a. pellagra
   b. beriberi
   c. scurvy
   d. rickets

5. Which of the following describes the fat-soluble vitamins?
   a. vitamins B and C
   b. easily absorbed and excreted
   c. stored extensively in tissues
   d. a and c

6. Which vitamin(s) is (are) present only in foods of animal origin?
   a. the active form of vitamin A
   b. vitamin B_{12}
   c. riboflavin
   d. a and b

7. The theory that vitamin C prevents or cures colds is well supported by research.
T F

8. Xerophthalmia results from advanced vitamin A deficiency and can lead to permanent blindness.
T F

9. A high blood level of homocysteine is associated with a deficiency of B vitamins and may increase the risk of heart disease.
T F

10. Vitamin A supplements can help treat acne.
T F

track it!

Diet Analysis PLUS ✛ Concepts in Action

start now! ·····⟩ If you haven't already done so, go to Diet Analysis Plus and track your diet for 3 days, including one weekend day. After you have recorded your foods for 3 days, from the Reports tab under the Nutrients heading click Intake vs Goals, select all 3 Days (choose all meals and snacks) to see how close you come to meeting the nutrient recommendations for a person of your age, sex, weight, and level of physical activity.

Analyze Your Vitamin Intake

The purpose of this exercise is to help you identify your food sources of water-soluble and fat-soluble vitamins. Many foods rich in vitamins work in harmony to provide a full complement of nutrients, which ultimately contributes to a health-promoting eating pattern.

1. Determine whether your food provides enough vitamins. From the Reports tab select Intake vs. Goals. Choose Day Two (all meals and snacks). Generate a report. Did your intakes on that day meet your DRI recommended intake values for vitamins for your age, sex and life-stage? If not, list those that fall short of the DRI goals. For all of the vitamins that exceeded your recommendations, check page C at the front of the

book to see if any also exceeded the Tolerable Upper Intake Levels (UL). Remember this report represents only a single day of your eating pattern and the shortfalls and excesses will even out for those who consume a varied diet as recommended in Canada's Food Guide.

2. Some fruits and vegetables are good sources of fat-soluble vitamins (see the Snapshots in this chapter). Have you met your minimum recommended number of servings of vegetables and fruit from Canada's Food Guide? Did you consume any fruits and vegetables listed in the Snapshots for the fat-soluble vitamins? Which ones?

3. From the Reports tab under the Advanced Analysis heading, select Source Analysis, and choose any day (include all meals and snacks). From the drop-down pick-list, select vitamin C (and do the same for folate), and generate a report for each vitamin. What is your best food source for vitamin C? And for folate? Were your best sources shown in the Snapshots for vitamin C and for folate?

4. After viewing the Intake vs. Goals report in item 1 above, if you fell short on any vitamin, what foods could you include that would bring you up to

the DRI recommended value? If you exceeded the UL for any of them find out which foods were responsible by clicking on the Report tab, and under the Advanced Analysis heading, click on Source Analysis and use the drop-down pick-list to find the nutrient and foods that contributed the most.

5. The Canada's Food Guide recommended number of servings for a young adult female suggest that a person who requires about 2,000 calories per day should consume 7 to 8 servings of vegetables and fruit (including at least 1 dark green and 1 orange vegetable) each day. Create a dish from vegetables or fruits that you enjoy. Get some ideas by using Figure 7–17 (pages 288–289) and/or the various Snapshots in this chapter. From the Track Diet tab, choose a different day from those for your 3-Day Food Record and enter the ingredients for your new dish. From the Reports tab, under the Advanced Analysis heading, select Source Analysis, and select one water-soluble and then one fat-soluble vitamin from the drop-down pick-list. Generate a report for each. Look for Silver (10 to 20%DV) or Gold (>20%DV) Stars next to the food items to identify the vitamin-rich foods from the report. What did you find?

Endnotes

1. R. Rodriguez-Melendez, J. B. Griffin, and J. Zempleni, Biotin supplementation increases expression of the cytochrome P45o 1B1 in Jurkat cells, increasing the occurrence of single-stranded DNA breaks, *Journal of Nutrition* 134 (2004): 2222–2228; B. N. Ames and P. Wakimoto, Are

vitamin and mineral deficiencies a major cancer risk? *Nature Reviews: Cancer* 2 (2002): 694–704.
2. S. Kato, Molecular mechanism of transcriptional control by nuclear vitamin receptors, *British Journal of Nutrition* 84 (2000): S229–S233.

3. S. Perrotta and coauthors, Vitamin A and infancy: Biochemical, functional, and clinical aspects, *Vitamins and Hormones* 66 (2003): 457–591; M. Clagett-Dame and H. F. DeLuca, The role of vitamin A in mammalian reproduction and embryonic development, *Annual Review of Nutrition* 22 (2002): 347–381.

4. J. Bastien and C. Rochette-Egly, Nuclear retinoid receptors and the transcription of retinoid-target genes, *Gene* 328 (2004): 1–16; L. N. Wei, Retinoid receptors and their coregulators, *Annual Review of Pharmacology and Toxicology* 43 (2003): 47–72; R. Zolfaghari and A. C. Ross, Recent advances in molecular cloning of fatty acid desaturatase genes and the regulation of their expression by dietary vitamin A and retinoic acid, *Prostaglandins, Leukotrienes and Essential Fatty Acids* 68 (2003): 171–179; J. E. Balmer and R. Blomhoff, Gene expression regulation by retinoic acid, *Journal of Lipid Research* 43 (2002): 1773–1808.

5. Balmer and Blomhoff, 2002 [see reference 4].

6. G. L. Johanning and C. J. Piyathilake, Retinoids and epigenetic silencing in cancer, *Nutrition Reviews* 61 (2003): 284–289.

7. R. Reifen, Vitamin A as an anti-inflammatory agent, *Proceedings of the Nutrition Society* 61 (2002): 397–400.

8. M. Maden and M. Hind, Retinoic acid, a regeneration-inducing molecule, *Developmental Dynamics* 226 (2003): 237–244; L. Bonet and coauthors, Vitamin A and the regulation of fat reserves, *Cellular and Molecular Life Sciences* 60 (2003): 1311–1321; Perrotta and coauthors, 2003 [see reference 3]; Clagett-Dame and DeLuca, 2002 [see reference 3].

9. A. C. Ross, Advances in retinoid research: Mechanisms of cancer chemoprevention, symposium introduction, *Journal of Nutrition* 133 (2003): 271S–272S.

10. C. Ballew and coauthors, Serum retinol distributions in residents of the United States: Third National Health and Nutrition Examination Survey, 1988–1994, *American Journal of Clinical Nutrition* 73 (2001): 586–593.

11. Standing Committee on the Scientific Evaluation of Dietary Reference Intakes, Food and Nutrition Board, Institute of Medicine, *Dietary Reference Intakes for Vitamin A, Vitamin K, Arsenic, Boron, Chromium, Copper, Iodine, Iron, Manganese, Molybdenum, Nickel, Silicon, Vanadium, and Zinc* (Washington, D.C.: National Academies Press, 2001), pp. 4-9–4-10.

12. M. A. Dijkhuizen and coauthors, Concurrent micronutrient deficiencies in lactating mothers and their infants in Indonesia, *American Journal of Clinical Nutrition* 73 (2001): 786–791.

13. E. Villamor and coauthors, Vitamin A supplements ameliorate the adverse effect of HIV-1, malaria, and diarrheal infections on child growth, *Pediatrics* 109 (2002), available at http://pediatrics.aappublications.org/content/109/1/e6.full; C. Duggan and W. Fawzi, Micronutrients and child health: Studies in international nutrition and HIV infection, *Nutrition Reviews* 59 (2001): 358–369.

14. P. S. Genaro and L. A. Martini, Vitamin A supplementation and risk of skeletal fracture, *Nutrition Reviews* 62 (2004): 65–67; K. Michaelsson and coauthors, Serum retinol levels and the risk of fractures, *New England Journal of Medicine* 348 (2003): 287–294; S. Johnasson and coauthors, Subclinical hypervitaminosis A causes fragile bones in rats, *Bone* 31 (2002): 685–689; D. Feskanich and coauthors, Vitamin A intake and hip fractures among postmenopausal women, *Journal of the American Medical Association* 287 (2002): 47–54; N. Binkley and D. Krueger, Hypervitaminosis A and bone, *Nutrition Reviews* 58 (2000): 138–144.

15. Genaro and Martini, 2004 [see reference 14]; K. L. Penniston and S. A. Tanumihardjo, Vitamin A in dietary supplements and fortified foods: Too much of a good thing? *Journal of the American Dietetic Association* 103 (2003): 1185–1187.

16. L. H. Allen and M. Haskell, Estimating the potential for vitamin A toxicity in women and young children, *Journal of Nutrition* 132 (2003): 2907S–2919S.

17. S. J. Hickenbottom and coauthors, Variability in conversion of C-carotene to vitamin A in men as measured by using a double-tracer study design, *American Journal of Clinical Nutrition* 75 (2002): 900–907; K. J. Yeum and R. M. Russell, Carotenoid bioavailability and bioconversion, *Annual Review of Nutrition* 22 (2002): 483–504.

18. A. Mazzone and A. dal Canton, Images in clinical medicine—Hypercarotenemia, *New England Journal of Medicine* 346 (2002): 821.

19. P. F. Jacques and coauthors, Long-term nutrient intake and early age-related nuclear lens opacities, *Archives of Ophthalmology* 119 (2001): 1009–1019; J. T. Landrum and R. A. Bone, Lutein, zeaxanthin, and the macular pigment, *Archives of Biochemistry and Biophysics* 385 (2001): 28–40.

20. B. R. Hammond Jr., B. R. Wooten, and J. Curran-Celentano, Carotenoids in the retina and lens: Possible acute and chronic effects on human visual performance, *Archives of Biochemistry and Biophysics* 385 (2001): 41–46.

21. C. Moore and coauthors, Vitamin D intake in the United States, *Journal of the American Dietetic Association* 104 (2004): 980–983; M. S. Calvo and S. J. Whiting, Prevalence of vitamin D insufficiency in Canada and the United States: Importance to health status and efficacy of current food fortification and dietary supplement use, *Nutrition Reviews* 61 (2003): 107–113; S. Nesby-O'Dell and coauthors, Hypovitaminosis D prevalence and determinants among African American and white women of reproductive age: Third National Health and Nutrition Examination Survey, 1988–1994, *American Journal of Clinical Nutrition* 76 (2002): 187–192.

22. S. Kato, Molecular mechanism of transcriptional control by nuclear vitamin receptors, *British Journal of Nutrition* 84 (2000): S229–S233.

23. E. Giovannucci, The epidemiology of vitamin D and cancer incidence and mortality: A review (United States), *Cancer Causes and Control* 16 (2005): 83–95; E. Giovannucci and coauthors, Prospective study of predictors of vitamin D status and cancer incidence and mortality in men, *Journal of the National Cancer Institute* 98 (2006): 451–459; M. T. Cantorna and coauthors, Vitamin D status, 1, 25-dihydroxyvitamin D3, and the immune system, *American Journal of Clinical Nutrition* 80 (2004): 1717S–1720S; M. F. Holick, Vitamin D: Importance in the prevention of cancers, type 1 diabetes, heart disease, and osteoporosis, *American Journal of Clinical Nutrition* 79 (2004): 362–371; J. B. Zella and H. F. DeLuca, Vitamin D and autoimmune diabetes, *Journal of Cell Biochemistry* 88 (2003): 216–222; A. Zitterman, Vitamin D in preventive medicine: Are we ignoring the evidence? *British Journal of Nutrition* 89 (2003): 552–572; I. A. van der Mei and coauthors, Past exposure to sun, skin phenotype, and risk of multiple sclerosis: Case-control study, *British Medical Journal* 327 (2003): 316–332; G. Wolf, Intestinal bile acids can bind to and activate the vitamin D receptor, *Nutrition Reviews* 60 (2002): 281–288.

24. P. Weisberg and coauthors, Nutritional rickets among children in the United States: Review of cases reported between 1986 and 2003, *American Journal of Clinical Nutrition* 80 (2004): 1697S–1705S; S. R. Kreiter and coauthors, Nutritional rickets in African American breast-fed infants, *Journal of Pediatrics* 137 (2000): 143–145.

25. M. K. M. Lehtonen-Veromaa and coauthors, Vitamin D and attainment of peak bone mass among peripubertal Finnish girls: A 3-y prospective study, *American Journal of Clinical Nutrition* 76 (2002): 1446–1453; T.A. Outila, M. U. M. Karkkainen, and C. J. E. Lamberg-Allardt, Vitamin D status affects serum parathyroid hormone concentrations during winter in female adolescents: Associations with forearm bone mineral density, *American Journal of Clinical Nutrition* 74 (2001): 206–210.

26. B. Liebman, Soaking up the D's: An interview with Michael F. Holick, *Nutrition Action Healthletter,* December 2003, pp. 1, 3–6.

27. Calvo and Whiting, 2003 [see reference 21].

28. Calvo and Whiting, 2003 [see reference 21]; V. Tangpricha and coauthors, Vitamin D insufficiency among free-living adults, *American Journal of Medicine* 112 (2002): 659–662.

29. M. F. Holic, Sunlight and vitamin D for bone health and prevention of autoimmune diseases, cancers, and cardiovascular disease, *American Journal of Clinical Nutrition* 80 (2004): 1678S–1688S; R. P. Heaney and coauthors, Human serum 25-hydroxycholecalciferol response to extended oral dosing with cholecalciferol, *American Journal of Clinical Nutrition* 77 (2003): 204–210.

30. E. R. Miller and coauthors, Meta-analysis: High-dosage vitamin E supplementation may increase all-cause mortality, *Annals of Internal Medicine* 142 (2005): 37–46, available at http://annals.org/article.aspx?articleid=718049; P. M. Kris-Etherton and coauthors, Antioxidant vitamin supplements and cardiovascular disease, *Circulation* 110 (2004): 637–641; J. E. Manson, S. S. Bassuk, and M. J. Stampfer, Does vitamin E supplementation prevent cardiovascular events? *Journal of Women's Health* 12 (2003): 123–136; L. Kritharides and R. Stocker, The use of antioxidant supplements in coronary heart disease, *Atherosclerosis* 164 (2002): 211–219.

31. Health Canada—It's Your Health: *The Safety of Vitamin E Supplements.* January 2006 (http://www.hc-sc.gc.ca/hl-vs/iyh-vsv/food-aliment/vitam-eng.php).

32. M. A. Beck, Nutritionally induced oxidative stress: Effect on viral disease, *American Journal of Clinical Nutrition* 71 (2000): 1676S–1679S.

33. E. R. Miller and coauthors (2005) [see reference 30].

34. C. T. Taylor and coauthors, Vitamin K to reverse excessive anticoagulation: A review of the literature, *Pharmacotherapy* 19 (1999): 1415–1425.

35. S.L. Booth and coauthors, Vitamin K intake and bone mineral density in women and men, *American Journal of Clinical Nutrition* 77 (2003): 512–516.

36. N. C. Binkley and coauthors, A high phylloquinone intake is required to achieve maximal osteocalcin g-carboxylation, *American Journal of Clinical Nutrition* 76 (2002): 1055–1060.

37. S. J. Padayatty and coauthors, Vitamin C as an antioxidant: Evaluation of its role in disease prevention, *Journal of the American College of Nutrition* 22 (2003): 18–35.

38. U.S. Preventive Task Force, Routine vitamin supplementation to prevent cancer and cardiovascular disease: Recommendations and rationale, *Annals of Internal Medicine* 139 (2003): 51–55; Padayatty and coauthors, 2003 [see reference 37].

39. Standing Committee on the Scientific Evaluation of Dietary Reference Intakes, Food and Nutrition Board, Institute of Medicine, 2000, p. 101.

40. A. Alberg, The influence of cigarette smoking on circulating concentrations of antioxidant micronutrients, *Toxicology* 180 (2002): 121–137.

41. A. M. Preston and coauthors, Influence of environmental tobacco smoke on vitamin C status in children, *American Journal of Clinical Nutrition* 77 (2003): 167–172; R. S. Strauss, Environmental tobacco smoke and serum vitamin C levels in children, *Pediatrics* 107 (2001): 540–542.

42. C. S. Johnston and D. L. Bowling, Stability of ascorbic acid in commercially available orange juices, *Journal of the American Dietetic Association* 102 (2002): 525–529.

43. K. J. Carpenter, Acute versus marginal deficiencies of nutrients, *Nutrition Reviews* 60 (2002): 277–280.

44. H. J. Powers, Riboflavin (vitamin B-2) and health, *American Journal of Clinical Nutrition* 77 (2003): 1352–1360.

45. P. A. Cotton and coauthors, Dietary sources of nutrients among US adults, 1994–1996, *Journal of the American Dietetic Association* 104 (2004): 921–930.

46. J. L. Parra and K. R. Reddy, Hepatotoxicity of hypolipidemic drugs, *Clinics in Liver Disease* 7 (2003): 415–433.

47. P. J. Stover, Physiology of folate and vitamin B_{12} in health and disease, *Nutrition Reviews* 62 (2004): S3–S4.

48. L. B. Bailey, G. C. Rampersaud, and G. P. A. Kauwell, Folic acid supplements and fortification affect the risk for neural tube defects, vascular disease and cancer: Evolving science, *Journal of Nutrition* 133 (2003): 1961S–1968S; G. C. Rampersaud, L. B. Bailey, and G. P. A. Kauwell, Relationship of folate to colorectal and cervical cancer: Review and recommendations for practitioners, *Journal of the American Dietetic Association* 102 (2002): 1273–1282; S. W. Choi and J. B. Mason, Folate and carcinogenesis: An integrated scheme, *Journal of Nutrition* 130 (2000): 129–132; Y. I. Kim, Methylenetetrahydrofolate reductase polymorphisms, folate, and cancer

risk: A paradigm of gene-nutrient interactions in carcinogenesis, *Nutrition Reviews* 58 (2000): 205–209.

49. A. Fleming, The role of folate in the prevention of neural tube defects: Human and animal studies, *Nutrition Reviews* 59 (2001): S13–S23.

50. J. G. Ray and coauthors, Association of neural tube defects and folic acid fortification in Canada, *Lancet* 360 (2002): 2047–2048; E. Gucciardi and coauthors, Incidence of neural tube defects in Ontario, 1986–1999, *Canadian Medical Association Journal* 167 (2002): 237–240.

51. I. A. Brouwer and coauthors, Low-dose folic acid supplementation decreases plasma homocysteine concentrations: A randomized trial, *American Journal of Clinical Nutrition* 69 (1999): 99–104.

52. S. P. Rothenberg, Increasing the dietary intake of folate: Pros and cons, *Seminars in Hematology* 36 (1999): 65–74.

53. J. L. Mills and coauthors, Low vitamin B-12 concentrations in patients without anemia: The effect of folic acid fortification of grain, *American Journal of Clinical Nutrition* 77 (2003): 1474–1477.

54. S. P. Stabler and R. H. Allen, Vitamin B_{12} deficiency as a worldwide problem, *Annual Review of Nutrition* 24 (2004): 299–326.

55. W. Hermann and J. Geisel, Vegetarian lifestyle and monitoring of vitamin B-12 status, *Clinica Chimica Acta International Journal of Clinical Chemistry* 326 (2002): 47–59.

56. R. Muhammad, Neurologic impairment in children associated with maternal dietary deficiency of cobalamin—Georgia, 2001, *Morbidity and Mortality Weekly Report* 52 (2003): 61–64.

57. K. M. Fairfield and R. H. Fletcher, Vitamins for chronic disease prevention in adults, *Journal of the American Medical Association* 287 (2002): 3116–3126.

58. E. Aufiero and coauthors, Pyridoxine hydrochloride treatment of carpal tunnel syndrome: A review, *Nutrition Reviews* 62 (2004): 96–104; A.A. Gerritsen and coauthors, Conservative treatment options for carpal tunnel syndrome: A systematic review of randomized controlled trials, *Journal of Neurology* 249 (2002): 272–280; R. Luboshitzky and coauthors, The effect of pyridoxine administration on melatonin secretion in normal men, *Neuroendocrinology Letters* 23 (2002): 213–217.

59. Fairfield and Fletcher, 2002 [see reference 57]; J. W. Miller, Does lowering plasma homocysteine reduce vascular disease risk? *Nutrition Reviews* 59 (2001): 242–244.

60. F. V. van Oort and coauthors, Folic acid and reduction of plasma homocysteine concentrations in older adults: A dose-response study, *American Journal of Clinical Nutrition* 77 (2003): 1318–1323; D. S. Wald, M. Law, and J. K. Morris, Homocysteine and cardiovascular disease: Evidence on causality from a meta-analysis, *British Medical Journal* 325 (2002): 1202–1208; B. J. Venn and coauthors, Dietary counseling to increase natural folate intake: A randomized placebo-controlled trial in free-living subjects

to assess effects on serum folate and plasma total homocysteine, *American Journal of Clinical Nutrition* 76 (2002): 758–765.

61. S. Friso and coauthors, Low plasma vitamin B-6 concentrations and modulation of coronary artery disease risk, *American Journal of Clinical Nutrition* 79 (2004): 992–998; Bailey, Rampersaud, and Kauwell, 2003 [see reference 48].

62. J. G. Ray and coauthors. Association of neural tube defects and folic acid food fortification in Canada, *Lancet* 360 (2002): 2047–2048; N. M. van der Put and coauthors, Folate, homocysteine and neural tube defects: An overview, *Experimental Biology and Medicine* 226 (2001): 243–270; P. F. Jacques and coauthors, The effect of folic acid fortification on plasma folate and total homocysteine concentrations, *New England Journal of Medicine* 340 (1999): 1449–1454.

63. Lengthy jail sentence for vendor of laetrile—a quack medication to treat cancer patients, *FDA News*, June 22, 2004, available at http://www.fda.gov/newsevents/newsroom/pressannouncements/2004/ucm108314.htm.

Consumer Corner 7

1. L. Pauling, *Vitamin C and the Common Cold* (San Francisco: Freeman, 1970).

2. B. Takkouche and coauthors, Intake of vitamin C and zinc and risk of common cold: A cohort study, *Epidemiology* 13 (2002): 38–44; H. Hemila and coauthors, Vitamin C, vitamin E, and beta-carotene in relation to common cold incidence in male smokers, *Epidemiology* 13 (2002): 32–37; H. Hemila, E. Chalker, and B. Douglas, Vitamin C for preventing and treating the common cold, *Cochrane Database of Systematic Reviews* 3 (2007), Art. no.: CD000980. Dd: 10.1002/14651858. CD000980.pub3.

3. H. Hemila and E. B. Chalker, Vitamin C for preventing and treating the common cold (Cochrane Review), *The Cochrane Library*, May 2013, available at http://summaries.cochrane.org/CD000980/vitamin-c-for-preventing-and-treating-the-common-cold; M. Van Straten and P. Josling, Preventing the common cold with a vitamin C supplement: A double-blind, placebo-controlled survey, *Journal of Manipulative and Physiological Therapeutics* 22 (1999): 530–533.

4. H. Hemila, Vitamin C supplementation and common cold symptoms: Factors affecting the magnitude of the benefit, *Medical Hypotheses* 52 (1999): 171–178.

5. C. J. Field, I. R. Johnson, and P. D. Schley, Nutrients and their role in host resistance to infection, *Journal of Leukocyte Biology* 71 (2002): 16–32; V. M. Victor, N. Guayerbas, and F. M. De, Changes in the antioxidant content of mononuclear leukocytes from mice with endotoxin-induced oxidative stress, *Molecular Cell Biochemistry* 229 (2002): 107–111.

6. M. Farva and coauthors, The problem of the placebo response in clinical trials for psychiatric disorders: Culprits, possible remedies, and a novel study design approach, *Psychotherapy and Psychosomatics* 72 (2003): 115–127.

7. Standing Committee on the Scientific Evaluation of Dietary Reference Intakes, Food

and Nutrition Board, Institute of Medicine, *Dietary Reference Intakes for Vitamin C, Vitamin E, Selenium, and Carotenoids* (Washington, D.C.: National Academies Press, 2000).

Controversy 7

1. R. H. Fletcher and K. M. Fairfield, Vitamins for chronic disease prevention in adults: Clinical applications, *Journal of the American Medical Association* 287 (2002): 3127–3129; W. C. Willet and M. J. Stampfer, What vitamins should I be taking, doctor? *New England Journal of Medicine* 345 (2001): 1819–1824.

2. K. Michaelsson and coauthors, Serum retinol levels and the risk of fracture, *New England Journal of Medicine* 348 (2003): 287–294; D. A. Bender, Daily doses of multivitamin tablets: Regular consumption will probably do you no good, with a few exceptions, *British Medical Journal* 325 (2002): 173–174; National Institutes of Health, Multivitamin/Mineral supplements and chronic disease prevention NIH State-of-the-Science Conference (Proceedings from meeting held in Bethesda, MD, May 15–17, 2006), *American Journal of Clinical Nutrition* 85 (Suppl) (2007): 251S–327S; S. J. Whiting and J. Adolphe, Current issues—The inside story: The continuing debate on the benefits and risks of supplemental vitamins and minerals, *Dietitians of Canada* (August 2008): 1–6.

3. Position of the American Dietetic Association: Food fortification and dietary supplements, *Journal of the American Dietetic Association* 101 (2001): 115–125.

4. U.S. Preventive Services Task Force, Routine vitamin supplementation to prevent cancer and cardiovascular disease, AHRQ publication no. APPIP03-0012, June 2003, available at http://innovations.ahrq.gov/content.aspx?id=950.

5. Michaelsson and coauthors, 2003 [see reference 2].

6. Committee on the Framework for Evaluating the Safety of Dietary Supplements, Institute of Medicine and National Research Council, *Dietary Supplements: A Framework for Evaluating Safety* (Washington, D.C.: National Academies Press, 2004), pp. ES1–ES14.

7. C. L. Taylor, Regulatory frameworks for functional foods and dietary supplements, *Nutrition Reviews* 62 (2004): 55–59.

8. Acting FDA Commissioner Dr. Lester M. Crawford outlines science-based plan for dietary supplement enforcement, *FDA News*, April 19, 2004, available at http://www.fda.gov/NewsEvents/Newsroom/PressAnnouncements/2004/ucm108286.htm.

9. M. Meadows, Ensuring the safety of dietary supplements, *FDA Consumer*, July/August 2004, available at http://permanent.access.gpo.gov/lps1609/www.fda.gov/fdac/features/2004/404_supp.html.

10. U.S. Food and Drug Administration, Center for Food Safety and Applied Nutrition, Claims that can be made for conventional foods and dietary supplements, September 2003, available at http://www.fda.gov/Food/IngredientsPackagingLabeling/LabelingNutrition/ucm111447.htm.

11. B. N. Ames, The metabolic tune-up: Metabolic harmony and disease prevention, *Journal of Nutrition* 133 (2003): 1544S–1548S.

12. R. J. Hillstrom, A. K. Yacapin-Ammons, and S. M. Lynch, Vitamin C inhibits lipid oxidation in human HDL, *Journal of Nutrition* 133 (2003): 3047–3051.

13. C. D. Morris and S. Carson, Routine vitamin supplementation to prevent cardiovascular disease: A summary of the evidence for the U.S. Preventive Services Task Force, *Annals of Internal Medicine* 139 (2003): 56–70.

14. Ames, 2003 [see reference 11].

15. Ames, 2003 [see reference 11].

16. Fletcher and Fairfield, 2002 [see reference 1].

17. P. M. Kris-Etherton and coauthors, Antioxidant vitamin supplements and cardiovascular disease: AHA science advisory, *Circulation* 110 (2004): 637–641.

18. U. S. Preventive Services Task Force, 2003 [see reference 4].

19. L. T. Chylack and coauthors, The Roche European American Cataract Trial (REACT): A randomized clinical trial to investigate the efficacy of an oral antioxidant micronutrient mixture to slow progression of age-related cataract, *Ophthalmic Epidemiology* 9 (2002): 49–80.

20. A. Martin and coauthors, Roles of vitamins E and C on neurodegenerative diseases and cognitive performance, *Nutrition Reviews* 60 (2002): 308–326; H. Chen and coauthors, Dietary patterns and adenocarcinoma of the esophagus and distal stomach, *American Journal of Clinical Nutrition* 75 (2002): 137–144.

21. E. R. Berton and coauthors, A population-based case-control study of carotenoid and vitamin A intake and ovarian cancer (United States), *Cancer Causes and Control* 12 (2001): 83–90; Standing Committee on the Scientific Evaluation of Dietary Reference Intakes, Food and Nutrition Board, Institute of Medicine, *Dietary Reference Intakes for Vitamin C, Vitamin E, Selenium, and Carotenoids* (Washington, D.C.: National Academies Press, 2000), p. 346; D. S. Michaud and coauthors, Intake of specific carotenoids and risk of lung cancer in 2 prospective US cohorts, *American Journal of Clinical Nutrition* 72 (2000): 990–997; M. L. Slattery and coauthors, Carotenoids and colon cancer, *American Journal of Clinical Nutrition* 71 (2000): 575–582; N. McKeown and coauthors, Antioxidants and breast cancer, *Nutrition Reviews* 57 (1999): 321–324; E. Giovannucci, Tomatoes, tomato-based products, lycopene, and cancer: Review of the epidemiologic literature, *Journal of the National Cancer Institute* 91 (1999): 317–331.

22. I. Min Lee and coauthors, C-carotene supplementation and incidence of cancer and cardiovascular disease: The Women's Health Study, *Journal of the National Cancer Institute* 91 (1999): 2102–2106.

23. R. A. Jacob, Evidence that diet modification reduces in vivo oxidant damage, *Nutrition Reviews* 57 (1999): 255–258.

24. A. Iannuzzi and coauthors, Dietary and circulating antioxidant vitamins in relation to carotid plaques in middle-aged women, *American Journal of Clinical Nutrition* 76 (2002): 582–587; M. Meydani, Effect of functional food ingredients: Vitamin E modulation of cardiovascular diseases and immune status in the elderly, *American Journal of Clinical Nutrition* 71 (2000): 1665S–1668S; L. A. Yochum, A. R. Folsom, and L. H. Kushi, Intake of antioxidant vitamins and risk of death from stroke in postmenopausal women, *American Journal of Clinical Nutrition* 72 (2000): 476–483.

25. S. Devaraj, A. Harris, and I. Jialal, Modulation of monocyte-macrophage function with a-tocopherol: Implications for atherosclerosis, *Nutrition Reviews* 60 (2002): 8–14; L. J. van Tits and coauthors, a-tocopherol supplementation decreases production of superoxide and cytokines by leukocytes ex vivo in both normolipidemic and hypertriglyceridemic individuals, *American Journal of Clinical Nutrition* 71 (2000): 458–464; M. Meydani, Vitamin E and prevention of heart disease in high-risk patients, *Nutrition Reviews* 58 (2000): 278–281.

26. P. Knekt and coauthors, Antioxidant vitamins and coronary heart disease risk: A pooled analysis of 9 cohorts, *American Journal of Clinical Nutrition* 80 (2004): 1508–1520; D. D. Waters and coauthors, Effects of hormone replacement therapy and antioxidant vitamin supplements on coronary atherosclerosis in post-menopausal women: A randomized controlled trial, *Journal of the American Medical Association* 288 (2002): 2432–2440; Collaborative Group of the Primary Prevention Project (PPP), Low-dose aspirin and vitamin E in people at cardiovascular risk: A randomized trial in general practice, *Lancet* 357 (2001): 89–95.

27. U.S. Preventive Services Task Force, 2003 [see reference 4]; I. Lin and coauthors, Vitamin C preserves endothelial function in patients with coronary heart disease after a high-fat meal, *Clinical Cardiology* 25 (2002): 219–224.

28. E. R. Miller and coauthors, Meta-analysis: high dosage vitamin E supplementation may increase all-cause mortality, *Annals of Internal Medicine* 142 (2005), e-pub available at http://annals.org/article.aspx?articleid=718049; S. L. Booth and coauthors, Effect of vitamin E supplementation on vitamin K status in adults with normal coagulation status, *American Journal of Clinical Nutrition* 80 (2004): 143–148.

29. D. Lee and coauthors, Does supplemental vitamin C increase cardiovascular disease risk in women with diabetes? *American Journal of Clinical Nutrition* 80 (2004): 1194–1200.

30. R. Rodriguez-Melendez, J. B. Griffin, and J. Zempleni, Biotin supplementation increases expression of the cytochrome P450 1B1 in Jurkat cells, increasing the occurrence of single-stranded DNA breaks, *Journal of Nutrition* 134 (2004): 2222–2228.

31. B. Liebman, Spin the bottle: How to pick a multivitamin, *Nutrition Action Healthletter*, January/February 2003, pp. 3–9.

32. L. Troppmann, K. Gray-Donald, and T. Johns, Supplement use: Is there any nutritional benefit? *Journal of the American Dietetic Association* 102 (2002): 818–825.

8 Water and Minerals

Do You Ever . . .

Buy bottled water because you think it is safer than tap water?

Blame "water weight" when you've gained a few pounds?

Skip milk products, believing that you no longer need the nutrients they supply?

Feel tired and wonder if you need an iron supplement?

Keep Reading . . .

Learning Objectives

After completing this chapter, you should be able to

LO 8.1 Identify the best beverage choices to obtain enough water for the body's needs.

LO 8.2 Describe the body's water sources and routes of water loss and name factors that influence the need for water.

LO 8.3 Discuss why electrolyte balance is critical for the health of the body.

LO 8.4 Describe the nutrients needed to maintain blood calcium levels and explain why this is important.

LO 8.5 Describe a diet that follows the DASH principles and specify who might benefit from such a diet and in what ways.

LO 8.6 Compare the availability of iron from plant and animal sources.

LO 8.7 Discuss the function and importance of copper, zinc, chromium, fluoride, and selenium in the body.

LO 8.8 Describe a diet that a young woman can follow to help prevent osteoporosis later in life.

Contents

"Ashes to ashes and dust to dust"—it is true that when the life force leaves the body, what is left behind becomes nothing but a small pile of ashes. Carbohydrates, proteins, fats, vitamins, and water are present at first, but they soon disappear.

The carbon atoms in all carbohydrates, fats, proteins, and vitamins combine with oxygen to produce carbon dioxide, which vanishes into the air; the hydrogens and oxygens of those compounds unite to form water, and this water, along with the water that was a large part of the body weight, evaporates. The ashes left behind are the **minerals**, a small pile that weighs only about 2.3 kilograms. The pile is not impressive in size, but those minerals are critical to the functioning of living tissue.

Consider calcium and phosphorus. If you could separate these two minerals from the rest of the pile, you would take away about three-fourths of the total. Crystals made of these two minerals, plus a few others, form the structure of the bones and so provide the architecture of the skeleton.

Run a magnet through the pile that remains and you pick up the iron. It doesn't fill a teaspoon, but it consists of billions and billions of iron atoms. As part of hemoglobin, these iron atoms are able to attach to oxygen and make it available at the sites inside the cells where metabolic work is taking place.

If you then extract all of the other minerals from the pile of ashes, leaving only copper and iodine, close the windows first. A slight breeze would blow these remaining bits of dust away. Yet the amount of copper in the dust is necessary for iron to hold and to release oxygen, and iodine is the critical mineral in the thyroid hormones. Figure 8–1 shows the amounts of the seven **major minerals** and a few of the **trace minerals** in the human body. Other minerals, such as gold and aluminum, are present in the body but are not known to be nutrients.

The distinction between major and trace minerals doesn't mean that one group is more important in the body than the other. A daily inadequacy of a few micrograms

---

minerals naturally occurring, inorganic, homogeneous substances; chemical elements.

major minerals essential mineral nutrients found in the human body in amounts larger than 5 g.

trace minerals essential mineral nutrients found in the human body in amounts less than 5 g.

Figure 8–1

Minerals in a 60-Kilogram (132-Pound) Person, in Grams

The major minerals are those present in amounts larger than 5 grams (a teaspoon). The essential trace minerals number a dozen or more: only four are shown. A pound is about 454 grams; thus, only calcium and phosphorus appear in amounts larger than a pound.

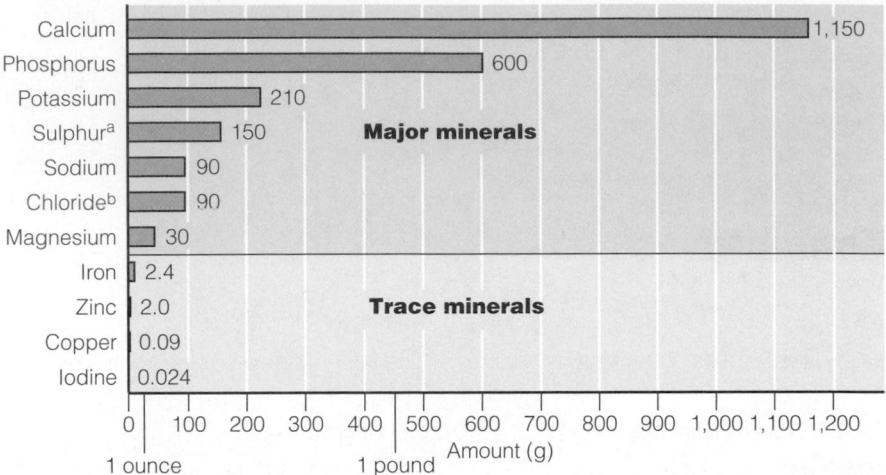

Mineral	Amount (g)
Calcium	1,150
Phosphorus	600
Potassium	210
Sulphur[a]	150
Sodium	90
Chloride[b]	90
Magnesium	30
Iron	2.4
Zinc	2.0
Copper	0.09
Iodine	0.024

Major minerals

Trace minerals

0   100   200   300   400   500   600   700   800   900   1,000   1,100   1,200
Amount (g)
1 ounce   1 pound

[a]Sulphur is a nonmetallic, yellow element; sulphate, a compound of sulphur and oxygen, is required by the body for making sulphur-containing molecules.
[b]Chlorine appears in the body as the chloride ion.

of iodine is just as serious as an inadequacy of several hundred milligrams of calcium. The major minerals are present in larger total quantities, however, so they influence the body fluids, which, in turn, affect the whole body.

This chapter begins with a discussion of water. Water is unique among the nutrients—standing alone as the most indispensable of all. The body needs more water each day than any other nutrient—50 times as much water as protein and 5,000 times as much water as vitamin C. You can survive a deficiency of any of the other nutrients for a long time, in some cases for months or years, but you

Water is the most indispensable nutrient.

can survive only a few days without water. In less than a day, a lack of water alters the body's chemistry and metabolism.

Our discussion begins with water's many functions. Next we examine how water and the major minerals mingle to form the body's fluids and how cells regulate the distribution of those fluids. Then we take up the specialized roles of each of the minerals.

Water

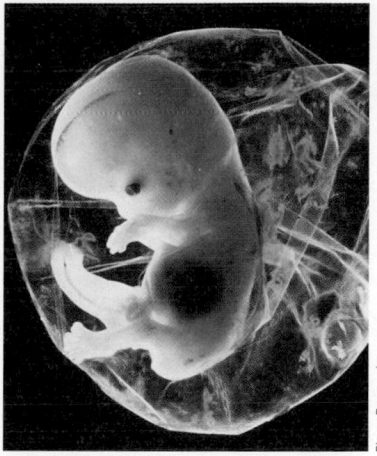

You began as a single cell bathed in a nourishing fluid. As you became a beautifully organized, air-breathing body of trillions of cells, each of your cells had to remain next to water to stay alive.

Water makes up about 60 percent of an adult person's weight—that's about 36 kilograms of water in a 60-kilogram person. All of this water in the body is not simply a river coursing through the arteries, capillaries, and veins. Some of the water is incorporated into the chemical structures of compounds that form the cells, tissues, and organs of the body. For example, proteins hold water molecules within them—water that is locked in and not readily available for any other use. Water also participates actively in many chemical reactions.

Human life begins in water.

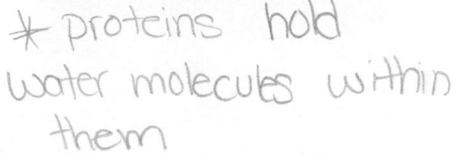

Why Is Water the Most Indispensable Nutrient?

Water brings to each cell the exact ingredients the cell requires and carries away the end products of the cell's life-sustaining reactions. The water of the body fluids is thus the transport vehicle for all nutrients and wastes. Without water, cells quickly die.

Water is nearly a universal solvent: it dissolves amino acids, glucose, minerals, and many other substances needed by the cells. Fatty substances are specially packaged with water-soluble proteins so that they, too, can travel freely in the blood (fatty acids bound to serum albumin) and lymph (triglycerides in lipoproteins).

Water is also the body's cleansing agent. Small molecules, such as the nitrogen wastes generated during protein metabolism, dissolve in the watery blood and must be removed before they build up to toxic concentrations. The kidneys filter these wastes from the blood and excrete them, mixed with water, as urine. When the kidneys become diseased, as can happen in diabetes and other disorders, toxins can build to life-threatening levels. A machine must then take over the task of cleansing the blood by filtering wastes into water contained in the machine.*

Water molecules resist being crowded together. Thanks to this incompressibility, water can act as a lubricant and a cushion for the joints, and it can protect sensitive tissue such as the spinal cord from shock. The fluid that fills the eye serves in a similar way to keep optimal pressure on the retina and lens. From the start of human life, a fetus is cushioned against shock by the bag of amniotic fluid in the mother's uterus. Water also lubricates the digestive tract, the respiratory tract, and all tissues that are moistened with mucus.

Yet another of water's special features is its ability to help maintain body temperature. The water of sweat is the body's coolant. Heat is produced as a by-product of energy metabolism and can build up dangerously in the body. To rid itself of this excess heat, the body routes its blood supply through the capillaries just under the skin. At the same time, the skin secretes sweat and its water evaporates. Converting water to vapour takes energy; therefore, as sweat evaporates, heat energy dissipates, cooling the skin and the underlying blood. The cooled blood then flows back to cool the body's core. Sweat evaporates continuously from the skin, usually in slight amounts that go unnoticed; thus, the skin is a major organ through which water is lost from the body. Lesser amounts are lost by way of exhaled breath and the feces.**,[1]

---

*The machine that cleanses the blood is a kidney dialysis machine.

** References are listed at the end of the chapter.

To sum up, water

- Carries nutrients throughout the body.
- Serves as the solvent for minerals, vitamins, amino acids, glucose, and other small molecules.
- Cleanses the tissues and blood of wastes.
- Actively participates in many chemical reactions.
- Acts as a lubricant around joints.
- Serves as a shock absorber inside the eyes, spinal cord, joints, and amniotic sac surrounding a fetus in the womb.
- Aids in maintaining the body's temperature.

KEY POINT

- Water provides the medium for transportation, acts as a solvent, participates in chemical reactions, provides lubrication and shock protection, and aids in temperature regulation in the human body.

The Body's Water Balance

Water is such an integral part of us that people are seldom conscious of water's importance, unless they are deprived of it. Since the body loses some water every day, a person must consume at least the same amount to avoid life-threatening losses, that is, to maintain **water balance**.

The total amount of fluid in the body is kept balanced by delicate mechanisms. Imbalances such as **dehydration** and **water intoxication/overhydration** can occur, but the balance is restored as promptly as the body can manage it. The body controls both intake and excretion to maintain water equilibrium.

The amount of the body's water varies by pounds at a time, especially in women who retain water during menstruation. Eating a meal high in salt can temporarily increase the body's water content; the body sheds the excess over the next day or so as the sodium is excreted. These temporary fluctuations in body water show up on the scale, but gaining or losing water weight does not reflect a change in body fat. Fat weight takes days or weeks to change noticeably, whereas water weight can change overnight.

KEY POINT

- Water makes up about 60 percent of the body's weight. A change in the body's water content can bring about a temporary change in body weight.

An extra drink of water benefits both young and old.

water balance the balance between water intake and water excretion, which keeps the body's water content constant.

dehydration loss of water. The symptoms progress rapidly, from thirst to weakness to exhaustion and delirium, and end in death.

water intoxication/overhydration a dangerous dilution of the body's fluids resulting from excessive ingestion of plain water. Symptoms are headache, muscular weakness, lack of concentration, poor memory, and loss of appetite.

Quenching Thirst and Balancing Losses

Thirst and satiety govern water intake.[2] When the blood is too concentrated (having lost water but not salt and other dissolved substances), the molecules and particles in the blood attract water out of the salivary glands, and the mouth becomes dry. The brain centre known as the hypothalamus (described in Chapter 3) plays the major role in monitoring the concentration of the blood. When the blood is too concentrated, or when the blood volume or pressure is too low, the hypothalamus initiates nerve impulses to the brain that register as "thirst." The hypothalamus also signals the pituitary gland to release a hormone that directs the kidneys to shift water back into the bloodstream from the pool destined for excretion. The kidneys themselves respond to the sodium concentration in the blood passing through them and secrete regulatory substances of their own. The net result is that the more water the body needs, the less it excretes. Figure 8–2 shows how intake and excretion naturally balance out.

Thirst lags behind a lack of water. When too much water is lost from the body and is not replaced, dehydration can threaten survival. A first sign of dehydration is thirst, the signal that the body has already lost up to 2 cups of its total fluid and that the need to obtain fluid is urgent. But suppose a thirsty person is unable to obtain fluid or, as in many elderly people, fails to perceive the thirst message. With a loss of just 5 percent of body fluid, perceptible symptoms appear: headache, fatigue, confusion or forgetfulness, and an elevated heart rate. Instead of "wasting" precious water in sweat, the dehydrated body diverts most of its water into the blood vessels to maintain the life-supporting blood pressure. Meanwhile, body heat builds up because sweating has ceased, creating the possibility of serious consequences (see Table 8–1). A water deficiency that develops slowly can switch on drinking behaviour in time to prevent serious dehydration, but one that develops quickly may not.

To ignore the thirst signal is to invite dehydration. People should stay attuned to thirst and drink whenever they feel thirsty to replace fluids lost throughout the day.[3] Older adults in whom thirst is blunted should drink regularly throughout the day, regardless of thirst.

At the other extreme from dehydration, water intoxication/overhydration occurs when too much plain water floods the body's fluids and disturbs their normal composition. Most victims have consumed several gallons of plain water in a few hours' time.[4] Water intoxication is rare, but when it occurs, immediate action is needed to reverse dangerously diluted blood before death ensues.

For more about water intoxication, see Chapter 10.

Figure 8–2

Water Balance—A Typical Example

Each day, water enters the body in liquids and foods, and some water is created in the body as a by-product of metabolic processes. Water leaves the body through the evaporation of sweat, in the moisture of exhaled breath, in the urine, and in the feces.

Water input (Total = 1,450–2,800 mL)

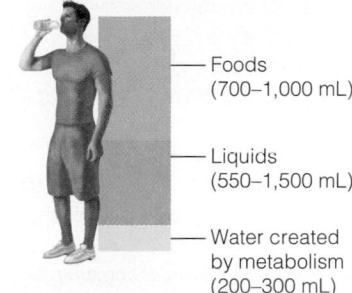

- Foods (700–1,000 mL)
- Liquids (550–1,500 mL)
- Water created by metabolism (200–300 mL)

Water output (Total = 1,450–2,800 mL)

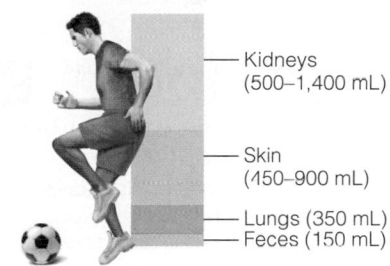

- Kidneys (500–1,400 mL)
- Skin (450–900 mL)
- Lungs (350 mL)
- Feces (150 mL)

- A 68-kg (150-lb) person contains 41 kg (90 lb) of water; a 5% loss of body fluid for this person amounts to about 2 kg (4½ lb) of water.

Table 8–1

Threats from Mild and Severe Dehydration and Chronic Lack of Fluid

Mild Dehydration (Loss of <5% Body Weight)	Severe Dehydration (Loss of >5% Body Weight)	Chronic Low Fluid Intake May Increase the Likelihood of
Thirst	Pale skin	Bladder, colon, and other cancers
Sudden weight loss	Bluish lips and fingertips	Cardiac arrest (heart attack) and
Rough, dry skin	Confusion; disorientation	other heart problems
Dry mouth, throat, body linings	Rapid, shallow breathing	Gallstones
Rapid pulse	Weak, rapid, irregular pulse	Kidney stones
Low blood pressure	Thickening of blood	Urinary tract infections
Lack of energy; weakness	Shock; seizures	
Impaired kidney function	Coma; death	
Reduced quantity of urine; concentrated urine		
Decreased mental functioning		
Decreased muscular work and athletic performance		
Fever or increased internal temperature		
Fainting		

Source: Based on Standing Committee on the Scientific Evaluation of Dietary Reference Intakes, Food and Nutrition Board, Institute of Medicine, Dietary References Intakes: Water, Potassium, Sodium, Chloride, and Sulfate *(Washington, D.C.: National Academies Press, 2005), pp. 4-31–4-48.*

Table 8–2

Factors That Increase Fluid Needs

These conditions increase a person's need for fluids:

- Alcohol consumption
- Cold weather
- Dietary fibre
- Diseases that disturb water balance, such as diabetes and kidney diseases
- Forced-air environments, such as airplanes and sealed buildings
- Heated environments
- High altitude
- Hot weather, high humidity
- Increased protein, salt, or sugar intakes
- Ketosis
- Medications (diuretics)
- Physical activity (see Chapter 10)
- Pregnancy and breast-feeding (see Chapter 13)
- Prolonged diarrhea, vomiting, or fever
- Surgery, blood loss, or burns
- Very young or old age

Water Content of Various Foods and Beverages

- 100% = water, diet soft drinks, seltzer (unflavoured), plain tea
- 95–99% = sugar-free gelatin dessert, clear broth, Chinese cabbage, celery, cucumber, lettuce, summer squash, decaffeinated black coffee
- 90–94% = Gatorade, grapefruit, fresh strawberries, broccoli, tomato
- 80–89% = sugar-sweetened soft drinks, milk, yogurt, egg white, fruit juices, low-fat cottage cheese, fresh apple, carrot
- 60–79% = low-Calorie mayonnaise, instant pudding, banana, shrimp, lean steak, pork chop, baked potato
- 40–59% = diet margarine, sausage, chicken, macaroni and cheese
- 20–39% = bread, cake, cheddar cheese, bagel, cooked oatmeal
- 10–19% = butter, margarine, regular mayonnaise, cooked rice
- 5–9% = peanut butter, popcorn
- 1–4% = ready-to-eat cereals, pretzels
- 0% = cooking oils, meat fats, shortening, white sugar

● Go to www.nelson.com/nutrition3ce and click on the Canadian Nutrient File link to see the water content of most other foods and beverages.

diuretic (dye-you-RET-ic) a compound, usually a medication, causing increased urinary water excretion; a "water pill."

KEY POINT

- Water losses from the body necessitate intake equal to output to maintain balance. The brain regulates water intake; the brain and kidneys regulate water excretion. Dehydration and water intoxication can have serious consequences.

How Much Water Do I Need to Drink in a Day?

Water needs vary greatly depending on the foods a person eats, the environmental temperature and humidity, the altitude, the person's activity level, and other factors (see Table 8–2). Because individual needs vary, adequate hydration can be maintained over a wide range of fluid intakes. As a general guideline, the Dietary Reference Intakes (DRI) committee recommends that, given a normal diet and moderate environmental conditions, men need about 13 cups (3.7 L) of fluid from beverages and drinking water, and women need about 9 cups (2.7 L). This amount of fluid provides about 80 percent of the day's need for water. Most of the rest is provided by the water consumed in foods. Nearly all foods contain some water: water constitutes up to 95 percent of the volume of most fruit and vegetables, and at least 50 percent of many meats and cheeses (see the margin). A small percentage of the day's fluid is generated in the tissues as energy-yielding nutrients in foods release water as a product of chemical breakdown.

Sweating increases water needs. Especially when performing physical work outdoors in hot weather, people can lose 3 to 5 litres of fluid in a day. An athlete training in the heat can sweat out more than 2 litres of fluid each hour.[5] The importance of maintaining hydration for athletes exercising in the heat cannot be overemphasized, and Chapter 10 provides detailed instructions on how, exactly, to hydrate the exercising body.

When people who normally abstain from caffeine drink a caffeine-containing beverage such as coffee, tea, or soda, their urine output increases somewhat more than it would for a similar amount of plain water. This is because caffeine acts as a **diuretic**. Research is mixed on whether any but the highest caffeine intakes, say, four or five cups of coffee, cause a net water deficit in the body; most people make up for small water losses by drinking additional fluid later. Also, people who habitually consume caffeine may adapt to its diuretic effects, losing no more fluid than when drinking other beverages.[6] Therefore, for most people, an occasional caffeinated beverage can contribute to the day's fluid requirement.[7] The Controversy section of Chapter 14 comes back to the effects of caffeine.

KEY POINT

- Many factors influence a person's need for water. The water of beverages and foods meets nearly all of the need for water, and a little more is supplied by the water formed during cellular breakdown of energy nutrients.

Are Some Kinds of Water Better for My Health Than Others?

Water occurs as **hard water** or **soft water**, a distinction that affects your health with regard to three minerals. Hard water has high concentrations of calcium and magnesium. Soft water's principal mineral is sodium. In practical terms, soft water makes more bubbles with less soap; hard water leaves a ring on the tub, a jumble of rocklike crystals in the teakettle, and a grey residue in the wash.

Soft water may seem more desirable, and some homeowners purchase water softeners that remove magnesium and calcium and replace them with sodium. Some evidence suggests, however, that soft water, even when it bubbles naturally from the ground, may aggravate hypertension and heart disease.[8] Mineral-rich hard water may oppose these conditions by virtue of its calcium content.[9]

Soft water also more easily dissolves certain contaminant metals, such as cadmium and lead, from pipes. Cadmium can harm the body, affecting enzymes by displacing zinc from its normal sites of action. Cadmium is also suspected of promoting bone fractures, kidney problems, and hypertension.[10] Lead is another toxic metal, and the body seems to absorb it more readily from soft water than from hard water, possibly because the calcium in hard water protects against its absorption. Old plumbing may contain cadmium or lead. People who live in old buildings should run the cold water tap a minute to flush out harmful minerals before drawing water for the first use in the morning and whenever no water has been drawn during the previous six hours.

> Lead poisoning is especially harmful to children (see Chapter 14).

KEY POINT

- Hard water is high in calcium and magnesium. Soft water is high in sodium, and it dissolves cadmium and lead from pipes.

Safety and Sources of Drinking Water

Remember that water is practically a universal solvent: it dissolves almost anything it encounters to some degree. Hundreds of contaminants—including disease-causing bacteria and viruses from human wastes, toxic pollutants from highway fuel runoff, spills and heavy metals from industry, organic chemicals such as pesticides from agriculture, and manure bacteria from farm animals—have been detected in public drinking water.

Public water systems remove some hazards; treatment includes the addition of a disinfectant (usually chlorine) to kill most microorganisms. Private well water is usually not chlorinated, so Canadians who drink water from private wells are likely to encounter microorganisms, mostly harmless, in their water.

Water quality is an important issue in Canada, where a number of deaths have been caused by unsafe water supplies. Health and environmental departments of the federal, provincial, territorial and municipal governments have responsibilities related to safe water. Health Canada has a website that reports on drinking water quality activities (http://www.hc-sc.gc.ca/ewh-semt/water-eau/drink-potab/index-eng.php). Note: This site also has a weblink to the August 2012 Guidelines for Canadian Drinking Water Quality—Summary Table (http://www.hc-sc.gc.ca/ewh-semt/alt_formats/pdf/pubs/water-eau/2012-sum_guide-res_recom/2012-sum_guide-res_recom-eng.pdf).

Some people fear that chlorine itself presents a danger to health. Large doses of by-products of water chlorination have been found to cause cancer-related changes in human cells and cancer in laboratory animals.[11] People consuming large amounts of chlorinated tap water a day have been reported to be somewhat more likely to develop colon, brain, and other cancers.[12] Conversely, men who take in 8 cups (2 L) of water from any source, chlorinated or not, have been found to be half as likely to develop bladder cancer as men who restrict water intake to less than a cupful.[13] Although most investigators acknowledge the possibility of a connection between consumption of chlorinated drinking water and cancer incidence, they also passionately defend chlorination as a benefit to public health. In areas of the world without chlorination, an estimated 25,000 people die *each day* from diseases caused by organisms carried by water and easily killed by chlorine. Substitutes for chlorine exist, but they are too expensive or too slow to be practical for treating a city's water, and some may create by-products of their own.

Meanwhile, what is a consumer to drink? One option is to drink tap water because municipal water is held to minimum standards for purity. Another option is to further purify tap water with home purifying equipment, which ranges in price from about $20 to $5,000. Some home systems do an adequate job of removing lead, chlorine, and other contaminants, but others only improve the water's taste. Many are not designed to remove microorganisms that are not affected by chlorine. Each system has advantages and drawbacks, and all require periodic maintenance or filter

Boil-Water Advisories

If your municipal water supply becomes contaminated from disease-causing bacteria, viruses, or parasites or has become cloudy at the source, a boil-water advisory may be issued by your local public health unit or other authority. If bottled water is not available at such times or you are concerned the water may not be safe to drink, Health Canada suggests the following measures:

- Bring tap water to a rolling boil for at least 1 min (and at least 2 min if you live at elevations above 2,000 m).
- Wash hands in a dilute solution containing unscented bleach (1 mL per litre of water) before preparing meals, changing diapers, etc.
- Such advisories will remain in effect for at least 48 h.

More information is available at http://www.hc-sc.gc.ca/ewh-semt/pubs/water-eau/boil-ebullition-eng.php.

hard water water with high calcium and magnesium concentrations.

soft water water with a high sodium concentration.

Table 8–3

Water Sources

- **aquifers** underground rock formations containing water that can be drawn to the surface for use.
- **ground water** water that comes from underground aquifers.
- **surface water** water that comes from lakes, rivers, and reservoirs.

replacements that vary in price. Not all companies or representatives are legitimate—some perform water tests that yield dramatic-appearing but meaningless results to sell unneeded systems. Verify all claims of contamination by checking reports from local municipal water agencies or by independently testing well water before buying any purifying system.

A third option is to use **bottled water**. Many people turn to bottled water as an alternative to tap water. Read the Consumer Corner in this chapter for more about bottled water. Whether water comes from the tap or is poured from a bottle, all water comes from the same sources—**surface water** and **ground water** (see Table 8–3).

Surface water flowing from lakes, rivers, and reservoirs fills about half of the nation's need for drinking water, mostly in major cities. Surface water is exposed to contamination by acid rain, petroleum products, pesticides, fertilizer, human and animal wastes, and industrial wastes that run directly from pavements, septic tanks, farmlands, and industrial areas into streams that feed surface water bodies. Surface water generally moves faster than ground water and stays above ground, where aeration and exposure to sunlight can cleanse it. The plants and microorganisms that live in surface water also filter it. These processes can remove some contaminants, but others stay in the water.

Ground water comes from protected **aquifers**, deep underground rock formations saturated with water. People in rural areas rely mostly on ground water pumped from private wells, and some cities tap this resource, too. Ground water can become contaminated from hazardous waste sites, dumps, oil and gas pipelines, and landfills, as well as downward from surface water bodies. Ground water moves slowly and is not aerated or exposed to sunlight, so contaminants break down more slowly than in surface water. To mingle with water in the aquifer, surface water must first "percolate," or seep, through soil, sand, or rock, which filters out some contaminants.

Given water's importance in the body, the world's supply of clean, wholesome water is a precious resource to be guarded. The remainder of this chapter addresses other important nutrients—the minerals.

KEY POINT

- Public drinking water is tested and treated for safety. All drinking water originates from surface water or ground water that is vulnerable to contamination from human activities.

Body Fluids and Minerals

Most of the body's water weight is contained inside the cells, and some water bathes the outsides of the cells. The remainder fills the blood vessels. How do cells keep themselves from collapsing when water leaves them and from swelling up when too much water enters them? The cells cannot regulate the amount of water directly by pumping it in and out because water slips across membranes freely. The cells can, however, pump minerals across their membranes. The major minerals form **salts** that dissolve in the body fluids; the cells direct where the salts go, and this determines where the fluids flow because water follows salt.

When mineral (or other) salts dissolve in water, they separate into single, electrically charged particles known as **ions**. Unlike pure water, which conducts electricity poorly, ions dissolved in water carry electrical current; for this reason, these electrically charged ions are called **electrolytes**. As Figure 8–3 shows, when dissolved particles, such as electrolytes, are present in unequal concentrations on either side of a water-permeable membrane, water flows toward the more concentrated side to equalize the concentrations. Cells and their surrounding fluids work in the same way. Think of a cell as a sack made of a water-permeable membrane. The sack is filled with watery fluid and suspended in a dilute solution of salts and other dissolved particles. Water flows freely between the fluids inside and outside the cell but generally moves from the more dilute solution toward the more concentrated one (the photo of salted eggplant slices on the next page shows this effect). To control the

bottled water drinking water sold in bottles.

salts compounds composed of charged particles (ions). An example is potassium chloride (K^+Cl^-).

ions (EYE-ons) electrically charged particles, such as sodium (positively charged) and chloride (negatively charged).

electrolytes compounds that partly dissociate in water to form ions, such as the potassium ion (K^+) and the chloride ion (Cl^-).

Figure 8–3

How Electrolytes Govern Water Flow

Water flows in the direction of the more highly concentrated solution.

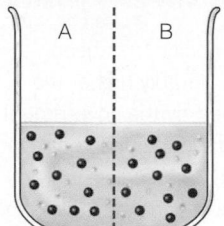

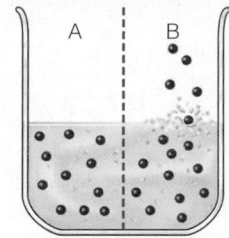

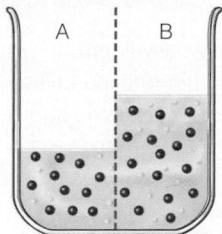

❶ With equal numbers of dissolved particles on both sides of a water-permeable divider, water levels remain equal.

❷ Now additional particles are added to increase the concentration on side B. Particles cannot flow across the divider. In the case of a cell, the divider (cell membrane) partitions fluids inside and outside the cell.

❸ Water can flow both ways across the divider but tends to move from side A to side B, where the concentration of dissolved particles is greater. The *volume* of water increases on side B, and the particle *concentrations* on sides A and B become equal.

Craig M. Moore

Water follows salt. Notice the beads of "sweat," formed on the right-hand slices of eggplant, which were sprinkled with salt. Cellular water moves across each cell's membrane (water-permeable divider) toward the higher concentration of salt (dissolved particles) on the surface.

flow of water, the body must spend energy moving its electrolytes from one compartment to another (see Figure 8–4). Figure 6–11 (page 219) introduced the proteins that form the pumps that move mineral ions across cell membranes. The result is **fluid and electrolyte balance**, the proper amount and kind of fluid in each compartment of the body.

If the fluid balance is disturbed, severe illness can develop quickly because fluid can shift rapidly from one compartment to another. For example, in vomiting or diarrhea, the loss of water from the digestive tract pulls fluid from between the cells in every part of the body. Fluid then leaves the cell interiors to restore balance. Meanwhile, the kidneys detect the water loss and attempt to retrieve water from the pool destined for excretion. To do this, they raise the sodium concentration outside the cells, and this pulls still more water out of them. The result is **fluid and electrolyte imbalance**, a medical emergency. Water and minerals lost in vomiting or diarrhea ultimately come from every body cell. This loss disrupts the heartbeat and threatens life. It is a cause of death among those with eating disorders.

The minerals help manage still another balancing act, the **acid–base balance**, or pH, mentioned in Chapters 3 and 6. In pure water, a small percentage of water molecules (H_2O) exist as positive (H) and negative (OH) ions, but they exist in equilibrium—the positive charges exactly equal the negatives. When dissolved in watery body fluids, some of the major minerals give rise to acids (H, or hydrogen, ions) and others to bases (OH). Excess H ions in a solution make it an acid; they lower the pH. Excess OH ions in a solution make it a base; they raise the pH.

Maintenance of body fluids at a nearly constant pH is critical to life. Even slight changes in pH drastically change the structure and chemical functions of most biologically important molecules. The body's proteins and some of its mineral salts help prevent changes in the acid–base balance of its fluids by serving as **buffers**—molecules that gather up or release H ions as needed to maintain the correct pH. The kidneys help control the pH balance by excreting more or less acid (H ions). The lungs also help by excreting more or less carbon dioxide. (Dissolved in the blood, carbon dioxide forms an acid, carbonic acid.) This tight control of the acid–base balance permits all other life processes to continue.

KEY POINT

- Mineral salts form electrolytes that help keep fluids in their proper compartments and buffer these fluids, permitting all life processes to take place.

Figure 8–4

Electrolyte Balance

Transport proteins in cell membranes maintain the proper balance of sodium (mostly outside the cells) and potassium (mostly inside the cells).

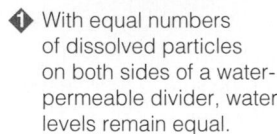

Cell membrane

Outside cell

Inside cell

Transport protein

Key
● Potassium
● Sodium

fluid and electrolyte balance maintenance of the proper amounts and kinds of fluids and minerals in each compartment of the body.

fluid and electrolyte imbalance failure to maintain the proper amounts and kinds of fluids and minerals in every body compartment; a medical emergency.

acid–base balance maintenance of the proper degree of acidity in each of the body's fluids.

buffers molecules that can help keep the pH of a solution from changing by gathering or releasing H ions.

Bottled Water in Canada

You can find information about the bottled water in Canada by referring to Health Canada's online document, "The Safety of Bottled Water,"[1] and its role in developing drinking water guidelines in a document entitled "Water Quality."[2]

Still, the great majority of people who buy bottled water say that it tastes better than the water from their taps. Most water-bottling plants disinfect their products with ozone, which, unlike chlorine, leaves no flavour or odour in the water. Other nutritional aspects of bottled water can be found elsewhere.[3]

Table 8–4 defines some terms that appear on labels. What you are unlikely to find on the label, however, is the water's mineral content. Some bottling companies will provide mineral information if a consumer requests it. For nutrition's sake, the best choice is a water rich in calcium and magnesium but low in sodium.[4] The calcium is as available from the water as from milk; absorption of magnesium is lower but improves when the water is consumed with a meal.[5]

Bottled water is unpredictable in its content of fluoride, a mineral important to the health of teeth and bones,

especially in growing children. As for vitamin-fortified bottled waters, these are simply liquid supplements. Read the Controversy section of Chapter 7 to determine if you need a supplement before paying for high-priced vitamin-fortified water, which is now available in both Canada and the United States.

If your water is dispensed from a water cooler, cleanse the cooler once a month by running 2 litres of white vinegar through it. Remove the vinegar residue by rinsing the cooler with 15 to 20 litres of tap water. The microbial content of water coolers has been found to be considerably higher than that recommended by the government. Regular cleaning reduces bacterial and mould growths that can cause serious infection and disease in those who ingest water contaminated with them.

Also, depending on the brand, bottled water can be expensive, and to help the environment, be sure to recycle the containers. If, however, you intend to use a refillable water bottle on a regular basis, be sure to clean it thoroughly and on a regular basis, as well.

The label on a water bottle may imply purity, but the product inside often falls far short.

Table 8–4

Water Terms That May Appear on Labels

- **artesian water** water drawn from a well that taps a confined aquifer in which the water is under pressure.
- **baby water** ordinary bottled water treated with ozone to make it safe but not sterile.
- **caffeine water** bottled water with caffeine added.
- **carbonated water** water that contains carbon dioxide gas, either naturally occurring or added, that causes bubbles to form in it; also called *bubbling* or *sparkling water*. Seltzer, soda, and tonic waters are legally soft drinks and are not regulated as water.
- **distilled water** water that has been vapourized and recondensed, leaving it free of dissolved minerals.
- **filtered water** water treated by filtration, usually through *activated carbon filters* that reduce the lead in tap water, or by *reverse osmosis* units, which force pressurized water across a membrane, removing lead, arsenic, and some microorganisms from tap water.
- **fitness water** lightly flavoured bottled water enhanced with vitamins, supposedly to enhance athletic performance (see Chapter 10).
- **mineral water** water from a spring or well that typically contains 250 to 500 parts per million (ppm) of minerals. Minerals give water a distinctive flavour. Many mineral waters are high in sodium.
- **natural water** water obtained from a spring or well that is certified to be safe and sanitary. The mineral content may not be changed, but the water may be treated in other ways, such as with ozone or by filtration.
- **public water** water from a municipal or county water system that has been treated and disinfected.
- **purified water** water that has been treated by distillation or other physical or chemical processes that remove dissolved solids. Because purified water contains no minerals or contaminants, it is useful for medical and research purposes.
- **spring water** water originating from an underground spring or well. It may be bubbly (carbonated) or "flat" or "still," meaning not carbonated. Brand names such as "Spring Pure" do not necessarily mean that the water comes from a spring.
- **vitamin water** bottled water with a few vitamins added; does not replace vitamins from a balanced diet and may worsen overload in people receiving vitamins from enriched food, supplements, and other enriched products such as "energy" bars.
- **well water** water drawn from ground water by tapping into an aquifer.

The Major Minerals

Canadian Daily Values for Minerals

The Canadian Daily Value reference standards for minerals that are used to indicate the %DV for minerals in Nutrition Facts tables on foods are based, in part, on the Recommended Daily Intake for minerals (http://www.inspection.gc.ca/english/fssa/labeti/guide/ch6e.shtml#a6_3_2). The Daily Value reference standards for the major minerals for persons two years of age and older are listed in Table 8–12 on pages 343–344 (also see discussion of percentage of daily values (%DV) on page 36 of Chapter 2 in the section Why Are Daily Values Used on Labels?). You can see that, currently, sodium and potassium are the only minerals listed that have the same Daily Values in Canada and the United States. The differences in Daily Values may be important if you are using %DV in foods to assess mineral intake.

Controversy 9 in Chapter 9 describes the problems of eating disorders.

Figure 3–11 (page 90) showed the pH of common substances; Figure 3–3 (page 79) depicted fluid movement in and around cells.

Although all of the major minerals help maintain the fluid balance, each one also has some special duties of its own. Table 8–11 (pages 342–343) summarizes the roles of the minerals discussed below.

Calcium

As Figure 8–1 showed, calcium is by far the most abundant mineral in the body. Nearly all (99%) of the body's calcium is stored in the bones and teeth, where it plays two important roles. First, it is an integral part of bone structure. Second, bone calcium serves as a bank that can release calcium to the body fluids if even the slightest drop in blood calcium concentration occurs. Many people have the idea that, once deposited in bone, calcium (together with the other minerals of bone) stays there forever—that once a bone is built, it is inert, like a rock. Not so. The minerals of bones are in constant flux (Figure 8–5), with formation and dissolution taking place every minute of the day and night.

Calcium and phosphorus are both essential to bone formation: calcium phosphate salts crystallize on a foundation material composed of the protein collagen. The resulting **hydroxyapatite** crystals invade the collagen and gradually lend more and more rigidity to a youngster's maturing bones until they are able to support the weight they will have to carry. During and after the bone-strengthening processes, fluoride may displace the "hydroxy" parts of these crystals, making **fluorapatite**. Fluorapatite resists bone-dismantling forces to help maintain bone integrity.

Teeth are formed in a similar way: hydroxyapatite crystals form on a collagen matrix to create the dentin that gives strength to the teeth (see Figure 8–6). The turnover of minerals in teeth is not as rapid as in bone, but some withdrawal and redepositing do take place throughout life. As in bone, fluoride hardens and stabilizes the crystals of teeth and makes the enamel resistant to decay.

Other roles for calcium are emerging as well. People with low intakes of calcium may be somewhat more likely to develop cancer of the colon and rectum than those with higher intakes.[14] Calcium from low-fat milk and milk products may also play a role in maintaining a healthy body weight.[15] Large, well-designed clinical studies are needed to confirm the effects of dietary calcium on cancer and body fatness.

Calcium in Body Fluids   Only about 1 percent of the body's calcium is in the fluids that bathe and fill the cells, but this tiny amount plays these major roles:

- Regulates the transport of ions across cell membranes and is particularly important in nerve transmission
- Helps maintain normal blood pressure (see Chapter 11)
- Plays an essential role in the clotting of blood

Major Minerals

- Calcium
- Chloride
- Magnesium
- Phosphorus
- Potassium
- Sodium
- Sulphate

hydroxyapatite (hi-DROX-ee-APP-uh-tight) the chief crystal of bone, formed from calcium and phosphorus.

fluorapatite (floor-APP-uh-tight) a crystal of bones and teeth, formed when fluoride displaces the "hydroxy" portion of hydroxyapatite. Fluorapatite resists being dissolved back into body fluid.

Figure 8–5

A Bone

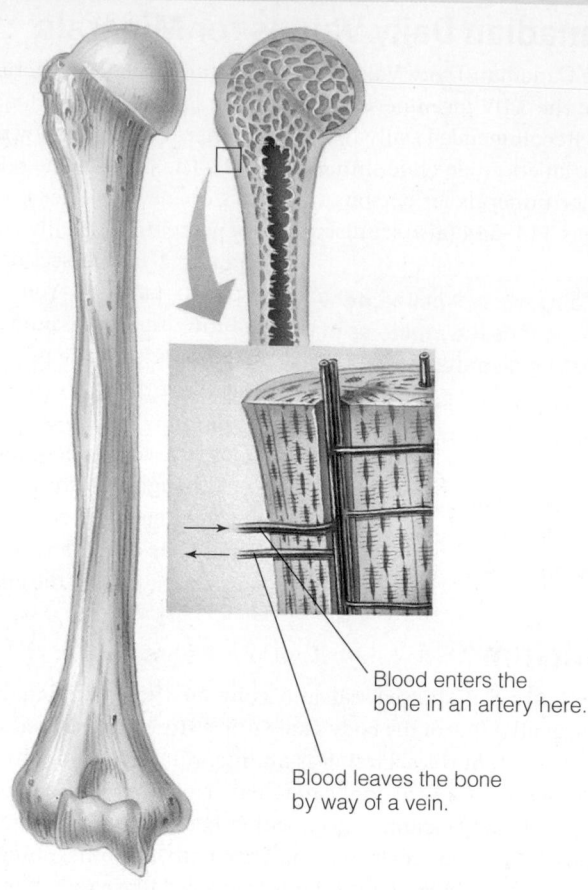

Bone is active, living tissue. Blood travels in capillaries throughout the bone, bringing nutrients to the cells that maintain the bone's structure and carrying away waste materials from those cells. It picks up and deposits minerals as instructed by hormones.

Bone derives its structural strength from the lacy network of crystals that lie along its lines of stress. If minerals are withdrawn to cover deficits elsewhere in the body, the bone will grow weak and ultimately will bend or crumble.

Blood enters the bone in an artery here.

Blood leaves the bone by way of a vein.

Figure 8–6

A Tooth

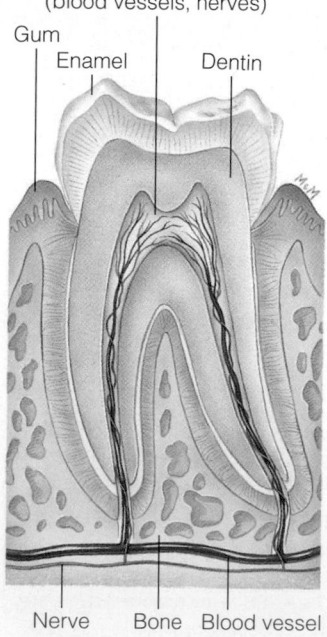

Pulp (blood vessels, nerves)

Gum

Enamel

Dentin

Nerve   Bone   Blood vessel

- Is essential for muscle contraction and therefore for the heartbeat
- Allows secretion of hormones, digestive enzymes, and neurotransmitters
- Activates cellular enzymes that regulate many processes

Because of its importance, blood calcium is tightly controlled.

Calcium and the Bones   The key to bone health lies in the body's calcium balance. Cells need continuous access to calcium, so the body maintains a constant calcium concentration in the blood. The skeleton serves as a bank from which the blood can borrow and return calcium as needed. Blood calcium is regulated not by a person's daily calcium intake or bone density but by hormones sensitive to blood calcium concentrations.* Thus, a person whose calcium intake is inadequate maintains normal blood calcium but at the expense of the bones.

The body is sensitive to an increased need for calcium, although it sends no signals to the conscious brain indicating calcium need. Instead, the body quietly increases the absorption of calcium from the intestine and prevents its loss from the kidneys. For example, more calcium is needed for growth, so infants and children absorb about 60 percent of ingested calcium and pregnant women absorb about 50 percent, compared with 25 percent in other healthy adults. The body of an adolescent hungers for calcium, absorbing and retaining more calcium from each meal than does the body of an adult.[16] The body also absorbs a higher percentage of calcium when less total calcium

---

*Calcitonin, made in the thyroid gland, is secreted whenever the calcium concentration in the blood rises too high. It acts to stop withdrawal from bone and to slow absorption somewhat from the intestine. Parathormone, from the parathyroid glands, has the opposite effect.

is provided in the diet.[17] It does this, in part, with the help of vitamin D-dependent upregulation of calcium transport into the intestinal cells. Deprived of calcium for months or years, an adult may double the calcium absorbed; when supplied for years with abundant calcium, the same person may absorb only about one-third the normal amount. These adjustments take time, though, and increased absorption cannot fully compensate for a reduced calcium intake. A person who suddenly cuts back on calcium is likely to lose calcium from the bones.

Despite the body's adjustments, some bone loss is an inevitable consequence of aging. By the late 20s, or 10 years after adult height is achieved, the skeleton no longer adds significantly to bone density.[18] After about 40 years of age, regardless of calcium intake, bones begin to lose density, but the loss can be slowed somewhat by a diet high in calcium along with sufficient physical activity.

To protect against bone loss, high calcium intakes early in life are recommended. A calcium-poor diet during the growing years may prevent a person from achieving **peak bone mass**.[19] Furthermore, a person whose calcium savings account is not sufficient is more likely to develop the fragile bones of **osteoporosis**, or adult bone loss. Too little calcium packed into the skeleton during childhood and young adulthood strongly predicts susceptibility to osteoporosis in adulthood. Osteoporosis constitutes a major health problem for many older people—its possible causes and prevention are the topics of this chapter's Controversy feature.

In Osteoporosis
Bones of older adults become brittle and fragile.

How Much Calcium Do I Need? Setting recommended intakes for calcium is difficult because absorption varies not only with age but also with a person's vitamin D status and the calcium content of the diet. The DRI committee took such variations into account and set recommendations for calcium at levels that produce maximum calcium retention. At lower intakes, the body does not store calcium to capacity; at greater intakes, the excess calcium is excreted and thus wasted.

The importance of vitamin D in calcium absorption was described in Chapter 7.

● The maximum daily dose (MDD) for single-ingredient supplements for calcium is 1,500 mg/d.

Recommended intakes are high for children and adolescents because people develop their peak bone mass during their growing years. Obtaining enough calcium at that time helps ensure that the skeleton starts adulthood with a high bone density. Despite the importance of consuming adequate calcium during the growing years, average intakes among today's youth are too low to meet recommendations. Snapshot 8–1 provides a look at some foods that are good or excellent sources of calcium, and this chapter's Food Feature on pages 345–348 focuses on foods that can help meet calcium needs.

Calcium in Canadian Foods

Canadian regulations for adding calcium to foods and beverages (fortification) differ from those in the United States. Some milk products, such as fluid milk or milk substitutes, contain added milk solids, thus increasing the amount of calcium in milk by up to 33 percent. Some fruit juice products, such as orange juice, have added milk solids or added calcium. These are often sold as calcium supplements. You should read the labels of these products carefully to compare calcium content and cost.

Consider this: What is the vitamin D intake or status of those using nonmilk products as major sources of calcium?

Keep in mind that the new nutrition labelling regulations include calcium among the core nutrients or food components that must be listed in the Nutrition Facts table. Also, Health Canada recently allowed food manufacturers to use a diet-related heath claim on foods meeting certain criteria, linking calcium, vitamin D, and physical activity with osteoporosis. But, as with all other diet-related health claims, the exact wording is prescribed. One example of such a claim is "A healthy diet with adequate calcium and vitamin D and regular physical activity help to achieve strong bones and may reduce the risk of osteoporosis." In addition, the Natural Health Products Directorate allows health claims on vitamin and mineral supplements that contain those nutrients at levels at or above the RDA/AI, for example, for calcium:

peak bone mass the highest attainable bone density for an individual; developed during the first three decades of life.

osteoporosis (OSS-tee-oh-pore-OH-sis) a reduction of the bone mass of older persons in which the bones become porous and fragile (*osteo* means "bones"; *poros* means "porous"); also known as *adult bone loss*.

The Major Minerals

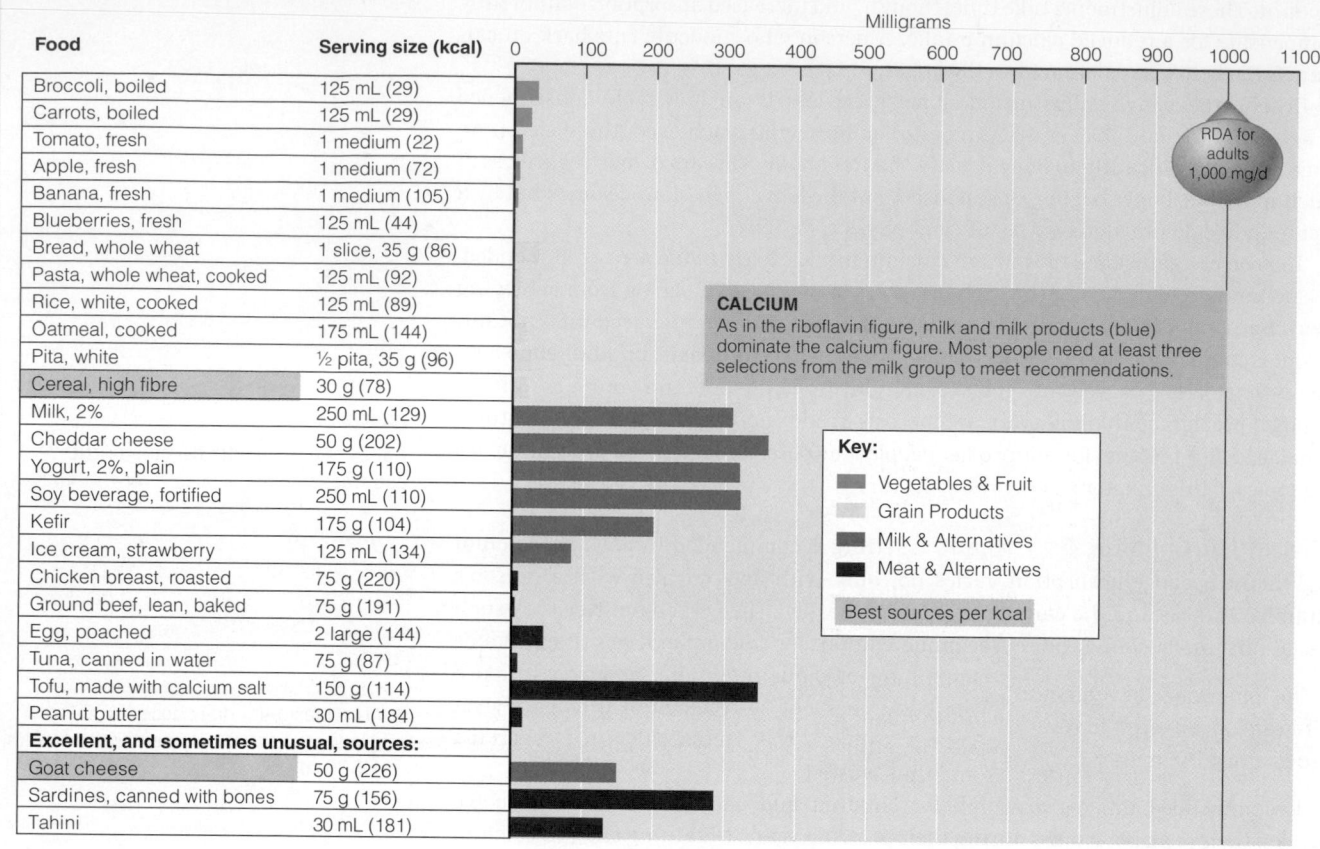

Food	Serving size (kcal)
Broccoli, boiled	125 mL (29)
Carrots, boiled	125 mL (29)
Tomato, fresh	1 medium (22)
Apple, fresh	1 medium (72)
Banana, fresh	1 medium (105)
Blueberries, fresh	125 mL (44)
Bread, whole wheat	1 slice, 35 g (86)
Pasta, whole wheat, cooked	125 mL (92)
Rice, white, cooked	125 mL (89)
Oatmeal, cooked	175 mL (144)
Pita, white	½ pita, 35 g (96)
Cereal, high fibre	30 g (78)
Milk, 2%	250 mL (129)
Cheddar cheese	50 g (202)
Yogurt, 2%, plain	175 g (110)
Soy beverage, fortified	250 mL (110)
Kefir	175 g (104)
Ice cream, strawberry	125 mL (134)
Chicken breast, roasted	75 g (220)
Ground beef, lean, baked	75 g (191)
Egg, poached	2 large (144)
Tuna, canned in water	75 g (87)
Tofu, made with calcium salt	150 g (114)
Peanut butter	30 mL (184)
Excellent, and sometimes unusual, sources:	
Goat cheese	50 g (226)
Sardines, canned with bones	75 g (156)
Tahini	30 mL (181)

CALCIUM
As in the riboflavin figure, milk and milk products (blue) dominate the calcium figure. Most people need at least three selections from the milk group to meet recommendations.

Key:
- Vegetables & Fruit
- Grain Products
- Milk & Alternatives
- Meat & Alternatives

Best sources per kcal

RDA for adults 1,000 mg/d

Recommended Dietary Allowance:
Adults: 1,000 mg/d (19–50 yr)
1,200 mg/d (51+ yr)

CCHS 2.2 Mean Intake
Men: ~1,100 mg/d
Women: ~870 mg/d

Tolerable Upper Intake Level:
Adults: 2,500 mg/d

Chief Functions:
Mineralization of bones and teeth; muscle contraction and relaxation, nerve functioning, blood clotting

Deficiency:
Stunted growth and weak bones in children; bone loss (osteoporosis) in adults

Toxicity:
Constipation; interference with absorption of other minerals; increased risk of kidney stone formation

"Adequate calcium as part of a healthy diet may reduce the risk of developing osteoporosis" (http://webprod.hc-sc.gc.ca/nhpid-bdipsn/monoReq.do?id=57&lang=eng). Additional information about how to meet calcium needs and reduce the risk of osteoporosis can be found later in this chapter's Food Feature and Controversy sections.

KEY POINT

- Calcium makes up bone and tooth structure and plays roles in nerve transmission, muscle contraction, and blood clotting. Calcium absorption rises when there is a dietary deficiency or an increased need, such as during growth.

Phosphorus

Phosphorus is the second-most abundant mineral in the body, but its concentration in the blood is less than half that of calcium. About 85 percent of the body's phosphorus is found combined with calcium in the crystals of the bones and teeth. The rest is everywhere else:

- Phosphorous salts are critical buffers, helping maintain the acid–base balance of cellular fluids.

- Phosphorus is part of the DNA and RNA of every cell and is thus essential for growth and renewal of tissues.

- Phosphorous compounds carry, store, and release energy in the metabolism of energy nutrients.

- Phosphorous compounds assist many enzymes and vitamins in extracting the energy from nutrients.

- Phosphorus forms part of the molecules of the phospholipids that are principal components of cell membranes (discussed in Chapter 5).

- Phosphorus is present in some proteins.

Despite all of these critical roles, the body's need for phosphorus is easily met by almost any diet, and deficiencies are unknown. As Snapshot 8–2 shows, animal protein is the best source of phosphorus (because phosphorus is abundant in the cells of animals). Phosphorus is also present in some soft drinks, such as cola beverages, but Canada's Food Guide recommends that we limit our intake of soft drinks and "Drink water regularly" as a Caloric-free way to satisfy our thirst.

- The mineral is *phosphorus*. The adjective form is spelled with an *-ous* (as in phosphorous salts).

- The maximum daily dose (MDD) for multiple-nutrient supplements for phosphorus is 2,000 mg/d.

KEY POINT

- Most of the phosphorus in the body is in the bones and teeth. Phosphorus helps maintain acid–base balance, is part of the genetic material in cells, assists in energy metabolism, and forms part of cell membranes. Under normal circumstances, deficiencies of phosphorus are unknown.

Magnesium

Magnesium barely qualifies as a major mineral: only about 30 grams is present in the body of a 60-kilogram person, over half of it in the bones. Most of the rest is in the muscles, heart, liver, and other soft tissues, with only 1 percent in the body fluids. The supply of magnesium in the bones can be tapped to maintain a constant blood level whenever dietary intake falls too low. The kidneys can also act to conserve magnesium.

Like phosphorus, magnesium is critical to many cell functions. It assists in the operation of more than 300 enzymes; is needed for the release and use of energy from the energy-yielding nutrients; and directly affects the metabolism of potassium, calcium, and vitamin D. Magnesium acts in the cells of all of the soft tissues, where it forms part of the protein-making machinery and is necessary for the release of energy. Magnesium and calcium work together for proper functioning of the muscles: calcium promotes contraction, and magnesium helps the muscles relax afterward. In the teeth, magnesium promotes resistance to tooth decay by holding calcium in tooth enamel.

Most Canadians receive more than the estimated average requirement (EAR) for magnesium from their diets.[20] Among those of African descent, whose magnesium intakes are much lower than those of other groups, chronic diseases occur in high numbers, leading to the suspicion that low intakes of magnesium-rich foods may contribute to disease development.[21] Snapshot 8–3 shows magnesium-rich foods. Magnesium is easily washed and peeled away from foods during processing, so slightly processed or unprocessed foods are the best sources. In some parts of the country, water contributes significantly to magnesium intakes, so people living in those regions need less from food.

A magnesium deficiency may occur as a result of inadequate intake, vomiting, diarrhea, alcoholism, or protein malnutrition. It may also occur in hospital clients who have been fed magnesium-poor fluids through a vein for too long or in people

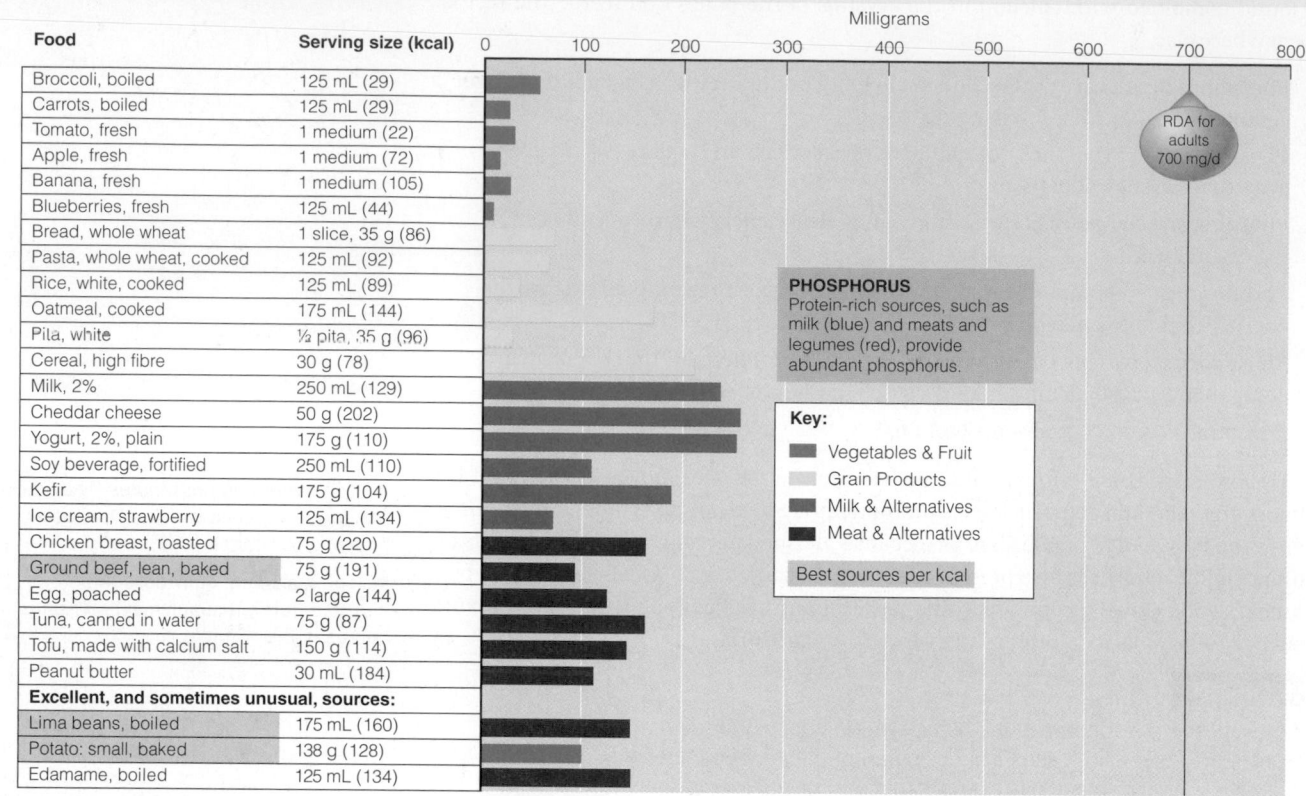

Food	Serving size (kcal)
Broccoli, boiled	125 mL (29)
Carrots, boiled	125 mL (29)
Tomato, fresh	1 medium (22)
Apple, fresh	1 medium (72)
Banana, fresh	1 medium (105)
Blueberries, fresh	125 mL (44)
Bread, whole wheat	1 slice, 35 g (86)
Pasta, whole wheat, cooked	125 mL (92)
Rice, white, cooked	125 mL (89)
Oatmeal, cooked	175 mL (144)
Pita, white	½ pita, 35 g (96)
Cereal, high fibre	30 g (78)
Milk, 2%	250 mL (129)
Cheddar cheese	50 g (202)
Yogurt, 2%, plain	175 g (110)
Soy beverage, fortified	250 mL (110)
Kefir	175 g (104)
Ice cream, strawberry	125 mL (134)
Chicken breast, roasted	75 g (220)
Ground beef, lean, baked	75 g (191)
Egg, poached	2 large (144)
Tuna, canned in water	75 g (87)
Tofu, made with calcium salt	150 g (114)
Peanut butter	30 mL (184)
Excellent, and sometimes unusual, sources:	
Lima beans, boiled	175 mL (160)
Potato: small, baked	138 g (128)
Edamame, boiled	125 mL (134)

PHOSPHORUS
Protein-rich sources, such as milk (blue) and meats and legumes (red), provide abundant phosphorus.

Key:
- Vegetables & Fruit
- Grain Products
- Milk & Alternatives
- Meat & Alternatives

Best sources per kcal

RDA for adults 700 mg/d

Recommended Dietary Allowance:
Adults: 700 mg/d

CCHS 2.2 Mean Intake:
Females: ~1,200 mg/d
Males: ~1,600 mg/d

Tolerable Upper Intake Level:
Adults (19–70 yr): 4,000 mg/d

Chief Functions:
Mineralization of bones and teeth; part of phospholipids, important in genetic material, energy metabolism, and buffering systems

Deficiency:
Muscular weakness, bone pain[a]

Toxicity:
Calcification of soft tissues, particularly the kidneys

[a]Dietary deficiency rarely occurs, but some drugs can bind with phosphorus, making it unavailable.

who are using diuretics. People whose drinking water provides adequate magnesium experience a lower incidence of sudden death from heart failure than other people. It seems likely that magnesium deficiency makes the heart unable to stop spasms once they start. Magnesium deficiency may also be related to cardiovascular disease (CVD), heart attack, and high blood pressure. A deficiency also causes hallucinations that can be mistaken for mental illness or drunkenness. Although intakes are often below those recommended, overt deficiency symptoms are rare in normal, healthy people.

Magnesium toxicity is rare, but it can be fatal. Toxicity occurs only with high intakes from nonfood sources such as supplements or magnesium salts. Accidental poisonings may occur in children with access to medicine chests and in older people

• The maximum daily dose (MDD) for single-ingredient supplements for magnesium is 500 mg/d.

Snapshot 8-3 ⟶ Magnesium

Food	Serving size (kcal)	Milligrams (0–400+)
Broccoli, boiled	125 mL (29)	
Carrots, boiled	125 mL (29)	
Tomato, fresh	1 medium (22)	
Apple, fresh	1 medium (72)	
Banana, fresh	1 medium (105)	
Blueberries, fresh	125 mL (44)	
Bread, whole wheat	1 slice, 35 g (86)	
Pasta, whole wheat, cooked	125 mL (92)	
Rice, white, cooked	125 mL (89)	
Oatmeal, cooked	175 mL (144)	
Pita, white	½ pita, 35 g (96)	
Cereal, high fibre	30 g (78)	
Milk, 2%	250 mL (129)	
Cheddar cheese	50 g (202)	
Yogurt, 2%, plain	175 g (110)	
Soy beverage, fortified	250 mL (110)	
Kefir	175 g (104)	
Ice cream, strawberry	125 mL (134)	
Chicken breast, roasted	75 g (220)	
Ground beef, lean, baked	75 g (191)	
Egg, poached	2 large (144)	
Tuna, canned in water	75 g (87)	
Tofu, made with calcium salt	150 g (114)	
Peanut butter	30 mL (184)	
Excellent, and sometimes unusual, sources:		
Spinach, boiled	125 mL (22)	
Pumpkin seeds, roasted	60 mL (330)	
Halibut, baked	75 g (105)	

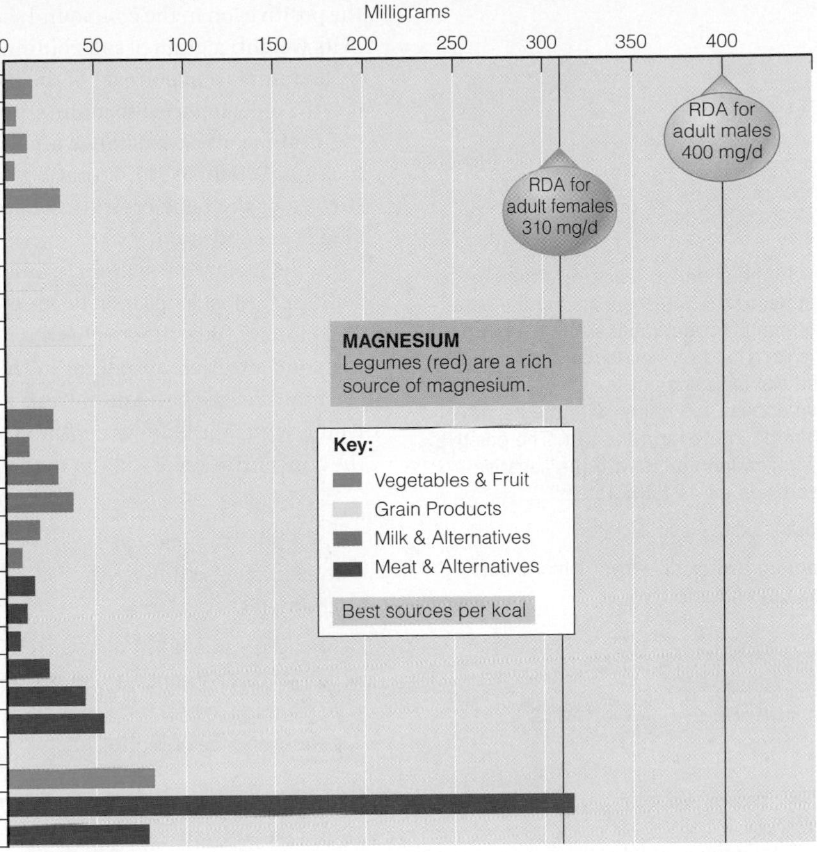

RDA for adult males 400 mg/d

RDA for adult females 310 mg/d

MAGNESIUM
Legumes (red) are a rich source of magnesium.

Key:
- Vegetables & Fruit
- Grain Products
- Milk & Alternatives
- Meat & Alternatives

Best sources per kcal

Recommended Dietary Allowance:
Men (19–30 yr): 400 mg/d
Women (19–30 yr): 310 mg/d

CCHS 2.2 Mean Intake:
Men: ~380 mg/d
Women: ~285 mg/d

Tolerable Upper Intake Level:
Adults: 350 mg/d[a]

Chief Functions:
Bone mineralization, protein synthesis, enzyme action, muscle contraction, nerve function, tooth maintenance, and immune function

Deficiency:
Weakness, confusion; if extreme, convulsions, uncontrollable muscle contractions, hallucinations, and difficulty in swallowing; in children, growth failure

Toxicity:
From nonfood sources only; diarrhea, pH imbalance, dehydration

[a]From nonfood sources, in addition to the magnesium provided by food.

who abuse magnesium-containing laxatives, antacids, and other medications. The consequences can be severe diarrhea, acid–base imbalance, and dehydration. For safety, use magnesium-containing medications with discretion.

KEY POINT

- Most of the body's magnesium is in the bones and can be drawn out for all cells to use in building protein and using energy. About one-third of Canadians aged 19–30 years consume less than the EAR of magnesium from their food.

Sodium

Salt has been known and valued throughout recorded history. "You are the salt of the earth" means that you are valuable. If "you are not worth your salt," you are worthless. Even our word *salary* comes from the Latin word for *salt*. Chemically, sodium is the positive ion in the compound sodium chloride (table salt) and makes up 40 percent of its weight: a gram of salt contains 400 milligrams of sodium.

Sodium is a major part of the body's fluid and electrolyte balance system because it is the chief ion used to maintain the volume of fluid outside cells. Sodium also helps maintain acid–base balance and is essential to muscle contraction and nerve transmission. Scientists think that 30 to 40 percent of the body's sodium is stored on the surface of the bone crystals, where the body can easily draw on it to replenish the blood concentration.

A deficiency of sodium would be harmful, but no known human diets lack sodium.[22] Most foods include more salt than is needed, and the body absorbs it freely. The kidneys filter the surplus out of the blood and into the urine. For example, when the concentration of sodium in the blood is high, the pituitary gland at the base of the brain releases an antidiuretic hormone that signals the kidneys to reabsorb more water, while the kidneys continue to excrete small amounts of sodium, thus reducing the concentration of sodium in the blood. They can also sensitively conserve sodium.

In the rare event of a deficiency, they can return to the bloodstream the exact amount needed. Small sodium losses occur in sweat, but the amount of sodium excreted in a day equals the amount ingested that day. But if sodium is so well controlled by the body, why do authorities urge people to limit their intakes? To understand why, you must first understand how sodium interacts with body fluids.

How Are Salt and "Water Weight" Related? If blood sodium rises, as it will after a person eats salted foods, thirst ensures that the person will drink water until the sodium-to-water ratio is restored. Then the kidneys excrete the extra water along with the extra sodium.

Dieters sometimes think that eating too much salt or drinking too much water will make them gain weight, but they do not gain fat, of course. They gain water, but a healthy body excretes this excess water immediately. Excess salt is excreted as soon as enough water is drunk to carry the salt out of the body. From this perspective, then, the way to keep body salt (and "water weight") under control is to control salt intake and drink more, not less, water.

If blood sodium drops, body water is lost, and both water and sodium must be replenished to avert an emergency. Overly strict use of low-sodium diets in the treatment of hypertension, kidney disease, or heart disease can deplete the body of needed sodium; so can vomiting, diarrhea, or extremely heavy sweating.

Sodium Intakes The recommended AI for sodium has been set at 1,500 milligrams for healthy, active young adults; at 1,300 for people ages 51 through 70; and at 1,200 for the elderly.[23] These amounts are sufficient to ensure an overall diet that provides adequate amounts of other needed nutrients. Because Canadian and U.S. intakes are much higher than these amounts, and because blood pressure rises with sodium intakes, the DRI committee set a Tolerable Upper Intake Level for sodium of 2,300 milligrams per day. It is recommended that people stay within the DRI sodium guidelines (see Table 8–5).

Adult Canadian males and females between 19 and 30 years old consume an average of about 4,000 milligrams and about 2,800 milligrams of sodium per day, respectively, which translates into between 7 and 10 grams of salt (see Figure 8–7).[24] This amount exceeds the Tolerable Upper Intake Level of 2,300 milligrams. Asian peoples, whose staple sauces and flavourings are based on soy sauce and monosodium glutamate (MSG or Accent), may consume the equivalent of 30 to 40 grams of salt per day.

- To the chemist, a salt results from the neutralization of an acid and a base. Sodium chloride, table salt, results from the reaction between hydrochloric acid and the base sodium hydroxide. The positive dodium ion unites with the negative chloride ion to form the salt. The positive hydrogen ion unites with the negative hydroxide ion to form water

Base + acid = salt + water

Sodium hydroxide + hydrochloric acid = sodium chloride + water

Table 8–5

Sodium and Salt Intake Guidelines

DRI Recommendations

- Recommended intakes for sodium:
  - Adults (19–50 years): 1,500 mg/d
  - Adults (51–70 years): 1,300 mg/d
  - Adults (71 years and older): 1,200 mg/d
- Tolerable Upper Intake Level for sodium and salt:
  - Adults (19 years and older): 2,300 mg sodium, or 5.6 g salt (sodium chloride) per day (http://www.nap.edu/openbook.php?record_id=10925)

Eating Well with Canada's Food Guide recommends

- "Limiting foods and beverages high in . . . salt (sodium) . . . potato chips, nachos and other salty snacks . . ." and that we read labels on foods to "Compare the Nutrition Facts . . . to choose foods that contain less . . . sodium" (go to http://www.hc-sc.gc.ca/fn-an/alt_formats/hpfb-dgpsa/pdf/food-guide-aliment/view_eatwell_vue_bienmang-eng.pdf and look for the "Eat Well" section at the bottom of the page or check it out on the back of the Food Guide).

For a brief summary of the kidneys' actions, see Chapter 3.

Too little sodium can pose a danger to endurance athletes performing in hot, humid conditions. See Chapter 10.

Canadian Salt and Sodium Intake Even with the exclusion of salt added at the table or while cooking, the usual intake of sodium by the vast majority of adults (19–70 years) not only exceeds the AI for sodium (1,300–1,500 mg/d), it also exceeds the Tolerable Upper Intake Level (2,300 mg/d) as well, a level beyond which health risk increases; however, it should be noted that females do consume significantly less than their male counterparts (http://www.hc-sc.gc.ca/fn-an/nutrition/sodium/index-eng.php). Also, the food grouping that contributed the greatest amount of sodium to the diet (~20%) was "pizza, sandwiches, submarines, hamburgers and hotdogs" followed by "soups" at ~7 percent.

Sodium and Blood Pressure Around the world, communities with high intakes of salt experience high rates of **hypertension**; CVD; and cerebral hemorrhage, a hypertension-related stroke.[25] As sodium intakes increase, average blood pressure rises with them in a stepwise fashion.[26] As blood pressure rises, the risk of death from CVD climbs steadily.[27]

The relationship between salt intakes and blood pressure is direct—the more salt a person eats, the higher the blood pressure goes.[28] Even small increases in sodium, even when salt intakes are low to begin with, have this effect—any amount of salt seems to raise the blood pressure. This effect occurs more strongly among more salt-sensitive people, including those with diabetes, hypertension, or kidney disease; those of African descent; those whose parents had high blood pressure; and anyone over age 50 because the blood pressure responds to salt more dramatically in older age.

Not surprisingly, genetics plays a role in the body's handling of dietary sodium and may be at the bottom of the variations in salt sensitivity observed among different groups of people. Certain genetic variations are known to cause high blood pressure, and researchers suspect that, while these relationships are complex, the genes affecting blood pressure do so by altering the kidneys' handling of sodium.[29]

Luckily, people can modify their salt response somewhat by consuming more potassium in the context of a nutritious diet. One proven dietary approach can help people reduce their sodium and increase their potassium intakes, thereby reducing their disease risks. The DASH (Dietary Approaches to Stop Hypertension) diet often achieves a lower blood pressure than restriction of sodium intake alone.[30] The DASH approach calls for greatly increased intakes of fruit and vegetables, with adequate amounts of nuts, fish, whole grains, and low-fat dairy products. At the same time, red meat, butter, and other high-fat foods and sweets are held to occasional small portions. Salt and sodium are greatly reduced.

When people consume the DASH diet with progressively lower sodium, their blood pressures fall responsively.[31] When the diet is modified to also provide foods with abundant magnesium, potassium, and calcium, as well as adequate protein and fibre, the average blood pressure drops even lower at each level of sodium intake. Low potassium intake on its own raises blood pressure, whereas high potassium intake appears to both help prevent and correct hypertension.[32] These beneficial nutrients come from consuming generous amounts of whole grains, fruit, vegetables, low-fat milk products, seeds, nuts, and legumes each day while limiting meats and other animal products.[33] For controlling hypertension, then, actions to reduce sodium and implement the dietary changes characterizing the DASH diet seem wise (see also Chapter 11).

Many Canadians have much to gain in terms of cardiovascular health and nothing to lose from cutting back on salt to at most 2,300 mg per day as part of an overall lifestyle strategy to reduce blood pressure. Physical activity should also be part of that lifestyle because regular moderate exercise reliably lowers the blood pressure.

Other valid reasons exist for most people to hold their salt intakes at or below the recommended maximum. For example, older people without clinical hypertension often die of stroke, and reducing dietary sodium may lower their blood pressure enough to reduce their stroke risk. Excess sodium in the diet also increases calcium excretion, an effect that could potentially compromise the integrity of the bones.[34] Excessive salt may also directly stress a weakened heart or aggravate kidney problems. The high salt intakes of many Asian peoples have been suggested as a possible cause for their greatly elevated rates of stomach cancer.

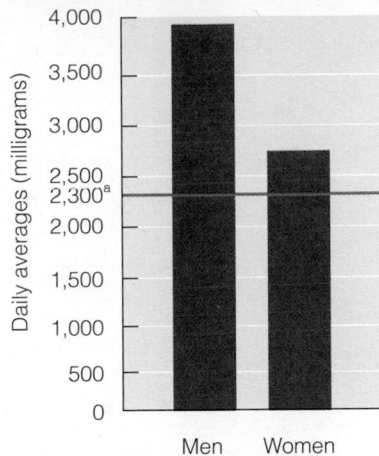

Figure 8–7

Sodium Intakes of Canadian Adults

[a]DRI Tolerable Upper Intake Level (UL).

Data from Statistics Canada: D. Garriguet, "Sodium consumption at all ages," Health Reports 18 (2007): (2), Catalogue no. 82-003. Reproduced and distributed on an "as is" basis with the permission of Statistics Canada.

● Sodium is not allowed to be used as a medicinal ingredient in supplements in Canada.

● A diet designed with the DASH eating plan (Table F-2 in Appendix F) fits well with Canada's Food Guide and meets the guidelines for sodium and potassium.

The Food Guide also Encourages People to

- Consume a sufficient amount of fruit and vegetables while staying within energy needs. For example, 7–10 servings of vegetables and fruit per day are recommended in a 2,000-Cal diet.
- Choose a variety of fruit and vegetables each day; in particular, select dark green and orange vegetables several times each week.

hypertension high blood pressure.

Sodium and Potassium on Canadian Labels Sodium is a core nutrient on all Nutrition Facts labels, with the amount expressed in both milligrams and as %DV (http://www.inspection.gc.ca/english/fssa/labeti/guide/ch6ae.shtml) under nutrition labelling regulations. Potassium is not a core nutrient. However, potassium content must be declared if the prepackaged food contains added potassium salts or if there is any claim or advertisement about the absence or reduced level of salt or sodium in the food. In these cases, the amount of potassium is stated in both milligrams and as a %DV. For example, "Salt-Free" or "Sodium-Free" means that less than 5 milligrams of sodium is present in the amount or serving of a stated size (these reference amounts or servings are regulated by Health Canada). Also, foods with <5 percent DV would not be considered high in sodium.

The labelling regulations also allow a health claim linking sodium and potassium to high blood pressure. The regulations provide prescribed wording of the claim. Potassium content must appear on the Nutrition Facts table when such a claim is made.

An example of a disease risk reduction health claim is "A healthy diet containing foods high in potassium and low in sodium may reduce the risk of high blood pressure, a risk factor for stroke and heart disease" (http://www.inspection.gc.ca/english/fssa/labeti/guide/ch8e.shtml).

Controlling Salt Intake Cutting down on salt and sodium may be easier than people believe, and Table 8–6 demonstrates how, with a few thoughtful food choices, a meal's sodium can be drastically reduced. Notice that in the meal in the left-hand column, sauces, dressings, and the salt added to corn, chips, pickles, and pie crust and sprinkled on foods are the major modifiable sources of sodium. Notice, too, that even without added sauces and salt, most foods contain enough sodium to easily meet most people's need. Foods eaten without salt may seem less tasty at first but, with repetition, tastes adjust, and the natural flavour becomes the preferred taste. As a result of greater awareness regarding the negative health effects of high salt intake, more and more "reduced-salt" and "low-salt" foods are finding their way onto our store shelves. Check them out; you may be surprised that the taste isn't that different—you might not even notice the difference! Also, remember that the recommendation is to consume less sodium, not eliminate salt altogether.

While an obvious step is to control the salt shaker, this source may contribute as little as 10 percent of the total salt consumed. As Figure 8–8 indicates, a more productive step is to cut down on processed and fast foods, the source of almost 75 percent of the salt in our diet. Often the least processed foods in each food group are not only lowest in sodium but also highest in potassium. As mentioned earlier, low potassium

---

Table 8–6

How to Cut Sodium from a Barbecue Lunch

Lunch #1 exceeds the whole day's Tolerable Upper Intake Level of 2,300 milligrams sodium. With careful substitutions, the sodium drops dramatically in the second lunch, but it still provides over 40 percent of the suggested maximum intake. In lunch #3, just two small changes—omitting the sauce and salt—cut the sodium by half again.

Lunch #1: Highest	Sodium (mg)	Lunch #2: Lower	Sodium (mg)	Lunch #3: Lowest	Sodium (mg)
▪ Chopped pork sandwich, with sauce	950	▪ Sliced pork sandwich with 1 tbs sauce	400	▪ Sliced pork sandwich, (no sauce)	210
▪ Creamed corn, ½ c	460	▪ Corn, 1 cob, soft margarine, salt	190	▪ Corn, 1 cob, soft margarine	50
▪ Potato chips, 8.5 g	340	▪ Coleslaw, ½ c	180	▪ Green salad, oil and vinegar	10
▪ Dill pickle, ½ medium	420	▪ Watermelon, slice	10	▪ Watermelon, slice	10
▪ Milk, 1%, 1 c	113	▪ Milk, 2%, 1 c	106	▪ Milk, 2%, 1 c	106
▪ Pecan pie, slice	480	▪ Ice cream, low fat, ½ c	80	▪ Ice cream, low fat, ½ c	80
Total	**2,763**	**Total**	**966**	**Total**	**766**

Figure 8–8

Sources of Sodium in the Canadian Diet

Unprocessed Foods

Those that are low in sodium contribute 15% of the total sodium in the Canadian diet.

Fresh foods higher in sodium
 Milk, 120 mg per 1 c
 Scallops, 260 mg per 90 g
Fresh meats, about 30 to 70 mg per 90 g
 Chicken, beef, fish, lamb, pork
Fresh vegetables, about 30 to 50 mg
 per ¹/2 c
 Celery, Chinese cabbage, sweet
 potatoes
Fresh vegetables, about 10 to 20 mg
 per ¹/2 c
 Broccoli, Brussels sprouts, carrots,
 corn, green beans, legumes,
 potatoes, salad greens
Grains (cooked without salt), about 0 to
 10 mg per ¹/2 c
 Barley, oatmeal,
 pasta, rice

Salt

Salt added at home, in cooking or at the table, contributes about 10% of the total sodium in the Canadian diet. Many seasonings and sauces also contribute salt and sodium.

Salts, about 2,000 mg per teaspoon
 Salt, sea salt, seasoned salt, onion
 salt, garlic salt[a]
Soy sauce, about 300 mg per teaspoon
Condiments and sauces, about 100 to 200 mg
 per tablespoon
 Barbecue sauce, ketchup, mustard,
 salad dressings, sweet pickle relish,
 taco sauce, Worcestershire sauce

[a]Note that herb seasoning blends may or may not contain substantial sodium; read the labels.

Processed Foods

These contribute 75% of the sodium in the Canadian diet.

Dry soup mixes (prepared), about 1,000
 to 2,000 mg per 1 c
 Bouillon cube or canned, noodle
 soups, onion soup, ramen
Smoked and cured meats, about 700 to
 2,000 mg per 60 g
 Canned ham products, corned or
 chipped beef, ham, lunch meats
Fast foods and TV dinners, about 700 to
 1,500 mg per serving
 Breakfast biscuit (cheese, egg, and
 ham), cheeseburger, chicken wings
 (10 spicy wings), frozen TV dinners,
 pizza (2 slices), taco, vegetarian soy
 burger (on bun)
Canned soups (prepared), about 700 to
 1,500 mg per 1 c
 Bean soup, beef or chicken soups,
 "hearty" soups, tomato soup,
 vegetable soup
Canned pasta, about 800 to 1,000 mg per
 serving
 Beefaroni, macaroni and cheese,
 ravioli
Hot dogs, about 500 to 700 mg per 60 g
 Hot dogs, smoked sausages
Foods prepared in brine, about 300 to 800
 mg per serving
 Anchovies (2 fillets), dill pickles (1),
 olives (5), sauerkraut ¹/2 c
Cheeses, processed, about 550 mg per 45 g
 Cheddar, Swiss
Pudding, instant, about 420 mg per ¹/2 c
 All flavours
Canned vegetables, about 200 to 450 mg
 per ¹/2 c
 Carrots, corn, green beans, legumes,
 peas, potatoes
Cereals, dry ready-to-eat, about 180 to 260 mg
 per 30 g
 Cheerios, cornflakes, corn bran,
 Cocoa Puffs, Total, others

intakes are thought to play an important role in the development of hypertension. Many people are unaware that foods high in sodium do not always taste salty. Who could guess by taste alone that half a cup of instant chocolate pudding provides almost one-fifth of the daily upper limit for sodium? Moral: Read the labels. In October 2007, Health Canada announced the formation of a multistakeholder "Working Group on Dietary Sodium Reduction" whose mandate was to "develop, implement and oversee a population-health strategy for the successful reduction of the sodium content of the diets of Canadians to be in line with the recommendations of the Institute of Medicine of the National Academies DRI Report" (http://www.hc-sc.gc.ca/fn-an/nutrition/sodium/related-info-connexe/strateg/reduct-strat-eng.php). They have since met several times to examine sodium intakes of Canadians and sources of salt in our diet, consulted with stakeholders regarding strategies for sodium reduction, and submitted their "Sodium Reduction Strategy for Canada" report to the minister of Health in July 2010 (http://www.hc-sc.gc.ca/fn-an/nutrition/sodium/related-info-connexe/strateg/reduct-strat-eng.php). Their multistage strategy includes reducing our daily intake of sodium from 3,400 milligrams/day to 2,300 milligrams/day by 2016 including ". . . voluntary reduction of sodium levels in processed food products and foods sold in food services establishments; education and awareness of consumers, industry, health professionals and other key stakeholders; and research," and putting into place monitoring and evaluation programs during this period. Since that time, Health Canada also released "Guidance for the Food Industry on Reducing Sodium in Processed Foods," a document intended to help the food industry continue its efforts to meet sodium targets by 2016 (http://www.hc-sc.gc.ca/fn-an/legislation/guide-ld/2012-sodium-reduction-indust-eng.php).

Also, for a brief overview of the role of sodium in health and disease, its function in food, and international initiatives to reduce sodium, see the Canadian Council of Food and Nutrition's (CCFN) Watching Brief entitled "Reducing Dietary Sodium Intake" at http://www.cfdr.ca/Downloads/CCFN-docs/Watching-Brief-on-Sodium---Nov15-08.aspx.

KEY POINT

- Sodium is the main positively charged ion outside the body's cells. Sodium attracts water. Thus, too much sodium (or salt) raises blood pressure and aggravates hypertension. Diets rarely lack sodium.

Potassium

Potassium is the principal positively charged ion *inside* the body's cells. It plays a major role in maintaining fluid and electrolyte balance and cell integrity, and it is critical to maintaining the heartbeat. The sudden deaths that occur during fasting or severe diarrhea and in children with kwashiorkor or people with eating disorders are thought to be due to heart failure caused by potassium loss.

> Kwashiorkor is described in Chapter 6.

Dehydration leads to a loss of potassium from inside cells. This condition is dangerous because when the cells of the brain lose potassium, the person loses the ability to notice the need for water. Adults are warned not to take diuretics (water pills) that cause potassium loss or to give them to children, except under a physician's supervision. Physicians prescribing diuretics will tell clients to eat potassium-rich foods to compensate for the losses. Depending on the diuretic, physicians may also advise a lower sodium intake. When taking diuretics, a person should alert all other health-care providers.

In healthy people, almost any reasonable diet provides enough potassium to prevent the dangerously low blood potassium that indicates a severe deficiency. The median intakes of Canadians (~3.3 g/d for males and 2.5 g/d for females) provide just over half of the daily 4,700 milligrams of potassium recommended by the DRI committee.[35] Although blood potassium may remain normal on such a diet, chronic diseases are more likely to occur. With low potassium intake, hypertension becomes worse, glucose tolerance is impaired, metabolic acidity increases, calcium losses from bones accelerate, and kidney stone formation becomes more likely. The amounts of fruit and vegetables recommended in both Canada's Food Guide and the DASH diet are sufficient to provide all of the needed potassium. Potassium chloride, a salt substitute for people with hypertension who must strictly limit salt, provides potassium but does not reverse many of the conditions associated with diets that lack potassium-rich foods.[36]

- Unlike sodium, potassium may exert a positive effect against hypertension and related ills.

Because potassium is found inside all living cells, and because cells remain intact unless foods are processed, the richest sources of potassium are fresh, whole foods (see Snapshot 8–4). Most vegetables and fruit are outstanding. Bananas, despite their fame as the richest potassium source, are only one of many rich sources, which also include oranges, potatoes, spinach, cantaloupe, and almonds. Nevertheless, bananas are readily available, are easy to chew, and have a sweet taste that almost everyone likes, so health-care professionals often recommend them.

Potassium from foods is safe, but potassium injected into a vein can stop the heart. Potassium chloride pills should *not* be used except on a physician's advice. Potassium overdoses are normally not life-threatening as long as they are taken by mouth because the presence of excess potassium in the stomach triggers a vomiting reflex that expels the unwanted substance. A person with a weak heart, however, should not

- Although no amount of potassium is allowed in supplements for children or adolescents, only up to 100 mg is allowed in multi-nutrient supplements for adults.

Snapshot 8-4 ⟶ Potassium

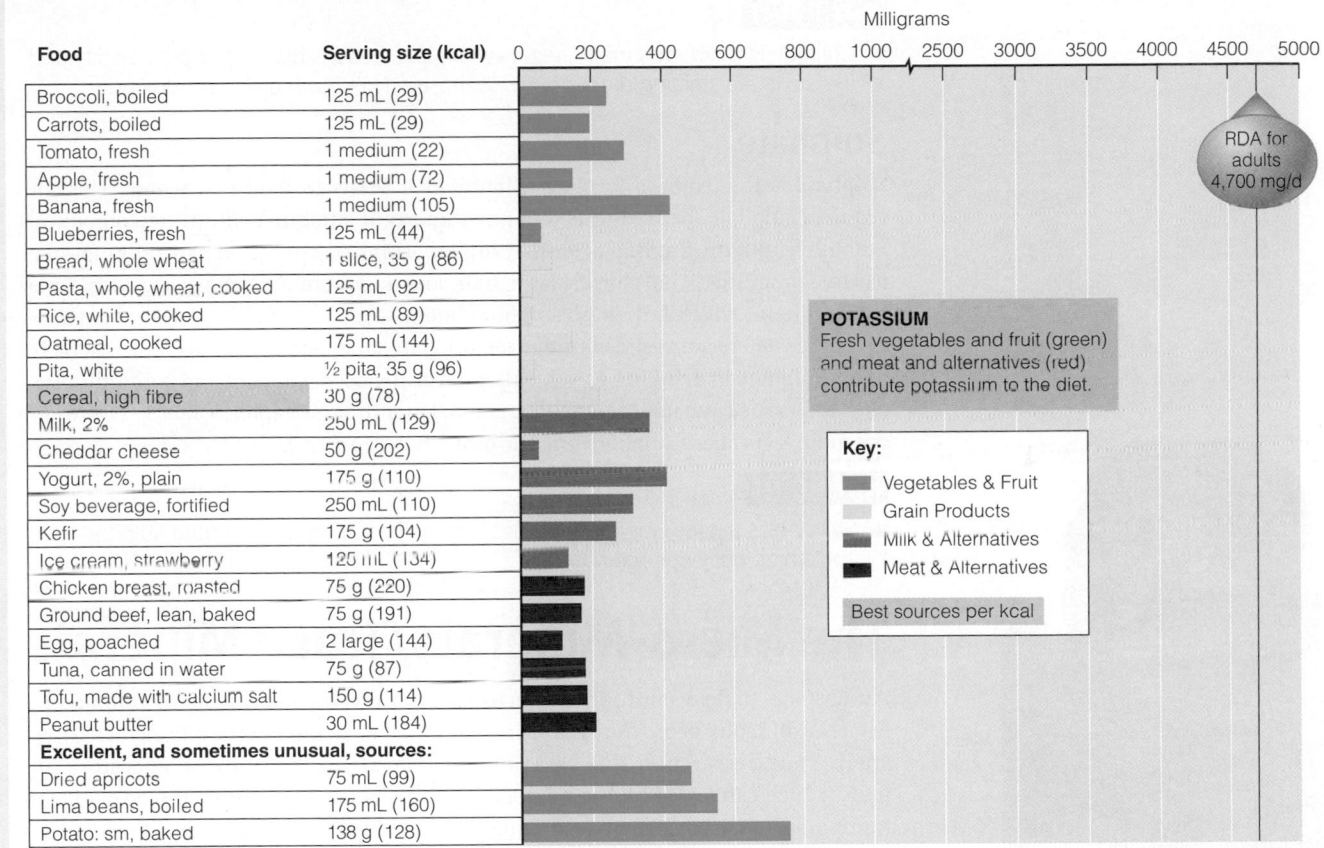

POTASSIUM
Fresh vegetables and fruit (green) and meat and alternatives (red) contribute potassium to the diet.

Key:
- Vegetables & Fruit
- Grain Products
- Milk & Alternatives
- Meat & Alternatives

Best sources per kcal

RDA for adults 4,700 mg/d

Adequate Intake:
Adults: 4,700 mg/d

CCHS 2.2 Mean Intake:
Men: ~3,550 mg/d
Women: ~2,675 mg/d

Chief Functions:
Maintains normal fluid and electrolyte balance; facilitates chemical reactions; supports cell integrity; assists in nerve functioning and muscle contractions

Deficiency:[a]
Muscle weakness, paralysis, confusion

Toxicity:
Muscle weakness; vomiting; for an infant given supplements, or when injected into a vein in an adult, potassium can stop the heart

[a]Deficiency accompanies dehydration.

go through this trauma, and a baby may not be able to withstand it. Several infants have died when well-meaning parents overdosed them with potassium supplements.

KEY POINT

- Potassium, the major positive ion inside cells, is important in many metabolic functions. Fresh whole foods are the best sources of potassium. Diuretics can deplete the body's potassium and so can be dangerous; potassium excess can also be dangerous.

Chloride

In its elemental form, chlorine forms a deadly green gas. In the body, the chloride ion plays important roles as the major negative ion. In the fluids outside the cells, it accompanies sodium and so helps maintain the crucial fluid balances (acid–base and electrolyte balances). The chloride ion also plays a special role as part of hydrochloric acid,

> The DRI committee set AI values for chloride; see inside front cover.

which maintains the strong acidity of the stomach necessary to digest protein. The principal food source of chloride is salt, both added and naturally occurring in foods, and no known diet lacks chloride.

KEY POINT

- Chloride is the body's major negative ion; it is responsible for stomach acidity and assists in maintaining proper body chemistry. No known diet lacks chloride.

Sulphate

Sulphate is the oxidized form of sulphur as it exists in food and water. The body requires sulphate for synthesis of many important sulphur-containing compounds. Sulphur-containing amino acids play an important role in helping strands of protein assume their functional shapes. Skin, hair, and nails contain some of the body's more rigid proteins, which have high sulphur contents.

There is no recommended intake for sulphate, and deficiencies are unknown. Too much sulphate in drinking water, either naturally occurring or from contamination, causes diarrhea and may damage the colon. Later in this chapter, Table 8–11 presents the main facts about sulphate and the other major minerals.

KEY POINT

- Sulphate is a necessary nutrient used to synthesize many important sulphur-containing body compounds.

The Micro-Minerals/Trace Minerals

An obstacle to determining the precise roles of the trace elements in humans has been the difficulty of providing an experimental diet lacking in the one element under study. Thus, research in this area is limited mostly to the study of laboratory animals, which can be fed highly refined, purified diets in environments free of all contamination. New laboratory techniques have enabled scientists to detect minerals in smaller and smaller quantities in living cells, and research is now rapidly expanding our knowledge about them. Intake recommendations for human beings have been established for nine trace minerals—see Table 8–7. Others are recognized as essential nutrients for some animals but have not been proven to be required for human beings.

Iodine

The body needs only an infinitesimally small quantity of iodine, but obtaining this amount is critical. Iodine is a part of thyroxine, the hormone made by the thyroid gland that is responsible for regulating the basal metabolic rate. Iodine must be available for thyroxine to be synthesized.

In iodine deficiency, the cells of the thyroid gland enlarge in an attempt to trap as many particles of iodine as possible. Sometimes the gland enlarges until it makes a visible lump in the neck, a **goitre**. People with iodine deficiency this severe become

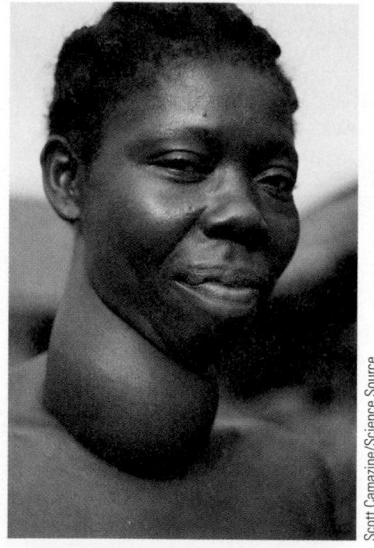

In iodine deficiency, the thyroid gland enlarges—a condition known as goitre.

Scott Camazine/Science Source

goitre (GOY-ter) enlargement of the thyroid gland due to iodine deficiency is *simple goitre*; enlargement due to an iodine excess is *toxic goitre*.

Table 8-7

Micro-Minerals/Trace Minerals

Human Intake Recommendations Established	Known Essential for Animals; Human Requirements under Study	Known Essential for Some Animals; No Evidence That Intake by Humans Is Ever Limiting
Iodine	Arsenic	Cobalt
Iron	Boron	
Zinc	Nickel	
Selenium	Silicon	
Fluoride	Vanadium	
Chromium		
Copper		
Manganese		
Molybdenum		

NOTE: The evidence for requirements and essentiality is weak for the trace minerals cadmium, lead, lithium, and tin.

sluggish and gain weight. Severe iodine deficiency during pregnancy causes extreme and irreversible mental and physical retardation in the infant, known as **cretinism**. Much of the mental retardation can be averted if the woman's deficiency is detected and treated within the first six months of pregnancy, but if treatment comes too late or not at all, the child may have an IQ as low as 20 (100 is average). Iodine deficiency is one of the world's most common and most preventable causes of mental retardation. Researchers hope to reverse the high rates of cretinism and goitre reported in developing nations by adding iodine to community food or water supplies.

The iodine in food varies because it reflects the soil in which plants are grown or on which animals graze. Iodine is plentiful in the ocean, so seafood is a dependable source. In the central parts of Canada that were never under the ocean or were heavily glaciated, the soil is poor in iodine. In those areas, the use of iodized salt and the consumption of foods shipped in from iodine rich areas have wiped out the iodine deficiency that once was widespread. Surprisingly, sea salt delivers little iodine because iodine becomes a gas and flies off into the air during the salt-drying process. In Canada, all table salt is iodized; in the United States, salt labels state whether the salt is iodized.

Excessive intakes of iodine can enlarge the thyroid gland just as a deficiency can. Canadian and U.S. intakes are above the recommended intake of 150 micrograms but still below the Tolerable Upper Intake Level of 1,100 micrograms per day for an adult.[37] Like chlorine and fluorine, iodine is a deadly poison in large amounts.

Much of the iodine in Canadian diets today comes from fast-food and other restaurant establishments, which use iodized salt with a liberal hand, and from bakery products and milk. The baking industry uses iodine-containing dough conditioners, and most dairies use iodine to disinfect milking equipment. One cup of milk supplies nearly half of one day's recommended intake of iodine, and less than a half-teaspoon of iodized salt meets the entire recommendation.

An iodine-containing medication, **potassium iodide**, effectively blocks damage to the thyroid gland caused by radioactive iodine released during nuclear radiation emergencies.* When given in the correct dosage within a certain time frame relative to radiation exposure, potassium iodide can greatly reduce the likelihood of thyroid cancer development.[38] When given in the wrong dosage or with faulty timing,

● The maximum daily dose (MDD) for iodine allowed in single-ingredient supplements for adults and adolescents is 800 µg/d.

cretinism (CREE-tin-ism) severe mental and physical retardation of an infant caused by the mother's iodine deficiency during pregnancy.

potassium iodide a medication approved by the U.S. FDA as safe and effective for the prevention of thyroid cancer caused by radioactive iodine that may be released during radiation emergencies.

---

*Potassium iodide works only to prevent thyroid cancer after exposure to radioactive iodine; it is not a general radioprotective agent. Read more at the Centres for Disease Control and Prevention website, http://www.bt.cdc.gov/radiation/ki.asp.

The Micro-Minerals/Trace Minerals

potassium iodide is useless or toxic. For this reason, concerned people who live near nuclear power plants are urged to rely on health professionals for guidance and to ignore quacks selling "antiradiation pills" on the Internet and elsewhere.[39]

KEY POINT

- Iodine is part of the hormone thyroxine, which influences energy metabolism. The deficiency diseases are goitre and cretinism. Iodine occurs naturally in seafood and in foods grown on land that was once covered by oceans; it is an additive in milk and bakery products. Large amounts are poisonous. Potassium iodide, appropriately administered, blocks some radiation damage to the thyroid during radiation emergencies.

Iron

Every living cell, whether plant or animal, contains iron. Most of the iron in the body is a component of two proteins: **hemoglobin** in red blood cells and **myoglobin** in muscle cells. Hemoglobin in the red blood cells carries oxygen from the lungs to tissues throughout the body. Myoglobin carries and stores oxygen for the muscles. Iron helps these proteins hold and carry oxygen and then release it.

> Chapter 6 described the influence of iron stores on the production of the protein hemoglobin.

All of the body's cells need oxygen to combine with the carbon and hydrogen atoms the cells release as they break down energy nutrients. The oxygen combines with these atoms to form the waste products carbon dioxide and water; thus, the body constantly needs fresh oxygen to keep the cells going. As cells of tissues use up and excrete their oxygen (as carbon dioxide and water), red blood cells shuttle in fresh oxygen supplies from the lungs. In addition to this major task, iron helps many enzymes use oxygen, and iron is needed to make new cells, amino acids, hormones, and neurotransmitters.

Iron is clearly the body's gold, a precious mineral to be hoarded. The liver packs iron sent from the bone marrow into new red blood cells and ships them out to the bloodstream. Red blood cells live for about three to four months. When they die, the spleen and liver break them down, salvage their iron for recycling, and send it back to the bone marrow to be kept until it is reused. The body does lose iron in nail clippings, hair cuttings, and shed skin cells, but only in tiny amounts. Bleeding can cause significant iron loss from the body, however.

The body has special provisions for obtaining iron. Only about 10 to 15 percent of dietary iron is absorbed, but if the body's supply of iron is diminished or if the need increases (say, during pregnancy), absorption can increase several-fold.[40] Once inside the body, iron is difficult to excrete, so absorption of iron is carefully controlled.[41] Just as absorption increases when iron is deficient, absorption declines when iron is abundant.[42]

Special measures are also needed to contain iron in the body. Left free, iron is a powerful oxidant that can start free-radical reactions that could damage cellular structures. Consequently, the body guards against iron's renegade nature. Protein carriers guard the body's iron molecules and keep them away from vulnerable body compounds, thereby preventing damaging reactions.[43] Iron's actions are thus tightly controlled.

> Chapter 7 described free radicals and their control.

The Genes and Iron Absorption Control of iron absorption depends partly on the activities of genes in the absorptive cells that line the intestine. Researchers believe that messages arising when the body lacks iron trigger these genes to produce more of the proteins that work to absorb iron.[44] With more iron-absorbing proteins, the intestinal cells can absorb more iron from each meal.[45] As the body's iron supply builds up in response, the genes receive the opposite message—to produce fewer of these proteins to prevent absorption of too much iron. By this method, the genes of the intestinal cells help balance the absorption of iron from the diet with the body's need for iron.

hemoglobin (HEEM-oh-globe-in) the oxygen-carrying protein of the blood; found in the red blood cells (*hemo* means "blood"; *globin* means "spherical protein").

myoglobin (MYE-oh-globe-in) the oxygen-holding protein of the muscles (*myo* means "muscle").

What Happens to a Person Who Lacks Iron? If absorption cannot compensate for losses or low dietary intakes, then iron stores are used up and iron deficiency sets in. **Iron deficiency** and **iron-deficiency anemia** are not one and the same, though they often occur together. The distinction between iron deficiency and its anemia is a matter of degree. People may be iron deficient, meaning that they have decreased iron stores (stage 1) or depleted iron stores (stage 2), without being anemic, or they may be iron deficient *and* anemic (stage 3). With regard to iron, the term **anemia** refers to severe depletion of iron stores resulting in low blood hemoglobin.

A body severely deprived of iron becomes unable to make enough hemoglobin to fill new blood cells, and anemia results. A sample of iron-deficient blood examined under the microscope shows cells that are smaller and lighter red than normal (see Figure 8–9). The undersized cells contain too little hemoglobin and thus deliver too little oxygen to the tissues. The diminished supply of oxygen limits the cells' energy metabolism and causes tiredness, apathy, and a tendency to feel cold.

Even slightly lowered iron levels cause fatigue and impair physical work capacity and productivity.[46] Many of the symptoms associated with iron deficiency are easily mistaken for behavioural or motivational problems (see Table 8–8). With reduced energy, people work less, play less, and think or learn less eagerly. (Lack of energy does not always mean an iron deficiency—see the Think Fitness feature.) Children deprived of iron become restless, irritable, unwilling to work or play, and unable to pay attention, and they may fall behind their peers academically. Some symptoms, such as irritability, disappear when iron intake improves, but others, such as academic failure, may linger after iron repletion.[47]

A curious symptom seen in some people with iron deficiency is an appetite for ice, clay, paste, soil, or other nonnutritious substances. This consumption of nonfood substances, or **pica**, is most often observed in poverty-stricken women and children, in the mentally ill, and in people with kidney failure who must have their blood cleansed by machine.[48] In some cases, pica clears up within days after iron is given, even before the red blood cells have had a chance to respond. Other times, pica is unresponsive to iron.

Figure 8–9
Normal and Anemic Blood Cells

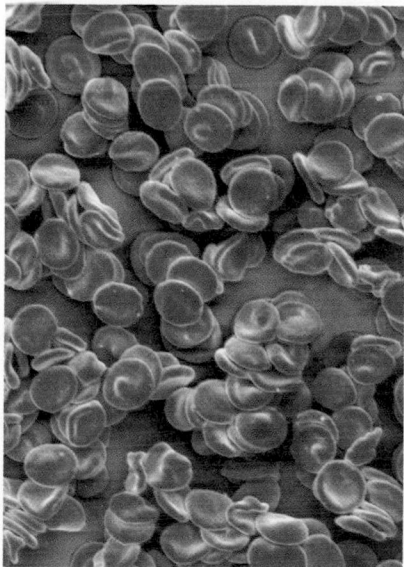

Normal red blood cells. Both size and colour are normal.

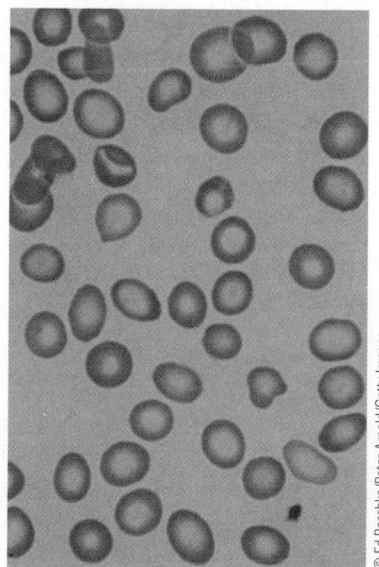

Blood cells in iron-deficiency anemia. These cells are small and pale because they contain less hemoglobin.

Iron deficiency the condition of having depleted iron stores, which, at the extreme, causes iron-deficiency anemia.

iron-deficiency anemia a form of anemia caused by a lack of iron and characterized by red blood cell shrinkage and colour loss. Accompanying symptoms are weakness, apathy, headaches, pallor, intolerance to cold, and inability to pay attention. (For other anemias, see the Index.)

anemia the condition of inadequate or impaired red blood cells; a reduced number or volume of red blood cells along with too little hemoglobin in the blood. The red blood cells may be immature and, therefore, too large or too small to function properly. Anemia can result from blood loss, excessive red blood cell destruction, defective red blood cell formation, and many nutrient deficiencies. Anemia is not a disease but a symptom of another problem; its name literally means "too little blood."

pica (PIE-ka) a craving for nonfood substances. Also known as *geophagia* (gee-oh-FAY-gee-uh) when referring to clay eating and *pagophagia* (pag-oh-FAY-gee-uh) when referring to ice craving (*geo* means "earth"; *pago* means "frost"; *phagia* means "to eat").

On hearing about symptoms of iron deficiency, tired people may jump to the conclusion that they need to take iron supplements to restore their pep.

More likely, they can obtain help by simply getting to bed on time and getting enough exercise. Few realize that too little exercise over weeks and months is

as exhausting as too much—the less you do, the less you're able to do, and the more fatigued you feel. The condition even has a name: "sedentary inertia."

Feeling fatigued, weak, and apathetic is a sign that something is wrong. It is not a sign that you necessarily need iron or other supplements. Three actions are called for

- First, get your diet in order.
- Second, get some exercise.
- Third, if symptoms persist for more than a week or two, consult a physician for a diagnosis.

Because pica sometimes occurs with iron deficiency and some soils contain iron, folklore has it that pica develops because the body craves what it needs—iron. Iron-rich clays and soils often contain substances that interfere with iron absorption, however, so eating clay and soil is unlikely to benefit iron status.[49] Instead, nutrition and health suffer when nonfood items displace nutritious foods from the diet and when toxic contaminants such as lead and dangerous blood-depleting parasites gain entrance to the body by way of contaminated clay and soil.[50]

> Iron deficiency makes children more susceptible to lead poisoning. See Chapter 14.

Causes of Iron Deficiency and Anemia   Iron deficiency is usually caused by malnutrition, that is, inadequate iron intake, either from sheer lack of food or from high consumption of the wrong foods. In developed countries, overconsuming foods rich in sugar and fat and poor in nutrients is often responsible for low iron intakes. Snapshot 8–5 shows some foods that are good or excellent sources of iron.

Among nonnutritional causes of anemia, blood loss is number one. Because 80 percent of the iron in the body is in the blood, losing blood means losing iron. Because of menstrual losses, women need one and a half times as much iron as men do. Women are especially vulnerable to iron deficiency because they not only need more iron than men but they also, on average, eat less food. Infants over six months of age, young children, adolescents, menstruating women, and pregnant women all have increased need for iron to support the growth of new body tissues or replace losses or, in the case of adolescent girls, both.

Worldwide, iron deficiency is the most common nutrient deficiency, affecting more than 1.2 billion people.[51] In developing countries, parasitic infections of the digestive tract cause people to lose blood daily. For their entire lives, they may feel fatigued and listless but never know why. Digestive tract problems such as ulcers, sores, and even inflammation can also cause blood loss severe enough to cause anemia.[52] Almost half of the preschool children and pregnant women in these countries suffer from iron-deficiency anemia.[53]

> Table 8–11 (pages 342–343) summarizes the effects of iron toxicity.

In Canada, iron deficiency is less prevalent, but women of childbearing age are still obtaining only 12 to 15 milligrams of iron per day, levels well below the 18 milligrams/day recommended for this group.[54]

- The maximum daily dose (MDD) of iron in nonprescription single-ingredient supplements is 45 mg/d (although higher doses may be available but only if you speak to the pharmacist or have a prescription).

Can a Person Take in Too Much Iron?   Iron is toxic in large amounts, and once absorbed inside the body, it is difficult to excrete. The healthy body defends against **iron overload** by controlling its entry: the intestinal cells trap some of the iron and hold it within their boundaries. When they are shed, these cells carry out of the intestinal tract the excess iron that they collected during their brief lives.[55] In healthy people, when iron stores fill up, less iron is absorbed, protecting them against iron overload.[56]

iron overload the state of having more iron in the body than it needs or can handle, usually arising from a hereditary defect. Also called *hemochromatosis.*

Snapshot 8-5 ⋯⋯⋙ Iron

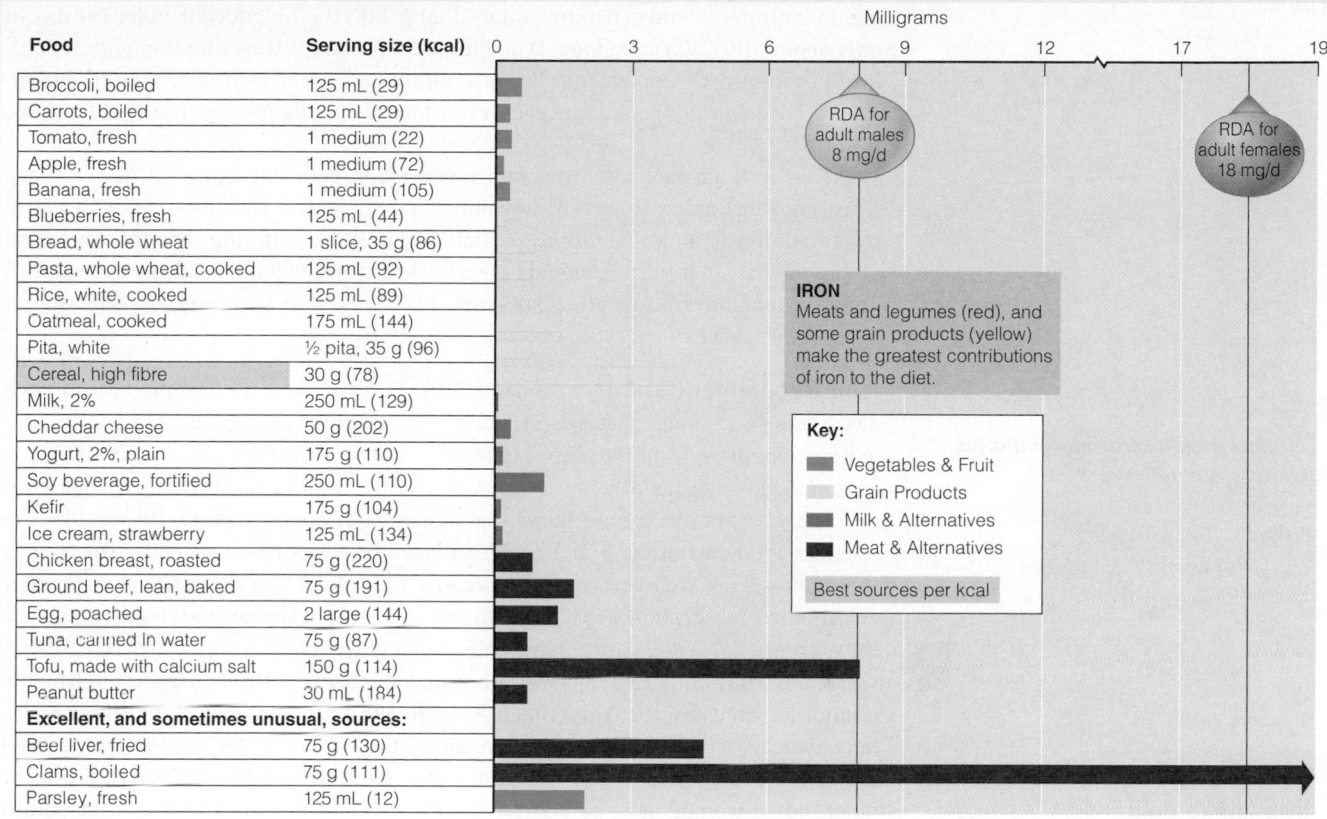

Food	Serving size (kcal)
Broccoli, boiled	125 mL (29)
Carrots, boiled	125 mL (29)
Tomato, fresh	1 medium (22)
Apple, fresh	1 medium (72)
Banana, fresh	1 medium (105)
Blueberries, fresh	125 mL (44)
Bread, whole wheat	1 slice, 35 g (86)
Pasta, whole wheat, cooked	125 mL (92)
Rice, white, cooked	125 mL (89)
Oatmeal, cooked	175 mL (144)
Pita, white	½ pita, 35 g (96)
Cereal, high fibre	30 g (78)
Milk, 2%	250 mL (129)
Cheddar cheese	50 g (202)
Yogurt, 2%, plain	175 g (110)
Soy beverage, fortified	250 mL (110)
Kefir	175 g (104)
Ice cream, strawberry	125 mL (134)
Chicken breast, roasted	75 g (220)
Ground beef, lean, baked	75 g (191)
Egg, poached	2 large (144)
Tuna, canned in water	75 g (87)
Tofu, made with calcium salt	150 g (114)
Peanut butter	30 mL (184)
Excellent, and sometimes unusual, sources:	
Beef liver, fried	75 g (130)
Clams, boiled	75 g (111)
Parsley, fresh	125 mL (12)

IRON
Meats and legumes (red), and some grain products (yellow) make the greatest contributions of iron to the diet.

Key:
- Vegetables & Fruit
- Grain Products
- Milk & Alternatives
- Meat & Alternatives

Best sources per kcal

RDA for adult males 8 mg/d

RDA for adult females 18 mg/d

DRI Recommended Intakes:
Men: 8 mg/d
Women (19–50 yr): 18 mg/d
Women (51+): 8 mg/d

CCHS 2.2 Mean Intake:
Women: ~12.5 mg/d
Men: ~17.5 mg/d

Tolerable Upper Intake Level:
Adults: 45 mg/d

Chief Functions:
Carries oxygen as part of hemoglobin in blood or myoglobin in muscles; required for cellular energy metabolism

Deficiency:
Anemia: weakness, fatigue, headaches; impaired mental and physical work performance; impaired immunity; pale skin, nail beds, and mucous membranes; concave nails; chills; pica

Toxicity:
GI distress; with chronic iron overload, infections, fatigue, joint pain, skin pigmentation, organ damage

NOTE: Dried figs contain 0.6 mg per ¼ c; raisins contain 0.8 mg per ¼ c.
- Some clams may contain less, but most types are iron-rich foods.
- Legumes contain phytates that reduce iron absorption. Soaking in water before cooking reduces phytates, and consuming legumes with vitamin C or meats increases iron absorption.
- Enriched cereals vary widely in iron content.

Iron overload, which has a strong genetic component, may occur more often than previously suspected, especially among Caucasian people.[57] In hereditary iron overload, the intestine continues to absorb iron at a high rate despite the excess iron building up in the body tissues.[58] Early symptoms are general and vague, such as fatigue, mental depression, and abdominal pains. Later, tissue damage occurs, with liver failure, abnormal heartbeats, and diabetes.[59] Infections are also likely because bacteria thrive on iron-rich blood. The effects are most severe in alcohol abusers because alcohol damages the intestine, impairing its defence against absorbing too much iron.

The danger of iron overload is an argument against high-level iron fortification of foods. Susceptible people would have trouble following a low-iron diet if most foods were doused with iron. A susceptible man choosing a single ounce of fortified cereal for breakfast, an ordinary ham sandwich at lunch, and a cup of chili with meat for dinner would consume almost double his recommended iron for the day in only about 800 Calories of food. Worsening the picture is the Canadian population's love of vitamin C supplements because vitamin C greatly enhances iron absorption.[60] For healthy people, however, even fortified foods pose virtually no risk for iron toxicity.[61]

As for iron supplements, they can reverse iron-deficiency anemia from dietary causes in short order. However, they may create oxidative reactions in the digestive tract that may damage its linings, particularly in those suffering with inflammation of these tissues.[62] Iron supplements are a leading cause of fatal accidental poisonings among Canadian children under six years old.[63] Therefore, keep iron supplements out of children's reach.

Iron Recommendations and Sources   Men need 8 milligrams of iron each day, and so do women past age 51. For women of childbearing age, the recommendation is higher—18 milligrams—to replace menstrual losses. During pregnancy, a woman needs significantly more—27 milligrams. Adult men rarely experience iron-deficiency anemia. If a man has a low hemoglobin concentration, his health-care provider should examine him for a blood-loss site. Vegetarians, because the iron in their foods is not well absorbed and because their diets lack factors from meat that enhance iron absorption, are advised to obtain 1.8 times the normal requirement (see the margin). Table 8–9 sums up iron recommendations.

To meet your iron needs, it is best to rely on foods because the iron from supplements is much less well absorbed than that from food. The usual Western mixed diet provides only about 5 to 6 milligrams of iron in each 1,000 Calories. An adult male who eats 2,500 Calories or more a day has no trouble obtaining his needed 8 milligrams or more, but a woman who eats fewer Calories and needs more iron cannot obtain her needed 18 milligrams unless she selects high-iron, low-Calorie foods from each food group. Pregnant women need an iron supplement.[64] No one should take iron supplements without a physician's recommendation, however.

Absorbing Iron   Iron occurs in two forms in foods. Some is bound into **heme**, the iron-containing part of hemoglobin and myoglobin in meat, poultry, and fish (look back at Figure 6–4 in Chapter 6, page 211). Some is nonheme iron, found in foods from plants and in the nonheme iron in meats. The form affects absorption. Heme iron is much more reliably absorbed than nonheme iron. Healthy people with adequate iron stores absorb heme iron at a rate of about 23 percent over a wide range of meat intakes. People absorb nonheme iron at rates of 2 to 20 percent, depending on dietary factors and iron stores.

Meat, fish, and poultry contain a factor (**MFP factor**) that promotes the absorption of nonheme iron from other foods eaten at the same time. Vitamin C can triple nonheme iron absorption from foods eaten in the same meal.[65] A system of calculating the amount of iron absorbed from a meal, based on these factors, is presented in Table 8–10.

Some substances impair iron absorption. They include the **tannins** of tea and coffee, the calcium and phosphorus in milk, and the **phytates** that accompany fibre in lightly processed legumes and whole-grain cereals.[66] Ordinary black tea is exceptional in its efficiency at reducing absorption of iron—clinical dietitians advise people with iron overload to drink it with their meals. For those who need more iron, the opposite advice applies—drink tea between meals, not with food.[67]

Thus, the amount of iron *absorbed* from a meal depends partly on the interaction between promoters and inhibitors of iron absorption. When you eat meat with legumes (e.g., ham and beans or chili with beans and meat), the iron from the meat is

---

To Calculate the DRI Recommendation for Vegetarians, Multiply by 1.8

- Vegetarian men:
  8 mg/d × 1.8 = 14 mg/d
- Vegetarian women (19 to 50 yr):
  18 mg/d × 1.8 = 32 mg/d

Table 8–9

Iron Intake Guidelines

DRI Recommendations

- Recommended intakes:
  - Men: 8 mg/d
  - Women: Childbearing years: 18 mg/d
  - 51 years and older: 8 mg/d
  - Pregnancy: 27 mg/d
- Tolerable Upper Intake Levels:
  - Infants and children: 40 mg/d
  - Adolescents and adults: 45 mg/d

---

heme (HEEM) the iron-containing portion of the hemoglobin and myoglobin molecules.

MFP factor a factor present in meat, fish, and poultry that enhances the absorption of nonheme iron present in the same foods or in other foods eaten at the same time.

tannins compounds in tea (especially black tea) and coffee that bind iron. Tannins also denature proteins.

phytates (FYE-tates) compounds present in plant foods (particularly whole grains) that bind iron and may prevent its absorption.

Table 8–10

Calculation of Iron Absorbed from Meals

You need to know three factors to calculate the amount of iron absorbed from a meal:

1. How much of the iron in the meal was heme iron, and how much was nonheme iron?
2. How much vitamin C was in the meal?
3. How much total meat, fish, and poultry (MFP factor) was consumed?

   (It is assumed that your iron stores are moderate; otherwise, you'd have to take this into consideration, too.) Write down the foods you eat at a typical meal; look up their iron content in the Canadian Nutrient File (link available at www.nelson.com/nutrition3ce), and then answer these questions:

1. How much iron was from animal tissues (MFP)? _____ mg
2. Forty percent of (1), on the average, is heme iron:
   (1) _____ mg × 0.40 = _____ mg heme iron
3. How much iron was from other sources? _____ mg
4. Add (3) and 60% of (1) to get nonheme iron:
   (3) _____ mg + 0.60 × (1) _____ mg = _____ mg nonheme iron
5. How much vitamin C was in the meal? _____ mg
   Less than 25 mg is low; 25 to 75 mg is medium; more than 75 mg is high:

   _____
6. How much MFP factor was in the meal? _____ oz
   Less than 90 g lean MFP is low; 30 to 90 g is medium; more than 90 g is high:

   _____
7. Now you can calculate the amount of each type of iron that was absorbed. Start with the heme iron. You absorbed 25% of the heme iron:
   (2) _____ mg × 0.25 = _____ mg heme iron absorbed
8. Consider your scores from (5) and (6). If either vitamin C or MFP factor was high or if both were medium, the availability of your nonheme iron was **high**. If neither was high but one was medium, the availability of your nonheme iron was **medium**. If both were low, your nonheme iron had **poor** availability. You absorbed:
   - High availability: 10% of the nonheme iron
   - Medium availability: 8% of the nonheme iron
   - Poor availability: 5% of the nonheme iron
9. Now you can calculate the nonheme iron absorbed. You absorbed _____ % of the nonheme iron, or:
   (4) _____ mg × (8) _____ % = _____ mg nonheme iron absorbed
10. Add the heme and nonheme iron from (7) and (9) together:
    (7) _____ mg heme iron absorbed
    + (9) _____ mg nonheme iron absorbed
    Total = _____ mg iron absorbed.

According to the DRI committee, if you are a man age 19 or older or a woman age 51 or older, you need to absorb about 1 mg per day. If you are a woman 11 to 50 years old, you need to absorb 1.5 mg per day on average. If you have higher menstrual losses than the average woman, you may need still more.

Dietary Factors That Increase Iron Absorption
- Vitamin C
- MFP factor

Factors That Hinder Iron Absorption
- Tea
- Coffee
- Calcium and phosphorus
- Phytates, tannins, and fibre

well absorbed, and MFP factor enhances iron absorption from the beans. The vitamin C from a slice of tomato and a leaf of lettuce in a sandwich will enhance iron absorption from the bread. The bit of vitamin C in dried fruit, strawberries, or watermelon helps absorb the nonheme iron in these foods. The meat and tomato in spaghetti sauce help absorb the iron from the spaghetti.

Cooking the sauce in an iron pan also adds more iron. Foods cooked in iron pans contain iron salts somewhat like those in supplements. The iron content of 100 grams of spaghetti sauce simmered in a glass dish is 3 milligrams, but it increases to 87 milligrams when the sauce is cooked in a black iron skillet. In the short time it takes to scramble eggs, a cook can triple the eggs' iron content by scrambling them in an iron pan. This iron salt is not as well absorbed as iron from meat, but some does get into the body, especially if the meal also contains MFP factor or vitamin C.

This chilli provides iron and MFP factor from meat, iron from legumes, and vitamin C from tomatoes. The combination of heme iron, nonheme iron, MFP factor, and vitamin C helps achieve maximum iron absorption.

The old-fashioned iron skillet adds supplemental iron to foods.

Courtesy of Ray Stanyard

The boy in this photo is 17 years old but is only 4 feet tall, the height of a 7-year-old in Canada. His genitalia are like those of a 7-year-old. The retardation is rightly ascribed to zinc deficiency, which is partially reversible when zinc is restored to the diet; however, better results are achieved when a broad mixture of micronutrients are provided. The photo was taken in Egypt by H. H. Sanstead MD, University of Texas-Galveston.

leavened (LEV-end) literally, "lightened" by yeast cells, which digest some carbohydrate components of the dough and leave behind bubbles of gas that make the bread rise.

KEY POINT

- Most iron in the body is contained in hemoglobin and myoglobin or occurs as part of enzymes in the energy-yielding pathways. Iron-deficiency anemia is a problem worldwide; too much iron is toxic. Iron is lost through menstruation and other bleeding; reduced absorption and the shedding of intestinal cells protect against overload. For maximum iron absorption, use meat, other iron sources, and vitamin C together.

Zinc

Zinc occurs in a very small quantity in the human body, but it works with proteins in every organ, helping nearly 100 enzymes to

- Make parts of the cells' genetic material.
- Make heme in hemoglobin.
- Assist the pancreas with its digestive functions.
- Help metabolize carbohydrate, protein, and fat.
- Liberate vitamin A from storage in the liver.

Besides helping enzymes function, zinc helps regulate gene expression in protein synthesis. Zinc also affects behaviour and learning; assists in immune function; and is essential to wound healing, sperm production, taste perception, fetal development, and growth and development in children. Zinc is needed to produce the active form of vitamin A in visual pigments. A protective role for zinc in oxidative damage is also under investigation.[68] When zinc deficiency occurs, it packs a wallop to the body, impairing all of these functions. Even a mild zinc deficiency can result in impaired immunity, abnormal taste, and abnormal vision in the dark.

Problem: Too Little Zinc
Zinc deficiency in human beings was first reported in the 1960s from studies with growing children and adolescent boys in the Middle East (see photo at left). Their native diets were typically low in animal protein and high in whole grains and beans; consequently, their diets were high in fibre and phytates, which bind zinc as well as iron. Furthermore, the bread was not **leavened**; in leavened bread, yeast breaks down phytates as the bread rises.

Since the first reports, zinc deficiency has been recognized elsewhere, and it affects much more than growth. It alters digestive function profoundly and causes diarrhea, which worsens the malnutrition already present, with respect not only to zinc but also to all nutrients. It drastically impairs the immune response, making infections likely.[69] Infections of the intestinal tract worsen malnutrition, including zinc malnutrition. Even mild zinc deficiency, brought on after one month of consuming a low-zinc diet, causes imbalances in the body's immune system that can increase susceptibility to infections. In developing countries, zinc treatment for children with infectious diseases reduces diarrhea and death.[70]

Normal vitamin metabolism depends on zinc, so zinc-deficiency symptoms often include vitamin-deficiency symptoms. Zinc deficiency also disturbs thyroid function and slows the body's energy metabolism, causing loss of appetite and slowing wound healing. In laboratory animals, a mild deficiency may reduce physical activity, memory, and attention span.[71] The symptoms are so pervasive that when faced with zinc deficiency, physicians are more likely to diagnose it as general malnutrition and sickness than as zinc deficiency.

Although severe zinc deficiencies are not widespread in developed countries, they occur among some groups, including pregnant women, young children, the elderly, and the poor. When pediatricians or other health workers evaluating children's health note poor growth accompanied by poor appetite, they should think zinc.

Problem: Too Much Zinc
Zinc is toxic in large quantities, and zinc supplements can cause serious illness or even death in high enough doses. Regular doses of zinc only a few milligrams above the recommended intake, taken over time, block copper

Chapter 8 Water and Minerals

absorption and lower the body's copper content. In animals, this effect leads to degeneration of the heart muscle. In high doses, zinc may reduce the concentration of beneficial high-density lipoproteins (HDL) in the blood.

High doses of zinc can also inhibit iron absorption from the digestive tract. A protein in the blood that carries iron from the digestive tract to tissues also carries some zinc. If this protein is burdened with excess zinc, little or no room is left for iron to be picked up from the intestine. The opposite is also true: too much iron leaves little room for zinc to be picked up, thus impairing zinc absorption. Zinc and iron are often found together in foods, but food sources are safe and never cause imbalances in the body. Supplements, in contrast, can easily do so. Zinc from lozenges and sprays sold for treatment of the common cold may or may not provide the intended relief, but their use contributes supplemental zinc to the body.[72]

Unlike excess iron, excess zinc has a normal escape route from the body. The pancreas secretes zinc-rich juices into the digestive tract, and some of these are excreted. Still, large overdoses from zinc supplements can overwhelm the escape route and cause toxicity.

 Food Sources of Zinc   Meats, shellfish, and poultry and milk and milk products are among the top providers of zinc in the Canadian diet (see Snapshot 8–6).[73] Among plant sources, some legumes and whole grains are rich in zinc, but the zinc is not as well absorbed as from meat. Most people meet the recommended 11 milligrams per day for men and 8 milligrams per day for women. Vegetarians are advised to eat varied diets that include whole-grain breads well leavened with yeast, which helps make zinc available for absorption.

KEY POINT

- Zinc assists enzymes in all cells. Deficiencies in children cause growth retardation with sexual immaturity. Zinc supplements can reach toxic doses, but zinc in foods is nontoxic. Animal foods are the best sources.

Selenium

Selenium has attracted the attention of the world's scientists for its role in protecting vulnerable body chemicals against oxidative destruction. Selenium assists a group of enzymes that, in concert with vitamin E, work to prevent the formation of free radicals and prevent oxidative harm to cells and tissues.[74] For example, cells of the immune system generate oxidizing compounds when they destroy foreign invaders, and the selenium-dependent enzymes reduce these compounds to harmless by-products that can be safely metabolized by body tissues. Selenium also plays roles in activating thyroid hormone, the hormone that regulates the body's rate of metabolism. Low blood selenium correlates with the development of some forms of cancers, especially prostate cancer in men.

Prostate cancer is the fourth leading cancer in men worldwide, and black men in the United States suffer the highest rate of all. Men who have adequate selenium in their bloodstreams develop prostate cancer less often than men whose blood measures are low.[75] Supplement supporters tout results like these as proof that men should take selenium supplements to ward off cancer, but no benefit is observed from taking extra selenium. Furthermore, supplements may slightly raise the risk of a form of skin cancer.[76] Studies reveal that only men whose blood is low in selenium in the first place benefit from supplements that correct their deficiency.[77] Clearly, adequate selenium is important but research is lacking to support taking selenium supplements in excess of the DRI recommended intake.

A deficiency of selenium can open the way for a specific type of heart disease (unrelated to the heart disease discussed in Chapters 5 and 11). The condition, first identified in China among people from areas with selenium-deficient soils, prompted researchers to place this mineral among the essential nutrients (see the inside front cover for selenium's intake recommendation).

- The maximum daily dose (MDD) for zinc in single-ingredient supplements ranges from 25 mg/d for zinc-picolinate to 50 mg/d for a non-picolinate source.

Milligrams

Food	Serving size (kcal)
Broccoli, boiled	125 mL (29)
Carrots, boiled	125 mL (29)
Tomato, fresh	1 medium (22)
Apple, fresh	1 medium (72)
Banana, fresh	1 medium (105)
Blueberries, fresh	125 mL (44)
Bread, whole wheat	1 slice, 35 g (86)
Pasta, whole wheat, cooked	125 mL (92)
Rice, white, cooked	125 mL (89)
Oatmeal, cooked	175 mL (144)
Pita, white	½ pita, 35 g (96)
Cereal, high fibre	30 g (78)
Milk, 2%	250 mL (129)
Cheddar cheese	50 g (202)
Yogurt, 2%, plain	175 g (110)
Soy beverage, fortified	250 mL (110)
Kefir	175 g (104)
Ice cream, strawberry	125 mL (134)
Chicken breast, roasted	75 g (220)
Ground beef, lean, baked	75 g (191)
Egg, poached	2 large (144)
Tuna, canned in water	75 g (87)
Tofu, made with calcium salt	150 g (114)
Peanut butter	30 mL (184)
Excellent, and sometimes unusual, sources:	
Oysters, steamed	75 g (100)
Crab, boiled	75 g (73)
Sirloin steak, lean, braised	75 g (164)

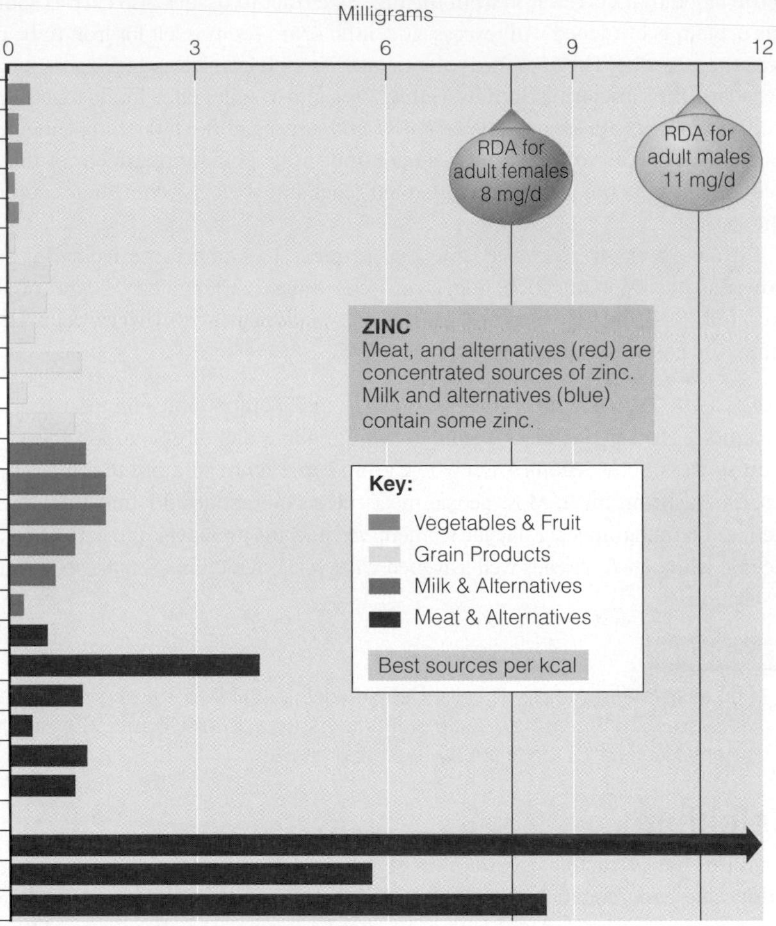

RDA for adult females 8 mg/d

RDA for adult males 11 mg/d

ZINC
Meat, and alternatives (red) are concentrated sources of zinc. Milk and alternatives (blue) contain some zinc.

Key:
Vegetables & Fruit
Grain Products
Milk & Alternatives
Meat & Alternatives

Best sources per kcal

DRI Recommended Intakes:
Men: 11 mg/d
Women: 8 mg/d

CCHS 2.2 Mean Intake:
Men: ~14 mg/d
Women: ~9.5 mg/d

Tolerable Upper Intake Level:
Adults: 40 mg/d

Chief Functions:
Activates many enzymes; associated with hormones; synthesis of genetic material and proteins, transport of vitamin A, taste perception, wound healing, reproduction

Chief Functions: Deficiency:[a]
Growth retardation, delayed sexual maturation, impaired immune function, hair loss, eye and skin lesions, loss of appetite

Toxicity:
Loss of appetite, impaired immunity, reduced copper and iron absorption, low HDL cholesterol (a risk factor for heart disease)

[a]A rare inherited form of zinc malabsorption causes additional and more severe symptoms.

Chapter 3 described how immune cells attack invaders with an "oxidative burst."

If you eat a normal diet composed of mostly unprocessed foods, you need not worry about selenium. It is widely distributed in foods such as meats and shellfish and in vegetables and grains grown on selenium-rich soil. Soils in Canada and the United States vary in selenium, but foods from many locations across these nations mingle together on supermarket shelves, ensuring that consumers are well supplied with selenium.

Toxicity is possible when people take selenium supplements over a long period. Selenium toxicity brings on symptoms such as hair loss, diarrhea, and nerve abnormalities. The Tolerable Upper Intake Level for selenium is set at 400 micrograms per day.

KEY POINT

- Selenium works with an enzyme system to protect body compounds from oxidation. A deficiency induces a disease of the heart. Deficiencies are rare in developed countries, but toxicities can occur from overuse of supplements.

- The maximum daily dose (MDD) for selenium in single-ingredient supplements is 400 µg/d.
- Although fluoride may be present in municipal water supplies, bottled water, toothpaste, and mouthwashes, it is not allowed in either single- or multiple-nutrient supplements.

Fluoride Helps Prevent Caries in Three Ways,
In Developing Teeth
- Forms decay-resistant crystals

In Erupted Teeth
- Promotes remineralization
- Reduces acidity of plaque

Fluoride

Fluoride is not essential to life, but it is beneficial in the diet because of its ability to inhibit the development of dental caries in both children and adults. Only a trace of fluoride occurs in the human body, but the crystalline deposits in bones and teeth are larger and more perfectly formed because this fluoride replaces the hydroxy portion of hydroxyapatite, forming the more decay-resistant fluorapatite in developing teeth. Once teeth have erupted through the gums, fluoride helps prevent dental caries by promoting the remineralization of early lesions of the enamel that might otherwise progress to form caries. Fluoride also acts directly on the bacteria of plaque, suppressing their metabolism and reducing the amount of acid they produce.

Drinking water is the usual source of fluoride. Data from Health Canada indicate that approximately 40 percent of Canadians have access to a fluoridated water supply (about 1 mg/L).[78] Fluoride is rarely present in bottled waters unless it was added at the source, as in bottled municipal tap water.

Where fluoride is lacking, the incidence of dental decay is very high, and fluoridation of water is recommended for public dental health.[79] Fluoridation is a practical, safe, and cost-effective way to help prevent dental caries in the young, and its widespread use has been a major factor in reducing U.S. dental caries.[80] Sufficient fluoride during the tooth-forming years of infancy and childhood gives lifetime protection against tooth decay. Some uninformed fluoride opponents claim that communities using fluoridated water have an increased cancer rate, but studies show no connection. Based on the accumulated evidence of its beneficial effects, fluoridation has been endorsed by the Canadian Dental Association (http://www.cda-adc.ca/_files/position_statements/Fluorides-English-2010-06-08.pdf).

In communities where the water contains too much fluoride—2 to 8 ppm—discoloration of the teeth, or **fluorosis**, may occur. Fluorosis occurs only during tooth development, never after the teeth have formed—and it is irreversible. Widespread availability of fluoridated toothpaste and mouthwash, foods made with fluoridated water, and fluoride-containing supplements has led to an increase in the mildest form of fluorosis. In this condition, characteristic discoloration can form in the tooth enamel; a more severe form is shown in Figure 8–10. To prevent fluorosis, people in areas with fluoridated water should limit other sources, such as fluoride-enriched formula for infants and fluoride supplements for infants or children unless prescribed by a physician. Children younger than six years should use only a pea-sized squeeze of toothpaste and should be told not to swallow their toothpaste when brushing their teeth. The Tolerable Upper Intake Level for fluoride for all people older than 8 years is 10 mg per day.

Canadian Population with Access to Fluoridated Water, 2007

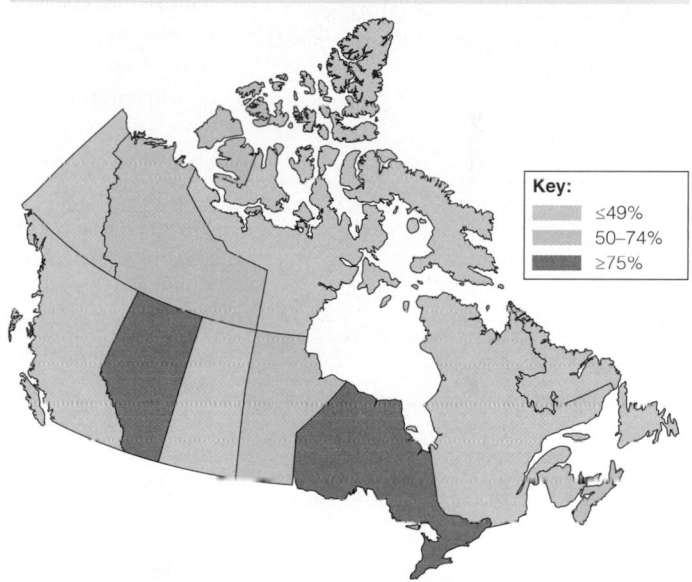

Key:
- ≤49%
- 50–74%
- ≥75%

Source: Danielle Rabb-Waytowich. Canadian population with access to Fluoridated water, 2007. "Water Fluoridation in Canada: Past and Present." Journal of the Canadian Dental Association 75(6), 2009. www.cda-adc.ca/jcda/vol-75/issue-6/451.html

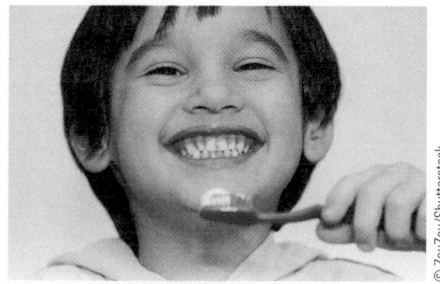

To prevent fluorosis, young children should not swallow toothpaste.

© ZouZou/Shutterstock

fluorosis (floor-OH-sis) discoloration of the teeth due to ingestion of too much fluoride during tooth development.

Figure 8–10

Fluorosis

The brown mottled stains on these teeth indicate exposure to high concentrations of fluoride during development.

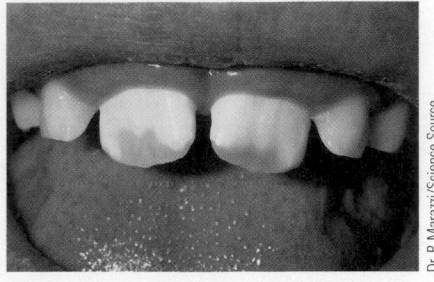

Dr. P. Marazzi/Science Source

- The maximum daily dose (MDD) for chromium in single-ingredient supplements is 500 µg/d.

Chromium

Chromium works closely with the hormone insulin to regulate and release energy from glucose. When chromium is lacking, insulin action is impaired, resulting in a diabeteslike condition of high blood glucose that resolves with chromium supplementation. Supplements of chromium cannot treat or cure the common forms of diabetes, and most people with diabetes are not chromium deficient.[81] Therefore, supplements are not recommended for management of type 2 diabetes. Diets high in simple sugars and low in whole, nutrient-dense foods deplete the body's supply of chromium.

Chromium-containing supplements will *not* build extra muscle tissue or melt off body fat or ward off its regain, as popular magazines may profess. Chromium supplements have been reported to slightly increase lean body mass in laboratory animals and sometimes in human beings tested under laboratory conditions. These results led to exaggerated claims for chromium's ability to bring about weight loss and muscle gain, but follow-up studies have shown no effect of chromium on body fat and lean tissue. Likewise, chromium supplementation does not lower blood cholesterol in people, an effect that has been implied in the "information" provided by supplement marketers.

Chromium compounds used in various industrial processes are known carcinogens and are responsible for many cases of cancer in exposed workers. The form of chromium in foods and supplements is nontoxic by comparison, and amounts of 200 micrograms per day seem to be safe. Supplements may cause skin eruptions, however, and taking large doses is ill-advised.[82]

Chromium is widely distributed in the food supply, especially in unrefined foods and whole grains. It exists in foods in complexes with other compounds that make it easily controlled and used by the body. Researchers use the terms *biologically active chromium* or *glucose tolerance factor* to describe these chromium-containing compounds. Chromium is lost during food processing, and chromium deficiencies become more likely as people depend more heavily on refined foods. The best chromium food sources are liver, whole grains, nuts, and cheeses. It is estimated that 90 percent of adults consume less than the recommended minimum intake of 50 micrograms a day.

Copper

One of copper's most vital roles is to help form hemoglobin and collagen. In addition, many enzymes depend on copper for its oxygen-handling ability. Copper plays roles in the body's handling of iron and, like iron, assists in reactions leading to the release of energy.[83] One copper-dependent enzyme helps control damage from free-radical activity in the tissues.* Researchers are investigating the possibility that a low-copper diet may contribute to heart disease by suppressing the activity of this enzyme.

Copper deficiency is rare but not unknown: it has been seen in severely malnourished infants fed a copper-poor milk formula.[84] Deficiency can severely disturb growth and metabolism, and in adults, it can impair immunity and blood flow through the arteries. Excess zinc interferes with copper absorption and can cause deficiency.

---

*The enzyme is superoxide dismutase.

Copper toxicity from foods is unlikely, but supplements can cause it. The Tolerable Upper Intake Level for adults is set at 10,000 micrograms (10 mg) per day. The best food sources of copper are organ meats, seafood, nuts, and seeds. Water may also supply copper, especially where copper plumbing pipes are used. In Canada, copper intakes are thought to be adequate.[85]

● The maximum daily dose (MDD) for copper in single-ingredient supplements is 8,000 µg/d.

KEY POINT

- Copper is needed to form hemoglobin and collagen and assists in many other body processes. Copper deficiency is rare.

Other Trace Minerals and Some Candidates

DRI intake recommendations have been established for two other trace minerals, molybdenum and manganese. Molybdenum functions as part of several metal-containing enzymes, some of which are giant proteins. Manganese works with dozens of different enzymes that facilitate body processes.

Several other trace minerals are now recognized as important to health. Boron influences the activity of many enzymes, and research suggests that a low intake of boron may enhance susceptibility to osteoporosis by way of its effects on calcium metabolism.[86] The richest food sources of boron are noncitrus fruits, leafy vegetables, nuts, and legumes. Cobalt is the mineral in the vitamin B_{12} molecule; the alternative name for vitamin B_{12}, *cobalamin*, reflects cobalt's presence. Nickel is important for the health of many body tissues; deficiencies harm the liver and other organs. Silicon is known to be involved in bone calcification in animals. Future research may reveal key roles played by other trace minerals, including barium, cadmium, lead, lithium, mercury, silver, tin, and vanadium. Even arsenic, a known poison and carcinogen, may turn out to be essential in tiny quantities.

All trace minerals are toxic in excess, and Tolerable Upper Intake Levels exist for boron, nickel, and vanadium (see page C at the front of the book). Overdoses are most likely to occur in people who take multiple nutrient supplements. The way to obtain the trace minerals is from food, which is not hard to do—just eat a variety of whole foods in the amounts recommended in Chapter 2. Some claim that organically grown foods contain more trace minerals than those grown with chemical fertilizers. Organic fertilizers do contain more trace minerals than do refined chemical fertilizers, and plants do take up some of the minerals they are given. Controversy 12 considers the merits and demerits of foods grown organically.

Research on the trace minerals is uncovering many interactions among them: an excess of one may cause a deficiency of another. A slight manganese overload, for example, may aggravate an iron deficiency. A deficiency of one mineral may open the way for another to cause a toxic reaction. Iron deficiency, for example, makes the body much more susceptible to lead poisoning. Good food sources of one are poor food sources of another, and factors that cooperate with some trace elements oppose others. The continuous outpouring of new information about the trace minerals is a sign that we have much more to learn. Tables 8–11 and 8–12 sum up what this chapter has said about the minerals and fill in some additional information. Also, to help integrate what you are learning about the recommendations for the minerals covered in this chapter, use Table 8–13 to find out the average amount young adult Canadians are consuming.

KEY POINT

- Many different trace elements play important roles in the body. All of the trace minerals are toxic in excess.

Table 8–13 helps us put into context the level of mineral intake by 19- to 30-year-old Canadians in relation to the DRI report recommendations. Notice also that while Tolerable Upper Intake Levels were not set for some of them, there are Maximum Daily Dosages for all of those available in single- or multi-ingredient supplements.

Table 8-11

The Minerals—A Summary

Mineral and Chief Functions in the Body	Deficiency Symptoms	Toxicity Symptoms	Significant Sources
Major Minerals			
Calcium			
The principal mineral of bones and teeth. Also acts in normal muscle contraction and relaxation, nerve functioning, regulation of cell activities, blood clotting, blood pressure, and immune defences	Stunted growth in children; adult bone loss (osteoporosis)	Constipation; urinary tract stone formation; kidney dysfunction; interference with absorption of other minerals	Milk and milk products, oysters, small fish (with bones), calcium-set tofu (bean curd), certain leafy greens, broccoli, legumes
Phosphorus			
Mineralization of bones and teeth; important in cells' genetic material, in cell membranes as phospholipids, in energy transfer, and in buffering systems	Appetite loss, bone pain, muscle weakness, impaired growth, and rickets in infants[a]	Calcification of nonskeletal tissues, particularly the kidney	Foods from animal sources, some legumes
Magnesium			
A factor involved in bone mineralization, the building of protein, enzyme action, normal muscular function, transmission of nerve impulses, proper immune function, and maintenance of teeth	Weakness; muscle twitches; appetite loss; confusion; if extreme, convulsions, bizarre movements (especially of eyes and face), hallucinations, and difficulty in swallowing. In children, growth failure[b]	Excess magnesium from abuse of laxatives (Epsom salts) causes diarrhea with fluid and electrolyte and pH imbalances	Nuts, legumes, whole grains, dark green vegetables, seafoods, chocolate, cocoa
Sodium			
Sodium, chloride, and potassium (electrolytes) maintain normal fluid balance and acid–base balance in the body. Sodium is critical to nerve impulse transmission	Muscle cramps, mental apathy, loss of appetite	Hypertension	Salt, soy sauce, seasoning mixes, processed foods, condiments, fast foods
Potassium			
Potassium facilitates reactions, including the making of protein; the maintenance of fluid and electrolyte balance; the support of cell integrity; the transmission of nerve impulses; and the contraction of muscles, including the heart	Deficiency accompanies dehydration; causes muscular weakness, paralysis, and confusion; can cause death	Causes muscular weakness; triggers vomiting; if given into a vein, can stop the heart	All whole foods: meats, milk, fruit, vegetables, grains, legumes
Chloride			
Chloride is part of the hydrochloric acid found in the stomach, necessary for proper digestion. Helps maintain normal fluid and electrolyte balance	Growth failure in children; muscle cramps, mental apathy, loss of appetite; can cause death (uncommon)	Normally harmless (the gas chlorine is a poison but evaporates from water); can cause vomiting	Salt, soy sauce; moderate quantities in whole, unprocessed foods; large amounts in processed foods
Major Minerals			
Sulphate			
A contributor of sulphur to many important compounds, such as certain amino acids, antioxidants, and the vitamins biotin and thiamin; stabilizes protein shape by forming sulphur-sulphur bridges (see Figure 6–10 in Chapter 6, p. 213)	None known; protein deficiency would occur first	Would occur only if sulphur amino acids were eaten in excess; this (in animals) depresses growth	All protein-containing foods

Table 8–11

The Minerals—A Summary (continued)

Mineral and Chief Functions in the Body	Deficiency Symptoms	Toxicity Symptoms	Significant Sources
Trace Minerals			
Iodine			
A component of the thyroid hormone thyroxine, which helps regulate growth, development, and metabolic rate	Goitre, cretinism	Depressed thyroid activity; goitrelike thyroid enlargement	Iodized salt; seafood; bread; plants grown in most parts of the country and animals fed those plants
Iron			
Part of the protein hemoglobin, which carries oxygen in the blood; part of the protein myoglobin in muscles, which makes oxygen available for muscle contraction; necessary for the use of energy	Anemia: weakness, fatigue, pale skin and mucous membranes, pale concave nails, headaches, inability to concentrate, impaired cognitive function (children), lowered cold tolerance	Iron overload: fatigue, abdominal pain, infections, liver injury, joint pain, skin pigmentation, growth retardation in children, bloody stools, shock	Red meats, fish, poultry, shellfish, eggs, legumes, green leafy vegetables, dried fruit
Zinc			
Associated with hormones; needed for many enzymes; involved in making genetic material and proteins, immune cell activation, transport of vitamin A, taste perception, wound healing, the making of sperm, and normal fetal development	Growth failure in children, dermatitis, sexual retardation, loss of taste, poor wound healing	Nausea, vomiting, diarrhea, loss of appetite, headache, immune suppression, decreased HDL, reduced iron and copper status	Protein-containing foods: meats, fish, shellfish, poultry, grains, yogurt
Selenium			
Assists a group of enzymes that defend against oxidation	Predisposition to a form of heart disease characterized by fibrous cardiac tissue (uncommon)	Nausea; abdominal pain; nail and hair changes; nerve, liver, and muscle damage	Seafoods, organ meats; other meats; whole grains and vegetables depending on soil content
Fluoride			
Helps form bones and teeth; confers decay resistance on teeth	Susceptibility to tooth decay	Fluorosis (discoloration) of teeth, nausea, vomiting, diarrhea, chest pain, itching	Drinking water if fluoride containing or fluoridated; tea; seafood
Chromium			
Associated with insulin; needed for energy release from glucose	Abnormal glucose metabolism	Possibly skin eruptions	Meat, unrefined grains, vegetable oils
Copper			
Helps form hemoglobin; part of several enzymes	Anemia; bone abnormalities	Vomiting, diarrhea; liver damage	Organ meats, seafood, nuts, seeds, whole grains, drinking water

[a]Seen only rarely in infants fed phosphorus-free formula or in adults taking medications that interact with phosphorus.

[b]A still more severe deficiency causes tetany, an extreme, prolonged contraction of the muscles similar to that caused by low blood calcium.

Table 8–12

Daily Value Reference Standards for Minerals in Canada for Persons 2 Years and Older Compared with U.S. Daily Value Reference Standards

Mineral	Canadian Daily Value (RDI)	U.S. Daily Value
Calcium	1,100 mg	1,000 mg
Phosphorus	1,100 mg	1,000 mg
		(continued)

Table 8-12

Daily Value Reference Standards for Minerals in Canada for Persons 2 Years and Older Compared with U.S. Daily Value Reference Standards (continued)

Mineral	Canadian Daily Value (RDI)	U.S. Daily Value
Magnesium	250 mg	400 mg
Sodium	2,400 mg	2,400 mg
Potassium	3,500 mg	3,500 mg
Iron	14 mg	18 mg
Zinc	9 mg	15 mg
Iodide	160 µg	150 µg
Selenium	50 µg	70 µg
Copper	2 mg	2 mg
Manganese	2 mg	2 mg
Chromium	120 µg	120 µg
Molybdenum	75 µg	75 µg
Chloride	3,400 mg	3,400 mg

Sources: Modified from Health Canada and Statistics Canada. 2009. Canadian Community Health Survey, Cycle 2.2, Nutrition (2004): Nutrient Intakes from Food – Provincial, Regional and National Summary Data Tables (Vol. 1–3), Cat No. 978-0-662-06542-5; Health Canada – Dietary Reference Intakes Report List, http://www.hc-sc.gc.ca/fn-an/nutrition/reference/dri_reprap_anref-list-eng.php; Health Canada – Natural Health Products Ingredients Database, http://webprod.hc-sc.gc.ca/nhpid-bdipsn/monosReq.do?langeng.

Table 8-13

Minerals: Females and Males 19–30 Years of Age

		Recommended Dietary Allowance/ Adequate Intake[1]	Current Intake (CCHS data)	Tolerable Upper Intake Level	MDD (NHPD Values) for Single- and Multi-Nutrient Supplements[2]
Boron	Females	n/a	n/a	20 mg/d	700 µg/d
(mg/d)	Males	n/a	n/a	20 mg/d	700 µg/d
Calcium	Females	1,000 mg/d	867 mg/d[3]	2.5 g/d	1,500 mg/d
(g/d)	Males	1,000 mg/d	1,107 mg/d[3]	2.5 g/d	1,500 mg/d
Chromium	Females	**25 µg/d**	n/a	ND	500 µg/d
	Males	**35 µg/d**	n/a	ND	500 µg/d
Copper	Females	900 µg/d	n/a	10,000 µg/d	8,000 µg/d
(µg/d)	Males	900 µg/d	n/a	10,000 µg/d	8,000 µg/d
Fluoride	Females	**3 mg/d**	n/a	10 mg/d	n/a
(mg/d)	Males	**4 mg/d**	n/a	10 mg/d	n/a
Iodine	Females	150 µg/d	n/a	1,100 µg/d	800 µg/d
(µg/d)	Males	150 µg/d	n/a	1,100 µg/d	800 µg/d
Iron	Females	18 mg/d	12.4 mg/d[4]	45 mg/d	45 mg/d
(mg/d)	Males	8 mg/d	17.6 mg/d[4]	45 mg/d	45 mg/d
Magnesium	Females	310 mg/d	284 mg/d[4]	350 mg/d	500 mg/d
(mg/d)	Males	400 mg/d	380 mg/d[4]	350 mg/d	500 mg/d

Chapter 8 Water and Minerals

Table 8–13

Minerals: Females and Males 19–30 Years of Age (continued)

		Recommended Dietary Allowance/ Adequate Intake[1]	Current Intake (CCHS data)	Tolerable Upper Intake Level	MDD (NHPD Values) for Single- and Multi-Nutrient Supplements[2]
Manganese	Females	**1.8 mg/d**	n/a	11 mg/d	9 mg/d
(mg/d)	Males	**2.3 mg/d**	n/a	11 mg/d	9 mg/d
Molybdenum	Females	45 µg/d	n/a	2,000 µg/d	2,000 µg/d
(µg/d)	Males	45 µg/d	n/a	2,000 µg/d	2,000 µg/d
Nickel	Females	n/a	n/a	1.0 mg/d	350 µg/d
(mg/d)	Males	n/a	n/a	1.0 mg/d	350 µg/d
Phosphorus	Females	700 mg/d	1,192 mg/d[4]	4 g/d	2,000 mg/d
(g/d)	Males	700 mg/d	1,659 mg/d[4]	4 g/d	2,000 mg/d
Potassium	Females	**4.7 g/d**	2,674 mg/d[4]	ND	100 mg/d
	Males	**4.7 g/d**	3,552 mg/d[4]	ND	100 mg/d
Selenium	Females	55 µg/d	n/a	400 µg/d	400 µg/d
	Males	55 µg/d	n/a	400 µg/d	400 µg/d
Silicon	Females	n/a	n/a	ND	84 mg/d
	Males	n/a	n/a	ND	84 mg/d
Vanadium	Females	n/a	n/a	1.8 mg/d	182 µg/d
(mg/d)	Males	n/a	n/a	1.8 mg/d	182 µg/d
Zinc	Females	8 mg/d	9.5 mg/d[4]	40 mg/d	50 mg/d
(mg/d)	Males	11 mg/d	14.2 mg/d[4]	40 mg/d	50 mg/d
Sodium	Females	**1.5 g/d**	2,743 mg/d[3]	2.3 g/d	n/a
(g/d)	Males	**1.5 g/d**	4,083 mg/d[3]	2.3 g/d	n/a
Chloride	Females	**2.3 g/d**	n/a	3.6 g/d	n/a
(g/d)	Males	**2.3 g/d**	n/a	3.6 g/d	n/a

ND = Not Determinable

n/a = Not Available

[1]IOM, DRI Reports (AI values are bolded).

[2]NHPD Single- and multi-nutrient supplement monographs.

[3]Data from CCHS 2.2, Volume 1.

[4]Data from CCHS 2.2, Volume 2.

Sources: Modified from Health Canada and Statistics Canada. 2009. Canadian Community Health Survey, Cycle 2.2, Nutrition (2004): Nutrient Intakes from Food—Provincial, Regional and National Summary Data Tables (Vol. 1-3), Cat No. 978-0-662-06542-5; Health Canada—Dietary Reference Intakes Report List, http://www.hc-sc.gc.ca/fn-an/nutrition/reference/dri_rep-rap_anref-list/index-eng.php; Health Canada—Natural Health Products Ingredients Database, http://webprod.hc-sc.gc.ca/nhpid-bdipsn/monosReq.do?lang=eng.

try it!

Food Feature

Meeting the Need for Calcium

The average woman consumes just a third of her recommended amount of calcium; men do somewhat better, with calcium intakes close to three-fourths of the recommendation. Low calcium intakes are associated with all sorts of major illnesses, including adult bone loss (see this chapter's Controversy section), high blood pressure and colon cancer (see Chapter 11), kidney stones, and even lead poisoning.

Consumption of one of the best sources of calcium—milk—has decreased in recent years, while consumption of other beverages, such as soft drinks, has increased dramatically. One national dairy group calls the situation a "national calcium crisis," and representatives of many national health and nutrition organizations agree. This Food Feature focuses on sources of calcium in the diet and provides guidance about how to meet the need for calcium.

Milk and Alternatives

Data from the Food Habits of Canadians study indicate that, together, fluid milk and cheese are traditional sources of ~50 percent of the calcium in the diet of adults 18 to 65 years old.[87] Milk is not only a significant source of calcium for Canadians; the Food Guide also recommends that we "have 500 mL (2 cups) of milk every day for adequate vitamin D."[88] People who do not use milk because of lactose intolerance, dislike, or allergy can obtain calcium from other sources, but care is needed; *wise* substitutions must be made.[89] This is especially true for children. Children who don't drink milk often have lower calcium intakes and poorer bone health than those who drink milk regularly, and they may also be smaller in stature.[90] Most of milk's many relatives are recommended choices: yogurt; **kefir**; buttermilk; cheese (especially the low-fat or fat-free varieties); and, for people who can afford the Calories, ice milk. Cottage cheese and frozen yogurt desserts contain about half the calcium of milk: 2 cups (500 mL) are needed to provide the amount of calcium in 1 cup (250 mL) of milk. Butter, cream, and cream cheese are almost pure fat and contain negligible calcium.

Tinker with milk products to make them more appealing. Add cocoa to milk and fruit to yogurt, make your own fruit smoothies from milk or yogurt, or add skim milk powder to any dish. The cocoa powder added to make chocolate milk does contain a small amount of oxalic acid, which binds with some of milk's calcium and inhibits its absorption, but the effect is insignificant. Sugar lends both sweetness and Calories to chocolate milk, so mix your chocolate milk at home, where you can control the amount of sugary chocolate added to the milk.

Vegetables

Among vegetables, rutabaga, broccoli, beet greens, turnip greens, mustard

Chocolate milk is an excellent source of calcium for those who can afford the extra Calories.

© National Dairy Council

greens, bok choy (a Chinese cabbage), and kale are good sources of available calcium. So are collard greens, green cabbage, kohlrabi, watercress, parsley, and probably some seaweeds, such as the **nori** popular in Japanese cookery. Certain other foods, including spinach, Swiss chard, and rhubarb, appear equal to milk in calcium content but provide very little or no calcium to the body because they contain binders that prevent calcium's absorption (see Figure 8–11). The presence of calcium binders does not make spinach an inferior food. Spinach is also rich in iron, beta-carotene, and dozens of other essential nutrients and potentially helpful phytochemicals. Just don't rely on it for calcium. Dark greens of all kinds are superb sources of riboflavin and indispensable for the vegan or anyone else who does not drink milk.

Calcium in Other Foods

For the many people who cannot use milk and milk products, small fish such as canned sardines and other canned fishes prepared with their bones are rich sources of calcium. One-third cup of almonds supplies about 100 milligrams of calcium along with almost 300 Calories—a high-energy calcium source. Stocks or extracts made from bones can be another rich source. The Vietnamese tradition of making fish stock from the bones helps account for their

Figure 8–11

Calcium Absorption from Food Sources

≥50% Absorbed	Cauliflower, watercress, Chinese cabbage, head cabbage, Brussels sprouts, rutabaga, kolhrabi, kale, mustard greens, bok choy, broccoli, turnip greens
≈30% Absorbed	Milk, yogurt, cheese, calcium-fortified soy milk, calcium-set tofu, calcium-fortified juices and drinks
≈20% Absorbed	Almonds, sesame seeds, beans (pinto, red, and white)
5% Absorbed	Spinach, rhubarb, Swiss chard

adequate calcium intake without the use of milk. Calcium-rich mineral water may also be a useful calcium source. Recent evidence seems to indicate that the calcium from mineral water, including hard tap water, may be as absorbable as the calcium from milk.[91] Many other foods contribute smaller, but still significant, amounts of calcium to the diet.

Calcium-Fortified Foods

Next in order of preference among non-milk sources of calcium are foods that contain large amounts of calcium salts by an accident of processing or by intentional fortification. In the processed category are soybean curd, or tofu (calcium salt is often used to coagulate it, so check the label); canned tomatoes (firming agents donate 63 mg per cup of tomatoes); **stone-ground flour** and self-rising flour; stone-ground whole and self-rising cornmeal; and blackstrap molasses.

Some food products available to Canadian consumers are fortified to add calcium to people's diets. The richest in calcium is high-calcium milk, that is, milk with extra calcium added; it provides more calcium per cup

---

kefir a yogurt-based beverage.

nori a type of seaweed popular in Asian, particularly Japanese, cooking.

stone-ground flour flour made by grinding kernels of grain between heavy wheels made of limestone, a kind of rock derived from the shells and bones of marine animals. As the stones scrape together, bits of the limestone mix with the flour, enriching it with calcium.

than any natural milk, 500 milligrams per 250 millilitres. Then comes calcium-fortified orange juice, with 300 milligrams per 250 millilitres, a good choice because, in some cases, the bioavailability of its calcium is comparable to that of milk. Calcium-fortified soy milk can also be prepared so that it contains more calcium than whole cow's milk. Soy-based infant formula is fortified with calcium, and no law prevents adults from using it in cooking for themselves, although it may be somewhat higher in fat than some other calcium-rich choices.

Finally, calcium supplements are available, sold mostly to people hoping to ward off osteoporosis. Controversy 8 in this chapter points out, however, that, while often useful, supplements are not magic bullets against bone loss.

Making Meals Rich in Calcium

For those who tolerate milk, many cooks slip extra calcium into meals by sprinkling a tablespoon or two of skim milk powder into almost everything. The added Calorie value is small, changes to the taste and texture of the dish are practically nil, but 2 tablespoons adds about 100 extra milligrams of calcium and moves adults closer to meeting the recommendation to obtain two to three cups of milk each day (see Figure 8–12). Here are some more tips for including calcium-rich foods in your meals:

At breakfast:

- Choose calcium-fortified orange or vegetable juice.
- Serve tea or coffee, hot or iced, with milk.
- Choose cereals, hot or cold, with milk.
- Cook hot cereals with milk instead of water; then mix in 2 tablespoons of skim milk powder.
- Make muffins or quick breads with milk and extra powdered skim milk.
- Add milk to scrambled eggs.
- Moisten cereals with flavoured yogurt.

At lunch:

- Add low-fat cheeses to sandwiches, burgers, or salads.
- Use a variety of green vegetables, such as watercress or kale, in salads and on sandwiches.

- Drink skim milk or calcium-fortified soy milk as a beverage or in a smoothie.
- Drink calcium-rich mineral water as a beverage (studies suggest significant calcium absorption).
- Marinate cabbage shreds or broccoli spears in low-fat Italian dressing for an interesting salad that provides calcium.
- Choose coleslaw over potato and macaroni salads.
- Mix the mashed bones of canned salmon into salmon salad or patties.
- Eat sardines with their bones.
- Stuff potatoes with broccoli and low-fat cheese.
- Try pasta such as ravioli stuffed with low-fat ricotta cheese instead of meat.
- Sprinkle parmesan cheese on pasta salads.

At supper:

- Toss a handful of thinly sliced green vegetables, such as kale or young turnip greens, with hot pasta; the greens wilt pleasingly in the steam of the freshly cooked pasta.
- Serve a green vegetable every night and try new ones—how about kohlrabi? It tastes delicious when cooked—like broccoli.
- Learn to stir-fry Chinese cabbage and other Asian foods.
- Try tofu (the calcium-set kind); this versatile food has inspired whole cookbooks devoted to creative uses.
- Add powdered skim milk to almost anything—meat loaf, sauces, gravies, soups, stuffings, casseroles, blended beverages, puddings, quick breads, cookies, brownies. Be creative.
- Choose frozen yogurt, ice milk, or custards for dessert.

Here is a shortcut for tracking the amount of calcium in a day's meals. To start, memorize these two facts:

1. A cup of low-fat 1% milk provides about 300 milligrams of calcium.

Figure 8–12

Milk and Alternatives Group Average Intakes[a]

On average, in Canada, between 65 and 85 percent of females and between 45 and 85 percent of males 17 years old and older fall far short of meeting the recommendation to obtain a minimum of two cups of milk, yogurt, or cheese each day.

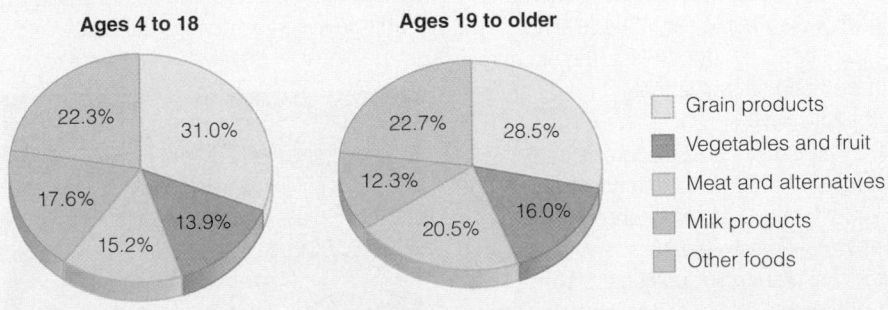

Ages 4 to 18

22.3% 31.0% 17.6% 15.2% 13.9%

Ages 19 to older

22.7% 28.5% 12.3% 20.5% 16.0%

- Grain products
- Vegetables and fruit
- Meat and alternatives
- Milk products
- Other foods

Note: Excludes women who were pregnant or breastfeeding.

[a]*Includes all forms of milk, yogurt, cheese, and frozen dairy desserts.*

Source: Findings from the Canadian Community Overview of Canadians' Eating Habits 2004 *by Didier Garriguet.*

Data Source: 2004 Canadian Community Health Survey: Nutrition.

2. Adults need 1,000 to 1,200 milligrams each day. Broken down in terms of "cups of milk," the need is 3⅓ to 4 cups each day.

To estimate calcium from an entire day's foods, not just milk, assign "cups of milk" points to various calcium sources. The goal is to achieve 3½ to 4 points per day:

- 1 point = 1 cup low-fat (1%) milk, yogurt, or calcium-fortified beverage, or 50 g cheese
- 1 point = 120 grams canned fish with bones

- ½ point = 1 cup ice cream, cottage cheese, or calcium-rich vegetables

Also, because bits of calcium are present in many foods (a bagel has about 50 mg, for example):

- 1 point = a well-balanced, adequate, and varied diet

Example: Say a day's calcium-rich foods include cereal and a cup of milk, a ham and cheese sandwich, and a broccoli and pasta salad.

- 1 point (cup of low-fat 1% milk) + 1 point (cheese) + ½ point (broccoli) = 2½ points

Add 1 point for the other foods eaten that day:

- 1 point + 2½ points = 3½ points

This day's foods provided a calcium intake approximately equal to the lower of the DRI committee's recommendation. The tips in this chapter offer many ways to aim higher.

Osteoporosis: Can Lifestyle Choices Reduce the Risks?

The Osteoporosis Society of Canada reports that 1.4 million Canadians suffer from osteoporosis (one in three women and one in five men will suffer from an osteoporotic fracture in their lifetime), with an estimated cost of treatment of $2.3 billion annually.*,[1]

Canadian Osteoporosis Society's Approach to Prevention, Diagnosis, and Management of Osteoporosis

See the 2010 Clinical Practice Guidelines for osteoporosis (including a brief video overview about them) at http://www.osteoporosis.ca/health-care-professionals/guidelines. This site also includes access to the full report published in the *Canadian Medical Association Journal*.[2] Many elderly

*Controversy references are listed separately at the end of the chapter.

people with hip fracture never walk or live independently again. About a fifth die from related complications within a year. Both men and women are urged to do whatever they can to prevent fractures related to osteoporosis.

Fractures from osteoporosis occur during the later years, but osteoporosis itself develops silently much earlier. Few young adults are aware that osteoporosis is sapping the strength of their bones; then suddenly, 40 years later, the hip gives way. People say, "She fell and broke her hip," but, in fact, the hip may have been so fragile that it broke *before* she fell.

The causes of osteoporosis are tangled. Insufficient dietary calcium and vitamin D certainly play roles, but physical activity, genetics, and other factors are also major potential players. This Controversy addresses several questions about osteoporosis: What is it? Who gets it? What can people do to reduce their risks? And where do dietary calcium and calcium supplements fit into the picture?

The Development of Osteoporosis

To understand how the skeleton loses minerals in later years, you must first know a few things about bones. Table C8–1 offers definitions of relevant terms. The photograph on this page shows a human leg bone sliced lengthwise, exposing the lattice of calcium-containing crystals (the **trabecular bone**) inside that are part of the body's calcium bank. Invested as savings during the

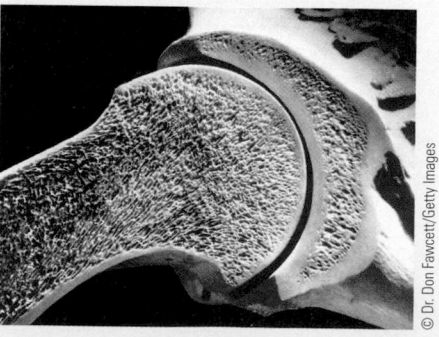

Photograph of sectioned bone.

Toward Prevention—Understanding the Causes of Osteoporosis

Scientists are searching for ways to prevent osteoporosis, but they must first establish its causes. In addition to the obvious factors of gender and advanced age, a person's chances of developing osteoporosis also depend both on genetic inheritance and on the environment. Environmental factors under study for their roles in lowering bone density include

- Poor nutrition involving calcium and vitamin D
- Estrogen deficiency in women
- Lack of physical activity
- Being underweight
- Use of tobacco and alcohol
- Possibly, excess protein, sodium, caffeine, and soft drinks and inadequate vitamin K

milk-drinking years of youth, these deposits provide a nearly inexhaustible fund of calcium. **Cortical bone** is the dense, ivory-like bone that forms the exterior shell of a bone and the shaft of a long bone (look closely at the photograph). Both types of bone are crucial to overall bone strength. Cortical bone forms a sturdy outer wall, and trabecular bone provides strength along the lines of stress.

The two types of bone handle calcium in different ways. The lacy crystals of the trabecular bone are tapped to raise blood calcium when the supply from the day's diet runs short; the calcium crystals are redeposited in bone when dietary calcium is plentiful. Trabecular bone, generously supplied with blood vessels, is more metabolically active than cortical bone, is more sensitive to hormones that govern calcium deposits and withdrawals from day to day, and readily gives up its minerals at the necessary rate whenever blood

calcium needs replenishing. Losses of trabecular bone begin to be significant for men and women in their mid-20s. Cortical bone's calcium can also be withdrawn, but slowly. Cortical bone loss begins at about age 40, and bone tissue dwindles steadily thereafter.

As bone loss continues and osteoporosis progresses (Figure C8–1), **bone density** declines, and bones become so fragile that the body's weight can overburden the spine; vertebrae may suddenly disintegrate and crush down, painfully pinching major nerves. Or they may compress into wedges, forming what is insensitively called "dowager's hump," the bent posture of many men and women as they "grow shorter" (see Figure C8–2). Wrists may break as trabecula-rich bone ends weaken, and teeth may loosen or fall out as the trabecular bone of the jaw recedes. As the cortical bone shell weakens as well, breaks often occur in the hip.

Bone Density and the Genes

Science may soon reveal a genetic basis for variations in bone density and development of osteoporosis.[3] Over 30 genes are under investigation in this regard, and each may interact with others and with environmental factors, such as vitamin D and calcium nutrition. Genes influence the activities of bone-forming cells and bone-dismantling cells, the cellular mechanisms that make collagen (the structural protein of bone formation), the mechanisms for absorbing and employing vitamin D, and many other contributors to bone metabolism.[4] Researchers hope that, once unsnarled, this tangle of genetic leads will help explain many of the remaining questions surrounding osteoporosis.

A classic approach to genetics includes studies of identical twins. Because such siblings have identical genes, a disease arising from genetic inheritance reliably appears in both twins. However, a study of elderly Finnish twins suggests that the fracture rates vary between twin siblings, underscoring the importance of environmental

Figure C8–1

Losses of Trabecular Bone

The image on the left shows healthy trabecular bone. The one on the right shows trabecular bone that has been affected by osteoporosis.

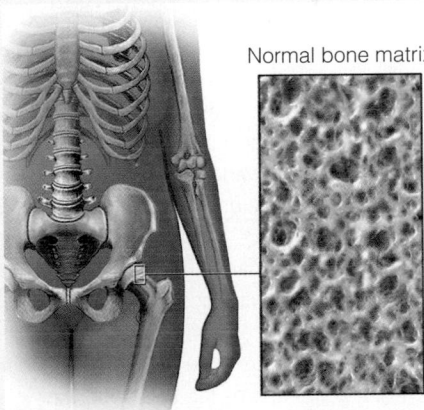
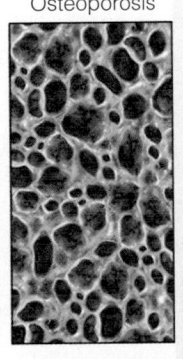

Normal bone matrix   Osteoporosis

© PHOTOTAKE Inc./Alamy

Loss of Height in a Woman Caused by Osteoporosis

The woman on the left is about 50 years old. On the right, she is 80 years old. Her legs have not grown shorter; only her back has lost length, due to collapse of her spinal bones (vertebrae). When collapsed vertebrae cannot protect the spinal nerves, the pressure of bones pinching the nerves causes excruciating pain.

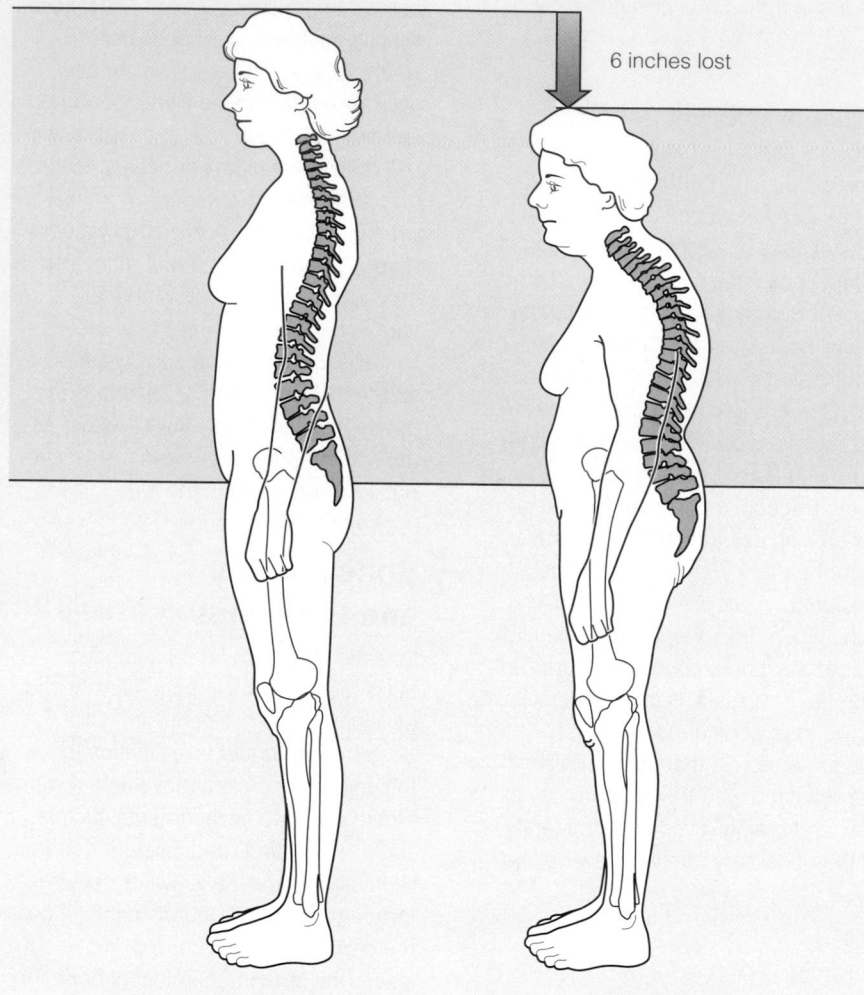

6 inches lost

50 years old

80 years old

factors in bone breaks.[5] By one estimate, genetic factors may account for about 35 percent of the variation in rates of serious fractures among the elderly, with environmental factors accounting for the rest.[6]

Genetic inheritance appears to most strongly influence the maximum bone mass attainable during growth.[7] It also influences the extent of a woman's bone loss during menopause, the time when women's estrogen production declines and menstruation ceases.

Risks of osteoporosis differ by race and ethnicity. People of African descent

have denser bones than do people of northern European extraction, and black women may lose bone at just half the rate of white women throughout aging.[8] These differences in bone density hold true for both sexes of all ages: hip fractures are three times as likely in 80-year-old white women as in black women of the same age.

Some ethnic groups have lower bone densities than do northern Europeans. Asians from China and Japan, Hispanics from Central and South America, and Inuit from St. Lawrence Island all have lower bone density than

do northern Europeans. Do lower bone densities forecast a higher rate of hip fractures in these groups? Not always. Chinese people living in Singapore have low bone density, but their hip fracture rates are among the lowest in the world. It may be that Chinese people have particularly strong hip bones or some other advantage that prevents fractures.

The message in all of these findings: although your genes may provide an inherited tendency for strong or weak bones, this genetic potential is tempered by individual life experiences. For example, those who attend to nutrition and physical activity attain their maximum bone density during growth, whereas those who overuse alcohol or use tobacco accelerate their bone losses, regardless of their genes.

Calcium and Vitamin D

An environmental factor that affects bone deposition and withdrawal is calcium and vitamin D nutrition during childhood, adolescence, and early adult life. Preteen children who consume extra calcium together with adequate vitamin D lay more calcium into the structure of their bones than children with less adequate intakes.

When people reach the bone-losing years of middle age, those who formed dense bones during youth have more bone tissue to lose before suffering ill effects—see Figure C8–3. Therefore, whatever factors help build strong bones in youth, including calcium nutrition, also protect against osteoporosis much later.

Women who seldom drank milk as children or teenagers have lower bone density and greater risk of fractures than those who drank milk regularly.[9] Even in childhood, those who avoid drinking milk may be more prone to fractures than their milk-drinking peers.[10] Simply put, growing children who do not get enough calcium do not develop strong bones.[11] Once compromised, bone strength may remain in jeopardy years later during adulthood. Milk is not the only food rich in calcium, but milk and milk products supply the most calcium to the Canadian diet by far. In addition, new research suggests that a protein in milk may increase

Two Women's Bone Mass History Compared

Woman A entered adulthood with enough calcium in her bones to last a lifetime. Woman B had less bone mass starting out and so suffered ill effects from bone loss later on.

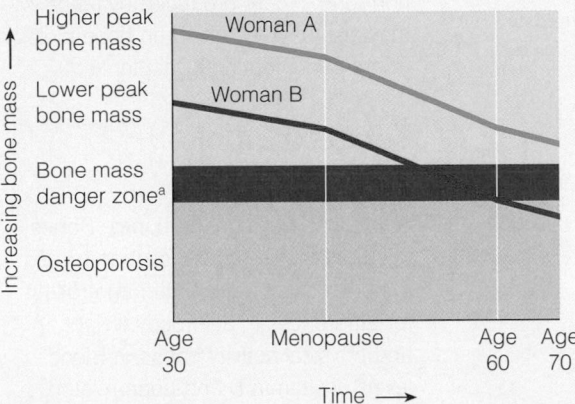

a*People with a moderate degree of bone mass reduction are said to have osteopenia and are at increased risk of fractures.*

Data from Standing Committee on the Scientific Evaluation of Dietary Reference Intakes, Food and Nutrition Board, Institute of Medicine, Dietary Reference Intakes for Calcium, Phosphrous, Magnesium, Vitamin D, and Fluoride (Washington, D.C.: National Academies Press, 1997) pp 4-10.

bone formation by supporting the activities of the bone-building cells.*,[12]

Calcium on Food Labels

Nutrition labelling regulations not only include calcium among the core nutrients or food components that must be listed in the Nutrition Facts table but also permit a disease risk reduction health claim about calcium and vitamin D and physical activity and a link to osteoporosis (http://www.inspection.gc.ca/english/fssa/labeti/guide/ch8e.shtml). The regulations prescribe the wording for such a claim, for example "A healthy diet with adequate calcium and vitamin D and regular physical activity help to achieve strong bones and may reduce the risk of osteoporosis."

Although dietary calcium and vitamin D in later life cannot make up for earlier deficiencies, they can help slow the rate of bone loss. Unfortunately, older people take in less calcium and vitamin D than others. After about age 65, they absorb less calcium, too, probably because aging skin is less efficient at making vitamin D. Also, many older people fail to go outdoors and so are deprived of the sunlight necessary to form vitamin D. Some of the hormones that regulate bone maintenance and calcium metabolism also change with age and accelerate bone mineral withdrawal.

Gender and Hormones

Gender is a powerful predictor of osteoporosis: men have greater bone density than women at maturity, and women have greater losses during menopause. Women thus account for more than two of three cases of osteoporosis. These facts may lull some men into believing that osteoporosis is a "woman's disease," but men suffering fractures each year from osteoporosis number in the millions.[13]

In women, bone dwindles rapidly when the hormone estrogen diminishes as menstruation ceases. Accelerated losses continue for six to eight years following menopause and then taper off, so women again lose bone at the same rate as their male counterparts. Losses of bone minerals continue throughout the remainder of a woman's lifetime, but not at the free-fall pace of the menopause years (see Figure C8–3).

Young women who cease menstruating (amenorrhea) lose bone rapidly. In some cases, diseased ovaries are to blame and must be removed; in others, the ovaries fail to produce sufficient estrogen because the women suffer from anorexia nervosa (see Controversy 9). The bone loss of anorexia nervosa remains long after recovery from the eating disorder.

If estrogen deficiency is a major cause of osteoporosis in women, what is the cause of bone loss in men? Men produce only a little estrogen, yet they resist osteoporosis better than women. It may be that the male sex hormone testosterone plays a role—men suffer more fractures after removal of diseased testes or when their testes lose function with aging. Thus, both male and female sex hormones appear to play roles in the development of osteoporosis.

Physical Activity

When people lie idle—for example, when they are confined to bed—the bones lose strength just as the muscles do. Astronauts who live without gravity for days or weeks at a time experience rapid and extensive bone losses. Table C8–2 ranks sedentary lifestyle with other detrimental influences on bone health, such as nutrient deficiencies and cigarette smoking.

Muscle strength and bone strength go together, and muscle use seems to promote bone strength. When bones of sedentary and active people are compared, the active bones are denser by far.[14] The hormones that promote

These young people are putting bone in the bank.

© Iofoto/Shutterstock

*The protein is lactoferrin.

Table C8–2

Risk and Protective Factors That Correlate with Osteoporosis

Risk Factors	Protective Factors
High Correlation	
Advanced age	Black race
Alcoholism, heavy drinking	Estrogens, long-term use
Chronic steroid use	
Female gender	
Rheumatoid arthritis	
Surgical removal of ovaries or testes	
Thinness or weight loss	
White race	
Moderate Correlation	
Chronic thyroid hormone use	Having given birth
Cigarette smoking	High body weight
Diabetes (insulin dependent, type 1)	High-calcium diet
Early menopause	Regular physical activity
Excessive antacid use	
Family history of osteoporosis	
Low-calcium diet	
Sedentary lifestyle	
Vitamin D deficiency	
Probably Important but Not Yet Proven	
Alcohol taken in moderation	Adequate vitamin K intake
Caffeine intake	
High-fibre diet	Low-sodium diet (later years)
High blood homocysteine	
High-protein diet	
Lactose intolerance	

synthesis of new muscle tissue also favour the building of bone; flexibility and muscle strength gained through physical activity also improve balance and help prevent falls from occurring.

To keep the bones healthy and to prevent falls, include weight-bearing exercises such as calisthenics, dancing, jogging, vigorous walking, or weight training every day.[15] Even sports or gardening, performed with vigour, can build bone strength and improve balance. In adolescence, regular physical activity, as well as an adequate calcium intake, is critical to maximize bone density.[16] Later on in adulthood, bone density benefits from a regular program of weight training.[17] Even past menopause, when most women are losing bone, a strong, fit body may help maintain the bones.[18]

Body Weight

After age and gender, the next risk factor for osteoporosis is being underweight or losing weight.[19] Women who are thin throughout life, and especially those who lose 10 percent or more of their body weight after the age of menopause, face a hip fracture rate twice as high as that of most other women. Heavier body weights and higher body fatness stress the bones and promote their maintenance.[20] Also, fat tissue serves as a storage depot for hormones, and abundant body fat may mean greater hormone stores. An appetite-controlling hormone, leptin, produced by fat cells may also have an effect on bone biology (more about leptin in Chapter 9).[21]

Tobacco Smoke and Alcohol

Smoking is hard on the bones. Bones of smokers are less dense than those of nonsmokers—even after controlling for differences in age, body weight, and physical activity habits.[22] Blood levels of vitamin D and bone-related hormones in smokers favour decreased calcium absorption and increased bone destruction.[23] Fortunately, quitting can reverse these damaging effects. Blood indicators shift beneficially after just six weeks of smoking cessation.[24] In time, bone density is similar for former smokers and nonsmokers.

People who are addicted to alcohol also experience more frequent fractures, and drinking can contribute to accidents and falls. Because alcohol (a diuretic) causes fluid excretion, it may induce excessive calcium losses through the urine. Heavy drinking may also upset the hormonal balance required for healthy bones or may be directly toxic to the bone-building cells, preventing their reproduction and diminishing their numbers.

Protein

Excess dietary protein causes the body to excrete calcium in the urine.[25] This finding suggests that a lifetime of consuming excess dietary protein could accelerate bone loss, especially when calcium intake is low.

Does a high-protein diet cause bone loss? Research is not entirely clear on this point, but some findings support the idea that it may, especially among well-nourished people eating a diet rich in animal protein but low in vegetables.[26] In experiments, people fed

Ratio of Vegetable to Animal Protein in the Diet and Hip Fracture Incidence Worldwide

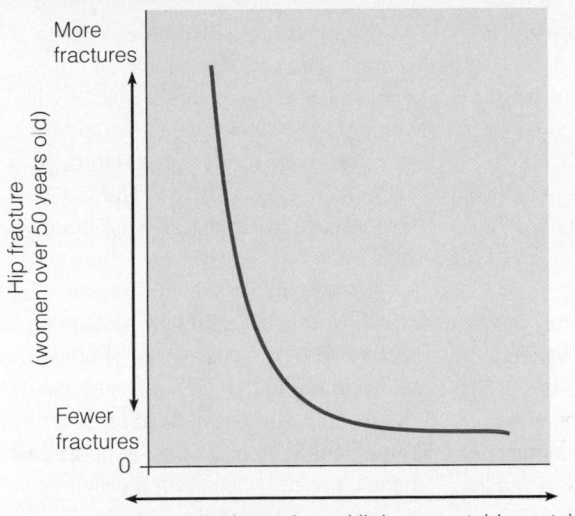

Source: Journals of Gerontology Series A: Biomedical Sciences Vol. 55 (10): M585-M592 (2000) Figure 2 (adapted), Lynda A. Frassetto, Karen M. Todd, R. Curtis Morris, Jr., and Anthony Sebastian. Worldwide Incidence of Hip Fracture in Elderly Women: Relation to Consumption of Animal and Vegetable Foods. Reprinted by permission of Oxford University Press.

increasing amounts of purified animal protein developed an increasingly negative calcium balance (they lost more calcium in the urine than they consumed from food). Figure C8–4 shows that in women around the world, hip fracture incidence drops when the ratio of vegetable to animal protein in the diet increases.[27]

Soy foods in particular, by virtue of their protein and phytochemicals, may help stem the rapid bone losses of the menopause years.[28] Research suggests that soy may indeed offer some protection, but foods, and not supplements, are the best choice, as Controversy 2 made clear.[29]

Vegetables themselves, and not their protein, may be the protective factor, however, because of their role in providing alkaline substances to the body. Before the body can use or store energy from the sulphur-containing amino acids in proteins, it must first cleave off the sulphur, which then forms sulphuric acid, one of the strongest acids known.[30] The body must act quickly to neutralize this excess acidity before it can upset the body's delicate acid–base balance. One way it does so is by withdrawing alkaline calcium salts from the bones and using the noncalcium part to buffer the acid. The calcium part is detected as "excess calcium" by the kidneys, which toss it out in the urine. Vegetables are rich sources of alkaline constituents that help neutralize acid, reducing the need for bone calcium withdrawal.

On the other side of the spectrum, obtaining sufficient protein is essential to bone health because protein deprivation also stimulates calcium losses and weakens bones.[31] Remember from the chapter that the mineral crystals of bone form on a protein matrix—collagen, mentioned earlier. Because the body stores no significant quantities of protein, it must be supplied by the diet. Especially in malnourished elderly people, restoring protein from animal or vegetable sources can often improve bone status and reduce the incidence of hip fractures. Also, some protein-rich foods from animals do not seem to produce a negative calcium balance. Milk is a good example. A milk-rich diet provides both protein and calcium and may help *oppose* withdrawal of calcium from the skeleton. With protein, as with other nutrients, then, it seems wise to follow a now familiar nutrition principle—a vegetable-rich diet based on adequacy, moderation, and variety is best.[32]

Sodium, Caffeine, Soft Drinks, Vitamin K, Homocysteine, and Others

A high sodium intake is also associated with urinary calcium excretion, and lowering sodium intakes seems to lessen calcium losses.[33] Study subjects eating the DASH diet (the high-vegetable, high-dairy diet described in Appendix F) at three sodium levels were compared with controls consuming a more "typical" Canadian diet.[34] Calcium losses were greatest in those consuming the highest levels of sodium and smallest in the lower sodium groups. In addition, the DASH diet is higher in calcium than most diets and had a beneficial effect on bone metabolism—blood indicators suggest that bone loss was slowing, while bone accretion was increasing.[35] Whether these effects were due to the abundant calcium or fruit and vegetables in the DASH diet is unknown.

Long-term evidence showing that a reduced sodium intake prevents osteoporosis is lacking, but no harm can come from recommending that people reduce sodium intakes.[36] Also, increasing potassium may help—some research shows that potassium may counteract the effects of sodium on calcium excretion.[37] The person who wishes to lower sodium and increase potassium should choose a diet rich in unprocessed or lightly processed foods such as fruit and vegetables while restricting heavily processed, convenience, or fast foods.

Heavy users of caffeinated beverages, such as coffee, tea, and colas, should be aware that some evidence links caffeine use and osteoporosis, although other findings tend to absolve caffeine use from posing a risk. It may be that ordinary caffeine intakes, say the amount in two cups of coffee, increase calcium losses only when calcium intakes are low. Such losses may be so small that the calcium in just one or two *tablespoons* of milk is enough to replace them.[38]

Cola beverages and other soft drinks may also have adverse effects on calcium, although the reasons are unclear. One idea is that the high concentration of fructose sweetener in the drinks may cause calcium loss.[39] Soft drinks also displace milk from the diet, especially in children and adolescents.

Rats given colas instead of water increase their fluid intake by three times, lose calcium in their urine, and dramatically reduce their intake of solid food.[40] Despite reduced food intake, the rats gain more weight than water-drinking controls, and their bones are significantly less dense. In children, an unexplained tendency to develop bone problems such as stress fractures has been reported to accompany high intakes of fruit juices or cola beverages but not other soft drinks.

Vitamin K plays important roles in the production of at least one bone protein that participates in bone maintenance.* People with hip fractures often have low intakes of vitamin K.[41] In a study of female athletes in whom strenuous exercise had lowered estrogen production, an increased vitamin K intake reduced markers of bone loss and increased markers of bone formation.

Elevated blood concentration of the amino acid homocysteine indicates a dietary deficit of folate, vitamin B_{12}, and vitamin B_6. A study from the Netherlands revealed that people with the highest homocysteine levels experienced twice as many hip and wrist fractures as people with lower levels.[42] Likewise, in the United States, the rate of hip fractures quadrupled in men with the highest homocysteine levels and doubled in women over those with lower homocysteine levels.[43] Whether such a relationship exists between hip fractures and plasma homocysteine levels in Canadian adults is unknown. No one can say yet whether elevated blood homocysteine contributes to osteoporosis, results from the disease process, or exists as an innocent bystander in those with osteoporosis.[44]

Magnesium also helps maintain bone mineral density.[45] Vitamin A is needed in the bone-remodelling process, but too much may be associated with osteoporosis.[46] Clearly, a well-balanced diet that supplies abundant fruit and vegetables and a full array of nutrients is central to bone health.[47] In contrast,

diets containing too much salt, candy, or colas and possibly caffeine are associated with bone losses.[48]

Review Table C8–2 (page 352) and the risk factors covered here. The more risk factors that apply to you, the greater your chances of developing osteoporosis in the future and the more seriously you should take the advice offered in this Controversy section.

Diagnosis and Medical Treatment

Diagnosis of osteoporosis includes measuring bone density using an advanced form of X-ray (DEXA, described in Chapter 9) or ultrasound.* A thorough examination also includes evaluating risk factors for fractures, such as race, family history, and physical inactivity.[49] Men with a family history of osteoporosis and all women should have a bone density test after they reach age 50.

Estrogen therapy can help non-menstruating women prevent further bone loss and reduce the incidence of fractures.[50] Estrogen therapy may also increase the risks for heart disease and breast cancer, however, so women and their health-care providers must carefully weigh any potential benefits against the potential risks.[51] A combination of drugs may be an option for some women.[52]

Several drugs are proving powerful allies in the struggle to reverse bone loss. Such drugs inhibit the activities of the bone-dismantling cells, thus allowing the bone-building cells to slowly shore up bone tissue with new calcium deposits.** The drugs have worked minor miracles in reversing even severe bone loss in some people, but for others, they are not tolerated or not effective.

Calcium Recommendations

As described earlier, bone strength later in life depends most on how well the bones were developed and maintained

during youth. Adequate calcium nutrition during the growing years is essential to achieving optimal peak bone mass.[53] Yet only 10 percent of girls and 25 percent of boys meet the recommendation for calcium during their bone-forming years.[54] The DRI committee recommends 1,300 milligrams of calcium, the amount in about 4 cups (1,000 mL) of milk, each day for everyone 9 through 18 years of age; 1,000 milligrams through age 50; and 1,200 milligrams thereafter.

How should you obtain this calcium? Nutritionists strongly recommend foods and beverages as your source of calcium and that you take supplements only when advised to do so by a physician. People can best support their bones' health by following the lifetime recommendations for healthy bones in Table C8–3. Calcium supplements cannot equal any of the actions listed in the table. By the way, some miraculous powers for preventing diseases have been attributed to calcium derived from marine coral, but this is just a marketing gimmick. "Coral calcium" may contain toxic metals or trigger allergic reactions in people with an allergy to shellfish. The advertiser was fined and banned from advertising further false health claims about coral calcium.[55]

Bone loss is not a calcium-deficiency disease comparable to iron-deficiency anemia. In iron-deficiency anemia, high iron intakes reliably reverse the condition. With respect to calcium balance, though, calcium intakes alone do little or nothing to reverse bone loss. Calcium and vitamin D supplements after the age of 50, however, do produce small but still beneficial effects on the bone mass and fracture rates. During the menopausal years, calcium supplements of 1 gram may slow, but cannot fully prevent, the inevitable bone loss.

Although calcium supplements are well tolerated by most people, taking self-prescribed calcium supplements entails possible risks (see Table C8–4) and cannot take the place of sound food choices and other healthy habits. The next section provides some details

*The vitamin K–dependent bone protein is osteocalcin.

*DEXA stands for dual X-ray absorptiometry.

**The drugs are bisphosphonates.

Table C8–3

A Lifetime Plan for Healthy Bones

Childhood

Ages	Goal	Guidelines
2 through 12 or 13 years (sexual maturity)	Grow strong bones	▪ Use milk as the primary beverage to meet the need for calcium within a balanced diet that provides all nutrients. ▪ Play actively in sports or other activities. ▪ Limit television and other sedentary entertainment. ▪ Drink fluoridated water.

Adolescence through Young Adulthood

Ages	Goal	Guidelines
13 or 14 through 30 years	Achieve peak bone mass	▪ Choose milk as the primary beverage, or if milk causes distress, include other calcium sources. ▪ Commit to a lifelong program of physical activity. ▪ Do not smoke or drink alcohol—if you have started, quit. ▪ Drink fluoridated water.

Mature Adult

Ages	Goal	Guidelines
31 through 50 years	Maximize bone retention	▪ Continue as for 13- to 30-year-olds. ▪ Adopt bone-strengthening exercises. ▪ Obtain the recommended amount of calcium from food. ▪ Take calcium supplements only if calcium needs cannot be met through foods.

Mature Adult

Ages	Goal	Guidelines
51 years and above	Minimize bone loss	▪ Continue as for 13- to 30-year-olds. ▪ Continue striving to meet the calcium need from diet. ▪ Continue bone-strengthening exercises. ▪ Obtain a bone density test; follow physician's advice concerning bone-restoring medications and supplements.

NOTE: The exact ages of cessation of bone accretion and onset of loss vary among people, but, in general, data indicate that the skeleton continues to accrete mass for approximately 10 years after adult height is achieved and begins to lose bone around age 35.

Based on data from Committee on Dietary Reference Intakes, Food and Nutrition Board, Institute of Medicine, Dietary Reference Intakes for Calcium, Phosphorus, Magnesium, Vitamin D, and Fluoride (Washington, D.C.: National Academies Press, 1997) p 91–112.

Table C8–4

Calcium Supplement Risks

People who take calcium supplements risk

- **Impaired iron status.** Calcium inhibits iron absorption.
- **Accelerated calcium loss.** Calcium-containing antacids that also contain aluminum and magnesium hydroxide cause a net calcium loss.
- **Urinary tract stones or kidney damage in susceptible individuals.** People who have a history of kidney stones should be monitored by a physician and choose calcium citrate if they must take supplements.
- **Exposure to contaminants.** Some preparations of bone meal and dolomites are contaminated with hazardous amounts of arsenic, cadmium, mercury, and lead.
- **Vitamin D toxicity.** Vitamin D, which is present in many calcium supplements, can be toxic. Users must eliminate other concentrated vitamin D sources.
- **Excess blood calcium.** This complication is seen only with doses of calcium fourfold or more as great as customarily prescribed.
- **Milk alkali syndrome.** This condition is rare, but not absent. It is characterized by high blood calcium, metabolic alkalosis, and renal failure. Early symptoms include irritability, headaches, and apathy.
- **Other nutrient interactions.** Calcium inhibits absorption of magnesium, phosphorus, and zinc.
- **Drug interactions.** Calcium and tetracycline form an insoluble complex that impairs both mineral and drug absorption.
- **GI distress.** Constipation, intestinal bloating, and excess gas are common.

Although better absorbed when taken with meals, avoid taking calcium supplements two hours before and for up to four hours after taking other medications.

about the variety of calcium supplements and the benefits and risks of taking them.

Calcium Supplements

Calcium supplements are available in three chemical forms. Simplest are the purified **calcium compounds**, such as calcium carbonate, citrate, gluconate, hydroxide, lactate, malate, or phosphate (be mindful that some may be related to constipation and necessitate changing supplements), and compounds of calcium with amino acids (called **amino acid chelates**). Second are mixtures of calcium with other compounds, such as calcium carbonate with magnesium carbonate, with aluminum salts (as in some **antacids**; see also Table C8–6), or with vitamin D. Third are powdered, calcium-rich materials such as **bone meal**, **powdered bone**, **oyster shell**, and **dolomite** (limestone). See Table C8–5 for calcium supplement terms.

If you are considering taking calcium supplements, you might ask yourself or your healthcare provider the following three questions:

Question 1: How well does the body absorb and use the calcium from various supplements? Based on research to date, many people seem to absorb calcium reasonably well—and about as well as from milk—from amino acid chelates and from calcium compounds such as calcium acetate, calcium carbonate, calcium citrate, calcium gluconate, calcium lactate, and calcium phosphate dibasic. People absorb calcium less well from a mixture of calcium and magnesium carbonates, from oyster shell calcium fortified with inorganic magnesium, from a chelated calcium-magnesium combination, and from calcium carbonate fortified with vitamins and iron. Some people absorb calcium better from milk and milk products than from even the most absorbable supplements. Calcium from mineral water may also be highly absorbable.[56] Table C8–6 lists some sources of supplemental calcium, the amount of calcium delivered,

Table C8–5

Calcium Supplement Terms

- **amino acid chelates** (KEY-lates) compounds of minerals (such as calcium) combined with amino acids in a form that favours their absorption. A *chelating agent* is a molecule that surrounds another molecule and can then either promote or prevent its movement from place to place (*chele* means "claw").
- **antacids** acid-buffering agents used to counter excess acidity in the stomach. Calcium-containing preparations (such as Tums) contain available calcium. Antacids with aluminum or magnesium hydroxides (such as Rolaids) can accelerate calcium losses.
- **bone meal or powdered bone** crushed or ground bone preparations intended to supply calcium to the diet. Calcium from bone is not well absorbed and is often contaminated with toxic materials such as arsenic, mercury, lead, and cadmium.
- **calcium compounds** the simplest forms of purified calcium. They include calcium carbonate, citrate, gluconate, hydroxide, lactate, malate, and phosphate. These supplements vary in the amount of calcium they contain, so read the labels carefully. A 500-mg tablet of calcium gluconate may provide only 45 mg of calcium, for example.
- **dolomite** a compound of minerals (calcium magnesium carbonate) found in limestone and marble. Dolomite is powdered and is sold as a calcium-magnesium supplement but may be contaminated with toxic minerals, is not well absorbed, and interacts adversely with absorption of other essential minerals.
- **oyster shell** a product made from the powdered shells of oysters that is sold as a calcium supplement but is not well absorbed by the digestive system.

Table C8–6

A Sampling of Supplemental Calcium Sources

Calcium Source	Typical Amount per Serving	Calories
Antacid medication, regular strength ("Tums" type)	500 mg per 2 tablets	10
Breads with "more" calcium[a]	80 mg per slice	70
Calcium-fortified candies or chewable candy supplements	500 mg per dozen	20
Calcium-fortified or "100% nutrient" cereals	1,000 mg per serving	110
Calcium-fortified skim milk and milk products	500 mg per 250 mL serving	100
Calcium-fortified orange juice or other fruit beverages	350 mg per 250 mL serving	110
Calcium pills	A wide variety of pills provide varying doses. Read the label.	Negligible
Meal replacer: cereal bars "with milk"	250 mg	160
Meal replacer: "complete nutrition" drinks	200–350 mg per 250 mL drink	360
Meal replacer: "energy" bars	300 mg per bar	230

[a]Bread, though not rich in calcium, is heavily consumed and may contribute significantly to many people's intakes.

and the form of the calcium along with the number of Calories in a dose or serving.

Question 2: How much calcium does the supplement provide? The Tolerable Upper Intake Level for calcium has been set at 2,500 milligrams. To be safe, supplements should provide less than this as foods also provide calcium. Read the label to find out how much a dose supplies. Calcium carbonate is 40 percent elemental calcium, whereas calcium gluconate is only 9 percent. A healthy young adult (with the exception of pregnant or lactating women in whom absorption increases) absorbs about 25 percent of the available calcium.

Question 3: Will the supplement be digested and the calcium be available for absorption? Manufacturers compress large quantities of calcium into small pills, and stomach acid often has difficulty penetrating the pill. To test whether a supplement will dissolve, drop it into 175 mL of vinegar and stir occasionally. A high-quality formulation will dissolve within half an hour. The chewable kind, because they are chewed into bits before swallowing, and calcium-fortified foods and beverages are not prone to this problem.

One last pitch: Think one more time before you decide to take supplements for calcium. The authors of this book are so impressed with the importance of using abundant, calcium-rich foods that we have worked out ways to do so at every meal. Seldom do nutritionists agree so unanimously. So, if you still think you might not be getting enough calcium from your regular diet, try the Osteoporosis Canada "Calcium Calculator" at http://www.osteoporosis.ca/osteoporosis-and-you/nutrition/calculate-my-calcium.

Self-Check

Answers to these Self-Check questions are in Appendix D.

1. Water balance is governed by the
   a. liver
   b. kidneys
   c. brain
   d. b and c

2. Which two minerals are the major constituents of bone?
   a. calcium and zinc
   b. phosphorus and calcium
   c. sodium and magnesium
   d. magnesium and calcium

3. All of the following are correct concerning zinc *except*
   a. in high doses, it may reduce the HDL concentration in the blood
   b. in high doses, it may inhibit iron absorption from the digestive tract
   c. fruit and vegetables are the best sources for zinc
   d. deficiencies in children retard growth

4. A deficiency of which mineral is a leading cause of mental retardation worldwide?
   a. iron
   b. iodine
   c. zinc
   d. chromium

5. Which mineral supplement is a cause of fatal accidental poisonings of children under six years old?
   a. iron
   b. sodium
   c. chloride
   d. potassium

6. After about 40 years of age, bones begin to lose density.
   T   F

7. The best way to control salt intake is to cut down on processed and fast foods.
   T   F

8. The most abundant mineral in the body is iron.
   T   F

9. Dairy foods such as butter, cream, and cream cheese are good sources of calcium, whereas vegetables such as broccoli are poor sources.
   T   F

10. All municipal water supplies in Canada are fluoridated.
    T   F

track it!

Diet Analysis
PLUS✚   Concepts in Action

start now! ┄┄❯ Using the Track Activity feature in Diet Analysis Plus, track your physical activity for one week, trying to increase your level of activity a little bit each day. See if you can walk briskly, bike, or jog for 30 minutes each day for a week.

Analyze Your Calcium Intake

The purpose of this exercise is to make you aware of your calcium intake and to give you ideas about how you might meet your DRI recommended intake. Using the Diet Analysis program that accompanies this text, complete the following.

1. From the Reports tab, under the Nutrients heading select DRI Report. Find your calcium information. What is the DRI Recommended Dietary Intake (RDA) for calcium for your profile?

2. From the Reports tab, under the Nutrients heading select Intake vs. Goals. Choose Day One (from your 3-day diet intake record) and include all meals and snacks. What percentage of your calcium DRI did you meet on that day? Was this intake typical?

3. From the Reports tab, under the Nutrients heading select Source Analysis. Choose Day One, include all meals and snacks. Select calcium from the drop-down pick-list and generate a report. What were the top three food sources of calcium that day? What were your three lowest sources? Which of your top sources matched those of the calcium Snapshot on page 318?

4. From the Reports tab, under the Advanced Analysis heading, select Source Analysis, choose Day Three, choose only breakfast, select calcium from the drop-down pick-list, and then generate a report. Did the calcium values of any of the foods surprise you? Which ones? How many milligrams of calcium did you consume at breakfast?

5. Now modify this report to include lunch, then dinner, then snacks. At which meal did you consume the most calcium? Which meal had the least calcium: breakfast, lunch, or dinner?

6. Many foods that are not Milk and Alternatives can provide calcium. Using the tips in the Food Feature in this chapter (pages 345–348), create a calcium-rich side dish without Milk and Alternatives items. Select the Track Diet tab, start a new day and enter the ingredients for your side dish. From the Reports tab, under the Advanced Analysis heading, select Source Analysis, select calcium from the drop-down pick-list, and generate a report. How much calcium was in this side dish? How absorbable was the calcium in these foods? (Check Figure 8–11 page 346 and also see Figure C6–1 in Chapter 6 for other calcium-rich foods.)

Endnotes

1. Standing Committee on the Scientific Evaluation of Dietary Reference Intakes, Food and Nutrition Board, Institute of Medicine, *Dietary Reference Intakes: Water, Potassium, Sodium, Chloride, and Sulfate* (Washington, D.C.: National Academies Press, 2005).

2. Standing Committee on the Scientific Evaluation of Dietary Reference Intakes, Food and Nutrition Board, Institute of Medicine, 2005, p. 4-26 [see reference 1].

3. American College of Sports Medicine. Exercise and Fluid Replacement—Position Stand. *Medicine and Science in Sports and Exercise* 39 (2007): 377–390; S. M. Jamal and M. J. Eisengerg, The nutritional value of bottled water, in T. Wilson and N. J. Temple, eds., *Beverage Impacts on Health and Nutrition* (Totowa, NJ: Humana Press, 2003), pp. 321–333.

4. J. W. Gardner, Death by water intoxication, *Military Medicine* 167 (2002): 432–434.

5. Standing Committee on the Scientific Evaluation of Dietary Reference Intakes, Food and Nutrition Board, Institute of Medicine, 2005, p. 4-49 [see reference 1].

6. A. C. Grandjean and coauthors, The effect of caffeinated, non-caffeinated, caloric and non-caloric beverages on hydration, *Journal of the American College of Nutrition* 19 (2000): 591–600.

7. Standing Committee on the Scientific Evaluation of Dietary Reference Intakes, Food and Nutrition Board, Institute of Medicine, 2005, p. 4-55 [see reference 1].

8. M. P. Sauvant and D. Pepin, Geographic variation of the mortality from cardiovascular disease and drinking water in a French small area (Puy de Dome), *Environmental Research* 84 (2000): 219–227.

9. H. Bohmer, H. Muller, and K. L. Resch, Calcium supplementation with calcium-rich mineral waters: A systematic review and meta-analysis of its bioavailability, *Osteoporosis International* 11 (2000): 938–943; R. Maheswaran and coauthors, Magnesium in drinking water supplies and mortality from acute myocardial infarction in north west England, *Heart* 82 (1999): 455–460.

10. S. Satarug and coauthors, A global perspective on cadmium pollution and toxicity in non-occupationally exposed population, *Toxicology Letters* 137 (2003): 65–83.

11. N. W. Woodruff and coauthors, Human cell mutagenicity of chlorinated and unchlorinated water and the disinfection byproduct 3-chloro-4-(dichloromethyl)-5- hydroxy-2(5H)-furanone (MX), *Mutation Research* 495 (2001): 157–168; S. F. Thai and coauthors, Detection of early gene expression changes by differential display in the livers of mice exposed to dichloroacetic acid, *Carcinogenesis* 22 (2001): 1317–1322.

12. K. P. Cantor and coauthors, Drinking water source and chlorination byproducts in Iowa. III. Risk of brain cancer, *American Journal of Epidemiology* 150 (1999): 552–560.

13. D. S. Michaud and coauthors, Fluid intake and the risk of bladder cancer in men, *New England Journal of Medicine* 340 (1999): 1390–1397.

14. A. Flood and coauthors, Calcium from diet and supplements is associated with reduced risk of colorectal cancer in a prospective cohort of women, *Cancer Epidemiology, Biomarkers and Prevention* 14 (2005): 126–132; V. Chia and P. A. Newcomb, Calcium and colorectal cancer: Some questions remain, *Nutrition Reviews* 62 (2004): 115–120.

15. M. B. Zemel and S. L. Miller, Dietary calcium and dairy modulation of adiposity and obesity risk, *Nutrition Reviews* 62 (2004): 125–131; S. J. Parikh and J. A. Yanovski, Calcium and adiposity, *American Journal of Clinical Nutrition* 77 (2003): 281–287; D. Teegarden, Calcium intake and reduction in weight or fat mass, *Journal of Nutrition* 133 (2003): 249S–251S; R. P. Heaney, K. M. Davies, and M. J. Barger-Lux, Calcium and weight: Clinical studies, *Journal of the American College of Nutrition* 21 (2002): 152–155.

16. M. E. Wastney and coauthors, Changes in calcium kinetics in adolescent girls induced by high calcium intake, *Journal of Clinical Endocrinology and Metabolism* 85 (2000): 4470–4475.

17. Standing Committee on the Scientific Evaluation of Dietary Reference Intakes, Food and Nutrition Board, Institute of Medicine, *Dietary Reference Intakes for Calcium, Phosphorus, Magnesium, Vitamin D, and Fluoride* (Washington, D.C.: National Academies Press, 1997), p. 72.

18. Standing Committee on the Scientific Evaluation of Dietary Reference Intakes, Food and Nutrition Board, Institute of Medicine, 1997, pp. 106–107 [see reference 17].

19. Standing Committee on the Scientific Evaluation of Dietary Reference Intakes, Food and Nutrition Board, Institute of Medicine, 1997, pp. 101–106 [see reference 17].

20. Health Canada, Food and nutrition: Canadian Community Health Survey Cycle 2.2 Nutrition Focus Vol. 2, available at http://www.hc-sc.gc.ca/fn-an/surveill/nutrition/commun/cchs_focus-volet_escc-eng.php; E. S. Ford and A. H. Mokdad, Dietary magnesium intake in a national sample of U.S. adults, *Journal of Nutrition* 133 (2003): 2879–2882.

21. E. S. Ford and A. H. Mokdad, 2003 [see reference 20].

22. L. Cordain and coauthors, Origins and evolution of the Western diet: Health implications for the 21st century, *American Journal of Clinical Nutrition* 81 (2005): 341–354.

23. Standing Committee on the Scientific Evaluation of Dietary Reference Intakes, Food and Nutrition Board, Institute of Medicine, 2005 [see reference 1].

24. Standing Committee on the Scientific Evaluation of Dietary Reference Intakes, Food and Nutrition Board, Institute of Medicine, 2005 [see reference 1].

25. J. Tuomilehto and coauthors, Urinary sodium excretion and cardiovascular mortality in Finland: A prospective study, *Lancet* 357 (2001): 848–851; L. Liu and coauthors, Comparative studies of diet-related factors and blood pressure among Chinese and Japanese: Results from the China-Japan Cooperative Research of the WHO-CARDIAC Study. Cardiovascular Disease and Alimentary Comparison, *Hypertension Research* 23 (2000): 413–420.

26. Standing Committee on the Scientific Evaluation of Dietary Reference Intakes, Food and Nutrition Board, Institute of Medicine, 2005 [see reference 1].

27. J. Stamler, The INTERSALT Study: Background, methods, findings, and implications, *American Journal of Clinical Nutrition* 65 (1997): 626S–642S.

28. U.S. Department of Agriculture and U.S. Department of Health and Human Services, *Dietary Guidelines for Americans*, 2010, available at http://www.health.gov/dietaryguidelines/2010.asp.

29. F. C. Luft, Present status of genetic mechanisms in hypertension, *Medical Clinics of North America* 88 (2004): 1–18; S. T. Turner and E. Boerwinkle, Genetics of blood pressure, hypertensive complications, and antihypertensive drug responses, *Pharmacogenomics* 4 (2003): 53–65.

30. N. M. Karanja and coauthors, Descriptive characteristics of the dietary patterns used in the Dietary Approaches to Stop Hypertension Trial, *Journal of the American Dietetic Association* 99 (1999): S19–S27; L. P. Svetkey and coauthors, Effects of dietary patterns on blood pressure: Subgroup analysis of the Dietary Approaches to Stop Hypertension (DASH) randomized clinical trial, *Archives of Internal Medicine* 159 (1999): 285–293.

31. F. M. Sacks and coauthors, Effects on blood pressure of reduced dietary sodium and the Dietary Approaches to Stop Hypertension (DASH) diet, *New England Journal of Medicine* 344 (2001): 3–10.

32. F. J. He and G. A. MacGregor, Beneficial effects of potassium, *British Medical Journal* 323 (2001): 497–501.

33. P.-H. Lin and coauthors, Food group sources of nutrients in the dietary patterns of the DASH-Sodium trial, *Journal of the American Dietetic Association* 103 (2003): 488–496.

34. P.-H. Lin and coauthors, The DASH diet and sodium reduction improve markers of bone turnover and calcium metabolism in adults, *Journal of Nutrition* 133 (2003): 3130–3136.

35. Standing Committee on the Scientific Evaluation of Dietary Reference Intakes, Food and Nutrition Board, Institute of Medicine, 2005 [see reference 1].

36. Standing Committee on the Scientific Evaluation of Dietary Reference Intakes, Food and Nutrition Board, Institute of Medicine, 2005, p. 5-35 [see reference 1].

37. Standing Committee on the Scientific Evaluation of Dietary Reference Intakes, Food and Nutrition Board, Institute of Medicine, *Dietary Reference Intakes for Vitamin A, Vitamin K, Arsenic, Boron, Chromium, Copper, Iodine, Iron, Manganese, Molybdenum, Nickel, Silicon, Vanadium, and Zinc* (Washington, D.C.: National Academies Press, 2001), p. 258.

38. Committee to Assess the Distribution and Administration of Potassium Iodide in the Event of a Nuclear Incident, *Distribution and Administration of Potassium Iodide in the Event of a Nuclear Incident* (Washington, D.C.: National Academies Press, 2003), pp. 1–5.

39. FDA attacks "anti-radiation pills," *Consumer Health Digest*, September 2003.

40. Standing Committee on the Scientific Evaluation of Dietary Reference Intakes, Food and Nutrition Board, Institute of Medicine, 2001, pp. 9–14 [see reference 37].

41. N. C. Andrews, Disorders of iron metabolism, *New England Journal of Medicine* 341 (1999): 1986–1995.

42. S. Miret, R. J. Simpson, and A. T. McKie, Physiology and molecular biology of dietary iron absorption, *Annual Review of Nutrition* 23 (2003): 283–301.

43. M. B. Reddy and L. Clark, Iron, oxidative stress, and disease risk, *Nutrition Reviews* 62 (2004): 120–124.

44. R. D. Baynes and M. H. Stipanuk, Iron, in *Biochemical and Physiological Aspects of Human Nutrition* (Philadelphia, PA: Saunders, 2000), pp. 711–740.

45. M. Wessling-Ressnick, Lessons learned from genetic and nutrition iron deficiencies, *Nutrition Reviews* 62 (2004): 212–220.

46. F. Verdon and coauthors, Iron supplementation for unexplained fatigue in non-anaemic women: Double blind randomised placebo controlled trial, *British Medical Journal* 326 (2003): available at http://www.bmj.com/content/326/7399/1124; J. Beard, Iron deficiency alters brain development and functioning, *Journal of Nutrition* 133 (2003): 1468S–1472S; E. M. Ross, Evaluation and treatment of iron deficiency in adults, *Nutrition in Clinical Care* 5 (2002): 220–224; J. D. Haas and T. Brownlie IV, Iron deficiency and reduced work capacity: A critical review of the research to determine a causal relationship, *Journal of Nutrition* 131 (2001): 676S–690S; S. Horton and C. Levin, Commentary on "evidence that iron deficiency anemia causes reduced work capacity," *Journal of Nutrition* 131 (2001): 691S–696S.

47. D. Pinero, B. Jones, and J. Beard, Variations in dietary iron alter behavior in developing rats, *Journal of Nutrition* 131 (2001): 311–318; Standing Committee on the Scientific Evaluation of Dietary Reference Intakes, Food and Nutrition Board, Institute of Medicine, 2001, pp. 9-5–9-6 [see reference 37].

48. C. I. Obialo and coauthors, Clay pica has no hematologic or metabolic correlate in chronic hemodialysis patients, *Journal of Renal Nutrition* 11 (2001): 32–36.

49. P. W. Harvey, P. B. Dexter, and I. Darnton-Hill, The impact of consuming iron from non-food sources on iron status in developing countries, *Public Health Nutrition* 3 (2000): 375–383.

50. M. Shannon, Severe lead poisoning in pregnancy, *Ambulatory Pediatrics* 3 (2003): 37–39; E. A. Rose, J. H. Porcerelli, and A. V. Neale, Pica: Common but commonly missed, *Journal of the American Board of Family Practice* 13 (2000): 353–358; J. F. Magnaval and coauthors, Highlights of human toxocariasis, *Korean Journal of Parasitology* 39 (2001): 1–11.

51. J. L. Beard and J. R. Connor, Iron status and neural functioning, *Annual Review of Nutrition* 23 (2003): 41–58.

52. B. Annibale and coauthors, Reversal of iron deficiency anemia after *Helicobacter pylori* eradication in patients with asymptomatic gastritis, *Annals of Internal Medicine* 131 (1999): 668–672.

53. World Health Organization, http://www.who .int/nut/ida.htm.

54. Standing Committee on the Scientific Evaluation of Dietary Reference Intakes, Food and Nutrition Board, Institute of Medicine, 2001 [see reference 37]; L. Johnson-Down and coauthors, Primary food sources of nutrients in the diet of Canadian adults, *Canadian Journal of Dietetic Practice and Research* 67 (2006): 7–13.

55. M. Wessling-Resnick, Iron transport, *Annual Review of Nutrition* 20 (2000): 129–151.

56. A. L. M. Heath and S. J. Fairweather-Tait, Health implications of iron overload: The role of diet and genotype, *Nutrition Reviews* 61 (2003): 45–62; J. R. Hunt and Z. K. Roughead, Adaptation of iron absorption in men consuming diets with high or low iron bioavailability, *American Journal of Clinical Nutrition* 71 (2000): 94–102.

57. L. M. Neff, Current directions in hemochromatosis research: Towards an understanding of the role of iron overload and the *HFE* gene mutations in the development of clinical disease, *Nutrition Reviews* 61 (2003): 38–42; M. R. Borgaonkar, Hemochromatosis: More common than you think, *Canadian Family Physician* 49 (2003): 36–43.

58. M. J. Nowicki and B. R. Bacon, Hereditary hemochromatosis in siblings: Diagnosis by genotyping, *Pediatrics* 105 (2000): 426–429; A. S. Tavill, Clinical implications of the hemochromatosis gene, *New England Journal of Medicine* 341 (1999): 755–757.

59. L. M. Neff, 2003 [see reference 57].

60. J. D. Cook and M. B. Reddy, Effect of ascorbic acid intake on nonheme-iron absorption from a complete diet, *American Journal of Clinical Nutrition* 73 (2001): 93–98.

61. A. L. M. Heath and S. J. Fairweather-Tait, 2003 [see reference 56].

62. A. E. O. Fisher and D. P. Naughton, Iron supplements: The quick fix with long-term consequences, *Nutrition Journal* 3 (2004), available at http://www.nutritionj.com/content/3/1/2.

63. M. Shannon, Ingestion of toxic substances by children, *New England Journal of Medicine* 342 (2000): 186–191; C. C. Morris, Pediatric iron poisonings in the United States, *Southern Medicine Journal* 93 (2000): 352–358.

64. Standing Committee on the Scientific Evaluation of Dietary Reference Intakes, Food and Nutrition Board, Institute of Medicine, 2001, p. 347 [see reference 37].

65. M. B. Reddy, R. F. Hurrell, and J. D. Cook, Estimation of nonheme-iron bioavailability from meal composition, *American Journal of Clinical Nutrition* 71 (2000): 937–943.

66. A. S. Sandberg, Bioavailability of minerals in legumes, *British Journal of Nutrition* 88 (2002): S281–S285.

67. I. M. Zijp, O. Korver, and L. B. Tijburg, Effect of tea and other dietary factors on iron absorption, *Critical Reviews in Food Science and Nutrition* 40 (2000): 371–398.

68. R. A. DiSivestro, Zinc in relation to diabetes and oxidative disease, *Journal of Nutrition* 130 (2000): 1509S–1511S.

69. C. F. Walker and R. E. Black, Zinc and the risk for infectious disease, *Annual Review of Nutrition* 24 (2004): 255–275.

70. T. A. Strand and coauthors, Effectiveness and efficacy of zinc for the treatment of acute diarrhea in young children, *Pediatrics* 109 (2002): 898–903; N. Bhandari and coauthors, Substantial reduction in severe diarrheal morbidity by daily zinc supplementation in young North Indian children, *Pediatrics* 109 (2002): e86; C. Duggan and W. Fawzi, Micronutrients and child health: Studies in international nutrition and HIV infection, *Nutrition Reviews* 59 (2001): 358–369; The Zinc Investigators' Collaborative Group, Therapeutic effects of oral zinc in acute and persistent diarrhea in children in developing countries: Pooled analysis of randomized controlled trials, *American Journal of Clinical Nutrition* 72 (2000): 1516–1522.

71. K. A. Keller, A. Grider, and J. A. Coffield, Age-dependent influence of dietary zinc restriction on short-term memory in male rats, *Physiology and Behavior* 72 (2001): 339–348.

72. B. H. McElroy and S. P. Miller, Effectiveness of zinc gluconate glycine lozenges (Cold-Eeze) against the common cold in school-aged subjects: A retrospective chart review, *American Journal of Therapeutics* 9 (2002): 472–475; I. Marshall, Zinc for the common cold, *Cochrane Database of Systematic Reviews* 2 (2000): CD001364; J. L. Jackson, E. Lesho, and C. Peterson, Zinc and the common cold: A meta-analysis revisited, *Journal of Nutrition* 130 (2000): 1512S–1515S; A. S. Prasad and coauthors, Duration of symptoms and plasma cytokine levels in patients with the common cold treated with zinc acetate: A randomized, double-blind, placebo-controlled trial, *Annals of Internal Medicine* 133 (2000): 245–252; R. B. Turner and W. E. Cetnarowski, Effect of treatment with zinc gluconate or zinc acetate on experimental and natural colds, *Clinical Infectious Diseases* 31 (2000): 1202–1208.

73. P. A. Cotton and coauthors, Dietary sources of nutrients among US adults, 1994–1996, *Journal of the American Dietetic Association* 104 (2004): 921–930.

74. D. H. Holben and A. M. Smith, The diverse role of selenium within selenoproteins: A review, *Journal of the American Dietetic Association* 99 (1999): 836–843.

75. T. M. Vogt and coauthors, Serum selenium and risk of prostate cancer in U.S. blacks and whites, *International Journal of Cancer* 103 (2003): 664–670.

76. A. J. Duffield-Lillico and coauthors, Selenium supplementation and secondary prevention of nonmelanoma skin cancer in a randomized trial, *Journal of the National Cancer Institute* 95 (2003): 1477–1481.

77. M. A. Moyad, Selenium and vitamin E supplements for prostate cancer: Evidence or embellishment? *Urology* 59 (2002): 9–19.

78. Health Canada, Fluoride and human health, July 2008, available at http://www.hc-sc.gc.ca/hl-vs/iyh-vsv/environ/fluor-eng.php.

79. Achievements in public health, 1900–1999: Fluoridation of drinking water to prevent dental caries, *Morbidity and Mortality Weekly Report* 48 (1999): 933–940.

80. Centers for Disease Control and Prevention, Recommendations for using fluoride to prevent and control dental caries in the United States, *Morbidity and Mortality Weekly Report* 50 (2001): 1–42; Position of the American Dietetic Association: The impact of fluoride on health, *Journal of the American Dietetic Association* 100 (2000): 1208–1213.

81. G. Y. Yeh and coauthors, Systematic review of herbs and dietary supplements for glycemic control in diabetes, *Diabetes Care* 26 (2003): 1277–1294; M. D. Althuis and coauthors, Glucose and insulin reponses to dietary chromium supplement: a meta-analysis, *American Journal of Clinical Nutrition* 76 (2002): 148–155.

82. J. F. Fowler Jr., Systemic contact dermatitis caused by oral chromium picolinate, *Cutis* 65 (2000): 116.

83. P. L. Fox, The copper-iron chronicles: The story of an intimate relationship, *Biometals* 16 (2003): 9–40; N. E. Hellman and J. D. Gitlin, Ceruloplasmin metabolism and function, *Annual Review of Nutrition* 22 (2002): 439–458.

84. Standing Committee on the Scientific Evaluation of Dietary Reference Intakes, Food and Nutrition Board, Institute of Medicine, 2001, p. 227 [see reference 37].

85. Standing Committee on the Scientific Evaluation of Dietary Reference Intakes, Food and Nutrition Board, Institute of Medicine, 2001, p. 245 [see reference 37].

86. T. A. Devirian and S. L. Volpe, The physiological effects of dietary boron, *Critical Reviews in Food Science and Nutrition* 43 (2003): 219–231.

87. L. Johnson-Down and coauthors, Primary food sources of nutrients in the diet of Canadian adults, *Canadian Journal of Dietetic Practice and Research* 67 (2006): 7–13.

88. Health Canada, *Eating Well with Canada's Food Guide.* 2007, Catalogue no. H164-38/1-2007E.

89. U.S. Department of Agriculture and U.S. Department of Health and Human Services, *Dietary Guidelines for Americans*, 2010, available at http://www.health.gov/dietaryguidelines/2010.asp.

90. R. E. Black and coauthors, Children who avoid drinking cow milk have low dietary calcium intakes and poor bone health, *American Journal of Clinical Nutrition* 76 (2002): 675–680.

91. A. Azoulay, P. Garzon, and M. J. Eisenberg, Comparison of the mineral content of tap water and bottled waters, *Journal of General Internal Medicine* 16 (2001): 168–175; H. Bohmer, H. Muller, and K. L. Resch, 2000 [see reference 9].

Consumer Corner 8

1. Health Canada. Healthy Living—The Safety of Bottled Water, 2010, available at http://www.hc-sc.gc.ca/hl-vs/iyh-vsv/food-aliment/bottled-embouteillee-eng.php.

2. Health Canada. Environmental and Workplace Health—Water Quality, 2012, available at http://www.hc-sc.gc.ca/ewh-semt/water-eau/index-eng.php.

3. National Sanitation Foundation, Consumer guide to bottled water, *Information for Consumers,* March 1998.

4. P. Garzon and M. J. Eisenberg, Variation in the mineral content of commercially available bottled waters: Implications for health and disease, *American Journal of Medicine* 105 (1998): 125–130.

5. M. Sabatier and coauthors, Meal effect on magnesium bioavailability from mineral water in healthy women, *American Journal of Clinical Nutrition* 75 (2002): 65–71.

Controversy 8

1. Osteoporosis Canada, About osteoporosis, available at http://www.osteoporosis.ca/about-osteoporosis-canada/.

2. Osteoporosis Society of Canada. 2010 Clinical Practice Guidelines for the Diagnosis and Management of Osteoporosis in Canada, available at http://www.osteoporosis.ca/health-care-professionals/guidelines/.

3. Y.-Z. Liu and coauthors, Molecular studies of identification of genes for osteoporosis: The 2002 update, *Journal of Endocrinology* 177 (2003): 147–196.

4. S. L. Teitelbaum and F. P. Ross, Genetic regulation of osteoclast development and function, *Nature Reviews: Genetics* 4 (2003): 638–649.

5. P. Kannus and coauthors, Genetic factors and osteoporotic fractures in elderly people: Prospective 25 year follow up of a nationwide cohort of elderly Finnish twins, *British Medical Journal* 319 (1999): 1334–1337.

6. A. J. MacGregor, H. Snieder, and T. D. Spector, Genetic factors and osteoporotic fractures in elderly people, letter, *British Medical Journal* 320 (2000): 1669.

7. S. M. Runyan and coauthors, Familial resemblance of bone mineralization, calcium intake, and physical activity in early-adolescent daughters, their mothers, and maternal grandmothers, *Journal of the American Dietetic Association* 103 (2003): 1320–1325.

8. J. A. Cauley and coauthors, Longitudinal study of changes in hip bone mineral density in Caucasian and African American women, *Journal of the American Geriatric Society* 53 (2005): 183–189.

9. H. J. Kalkwarf, J. C. Khoury, and B. P. Lanphear, Milk intake during childhood and adolescence, adult bone density, and osteoporotic fractures in US women, *American Journal of Clinical Nutrition* 77 (2003): 257–265.

10. A. Goulding and coauthors, Children who avoid drinking cow's milk are at increased risk for prepubertal bone fractures, *Journal of the American Dietetic Association* 104 (2004): 250–253.

11. J. S. Volek and coauthors, Increasing fluid milk favorably affects bone mineral density responses to resistance training in adolescent boys, *Journal of the American Dietetic Association* 103 (2003): 1353–1356; R. E. Black and coauthors, Children who avoid drinking cow milk have low dietary calcium intakes and poor bone health, *American Journal of Clinical Nutrition* 76 (2002): 675–680.

12. J. Cornish and coauthors, Lactoferrin is a potent regulator of bone cell activities and increases bone formation in vivo, *Endocrinology* 145 (2004): 4366–4374.

13. J. M. Campion and M. J. Maricic, Osteoporosis in men, *American Family Physician* 67 (2003): 1551–1526.

14. S. M. Runyan and coauthors, 2003 [see reference 7].

15. W. Kemmler and coauthors, The Erlangen Fitness Osteoporosis Prevention Study: A controlled exercise trial in early postmenopausal women with low bone density—first-year results, *Archives of Physical Medicine and Rehabilitation* 84 (2003): 673–682; M. C. Wang and coauthors, Diet in midpuberty and sedentary activity in prepuberty predict peak bone mass, *American Journal of Clinical Nutrition* 77 (2003): 495–503; S. J. Stear and coauthors, Effect of a calcium and exercise intervention on the bone mineral status of 16–18-y-old adolescent girls, *American Journal of Clinical Nutrition* 77 (2003): 985–992.

16. J. E. Layne and M. E. Nelson, The effects of progressive resistance training on bone density: A review, *Medicine and Science in Sports and Exercise* 31 (1999): 25–30.

17. E. C. Cussler and coauthors, Weight lifted in strength training predicts bone change in postmenopausal women, *Medicine and Science in Sports and Exercise* 35 (2003): 10–17.

18. L. M. Salamone and coauthors, Effect of a lifestyle intervention on bone mineral density in premenopausal women: A randomized trial, *American Journal of Clinical Nutrition* 70 (1999): 97–103.

19. S. Gillette-Guyonnet and coauthors, Body composition and osteoporosis in elderly women, *Gerontology* 46 (2000): 189–193.

20. S. Gillette-Guyonnet and coauthors, 2000 [see reference 19].

21. J. C. Fleet, Leptin and bone: Does the brain control bone biology? *Nutrition Reviews* 58 (2000): 209–211.

22. P. Gerdhem and K. J. Obrant, Effects of cigarette-smoking on bone mass as assessed by dual-energy X-ray absorptiometry and ultrasound, *Osteoporosis International* 13 (2002): 932–936; K. D. Ward and R. C. Klesges, A meta-analysis of the effects of cigarette smoking on bone mineral density, *Calcified Tissue International* 68 (2001): 259–270.

23. P. B. Rapuri and coauthors, Smoking and bone metabolism in elderly women, *Bone* 27 (2000): 429–436; A. P. Hermann and coauthors, Premenopausal smoking and bone density in 2015 perimenopausal women, *Journal of Bone and Mineral Research* 15 (2000): 780–787.

24. C. Oncken and coauthors, Effects of smoking cessation or reduction on hormone profiles and bone turnover in postmenopausal women, *Nicotine and Tobacco Research* 4 (2002): 451–458.

25. B. Dawson-Hughes, Interaction of dietary calcium and protein in bone health in humans, *Journal of Nutrition* 133 (2003): 852S–854S.

26. D. E. Sellmeyer and coauthors, A high ratio of dietary animal to vegetable protein increases the rate of bone loss and the risk of fracture in postmenopausal women, *American Journal of Clinical Nutrition* 73 (2001): 118–122.

27. L. A. Frassetto and coauthors, Worldwide incidence of hip fracture in elderly women: Relation to consumption of animal to vegetable foods, *Journals of Gerontology Series A: Biological Sciences and Medical Sciences* 55 (2000): M585–M592.

28. R. Brynin, Soy and its isoflavones: A review of their effects on bone density, *Alternative Medicine Review* 7 (2002): 317–327.

29. B. H. Arjmandi and coauthors, Soy protein has a greater effect on bone in post-menopausal women not on hormone replacement therapy, as evidenced by reducing bone resorption and urinary calcium excretion, *Journal of Clinical Endocrinology and Metabolism* 88 (2003): 1048–1054; T. Uesugi, Y. Fukui, and Y. Yamori, Beneficial effects of soybean isoflavone supplementation on bone metabolism and serum lipids in postmenopausal Japanese women: A four-week study, *Journal of the American College of Nutrition* 21 (2002): 97–102.

30. L. K. Massey, Dietary animal and plant protein and human bone health: A whole foods approach, *Journal of Nutrition* 133 (2003): 862S–865S.

31. J. Bell, Elderly women need dietary protein to maintain bone mass, *Nutrition Reviews* 60 (2002): 337–341; B. Dawson-Hughes and S. S. Harris, Calcium intake influences the association of protein intake with rates of bone loss in elderly men and women, *American Journal of Clinical Nutrition* 75 (2002): 773–779; J. H. E. Promislow and coauthors, Protein consumption and bone mineral density in the elderly: The Rancho Bernardo Study, *American Journal of Epidemiology* 155 (2002): 636–644.

32. J. Raloff, Do meat and dairy harm aging bones? *Science News* 159 (2001): 20.

33. M. Harrington and K. D. Cashman, High salt intake appears to increase bone resorption in postmenopausal women but high potassium intake ameliorates this adverse effect, *Nutrition Reviews* 61 (2003): 179–183.

34. P.-H. Lin and coauthors, The DASH diet and sodium reduction improve markers of bone turnover and calcium metabolism in adults, *Journal of Nutrition* 133 (2003): 3130–3136.

35. L. Doyle and K. D. Cashman, The DASH diet may have beneficial effects on bone health, *Nutrition Reviews* 62 (2004): 215–220.

36. Standing Committee on the Scientific Evaluation of Dietary Reference Intakes, Food and Nutrition Board, Institute of Medicine, *Dietary Reference Intakes for Water, Potassium, Sodium, Chloride, and Sulfate* (Washington, D.C.: National Academies Press, 2004), pp. 6-89–6-92; F. P. Cappuccio and coauthors, Unraveling the links between calcium excretion, salt intake, hypertension, kidney stones and bone metabolism, *Journal of Nephrology* 13 (2000): 169–177.

37. D. E. Sellmeyer, M. Schloetter, and A. Sebastin, Potassium citrate prevents increased urine calcium excretion and bone resorption

induced by a high sodium chloride diet, *Journal of Clinical Endocrinology and Metabolism* 87 (2002): 2008–2012.

38. R. P. Heaney, Effects of caffeine on bone and the calcium economy, *Food and Chemical Toxicology* 40 (2002): 1263–1270.

39. D. B. Milne and F. H. Nielsen, The interaction between dietary fructose and magnesium adversely affects macromineral homeostasis in men, *Journal of the American College of Nutrition* 19 (2000): 31–37.

40. F. Garcia-Contreras and coauthors, Cola beverage consumption induces bone mineralization reduction in ovariectomized rats, *Archives of Medical Research* 31 (2000): 360–365.

41. N. C. Binkley and coauthors, A high phylloquinone intake is required to achieve maximal osteocalcin g-carboxylation, *American Journal of Clinical Nutrition* 76 (2002): 1055–1060; S. L. Booth and coauthors, Dietary vitamin K intakes are associated with hip fracture but not with bone mineral density in elderly men and women, *American Journal of Clinical Nutrition* 71 (2000): 1201–1208.

42. J. B. J. van Meurs and coauthors, Homocysteine levels and the risk of osteoporotic fracture, *New England Journal of Medicine* 350 (2004): 2033–2041.

43. R. R. McLean and coauthors, Homocysteine as a predictive factor for hip fracture in older persons, *New England Journal of Medicine* 350 (2004): 2042–2049.

44. L. G. Raisz, Homocysteine and osteoporotic fractures: Culprit or bystander? *New England Journal of Medicine* 350 (2004): 2089–2090.

45. K. L. Tucker and coauthors, Potassium, magnesium, and fruit and vegetable intakes are associated with greater bone mineral density in elderly men and women, *American Journal of Clinical Nutrition* 69 (1999): 727–736.

46. K. Michaelsson and coauthors, Serum retinol levels and the risk of fractures, *New England Journal of Medicine* 348 (2003): 287–294; D. Feskanich and coauthors, Vitamin A intake and hip fractures among postmenopausal women, *Journal of the American Medical Association* 287 (2002): 47–54; S. Johnasson and coauthors, Subclinical hypervitaminosis A causes fragile bones in rats, *Bone* 31 (2002): 685–689; N. Binkley and D. Krueger, Hypervitaminosis A and bone, *Nutrition Reviews* 58 (2000): 138–144.

47. K. L. Tucker and coauthors, Bone mineral density and dietary patterns in older adults: The Framingham Osteoporosis Study, *American Journal of Clinical Nutrition* 76 (2002): 245–252; S. A. New and coauthors, Dietary influences on bone mass and bone metabolism: Further evidence of a positive link between fruit and vegetable consumption and bone health? *American Journal of Clinical Nutrition* 71 (2000): 142–151.

48. M. Harrington and K. D. Cashman, 2003 [see reference 33]; K. L. Tucker and coauthors, 2002 [see reference 47]; P. B. Rapuri and coauthors, Caffeine intake increases the rate of bone loss in elderly women and interacts with vitamin D receptor genotypes, *American Journal of Clinical Nutrition* 74 (2001): 694–700.

49. D. J. van der Voort and coauthors, Screening for osteoporosis using easily obtainable biometrical data: Diagnostic accuracy of measured, self-reported and recalled BMI, and related costs of bone mineral density measurements, *Osteoporosis International* 11 (2000): 233–239.

50. H. J. Kloosterboer and A. G. Ederveen, Pros and cons of existing treatment modalities in osteoporosis: A comparison between tibolone, SERMs and estrogen (1/2 progestogen) treatments, *Journal of Steroid Biochemistry and Molecular Biology* 83 (2002): 157–165; R. A. Sayegh and P. G. Stubblefield, Bone metabolism and the perimenopause overview, risk factors, screening, and osteoporosis preventive measures, *Obstetrics and Gynecology Clinics of North America* 29 (2002): 495–510.

51. R. T. Chlebowski and coauthors, Influence of estrogen plus progestin on breast cancer and mammography in healthy postmenopausal women: The Women's Health Initiative Randomized Trial, *Journal of the American Medical Association* 289 (2003): 3243–3253; C. G. Solomon and R. G. Dluhy, Rethinking postmenopausal hormone therapy, *New England Journal of Medicine* 348 (2003): 579–580; Writing Group for the Women's Health Initiative Investigators, Risks and benefits of estrogen plus progestin in healthy postmenopausal women: Principal results from the Women's Health Initiative Randomized Controlled Trial, *Journal of the American Medical Association* 288 (2002): 321–333; O. Ylikorkala and M. Metsa-heikkila, Hormone replacement therapy in women with a history of breast cancer, *Gynecological Endocrinology* 16 (2002): 469–478.

52. S. L. Greenspan, N. M. Resnick, and R. A. Parker, Combination therapy with hormone replacement and alendronate for prevention of bone loss in elderly women: A randomized controlled trial, *Journal of the American Medical Association* 289 (2003): 2525–2533.

53. D. Teegarden and coauthors, Previous milk consumption is associated with greater bone density in young women, *American Journal of Clinical Nutrition* 69 (1999): 1014–1017.

54. NIH Consensus Development Panel, Osteoporosis prevention, diagnosis, and therapy, *Journal of the American Medical Association* 285 (2001): 785–795.

55. Federal Trade Commission, Kevin Trudeau banned from infomercials, September 7, 2004, available at http://www.ftc.gov/opa/2004/09/trudeaucoral.htm.

56. J. Guillemant and coauthors, Mineral water as a source of dietary calcium: Acute effects on parathyroid function and bone resorption in young men, *American Journal of Clinical Nutrition* 71 (2000): 999–1002.

9 Energy Balance and Healthy Body Weight

Do You Ever . . .

Wish you could control your body weight, once and for all?

Feel tempted by a favourite treat when you don't feel hungry?

Wonder how extra Calories from food become fat on your body?

Try fad diets to lose weight?

Keep Reading . . .

Learning Objectives

After completing this chapter, you should be able to

LO 9.1 Define the term *central obesity*, and discuss the primary health risks associated with it.

LO 9.2 Describe the role of BMR in determining an individual's daily energy needs, and explain the other factors that determine energy need.

LO 9.3 Calculate the BMI when given height and weight information for various people, and describe the implications of their BMI for health.

LO 9.4 Compare and contrast the roles of the hormones ghrelin and leptin in appetite regulation, and name some other influences that affect appetite.

LO 9.5 Discuss the potential impact of "outside the body" factors on weight control efforts.

LO 9.6 Develop a healthy eating plan that includes controlled portions and nutrient-dense foods for weight control.

LO 9.7 Defend the importance of behaviour modification in maintaining a healthy body composition over the long term.

LO 9.8 Compare and contrast the characteristics of anorexia nervosa and bulimia nervosa, and provide strategies for combatting eating disorders.

Contents

A re you pleased with your body weight? If you answered yes, you are a rare individual. Nearly all people in our society think they should weigh more or less (mostly less) than they do. Their primary concern is usually appearance, but they often correctly perceive that physical health is somehow related to weight. At the extremes, both **overweight** and **underweight** present risks to health.*,[1]

People also think of their weight as something they should control, once and for all. Three misconceptions in that sentence frustrate their efforts, however—the focus on weight, the focus on *controlling* weight, and the focus on a short-term endeavour. Simply put, it isn't your weight you need to control; it's the fat in your body in proportion to the lean—your **body composition.** And controlling body composition directly isn't possible—you can only control your *behaviour.* Sporadic bursts of activity, such as "dieting," are not effective; the behaviours that achieve and maintain a healthy body weight take a lifetime of commitment.

This chapter starts out by presenting the problems associated with deficient and excessive body fatness and then examines how the body manages its energy budget. The following sections show how to judge body weight on the sound basis of health and describe theories about the causes of obesity. Finally, the chapter reveals how the body gains and loses weight and suggests lifestyle strategies for achieving and maintaining a healthy body weight.

overweight overfatness of a moderate degree; defined as a body mass index (BMI) of 25.0 through 29.9. BMI is defined later.

underweight too little body fat for health; defined as having a body mass index of less than 18.5.

body composition the proportions of muscle, bone, fat, and other tissue that make up a person's total body weight.

---

*Reference notes are listed at the end of the chapter.

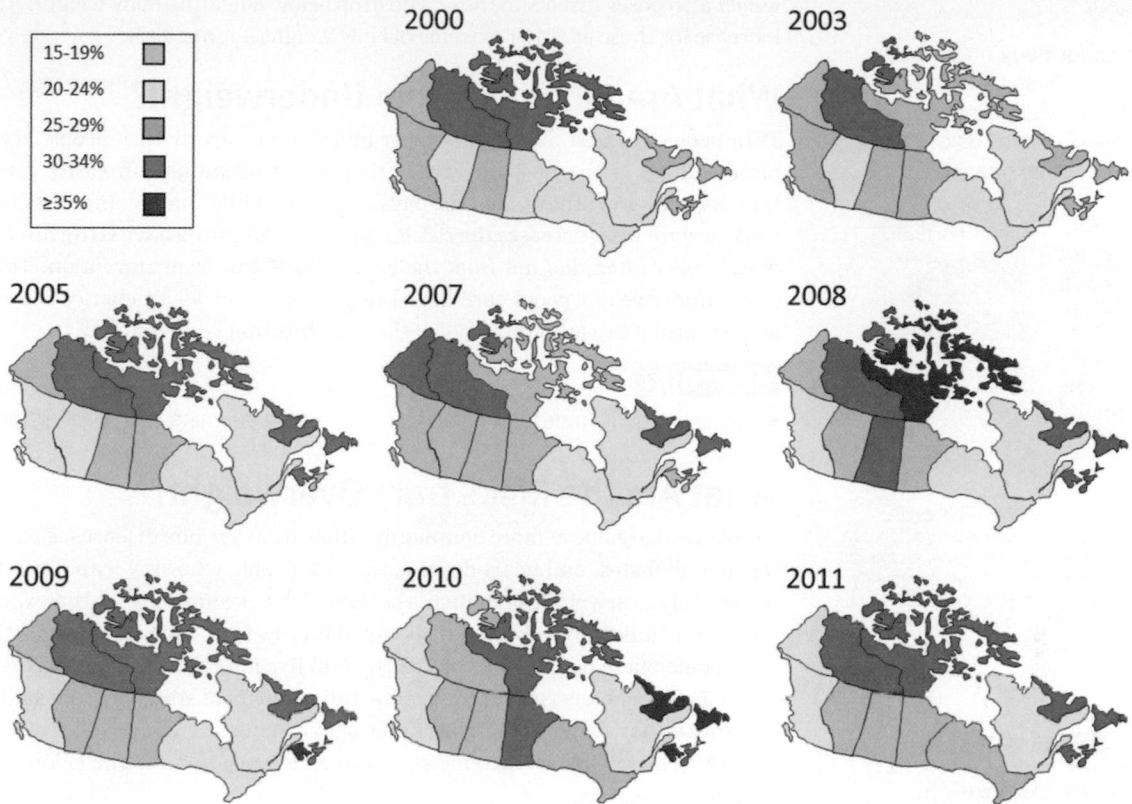

Figure 9-1

The Increasing Prevalence of Obesity among Canadian Adults (2000–2011)

15-19%	☐
20-24%	☐
25-29%	☐
30-34%	☐
≥35%	☐

2000 2003
2005 2007 2008
2009 2010 2011

Source: From Carolyn Gotay et al. "Updating the Canadian Obesity Maps: An Epidemic in Progress." Canadian Journal of Public Health, Vol 104, No 1 (2013). Published by Canadian Public Health Association. http://journal.cpha.ca/index.php/cjph/article/view/3513/2754

The Problems of Too Little or Too Much Body Fat

Both deficient and excessive body fat present risks to health. In Canada, too little body fat is not a widespread problem. **Obesity**, in contrast, is an escalating epidemic—see Figure 9–1. In 2008, 37 percent of Canadian adults were overweight, and about 23 percent met the definition of obesity (see Figure 9–2). Additionally, one of every five children and teenagers in Canada is overweight.

Health Canada has been monitoring the prevalence of overweight and obesity using data collected by the 1985 and 1990 Health Promotion Surveys; 1994, 1996, and 1998 Population Health Surveys; and 2000 and 2004 Canadian Community Health Surveys (CCHS).[2] These data also reveal that the overweight- and obesity-related mortality rate has also increased in every province, with higher levels in eastern Canada. Based on the results of the CCHS, 15 percent of the population was obese in 2000–2001, a rate that had tripled in the past few decades.[3]

The first report of the CCHS (2000/2001) presented statistics about the body mass index (BMI) of Canadians from 1994/1995 to 2000/2001.[4] Figure 9–1 presents the Canadian proportions for each BMI category. It should be noted that BMI values are based on self reported height and weight. For children 7 to 13 years, the rate of obesity increased by 1.5 to 5 times between 1981 and 2001.[5] For example, the rate of obesity rose from 2 to 10 percent among girls, and the rate of overweight rose from 9 to 20 percent among boys. More recent data from the CCHS (2004) Cycle 2.2 using measured data revealed that for children 2 to 17 years, 18 percent were considered

obesity overfatness with adverse health effects, as determined by reliable measures and interpreted with good medical judgment. Obesity is officially defined as a body mass index of 30 or higher.

Figure 9–2

Body Weights among Canadian Adults

BMI stands for body mass index, an index of a person's weight in relation to height, associated with degree of health risk. BMI is defined on the next page.

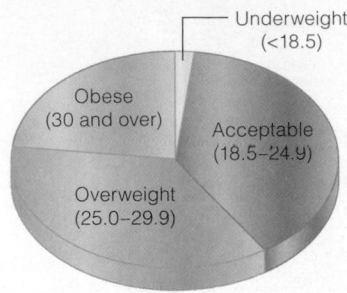

Source: Statistics Canada, Michael Tjepkema, "Prevalence of Obesity in Canada: Measured Obesity: Adult obesity in Canada: Measured height and weight," Nutrition: Findings from the Canadian Community Health Survey, *Catalogue no. 82-620-MWE2005001 ISSN: 1716-6713. Reproduced and distributed on an "as is" basis with the permission of Statistics Canada.*

Figure 9–3

Underweight, Overweight, and Mortality

This J-shaped curve describes the relationship between body mass index (BMI) and mortality.
It shows that both underweight and overweight present risks of a premature death.

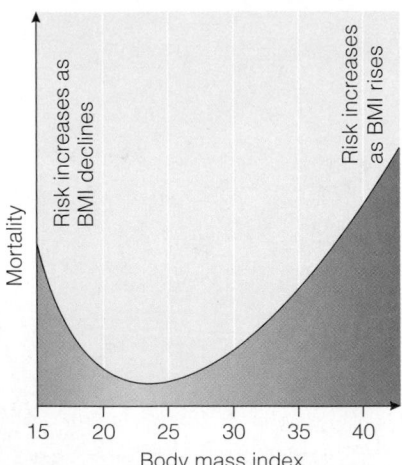

wasting the progressive, relentless loss of the body's tissues that accompanies certain diseases and shortens survival time.

overweight and 8 percent were considered obese, a combined rate of 26 percent (http://www.statcan.gc.ca/pub/82-620-m/2005001/pdf/4193660-eng.pdf).

While obesity and overweight have taken the spotlight, the problem of *underweight* also poses threats to those who drop below a healthy body weight. Risks to life increase for those at either extreme of body weight (Figure 9–3).

What Are the Risks from Underweight?

Thin people die first during a siege or in a famine. Overly thin people are also at a disadvantage in the hospital, where their nutrient status can easily deteriorate if they have to go without food for days at a time while undergoing tests or surgery. Underweight also increases the risk for any person fighting a **wasting** disease. People with cancer often die, not from the cancer itself, but from starvation. Thus, excessively underweight people are urged to gain body fat as an energy reserve and to acquire protective amounts of all of the nutrients that can be stored.

KEY POINT

- Deficient body fatness threatens survival during a famine or in wasting diseases.

What Are the Risks from Overweight?

People who are obese more commonly suffer from serious diseases, such as hypertension, diabetes, and heart disease, than do people who stay lean. Even those just moderately overweight may increase their risks, assuming that the excess weight is fat, not muscle.[6] Body weight is not the only factor in illness causation, however; some obese people remain healthy and live long despite their excess body fatness.[7] Researchers suspect that genetic inheritance, abstinence from smoking, and cardiovascular fitness help determine who among the obese stays well and who falls ill.[8] The trouble is, no one can tell to which group he or she belongs until serious diseases set in.

To underestimate the threat from obesity is to invite calamity. People die each year from obesity-related diseases, and the risk of dying increases proportionally with increasing weight, although all-cause mortality and being overweight has been challenged.[9] Over 70 percent of obese people suffer from at least one other major health problem. Excess weight causes up to half of all cases of hypertension, thereby increasing the risk of heart attack and stroke.[10] Cardiovascular disease (CVD) rates rise with central obesity, as described next. Currently, only tobacco contributes to more preventable illnesses and premature deaths.

The health risks of overfatness are so many that obesity has been declared a chronic disease by some health organizations (including the American Medical Association at its 2013 Annual Meeting; see http://www.ama-assn.org/ama/pub/news/news/2013/2013-06-18-new-ama-policies-annual-meeting.page). In addition to hypertension and CVD, obesity triples a person's risk of developing diabetes and all of its associated ills. Even modest weight gain raises diabetes risk, and the risk appears greater for people of European descent than for those of African descent.[11] If hypertension, CVD, or diabetes runs in your family, you urgently need to attend to controlling body fatness.

Obese adults are also threatened by other risks. Among them are abdominal hernias, arthritis, complications in pregnancy and surgery, flat feet, gallbladder disease, gout, high blood lipids, kidney stones, liver malfunction, respiratory problems (including Pickwickian syndrome, a breathing blockage linked to sudden death), sleep apnea (dangerous abnormal breathing during sleep), some cancers, varicose veins, and even a high accident rate.[12] Moreover, after the effects of diagnosed diseases are taken into account, the risk of death from other causes remains almost twice as high for people with lifelong obesity as for others. Even modest weight loss often improves these maladies. An older obese man, for example, often gains relief from arthritis pain and reduces his blood pressure with the loss of 10 percent of his body weight.

KEY POINT

- Most obese people suffer illnesses, and obesity is considered a chronic disease.

Figure 9–4

Visceral Fat and Subcutaneous Fat

The fat deep within the body's abdominal cavity may pose an especially high risk to health.

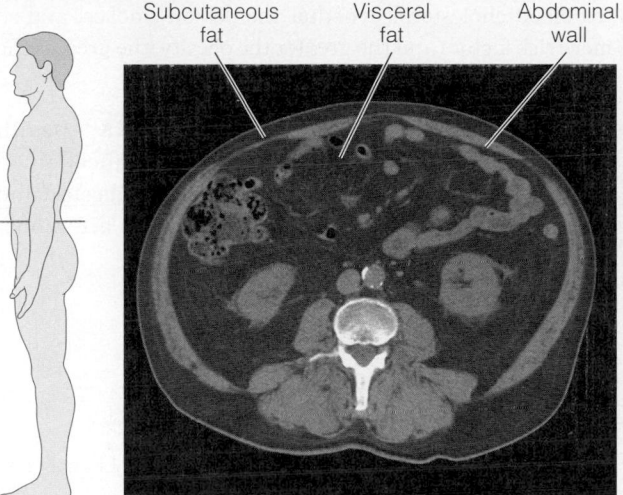

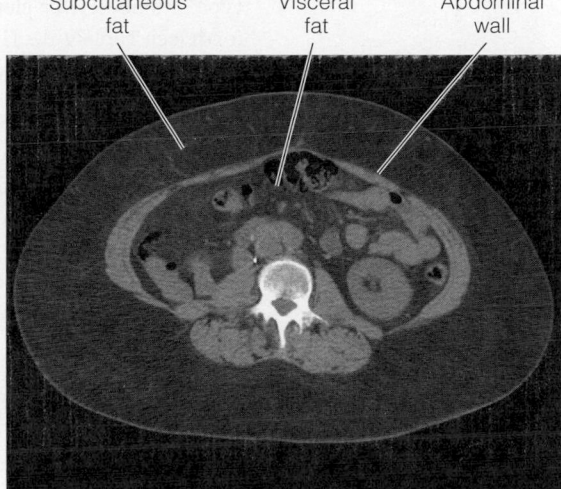

Subcutaneous fat   Visceral fat   Abdominal wall   Subcutaneous fat   Visceral fat   Abdominal wall

Male: BMI 29   Female: BMI 32

Reprinted from *The Lancet*, Vol 380, Bezzocchi, Alberto, "How fat is fat?" p. e1.Copyright (2012), with permission from The Lancet via Copyright Clearance Center.

Central Obesity   Even more than total fatness, fat that collects deep within the central abdominal area of the body, called **visceral fat**, may be especially dangerous with regard to risks of diabetes, stroke, hypertension, and coronary artery disease (Figure 9–4).[13] The risk of death from all causes may be higher in those with **central obesity** than in those whose fat accumulates elsewhere in the body. The health risks of obesity seem to run on a continuum: normal weight brings no extra risk, central obesity carries severe risks, and other forms of obesity fall somewhere in between.

Why should fat in the abdomen bring extra risk to the heart? Some researchers suspect that differences in fat mobility are part of the explanation. Visceral fat, which is readily released into the bloodstream, may make a significant contribution to the blood's daily burden of cholesterol-carrying lipoproteins, LDL, thereby increasing heart disease risk.[14] Fat layers lying just beneath the skin (**subcutaneous fat**) of the abdomen, thighs, hips, and legs also release fat, but sluggishly, and so, theoretically, may contribute less to blood lipids.[15]

Men of all ages and women who are past menopause are more prone to develop the "apple" profile of central obesity, whereas women in their reproductive years develop more of a "pear" profile (fat around the hips and thighs). Some women change profile at menopause, and lifelong "pears" may suddenly face increased risks of diseases that accompany excess visceral fat. Smokers, too, may carry more of their body fat centrally. Although a smoker may weigh less than the average nonsmoker, the smoker's waist measurement may be greater, leading to the theory that smoking directly affects body fat distribution. Two other factors also affect body fat distribution. Moderate-to-high intakes of alcohol have a positive association with central obesity, and higher levels of physical activity have a negative association.[16] A later section explains how to judge whether a person carries too much fat around the middle.

KEY POINT

- Central obesity may be more hazardous to health than other forms of obesity.

How Fat Is Too Fat for Health?   People want to know exactly how fat is too fat for health, and although the answer is not the same for everyone, scientists have developed guidelines. Obesity experts commonly evaluate risks to health from obesity using three indicators, discussed in more detail in a later section. The first of these is a person's **body mass index (BMI)**. The BMI, which defines average relative weight

Factors Affecting Body Fat Distribution
- Menopause in women
- Smoking
- Alcohol intake
- Physical activity

Who's Trying to Lose Weight?
- 70% of overweight women
- 48% of overweight men

Source: "How Canadian Weigh In." Canadians and Healthy Eating. Nutrition Highlights from the National Population Health Survey, 1994-1995, p. 8 Cat. No. H49-107/1997E http://publications.gc.ca/collections/Collection/H49-107-1997E.pdf

visceral fat fat stored within the abdominal cavity in association with the internal abdominal organs; also called *intra-abdominal fat*.

central obesity excess fat in the abdomen and around the trunk.

subcutaneous fat fat stored directly under the skin (*sub* means "beneath"; *cutaneous* refers to the skin).

body mass index (BMI) an indicator of obesity or underweight, calculated by dividing the weight of a person by the square of the person's height.

for height in people older than 20 years, often correlates with degree of body fatness and disease risks.[17]

The second indicator is waist circumference, reflecting the degree of visceral fatness in proportion to body fatness (see Figure 9–4). The third indicator is the person's disease risk profile, which takes into account whether the person has hypertension, type 2 diabetes, or elevated blood cholesterol; whether the person smokes; and so forth (see Table 9–1). The more risk factors and the greater the obesity, the greater the urgency to control body fatness.

 Canadian Guidelines for Body Weight Classification in Adults Health Canada published the Canadian Guidelines for Body Weight Classification in Adults in 2003, based on a technical report developed by Health Canada staff and an expert working group of Canadian researchers.[18] The BMI ranges are shown in Table 9–2.

Table 9–1

Indicators of an Urgent Need for Weight Loss

The U.S. National Heart, Lung, and Blood Institute states that aggressive treatment may be needed for critically obese people who also have any of the following:

- Established CVD
- Established type 2 diabetes, or impaired glucose tolerance
- Sleep apnea, a disturbance of breathing in sleep, including temporary stopping of breathing

The same urgency for treatment exists for an obese person with any three of the following:

- Hypertension
- High LDL
- Smoking
- Low HDL cholesterol
- Sedentary lifestyle
- Age older than 45 years (men) or 55 years (women)
- Heart disease of an immediate family member before age 55 (male) or 65 (female)

Source: National Heart, Lung, and Blood Institute, National Institute of Health, The Practical Guide: Identification, Evaluation, and Treatment of Overweight and Obesity in Adults. *NIH Publication, no 00-4084 (Washington, D.C.: Government Printing Office, 2000)*

Table 9–2

Canadian BMI Categories and Levels of Health Risk

BMI	Category	Level of Risk
<18.5	Underweight	Increased risk
18.5–24.9	Normal weight	Least risk
25.0–29.9	Overweight	Increased risk
30 and over	Obese	
30.0–34.9	Obese Class I	High risk
35.0–39.9	Obese Class II	Very high risk
≥40.0	Obese Class III	Extremely high risk

Source: Canadian Guidelines for Body Weight Classification in Adults, Health Canada, http://www.hc-sc.gc.ca/ fn-an/nutrition/weights-poids/guide-ld-adult/weight_book_tc-livres_des_poids_tm_e.html

The guidelines also identify waist circumference as an important indicator of health risk. Increased risk of type 2 diabetes, coronary heart disease, and hypertension is associated with a waist circumference for:

- men > 102 cm (40 in.) and
- women > 88 cm (35 in.)

 The full report and a Quick Reference Tool for Professionals are available from the Health Canada website at http://www.hc-sc.gc.ca/fn-an/nutrition/weights-poids/guide-ld-adult/index-eng.php. The "2006 Canadian Clinical Practice Guidelines on the Management and Prevention of Obesity in Adults and Children," which includes recommendations to screen not only adults but also children and adolescents for overweight and obesity, is also available online (http://www.cmaj.ca/cgi/content/full/176/8/S1).

Fitness of the heart and lungs gained through regular physical activity improves the health of the heart and longevity, independent of BMI.[19] Normal-weight fit people have the lowest risk of mortality from chronic diseases, but among those who are overweight, fitness may be a greater determinant of the risk of death than overfatness.[20] A healthy body weight supports good health, but fitness also clearly contributes.

KEY POINT

- Experts estimate health risks from obesity using BMI values, waist circumference, and a disease risk profile. Fit people are healthier than others, regardless of body fatness.

Social and Economic Costs of Obesity   Although some overfat people escape health problems, no one who is fat in our society quite escapes the social and economic handicaps. Fat people are more likely to be judged on their appearance than on their character.[21] Our society places enormous value on thinness, especially for women, and fat people are less sought after for romance, less often hired, and less often admitted to college/university. They pay higher insurance premiums, and they pay more for clothing. As a result, numerous agencies are drawing attention to these issues (e.g., the Canadian Obesity Network, http://www.obesitynetwork.ca), and ongoing efforts are needed to reduce these types of prejudice.

As mentioned earlier, the vast majority of overweight women and almost half of overweight men are trying to lose weight. The assumption is that every overweight person can and should achieve slenderness. Yet most overweight people cannot—for whatever reason—become slender. By one reckoning, only 5 percent of all people who successfully lose weight maintain their losses; other estimates are more optimistic but still predict that the majority of dieters' lost weight will creep back over time.[22]

Prejudice defines obese people by their appearance rather than by their character, often stereotyping them as lazy, stupid, and self-indulgent. Obese people suffer emotional pain when others treat them with hostility and contempt. Subtle blaming for an apparent lack of the discipline to resolve their weight problem often becomes internalized as guilt and self-deprecation. Even health-care professionals, including dietitians, can be among the chief offenders. To free our society of its obsession with body weight and prejudice against obesity, activists are speaking out for acceptance of body weight and respect for individuals.

KEY POINT

- Overfatness presents social and economic handicaps as well as physical ills. Judging people by their body weight is a form of prejudice in our society.

The Body's Energy Balance

What happens inside the body when you eat too much or too little food? The body ends up with an unbalanced energy budget—you have taken in more or less food energy than you spent. The mechanisms by which the body handles its energy underlie changes that occur in body composition.

Being active—even if overweight—is healthier than being sedentary. With a BMI of 36, aerobics instructor Jennifer Portnick is considered obese, but her daily workout routine helps reduce the risks to her health.

© Peter Berrik/Shutterstock

When more food energy is consumed than is needed, excess fat accumulates in the fat cells in the body's **adipose tissue**, where it is stored. When energy supplies run low, stored fat is withdrawn. The daily energy balance can therefore be stated like this: Change in energy stores equals food energy taken in minus energy spent on metabolism and muscle activities. More simply:

$$\text{Change in energy stores} = \text{Energy in} - \text{Energy out}$$

Too much or too little fat on the body today does not necessarily reflect today's energy budget. Small imbalances in the energy budget compound over time.

Energy In and Energy Out

The energy in foods and beverages is the only contributor to the "energy in" side of the energy balance equation. Before you can decide how much food will supply the energy you need in a day, you must first become familiar with the amounts of energy in foods and beverages. One way to do so is to look up Calorie amounts associated with foods and beverages online in the Canadian Nutrient File 2010 at http://www .hc-sc.gc.ca/fn-an/nutrition/fiche-nutri-data/index-eng.php. Alternatively, computer programs can provide this information in the blink of an eye for those with computer access. Such numbers are always fascinating to people concerned with managing body weight.

For example, an apple gives you 70 Calories from carbohydrate; a regular-size chocolate bar gives you about 250 Calories, mostly from fat and carbohydrate. You may already know that for each 3,500 Calories you eat in excess of expenditures, you store approximately half a kilogram (1 lb) of body fat.

On the "energy out" side of the equation, no easy method exists for determining the energy an individual spends and therefore needs. Energy expenditures vary so widely among individuals that estimating an individual person's need requires knowing something about the person's lifestyle and metabolism.

KEY POINT

- The "energy in" side of the body's energy budget is measured in Calories taken in each day in the form of foods and beverages. The number of Calories in foods and beverages can be obtained from published tables or computer diet analysis programs. No easy method exists for determining the "energy out" side of a person's energy balance equation.

Estimated Energy Requirements

A person wishing to know how much energy he or she needs in a day might look up his or her **Estimated Energy Requirement (EER)** value listed on the inside front cover of this book. The list of numbers there seems to imply that for the given age and gender groups, the number of Calories needed to meet the daily requirement can be stated as precisely as, say, the recommended intake for vitamin A. These values, however, are appropriate only for those exactly matching the characteristics of the "reference man and woman" (see the margin). People who deviate in any way from these characteristics must use other methods for determining energy requirements, and almost everyone deviates.

Instructions for determining whether you are sedentary, lightly active, active, or very active are provided in Appendix E. About 80 percent of people in the United States and Canada fall into the sedentary or lightly active categories.

Taller people need proportionately more energy than shorter people to balance their energy budgets because their greater surface area allows more energy to escape as heat. Older people generally need less than younger people due to slowed metabolism and reduced muscle mass, which occur in part because of reduced physical activity. (As Chapter 14 points out, these losses may not be inevitable for people who stay active.) On average, energy need diminishes by 5 percent per decade beyond the age of 30 years.

In reality, no one is average. In any group of 20 similar people with similar activity levels, one may expend twice as much energy per day as another. A 60-year-old

---

- About half a kilogram (1 lb) body fat = 3,500 Cal.

- Pure fat is worth 9 Cal per gram. About half a kilogram (1 lb) of it, then, would store 4,500 Cal. A pound of body fat is not pure fat, though; it contains water, protein, and other materials of living tissue—hence the lower Calorie value.

The DRI Committee Sets EER for a Reference Man and Woman

- Reference man: "Active" physical activity level, 22.5 BMI, 154 cm tall, weighing 70 kg (154 lb).
- Reference woman: "Active" physical activity level, 21.5 BMI, 140 cm tall, weighing 57 kg (126 lb).

adipose tissue the body's fat tissue. Adipose tissue performs several functions, including the synthesis and secretion of the hormone leptin involved in appetite regulation.

Estimated Energy Requirement (EER) the DRI recommendation for energy intake, accounting for age, gender, weight, height, and physical activity. Also defined in Chapter 2.

person who bikes, swims, or walks briskly each day may need as many Calories as a sedentary person of 30. Clearly, with such a wide range of variation, a necessary step in determining any person's energy need is to study that person.

KEY POINT

- The DRI committee sets Estimated Energy Requirements for a reference man and woman. People's energy needs vary greatly.

How Many Calories Do I Need Each Day?

Simply put, you need to take in enough Calories to cover your energy expenditure each day—your energy budget must balance. One way to estimate your energy need is to monitor your food intake and body weight over a period of time in which your activities are typical and are sufficient to maintain your health. If you keep an accurate record of all of the foods and beverages you consume and if your weight is in a healthy range and has not changed during the past few months, you can conclude that your energy budget is balanced. Your average daily Calorie intake is sufficient to meet your daily output—your need, therefore, is the same as your current intake.[23] At least three, and preferably seven, days or more of honest record-keeping are necessary because intakes and activities fluctuate from day to day.

An alternative method of determining energy need is based on energy output. The two major ways in which the body spends energy are (1) to fuel its **basal metabolism** and (2) to fuel its **voluntary activities**. Basal metabolism requires energy to support the body's work that goes on all of the time without our conscious awareness. A third energy component, the body's metabolic response to food, or the **thermic effect of food (TEF)**, uses up about 5 to 10 percent of a meal's energy value in stepped-up metabolism in the five or so hours after the meal.

Basal metabolism consumes a surprisingly large amount of fuel, and the **basal metabolic rate** (BMR) varies from person to person (see Figure 9–5). Depending on activity level, a person whose total energy needs are 2,000 Calories a day may spend as many as 1,000 to 1,600 of them to support basal metabolism. The hormone thyroxine directly controls basal metabolism—the less secreted, the lower the energy requirements for basal functions. The rate is lowest during sleep.* Many other factors also affect the BMR (see Table 9–3).

People often wonder whether they can speed up their metabolism to spend more daily energy. You cannot speed up your BMR very much *today*. You can, however, amplify the second component of your energy expenditure—your voluntary activities. If you do, you will spend more Calories today, and if you keep doing so day after day, your BMR will also increase.[24] Lean tissue is more metabolically active than fat tissue, so a way to speed up your BMR to the maximum possible rate is to make endurance and strength-building activities a daily habit so that your body composition moves toward the lean. A warning: some ads for weight-loss diets claim that certain substances, such as grapefruit or herbs,

> Chapter 10 is devoted to presenting details of how the body spends its energy during activity.

can elevate the BMR and thus promote weight loss. This claim is false. Any meal temporarily steps up energy expenditure due to the thermic effect of food; in the context of a mixed diet, the differences among foods are not large enough to be worth notice.

In voluntary activities, energy spent depends somewhat on your personal style. In general, the heavier the weight of the body parts you move in your activity and the longer the time you invest, the more Calories you expend.

KEY POINT

- Two major components of the "energy out" side of the body's energy budget are basal metabolism and voluntary activities. A third component of energy expenditure is the thermic effect of food. Many factors influence the basal metabolic rate.

---

*A measure of energy output taken while the person is awake but relaxed yields a slightly higher number called the *resting metabolic rate*, sometimes used in research.

The Body's Energy Balance

Figure 9–5

Components of Energy Expenditure

In most people, basal metabolism represents the person's largest expenditure of energy, followed by physical activity and the thermic effect of food.

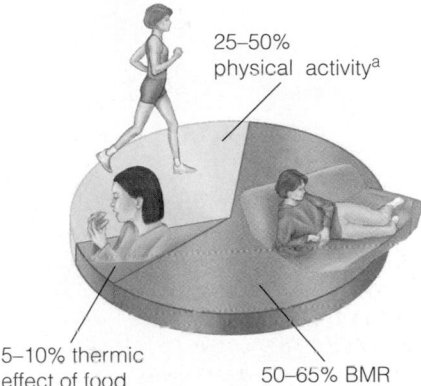

25–50% physical activity[a]

5–10% thermic effect of food

50–65% BMR

[a]For a sedentary person, physical activity may account for less than half as much energy as basal metabolism, whereas a very active person's activity may equal the energy cost of basal metabolism.

Source: Evaluation of Dietary Reference Intakes, Food and Nutrition Board, Institute of Medicine, Dietary Reference Intakes for Energy, Carbohydrate, Fibre, Fat, Fatty Acids, Cholesterol, Protein, and Amino Acids (Washington, D.C.: National Academies Press, 2002), p. 5–7.

basal metabolism the sum total of all of the involuntary activities that are necessary to sustain life, including circulation, respiration, temperature maintenance, hormone secretion, nerve activity, and new tissue synthesis, but excluding digestion and voluntary activities. Basal metabolism is the largest component of the average person's daily energy expenditure.

voluntary activities intentional activities (such as walking, sitting, or running) conducted by voluntary muscles.

thermic effect of food (TEF) the body's speeded-up metabolism in response to having eaten a meal; also called diet-induced thermogenesis.

basal metabolic rate (BMR) the rate at which the body uses energy to support its basal metabolism.

Table 9–3

Factors That Affect the BMR

Factor	Effect on BMR
Age	The BMR is higher in youth; as lean body mass declines with age, the BMR slows. Continued physical activity may prevent some of this decline.
Height	Tall people have a larger surface area, so their BMRs are higher.
Growth	Children and pregnant women have higher BMRs.
Body composition	The more lean tissue, the higher the BMR. A typical man has greater lean body mass than a typical woman, making his BMR higher.
Fever	Fever raises the BMR.
Stress	Stress hormones raise the BMR.
Environmental temperature	Adjusting to either heat or cold raises the BMR.
Fasting/starvation	Fasting/starvation hormones lower the BMR.
Malnutrition	Malnutrition lowers the BMR.
Thyroxine	The thyroid hormone thyroxine is a key BMR regulator; the more thyroxine produced, the higher the BMR.

The DRI Method of Estimating Energy Requirements

The DRI committee sets EER values by taking into account the ways in which energy is spent and by whom:

- *Gender.* Women generally have less lean body mass than men; in addition, women's menstrual hormones influence the BMR, raising it just prior to menstruation.

- *Age.* Because the BMR declines by an average of 5 percent per decade, age is a determining factor when calculating EER values.

- *Physical activity.* To estimate the energy spent on physical activity, the DRI committee clusters various activities according to the typical intensity of a day's efforts.

- *Body size and weight.* The higher BMR of taller and heavier people calls for height and weight to be factored in when estimating a person's EER.

Figure 9–6 explains how to determine your own EER, sufficient to maintain your present weight. Keep in mind, however, that due in part to biological variability, there may be as much as 20 percent error in the final calculation and that such calculations may be inaccurate when applied to elderly individuals and various ethnic groups. It requires a factor for physical activity that you can calculate by following the instructions given in Appendix E. Alternatively, the item in the margin at the top of the next page offers a quick and easy but more approximate way to determine your energy need.

Balancing food energy intake with physical activity can add to life's enjoyment.

© Blazej Lyjak/Shutterstock

Chapter 9 Energy Balance and Healthy Body Weight

NEL

Figure 9-6

How to Calculate Your Estimated Energy Requirement (EER)

A Quick and Easy Estimate of Energy Need
- Men: kg body weight × 24 = Cal/day
- Women: kg body weight × 22 = Cal/day

To convert pounds to kilograms, divide by 2.2.

1. Find the equation for your gender below.
2. Insert your age in years, your weight (wt) in kilograms, and your height (ht) in metres. To convert pounds to kilograms, divide by 2.2 (see the example below). Convert inches to metres by dividing by 39.37 (see example).
3. The final number needed to complete the equation is your physical activity factor (PA) as listed in the table at the end of this figure. To determine whether you are typically sedentary, low active, active, or very active, turn to Appendix E and follow the instructions to obtain your PA factor. The DRI committee provided these instructions because people tend to greatly overestimate their activity levels.
4. With your PA factor in place, proceed with your calculations.

Equations:

Women age 19 years and older:

$$EER = 354 - 6.91 \times age + PA \times [(9.36 \times wt) + (726 \times ht)]$$

Men age 19 years and older:

$$EER = 662 - 9.53 \times age + PA \times [(15.91 \times wt) + (539.6 \times ht)]$$

Example:

An active, 30-year-old man, 5 feet 11 inches (or 71 inches) tall, weighing 178 pounds. Convert pounds (lb) to kilograms and inches (in) to metres and insert them, along with his age, into the equation:

$$178 \text{ lb} \div 2.2 \text{ lb/kg} = 80.9 \text{ kg}$$
$$71 \text{ in} \div 39.37 \text{ in/m} = 1.8 \text{ m}$$
$$EER = 662 - 9.53 \times age + PA \times [(15.91 \times wt) + (539.6 \times ht)]$$
$$EER = 662 - 9.53 \times 30 + PA \times [(15.91 \times 80.9) + (539.6 \times 1.8)]$$

Determine his PA factor by following the instructions in Appendix E. This man's daily activity places him in the "Active" category in the table below. Insert his PA factor of 1.25 (from the second column of the table) into the equation.

$$EER = 662 - 9.53 \times 30 + 1.25 \times [(15.91 \times 80.9) + (539.6 \times 1.8)]$$

With all of the appropriate numbers in place, it is now possible to calculate as follows. (A reminder: perform functions within brackets and parentheses first, and multiplication before addition and subtraction.)

$$EER = 662 - 9.53 \times 30 + 1.25 \times [(15.91 \times 80.9) + (539.6 \times 1.8)]$$
$$EER = 662 - 9.53 \times 30 + 1.25 \times (1,287 + 971)$$
$$EER = 662 - 9.53 \times 30 + 1.25 \times 2,258$$
$$EER = 662 - 286 + 2,823$$
$$EER = 3,199$$

The EER for this man is about 3,200 Calories per day. His actual requirement probably falls within a range of perhaps 10 percent above and below this value.

Physical Activity Levels and PA Factors[a]

Description	Men's PA Factors	Women's PA Factors
Sedentary	1.0	1.0
Low active	1.11	1.12
Active	1.25	1.27
Very active	1.48	1.45

[a]*Appendix E provides instructions for determining your physical activity level, including Table E.1, which provides multiplying factors for determining the Physical Activity Level Scores for various activities.*

- The DRI committee has established a method for determining an individual's approximate energy requirement.

Body Weight versus Body Fatness

For most people, weighing on a scale provides a convenient and accessible way to measure body fatness, but researchers and health-care providers require more accurate assessments. This section describes some of the preferred methods of assessing overweight and underweight.

Body Mass Index

BMI values correlate significantly with body fatness, and experts use them to help evaluate a person's health risks associated with underweight or overweight. The inside back cover of this book provides tables of values in which to find and evaluate BMI values of both adults and adolescents.

No one can tell you exactly how much you should weigh, but with health as a value, you have a starting framework in the BMI table. Your weight should fall within the range that best supports your health. As a general guideline, overweight for adults is defined as a BMI of 25.0 through 29.9 and obesity as a BMI equal to or greater than 30. Racial differences are apparent when health risks are evaluated by way of BMI values—the risks associated with a high BMI appear to be greater for white people than for black people.[25] In fact, the health risks associated with obesity may not become apparent in some black women until a BMI of 37.[26]

> BMI was defined earlier on page 367.

The BMI values are most accurate in assessing degrees of obesity and are less useful for evaluating nonobese people's body fatness. The BMI values have two major drawbacks: they fail to indicate how much of a person's weight is fat and where that fat is located. These drawbacks limit the value of the BMI for use with

- Athletes (because their highly developed musculature falsely increases their BMI values)

- Pregnant and lactating women (because their increased weight is normal during childbearing)

- Adults over 65 (because BMI values are based on data collected from younger people and because people "grow shorter" with age)

The bodybuilder in the margin proves this point: with a BMI over 30, he would be classified as obese by BMI standards alone. Yet a clinician would find that his percentage of body fat is well below average and his waist circumference is within a healthy range. A diagnosis of obesity or overweight requires a BMI value plus some measure of body composition and fat distribution. There is no easy way to look inside a living person to measure bones and muscles, but several indirect measures can provide an approximation.

KEY POINT

- The BMI values mathematically correlate heights and weights with risks to health. They are especially useful for evaluating the health risks of obesity but fail to measure body composition or fat distribution.

Measures of Body Composition and Fat Distribution

A person who stands about 180 centimetres tall and weighs 68 kilograms (150 lb) carries about 14 of those kilograms as fat. The rest is mostly water and lean tissues: muscles; organs such as the heart, brain, and liver; and the bones of the skeleton (see Figure 9–7). This lean tissue is vital to health. The person who seeks to lose weight wants to lose fat, not this precious lean tissue. And for someone who wants to gain weight, it is desirable to gain lean and fat in proportion, not just fat.

Many bodybuilders would be judged to be obese by BMI standards alone. For example, their bodies may contain only 8 percent of their weight as fat, less than the average percentage for men, and their waist circumferences are likely within a healthy range.

© Damir Spanic/iStockphoto

Figure 9–7

Average Body Composition of Men and Women

The substantially greater fat tissue of women is normal and necessary for reproduction. Normal body fat percentages for people in the healthy BMI range are as follows:

- Male: 12–20%
- Female: 20–30%

36% muscle
24% organs
27% fat
13% bone

45% muscle
25% organs
15% fat
15% bone

© Andersen Foss/Blend Images/Jupiter Images

© rubberball/JupiterImages

Source: Data from R. E. C. Wildman and D. M. Medeiros, Advanced Human Nutrition *(Boca Raton, Fla.: CRC Press, 2000), pp. 321-323.*

Techniques for estimating body fatness include the following (see Figure 9–8):

- *Anthropometry.* Direct body measurements include the **fatfold test** and waist circumference. Fatfold measurements taken by a trained technician with standard calipers provide an accurate estimate of total body fat and a fair assessment of the fat's location (see Figure 9–8).[27] Waist circumference indicates visceral fatness (see Figure 9–9); above a certain girth, disease risks rise—even when BMI values are normal.[28]

KEY POINT

- A clinician can determine the percentage of fat in a person's body by measuring fatfolds, body density, or other parameters. Distribution of fat can be estimated by radiographic techniques, and central adiposity can be assessed by measuring waist circumference.

- *Density* (the measurement of body weight compared with volume). Lean tissue is denser than fat tissue, so the denser a person's body is, the more lean tissue it must contain. Density can be determined by **underwater weighing** or **air displacement plethysmography (ADP)**.

- *Conductivity.* Only lean tissue and water conduct electrical current; **bioelectrical impedance** measures how well a tiny harmless electrical charge is conducted through the lean tissue of the body (see Figure 9–8).

- *Radiographic techniques.* New technology yields images of body tissues and an assessment of body composition. For example, **dual energy X-ray absorptiometry (DEXA)** measures two beams of X-ray energy as they pass harmlessly through body tissues, giving high-quality assessments of total body fatness, fat distribution, and bone density (see Figure 9–8).[29]

fatfold test measurement of the thickness of a fold of skin on the back of the arm (over the triceps muscle), below the shoulder blade (subscapular), or in other places, using a caliper (depicted in Figure 9–8); also called *skinfold* test.

underwater weighing a measure of density and volume used to determine body fat content.

air displacement plethysmography (ADP) uses a piece of equipment referred to as the Bod Pod to measure air displacement by your body to estimate and track body composition changes over time.

bioelectrical impedance (im-PEE-dense) a technique for measuring body fatness by measuring the body's electrical conductivity.

dual energy X-ray absorptiometry (ab-sorp-tee-OM-eh-tree) **(DEXA)** a noninvasive method of determining total body fat, fat distribution, and bone density by passing two low-dose X-ray beams through the body. Also used in evaluation of osteoporosis.

Figure 9–8

Three Methods of Assessing Body Fatness[a]

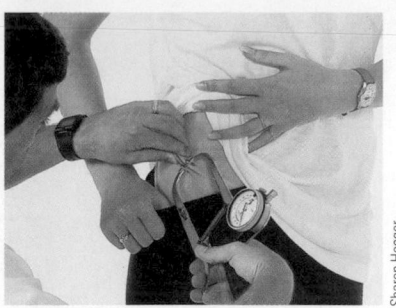

Fatfold measures can yield accurate results when a trained technician measures body fat by using a caliper to gauge the thickness of a fold of skin. Measurements are taken on the back of the arm (over the triceps), below the shoulder blade (subscapular), and in other places (including lower body sites) and are then compared with standards.

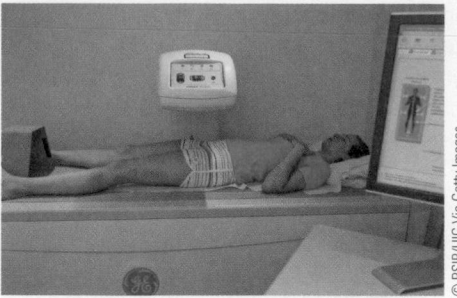

Dual energy X-ray absorptiometry (DEXA) employs two low-dose X-rays that differentiate among fat-free soft tissue (lean body mass), fat tissue, and bone tissue, providing a precise measurement of total fat and its distribution in all but extremely obese subjects.

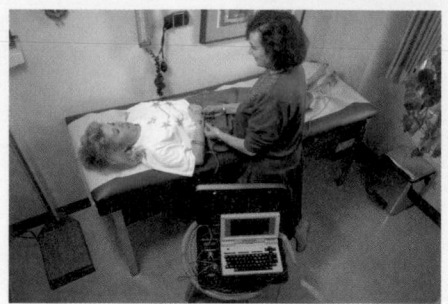

Bioelectrical impedance is simple, painless, and accurate when properly administered; the method determines body fatness by measuring conductivity. Lean tissue conducts a mild electric current; fat tissue does not.

[a]*Other methods include underwater weighing (hydrodensitometry), computed tomography, air displacement plethysmography (ADP), and magnetic resonance imaging.*

Figure 9–9

Measuring Waist Circumference

Using a nonstretching tape measure, measure around the body near the belly button. (The skeleton shows the tape position relative to the hip bone.) Exhale normally while taking the measurement. A healthy waist circumference for men is no larger than 102 centimetres (40 in.) and for women no larger than 88 centimetres (35 in.).

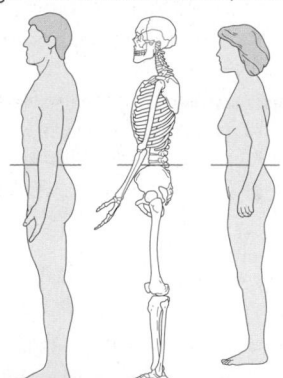

For a fair indication of whether you develop fat centrally, measure your waist as shown in Figure 9–8; then compare your measurement with these cut-off points:

• Men: 102 cm (40 in.)
• Women: 88 cm (35 in.)

Anyone with a waist measurement larger than these standards may carry an increased risk of disease along with the extra girth.

Each technique has strengths and weaknesses, but in all cases, the accuracy of the results depends on the skill of the clinician employing the technique and interpreting the results.

How Much Body Fat Is Ideal?

After you have a body fatness estimate, the question arises: What is the "ideal" amount of fat for a body to have? This prompts another question: Ideal for what? If the answer is "society's approval," be aware that fashion is fickle and many popular body shapes are not achievable by most people. Overweight children in particular suffer when they learn to dislike the bodies they have (see this chapter's Controversy).[30]

If the answer is "health," then the ideal depends partly on your gender and your age. A man of normal weight will have between 12 and 20 percent of body weight as fat, and a woman will have between 20 and 30 percent. Researchers draw the line when body fat exceeds 22 percent in young men, 25 percent in older men, 32 percent in younger women, and 35 percent in older women; age 40 is the dividing line between younger and older.

Besides gender and age, standards differ because of lifestyle and stage of life. For example, competitive endurance athletes need just enough body fat to provide fuel, insulate the body, and permit normal fat-soluble hormone activity but not so much fat as to weigh them down. An Arctic fisherman, in contrast, needs a blanket of extra fat to insulate against the cold. For a woman starting pregnancy, the outcome is compromised if she begins with too much or too little body fat. Below a threshold for body fat content set by heredity, some individuals become infertile, develop depression or abnormal hunger regulation, or become unable to keep warm. These thresholds are not the same for each function or in all individuals, and much remains to be learned about them.

KEY POINT

■ No single body composition weight suits everyone; needs vary by gender, lifestyle, and stage of life.

The Mystery of Obesity

Why do some people get fat? Why do some stay thin? Is weight controlled by hereditary metabolic factors or by environmental influences? Is it a matter of eating behaviours—and if so, what directs these behaviours, internal controls or a person's free will? Many factors, some of them *conflicting*, correlate with obesity (the margin lists some of them for interest), but *cause* is elusive. This section sorts through the pieces of the obesity puzzle, but no law says that only one cause must prevail. In all likelihood, internal and external factors operate together and in different combinations, beginning with the appetite and its controls.

Why Did I Eat That?

To repeat, food intake represents the "energy in" side of the body's energy budget. Scientists hope that by discovering how food intake is regulated in the body, they can devise effective strategies against obesity.[31] Eating behaviour seems to be regulated by a series of signals that fall into two broad functional categories: "go" mechanisms that stimulate eating and "stop" mechanisms that signal the body to cease or refrain from eating. One view of the process of food intake regulation is summarized in Figure 9–10.

"Go" Signals—Hunger and Appetite Most people recognize **hunger** as a strong, unpleasant sensation that signals a need for food, prompting them to search out food and eat. Hunger makes itself known roughly four to six hours after eating, after the food has left the stomach and much of the nutrient mixture has been absorbed by the intestine. Hunger is triggered by a contracting empty stomach, an empty small intestine, the stomach hormone **ghrelin** produced between meals, and chemical and nervous signals in the brain. Other factors influencing hunger may include the nutrients present in the bloodstream, the size and composition of the preceding meal, the weather (heat reduces food intake; cold increases it), exercise, sex hormones, and physical and mental illnesses.

The body's hunger response adapts quickly to changes in food intake. A person who restricts the amount of food consumed at each meal may feel extra hungry for a few days, but then hunger may diminish for a time. During this period, a large meal may make the person feel uncomfortably full, partly because the stomach's capacity has adapted to a smaller quantity of food. At this time, a dieter may report, "My stomach has shrunk," but the stomach organ itself doesn't shrink except in prolonged starvation.

Stomach adaptation may seem to be good news for dieters, but at some point in food deprivation, hunger returns with a vengeance and can lead to bouts of overeating that more than make up for the Calories lost during the deprivation period. And just as the stomach's capacity can adapt to small meals, it quickly adapts to larger and larger quantities of food, until a meal of normal size no longer satisfies. This observation may partly explain why obesity is on the rise: popular demand has led to larger and larger servings of food, and stomachs have adapted to accommodate them.

Figure 2–9 on page 52 in Chapter 2 demonstrated how portion sizes have increased over recent decades.

Hunger is just one signal determining whether a person will eat. **Appetite** also initiates eating and, sometimes, overeating. A person can experience appetite without hunger. For example, seeing and smelling a freshly baked apple pie after finishing a big meal can stimulate release of the brain's **endorphins**, pleasure molecules that create an appetite for the pie despite an already full stomach. In contrast, a person who is ill or under stress may physically need food but have no appetite.

Other factors affecting appetite are as follows:

- Hormones (for example, the sex hormones influence food consumption)
- Inborn appetites (inborn preferences for fatty, salty, and sweet tastes)[32]
- Learned preferences, aversions, and timings (for example, cravings for favourite foods, fear of new foods, eating according to the clock, desiring larger portions)

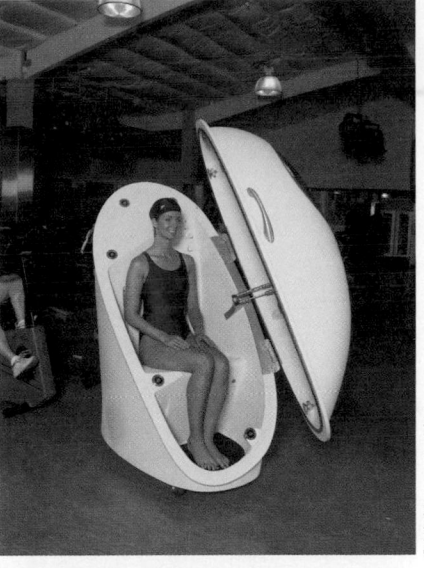

The Bod Pod is a tool for measuring a person's body fatness using air displacement plethysmography (ADP).

© Life Measurement, Inc.

Research Has Linked Obesity with

- Birth order; number of brothers
- Divorced/single parents; nonprofessional or unemployed parents
- Early menstruation
- Ethnicity
- Exposure to a variety of foods; fast-food consumption
- Fat intake; protein intake; carbohydrate intake
- Sugar-sweetened beverage consumption and weight gain
- Increased wealth (in developing nations)
- Less leisure time; international travel; geographic location
- Lower education level; lower social class
- Maternal famine or obesity during gestation
- Meal skipping; meals eaten away from home
- Napping habits; sleep deprivation
- Less frequent alcohol intake; high alcohol intake
- Sedentary behaviour; television watching
- Substandard housing
- Many more

Sources: Adapted from L. Grivetti, Psychology and cultural aspects of energy, Nutrition Reviews 59 (2001): S5,S12; V.S. Malik and others, American Journal of Clinical Nutrition 84(2) 104:274,288.

hunger the physiological need to eat, experienced as a drive for obtaining food; an unpleasant sensation that demands relief.

ghrelin (GREH-lin) a hormone released by the stomach that signals the hypothalamus of the brain to stimulate eating.

Figure 9–10

Hunger, Appetite, Satiation, and Satiety

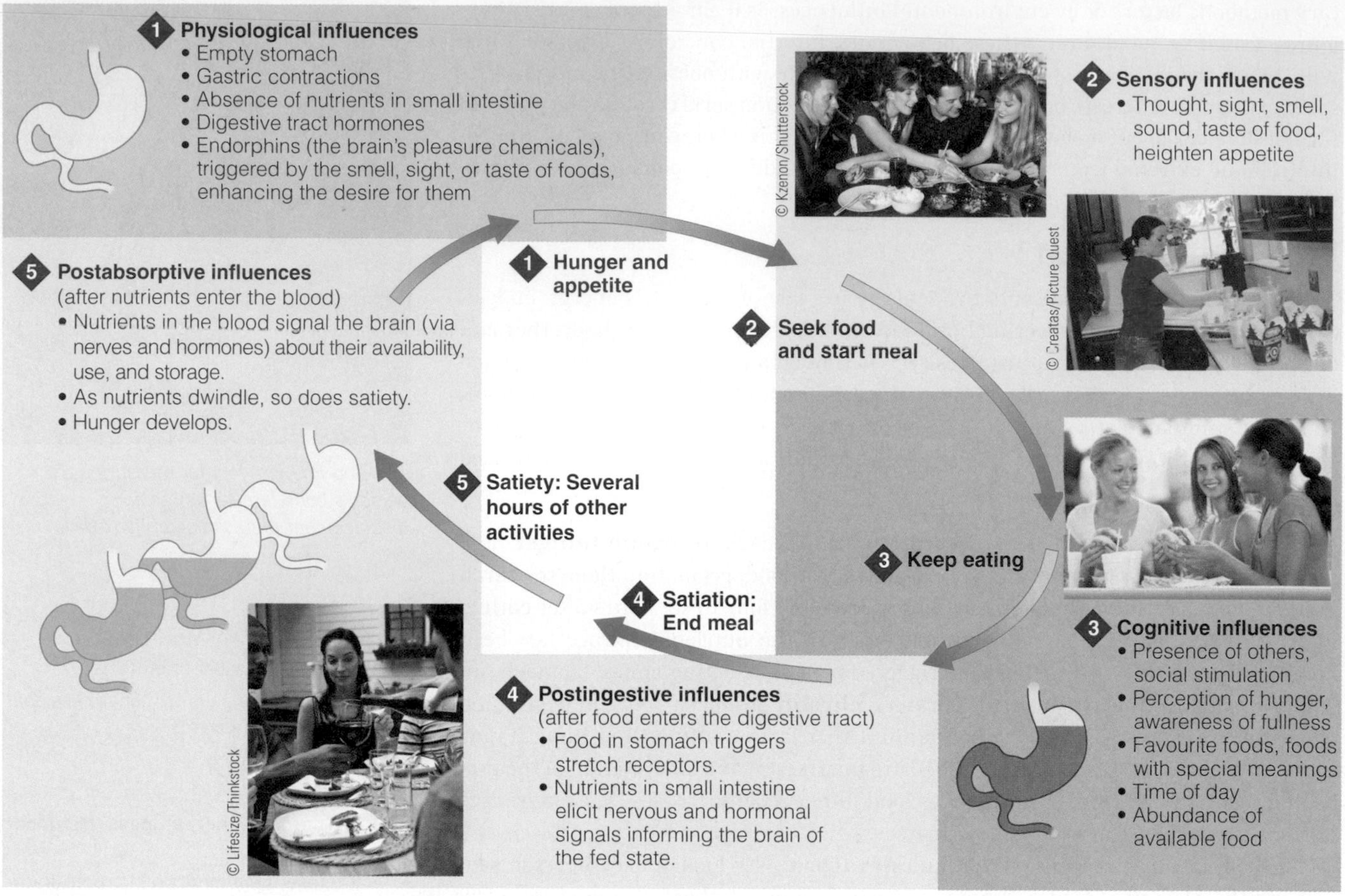

1 Physiological influences
- Empty stomach
- Gastric contractions
- Absence of nutrients in small intestine
- Digestive tract hormones
- Endorphins (the brain's pleasure chemicals), triggered by the smell, sight, or taste of foods, enhancing the desire for them

5 Postabsorptive influences
(after nutrients enter the blood)
- Nutrients in the blood signal the brain (via nerves and hormones) about their availability, use, and storage.
- As nutrients dwindle, so does satiety.
- Hunger develops.

1 Hunger and appetite

2 Seek food and start meal

5 Satiety: Several hours of other activities

4 Satiation: End meal

2 Sensory influences
- Thought, sight, smell, sound, taste of food, heighten appetite

3 Keep eating

3 Cognitive influences
- Presence of others, social stimulation
- Perception of hunger, awareness of fullness
- Favourite foods, foods with special meanings
- Time of day
- Abundance of available food

4 Postingestive influences
(after food enters the digestive tract)
- Food in stomach triggers stretch receptors.
- Nutrients in small intestine elicit nervous and hormonal signals informing the brain of the fed state.

© Kzenon/Shutterstock
© Creatas/Picture Quest
© Monkey Business/fotolia
© Lifesize/Thinkstock

- Customary eating habits (e.g., whether or not each meal includes dessert)
- Social interactions (cultural or religious acceptability of foods, companionship)
- Some disease states (obesity may be associated with increased taste sensitivity, whereas colds, flu, and zinc deficiency reduce taste sensitivity)
- Appetite stimulants or depressants and mood-altering drugs affecting food intake
- Environmental conditions (people often prefer hot foods in cold weather and vice versa)

KEY POINT

- Hunger is stimulated by an absence of food in the digestive tract. Appetite can occur with or without hunger.

"Stop" Signals—Satiation and Satiety   At some point during a meal, the brain receives messages from several sources that enough food has been eaten.[33] Often called **satiation**, this condition originates from the presence of food in the upper digestive tract (consult Figure 9–10 again). When the stomach stretches to accommodate a meal, nerve receptors in the stomach fire, sending a signal to the brain that the stomach is full. As nutrients from the meal enter the small intestine, they stimulate receptor nerves and trigger the release of hormones that provide the brain with information about the meal just eaten. The brain also detects absorbed nutrients passing by in the blood and releases neurotransmitters that suppress food intake in response. Together, stomach distention and nutrients in the small intestine trigger signals that inform the brain's

Chapter 3 described the brain's hypothalamus.

appetite the psychological desire to eat; a learned motivation and a positive sensation that accompanies the sight, smell, or thought of appealing foods.

endorphins (en-DOOR-fins) endogenous opiates; compounds of the brain whose actions mimic those of opiate drugs (morphine, heroin) in reducing pain and producing pleasure. In appetite control, endorphins are released on seeing, smelling, or tasting delicious food and are believed to enhance the drive to eat or continue eating.

satiation (SAY-she-AY-shun) the perception of fullness that builds throughout a meal, eventually reaching the degree of fullness and satisfaction that halts eating. Satiation generally determines how much food is consumed at one sitting.

hypothalamus about the size and nature of the meal. The response: satiation occurs; the eater feels full and stops eating.

After a meal, the feeling of **satiety** continues to suppress hunger and allows for a period of some hours in which the person is free to dance, study, converse, wonder, fall in love, and concentrate on endeavours other than eating. At some later point, signals from the digestive tract once again sound the alert that more food is needed.

Hunger and satiety are not equal in strength. Hunger, a life-or-death drive for survival, strongly stimulates eating behaviour, whereas satiation and satiety exert weaker control over food intake and often can be ignored. The regulation of the human appetite is thus unbalanced, tipping in favour of food consumption.[34] People attempting to reduce their food intakes often must fight against this imbalance. After hours of annoying hunger pains, they may overeat when mealtime arrives but regret it later, vowing to "do better" by starving again. A destructive cycle of starving and binge eating ensues, with no weight loss to show for the effort. Researchers are exploring both the body's satiety mechanisms and the satiety value of foods in hopes of devising ways of assisting people who must reduce their food intakes for health.

KEY POINT

- Satiation occurs when the digestive organs signal the brain that enough food has been consumed. Satiety is the feeling of fullness that lasts until the next meal. Hunger outweighs satiety in the appetite control system.

Leptin: A Satiety Hormone   **Leptin** is a peptide hormone primarily produced by the adipose tissue. Leptin travels to the brain via the bloodstream and is directly linked with both appetite control and body fatness. Some leptin is also produced in the stomach, where it may contribute to satiety.[35] As part of the brain's appetite-regulating chemistry, leptin suppresses appetite and food intake between meals.[36] Leptin operates on a feedback mechanism—a gain in body fatness stimulates leptin production, which, in turn, reduces food consumption, resulting in fat loss. Fat loss brings the opposite effect—suppression of leptin and increased appetite.[37] Thus, the fat tissue that produces leptin is ultimately controlled by it.[38]

A peptide is a molecule made of two or more amino acids linked together (see Chapter 6).

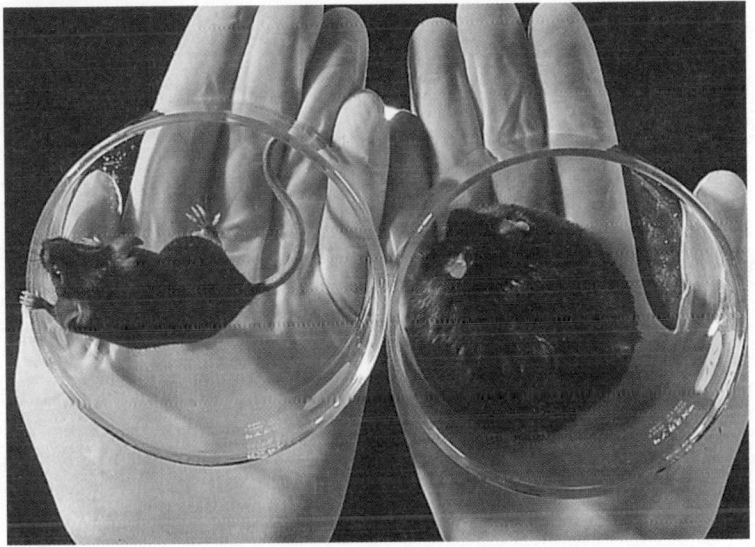

The mouse on the right is genetically obese—it lacks the gene for producing leptin. The mouse on the left is also genetically obese but remains lean because it receives leptin.

© Remi BENALI/Gamma-Rapho/Getty Images

The discovery of leptin dramatically changed the scientific view of adipose tissue. Once viewed as a metabolically sluggish storage depot for lipids, fat tissue has gained respect as a hormonally active regulatory tissue with widespread effects on the body.[39] In addition to its appetite function, leptin signals the female reproductive system about body fat reserves, may assist in the sexual maturation process, stimulates growth of new blood vessels in the cornea of the eye and elsewhere, has a constricting effect on the arteries, assists in the formation of blood cells in bone marrow, and helps support a normal immune response.[40] Scientists hope to one day harness the power of leptin for treating obesity, but, so far, clinical trials have been disappointing.[41]

KEY POINT

- The adipose tissue hormone leptin suppresses the appetite in response to a gain in body fat.

Energy Nutrients and Satiety   A popular idea today is that foods high in fat, protein, or slowly digested carbohydrates may sustain satiety longer than foods made from refined grains—that is, a food's satiety value may be influenced by its

satiety (sah-TIE-eh-tee) the perception of fullness that lingers in the hours after a meal and inhibits eating until the next mealtime. Satiety generally determines the length of time between meals.

leptin an appetite-suppressing hormone produced in the fat cells that conveys information about body fatness to the brain; believed to be involved in the maintenance of body composition (*leptos* means "slender").

glycemic index.[42] Thus far, research results are mixed: a recent review of the literature describes at least 15 studies in which a diet ranking low on the glycemic index reduced or delayed hunger and another 16 studies that found the opposite effect or no effect.[43] In the negative studies, a diet based on refined-grain foods such as soft breads, crackers and chips, certain cereals, and potatoes was just as satisfying as the diets based on low-glycemic index foods, and weight loss was practically identical on both diets.[44]

> The glycemic index was defined in Chapter 4 (page 134).

Of the three energy-yielding nutrients, protein is perhaps the most satiating.[45] A meal providing protein may quickly lend a feeling of fullness, an effect that could account for some of the popularity of high-protein weight-loss diets. (This chapter's Consumer Corner addresses these diets.) Fat in food is also well known for its satiety effects. Fat or protein in a meal triggers the release of a hormone produced by the intestine that slows stomach emptying and prolongs the feeling of fullness after a meal.[46] Researchers have also reported increased satiety from foods high in fibre or water and even from foods that have been puffed up with air.[47] As dieters await news of foods that might be useful against hunger, researchers have not yet identified any one food, nutrient, or attribute that is especially effective.

KEY POINT

- Some foods may confer greater satiety than others.

Inside-the-Body Causes of Obesity

Although interesting and important, findings about appetite regulation do not fully explain why some people gain too much body fatness while others stay lean. On the opposite side of the energy budget, the "energy out" side, many theories have emerged to explain obesity in terms of metabolic function. Whenever discussions turn to metabolism, the topic of genetics follows close behind.

Selected Metabolic Theories of Obesity   Metabolic theories attempt to explain variations in the ease with which people gain or lose weight when eating more or less food energy than they expend. When given an extra 1,000 Calories of food a day for 100 days, some people gain 14 kilograms (30 lb), but others gain less than 4.5 kilograms (10 lb). Those who gain more use Calories efficiently: they have a "thrifty" metabolism. Similarly, some people lose more weight faster than others on comparable exercise regimens. The **set-point theory**, which states that the body somehow strives to achieve and maintain a particular body weight, offers an explanation for this phenomenon (see Table 9–4).

One area of difference in energy expenditure involves production of heat, or **thermogenesis**. In metabolic processes, enzymes "waste" a small percentage of energy, radiated away as heat. Some processes, however, expend copious energy in thermogenesis, producing abundant heat without performing any useful work. In radiating more energy away as heat, the body can spend more, rather than store more, excess energy. It may seem logical, then, to strive to manipulate metabolic enzymes to step up thermogenesis, but caution is required. At a level of activity not far beyond that of normal functioning, energy-wasting activity kills the cells.[48]

KEY POINT

- Metabolic theories attempt to explain obesity on the basis of molecular functioning.

Genetics and Obesity   Genetic makeup greatly influences how efficiently the body uses up or stores energy. A few relatively rare types of obesity arise primarily from genetic causes. That is, a few known genetic differences change metabolic processes in ways that reliably cause excessive gains of body fat.[49] In the great majority of obesity cases, however, an inherited *tendency* toward developing obesity is evident but is not the only determinant.

set-point theory the theory that the body tends to maintain a certain weight by means of its own internal controls.

thermogenesis the generation and release of body heat associated with the breakdown of body fuels. *Adaptive thermogenesis* describes adjustments in energy expenditure related to changes in environment such as cold and to physiological events such as underfeeding or trauma.

Table 9–4

Selected Theories of Metabolic Causes of Obesity

Theory	Mechanism of Action
Enzyme theory	Excess fat storage may stem from elevated concentrations of an enzyme, **lipoprotein lipase (LPL)**, that enables fat cells to store triglycerides. The more LPL, the more easily fat cells store lipid, and the more likely the body will remain obese. The fat cells of obese people contain more LPL than the fat cells of lean people and therefore reach a large size quickly.
Fat cell number theory	Body fatness is determined by both the number and the size of fat cells. Fat cells increase in number during the growing years, tapering off in adulthood. Fat cell number may increase more rapidly in obese children than in lean children, leading to a lifelong tendency toward obesity.
Set-point theory	The body may "choose" a weight it wants to be and defend that weight by regulating behaviours and metabolic activities. Just as a thermostat setting triggers a heater to run when air temperature falls and turn off when warmth is restored, whenever weight is lost or gained, the set-point mechanism changes metabolic energy expenditure to restore the "chosen" body weight. The theories of thermogenesis, below, explain possible mechanisms by which the body defends its set point.
Thermogenesis I: Energy-wasting proteins and brown fat theory	Proteins control the body's heat production, or thermogenesis. A type of adipose tissue, brown fat, has abundant energy-wasting proteins that specialize in converting energy to heat. Whereas regular white fat cells have a sluggish metabolism and conserve and store fat energy, brown fat cells actively metabolize fat, releasing its stored energy as heat. Brown fat is more abundant in lean animals than in fat ones, and this theory states that a person with more brown fat and therefore more energy-wasting proteins may stay leaner. Human infants have abundant brown fat, but the amount dwindles with age.
Thermogenesis II: Adaptive thermogenesis theory	Many tissues, such as muscle, spleen, and bone marrow, convert stored energy into heat in response to cold temperature, physical conditioning, overfeeding, starvation, trauma, and other stress. Heat is also produced to "waste" fuel without useful work when energy supplies are too high; conversely, with low energy supplies, energy is conserved. Genetic inheritance is thought to determine the efficiency of this system. Dieters' efforts are often thwarted when, on reducing food intake, metabolism slows and heat production diminishes.
Thermogenesis III: Diet-induced thergenesis theory	The thermic effect of food varies between obese and nonobese people. In lean people who have just eaten a meal, energy use speeds up for a while, but in many obese people, no change in energy use occurs after eating. In theory, this small difference in energy expenditure may account for an accumulation of body fat, but no studies have shown this conclusively. Overweight people often spend more energy each day than lean people do because their heavier bodies require more energy to move and maintain.

The role of genetics in obesity is demonstrated in children, whose body fatness often closely resembles that of their biological parents.[50] For someone with at least one obese parent, the chance of becoming obese is estimated to fall between 40 and 70 percent. Adopted children tend to be similar in weight to their biological parents, not to their adoptive parents. Studies of twins bear this out: identical twins (assumed to have identical genes) are twice as likely as fraternal twins to weigh the same when reared apart in similar households. When identical twins are reared apart in household environments that *differ* in terms of smoking, eating behaviours, nutrient intakes, and physical activity, however, their weights are more often related to adoptive parents' lifestyle habits.[51] Such findings demonstrate that although genetic inheritance strongly influences a person's tendency to become obese, lifestyle choices determine whether that tendency is realized.[52]

If certain genes carry the instructions for making proteins involved in energy metabolism, then these genes might reasonably be expected to vary between fat and lean people. So far, however, the search for new obesity treatments through genetic research has been disappointing. For example, great scientific interest followed the discovery of a gene whose protein product seemed promising for influencing thermogenesis or fat metabolism in ways that oppose obesity.[53] In animals,

lipoprotein lipase (LPL) an enzyme mounted on the surface of fat cells that splits triglycerides in the blood into fatty acids and glycerol to be absorbed into the cells for reassembly and storage.

evidence of this protein is widespread in the body tissues of the leanest animals. In some children, a slight variation of the gene that produces the protein is associated with overfatness.[54] Further study, however, dashed early hopes for a genetic switch to control obesity. The protein's function now appears more related to immunity than to energy regulation or fat metabolism.[55]

> To review protein synthesis, see Figure 6–6 on page 212 in Chapter 6.

Genes clearly influence a person's tendency to gain weight or stay lean, but does this mean that obesity is inevitable in those whose genes predispose them to develop it? This fatalistic view is put to rest by a simple observation: obesity rates have greatly increased in recent decades wherever people enjoy conditions of prosperity and abundance. During the same time, the human genome has remained constant. This means that although an individual's genetic inheritance may make obesity likely, the disease of obesity cannot develop unless the environment—factors outside the body—provides the means of doing so.

KEY POINT

- A person's genetic inheritance greatly influences the likelihood of obesity. Genetic researchers are identifying potential genetic links with obesity development.

Outside-the-Body Causes of Obesity

Food is a source of pleasure. Being creatures of free will, people can override signals of satiety and hunger and eat whenever they wish, especially when tempted with delicious options and large servings. People also seek ease, and our increasing dependence on labour-saving inventions, such as automobiles and elevators, greatly decreases the energy we spend in activities required for daily living.

External Cues to Overeating Almost everyone has had the experience of walking into a food store, not feeling particularly hungry, and, after viewing the vast array of goodies, walking out snacking on a favourite treat. A classic experiment showed that *variety* influences animals to eat even if they are not hungry. Rats, known to maintain body weight with precision when fed standard rat chow, rapidly became obese when fed "cafeteria style" on a variety of rich, palatable foods. Many people, too, are prone to overconsume when presented with a wide variety of delectable foods, such as sweets, snacks, condiments, and main dishes, often without being aware of doing so.[56] Conversely, consumption of a wide variety of *vegetables* but few treats correlates with lower body fatness.[57]

Overeating also occurs in response to complex human sensations such as loneliness, yearning, craving, addiction, or compulsion. Some people experience food cravings when feeling down or depressed. Favourite foods pick them up for a while. Other people respond to other external stimuli such as the time of day ("I'm not hungry, but it's time for lunch").

Any kind of stress can cause overeating. ("What do I do when I'm grieving? Eat. What do I do when I'm concentrating? Eat!") The familiar foods that stressed people favour even have a calming name—*comfort* foods.[58] Although food availability, cravings, and stress can lead to the overconsumption of food energy, they cannot fully explain obesity development because even many thin people are susceptible to them and other people cannot eat at all when under stress.

Food Pricing, Availability, and Advertising High-Calorie fast foods are relatively inexpensive, widely available, heavily advertised, and wonderfully delicious, but a steady diet of them correlates with obesity.[59] By one estimate, 40 percent of the recent jump in U.S. body weights may be due to low food prices alone.[60] Controversy 11 in Chapter 11 revisits these issues, but consider the following: if price, availability, and advertising attract consumers of fast foods, can they do the same for nutritious, low-Calorie choices such as fruit, vegetables, or yogurt? At least one experiment seems to indicate that they can. When researchers dropped the price of more nutritious options by half and made them readily available in workplace vending machines and school cafeterias, adults and students alike quadrupled their purchases of fresh fruit and doubled their purchases of baby carrot sticks.[61]

Enjoying an occasional Calorie-rich treat or meal does not destine the eater for obesity, but such foods are widely advertised, available, and inexpensive, making overconsumption of Calories likely. Moderation remains a bedrock of nutrition common sense and holds true with regard to all kinds of foods.

Physical Inactivity   Some people may be obese not because they eat too much but because they move too little. Diet histories from obese people often report energy intakes that are similar to, or even less than, those of others. (Diet histories may not be accurate records of actual intakes, though; people commonly underreport intakes of high-Calorie foods.[62]) Some obese people are so inactive, however, that even when they eat less than lean people, they still have an energy surplus.

Such inactivity is a recent phenomenon. One hundred years ago, 30 percent of the energy used in farm and factory work came from human muscle power; today, only 1 percent does. The same trend follows at home, at work, at school, at play, and in transportation.[63]

Conversely, people who are sufficiently active can eat enough food to obtain the nutrients they need without the threat of weight gain. This activity must be the active kind, not passive motion such as being jiggled by a machine at a health spa or being massaged. It takes active moving of muscles to affect energy balance.

Despite benefits to body composition and health from regular physical activity, Canada seems locked in an epidemic of inactivity. For many people, television watching, video games, and computer entertainment have all but replaced outdoor work and play as the major leisure time activity. The Think Fitness feature underscores the importance of physical activity in weight management, and Table 9–5 lists the energy costs of some activities.

- Controversy 11 explores some issues regarding the roles of society in the current obesity epidemic and discusses potential actions to reduce the nation's fatness.

Physical Activity for Weight Loss or Maintenance

1. Choose moderate activities.
2. Move large muscle groups.
3. Invest longer times in physical activity.
4. Adopt informal strategies to be more active.

Physical Activity for Building Lean Body Mass

1. Choose strength-building exercises.
2. Use a balanced exercise routine.
3. Perform exercises with increasing intensity.
4. Adopt informal strategies to be more active.

Think Fitness ⟵ move it!   Activity for a Healthy Body Weight

Some people believe that physical activity must be long and arduous to achieve fat loss. Not so. A brisk, 30-minute walk each day can help significantly.[64] To achieve the DRI committee's "active lifestyle" category requires walking for an hour a day.[65] A useful strategy is to incorporate bits of physical activity into your daily schedule in many simple, small-scale ways. Work in the garden; work your abdominal muscles while you stand in line; stand up straight; walk up stairs; fidget while sitting down; tighten your buttocks each time you get up from your chair. Small energy expenditures add up to significant contributions. The items in the margin above provide some tips for staying active, and many more details are found in Chapter 10.

End of Story?   Anyone involved in a good mystery wants to know how it ends. In the case of the causes of obesity, no one yet knows which of the suspects is the real culprit, and until evidence proves otherwise, any or all may be guilty as charged. In real life, the best way for most people to attain a healthy body weight boils down to control in three areas: diet, physical activity, and behaviour. Later sections focus on these three areas. The next section delves into the details of how, exactly, the body loses and gains weight. For further information on the current obesity epidemic and how we can gain some control, see Controversy 11 in Chapter 11.

The Mystery of Obesity

Table 9-5

Energy Spent in Activities

To determine the Calorie cost of an activity, multiply the number listed by your weight in pounds. Then multiply by the number of minutes spent performing the activity. Example: Jessica (57 kg) rode a horse at a trot for 25 min: 0.114 × 57 = 6.5; 6.5 × 25 = 163.

Activity	Cal/kg body weight/min
Aerobic dance (vigorous)	0.136
Basketball (vigorous, full court)	0.213
Bicycling	
21 km/h	0.099
24 km/h	0.108
27 km/h	0.125
30 km/h	0.167
34 km/h	0.198
37 km/h	0.240
40 km/h	0.306
Canoeing (flat water, moderate pace)	0.099
Cross-country skiing, 13 km/h	0.229
Golf (carrying clubs)	0.099
Handball	0.172
Horseback riding (trot)	0.114
Rowing (vigorous)	0.213
Running	
8 km/h	0.134
10 km/h	0.163
12 km/h	0.207
14 km/h	0.227
16 km/h	0.251
18 km/h	0.288
Soccer (vigorous)	0.213
Studying	0.024
Swimming	
18 m/min	0.070
41 m/min	0.128
45 m/min	0.154
Table tennis (skilled)	0.099
Tennis (beginner)	0.070
Walking (brisk pace)	
6 km/h	0.077
7 km/h	0.106
Weightlifting	
Light-to-moderate effort	0.053
Vigorous effort	0.106
Wheelchair basketball	0.185
Wheeling self in wheelchair	0.066

KEY POINT

- Studies of human behaviour identify stimuli that lead to overeating. Food pricing, availability, and advertising influence food choices. Physical inactivity is clearly linked with overfatness.

How the Body Loses and Gains Weight

The causes of obesity may be complex, but the body's energy balance is straightforward. The balance between the energy you take in and the energy you spend determines whether you will gain, lose, or maintain body *fat*. A change in body *weight* of a pound or two may not indicate a change in body fat—it can reflect shifts in body fluid content, in bone minerals, in lean tissues such as muscles, or in the contents of the bladder or digestive tract. A change often correlates with the time of day: people generally weigh the least before breakfast. One of the most important things for people concerned with weight control to realize is that quick, large changes in weight are not usually changes in fat alone—or even at all.

The type of tissue lost or gained depends on how you go about losing or gaining it. To lose fluid, for example, you can take a "water pill" (diuretic), which will cause the kidneys to siphon extra water from the blood into the urine. Or you can engage in intense exercise while wearing heavy clothing in hot weather and lose abundant fluid in sweat. (Both practices are dangerous and are not being recommended here.) To gain water weight, you can overconsume salt and water; for a few hours, your body will retain water until it manages to excrete the salt. (This, too, is not recommended.) Most quick weight-change schemes promote large changes in body fluids that register dramatic, but temporary, changes on the scale and accomplish little weight change in the long run.

> Chapter 8 gave details about the body's water balance.

One other practice is not recommended: smoking. Each year, many adolescents, especially girls, take up smoking to control weight.[66] Nicotine blunts feelings of hunger, so when hunger strikes, a smoker can reach for a cigarette instead of food. Fear of weight gain sometimes deters people from quitting smoking. Smokers do tend to weigh less than nonsmokers, and many gain weight when they stop smoking. The best advice to smokers wanting to quit seems to be to adjust diet and exercise habits to maintain weight during and after cessation. The best advice to a person flirting with the idea of taking up smoking for weight control is don't do it—many thousands of people who became addicted as teenagers die from tobacco-related illnesses each year.

Moderate Weight Loss versus Rapid Weight Loss

Being able to eat periodically, store fuel, and then use up that fuel between meals is a great advantage. The between-meal interval is normally about 4 to 6 waking hours—about the length of time the body takes to use up most of the readily available fuel—or 12 to 18 hours at night, when body systems slow down and the need is less.

When you eat less food energy than you need, your body draws on its stored fuel to keep going. If a person exercises appropriately, moderately restricts Calories, and consumes an otherwise balanced diet that meets protein and carbohydrate needs, the body is forced to use up its stored fat for energy. Gradual weight loss will occur. This is preferred to rapid weight loss because lean body mass is spared and fat is lost.

The Body's Response to Fasting
If a person doesn't eat for, say, three whole days, then the body makes one adjustment after another. Less than a day into the fast, the liver's glycogen is essentially exhausted.[67] Where, then, can the body obtain *glucose* to keep its nervous system going? Not from the muscles' glycogen because that is reserved for the muscles' own use. Not from the abundant fat stores most people carry because these are of no use to the nervous system. Fat cannot be converted to glucose—the body

lacks enzymes for this conversion.* The muscles, heart, and other organs use fat as fuel, but at this stage, the nervous system needs glucose. The body does, however, possess enzymes that can convert protein to glucose. Therefore, the underfed body sacrifices the proteins in its lean tissue to supply raw materials from which to make glucose.

If the body were to continue to consume its lean tissue unchecked, death would ensue within about 10 days. After all, in addition to skeletal muscle, the blood proteins, liver, digestive tract linings, heart muscle, and lung tissue—all vital tissues—are being burned as fuel. (Fasting or starving people remain alive only until their stores of fat are gone or until half of their lean tissue is gone, whichever comes first.) To prevent this, the body plays its last ace: it converts fat into compounds that the nervous system can adapt for use and so forestalls the end. This process is ketosis, first mentioned in Chapter 4 as an adaptation to prolonged fasting or carbohydrate deprivation.

In ketosis, instead of breaking down fat molecules all the way to carbon dioxide and water, the body takes partially broken-down fat fragments and combines them to make **ketone bodies**, compounds that are normally kept to low levels in the blood. It converts some amino acids—those that cannot be used to make glucose—to ketone bodies, too. These ketone bodies circulate in the bloodstream and help feed the brain; about half of the brain's cells can make the enzymes needed to use ketone bodies for energy. After about 10 days of fasting, the brain and nervous system can meet most of their energy needs using ketone bodies.

Thus, indirectly, the nervous system begins to feed on the body's fat stores. Ketosis reduces the nervous system's need for glucose, spares the muscle and other lean tissue from being devoured quickly, and prolongs the starving person's life. Thanks to ketosis, a healthy person starting with average body fat content can live totally deprived of food for as long as six to eight weeks. Figure 9–11 reviews how energy is used during both feasting and fasting.

Respected, wise people in many cultures have practised fasting as a periodic discipline. The body tolerates short-term fasting, and at least in animal studies, short-term fasting seems to benefit the body in some ways (see Chapter 14), although there is no evidence that the body becomes internally "cleansed," as some believe.[68] Fasting may harm the body, however, when ketosis upsets the acid–base balance of the blood or when fasting promotes excessive mineral losses in the urine. In as little as 24 hours of fasting, the intestinal lining begins to lose its integrity.[69] Food deprivation also leads to a tendency to overeat or even binge when food becomes available. The effect seems to last beyond the point when weight is restored to normal; people with eating disorders often report that a fast or a severely restricted diet heralded the beginning of their loss of control over eating. This indictment applies to extreme dieting and fasting but not to the moderate weight-management strategies described later in this chapter.[70]

If you want to lose weight, fasting is not the best way. While the body's lean tissues continue to be degraded, tissues are deprived of nutrients they need to assemble new enzymes, red and white blood cells, and other vital components. The body also slows its metabolism to conserve energy. A diet only moderately restricted in Calories promotes a greater rate of *weight* loss, a faster rate of *fat* loss, and the retention of more lean tissue than a severely restricted fast. Additionally, moderate diets are sustainable—they provide the best chance at long-term weight management.

The Body's Response to a Low-Carbohydrate Diet Any diet too low in carbohydrate brings about responses that are similar to fasting. As carbohydrate runs out, the body breaks down fat and protein for energy and forms ketone bodies to feed the brain. To prevent these effects, the DRI committee sets a minimum intake for carbohydrate at 130 grams per day but recommends far more for health—between 45 and 65 percent of total Calories from carbohydrate, an amount associated with low chronic disease risks.

Low-carbohydrate, high-protein diets have been heavily promoted for weight loss, and they take many guises, each enjoying a new surge of popularity that subsequently fades away. These diets continue to sell, however, thanks to a sizable weight loss in the early stages of dieting that inspires new dieters to keep trying the diets. The sales

---

*Glycerol, which makes up 5 % of fat, can yield glucose but is a negligible source.

How the Body Loses and Gains Weight

Smoking May Keep Some People's Weight Down, but at What Cost?

- Cancer
- Chronic lung diseases
- Heart disease
- Low-birthweight babies
- Miscarriage
- Osteoporosis
- Shortened life span
- Sudden infant death
- Many others

In Early Food Deprivation

- The nervous system cannot use fat as fuel; it can use only glucose.
- Body fat cannot be converted to glucose.
- Body protein can be converted to glucose.

In Later Food Deprivation

- Ketone bodies help feed the nervous system and so help spare tissue protein.

ketone bodies acidic compounds derived from fat and certain amino acids. Normally rare in the blood, they help feed the brain during times when too little carbohydrate is available. Also defined in Chapter 4.

Figure 9–11

Feasting and Fasting

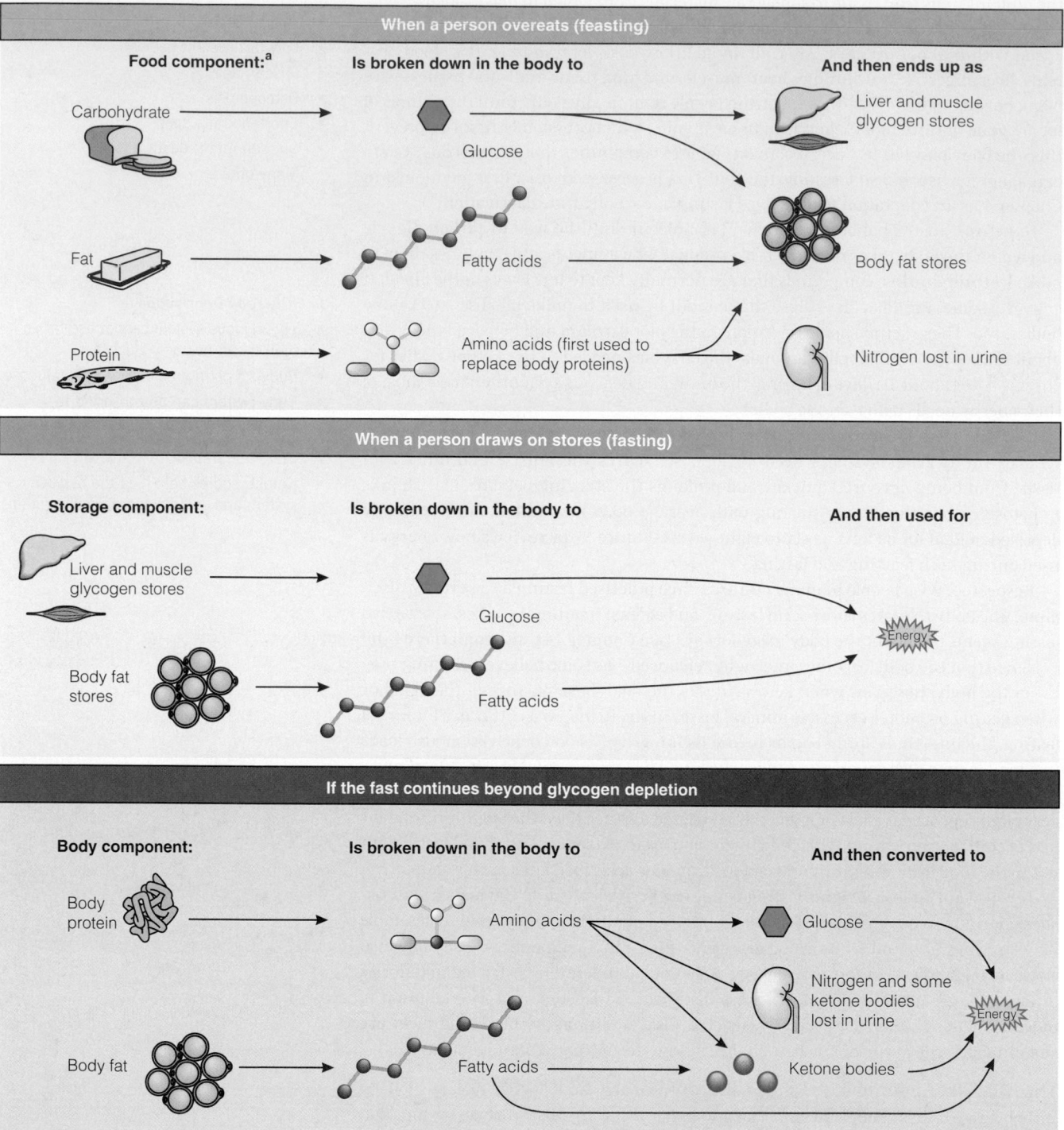

When a person overeats (feasting)

Food component:[a]   Is broken down in the body to   And then ends up as

Carbohydrate → Glucose → Liver and muscle glycogen stores

Fat → Fatty acids → Body fat stores

Protein → Amino acids (first used to replace body proteins) → Nitrogen lost in urine

When a person draws on stores (fasting)

Storage component: Is broken down in the body to   And then used for

Liver and muscle glycogen stores → Glucose → Energy

Body fat stores → Fatty acids → Energy

If the fast continues beyond glycogen depletion

Body component: Is broken down in the body to   And then converted to

Body protein → Amino acids → Glucose → Energy

Nitrogen and some ketone bodies lost in urine

Body fat → Fatty acids → Ketone bodies → Energy

[a]Alcohol is not included because it is a toxin and not a nutrient, but it does contribute energy to the body. After detoxifying the alcohol, the body uses the remaining two-carbon fragments to build fatty acids and stores them as fat.

pitch is that "you'll never feel hungry" and "you'll lose weight fast—faster than you would on any ordinary diet." Both of these claims are true but also misleading. Loss of appetite accompanies any low-Calorie diet. Large initial losses of water and glycogen occur when carbohydrate is lacking, but this kind of weight loss rapidly reverses when people begin eating normally again. The Consumer Corner on pages 389–390 examines some of the claims and scientific evidence surrounding these diets.[71]

- When energy balance is negative, glycogen returns glucose to the blood. When glycogen runs out, body protein is called upon for glucose. Fat also supplies fuel as fatty acids. If glucose runs out, fat supplies fuel as ketone bodies, but ketosis can be dangerous. Both prolonged fasts and low-carbohydrate diets are ill advised.

Weight Gain

What happens inside the body when a person does not use up all of the food energy taken in? Previous chapters have already provided the answer—the energy-yielding nutrients contribute the excess to body stores as follows (see also Figure 9–11):

- Protein is broken down to amino acids for absorption. Inside the body, these may be used to replace lost body *protein* and, in a person who is exercising, to build new muscle and other lean tissue. Excess protein is not stored in specific protein storage tissues. Excess amino acids have their nitrogen removed and are used for energy or are converted to *glucose* or *fat*.

- Fat is broken down to glycerol and fatty acids for absorption. Inside the body, the fatty acids can be broken down for energy or stored as body *fat* with great efficiency. The glycerol enters a pathway similar to carbohydrate.

- Carbohydrate (other than fibre) is broken down to sugars for absorption. In the body tissues, excesses of these may be built up to *glycogen* and stored, used for energy, or converted to *fat* and stored.

- Alcohol is easily absorbed intact and is either used for fuel or converted into body fat for storage.[72]

People who have healthy body weight consume more, not less, carbohydrate-rich food.

- Names of some low-carbohydrate, high-protein diets: Atkins New Diet Revolution, Calories Don't Count Diet, Protein-Power Diet, the Carbohydrate Addict's Diet, the Lo-Carbo Diet, and the Zone Diet. New ones keep coming out, but they are essentially the same diet.

Although three kinds of energy-yielding nutrients and alcohol may enter the body, they become only two kinds of energy stores: glycogen and fat. Glycogen stores amount to about three-fourths of a pound; fat stores can amount to many pounds. Remember from Chapter 6 that when excess protein is converted to fat, it cannot be recovered later as protein because the nitrogen is stripped from the amino acids and excreted in the urine. Thus, if you eat enough of any food, whether it's steak, brownies, or baked beans, any excess will be turned to fat within hours. Weight gain comes from spending less food energy than is taken in. Weight can be gained as body fat or as lean tissue, depending mostly upon whether the eater is also exercising.

Ethanol, the alcohol of alcoholic beverages, has been shown to slow down the body's use of fat for fuel by as much as a third, causing more fat to be stored. This storage is primarily in the visceral fat tissue of the "beer drinker's belly" and also on the thighs, legs, or anywhere the person tends to store surplus fat. Alcohol, therefore, is fattening, both through the Calories it provides and through its effects on fat metabolism.* The obvious conclusion is that weight control and abundant alcohol intake cannot easily coexist.

Chapter 10 further discusses muscle gains in response to exercise.

These points are worth repeating:

- Any food can make you fat if you eat enough of it. A net excess of energy is almost all stored in the body as fat in fat tissue.

- Fat from food is particularly easy for the body to store as fat tissue.

- Protein is not stored in the body except in response to exercise; it is present only as working tissue. Protein is converted to glucose to help feed the brain when carbohydrate is lacking; excess protein can be converted to fat.

- Alcohol both delivers Calories and encourages storage of body fat.

- Too little physical activity encourages body fat accumulation.

Each gram of alcohol presents 7 Calories of energy to the body—energy that is easily stored as body fat.

- When energy balance is positive, carbohydrate is converted to glycogen or fat, protein is converted to fat, and food fat is stored as fat. Alcohol delivers Calories and encourages fat storage.

---

*People addicted to alcohol are often overly thin because of diseased organs, depressed appetite, and subsequent malnutrition.

Figure 9–12

Reasonable Goals versus Unreasonable Expectations

Achieving and Maintaining a Healthy Body Weight

Obese women achieved remarkable success during a year's weight-loss program, but they were disappointed because they had set unrealistic expectations at the outset.

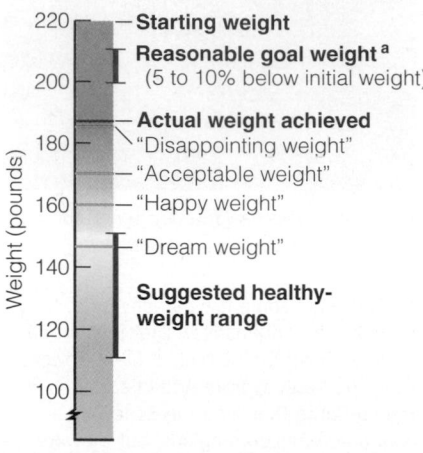

- **Starting weight**
- **Reasonable goal weight**[a] (5 to 10% below initial weight)
- **Actual weight achieved**
  - "Disappointing weight"
  - "Acceptable weight"
  - "Happy weight"
  - "Dream weight"
- **Suggested healthy-weight range**

[a]Reasonable goal weights reflect pounds lost over one year's time. Given more time, reasonable goals may eventually fall within the suggested healthy-weight range.

Source: Based on Foster GD, Wadden TA, Vogt RA, et al. "What is a reasonable weight loss? Patients' expectations and evaluations of obesity treatment outcomes." Journal of Consulting and Clinical Psychology 1997;65(1):79-85

Before setting out to change your body weight, think about your motivation for doing so. Many people in our society are dissatisfied with their body weight, not because of potential health risks or compromised daily living but because their weight fails to meet society's ideals of attractiveness. Unfortunately, this kind of thinking sets people up for disappointment because they set unrealistic goals. The human body is not infinitely malleable—few overweight people will ever become rail-thin, even with the right diet, exercise habits, and behaviours. Likewise, most underweight people will remain on the slim side even after putting on some heft.

Research clarifies the disparity between lofty expectations and reasonable goals.[73] At the start of a year on a weight-loss program, obese women named four potential outcomes: their "dream," "happy," "acceptable," and "disappointing" weights (see Figure 9–12). All of these, even the "disappointing" weights, were far lower than reasonable goals recommended by experts. By the end of the year, the women had lost an average of 16 kilograms (35 lb), or 16 percent of their starting weight. Despite experiencing remarkable physical, social, and psychological benefits, the women felt discouraged because they had not met even their "disappointing" weight. In truth, their discouragement reflected only their unrealistic expectations.

The truth is that overweight takes years to accumulate and cannot be changed overnight. Achieving a healthy weight is possible, but it takes time, patience, and perseverance. People willing to take one step at a time, even if it feels like just a baby step, are on the path toward meeting their individual goals.

Modest weight loss, even for the person who is still overweight, can lead to rapid improvements in control over diabetes, blood pressure, and blood lipids. As fitness builds, stair climbing, walking, and other tasks of daily living become noticeably easier. Adopting health or fitness as the ideal rather than some ill-conceived image of beauty can avert much misery, and Table 9–6 offers some tips to that end. The rest of this chapter stresses health and fitness as goals and uses weight only as a convenient gauge for progress. As mentioned, changes in three realms produce results: diet and physical activity (next sections) and behaviour (see this chapter's Food Feature, pages 403–404).

Table 9–6

Tips for Accepting a Healthy Body Weight

- Value yourself and others for human attributes other than body weight. Realize that prejudging people by weight is as harmful as prejudging them by race, religion, or gender.

- Use only positive, nonjudgmental descriptions of your body; never use degrading negative descriptions.

- Accept positive comments from others.

- Avoid checking your weight or appearance frequently; focus on your whole self, including your intelligence, social grace, and professional and scholastic accomplishments.

- Accept that no magic diet exists.

- Stop dieting to lose weight. Adopt a healthy eating and exercise lifestyle permanently.

- Follow Canada's Food Guide (Chapter 2). Never restrict food intake below the minimum levels that meet nutrient needs.

- Become physically active, not because it will help you get thin but because it will enhance your health.

- Seek support from loved ones. Tell them of your plan for a healthy life in the body you have been given.

- Seek professional counselling, not from a weight-loss counsellor but from someone who can help you make gains in self-esteem without weight as a factor.

- Join with others to fight weight discrimination and fashion stereotypes. (Search the Internet for credible information on this topic or for the names of groups, see the nutrition resources in Appendix G, available online at www.nelson.com/nutrition3ce).

Popular High-Protein, Low-Carbohydrate Diets

Many popular diet books have hooked millions of overweight, meat-loving readers with this tempting advice: eat unlimited Calories of protein and fat, and you'll lose weight and be healthy provided that you avoid carbohydrates.* Do these book authors really present "revolutionary" new evidence, as they claim?

An assumption of the low-carbohydrate diets seems to be that if carbohydrate intakes are low, then Calories in other energy-yielding nutrients will somehow fail to increase body fatness (see Table 9–7). Will eating more protein-rich and fat-rich foods lead to weight loss? According to a recent study on weight loss, Calories count, not the proportion of carbohydrate, fat, and protein in the diet.[†]

Weight Loss

Scientific evidence is mixed on whether a high-protein, low-carbohydrate diet produces leanness. Some results follow.

Studies Reporting Negative Findings

In a population study of almost 20,000 people, those consuming a high-protein diet had *higher* BMI values than people consuming more balanced diets.[‡, 1] In the laboratory, when researchers hold energy intakes constant, no difference is observed in weight loss between subjects eating a high-protein, low-carbohydrate diet and those eating a diet lower in protein and higher in carbohydrate.[2]

Studies Reporting Positive Findings

The picture changes in clinical studies where energy intakes vary—that is, when people living outside the laboratory freely choose how much food (and how many Calories) to consume. Severely obese people choosing from a high-protein, low-carbohydrate diet lost more weight on average during a six-month study than did subjects on a low-fat adequate-carbohydrate diet.[3] In a 12-month study of this type, weight loss was achieved on both diets, but the average losses were greater on the low-carbohydrate diet, especially during the first three months.[4] At six months, the weight-loss gap between the groups had narrowed, and by the end of a year, it had all but vanished. At 12 months, both groups were regaining their lost weight, but the rate of regain differed significantly: the low-carbohydrate group regained rapidly, while the low-fat group remained more stable.

The Science behind the Findings

On further analysis, several other points can be made about the studies just described: the weight-loss difference in these studies was small; one study was of short duration; and in both, a large number of subjects dropped out before data collection was complete. Those dropping out are likely to have not been losing weight, and omitting these negative data from the analysis may have slanted the results.[5]

How do scientists explain the greater initial weight loss observed with high-protein diets? Two partial explanations have been put forward. The first concerns water and glycogen: when glycogen stores are lost, as in low-carbohydrate diets, substantial water weight loss follows. Water can account for much, but not all, of the extra weight lost and rapidly regained by people on a low-carbohydrate weight-loss

diet. Unfortunately, the studies did not investigate whether the lost weight was mainly water, lean tissue, or fat.

A second partial explanation is that diet records indicate that people on low-carbohydrate diets generally consume fewer Calories.[6] This may reflect the higher satiety value of protein and fat—those who feel fuller after a meal due to the hormonal response of the digestive tract to protein or fat may be less tempted by between-meal snacks, or they may eat less food at subsequent meals. Simple arithmetic also comes into play: people omitting Calories of carbohydrate-rich foods do not replace them with additional Calories of high-protein foods.[7] When they strip a burrito of its carbohydrate-rich beans, tortilla wrapper, and chopped vegetables, they are left with a tiny pile of ground beef and a sprinkle of cheese for their meal. Likewise, when ordering a steak dinner, they consume a lone piece of meat, without the Calories (and nutrients) of the milk, potato, and whole-grain roll to accompany it.

Thus, when weight loss occurs on high-protein, low-carbohydrate diets, it is because people lose water and eat fewer Calories by eating less food and not because of some metabolic hocus-pocus. According to a diet evaluation by scientists from the U.S. Department of Agriculture, most people who recently lost substantial weight and kept it off were eating diets high in carbohydrates and low in fat.[8] In addition to producing weight loss, those diets received high scores for nutrition quality.*

Health Concerns

Diet books recommend replacing carbohydrate-rich foods in the diet with those rich in protein. To discuss the health effects of doing so requires addressing the effects of both high intakes of protein and low intakes of carbohydrate.

---

*For scientific evaluations of popular diets, see B. Liebman, Weigh the diet books, Nutrition Action Healthletter, January/February 2004, pp. 1–8; S. T. St. Jeor and coauthors, Dietary protein and weight reduction: A statement for healthcare professionals from the Nutrition Committee of the Council on Nutrition, Physical Activity, and Metabolism of the American Heart Association, Circulation 104 (2001): 1869–1874.

[†]F. M. Sacks and coauthors, Comparison of weight-loss diets with different compositions of fat, protein and carbohydrates, New England Journal of Medicine 360 (2009): 859–873, available at http://content.nejm.org/cgi/content/abstract/360/9/859.

[‡]Consumer Corner references are listed separately at the end of the chapter.

*Based on the Healthy Eating Index, a measure of how well the diet meets U.S. dietary recommendations (see Chapter 2).

High Protein and Animal Fat Intakes

The world's nutrition authorities agree that a steady diet of foods high in protein often presents too much saturated fat and cholesterol in the form of excessive bacon, eggs, hamburger, sausages, and cheeses—staple foods of high-protein, low-carbohydrate diets. Such a diet clearly raises the risk for heart and artery disease.[9]

In addition, saturated fats from animal sources are implicated in worsening a woman's risk of breast cancer.[10] Although early results were mixed, the link seems more certain following adjustments in research methods.[11] For example, in a study of over 90,000 nurses aged 26 to 46, breast cancer risk was one-third higher in those with the highest intakes of animal (but not vegetable) fats.[12] The DRI committee recognizes links between high-protein diets and increased risks of heart disease, osteoporosis, and kidney stones and worsening of kidney disease, cancer, and obesity.[13]

Low Carbohydrate Intakes

The low-carbohydrate diet books suggest that by lowering carbohydrate intake, the dieter can lose weight, lower blood cholesterol, and lower blood pressure, thus lowering the risk of diseases. Researchers are investigating these health claims, but so far they report mixed results or results that are hard to interpret with regard to heart disease. What is absolutely certain, however, is that consumption of more whole grains, fruit, vegetables, and low-fat milk products correlates with lean body composition and robust good health—evidence from many studies confirms

this. Fad diet authors often promote and profit from supplements or meal replacers that they claim will provide the elements missing from their diets, but such concoctions cannot replace the benefits lost when people eliminate whole classes of nutritious foods.[14]

Further, a diet low enough in carbohydrate to produce chronic ketosis presents problems of its own, such as deficiencies of vitamins and minerals, impaired mood, and inadequate glycogen stores to feed the brain or support vigorous physical activity, as discussed in Chapter 4.[15] And diet book claims about damage to healthy individuals from the body's normal insulin response to starchy or sweet foods are incorrect. In healthy people, insulin protects the body from the buildup of glucose; only in those with abnormalities such as insulin resistance does elevated blood insulin signify a potential threat. Healthful diets that include starchy or sweet foods

do not cause insulin resistance, but a diet enriched with saturated fats may worsen it.[16] Table 9–7 summarizes some of the high-protein diet claims and presents the science that disputes those claims.

Conclusion

Claims that weight and health can be improved by eliminating or greatly reducing intakes of whole grains, vegetables, milk, and fruit are baseless. To omit such foods is to lose out on nutrients, fibres, and phytochemicals with proven health benefits. High-fibre whole grains may support weight-loss efforts better than highly refined starches and sweet treats, but this is probably due to the satiety value of fibre.[17] Paradoxically, the fastest path to lasting weight management turns out to be the slowest one—planning a diet based on nutrient adequacy and other sound diet principles, making time to exercise, and changing behaviours permanently.[18]

Table 9–7

Assumptions and Science Concerning High-Protein Diets

Assumption: Restricting carbohydrates alone will shift metabolism and cause weight loss.
Science: Weight loss follows restricted food energy intake or increased energy output; shifting the proportion of energy nutrients in meals without reducing Calories does not produce weight loss.

Assumption: Eating more protein makes people lean.
Science: In population studies, the higher the protein intake, the higher the BMI.

Assumption: Insulin release causes obesity and disease.
Science: Insulin plays roles in the transport of glucose into cells and in the storage of excess nutrients, including fat. Insulin cannot cause fat storage and weight gain in a person whose energy budget is balanced.

Assumption: High-protein foods cause greater energy expenditure.
Science: The thermic effect of food is slightly higher for protein than for carbohydrate or fat, but the increase is so slight as to be insignificant to weight-loss efforts.

Sources: A. Trichopoulou and coauthors, "Lipid, protein and carbohydrate intake in relation to body mass index," European Journal of Clinical Nutrition 56 (2002): 37–43. J. C. Brüning and coauthors, Role of brain insulin receptor in control of body weight and reproduction, Science 289 (2000): 2122–2125.

What Diet Strategies Are Best for Weight Loss?

This section reveals diet-related changes that most often lead to successful weight loss and maintenance. Setting appropriate goals is step number one. Also, keep in mind the following statement from the *2006 Canadian Clinical Practice Guidelines on the Management and Prevention of Obesity in Adults and Children*: "We recommend an energy-reduced diet and regular physical activity as the first treatment option for overweight and obese adults ... to achieve clinically important weight loss."[74] Also, keep in mind that common behaviours of the more than 10,000 members of the U.S. National Weight Control Registry (http://www.nwcr.ws) who have lost at least 13.5 kilograms (30 lb) and kept it off for more than one year were to eat a lower-Calorie diet and to exercise every day.

Setting Goals   For the overweight person, a reasonable first goal might be to prevent further weight gain. With this accomplishment, a subsequent goal might be to reduce body weight by about 5 to 10 percent over a year's time. New goals can be built on prior achievements, and a lifetime goal may be to maintain the new healthier body weight. Weight maintenance often proves the most difficult.

Once you have identified your overall target, set smaller goals for the dietary, physical activity, and behavioural changes necessary to achieve the desired result. These changes do not produce a dramatic weight loss overnight, but if you faithfully employ them, you can lose a pound or two of body fat each week, safely and effectively. Losses greater or faster than these are not recommended because they are almost invariably followed by rapid regain and could also lead to the rapid re-release of fat-soluble toxins stored in adipose tissue. Also, rapid weight loss through excessive restriction can cause gallbladder stones or dangerous electrolyte imbalances. It's better to take your time and achieve a lasting change.

Keeping Records   Keeping records is critical. Recording your food intake and exercise can help you spot trends and identify areas needing improvement. Changes in body weight can provide a rough estimate of changes in body fatness. In addition to weight, measure your waist circumference to track changes in central adiposity.

It's Your Diet, So You'd Better Plan It   Contrary to the claims of faddists, no particular food plan is magical, and no particular food must be either included or excluded. You are the one who will have to live with the plan, so you had better be the one to design it. Remember, you are adopting a healthy eating plan for the long run, so it must consist of satisfying foods that you like, that are readily available, and that you can afford.

As for fad diets, only those that reduce Calorie intake produce weight loss, and it does not appear to matter which macronutrients they emphasize.[75] Table 9–8 exposes some of the untrue claims made by the sellers of fad diets, and Table 9–9 (page 393) provides a way to judge weight-loss plans according to standard nutrition principles.

Choosing Realistic Calorie Intakes   Guidelines for a weight-loss diet are outlined in Table 9–10 on page 394 . For those with a BMI greater than 35, reducing intake by 500 to 1,000 Calories per day will produce the desired loss. This should amount to an intake of about 1,000 to 1,200 Calories per day for most women and 1,200 to 1,600 Calories per day for most men; recent research on dieting by overweight adults indicates that "a Calorie is a Calorie" regardless of the macronutrient content of the diet.[76] Such an intake will allow most people to lose weight while still meeting nutrient needs, as demonstrated in Table 2–3 in Chapter 2 (page 47). Diets providing energy intakes lower than about 800 Calories—the so-called very-low-Calorie diets—are notoriously unsuccessful at achieving lasting weight loss, lack necessary nutrients, and may set in motion the unhealthy behaviours of eating disorders (see the Controversy feature later in this chapter) and so are not recommended. For those with a BMI ranging from 27 to 35, reducing intake by 300 to 500 Calories per day will result in a loss of 0.25 to 0.50 kilograms (1/2 to 1 lb) per week (for further information on how to gain control, see Controversy 11 in Chapter 11). If you plan

Table 9–8

Lies and Truths of Fad Diets

Lie: You'll lose weight fast without counting Calories or exercising because the diet or product alters metabolism.
Truth: No known trick of metabolism produces significant weight loss without diet or exercise.

Lie: On this diet, you can eat all you want and still lose weight.
Truth: Unless the diet is composed entirely of celery or lettuce, basic laws governing energy disprove this claim—energy consumed must be used to fuel the body or stored as fat.

Lie: You'll never regain the weight, even after you stop using the diet or product.
Truth: Maintenance of a new lower weight requires lifelong changes in diet and exercise.

Lie: Eat all of the fat, sugar, or other foods you want and lose a kilogram every day because the product blocks absorption of energy nutrients.
Truth: Losing a kilogram of body fat per week through malabsorption would require passing about 1,000 Cal of undigested fat or carbohydrate out of the digestive tract each day, an implausible outcome, and losing a kilogram a day in this manner is physically impossible.

Lie: Lose more than 1.5 kg per week without medical supervision.
Truth: Weight loss in this range carries substantial risks to health and even to life, making medical supervision prudent.

Lie: This product is 100% successful in producing weight loss.
Truth: The causes of obesity are multiple, and even prescription medications and stomach-shrinking surgeries are not 100% effective.

Lie: You'll lose weight just by wearing the product or rubbing it on the skin.
Truth: No over-the-counter patch, cream, wrap, ring, bracelet, other jewellery, shoe inserts, or other gimmick is known to cause loss of weight or fat.

Lie: Reset your genetic code to be thin.
Truth: You inherited your genes, and no diet can alter them.

Lie: Stress hormones make you fat.
Truth: Supplements sold to block stress hormones and produce weight loss do neither.

Lie: High-protein diets are so popular because they are the best way to lose weight.
Truth: See this chapter's Consumer Corner.

Lie: High-protein diets energize the brain.
Truth: The brain depends on carbohydrate for energy.

Lie: Dietitians know nothing about "modern" nutrition.
Truth: Dietitians are, by training and experience, nutrition experts who rely on scientific approaches and cannot be swayed by the claims of quacks.

Sources: Federal Trade Commission, Deception in Weight-Loss Advertising Workshop: Seizing Opportunities and Building Partnerships to Stop Weight-Loss Fraud, a Federal Trade Commission Staff Report, December 2003, available at http:// www.ftc.gov; Food and Drug Administration, Counting Calories: Report of the Working Group on Obesity, March 12, 2004, available at http://www.cfsan.fda.gov/~dms/owg-rpt.html; S. Barrett, Impossible weight-loss claims: Summary of a Federal Trade Commission report, December 16, 2003, available at http://www.quackwatch.org.

resolutely to include the amount of food from each food group that you need each day, you will find that you will have little appetite left for high-Calorie foods.

Balancing Carbohydrates, Fats, and Protein Healthy diets based on abundant fresh fruits and vegetables, low-fat milk products, legumes, lean meats, fish, poultry, and whole grains are high in carbohydrates, adequate in protein and fibre, and low in the kinds of fats associated with diseases. They are also best for managing weight. Earlier chapters described the importance of each of the energy-yielding nutrients to health. Therefore, diets for weight management should provide all three within the DRI recommended intake ranges (see the margin).

Crunchy, wholesome, high-fibre, unprocessed or lightly processed foods offer bulk and satiety for far fewer Calories than smooth, quickly consumed, refined foods. Thus, choosing whole grains and starchy vegetables in place of most refined grains and added fats and sugars benefits both weight and nutrition. Choose fats sensibly by avoiding sources of saturated and *trans* fats and including enough of the health-supporting fats (details in Controversy 5) to provide satiety but not so much

The DRI Recommends
- 45 to 65% of Calories from carbohydrate
- 20 to 35% of Calories from fat
- 10 to 35% of Calories from protein

Table 9–9

Rating Sound and Unsound Weight-Loss Schemes

Each diet or program starts with 160 points and is rated on 12 factors. Whenever a plan falls short of ideals, subtract points in the third column as instructed. A plan that loses more than 20 points might still be of value but deserves careful scrutiny.

Factor	Does the Diet or Program	Start
		160 points
Calories	Provide a reasonable number of Calories (not fewer than 1,200 Cal for an average-size person)? If not, subtract 10.	_____
Protein	Provide enough, but not too much, protein (at least the recommended intake, but not more than twice that much)? If no, subtract 10.	_____
Fat	Provide enough fat for balance but not so much fat as to go against current recommendations (about 30% of Calories from fat)? If no, subtract 10.	_____
Carbohydrate	Provide enough carbohydrate to spare protein and prevent ketosis (130 g of carbohydrate for the average-size person)? Is it mostly complex carbohydrate (not more than 10% of the Calories as concentrated sugar)? If no to either or both, subtract 10.	_____
Vitamins and minerals	Offer a balanced assortment of vitamins and minerals by including foods from all food groups and subgroups of Figure 2–4 on page 38 in Chapter 2? If it omits a food group (e.g., meats), does it provide a suitable food (not supplement) substitute? For each food group omitted and not adequately substituted for, subtract 10 points.	_____
Variety	Offer variety, in the sense that different foods can be selected each day? If you'd classify it as boring or monotonous, subtract 10.	_____
Ordinary foods	Consist of ordinary foods that are available locally (e.g., in the main grocery stores) at the prices people normally pay? Or does the dieter have to buy special, expensive, or unusual foods to adhere to the diet? If you would class it as "bizarre" or "requiring special foods," subtract 10.	_____
False promises	Promise dramatic, rapid weight loss (substantially more than 1% of total body weight per week)? If yes, subtract 10.	_____
Lifestyle changes	Encourage permanent, realistic lifestyle changes, including regular exercise and the behavioural changes needed for weight maintenance? If not, subtract 10.	_____
Reasonable costs	Misrepresent salespeople as "counsellors" supposedly qualified to give guidance in nutrition and/or general health without a profit motive, or collect large sums of money at the start, or require that clients sign contracts for expensive, long-term programs? If so, subtract 10.	_____
Warnings of risks	Fail to inform clients about the risks associated with weight loss in general or the specific program being promoted? If so, subtract 10.	_____
No gimmicks or mandatory supplements	Promote unproven or spurious weight-loss aids such as human chorionic gonadotrophin hormone (hormones can be dangerous; reject such a plan immediately), starch blockers, diuretics, sauna belts, body wraps, passive exercise, ear stapling, any type of injections, acupuncture, electric muscle-stimulating devices, spirulina, amino acid supplements (e.g., arginine, ornithine), glucomannan, appetite suppressants, "unique" ingredients, and so forth? If so, subtract 10.	_____
	Total points:	_____

as to oversupply Calories. Lean meats or other low-fat protein sources also play an important role: 30 grams of lean ham contains about the same number of Calories as 30 grams of bread, but the ham produces greater satiety. Limit these foods but don't eliminate them. Do strictly limit alcohol, which provides abundant Calories but no nutrients. Furthermore, alcohol reduces inhibitions and can sabotage even the most committed dieter's plans, at least temporarily.

Table 9–10

Recommendations for a Weight-Loss Diet

Nutrient	Recommended Intake
Calories	
For people with BMI ≥ 35	Approximately 500 to 1,000 Cal per day reduction from usual intake
For people with BMI between 27 and 35	Approximately 300 to 500 Cal per day reduction from usual intake
Total fat	35% or less of total Calories
Saturated fatty acids[a]	8 to 10% of total Calories
Monounsaturated fatty acids	Up to 15% of total Calories
Polyunsaturated fatty acids	Up to 10% of total Calories
Cholesterol[a]	<300 mg per day
Protein[b]	Approximately 15% of total Calories
Carbohydrate[c]	55% or more of total Calories
Sodium/Sodium chloride[d]	No more than 2,300 mg of sodium or approximately 6 g of sodium chloride (salt) per day
Calcium	1,000 to 1,500 mg per day
Fibre[c]	25 g per day for females and 38 g per day for males

[a]People with high blood cholesterol should aim for less than 7% of Calories from saturated fat and 200 mg cholesterol per day.

[b]Protein should be derived from plant sources and lean sources of animal protein.

[c]Carbohydrates and fibre should be derived from vegetables, fruit, and whole grains.

[d]The Tolerable Upper Intake Level for salt is 5.8 g.

Of Critical Importance: Portion Sizes Remember to pay careful attention to portion sizes—the monstrous helpings served by restaurants and sold in packages are the enemy of the person striving to control weight. Most people choose portions that are familiar, not scientific, so almost every dieter needs to retrain by using measuring cups for a while to learn to judge portion sizes.[77] Losing track of amounts of fat is especially to be avoided—fat grams add up quickly and contribute more Calories than do grams of carbohydrate or protein.

Most people will eat more at a sitting when presented with larger portions than when provided with smaller portions.[78] Yet, at the end of the meal, they report about the same sensation of fullness whether the portions were large or small. The trick seems to be to eat just until satisfied and then to stop, because satisfaction diminishes with continued eating while unneeded Calories mount up.

Keep in mind that eating large portions of reduced-Calorie foods can defeat their purpose—stick with a reduced-Calorie cookie or two, not half the bag. Stay focused on Calories and portion sizes—don't be distracted by product claims for reduction of a particular nutrient, be it fat or carbohydrate. Read labels and compare Calories per serving.

Using the Concept of Energy Density To lower Calorie intakes, most people must learn how to reduce the Calories in their diet. One way to do this is to reduce the **energy density** of the diet.[79] As Figure 9–13 demonstrates, foods containing substantial water or fibre and those low in fat help lower a meal's energy density, providing more food and greater satiety for fewer Calories. For example, selecting grapes with

energy density a measure of the energy provided by a food relative to its weight (Calories per gram).

Figure 9–13

Examples of Energy Density

The larger meals on the right weigh more, provide more fibre, and take far more time to enjoy than the meals on the left, yet the meals in both columns provide equal Calories. Much of the additional weight of the meals on the right is made up of water. Note that the hamburger is a modest serving of very lean beef, not the huge fatty burger typical of fast-food restaurants. Keep in mind that even foods of lower energy density can be overconsumed, so watch total Calories as well as energy density of foods.

Caesar salad; croutons (fast-food size).

$$\frac{500 \text{ Cal}}{280 \text{ g total weight}} = 1.78 \text{ energy density}$$

Mixed salad with 90 g chicken breast, mixed vegetables, almonds, cranberries, and 3 tbs low-Calorie dressing; whole-wheat dinner roll with 45 g lean ham.

$$\frac{500 \text{ Cal}}{570 \text{ g total weight}} = 0.88 \text{ energy density}$$

Large hot dog on bun; ½ c potato salad.

$$\frac{650 \text{ Cal}}{265 \text{ g total weight}} = 2.45 \text{ energy density}$$

Homemade very lean (8% fat) 90 g hamburger on whole-wheat bun; grilled vegetables with 1 tsp margarine; ½ c pork and beans; slice watermelon.

$$\frac{650 \text{ Cal}}{810 \text{ g total weight}} = 0.8 \text{ energy density}$$

Chapter 1 described the similar concept of nutrient density—the nutrient contribution of a food per Calorie.

their high water content instead of the same weight of their dehydrated counterparts (raisins) decreases the energy density. Likewise, a cupful of fibre-rich, water-rich broccoli delivers about a quarter of the energy (Calories) in a cupful of starch-rich potatoes.

A way to evaluate foods for their energy density is to compare them mathematically according to their Calories per gram. To demonstrate, compare carrot sticks with French fries. To calculate the energy density of the carrot sticks delivering 31 Calories and weighing 72 grams, divide Calories (31 Cal) by weight in grams (72 g):

$$\frac{31 \text{ Cal}}{72 \text{ g}} = 0.43 \text{ Cal/g}$$

● In general, foods high in fat or low in water, such as cookies or chips, rank high in energy density; foods high in water and fibre, such as fruit and vegetables, rank lower.

Do the same for the fries, contributing 167 Cal and weighing 50 g:

$$\frac{167\ Cal}{50\ g} = 0.43\ Cal/g$$

The higher the result, the more Calories per gram and the greater the energy density. Importantly, the *energy* density of foods does not reflect their *nutrient* density (nutrients per Calorie). This distinction is demonstrated in beverages, which, because of their high water content, all weigh about the same amount. The energy density of low-fat 1% or 2% milk, for example, almost equals that of sugary soft drinks, but these beverages rank far apart in measures of nutrient density and therefore in their contributions toward a nutritious diet.

Consider Milk and Milk Products   In a recent study, calcium intake in the form of low-fat milk and milk products correlated with a healthy body weight; in several other studies, higher calcium intake correlates with lower body fatness.[80] Whether or not milk products or calcium turn out to affect fat metabolism directly, low-fat yogurt, skim milk, and fat-free cheeses remain nutritious lower-Calorie foods for the weight-loss dieter. When skim milk replaces sugary soft drinks and punches, the benefits may be greater still.[81] Among 50,000 nurses, those who increased their consumption of pop or fruit punch by as little as 350 millilitres daily gained much more weight on average than those who consumed less than one pop per month.[82]

 Demonstration Diet   The meals shown in Figure 9–14 demonstrate how meals look before and after trimming 1,100 Calories. The full-Calorie meals, shown on the left side of the figure, have been modified in both portion sizes and energy density to produce the meals on the right. Some 350 Calories were trimmed from the 3,400-Calorie meals by reducing added sugars—reducing syrup served at breakfast and swapping apple pie for gelatin at lunch. (The diet planner kept the brownie at supper, however—pleasure matters, too.) These changes alone, repeated each day for one week, produce a Calorie reduction more than sufficient to make a 1-kilogram (2-pound) difference in the person's body weight.

Meal Spacing   Three meals a day is standard in our society, but no law says you can't have four or five—be sure they are smaller, of course. People who eat small, frequent meals are reported to be successful at weight loss and maintenance. Make sure that mild hunger, not appetite, is prompting you to eat. Also, eat regularly, before you become extremely hungry. When you do decide to eat, eat the entire meal you have planned for yourself. Then don't eat again until the next meal or snack. Save Calorie-free or favourite foods or beverages for a planned snack at the end of the day if you need insurance against late-evening hunger.

One meal you should strive to include is breakfast. People who skip breakfast are more often overweight than breakfast eaters.[83] Those who consume the majority of their daily Calories after six o'clock in the evening also often find it harder to lose weight than people who eat earlier in the day.[84] Much evidence supports the health effects of breakfast, and eating breakfast may reduce food intake all day long.

KEY POINT

- To achieve and maintain a healthy body weight, set realistic goals, keep records, and expect to progress slowly. Watch energy density, make the diet adequate and balanced, limit Calories, reduce alcohol, and eat regularly, especially at breakfast.

Physical Activity for Weight Loss

To prevent weight gain and support loss, a person typically must spend about 30 to 60 minutes in moderate physical activity each day in addition to the activities of daily life.[85] To be considered an "active individual," one is expected to expend the equivalent amount of energy to that of walking 11 kilometres per day at a rate of 5 to 6 kilometres per hour. People who combine diet and exercise typically lose more fat,

Chapter 10 presents the many health benefits of physical activity.

Figure 9–14

Calories in Two Sets of Meals

About 3,400 Cal

2% milk, 1 c, 121 Cal
Orange juice, 1 c, 112 Cal
Whole-grain waffles, 2 each, 402 Cal
    Soft margarine, 2 tsp, 68 Cal
    Syrup, 4 tbs, 210 Cal
Banana slices, ½ c, 69 Cal
              Breakfast total: 982

About 2,300 Cal

Skim milk, 1 c, 108 Cal
Orange juice, 1 c, 112 Cal
Whole grain waffle, 1, 201 Cal
    Soft margarine, 1 tsp, 34 Cal
    Syrup, 2 tbs, 105 Cal
Banana slices, ½ c, 69 Cal
              Breakfast total: 604

2% milk, 1 c, 121 Cal
Hamburger, quarter-pound, 430 Cal
French fries, large (about 50), 540 Cal
Ketchup, 2 tbs, 32 Cal
Apple pie, 1, 225 Cal
            Lunch total: 1,348

Skim milk, 1 c, 108 Cal
Cheeseburger, small, 330 Cal
Green salad, 1 c, with light dressing,
    1 tbs, 67 Cal; croutons, ½ c, 50 Cal
French fries, regular (about 30), 210 Cal
Ketchup, 1 tbs, 16 Cal
Gelatin dessert, sugar-free, 20 Cal
             Lunch total: 776

Italian bread, 2 slices, 162 Cal
    Soft margarine, 2 tsp, 68 Cal
Stewed skinless chicken breast,
115 g, 202 Cal
Tomato sauce, ½ c, 40 Cal
Brown rice, 1 c, 216 Cal
Mixed vegetables, ½ c, 59 Cal
Regular cheese sauce, ¼ c, 121 Cal
Brownie, 1, 224 Cal
        Supper total: 1,092
        Day's total: 3,422

Italian bread, 1 slice, 81 Cal
    Soft margarine, 1 tsp, 34 Cal
Stewed skinless chicken breast,
115 g, 202 Cal
Tomato sauce, ½ c, 40 Cal
Brown rice, 1 c, 216 Cal
Mixed vegetables, ½ c, 59 Cal
Low-fat cheese sauce, ¼ c, 85 Cal
Brownie, 1, 224 Cal
         Supper total: 941
         Day's total: 2,321

Source: Data from ESHA Research, The Food Processor Nutrition and Fitness Software version 8.3, 2004.

retain more muscle, and regain less weight than dieters who do not exercise. Regular exercise often seems to help people follow their diet plans more closely—and maintain weight losses more effectively.[86] Physical activity also reduces abdominal obesity, and this change improves blood pressure, insulin resistance, and fitness of the heart and lungs, even without weight loss.[87]

Increasing Metabolism and Reducing Appetite In addition to burning off Calories directly, activity also contributes to energy expenditure in an indirect way—by speeding up metabolism. This speeding up occurs both immediately and over the long term. For several hours following intense and prolonged exercise, metabolism remains slightly elevated, thus raising the Calorie cost of performing the activity by about 15 percent. Over the long term, as more metabolically active lean tissue gradually increases, so does energy spent on basal metabolism. More beneficial changes in body composition invariably follow: body fat decreases while lean body mass increases, with concurrent gains in health.[88]

Physical activity may also help control appetite. Many people fear that exercising will increase their hunger, but this is not entirely true. Active people do have healthy appetites, but immediately after a workout, appetite is suppressed by the circulating lipids and glucose released from storage to fuel exercise—a state that mimics the fed state from the body's point of view. Activity also helps reduce stress, even stress caused by dieting. And stress often leads to inappropriate eating.

Choosing Activities   The best activities are those you enjoy and that are safe to perform. What schedule of physical activity is best? It doesn't seem to matter much from a weight-loss point of view; benefits come from many kinds of routines—and any activity is better than being sedentary.[89] An expenditure of at least 2,000 Calories per week in some sort of physical activity is especially helpful for weight management.[90] Most important: perform at a comfortable pace within your current abilities. Those rushing to improve are practically guaranteed an injury.

Health-care professionals frequently advise people to engage in activities of low-to-moderate intensity for a long duration, such as an hour-long brisk walk. The reasoning behind such advice is that people exercising at low-to-moderate intensity are more likely to stick with their activity for longer times and are less likely to injure themselves. For those at higher fitness levels, higher-intensity activities may be performed for shorter periods to gain similar benefits.[91] An 80-kilogram (175-lb) person who replaces a 30-minute television program with a 3-kilometre daily walk can spend enough energy to lose (or at least not gain) 8 kilograms (18 pounds) in a year.

In addition to planned exercise, fitness can be gained through hundreds of energy-spending activities required for daily living: taking the stairs instead of the elevator, biking instead of driving, raking leaves instead of using a blower, and many, many others. One suggested goal is to take 10,000 steps a day. Wearing a pedometer makes tracking a day's activities easy. However you do it, be active. Walk. Swim. Dance. Cycle. Skip. Enjoy moving—and move often.

Spot Reducing   People sometimes ask about "spot reducing." Unfortunately, muscles do not "own" the fat that surrounds them. Fat cells all over the body release fat in response to the demand of physical activity for use by whatever muscles are active. Exercise cannot remove the fat from any one particular area.

Exercise can help with trouble spots in two other ways, though. During aerobic exercise, abdominal fat readily releases its stores, providing fuel to the physically active body and reducing fat in the abdomen. Another way exercise can help is by improving the strength and tone of muscles in a trouble area, improving the overall appearance of the area. Strength and flexibility will help cure associated posture problems. A combination of aerobic, strength, and flexibility workouts is best for improving health; fitness; and, as a side benefit, body contours.

KEY POINT

- Physical activity greatly augments diet in weight-loss efforts. Improvements in health and body composition follow an active lifestyle.

What Strategies Are Best for Weight Gain?

Should a thin person try to gain weight? Not necessarily. If you are healthy at your present weight, stay there. If your physician has advised you to gain; if you are excessively tired; if you are unable to keep warm; if you fall into the "underweight" category of the BMI table (see page Z at the back of the book); or if, for women, you have missed at least three consecutive menstrual periods, you may be in danger from a too-low body weight.

Physical Activity to Gain Muscle and Fat   A healthful weight gain is best achieved through physical activity, particularly strength training (see Chapter 10 for details), combined with a high-Calorie diet. Diet alone can bring about weight gain, but the gain will be mostly fat. For someone facing a wasting disease, the gain of fat tissue may be a welcome sign of improvement. For an athlete, however, such a gain can impair performance. For most people, physical activity is an essential component of a sound weight-gain plan. Many an underweight person has simply been too busy (for months) to eat or to exercise enough to gain or to maintain weight.

As important to weight gain as exercise are the Calories to support that activity—otherwise you will lose weight. If you eat just enough to fuel the activity, you will build muscle, but at the expense of body fat; that is, fat will be burned to support the muscle building. If you eat more, you will gain both muscle and fat. To gain a pound of muscle and fat requires taking in about 3,000 extra Calories.* Conventional advice on diet to the person building muscle is to eat about 700 to 1,000 Calories a day above normal energy needs; this range supports both the added activity and the formation of new muscle.

Choose Foods with High Energy Density   The weight gainer needs *nutritious* energy-dense foods. No matter how many sticks of celery you consume, you won't gain weight because celery simply doesn't offer enough Calories per bite. Energy-dense foods (the very ones the weight-loss dieter is trying to avoid) are often high in fat, but their energy is spent in building new tissue, and if the fat is mostly unsaturated, such foods will not contribute to heart disease. Be sure your choices are nutritious; a steady diet of chips and candy may add pounds but also threaten nutrient deficiencies.

Choose peanut butter instead of lean meat, avocado instead of cucumber, olives instead of pickles, whole-wheat muffins instead of whole-wheat bread, and flavoured milk drinks instead of milk. When you do eat celery, stuff it with tuna salad (use oil-packed tuna); choose flavoured coffee drinks over plain coffee; use olive oil or canola oil dressings on salads, whipped toppings on fruit, and soft or liquid margarine on potatoes. Because fat contains more than twice as many Calories per teaspoon as sugar, it adds Calories without adding much bulk, and its energy is in a form that is easy for the body to store.

Portion Sizes and Meal Spacing   Increasing portion sizes increases Calorie intakes. Choose extra slices of meats and cheeses on sandwiches; use larger plates, bowls, and glasses to disguise the appearance of the larger portions. Expect to feel full. Most underweight individuals are accustomed to small quantities of food. When they begin eating significantly more food, they complain of uncomfortable fullness. This feeling is normal, and it passes as the stomach gradually adapts to the extra food.

Eat frequently. Make three sandwiches in the morning and eat them between classes in addition to the day's three regular meals. Spend time making foods appealing—the more varied and palatable, the better. If you fill up fast during a meal, start with the main course or a meat- or cheese-filled appetizer, not carrot sticks. Drink between meals, not with them, to save space for higher-Calorie foods. Make milkshakes of milk, a frozen banana, a tablespoon of vegetable oil, and flavourings to drink between meals.

Weight-Gain Supplements   Most "weight-gain" supplements advertised to add body weight are useless without physical activity and confer no special benefits beyond adding Calories and a few nutrients. Ordinary items like instant breakfast powders or milk flavouring powders mixed with milk can do the same thing for a fraction of the supplement cost.

People's hormone status also affects their ability to gain weight, but taking steroids and other drugs to enhance weight gain is a bad idea—see Controversy 10 in Chapter 10.

Of the weight gained in a day, only 15 to 30 grams is protein tissue, so no special protein supplements can help speed gain of lean tissue. Ordinary food in abundance, along with exercise to work the nutrients into place, supports efforts to gain muscle and weight.

Avoid Tobacco   Smoking tobacco depresses the appetite and makes taste buds and olfactory (smelling) organs less sensitive. A person who smokes should quit before trying to gain weight. Quitters find that appetite picks up, food tastes and smells better, and the body reaps numerous benefits.

KEY POINT

- Weight gain requires a diet of Calorie-dense foods, eaten frequently throughout the day. Physical activity builds lean tissue, and no special supplements can speed the process.

---

*Theoretically, it takes an excess of 2,000 to 2,500 Cal to gain half a kilogram of only lean tissue and about 3,500 Cal to gain half a kilogram of fat.

Table 9–11

Pharmaceutical Treatments of Obesity[a]

Names	Actions	Known Side Effects	Comments
Prescription Drugs			
Orlistat Trade name: Xenical	Inhibits pancreatic lipase activity, thus blocking dietary fat absorption by about 30%	Gas, frequent bowel movements, and reduced absorption of fat-soluble vitamins	Most effective with a nutritionally balanced, reduced-Calorie, low-fat diet
Over-the-Counter Drugs and Products			
Benzocaine Trade names: Diet Ayds (candy) or Slim Mint (gum)	Anesthetizes the tongue, reducing taste sensations	None known	Only over-the-counter weight-loss medication with FDA approval
Phenylpropanolamine (PPA) (also called norephedrine)	Appetite suppressant; nasal and sinus decongestant	Dry mouth, rapid pulse, nervousness, sleeplessness, hypertension, irregular heartbeat, kidney failure, liver damage, liver failure, seizures, and hemorrhagic strokes (bleeding in the brain)	The FDA has removed PPA from drug products and has warned consumers not to consume products containing it (check labels).
Ephedrine, *Ephedra*, or ma huang	Enhances effects of the stress hormone norepinephrine, including reduced appetite	Nervousness, headache, insomnia, dizziness, palpitations, skin flush, serious heart problems; almost 1,400 reported adverse events, including death	Prohibited by the FDA but available via the Internet. Consumers owning products should stop taking them (check labels).
Bitter orange extract Trade names: Xendrine EFX, Metabolife Ultra, NOW Diet Support	Often a replacement for ephedrine, this stimulant mimics *Ephedra* in chemical composition and function	High blood pressure; increased risk of heart arrhythmias, heart attack, stroke	The FDA has currently taken no action against bitter orange extract.
"Carb blockers," "fat blockers" or "binders," chromium picolinate, chitosan, many others	None known	Not studied	The FDA and the Federal Trade Commission have begun taking action against products falsely claimed to produce weight or fat loss.

[a]For answers to drug-related questions, visit Health Canada's Drugs and Health Products website at http://www.hc-sc.gc.ca/dhp-mps/index-eng.php, then click on the Drug Products Database or the Licensed Natural Health Products Database link on the right side of the page. You can also call your Provincial Telehealth office or local pharmacist.

Drugs and Surgery to Treat Obesity

To someone fatigued from years of battling overweight, the idea of taking pills or undergoing surgery might seem attractive. These approaches can save the lives of obese people at critical risk, but they also carry serious risks of their own.

Each year, a million and a half U.S. citizens take prescription weight-loss medications. Of these, a quarter are not overweight.[92] In pursuit of a particular body form, physicians and patients alike seem willing to take the considerable risks that drug side effects present. Table 9–11 presents some of the known side effects and other details about weight-loss medications currently on the market.

People with a BMI of 30 or above and those with elevated disease risks may benefit from prescription medication, along with diet, exercise, and behaviour therapy, to bring their weight down. A person with **extreme obesity**, that is, someone whose BMI is 40 or above (35 with coexisting disease), urgently needs to reduce body fatness, and surgery may be an option for those healthy enough to withstand it.[93] Surgical procedures effectively limit food intake by reducing the size of the stomach and

extreme obesity clinically severe overweight, presenting very high risks to health; the condition of having a BMI of 40 or above; also called *morbid obesity*.

delaying the passage of food from the stomach into the intestine (see Figure 9–15), leading to significant weight loss in most patients.[94] Weight loss, in turn, often brings rapid improvements to such threats as diabetes, high blood cholesterol, hypertension, and sleep apnea.[95] The surgery is not a sure cure for obesity, however. A few people do not lose the expected pounds, and some who lose initially regain all of the lost weight in a few years.

The long-term safety and effectiveness of gastric surgery depend, in large part, on compliance with dietary instructions. Complications immediately following surgery often include infections, nausea, vomiting, and dehydration; in the long term, vitamin and mineral deficiencies and psychological problems may develop. Lifelong medical supervision is necessary for those who choose the surgical route, but in many suitable candidates, the benefits of weight loss may prove worth the substantial risks.

Another surgical procedure is used not primarily to treat obesity but to remove external body fat. Plastic surgeons can extract some fat deposits by lipectomy, or "liposuction." People consenting to this cosmetic procedure expect an improved body shape, but an unusually large number of lawsuits against surgeons performing it indicate that many people are disappointed with the outcome.[96] If the fat is gained back after liposuction, as often happens, it can form a lumpy, dimpled layer that looks worse than the original fat. Lipectomy is popular in part because it seems safe, but there can be serious complications, even death, from the surgery.[97]

Herbal Products Herbal weight-loss products are wildly popular, but their effectiveness and safety have not been proven. People may falsely believe that "natural" herbs are never harmful to the body, but many herbs contain poisonous toxins. Belladonna and hemlock are infamous examples, but many lesser-known herbs, such as sassafras, contain toxins as well. Furthermore, because weight-loss herbs are marketed in the United States as "dietary supplements," manufacturers need not present scientific evidence of their safety or effectiveness to the U.S. FDA before marketing them. Evidence about safety is gathered only through reports of consumers who sicken or die after purchasing and using herbal remedies.

A now familiar example is *Ephedra* (also called *ma huang*), a herb that showed promise as a weight-loss drug in preliminary studies. Immediately, *Ephedra*-containing pills and preparations for dieters and athletes flooded the market. Nearly 1,400 consumers of these products reported ill effects, including cardiac arrest, abnormal heartbeats, hypertension, strokes, and seizures; 81 people died. Canada banned *Ephedra*, and after many years of gathering required documentation, the U.S. FDA has also banned sales of dietary supplements containing *Ephedra* and its active constituent, ephedrine.[98] The World Health Organization has called for worldwide controls on *Ephedra* sales.[99] Another diet aid to avoid is known as TRIAC, a powerful hormone that interferes with normal thyroid functioning and has caused heart attack and stroke (see Controversy 10 in Chapter 10).* Many other "herbal" additives have turned out to be kidney or liver toxins or cancer-causing agents.

Herbal laxatives containing senna, aloe, rhubarb root, cascara, castor oil, or buckthorn are sold as "dieter's tea" because they can cause a temporary water loss of a pound or two. Users commonly report nausea, vomiting, diarrhea, cramping, and fainting. Such "teas" are suspected of contributing to the deaths of four women who used them and also drastically reduced their food intakes. Some herbs may be useful for other purposes, but herbs and supplements do not produce weight loss, and they clearly fail the safety test.[100] Read labels and don't take products containing these substances or any others not proven safe in laboratory studies. The risks of doing so are too high. To identify the status of herbs or natural products for which there are claims relating to weight loss, check the Natural Health Products Directorate website (go to http://www.hc-sc .gc.ca/dhp-mps/prodnatur/index-eng.php, and then click on Licensed Natural Health Products Database).

*The product name was Triax Metabolic Accelerator.

Figure 9–15

An Example of Obesity Surgery

In one common surgery, the surgeon constructs a small stomach pouch and restricts the outlet from the stomach to the intestine.

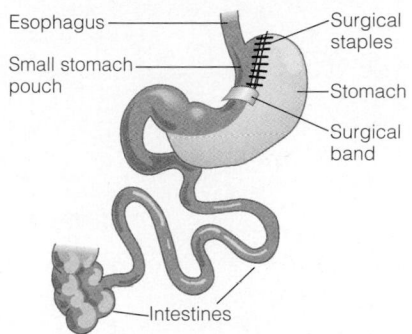

Esophagus — Surgical staples
Small stomach pouch — Stomach
— Surgical band
— Intestines

In one common surgery, the surgeon constructs a small stomach pouch and restricts the outlet from the stomach to the intestine.

Other Gimmicks   Steam baths and saunas do not melt the fat off the body, although they may dehydrate you so that you lose water weight. Brushes, sponges, wraps, creams, and massages intended to move, burn, or break up **cellulite** are useless for fat loss. Cellulite—the rumpled, dimpled fat tissue on the thighs and buttocks—is simply fat, awaiting the body's call for energy. The FDA has sent letters in the past warning supplement distributors to stop claiming that their products

- Block starch, fat, or sugar absorption.
- "Neutralize" starch, fat, or sugar in a meal.
- Promote weight loss with no effort.[101]

Such misleading claims distract people from the serious business of planning helpful weight-management strategies.

KEY POINT

- For people whose obesity threatens their health, medical science offers drugs and surgery. The effectiveness of herbal products and other gimmicks has not been demonstrated, and they may prove hazardous.

Once I've Changed My Weight, How Can I Stay Changed?

One reason gimmicks fail at weight control is that they fail to produce lasting change. Millions have experienced the frustration of achieving a desired change in weight only to see their hard work visibly slipping away: "I have lost 200 pounds, but I was never more than 20 pounds overweight." Disappointment, frustration, and self-condemnation are common in dieters who find they have slipped back to their original weight or even higher.[102] What makes the difference between a successful, long-term weight-control program and one that doesn't stick? How can you maintain a healthy body weight?

A key to weight maintenance is accepting it as a lifelong endeavour, not a goal to be achieved and then forgotten. Acceptance helps prepare the mind for making permanent changes. People who maintain a loss continue to employ the behaviours that reduce Calorie intakes and increase expenditures through exercise. They cultivate the habits of people who maintain a healthy weight, such as eating diets higher in carbohydrate, lower in fat, and higher in fruit and vegetables than average. Those who maintain healthy weight also generally

- Are more physically active than most people, for example, walking about 6.5 kilometres each day.[103]
- Monitor fat grams, Calorie intake, and body weight.
- Do not vary much in food intake from weekdays to weekends.[104]
- Believe they have the ability to control their weight, an attribute known as **self-efficacy**, even in the face of previous failures.
- Develop social support systems.
- Eat controlled portions at planned times and eat them at a leisurely pace.
- Eat high-fibre foods, particularly whole grains, and consume sufficient water each day.[105]
- Cultivate and honour realistic expectations regarding body size and shape.

The importance of exercise cannot be overstated. Those who endeavour to lose weight without exercise often become trapped in endless repeating rounds of weight loss and regain—"yo-yo" dieting. Weight-loss efforts often precede large weight gains, and a history of such **weight cycling** can predict a person's future success (or lack thereof) in maintaining weight.[106] Weight cycling may even damage the dieter's health by weakening the immune response, making diseases more likely to occur.[107]

Self-acceptance and self-efficacy also predict success, while self-hate and feelings of inadequacy predict failure. A paradox of behaviour change is that it takes an attitude of self-acceptance (loving the overweight self) to lay the foundation for changing

cellulite a term popularly used to describe dimpled fat tissue on the thighs and buttocks; not recognized in science.

self-efficacy a person's belief in his or her ability to succeed in an undertaking.

weight cycling repeated rounds of weight loss and subsequent regain, with reduced ability to lose weight with each attempt; also called *yo-yo dieting*.

that self. Thinking habits turn out to be as important to achieving a healthy body weight as eating habits are, and thinking habits can be changed. "Positive self-talk" is a concept worth cultivating—many people succeed because their mental dialogue supports, rather than degrades, their efforts. This chapter's Food Feature explores how a person can modify daily behaviours into healthy lifelong habits.

KEY POINT

- People who succeed at maintaining lost weight keep to their eating routines, keep exercising, and keep track of Calorie and fat intakes and body weight. The more traits related to positive self-image and self-efficacy a person possesses or cultivates, the more likely that person will succeed.

try it!
Food Feature

Behaviour Modification for Weight Control

Supporting both diet and exercise is the technique of **behaviour modification**, which cements into place all of the behaviours that lead to and perpetuate the desired body composition. Behaviour modification is based on the knowledge that habits drive behaviours.

How Does Behaviour Modification Work?

Suppose a friend tells you about a shortcut to class. To take it, you must make a left-hand turn at a corner where you now turn right. You decide to try the shortcut the next day, but when you arrive at the familiar corner, you turn right as always. Not until you arrive at class do you realize that you failed to turn left, as you had planned. You can learn to turn left, of course, but at first you will have to make an effort to remember to do so. After a while, the new behaviour will become as automatic as the old one was.

For those striving to lose weight, learning to say "No, thank you" might be among the first habits to establish. Learning to not "clean your plate" might be another. Once you identify the behaviours you need to change, do not attempt to modify all of them at once. No one who attempts too many changes at one time is successful. Set

your priorities and begin with a behaviour you can handle—then practise it until it becomes habitual and automatic. Then select another.

Applying Behaviour Modification

Behaviour researchers have identified six elements of behaviour modification to use to replace old eating habits with new ones:

1. Eliminate inappropriate eating cues.
2. Suppress the cues you cannot eliminate.
3. Strengthen cues to appropriate eating and exercise.
4. Repeat the desired eating and exercise behaviours.
5. Arrange or emphasize negative consequences for inappropriate eating.
6. Arrange or emphasize positive consequences for appropriate eating and exercise behaviours.

Table 9–12 provides specific examples of putting these six elements into action. Before doing so, however, you must establish a baseline, a record of your present eating behaviours against which to measure future progress. Keep a diary so that you can learn what particular eating stimuli, or cues, affect you.

To begin, set about eliminating or suppressing the cues that prompt you to eat inappropriately. An overeater's life may include many such cues: watching television, talking on the telephone, entering a convenience store, studying late at night. Resolve that you will no longer respond to such cues by eating. Respond only to one set of cues designed by you, in one particular place in one particular room. If some cues to inappropriate eating behaviour cannot be eliminated, suppress them, as described in Table 9–12; then strengthen the appropriate cues and reward yourself for doing so. The list in the margin suggests some activities and rewards to substitute for eating.

Activities and rewards to substitute for eating:

- Attending sporting events
- Enjoying leisure activities
- Exercising or playing sports
- Gardening
- Getting praise from others
- Going to a movie or play
- Listening to music
- Napping
- Praising yourself
- Reading
- Receiving token rewards (stickers, stars)

behaviour modification alteration of behaviour using methods based on the theory that actions can be controlled by manipulating the environmental factors that cue, or trigger, the actions.

- Redecorating
- Relaxing
- Saving money for future treats
- Shopping
- Taking a bubble bath
- Telephoning
- Tidying your room or house
- Vacationing
- Working on hobbies or crafts

In addition, be aware that the food marketing industry spends huge sums each year to modify consumers' behaviours in the opposite direction—toward increasing their food consumption (details in Controversy 11). Watch out particularly for foods sold in large packages or large portions on platter-size plates. The larger the package or portion, the greater the amount of food the average person consumes at a sitting.[108]

As you progress in your new behaviours of physical activity and sensible eating, enjoy your new, emerging fit and healthy self.

● Reminder: The three lifestyle components leading to healthy body weight are diet, physical activity, and behaviour modification.

Table 9–12

Applying Behaviour Modification to Control Body Fatness

1. Eliminate inappropriate eating cues:
   - Don't buy problem foods.
   - Eat only in one room at the designated time.
   - Shop when not hungry.
   - Avoid vending machines, fast-food restaurants, and convenience stores.
   - Turn off the television, video games, and computer.

2. Suppress the cues you cannot eliminate:
   - Serve individual plates; don't serve "family style."
   - Measure your portions; avoid large servings or packages of food.
   - Make small portions look large by spreading them over the plate.
   - Create obstacles to consuming problem foods—wrap them and freeze them, making them less quickly accessible.
   - Control deprivation; plan and eat regular meals.
   - Plan to spend only one hour in sedentary activities, such as watching television or using a computer.

3. Strengthen cues to appropriate eating and exercise:
   - Share appropriate foods with others.
   - Store appropriate foods in convenient spots in the refrigerator.
   - Learn appropriate portion sizes.
   - Plan appropriate snacks.
   - Keep sports and play equipment by the door.

4. Repeat the desired eating and exercise behaviours:
   - Slow down eating—put down utensils between bites.
   - Always use utensils.
   - Leave some food on your plate.
   - Move more—shake a leg, pace, stretch often.
   - Join groups of active people and participate.

5. Do not emphasize negative consequences for inappropriate eating:
   - Ask that others respond neutrally to your deviations (make no comments—even negative attention is a reward).
   - If you slip, don't punish yourself.

6. Arrange or emphasize positive consequences for appropriate eating and exercise behaviours:
   - Buy tickets to sports events, movies, concerts, or other nonfood amusement.
   - Indulge in a new small purchase.
   - Get a massage; buy some flowers.
   - Take a hot bath; read a good book.
   - Treat yourself to a lesson in a new active pursuit such as horseback riding, handball, or tennis.
   - Praise yourself; visit friends.
   - Nap; relax.

The Perils of Eating Disorders

The National Eating Disorder Information Centre in Toronto estimates that 200,000 to 300,000 women aged 13 to 40 have anorexia nervosa and twice as many have bulimia (http://www.nedic.ca/MMWIP/b281a6a6793a4529/f19261a0cdcad338.shtml).

This organization promotes the non-diet approach to a healthy lifestyle:

- The National Eating Disorder Information Centre (NEDIC) provides information through a toll-free phone number (1-866-633-4220 or 416-340-4156) and a website (http://www.nedic.ca). The website includes a guide for family and friends and numerous weblinks to other websites dedicated to helping those with eating disorder issues: Canadian sites (e.g., http://www.bana.ca and http://www.hopesgarden.org), U.S. sites (e.g., http://www.nationaleatingdisorders.org and http://www.gurze.com), and

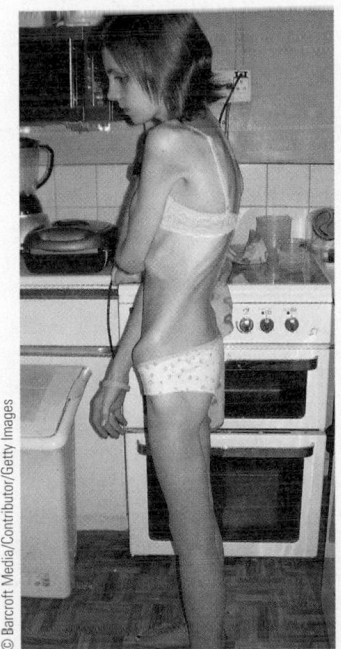

A woman with anorexia nervosa

international sites (e.g., http://www.alda.org.ar).

For additional information and resources, you may wish to consult programs for eating disorders available at your college or university, or in your community.

Primarily girls and women suffer from the **eating disorders** of **anorexia nervosa** and **bulimia nervosa**. Many more suffer from **binge eating disorder, EDNOS**, or other related conditions that imperil the sufferer's well-being. White women are most likely to have an eating disorder, although men and ethnic women are by no means immune.*,[1]

An estimated 85 percent of eating disorders start during adolescence.[2] In a U.S. national survey of over 6,700 adolescents in Grades 5 through 12, almost half of the girls and a fifth of the boys reported having dieted to lose weight.[3] Disordered eating occurred among 13 percent of the girls and 7 percent of the boys. A survey at a major university found that only 8 percent of the students were overweight by objective measure (BMI), yet more than half of the students reported themselves to be overweight. Half of the students found to be *underweight* according to the BMI charts made that claim. These behaviours and attitudes are much less prevalent in most other societies, although the incidence often increases when body image becomes central to self-worth.[4]

Why do so many people in our society suffer from eating disorders? Excessive pressure to be thin is at least partly to blame. When low body weight becomes an important goal, people begin to view normal, healthy body weight as too fat, and some take unhealthy actions to lose weight. Severe restriction of food intake can create intense stress and extreme

*Controversy references are listed separately at the end of the chapter.

hunger that lead to binges.[5] Painful emotions such as anger, jealousy, or disappointment may be turned inward by youngsters who express dissatisfaction with body weight or say they "feel fat." As weight loss and diet restraint become more and more a focus, psychological problems worsen, and the likelihood of developing full-blown eating disorders intensifies.[6] Table C9–1 defines eating disorder terms.

Eating Disorders in Athletes

Athletes and dancers are at special risk for eating disorders. In females, three associated medical problems form the **female athlete triad**: disordered eating, amenorrhea (cessation of menstruation), and osteoporosis (see Figure C9–1).[7] In males, disordered eating brings on many of the same physical problems affecting female counterparts.

The Female Athlete Triad

At age 14, Suzanne was a top contender for a spot on the state gymnastics team. Each day her coach reminded team members that they would not qualify for competition if they weighed more than a few ounces above their assigned weights. The coach chastised gymnasts who gained weight. Suzanne weighed herself several times a day to make sure that she had not exceeded her 36-kilogram limit. Suzanne dieted and exercised to an extreme, and unlike many of her friends, she never began to menstruate. A few months before her fifteenth birthday, Suzanne's coach dropped her back to the second-level team. Suzanne blamed her poor performance on a slow-healing stress fracture. Mentally stressed and physically exhausted, she quit gymnastics and began overeating between

Eating Disorder Terms

- **anorexia nervosa** an eating disorder characterized by a refusal to maintain a minimally normal body weight, self-starvation to the extreme, and a disturbed perception of body weight and shape; seen (usually) in teenage girls and young women (*anorexia* means "without appetite"; *nervos* means "of nervous origin").
- **binge eating disorder** an eating disorder whose criteria are similar to those of bulimia nervosa, excluding purging or other compensatory behaviours.
- **bulimia** (byoo-LEEM-ee-uh) **nervosa** recurring episodes of binge eating combined with a morbid fear of becoming fat; usually followed by self-induced vomiting or purging.
- **cathartic** a strong laxative.
- **cognitive therapy** psychological therapy aimed at changing undesirable behaviours by changing underlying thought processes contributing to these behaviours; in anorexia, a goal is to replace false beliefs about body weight, eating, and self-worth with health-promoting beliefs.
- **eating disorder** a disturbance in eating behaviour that jeopardizes a person's physical or psychological health.
- **EDNOS** eating disorder not otherwise specified.
- **emetic** (em-ETT-ic) an agent that causes vomiting.
- **female athlete triad** a potentially fatal triad of medical problems seen in female athletes: disordered eating, amenorrhea, and osteoporosis.

periods of self-starvation. Suzanne had developed the dangerous combination of problems that characterize the female athlete triad—disordered eating, amenorrhea, and weakening of the bones.[8]

Female athletes, in keeping with their coaches' recommendations, often compare themselves to unsuitable weight standards. An ultraslim appearance has long been considered desirable in activities such as dancing, gymnastics, and figure skating. This puts the athlete in a bind since an athlete's body must be heavier for a given height than a nonathlete's body because it contains more healthy muscle and dense bone tissue and less fat. Most weight standards appropriate for the general population fall far from the mark with regard to athletes' bodies—the photo in this chapter of an athlete with a high BMI demonstrated this. For athletes, body composition measures such as fatfold measures yield more useful information.

The Female Athlete Triad

In the female athlete triad, extreme weight loss causes both cessation of menstruation (amenorrhea) and excessive loss of calcium from the bones. The hormone disturbances associated with amenorrhea also contribute to osteoporosis, making the female athlete triad extraordinarily harmful to the bones.

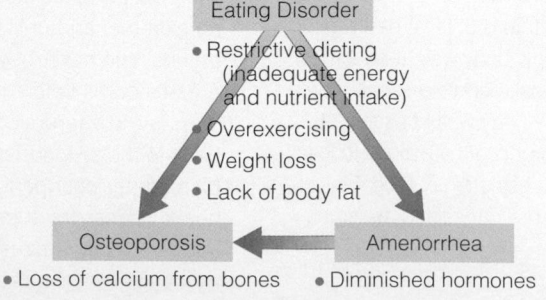

Eating Disorder
- Restrictive dieting (inadequate energy and nutrient intake)
- Overexercising
- Weight loss
- Lack of body fat

Osteoporosis
- Loss of calcium from bones

Amenorrhea
- Diminished hormones

The prevalence of amenorrhea among premenopausal women in the United States is about 2 to 5 percent overall, but it may be as high as 66 percent among female athletes. Amenorrhea is *not* a normal adaptation to strenuous physical training but a symptom of something going wrong, and it is particularly hazardous to the bones.[9] For most people, weight-bearing exercise helps protect bones against the calcium losses of osteoporosis. For young women with anorexia nervosa, however, strenuous activity can imperil their bones, even after recovery from the eating disorder.[10] Vigorous training along with low food energy intakes and other stressors may cause bone loss even without obvious menstrual irregularities.[11] Such bone losses may increase the risks of stress fractures today and of osteoporosis in later life (see Figure C9–1).

Male Athletes and Eating Disorders

Male athletes and dancers who face pressure to achieve a certain body weight often develop eating disorders, although they may deny having them in the mistaken belief that the disorders strike only women.[12] On average, male teenagers carry about 15 percent of body weight as fat, but some high school wrestlers, gymnasts, and figure skaters strive for only 5 percent body fat.

Wrestlers, for example, are required to "make weight" to compete in the lowest possible weight class to face the smallest possible opponents. To that end, wrestlers starve themselves, don rubber suits, sweat in steam rooms, and take diuretics to shed water weight before weighing in for competition. These practices were responsible for the deaths of three college athletes in the past and have caused untold misery and harm to many others. Athletes engaging in these practices actually compromise their athletic abilities. The diminished anaerobic strength, reduced endurance, decreased oxygen capacity, and general weakness caused by food deprivation and dehydration can hobble performance, an effect lasting days after food and water are replenished.

Male athletes are also susceptible to weight-*gain* problems, in which athletes with well-muscled bodies see themselves as underweight and weak. Such a distorted body image leads to frequent weighing, excessive exercise, overuse of special diets or protein supplements, or even the abuse of steroid drugs in the attempt to bulk up their muscles.

Young athletes and their coaches must be educated about links between inappropriate body-weight ideals, improper weight-loss techniques, eating disorder development, effective sports nutrition, and safe weight-control methods. For all young people's activities, idealistic artistic standards based on slim appearance or low body weight should be replaced with performance-based standards. Table C9–2 provides some suggestions to help athletes and dancers protect themselves against developing eating disorders. The next sections describe eating disorders that anyone, athlete or nonathlete, may experience.

Anorexia Nervosa

Julie is 18 years old and is a super-achiever in school. She watches her diet with great care and exercises daily, maintaining a heroic schedule of self-discipline. She is thin, but she is determined to lose more weight. She is 168 centimetres (5 ft 6 in.) tall and weighs 38 kilograms (85 pounds). She has anorexia nervosa.

Characteristics of Anorexia Nervosa

Julie is unaware that she is undernourished, and she sees no need to obtain treatment. She stopped menstruating several months ago and is moody and chronically depressed. She insists that she is too fat, although her eyes are sunk in deep hollows in her face. Although she is close to physical exhaustion, she no longer sleeps easily. Her family is concerned, and although reluctant to push her, they have finally insisted that she see a psychiatrist. Julie's psychiatrist has prescribed group therapy as a start but warns that if Julie does not begin

Women with anorexia nervosa see themselves as fat, even when they are dangerously underweight.

to gain weight soon, she will need to be hospitalized.

Most anorexia nervosa victims come from middle- or upper-class families. Men account for only 1 or 2 in 20 cases in the general population, although the incidence among male athletes and dancers may be much higher.

No one knows for certain what causes anorexia nervosa. Central to its diagnosis is a distorted body image that overestimates body fatness. When Julie looks at herself in the mirror, she sees her 85-pound body as fat. The more Julie overestimates her body size, the more resistant she is to treatment and the more unwilling to examine her faulty values and misconceptions. Malnutrition is known to affect brain functioning and judgment in this way. People with anorexia nervosa cannot recognize it in themselves; only professionals can diagnose it. Table C9–3 shows a summary of the criteria that experts use.

The Role of the Family

Certain family attitudes, and especially parental attitudes, stand accused of contributing to eating disorders. Families of persons with anorexia nervosa are

---

Table C9–2

Tips for Combatting Eating Disorders

General Guidelines

- Never restrict food intakes to below the amounts suggested for adequacy by Canada's Food Guide (Chapter 2).
- Eat frequently. People often do not eat frequent meals because of time constraints, but eating can be incorporated into other activities, such as snacking while studying or commuting. The person who eats frequently never gets so hungry as to allow hunger to dictate food choices.
- If not at a healthy weight, establish a reasonable weight goal based on a healthy body composition.
- Allow a reasonable time to achieve the goal. A reasonable rate for losing excess fat is about 1% of body weight per week.
- Establish a weight-maintenance support group with people who share interests.

Specific Guidelines for Athletes and Dancers

- Replace weight-based goals with performance-based goals.
- Remember that eating disorders impair physical performance. Seek confidential help in obtaining treatment if needed.
- Restrict weight-loss activities to the off-season.
- Focus on proper nutrition as an important facet of your training, as important as proper technique.

Table C9–3

Summary of Criteria for Diagnosis of Anorexia Nervosa

A person with anorexia nervosa demonstrates the following:

A. Restriction of energy intake relative to requirements, leading to a significantly low body weight in the context of age, sex, developmental trajectory, and physical health. *Significantly low weight* is defined as a weight that is less than the minimally normal.

B. Intense fear of gaining weight or becoming fat, or persistent behavior that interferes with weight gain, even though at a significantly low weight.

C. Disturbance in the way in which one's body weight or shape is experienced, undue influence of body weight or shape on self-evaluation, or persistent lack of recognition of the seriousness of the current low body weight.

Two types of anorexia nervosa include

- Restricting type: during the last 3 months, the individual has not engaged in recurrent episodes of binge eating or purging behaviour (i.e., self-induced vomiting or the misuse of laxatives, diuretics, or enemas). This subtype describes presentations in which weight loss is accomplished primarily through dieting, fasting, and/or excessive exercise.

- Binge eating/purging type: during the last 3 months, the individual has engaged in recurrent episodes of binge eating or purging behaviour (i.e., self-induced vomiting or the misuse of laxatives, diuretics, or enemas).

likely to be critical and to overvalue outward appearances while undervaluing inner self-worth. Parents may oppose one another's authority and vacillate between defending the anorexic child's behaviour and condemning it, confusing the child and disrupting normal parental control. In the extreme, parents may even be sexually abusive or abusive in other ways.

Julie is a perfectionist, just as her parents are: She identifies so strongly with her parents' ideals and goals that she cannot get in touch with her own identity. She is respectful of authority but sometimes feels like a robot, and she may act that way, too: polite but controlled, rigid, and unspontaneous.[13] For Julie, rejecting food is a way of gaining control.

Self-Starvation

How can a person as thin as Julie continue to starve herself? Julie uses tremendous discipline to strictly limit her portions of low-Calorie foods. She will deny her hunger, and having become accustomed to so little food, she feels full after eating only a half-dozen carrot sticks. She can recite the Calorie contents of dozens of foods and the Calorie

costs of as many exercises. If she feels that she has gained an ounce of weight, she runs or jumps rope until she is sure she has exercised it off. She drinks water incessantly to fill her stomach, risking dangerous mineral imbalances. If she fears that the food energy she has eaten exceeds the exercise she has done, she takes laxatives to hasten the passage of food from her system, not knowing that laxatives reduce water absorption but not food energy absorption. Her other methods of staying thin are so effective that she is unaware that laxatives have no effect on body fat. She is desperately hungry. In fact, she is starving, but she doesn't eat because her need for self-control dominates other needs.

Physical Perils

From the body's point of view, anorexia nervosa is starvation and thus brings the same damage as classic protein-energy malnutrition (described in Chapter 6). The person with anorexia depletes the body tissues of needed fat and protein.[14] In young people, growth ceases and normal development falters. They lose so much lean tissue that BMR slows. In athletes, the loss of

lean tissue handicaps physical performance. The heart pumps inefficiently and irregularly, the heart muscle becomes weak and thin, the heart chambers diminish in size, and the blood pressure falls.[15] Electrolytes that help regulate the heartbeat go out of balance. Many deaths in people with anorexia are due to heart failure.

Starvation brings neurological, digestive, and circulation consequences as well. The brain loses significant amounts of tissue, nerves function abnormally, the electrical activity of the brain becomes abnormal, and insomnia is common. Digestive functioning becomes sluggish, the stomach empties slowly, and the lining of the intestinal tract shrinks. The ailing digestive tract fails to digest food adequately, even if the victim does eat. The pancreas slows its production of digestive enzymes. Diarrhea sets in, further worsening malnutrition.

Changes in the blood include anemia, impaired immune response, altered blood lipids, high concentrations of vitamins A and E, and low blood proteins. Dry skin, low body temperature, and the development of fine body hair (the body's attempt to keep warm) also occur. In adulthood, both women and men lose their sex drives. Mothers with anorexia nervosa may severely underfeed their children, who then fail to grow and suffer the other harms typical of starvation.

Treatment of Anorexia Nervosa

Treatment of anorexia nervosa requires a multidisciplinary approach that addresses two issues and behaviours: those relating to food and weight and those involving relationships with oneself and others.[16] Teams of physicians, nurses, psychiatrists, family therapists, and dietitians work together to treat people with anorexia nervosa. Appropriate diet is crucial for normalizing body weight and must be crafted individually.[17] Clients are seldom willing to eat for themselves, but if they are, chances are they can recover without other interventions.

Professionals classify clients based on the risks posed by the degree of malnutrition present.* Clients with low risks may benefit from family counselling, **cognitive therapy**, behaviour modification, and nutrition guidance; those with greater risks may also need other forms of psychotherapy and supplemental formulas to provide extra nutrients and energy. High-risk clients may require involuntary hospitalization and may need to be force-fed by tube at first to forestall death. This step causes psychological trauma. Drugs are commonly prescribed, but, to date, their usefulness is limited.

Stopping weight loss is a first goal of treatment; establishing regular eating patterns is next. At first, progress is slow partly owing to a speeded-up metabolic rate and an increased thermic response to food that occur upon refeeding. As small gains of body fat occur, blood concentration of the appetite-suppressing hormone leptin begins creeping up, too, causing researchers to speculate that leptin may contribute to difficulties in weight restoration.

Few people with anorexia nervosa seek treatment on their own, and denial makes treatment difficult. Almost half of the women who are treated can maintain their body weight within 15 percent of a healthy weight; at that weight, many of them begin menstruating again.[18] The other half have poor or fair outcomes of treatment, and two-thirds of those treated continue a mental battle with recurring morbid thoughts about food and body weight. Many, fearing the growing pads of fat on hips and abdomen, relapse into abnormal eating behaviours.[19] About 1,000 women die of anorexia nervosa each year, mostly from heart abnormalities brought on by malnutrition or from suicide.[20] Anorexia nervosa has one of the highest mortality rates among psychiatric disorders.[21]

Before drawing conclusions about someone who is extremely thin, remember that diagnosis of anorexia nervosa requires professional assessment.

*Indicators of malnutrition include a low percentage of body fat, low blood proteins, and impaired immune response.

People seeking help for anorexia nervosa for themselves or for others should visit the National Eating Disorder Information Centre website or call to get started. Appendix G, available online at www.nelson.com/nutrition3ce, lists the needed resources.

Bulimia Nervosa

Sophia is a 20-year-old flight attendant, and although her body weight is healthy, she thinks constantly about food. She alternately starves herself and then secretly binges; when she has eaten too much, she vomits. Few people would fail to recognize that these symptoms signify bulimia nervosa.

Characteristics of Bulimia Nervosa

Bulimia nervosa is distinct from anorexia nervosa and is much more prevalent, although the true incidence is difficult to establish. People with bulimia nervosa often suffer in secret and, when asked, may deny the existence of a problem. More men suffer from bulimia nervosa than from anorexia nervosa, but bulimia nervosa is still most common in women. Based on a questionnaire, one study estimates that 19 percent of female college students

experience bulimic symptoms. A true diagnosis of bulimia nervosa is based on the criteria listed in Table C9–4; note however, only a summary of these criteria are shown.

Like the typical person with bulimia nervosa, Sophia is single, female, and white. She is well educated and close to her ideal body weight, although her weight fluctuates over a range of 10 pounds (4.5 kg) or so every few weeks.

Sophia seldom lets her bulimia nervosa interfere with her work or other activities. From early childhood, she has been a high achiever but emotionally dependent on her parents. As a young teen, Sophia cycled on and off crash diets. She feels anxious at social events and cannot easily establish close relationships. She is usually depressed, is often impulsive, and has low self-esteem.[22] When crisis hits, Sophia responds by replaying events, worrying excessively, seeking solace in alcohol and tobacco, and blaming herself but never asking for help—behaviours that are barriers to effective coping.[23]

The Role of the Family

Families of bulimic people are observed to be externally controlling but emotionally uninvolved with their children,

Table C9–4

Summary of Criteria for Diagnosis of Bulimia Nervosa

A person with bulimia nervosa demonstrates the following:

A. Recurrent episodes of binge eating. An episode of binge eating is characterized by both of the following:
   1. Eating, in a discrete period of time (e.g., within any 2-hour period), an amount of food that is definitely larger than what most individuals would eat in a similar period of time under similar circumstances.
   2. A sense of lack of control over eating during the episode (e.g., a feeling that one cannot stop eating or control what or how much one is eating).
B. Recurrent inappropriate compensatory behaviours in order to prevent weight gain, such as self-induced vomiting; misuse of laxatives, diuretics, or other medications; fasting; or excessive exercise.
C. The binge eating and inappropriate compensatory behaviours both occur, on average, at least once a week for 3 months.
D. Self-evaluation is unduly influenced by body shape and weight.
E. The disturbance does not occur exclusively during episodes of anorexia nervosa.

resulting in a stifling negative self-image believed to perpetuate bulimia (see Figure C9–2). Dieting, arguments, criticism of body shape or weight, minimal affection and caring, and other weaknesses are common in the families of people with bulimia.[24] Typically, the family has "secrets" that are hidden from outsiders. Bulimic women who report having been abused sexually or physically by family members or friends may continually suffer a sense of being unable to gain control.

Should the person with bulimia nervosa begin making the needed changes toward recovery, others in the family may feel threatened. Family cooperation is important, however, because making changes within a family requires effort from everyone. Such effort is well spent, for changing destructive family interactions can greatly benefit the person who has begun to fight against bulimia nervosa.

Binge Eating and Purging

A bulimic binge is unlike normal eating, and the food is not consumed for its nutritional value. During a binge, Sophia's eating is accelerated by her hunger from previous Calorie restriction (Figure C9–2). She regularly takes in extra food approaching 1,000 Calories at each binge, and she may have several binges in a day.[25] Typical binge foods are easy-to-eat, low-fibre, smooth-textured, high-fat, and high-carbohydrate foods, such as cookies, cakes, and ice cream, and she eats the entire bag of cookies, the whole cake, and every spoonful in a carton of ice cream. By the end of the binge, she has vastly overcorrected for her attempts at Calorie restriction at other times.

The binge is a compulsion and usually occurs in several stages: "anticipation and planning, anxiety, urgency to begin, rapid and uncontrollable consumption of food, relief and relaxation, disappointment, and finally shame or disgust." Then, to purge the food from her body, she may use a cathartic—a strong laxative that can injure the lower intestinal tract. Or she may induce vomiting, using an emetic—a drug intended as first aid for poisoning. After the binge, she pays the price with hands scraped raw against the teeth during induced vomiting; swollen neck glands and reddened eyes from straining to vomit; and the bloating, fatigue, headache, nausea, and pain that follow.

Physical and Psychological Perils

Purging may seem to offer a quick and easy solution to the problems of unwanted Calories and body weight, but bingeing and purging have serious physical consequences. Fluid and electrolyte imbalances caused by vomiting or diarrhea can lead to abnormal heart rhythms and injury to the kidneys. Urinary tract infections can lead to kidney failure. Vomiting causes irritation and infection of the pharynx, esophagus, and salivary glands; erosion of the teeth; and dental caries. The esophagus or stomach may rupture or tear. Overuse of emetics can lead to death by heart failure.

Unlike Julie, Sophia is aware that her behaviour is abnormal, and she is deeply ashamed of it. She wants to recover, and this makes recovery more likely for her than for Julie, who clings to denial.

Treatment of Bulimia Nervosa

To gain control over food and establish regular eating patterns requires adherence to a structured eating plan. The person may also benefit from a regular exercise program.[26] Restrictive dieting is forbidden for it almost always precedes and may even trigger binges. Steady maintenance of weight and prevention of relapse into cyclic gains and losses are the goals. Many a former bulimia nervosa sufferer has taken a major step toward recovery by learning to consistently eat enough food to satisfy hunger needs (at least 1,600 Cal a day). Table C9–5 offers some ways to begin correcting the eating problems of bulimia nervosa. About half of women receiving a diagnosis of bulimia nervosa may recover completely after 5 to 10 years, with or without treatment, but treatment probably speeds the recovery process. If Sophia's depression deepens, she may benefit from antidepressant medication.

Binge Eating Disorder

Anorexia nervosa and bulimia nervosa are distinct eating disorders, yet they sometimes overlap. People with both conditions share an overconcern with body weight and the tendency to drastically undereat. Both may purge. The two disorders can also appear in the same person, or one can lead to the other. Other people have eating disorders that fall short of anorexia nervosa or bulimia nervosa but share some of their features, such as fear of body fatness. One such condition is binge eating disorder (defined earlier in Table C9–1).

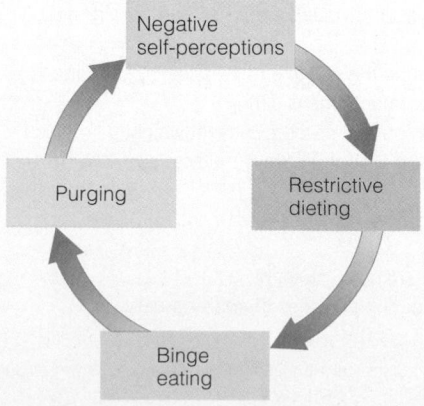

A typical binge consists of easy-to-eat, low-fibre, smooth-textured, high-Calorie foods.

© C. McGregor

Diet Strategies for Combatting Bulimia Nervosa

Planning principles:

- Plan meals and snacks; record plans in a food diary prior to eating.
- Plan meals and snacks that require eating at the table and using utensils.
- Refrain from finger foods.
- Refrain from "dieting" or skipping meals.

Nutrition principles:

- Eat a well-balanced diet and regularly timed meals consisting of a variety of foods.
- Include raw vegetables, salad, or raw fruit at meals to prolong eating times.
- Choose whole-grain, high-fibre breads, pasta, rice, and cereals to increase bulk.
- Consume adequate fluid, particularly water.

Other tips:

- Choose meals that provide protein and fat for satiety and bulky, fibre-rich carbohydrates for immediate feelings of fullness.
- Try including water-rich foods, such as clear broth, for satiety (see Water Content of Various Foods and Beverages in Chapter 8, in the margin under Table 8-2).
- Consume the amounts of food specified in Canada's Food Guide (Chapter 2).
- For convenience (and to reduce temptation), select foods that naturally divide into portions. Select one potato rather than rice or pasta that can be overloaded onto the plate; purchase yogurt and cottage cheese in individual containers; look for small packages of precut steak or chicken; choose frozen dinners with metered portions.
- Include 30 minutes or more of physical activity on most days—exercise may be an important tool in controlling bulimia.

Table C9–6

Summary of Criteria for Diagnosis of Binge-Eating Disorder

A person with a binge eating disorder demonstrates the following:

A. Recurrent episodes of binge eating. An episode of binge eating is characterized by both of the following:
  1. Eating, in a discrete period of time (e.g., within any 2-hour period), an amount of food that is definitely larger than what most people would eat in a similar period of time under similar circumstances
  2. Sense of lack of control over eating during the episode (e.g., a feeling that one cannot stop eating or control what or how much one is eating)

B. The binge-eating episodes are associated with at least three (or more) of the following:
  1. Eating much more rapidly than normal
  2. Eating until feeling uncomfortably full
  3. Eating large amounts of food when not feeling physically hungry
  4. Eating alone because of being embarrassed by how much one is eating
  5. Feeling disgusted with oneself, depressed, or very guilty afterward

C. Marked distress regarding binge eating is present.

D. The binge eating occurs, on average, at least once a week for 3 months.

E. The binge eating is not associated with the recurrent use of inappropriate compensatory behaviors as in bulimia nervosa and does not occur exclusively during the course of bulimia nervosa or anorexia nervosa.

Source: Reprinted with permission from the Diagnostic and Statistical Manual of Mental Disorders, Fifth Edition (DSM-5), (Copyright ©2013). American Psychiatric Association. All Rights Reserved.

Up to half of all people who restrict eating to lose weight periodically binge without purging, including about one-third of obese people who regularly engage in binge eating. Obesity itself, however, does not constitute an eating disorder. Table C9–6 lists a summary of the official diagnostic criteria for binge eating disorder.

Clinicians note differences between people with bulimia nervosa and those with binge eating disorder.[27] People with binge eating disorder consume less during a binge, rarely purge, and exert less restraint during times of dieting. Similarities also exist, including feeling out of control, disgusted, depressed, embarrassed, guilty, or distressed because of their self-perceived gluttony.[28] Binge eating behaviour responds more readily to treatment than other eating disorders, and resolving such behaviours can be a first step to authentic weight control. Successful treatment also improves physical health, mental health, and the chances of breaking the cycle of rapid weight losses and gains.

Eating Disorders in Society

Most experts agree that eating disorders have many causes: sociocultural, psychological, hereditary, and probably also neurochemical. Proof that society plays a role in eating disorders is their demographic distribution: they are known only in developed nations, and they become more prevalent as wealth increases and food becomes plentiful.

No doubt our society sets unrealistic ideals for body weight, especially for women, and devalues those who do not conform to them. The Miss America beauty pageant, for example, puts forth a role model of female desirability. No winner has ever been overweight, and thinner and thinner women have worn the Miss America crown over the years.[29] Magazines and other media convey the message that to be thin is to be happy; eating disorders are not a form of rebellion against these unrealistic ideals but rather an exaggerated acceptance of them. Body dissatisfaction is a primary factor in the development of eating disorders.[30]

Even professionals, including physicians and dietitians, tend to praise people for losing weight and to suggest weight loss to people who do not need it. As a result, normal-weight girls as young as five years old fear that they are too fat and are placed "on diets."[31] In addition, an increasing number of girls younger than 18 are poorly nourished.[32] Some eat so little food that normal growth ceases; thus, they miss out on their adolescent growth spurts and may never catch up.

Perhaps a young person's best defence against these disorders is to learn about normal, expected growth patterns, especially the characteristic weight gain of adolescence (see Chapter 14), and to learn respect for the inherent wisdom of the body. When people discover and honour the body's real needs for nutrition and exercise, they become unwilling to sacrifice health for conformity.

Self-Check

Answers to these Self-Check questions are in Appendix D.

1. All of the following are health risks associated with excessive body fat except
    a. respiratory problems
    b. sleep apnea
    c. gallbladder disease
    d. low blood lipids

2. Which of the following statements about basal metabolic rate (BMR) is correct?
    a. The greater a person's age, the higher the BMR.
    b. The more thyroxine produced, the higher the BMR.
    c. Fever lowers the BMR.
    d. Pregnant women have lower BMRs.

3. Body density (the measurement of body weight compared with volume) is determined by which technique?
    a. fatfold test
    b. bioelectrical impedance
    c. underwater weighing
    d. all of the above

4. The obesity theory stating that the body chooses to be at a specific desired weight is the
    a. set-point theory
    b. enzyme theory
    c. fat cell number theory
    d. external cue theory

5. Which of the following explains the great initial weight loss with a high-protein diet?
    a. increased basal metabolic rate
    b. increased thermic effect of protein
    c. lost glycogen and water
    d. urinary ketone loss

6. Which of the following is a possible physical consequence of fasting?
    a. loss of lean body tissues
    b. lasting weight loss
    c. body cleansing
    d. all of the above

7. The thermic effect of food plays a major role in energy expenditure.
    T   F

8. The nervous system cannot use fat as fuel; it can use only glucose.
    T   F

9. The BMI standard is an excellent tool for evaluating obesity in athletes and the elderly.
    T   F

10. A diet too low in carbohydrate brings about responses that are similar to fasting.
    T   F

track it!

Diet Analysis PLUS +

Concepts in Action

start now! ···> If you are not currently exercising regularly, try this: go to Diet Analysis Plus online and create an alternative profile, adding in 30 minutes of moderate to vigorous physical activity for each day on which you have tracked your food intake. Go to the Reports tab; then choose Energy Balance. What differences do you see when you compare this report with the report you created under your original profile?

Analyze Your Energy Balance

The purpose of this exercise is to help you to use critical thinking to evaluate correlations between nutrition, physical activity, and body weight.

1. Your Calorie intake represents the "energy in" part of your energy balance. From the Reports tab, under the Nutrients heading, select Energy Balance, choose Day One of your 3-Day intake, include all meals and snacks, and check your Net kcal for the day. How does it compare to the DRI Estimated Energy Requirement (EER) for the reference man or woman of your age, as listed on the inside front cover of the text?

2. Energy balance is affected not just by food eaten but also by energy expended. Compare the effects of two levels of activity on your energy balance. You've already generated an Energy Balance report for Day One. From the DA+ home page, select the Track Activity tab, and add a new 30-minute activity for Day One. Hint: Your text has some ideas listed in Table 9–5 on page 383. Next, compare the Energy Balance report with and without the added activity. What changes do you see?

3. If you want to lose body fat, you must expend more energy than you take in. Look over your 3-Day food record. Is there a day that you were in positive energy balance (took in more energy than you used)? If so, develop a revised food record for that day with the goal of reducing Calories but still maintaining a wholesome and satisfying diet. Now, select the Track Diet tab to evaluate the revised meal plan. Did you succeed in trimming Calories but still consume the recommended nutrients? How many Calories did you trim?

4. All three energy-yielding nutrients can contribute excess Calories, but fat is the least satiating, most highly caloric per gram, and most easily consumed without awareness. From the Reports tab, under the Advanced heading, select Source Analysis, choose all meals and snacks, and then select Fat, Total from the drop-down pick-list. Evaluate your daily food records for total fat. Then choose the day that contained the most fat in grams or the highest percentage of Calories from fat. Find the foods that contributed the most fat to your intake. What would you say led to higher intake of fat on that day as compared to the others? Which part of the day did you consume the most fat? Were you aware that you were doing so?

Endnotes

1. A. Thorogood and coauthors, Relation between body mass index and mortality in an unusually slim cohort, *Journal of Epidemiology and Community Health* 572 (2003): 130–133.

2. P. T. Katzmarzyk, C. L. Craig, and C. Bouchard, Underweight, overweight and obesity: Relationships with mortality in the 13-year follow up of the Canada Fitness Study, *Journal of Clinical Epidemiology* 54 (2001): 916–920.

3. P. T. Katzmarzyk and C. I. Arden, Overweight and obesity mortality trends in Canada, 1885–2000, *Canadian Journal of Public Health* 95 (2004): 16–20.

4. I. Strychar, Fighting obesity: A call to arms, *Canadian Journal of Public Health* 95 (2004): 12–14; M. Tjepkema, Measured obesity—adult obesity in Canada: Measured height and weight, available at http://www.statcan.gc.ca/pub/82-620-m/2005001/article/adults-adultes/8060-eng.htm.

5. Canadian Population Health Initiative, Improving the health of Canadians: Summary Report, available at https://secure.cihi.ca/free_products/IHC2004_sumrev_e.pdf.

6. J. K. Alexander, Obesity and coronary heart disease, *American Journal of the Medical Sciences* 321 (2001): 215–224.

7. A. H. Mokdad and coauthors, Prevalence of obesity, diabetes, and obesity-related health risk factors, 2001, *Journal of the American Medical Association* 289 (2003): 76–79; K. R. Fontaine and coauthors, Years of life lost due to obesity, *Journal of the American Medical Association* 289 (2003): 187–193.

8. J. C. Peters, The challenge of managing body weight in the modern world, *Asia Pacific Journal of Clinical Nutrition* 11 (2002): S714–S717.

9. M.-P. St-Onge and S. B. Heymsfield, Overweight and obesity status are linked to lower life expectancy, *Nutrition Reviews* 61 (2003): 313–316; D. B. Allison and coauthors, Annual deaths attributable to obesity in the United States, *Journal of the American Medical Association* 282 (1999): 1530–1538.

10. U.S. Department of Human & Health Services. Screening for and management of obesity in adults: U.S. Preventive Services Task Force recommendation statement (2012). available at http://www.guideline.gov/content.aspx?id=37710.

11. Centers for Disease Control and Prevention, Prevalence of overweight and obesity among adults with diagnosed diabetes—United States, 1988–1994 and 1999–2002, *Morbidity and Mortality Weekly Reports* 53 (2004): 1066–1068.

12. G. R. Dagenais and coauthors, Prognostic impact of body weight and abdominal obesity in women and men with cardiovascular disease, *American Heart Journal* 149 (2005): 54–60; E. N. Taylor, M. J. Stampfer, and G. C. Curhan, Obesity, weight gain, and the risk of kidney stones, *Journal of the American Medical Association* 293 (2005): 455–462; E. E. Calle and coauthors, Overweight, obesity, and mortality from cancer in a prospectively studied cohort of U.S. adults, *New England Journal of Medicine* 348 (2003): 1625–1638.

13. T. B. Nguyen-Duy and coauthors, Visceral fat and liver fat are independent predictors of metabolic risk factors in men, *American Journal of Physiology. Endocrinology and Metabolism* 284 (2003): 558–561; G. Davi and coauthors, Platelet activation in obese women—Role of inflammation and oxidant stress, *Journal of the American Medical Association* 288 (2002): 2008–2014; J. M. Oppert and coauthors, Anthropometric estimates of muscle and fat mass in relation to cardiac and cancer mortality in men: The Paris Prospective Study, *American Journal of Clinical Nutrition* 75 (2002): 1107–1113.

14. F. X. Pi-Sunyer, The epidemiology of central fat distribution in relation to disease, *Nutrition Reviews* 62 (2004): S120–S126.

15. P. R. Jones and D. A. Edwards, Areas of fat loss in overweight young females following an 8-week period of energy intake reduction, *Annals of Human Biology* 26 (1999): 151–162.

16. R. A. Breslow and B. A. Smothers, Drinking patterns and body mass index in never smokers, *American Journal of Epidemiology* 161 (2005): 368–376; C. A. Holcomb, D. L. Heim, and T. M. Loughin, Physical activity minimizes the association of body fatness with abdominal obesity in white, premenopausal women: Results from the Third National Health and Nutrition Examination Survey, *Journal of the American Dietetic Association* 104 (2004): 1859–1862; J. M. Dorn and coauthors, Alcohol drinking patterns differentially affect central adiposity as measured by abdominal height in women and men, *Journal of Nutrition* 133 (2003): 2655–2662.

17. J. Stevens and coauthors, Evaluation of WHO and NHANES II standards for overweight using mortality rates, *Journal of the American Dietetic Association* 100 (2000): 825–827.

18. Health Canada, *Canadian Guidelines for Body Weight Classification in Adults* (Ottawa, ON:

Health Canada Publications Centre, 2003), available at http://www.hc-sc.gc.ca/fn-an/nutrition/weights-poids/guide-ld-adult/index-eng.php.

19. T. R. Wessel and coauthors, Relationship of physical fitness vs. body mass index with coronary artery disease and cardiovascular events in women, *Journal of the American Medical Association* 292 (2004): 1179–1187; S. W. Farrell and coauthors, The relation of body mass index, cardiorespiratory fitness, and all-cause mortality in women, *Obesity Research* 10 (2002): 417–423; C. D. Lee and S. N. Blair, Cardiorespiratory fitness and smoking-related and total cancer mortality in men, *Medicine and Science in Sports and Exercise* 34 (2002): 735–739; C. D. Lee and S. N. Blair, Cardiorespiratory fitness and stroke mortality in men, *Medicine and Science in Sports and Exercise* 34 (2002): 592–595.

20. T. S. Church and coauthors, Exercise capacity and body composition as predictors of mortality among men with diabetes, *Diabetes Care* 27 (2004): 83–88.

21. N. S. Wellman and B. Friedberg, Causes and consequences of adult obesity: Health, social and economic impacts in the United States, *Asia Pacific Journal of Clinical Nutrition* 11 (2002): S705–S709.

22. M. R. Lowe, K. Miller-Kovach, and S. Phelan, Weight-loss maintenance in overweight individuals one to five years following successful completion of a commercial weight-loss program, *International Journal of Obesity and Related Metabolic Disorders* 25 (2001): 325–331.

23. Standing Committee on the Scientific Evaluation of Dietary Reference Intakes, Food and Nutrition Board, Institute of Medicine, *Dietary Reference Intakes for Energy, Carbohydrate, Fiber, Fat, Fatty Acids, Cholesterol, Protein, and Amino Acids* (Washington, D.C.: National Academies Press, 2002), p. 13-12.

24. M. Gilliat-Wimberely and coauthors, Effects of habitual physical activity on the resting metabolic rates and body compositions of women aged 35 to 50 years, *Journal of the American Dietetic Association* 101 (2001): 1181–1188.

25. J. Stevens and coauthors, The effect of decision rules on the choice of a body mass index cutoff for obesity: Examples from African American and white women, *American Journal of Clinical Nutrition* 75 (2002): 986–992; J. Stevens, Obesity and mortality in African-Americans, *Nutrition Reviews* 58 (2000): 346–353.

26. J. E. Manson and S. S. Bassuk, Obesity in the United States: A fresh look at its high toll, *Journal of the American Medical Association* 289 (2003): 229–230.

27. I. Janssen and coauthors, Body mass index and waist circumference independently contribute to the prediction of nonabdominal, abdominal subcutaneous, and visceral fat, *American Journal of Clinical Nutrition* 75 (2002): 683–688.

28. I. Lofgren and coauthors, Waist circumference is a better predictor than body mass index of coronary heart disease risk in overweight premenopausal women, *Journal of Nutrition* 134 (2004): 1071–1076.

29. G. Panotopoulos and coauthors, Dual X-ray absorptiometry, bioelectrical impedance, and near infrared interactance in obese women, *Medicine and Science in Sports and Exercise* 33 (2001): 665–670.

30. J. Wardle, J. Waller, and E. Fox, Age of onset and body dissatisfaction in obesity, *Addictive Behaviors* 27 (2002): 561–573.

31. L. J. Harnack, R. W. Jeffrey, and K. N. Boutelle, Temporal trends in energy intake in the United States: An ecologic perspective, *American Journal of Clinical Nutrition* 71 (2000): 1478–1484.

32. A. S. Levine, C. M. Kotz, and B. A. Gosnell, Sugars and fats: The neurobiology of preference, *Journal of Nutrition* 133 (2003): 831S–834S.

33. D. E. Gerstein and coauthors, Clarifying concepts about macronutrients' effects on satiation and satiety, *Journal of the American Dietetic Association* 104 (2004): 1151–1153; S. C. Woods, Gastrointestinal satiety signals I. An overview of gastrointestinal signals that influence food intake, *American Journal of Physiology. Gastrointestinal and Liver Physiology* 286 (2004): G7–G13.

34. A. Prentice and S. Jebb, Energy intake/physical activity interactions in the homeostasis of body weight regulation, *Nutrition Reviews* 62 (2004): S98–S104.

35. C. Pico and coauthors, Gastric leptin: A putative role in the short-term regulation of food intake, *British Journal of Nutrition* 90 (2003): 735–741; M. J. Lewin and A. Bado, Gastric leptin, *Microscopy Research and Technique* 53 (2001): 372–376.

36. R. B. Ceddia, W. N. William, Jr., and R. Curi, The response of skeletal muscle to leptin, *Frontiers in Bioscience* 6 (2001): D90–D97.

37. J. Williams and S. Mobarhan, A critical interaction: Leptin and ghrelin, *Nutrition Reviews* 61 (2003): 391–393; D. E. Cummings and M. W. Schwartz, Genetics and pathophysiology of human obesity, *Annual Reviews of Medicine* 54 (2003): 453–471.

38. E. Faloia and coauthors, Adipose tissue as an endocrine organ? A review of some recent data, *Eating and Weight Disorders* 5 (2000): 116–123.

39. M. W. Rajala and P. E. Scherer, Minireview: The adipocyte—At the crossroads of energy homeostasis, inflammation, and atherosclerosis, *Endocrinology* 144 (2003): 3765–3773; I. Sadaf Farooqi and coauthors, Beneficial effects of leptin on obesity, T cell hyporesponsiveness, and neuroendocrine/metabolic dysfunction of human congenital leptin deficiency, *Journal of Clinical Investigation* 110 (2002): 1093–1103; R. L. Bradley, K. A. Cleveland, and B. Cheatham, The adipocyte as a secretory organ: Mechanisms of vesicle transport and secretory pathways, *Recent Progress in Hormone Research* 56 (2001): 329–358.

40. C. K. Welt and coauthors, Recombinant human leptin in women with hypothalamic amenorrhea, *New England Journal of Medicine* 351 (2004): 987–997; S. Shalitin and M. Phillip, Role of obesity and leptin in the pubertal process and pubertal growth—A review, *International Journal of Obesity and Related Metabolic Disorders* 27 (2003): 869–874.

41. R. B. Ceddia, W. N. William, Jr., and R. Curi, 2001 [see reference 36]; M. S. Westerterp-Plantenga and coauthors, Effects of weekly administration of pegylated recombinant human OB protein on appetite profile and energy metabolism in obese men, *American Journal of Clinical Nutrition* 74 (2001): 426–434.

42. M. Yao and S. B. Roberts, Dietary energy and weight regulation, *Nutrition Reviews* 59 (2001): 247–258.

43. W. J. Pasman and coauthors, Effect of two breakfasts, different in carbohydrate composition, on hunger and satiety and mood in healthy men, *International Journal of Obesity and Related Metabolic Disorders* 27 (2003): 663–668; D. B. Pawlak, C. B. Ebbeling, and D. S. Ludwig, Should obese patients be counselled to follow a low-glycaemic index diet? Yes, *Obesity Reviews* 3 (2002): 235–243; J. C. Brand-Miller and coauthors, Glycemic index and obesity, *American Journal of Clinical Nutrition* 76 (2002): 281S–285S.

44. A. Raben, Should obese patients be counselled to follow a low-glycaemic index diet? No, *Obesity Reviews* 3 (2002): 245–256.

45. A. R. Skov and coauthors, Randomized trial on protein vs carbohydrate in ad libitum fat reduced diet for the treatment of obesity, *International Journal of Obesity and Related Metabolic Disorders* 23 (1999): 528–536.

46. T. H. Moran and K. P. Kinzig, Gastrointestinal satiety signals II. Cholecystokinin, *American Journal of Physiology. Gastrointestinal and Liver Physiology* 286 (2004): G183–G188.

47. E. M. Kovacs and coauthors, The effect of guar gum addition to a semisolid meal on appetite related to blood glucose, in dieting men, *European Journal of Clinical Nutrition* 56 (2002): 771–778; N. C. Howarth, E. Saltzman, and S. B. Roberts, Dietary fiber and weight regulation, *Nutrition Reviews* 59 (2001): 129–139; B. J. Rolls, E. A. Bell, and B. A. Waugh, Increasing the volume of food by incorporating air increases satiety in men, *American Journal of Clinical Nutrition* 72 (2000): 361–368; B. J. Rolls, E. A. Bell, and M. L. Thorwart, Water incorporated into a food but not served with a food decreases energy intake in lean women, *American Journal of Clinical Nutrition* 70 (1999): 448–455.

48. L. P. Kozak and M. E. Harper, Mitochondrial uncoupling proteins in energy expenditure, *Annual Review of Nutrition* 20 (2000): 339–363.

49. S. O'Rahilly and coauthors, Minireview: Human obesity—Lessons from mono-genetic disorders, *Endocrinology* 144 (2003): 3757–3764.

50. S. O'Rahilly and coauthors, 2003 [see reference 49]; M. S. Treuth and coauthors, Familial resemblance of body composition in prepubertal girls and their biological parents, *American Journal of Clinical Nutrition* 74 (2001): 529–533; L. Perusse and C. Bouchard, Genotype-environment interaction in human obesity, *Nutrition Reviews* 57 (1999): S31–S38.

51. P. Hakala and coauthors, Environmental factors in the development of obesity in identical twins, *International Journal of Obesity and Related Metabolic Disorders* 23 (1999): 746–753.

52. B. E. Levin and A. A. Dunn-Meynell, Defense of body weight depends on dietary composition and palatability in rats with diet-induced

obesity, *American Journal of Physiology: Regulatory, Integrative and Comparative Physiology* 282 (2002): R46–R54; L. Perusse and C. Bouchard, Gene-diet interactions in obesity, *American Journal of Clinical Nutrition* 72 (2000): 1285S–1290S.

53. D. E. Cummings and M. W. Schwartz, Genetics and pathophysiology of human obesity, *Annual Review of Medicine* 54 (2003): 453–471; J. Altman, Weight in the balance, *Neuroendocrinology* 76 (2002): 131–136; G. Wolf, The uncoupling proteins UCP2 and UCP3 in skeletal muscle, *Nutrition Reviews* 59 (2001): 56–57.

54. J. A. Yanovski and coauthors, Associations between uncoupling protein 2, body composition, and resting energy expenditure in lean and obese African American, white, and Asian children, *American Journal of Clinical Nutrition* 71 (2000): 1405–1412.

55. J. Nedergaard and B. Cannon, The "novel" "uncoupling" proteins UCP2 and UCP3: What do they really do? Pros and cons for suggested functions, *Experimental Physiology* 88 (2003): 65–84; G. Argyropoulos and M. Harper, Molecular biology of thermoregulation, invited review: Uncoupling proteins and thermoregulation, *Journal of Applied Physiology* 92 (2001): 2187–2198.

56. B. Wansink, as quoted in Food illusions: Why we eat more than we think, *Nutrition Action Healthletter*, March 2004, pp. 3–6; M. A. McCrory and coauthors, Dietary variety within food groups: Association with energy intake and body fatness in men and women, *American Journal of Clinical Nutrition* 69 (1999): 440–447.

57. E. Kennedy, Diet diversity, diet quality, and body weight regulation, *Nutrition Reviews* 62 (2004): S78–S79.

58. M. F. Dallman and coauthors, Chronic stress and obesity: A new view of "comfort food," *Proceedings of the National Academy of Sciences of the United States of America* 100 (2003): 11696–11701.

59. J. K. Binkley, J. Eales, and M. Jekanowski, The relation between dietary change and rising U.S. obesity, *International Journal of Obesity and Related Metabolic Disorders* 24 (2000): 1032–1039.

60. T. Philipson and coauthors, The economics of obesity: A report on the workshop held at the USDA's Economic Research Service, May 2004, available at http://www.ers.usda.gov/publications/efan04004/.

61. J. N. Variyam, The price is right: Economics and the rise in obesity, *Amber Waves*, February 2005, available at http://nifa.usda.gov/nea/food/pdfs/roundtable_references_price.pdf; S. A. French, Pricing effects on food choices, *Journal of Nutrition* 133 (2003): 841S–843S.

62. A. H. C. Goris, M. S. Westerterp-Plantenga, and K. R. Westerterp, Undereating and underrecording of habitual food intake in obese men: Selective underreporting of fat intake, *American Journal of Clinical Nutrition* 71 (2000): 130–134.

63. M. Wei and coauthors, The association between cardiorespiratory fitness and impaired glucose and type 2 diabetes mellitus in men, *Annals of Internal Medicine* 130 (1999): 89–96.

64. Even moderate amounts of exercise can prevent weight gain, *FDA Consumer*, March/April, 2004, p. 5.

65. C. A. Slentz and coauthors, Effects of the amount of exercise on body weight, body composition, and measures of central obesity: STRRIDE—a randomized controlled study, *Archives of Internal Medicine* 164 (2004): 31–39; Committee on the Scientific Evaluation of Dietary Reference Intakes, Food and Nutrition Board, Institute of Medicine, 2002, p. 12-1 [see reference 23].

66. J. Cawley, S. Markowitz, and J. Tauras, Lighting up and slimming down: The effects of body weight and cigarette prices on adolescent smoking initiation, *Journal of Health Economics* 23 (2004): 293–311; S. E. Saarni and coauthors, Intentional weight loss and smoking in young adults, *International Journal of Obesity and Related Metabolic Disorders* 28 (2004): 796–802.

67. M. M. McGrane, Carbohydrate metabolism—Synthesis and oxidation, in M. H. Stipanuk, ed., *Biochemical and Physiological Aspects of Human Nutrition* (Philadelphia, PA: W. B. Saunders, 2000), p. 192.

68. R. M. Anson and coauthors, Intermittent fasting dissociates beneficial effects of dietary restriction on glucose metabolism and neuronal resistance to injury from Calorie intake, *Proceedings of the National Academy of Sciences* 100 (2003): 6216–6220; R. Wan, S. Camandola, and M. P. Mattson, Intermittent fasting and dietary supplementation with 2-deoxy-D-glucose improve functional and metabolic cardiovascular risk factors in rats, *The Journal of FASEB* 17 (2003): 1133–1134.

69. R. P. Ferraris and H. V. Carey, Intestinal transport during fasting and malnutrition, *Annual Review of Nutrition* 20 (2000): 195–219.

70. National Task Force on the Prevention and Treatment of Obesity, Dieting and the development of eating disorders in overweight and obese adults, *Archives of Internal Medicine* 260 (2000): 2581–2589.

71. J. Eisenstein and coauthors, High-protein weight-loss diets: Are they safe and do they work? A review of the experimental and epidemiologic data, *Nutrition Reviews* 60 (2002): 189–200.

72. A. Raben and coauthors, Meals with similar energy densities but rich in protein, fat, carbohydrate, or alcohol have different effects on energy expenditure and substrate metabolism but not on appetite and energy intake, *American Journal of Clinical Nutrition* 77 (2003): 91–100.

73. G. D. Foster and coauthors, Obese patients' perceptions of treatment outcomes and the factors that influence them, *Archives of Internal Medicine* 161 (2001): 2133–2139.

74. D. C. W. Lau and coauthors for members of the Obesity Canada Clinical Practice Guidelines Expert Panel, 2006 Canadian clinical practice guidelines on the management and prevention of obesity in adults and children [Summary], *Canadian Medical Association Journal* 176, 8 (2007): S1–S13; J. E. Donnelly and coauthors, ACSM position stand: Appropriate physical activity intervention strategies for weight loss and prevention of weight regain for adults, *Medicine and Science in Sports and Exercise* 41(2) (2009): 459–471.

75. F. M. Sacks and coauthors, Comparison of weight-loss diets with different compositions of fat, protein and carbohydrates, *New England Journal of Medicine* 360, 9 (2009): 859–873.

76. National Heart, Lung, and Blood Institute, National Institutes of Health, *The Practical Guide: Identification, Evaluation, and Treatment of Overweight and Obesity in Adults*, NIH publication no. 00-4084 (Washington, D.C.: Government Printing Office, 2000), p. 26.

77. T. V. Kral, L. S. Roe, and B. J. Rolls, Does nutrition information about the energy density of meals affect food intake in normal-weight women? *Appetite* 39 (2002): 137–145; B. J. Rolls and E. A. Bell, Dietary approaches to the treatment of obesity, *Medical Clinics of North America* 84 (2000): 401–418, vi.

78. E. A. Bell and B. J. Rolls, Energy density of foods affects energy intake across multiple levels of fat content in lean and obese women, *American Journal of Clinical Nutrition* 73 (2001): 1010–1018.

79. A. Drewnowski and coauthors, Dietary energy density and body weight: Is there a relationship? *Nutrition Reviews* 62 (2004): 403–413; T. V. E. Kral, L. S. Roe, and B. J. Rolls, Combined effects of energy density and portion size on energy intake in women, *American Journal of Clinical Nutrition* 79 (2004): 962–968.

80. M. B. Zemel and S. L. Miller, Dietary calcium and dairy modulation of adiposity and obesity risk, *Nutrition Reviews* 62 (2004): 125–131; S. J. Parikh and J. A. Yanovski, Calcium and adiposity, *American Journal of Clinical Nutrition* 77 (2003): 281–287; D. Teegarden, Calcium intake and reduction in weight or fat mass, *Journal of Nutrition* 133 (2003): 249S–251S; R. P. Heaney, K. M. Davies, and M. J. Barger-Lux, Calcium and weight: Clinical studies, *Journal of the American College of Nutrition* 21 (2002): 152–155.

81. G. A. Bray, S. J. Nielsen, and B. M. Popkin, Consumption of high-fructose corn syrup in beverages may play a role in the epidemic of obesity, *American Journal of Clinical Nutrition* 79 (2004): 537–543; R. Novotny and coauthors, Dairy intake is associated with lower body fat and soda intake with greater weight in adolescent girls, *Journal of Nutrition* 134 (2004): 1905–1909.

82. M. B. Schulze and coauthors, Sugar-sweetened beverages, weight gain, and incidence of type 2 diabetes in young and middle-aged women, *Journal of the American Medical Association* 292 (2004): 927–934.

83. M. Y. Bertone and coauthors, Association between eating patterns and obesity in a free-living US adult population, *American Journal of Epidemiology* 158 (2003): 85–92.

84. L. A. Pawlow, P. M. O'Neil, and R. J. Malcolm, Night eating syndrome: Effects of brief relaxation training on stress, mood, hunger, and eating patterns, *International Journal of Obesity and Related Metabolic Disorders* 27 (2003): 970–978; M. E. Gluck, A. Geliebter, and T. Satov, Night eating syndrome is associated with depression, low self-esteem, reduced daytime hunger, and less weight loss in obese outpatients, *Obesity Research* 9 (2001): 264–267.

85. U.S. Department of Agriculture and U.S. Department of Health and Human Services,

Dietary Guidelines for Americans 2010, available at http://www.health.gov/dietaryguidelines/2010 .asp; S. N. Blair, M. J. LaMonte, and M. Z. Nichaman, The evolution of physical activity recommendations: How much is enough? *American Journal of Clinical Nutrition* 79 (2004): 913S–920S; Committee on the Scientific Evaluation of Dietary Reference Intakes, Food and Nutrition Board, Institute of Medicine, 2002 [see reference 23].

86. J. W. Anderson and coauthors, Long-term weight-loss maintenance: A meta-analysis of US studies, *American Journal of Clinical Nutrition* 74 (2001): 579–584.

87. J. F. Carroll and C. K. Kyser, Exercise training in obesity lowers blood pressure independent of weight change, *Medicine and Science in Sports and Exercise* 34 (2002): 596–601; B. Gutin and coauthors, Effects of exercise intensity on cardiovascular fitness, total body composition, and visceral adiposity of obese adolescents, *American Journal of Clinical Nutrition* 75 (2002): 818–826; R. Ross and coauthors, Reduction in obesity and related comorbid conditions after diet-induced weight loss or exercise induced weight loss in men: A randomized, controlled trial, *Annals of Internal Medicine* 133 (2000): 92–103.

88. B. R. Gutin and coauthors, 2002 [see reference 87]; Ross and coauthors, 2000 [see reference 87]; G. Benedetti and coauthors, Body composition and energy expenditure after weight loss following bariatric surgery, *Journal of the American College of Nutrition* 19 (2000): 270–274.

89. W. D. Schmidt, C. J. Biwer, and L. K. Kalscheuer, Effects of long versus short bout exercise on fitness and weight loss in overweight females, *Journal of the American College of Nutrition* 20 (2001): 494–501.

90. American College of Sports Medicine, Position stand: Appropriate intervention strategies for weight loss and prevention of weight regain for adults, *Medicine and Science in Sports and Exercise* 33 (2001): 2145–2156.

91. National Heart, Lung, and Blood Institute, National Institutes of Health, 2000, p. 29 [see reference 76].

92. L. K. Khan and coauthors, Use of prescription weight loss pills among U.S. adults in 1996–1998, *Annals of Internal Medicine* 134 (2001): 282–286.

93. E. C. Mun, G. L. Blackburn, and J. B. Matthews, Current status of medical and surgical therapy for obesity, *Gastroenterology* 120 (2001): 669–681.

94. FDA approves implanted stomach band to treat severe obesity, *FDA Talk Paper*, June 5, 2001, available at http://www.fda.gov/downloads/ AdvisoryCommittees/CommitteesMeetingMaterials/ MedicalDevices/MedicalDevicesAdvisoryCommittee/ Gastroenterology-UrologyDevicesPanel/ UCM302772.pdf.

95. H. Buchwald and coauthors, Bariatric surgery: A systematic review and meta-analysis, *Journal of the American Medical Association* 292 (2004): 1724–1737.

96. J. G. Bruner and R. H. de Jong, Lipoplasty claims experience of U.S. insurance companies, *Plastic and Reconstructive Surgery* 107 (2001): 1285–1291.

97. R. B. Rao, S. F. Ely, and R. S. Hoffman, Deaths related to liposuction, *New England Journal of Medicine* 340 (1999): 1471–1475.

98. Food and Drug Administration, FDA News Release: FDA Acts to Remove Ephedra-Containing Dietary Supplements from Market, November 2004, available at http://www.fda.gov/NewsEvents/Newsroom/ PressAnnouncements/2004/ucm108379.htm.

99. S. Barrett, ed., California restricts ephedra "supplements," *Consumer Health Digest*, October 21, 2003, available at http://www.ncahf.org/ digest03/03-41.html; W. K. Jones, Safety of dietary supplements containing ephedrine alkaloids, FDA Public Meeting Summary, August 2000, available at http://www.erowid.org/ chemicals/ephedrine/ephedrine_info2.shtml.

100. M. H. Pittler and E. Ernst, Dietary supplements for body-weight reduction: A systematic review, *American Journal of Clinical Nutrition* 79 (2004): 529–536.

101. Food and Drug Administration, FDA warns distributors of dietary supplements promoted online for weight loss, *FDA News*, April 1, 2004, available at http://www.fda.gov/newsevents/newsroom/pressannouncements/2004/ucm108274.htm.

102. J. P. Ikeda and coauthors, Self-reported dieting experiences of women with body mass indexes of 30 or more, *Journal of the American Dietetic Association* 104 (2004): 972–974.

103. 1,800 Calories, 4 miles keep the weight off, *In Diabetes Today*, November 17, 2004, available at http://usatoday30.usatoday.com/news/health/ 2004-11-16-activities_x.htm.

104. A. Groin and coauthors, Promoting long-term weight control: does dieting consistency matter? *International Journal of Obesity and Related Metabolic Disorders* 28 (2004): 278–281.

105. P. Koh-Banerjee and coauthors, Changes in whole-grain, bran, and cereal fiber consumption in relation to 8-y weight gain among men, *American Journal of Clinical Nutrition* 80 (2004): 1237–1245; N. C. Howarth, E. Saltzman, and S. B. Roberts, 2001 [see reference 47].

106. A. E. Field and coauthors, Relation between dieting and weight change among preadolescents and adolescents, *Pediatrics* 112 (2003): 900–906; A. Kroke and coauthors, Recent weight changes and weight cycling as predictors of subsequent two year weight change in a middle-aged cohort, *International Journal of Obesity and Related Metabolic Disorders* 26 (2002): 403–409.

107. E. D. Shade and coauthors, Frequent intentional weight loss is associated with lower natural killer cell cytotoxicity in postmenopausal women: Possible long-term immune effects, *Journal of the American Dietetic Association* 104 (2004): 903–912.

108. B. Wansink, Environmental factors that increase the food intake and consumption volume of unknowing consumers, *Annual Review of Nutrition* 24 (2004): 455–479.

Consumer Corner 9

1. A. Trichopoulou and coauthors, Lipid, protein and carbohydrate intake in relation to body mass index, *European Journal of Clinical Nutrition* 56 (2002): 37–43.

2. J. Eisenstein and coauthors, High-protein weight-loss diets: Are they safe and do they work? A review of the experimental and epidemiologic data, *Nutrition Reviews* 60 (2002): 189–200.

3. F. F. Samaha and coauthors, A low-carbohydrate diet as compared with a low-fat diet in severe obesity, *New England Journal of Medicine* 348 (2003): 2074–2081.

4. G. D. Foster and coauthors, A randomized trial of a low-carbohydrate diet for obesity, *New England Journal of Medicine* 348 (2003): 2082–2090.

5. J. H. Ware, Interpreting incomplete data in studies of diet and weight loss, *New England Journal of Medicine* 348 (2003): 2136–2137.

6. A. C. Buchholz and D. A. Schoeller, Is a caloric a calorie? *American Journal of Clinical Nutrition* 79 (2004): 899S–906S.

7. D. K. Layman and coauthors, A reduced ratio of dietary carbohydrate to protein improves body composition and blood lipid profiles during weight loss in adult women, *Journal of Nutrition* 133 (2003): 411–417; D. M. Bravata and coauthors, Efficacy and safety of low-carbohydrate diets, *Journal of the American Medical Association* 289 (2003): 1837–1850; M. R. Freedman, J. King, and E. Kennedy, Popular diets: A scientific review, *Obesity Research* 9 (2001): 1S–5S; A. Golay and coauthors, Similar weight loss with low-energy food combining or balanced diets, *International Journal of Obesity and Related Metabolic Disorders* 24 (2000): 492–496.

8. E. T. Kennedy and coauthors, Popular diets: Correlation to health, nutrition, and obesity, *Journal of the American Dietetic Association* 101 (2001): 411–420.

9. L. E. Kelemen and coauthors, Associations of dietary protein with disease and mortality in a prospective study of postmenopausal women, *American Journal of Epidemiology* 161 (2005): 239–249; Joint WHO/FAO Expert Consultation, Diet, Nutrition and the Prevention of Chronic Diseases (Geneva, Switzerland: World Health Organization, 2003); National Heart, Lung, and Blood Institute, Facts about the Dash Eating Plan, NIH publication no. 03-4082, revised 2003; Executive Summary of the Third Report of the National Cholesterol Education Program (NCEP) Expert Panel on Detection, Evaluation, and Treatment of High Blood Cholesterol in Adults (Adult Treatment Panel III), 2002, NIH publication no. 02-5215; Nutrition Committee of the American Heart Association, AHA dietary guidelines revision 2000: A statement for healthcare professionals from the nutrition committee of the American Heart Association, *Circulation* 102 (2000): 2284–2299.

10. E. Cho and coauthors, Premenopausal fat intake and risk of breast cancer, *Journal of the National Cancer Institute* 95 (2003): 1079–1085.

11. S. A. Bingham and coauthors, Are imprecise methods obscuring a relation between fat and breast cancer? *Lancet* 362 (2003): 212–214.

12. E. Cho and coauthors, 2003 [see reference 10].

13. Standing Committee on the Scientific Evaluation of Dietary Reference Intakes, Food and

Nutrition Board, Institute of Medicine, Dietary Reference Intakes for Energy, Carbohydrate, Fiber, Fat, Fatty Acids, Cholesterol, Protein, and Amino Acids (Washington, D.C.: National Academies Press, 2002).

14. S. A. Bowman and J. T. Spence, A comparison of low-carbohydrate vs. high-carbohydrate diets: Energy restriction, nutrient quality and correlation to body mass index, *Journal of the American College of Nutrition* 21 (2002): 268–274.

15. B. D. Butki, J. Baumstark, and S. Driver, Effects of a carbohydrate-restricted diet on affective responses to acute exercise among physically active participants, *Perceptual and Motor Skills* 96 (2003): 607–615; J. Achten and coauthors, Higher dietary carbohydrate content during intensified running training results in better maintenance of performance and mood state, *Journal of Applied Physiology* 96 (2004): 1331–1340; R. Gruetter, Glycogen: The forgotten cerebral energy store, *Journal of Neuroscience Research* 74 (2003): 179–183; I. Y. Choi, E. R. Seaquist, and R. Gruetter, Effect of hypoglycemia on brain glycogen metabolism in vivo, *Journal of Neuroscience Research* 72 (2003): 25–32; Standing Committee on the Scientific Evaluation of Dietary Reference Intakes, Food and Nutrition Board, Institute of Medicine, 2005 [see reference 13]; S. T. Reddy and coauthors, Effect of low-carbohydrate high-protein diet on acid-base balance, stone-forming propensity, and calcium metabolism, *American Journal of Kidney Disease* 40 (2002): 265–274; H. R. Lieberman, C. M. Falco, and S. S. Slade, Carbohydrate administration during a day of sustained aerobic activity improves vigilance, as assessed by a novel ambulatory monitoring device, and mood, *American Journal of Clinical Nutrition* 76 (2002): 120–127.

16. C. Lara-Castro and W. T. Garvey, Diet, insulin resistance, and obesity: zoning in on data for Atkins dieters living in South Beach, *Journal of Clinical Endocrinology and Metabolism* 89 (2004): 4197–4205.

17. S. Liu and coauthors, Relation between changes in intakes of dietary fiber and grain products and changes in weight and development of obesity among middle-aged women, *American Journal of Clinical Nutrition* 78 (2003): 920–927.

18. FDA Working Group on Obesity, Calories Count: Report of the Working Group on Obesity, March 2004, available at http://www.fda.gov/ohrms/dockets/ac/04/briefing/4039b1_01_cal-ories%20count.pdf; W. M. Mueller-Cunningham, R. Quintana, and S. E. Kasim-Karakas, An ad libitum, very low-fat diet results in weight loss and changes in nutrient intakes in post-menopausal women, *Journal of the American Dietetic Association* 103 (2003): 1600–1606.

Controversy 9

1. C. A. Arriaza and T. Mann, Ethnic differences in eating disorder symptoms among college students: The confounding role of body mass index, *Journal of American College Health* 49 (2001): 309–315.

2. Position of the American Dietetic Association: Nutrition intervention in the treatment of anorexia nervosa, bulimia nervosa, and eating disorders not otherwise specified (EDNOS), *Journal of the American Dietetic Association* 101 (2001): 810–819.

3. A. E. Field and coauthors, Relation between dieting and weight change among preadolescents and adolescents, *Pediatrics* 112 (2003): 900–906; D. Neumark-Sztainer and P. J. Hannan, Weight-related behaviors among adolescent girls and boys: Results from a national survey, *Archives of Pediatrics and Adolescent Medicine* 154 (2000): 569–577.

4. G. Tsai, Eating disorders in the Far East, *Eating and Weight Disorders* 5 (2000): 183–197.

5. J. A. McLean, S. I. Barr, and J. C. Prior, Cognitive dietary restraint is associated with higher urinary cortisol excretion in healthy premenopausal women, *American Journal of Clinical Nutrition* 73 (2001): 7–12.

6. E. Cooley and T. Toray, Disordered eating in college freshman women: A prospective study, *Journal of American College Health* 49 (2001): 229–235.

7. K. Kazis and E. Iglesias, The female athlete triad, *Adolescent Medicine* 14 (2003): 87–95.

8. K. Kazis and E. Iglesias 2003 [see reference 7].

9. N. H. Golden, A review of the female athlete triad (amenorrhea, osteoporosis and disordered eating), *International Journal of Adolescent Medicine and Health* 14 (2002): 9–17.

10. D. Hartman and coauthors, Bone density of women who have recovered from anorexia nervosa, *International Journal of Eating Disorders* 28 (2000): 107–112.

11. K. L. Cobb and coauthors, Disordered eating, menstrual irregularities, and bone mineral density in female runners, *Medicine and Science in Sports and Exercise* 35 (2003): 711–719.

12. Are you finding and treating males with eating disorders at your school? *School Health Professional*, August 2000, pp. 1–2.

13. V. Vidovic, N. Henigsberg, and V. Juresa, Anxiety and defense styles in eating disorders, *Collegium antropologicum* 27 (2003): 125–134.

14. K. P. Kerruish and coauthors, Body composition in adolescents with anorexia nervosa, *American Journal of Clinical Nutrition* 75 (2002): 31–37.

15. C. Romano and coauthors, Reduced hemodynamic load and cardiac hypotrophy in patients with anorexia nervosa, *American Journal of Clinical Nutrition* 77 (2003): 308–312; C. Panagiotopoulos and coauthors, Electrocardiographic findings in adolescents with eating disorders, *Pediatrics* 105 (2000): 1100–1105.

16. Committee on Adolescence, Identifying and treating eating disorders, *Pediatrics* 111 (2003): 204–211; Position of the American Dietetic Association, 2001 [see reference 2].

17. A. E. Becker and coauthors, Eating disorders, *New England Journal of Medicine* 340 (1999): 1092–1098.

18. H. C. Steinhausen, The outcome of anorexia nervosa in the 20th century, *American Journal of Psychiatry* 159 (2002): 1284–1293.

19. M. Misra and coauthors, Regional body composition in adolescents with anorexia nervosa and changes with weight recovery, *American Journal of Clinical Nutrition* 77 (2003): 1361–1367; L. Mayer, Body composition and anorexia nervosa: Does physiology explain psychology? *American Journal of Clinical Nutrition* 73 (2001): 851–852; S. Grinspoon and coauthors, Changes in regional fat distribution and the effects of estrogen during spontaneous weight gain in women with anorexia nervosa, *American Journal of Clinical Nutrition* 73 (2001): 865–869.

20. M. B. Tamburrino and R. A. McGinnis, Anorexia nervosa: A review, *Panminerva Medica* 44 (2002): 301–311.

21. P. K. Keel and coauthors, Predictors of mortality in eating disorders, *Archives of General Psychiatry* 60 (2003): 179–183.

22. J. Gutzwiller, J. M. Oliver, and B. M. Katz, Eating dysfunctions in college women: The roles of depression and attachment to fathers, *Journal of American College Health* 52 (2003): 27–32.

23. M. L. Granner, D. A. Abood, and D. R. Black, Racial differences in eating disorder attitudes, cigarette, and alcohol use, *American Journal of Health Behavior* 25 (2001): 83–99.

24. D. Neumark-Sztainer and coauthors, Disordered eating among adolescents: Associations with sexual/physical abuse and other familial/psychosocial factors, *International Journal of Eating Disorders* 28 (2000): 249–258.

25. J. L. Guss and coauthors, Binge size increases with body mass index in women with binge-eating disorder, *Obesity Research* 10 (2002): 1021–1029.

26. J. Sundgot-Borgen and coauthors, The effect of exercise, cognitive therapy, and nutritional counseling in treating bulimia nervosa, *Medicine and Science in Sports and Exercise* 34 (2002): 190–195.

27. A. E. Dingemans, M. J. Bruna, and E. F. van Furth, Binge eating disorder: A review, *International Journal of Obesity and Related Metabolic Disorders* 26 (2002): 299–307.

28. D. M. Ackard and coauthors, Overeating among adolescents: Prevalence and associations with weight-related characteristics and psychological health, *Pediatrics* 111 (2003): 67–74.

29. S. Rubinstein and B. Caballero, Is Miss America an undernourished role model? *Journal of the American Medical Association* 283 (2000): 1569.

30. J. Polivy and C. P. Herman, Causes of eating disorders, *Annual Review of Psychology* 53 (2002): 187–213.

31. J. A. Shunk and L. L. Birch, Girls at risk for overweight at age 5 are at risk for dietary restraint, disinhibited overeating, weight concerns, and greater weight gain from 5 to 9 years, *Journal of the American Dietetic Association* 104 (2004): 1120–1126.

32. Federal Interagency Forum on Child and Family Statistics. America's Children: Key National Indicators of Well-Being, 2013, (Washington, D.C.: Government Printing Office), available at http://www.nichd.nih.gov/publications/pubs/Documents/Americas_Children_2013_DRAFT.pdf.

10 Nutrients, Physical Activity, and the Body's Responses

Wonder if physical activity can help you live longer?

Wish for foods or beverages to help you feel stronger and go longer when competing?

Take vitamin pills right before a race or a game to improve your performance?

Drink sports drinks instead of water, but wonder why?

Keep Reading . . .

Learning Objectives

Contents

In the body, nutrition and physical activity are interactive—each influences the other. The working body demands all three energy-yielding nutrients—carbohydrate, lipid, and protein—to fuel activity. The body also needs protein and a host of supporting nutrients to build lean tissue. Physical activity, in turn, benefits the body's nutrition by helping to regulate the use of fuels, by pushing the body composition toward the lean, and by increasing the daily Calorie allowance. With more Calories come more nutrients and other beneficial constituents of foods.

For those just beginning to increase fitness, be assured that improvement is not only possible but an inevitable result of becoming more active. As you improve your physical fitness, you not only *feel* better and stronger, but you *look* better, too. Physically fit people walk with confidence and purpose because posture and self-image improve along with physical fitness.

If you are already physically fit, the following description applies: You move with ease and balance. You have endurance, and your energy lasts for hours. You are strong and meet daily physical challenges without strain. What's more, you are prepared to meet mental and emotional challenges, too, because physical fitness also supports mental and emotional energy and resilience. Sounds good, doesn't it?

This chapter is written for active people who train like athletes. Casual athletes (those who compete only with their own goals) and competitive athletes (those who compete with others) are cut from the same cloth with regard to their food and fluid needs. The chapter refers to "you" to make the connection between academic thinking and personal choices. To understand the interactions between physical activity and nutrition, you must first know a few things about fitness, its benefits, and **training** to develop fitness.

training regular practice of an activity, which leads to physical adaptations of the body with improvement in flexibility, strength, or endurance.

Fitness

Fitness depends on a certain minimum amount of **physical activity** or **exercise**. Physical activity and exercise both involve bodily movement, muscle contraction, and enhanced energy expenditure, but, by definition, a distinction is made between the two terms. Exercise is often considered to be a vigorous, structured, and planned type of physical activity. Because this chapter focuses on the active body's use of energy nutrients—whether that body is pedalling a bike across campus or pedalling a stationary bike in a gym—for our purposes, the terms *physical activity* and *exercise* will be used interchangeably.

Benefits of Fitness

People who regularly engage in just moderate physical activity live longer on average than those who are physically inactive.[*,1] Yet, despite an increasing awareness of the health benefits that physical activity confers, approximately 50 percent of adults in Canada are inactive.[2] A sedentary lifestyle ranks with smoking and obesity as a powerful risk factor for developing the major killer diseases of our time—cardiovascular disease (CVD), some forms of cancer, stroke, diabetes, and hypertension.[3] In the United States, every year an estimated $24 billion is spent on health-care costs attributed to physical inactivity.[4]

Monitoring Physical Activity in Canada

The Canadian Fitness and Lifestyle Research Institute monitors the physical activity of Canadians, providing data for each of the provinces and the territories, as a group.[5] Data are collected and analyzed from the National Population Health Surveys and the Canadian Community Health Survey (CCHS). A report from the 2007–2009 Canadian Health Measures Survey (Cycle 1) revealed the following: "Between 1981 and 2009, fitness levels of Canadian children and youth, as well as those of adults, declined significantly" and "Among adults, decreases in fitness levels over the same period were particularly pronounced for young adults aged 20 to 39" (http://www.statcan.gc.ca/daily-quotidien/100113/dq100113a-eng.htm). In the fall of 2010 the ministers responsible for physical activity, recreation, and sport endorsed "The Integrated Pan-Canadian Healthy Living Strategy," which includes a new set of targets for increases in healthy eating, physical activity, and healthy weights by 2015 (see the sidebar on this page). Also, CCHS data for 2011 reveal that about 54 percent of Canadians 12 and older were at least "moderately active" or the "equivalent to walking at least 30 minutes a day or taking an hour-long exercise class at least three times a week" (http://www.statcan.gc.ca/pub/82-625-x/2012001/article/11667-eng.htm).

As a person becomes physically active, the health of the entire body improves. Compared with unfit people, physically fit people enjoy:

- *More restful sleep.* Rest and sleep occur naturally after periods of physical activity. During rest, the body repairs injuries, disposes of wastes generated during activity, and builds new physical structures.
- *Better nutritional health.* Physical activity expends energy and thus allows people to eat more food. If they choose wisely, active people will consume more nutrients and be less likely to develop nutrient deficiencies.
- *Improved body composition.* A balanced program of physical activity limits body fat and increases or maintains lean tissue. Thus, physically active people have relatively less body fat than sedentary people at the same body weight.[6]
- *Improved bone density.* Weight-bearing physical activity builds bone strength and protects against osteoporosis.[7]
- *Enhanced resistance to colds and other infectious diseases.* Fitness enhances immunity.[†,8]

The "Integrated Pan-Canadian Healthy Living Strategy" 2010 Targets Are as Follows:

Healthy Eating

- By 2015, increase by 20% the proportion of Canadians who make healthy food choices according to the Canadian Community Health Survey (CCHS) and Statistics Canada (SC)/Canadian Institute for Health Information (CIHI) health indicators.

Physical Activity

- By 2015, increase by 20% the proportion of Canadians who participate in regular physical activity based on 30 min/d of moderate to vigorous activity as measured by the CCHS and the Physical Activity Benchmarks/Monitoring Program.

Healthy Weights

- By 2015, increase by 20% the proportion of Canadians at a "normal" body weight based on a body mass index (BMI) of 18.5 to 24.9 as measured by the National Population Health Survey (NPHS), CCHS, and SC/CIHI health indicators.

Source: The Integrated Pan-Canadian Healthy Living Strategy 2005, *The Secretariat for the Intersectoral Healthy Living Network in partnership with the F/P/T Healthy Living Task Group and the F/P/T Advisory Committee on Population Health and Health Security (ACPHHS) Cat. N° HP10-1/2005 http://www.phac-aspc.gc.ca/hl-vs-strat/pdf/hls_e.pdf*

physical activity or exercise bodily movement produced by muscle contractions that substantially increase energy expenditure.

exercise planned, structured, and repetitive bodily movement that promotes or maintains physical fitness.

---

*References are listed at the end of the chapter.
†Moderate physical activity can stimulate immune function. Intense, vigorous, prolonged activity such as marathon running, however, may compromise immune function.

- *Lower risks of some types of cancers.* Lifelong physical activity may help protect against colon cancer, breast cancer, and some other cancers.[9]

- *Stronger circulation and lung function.* Physical activity that challenges the heart and lungs strengthens both the circulatory and the respiratory system.

- *Lower risks of CVD.* Physical activity lowers blood pressure, slows resting pulse rate, lowers total blood cholesterol, and raises HDL cholesterol, thus reducing the risks of heart attacks and strokes.[10] Some research suggests that physical activity may reduce the risk of CVD in another way as well—by reducing intra-abdominal fat stores.[11]

- *Lower risks of type 2 diabetes.* Physical activity normalizes glucose tolerance.[12] Regular physical activity reduces the risk of developing type 2 diabetes and benefits those who already have the condition.

- *Reduced risk of gallbladder disease (women).* Regular physical activity reduces women's risk of gallbladder disease—perhaps by facilitating weight control and lowering blood lipid levels.[13]

- *Lower incidence and severity of anxiety and depression.* Physical activity may improve mood and enhance the quality of life by reducing depression and anxiety.[14]

- *Stronger self-image.* The sense of achievement that comes from meeting physical challenges promotes self-confidence.

- *Longer life and higher quality of life in the later years.* Active people have a lower mortality rate than sedentary people.[15] Even a 3-km walk daily can add years to a person's life. In addition to extending longevity, physical activity supports independence and mobility in later life by reducing the risk of falls and minimizing the risk of injury should a fall occur.[16]

You don't have to run marathons to reap the health rewards of physical activity.[17] For health's sake, the Canadian Society for Exercise Physiology recommends that Canadians 18–64 years old "... accumulate at least 150 minutes of moderate- to vigorous-intensity physical activity per week, in bouts of 10 minutes or more" (http://www.csep.ca/english/view.asp?x=804). These Canadian Physical Activity Guidelines, summarized in the margin, are shown in Figure 10–1 and have been endorsed by Health Canada and the Public Health Agency of Canada. You may have also heard about other similar guidelines, such as those from the Dietary Reference Intakes (DRI) committee and the American College of Sports Medicine (ACSM), that specify that people need to spend an accumulated minimum of 30 minutes in some sort of physical activity on most days of each week.[18] The latter two authorities, however, advise that 30 minutes of physical activity each day may not be enough for adults to maintain a healthy body weight (BMI of 18.5 to 24.9) and recommend at least 60 minutes of moderately intense activity such as walking or jogging each day.[19] The hour or more of activity can be split into shorter sessions throughout the day—two 30-minute sessions or four 15-minute sessions, for example.[20]

For many people, the health benefits of regular, moderate physical activity are reward enough. Others, however, seek the kinds and amount of physical activity that will not only benefit health but also improve their physical fitness or their performance in sports. The kinds and amounts of physical activity that improve physical fitness also provide still greater health benefits (further reduction of CVD risk and improved body composition, for example).[21]

KEY POINT

- Physical activity and fitness benefit people's physical and psychological well-being and improve their resistance to disease. Physical activity to improve physical fitness offers additional personal benefits.

The Public Health Agency of Canada encourages Canadians to be more active, providing numerous e-resources to help Canadians realize the importance of physical activity for good health, along with "Tips to get active" (http://www.phac-aspc.gc.ca/hp-ps/hl-mvs/pa-ap/index-eng.php). Physical activity guides for seniors, children, youth, and families with either children or youth are also available from

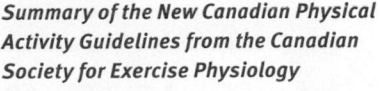

Summary of the New Canadian Physical Activity Guidelines from the Canadian Society for Exercise Physiology

Minimum Recommendations by Age Group (Years)

Ages 5–11 & 12–17

60 minutes of moderate- to vigorous-intensity physical activity daily; should include:

- vigorous-intensity activities 3 days per week, e.g., running, playing soccer; and
- activities for strengthening muscle and bone 3 days per week, e.g., skipping, jumping.

Ages 18–64

150 minutes of moderate- to vigorous-intensity aerobic physical activity per week, 10 or more minutes at a time, e.g., brisk walking, biking. It is also beneficial to add muscle- and bone-strengthening activities 2 days per week, e.g., weight training.

Ages 65+

150 minutes of moderate- to vigorous-intensity aerobic physical activity per week, 10 or more minutes at a time, e.g., brisk walking, swimming, fast dancing.

It is also beneficial to add muscle- and bone-strengthening activities 2 days per week, e.g., lifting, carrying.

Sources: Modified from M. S. Tremblay and coauthors. "New Canadian Physical Activity Guidelines." Applied Physiology, Nutrition and Metabolism 36: 36–46 (2011) doi:10.1139/H11-009; Canadian Society for Exercise and Physiology: Canadian Physical Activity Guidelines, available at http://www.csep.ca/english/view.asp?x–804.

Canadian Physical Activity Guidelines

FOR ADULTS - 18–64 YEARS

Guidelines

 To achieve health benefits, adults aged 18–64 years should accumulate at least 150 minutes of moderate- to vigorous-intensity aerobic physical activity per week, in bouts of 10 minutes or more.

 It is also beneficial to add muscle and bone strengthening activities using major muscle groups, at least 2 days per week.

 More physical activity provides greater health benefits.

Let's talk intensity!

Moderate-intensity physical activities will cause adults to sweat a little and to breathe harder. Activities like:

- Brisk walking
- Bike riding

Vigorous-intensity physical activities will cause adults to sweat and be 'out of breath'. Activities like:

- Jogging
- Cross-country skiing

Being active for at least **150 minutes** per week can help reduce the risk of:

- Premature death
- Heart disease
- Stroke
- High blood pressure
- Certain types of cancer
- Type 2 diabetes
- Osteoporosis
- Overweight and obesity

And can lead to improved:

- Fitness
- Strength
- Mental health (morale and self-esteem)

Pick a time. Pick a place. Make a plan and move more!

☑ Join a weekday community running or walking group.
☑ Go for a brisk walk around the block after dinner.
☑ Take a dance class after work.
☑ Bike or walk to work every day.

☑ Rake the lawn, and then offer to do the same for a neighbour.
☑ Train for and participate in a run or walk for charity!
☑ Take up a favourite sport again or try a new sport.
☑ Be active with the family on the weekend!

Now is the time. Walk, run, or wheel, and embrace life.

www.csep.ca/guidelines

Source: Canadian Physical Activity Guidelines, © 2011. Used with permission from the Canadian Society for Exercise Physiology, www.csep.ca/guidelines.

the Canadian Society for Exercise Physiology website (Canadian Physical Activity Guidelines: http://www.csep.ca/english/view.asp?x=804) along with Canadian Sedentary Behaviour Guidelines for children and youth up to 17 years old. A free online interactive flipbook that contains all of the Canadian physical activity and sedentary guidelines (a useful tool for the whole family) is also just a click away on the above website.

Nutrition and Physical Activity on the Net

- Canadian Society for Exercise Physiology: http://www.csep.ca/english/view.asp?x=804
- Coalition for Active Living: http://www.activeliving.ca
- Canadian Fitness and Lifestyle Research Institute: http://www.cflri.ca
- Coaching Association of Canada: http://www.coach.ca

The Essentials of Fitness

To be physically fit, you need to develop enough **flexibility**, **muscle strength**, **muscle endurance**, and **cardiorespiratory endurance** to allow you to meet the everyday demands of life with some to spare, and you need to achieve a reasonable body composition. A person who practises a physical activity *adapts* by becoming better able to perform it after each session—with more flexibility, more strength, and more endurance.

How Do My Muscles Become Physically Fit?   People shape their bodies by what they choose to do and not do. Muscle cells and tissues respond to an **overload** of physical activity by gaining strength and size, a response called **hypertrophy**. The opposite is also true: if not called on to perform, muscles dwindle and weaken, a response called **atrophy**. Thus, cyclists often have well-developed legs but less arm or chest strength; a tennis player may have one superbly strong arm, while the other is just average. A variety of physical activities produce the best overall fitness, and, to this end, people need to work different muscle groups from day to day. For balanced fitness, stretching enhances flexibility, weight training develops muscle strength and endurance, and **aerobic** activity improves cardiorespiratory endurance. It makes sense to give muscles a rest, too, because it takes a day or two to replenish muscle fuel supplies and to repair wear and tear incurred through physical activity.

Periodic rest also gives muscles time to adapt to an activity. During rest, muscles build more of the equipment required to perform the activity that preceded the rest. The muscle cells of a superbly trained weightlifter, for example, store extra granules of glycogen, build up strong connective tissues, and add bulk to the special proteins that contract the muscles, thereby increasing the muscles' ability to perform.* In the same way, the muscle cells of a distance swimmer develop huge stocks of **myoglobin**, the muscles' oxygen-handling protein, and other equipment needed to burn fat and to sustain prolonged exertion. Therefore, if you wish to become a better jogger, swimmer, or biker, you should train mostly by jogging, swimming, or biking. Your performance will improve as your muscles develop the specific equipment they need to do the activity. See the margin notes for an example of a weekly balanced fitness program.

> Extremes in physical activity, together with severely restricted energy intakes, may be detrimental to bone health in some young women. Such women risk developing the "female athlete triad," discussed in Controversy 9.

KEY POINT

- The components of fitness are flexibility, muscle strength, muscle endurance, and cardiorespiratory endurance. To build fitness, a person must engage in physical activity. Muscles adapt to activities they are called upon to perform repeatedly.

*All muscles contain a variety of muscle fibres, but there are two main types—slow twitch (also called *red fibres*) and fast twitch (also called *white fibres*). Slow-twitch fibres contain extra metabolic equipment to perform fat-burning aerobic work; the fast-twitch type store extra glycogen for anaerobic work. Muscle fibres of one type take on some of the characteristics of the other as an adaptation to exercise.

A Sample Balanced Fitness Program

Monday, Wednesday, Friday
- 5 minutes of warm-up activity
- 45 minutes of aerobic activity
- 10 minutes of cool-down activity and stretching

Tuesday, Thursday, Saturday
- 5 minutes of warm-up activity
- 30 minutes of weight training
- 10 minutes of cool-down activity and stretching

Saturday and/or Sunday
- Sports, walking, hiking, biking, or swimming

---

flexibility the capacity of the joints to move through a full range of motion; the ability to bend and recover without injury.

muscle strength the ability of muscles to work against resistance.

muscle endurance the ability of a muscle to contract repeatedly within a given time without becoming exhausted.

cardiorespiratory endurance the ability to perform large-muscle dynamic exercise of moderate to high intensity for prolonged periods.

overload an extra physical demand placed on the body; an increase in the frequency, duration, or intensity of an activity. A principle of training is that for a body system to improve, it must be worked at frequencies, durations, or intensities that increase by increments.

hypertrophy (high-PURR-tro-fee) an increase in size (e.g., of a muscle) in response to use.

atrophy (AT-tro-fee) a decrease in size (for example, of a muscle) because of disuse.

aerobic (air-ROH-bic) requiring oxygen. Aerobic activity strengthens the heart and lungs by requiring them to work harder than normal to deliver oxygen to the tissues.

myoglobin the muscles' iron-containing protein that stores and releases oxygen in response to the muscles' energy needs.

Fitness

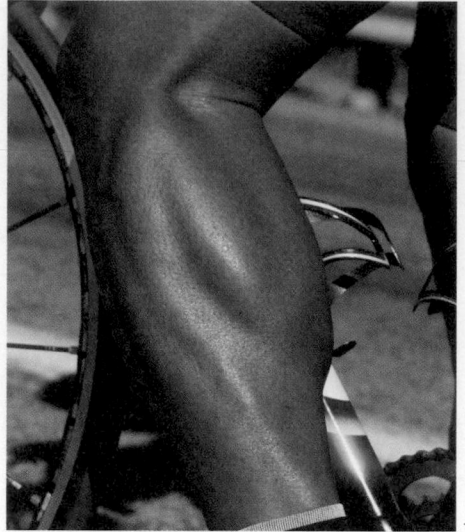

Bodies are shaped by the activities they perform.

How Does Weight Training Benefit Health and Fitness? **Weight training** has long been recognized as a method to build lean body mass and develop and maintain muscle strength and endurance. Additional benefits of weight training have recently emerged: progressive weight training also helps prevent and manage several chronic diseases, including CVD, and enhances psychological well-being.[22]

By promoting strong muscles in the back and abdomen, weight training can improve posture and reduce the risk of back injury. Weight training can also help prevent the decline in physical mobility that often accompanies aging. Older adults, even those in their eighties, who participate in weight-training programs not only gain muscle strength but also improve their muscle endurance, which enables them to walk significantly longer before exhaustion. Leg strength and walking endurance are powerful indicators of an older adult's physical abilities.

Yet another benefit is that weight training can help maximize and maintain bone mass.[23] Research shows that even in women past menopause (when most women are losing bone), a one-year program of weight training improves bone density; the more weight lifted, the greater the improvement.[24]

Weight training can emphasize either muscle strength or muscle endurance. To emphasize muscle strength, combine high resistance (heavy weight) with a low number of repetitions. To emphasize muscle endurance, combine less resistance (lighter weight) with more repetitions. Weight training enhances performance in other sports, too. Swimmers can develop a more efficient stroke and tennis players a more powerful serve when they train with weights.[25]

KEY POINT

- Weight training offers health and fitness benefits to adults. Weight training reduces the risk of CVD, improves older adults' physical mobility, and helps maximize and maintain bone mass.

How Does Cardiorespiratory Training Benefit the Heart? Although weight training provides some cardiovascular benefits, the kind of exercise most famous for improving the health of the heart is cardiorespiratory endurance training. You have felt your heartbeat pick up its pace during physical activity. Cardiorespiratory endurance determines how long you can remain active with an elevated heart rate—it is the ability of the heart and lungs to sustain a given physical demand. Working muscles need abundant oxygen to produce energy, and the heart and lungs work together to provide that oxygen. Thus, cardiorespiratory endurance training is aerobic.

The body's adaptation to the demands of regular aerobic activity involves a complex sequence of heart-healthy events. As cardiorespiratory endurance improves, the body

weight training the use of free weights or weight machines to provide resistance for developing muscle strength and endurance. A person's own body weight may also be used to provide resistance as when a person does pushups, pullups, or situps. Also called *resistance training*.

delivers oxygen more efficiently. With cardiorespiratory endurance, the total blood volume and the number of red blood cells increase, so the blood can carry more oxygen. The heart muscle becomes stronger and larger, and its **cardiac output** increases. Each beat empties the heart's chambers more completely, so the heart pumps more blood per beat—its **stroke volume** increases. This makes fewer beats necessary, so the pulse rate falls. The muscles that inflate and deflate the lungs gain strength and endurance, so breathing becomes more efficient. Blood moves easily through the blood vessels because the muscles of the heart contract powerfully, and contraction of the skeletal muscles pushes the blood through the veins. Such improvements keep resting blood pressure normal. Figure 10–2 shows the major relationships among the heart, lungs, and muscles. The improvements that come with cardiorespiratory endurance also raise blood HDL, the lipoprotein associated with lower heart disease risk.

> The importance of HDL to heart health is a topic of the next chapter.

Figure 10–2

Delivery of Oxygen by the Heart and Lungs to the Muscles

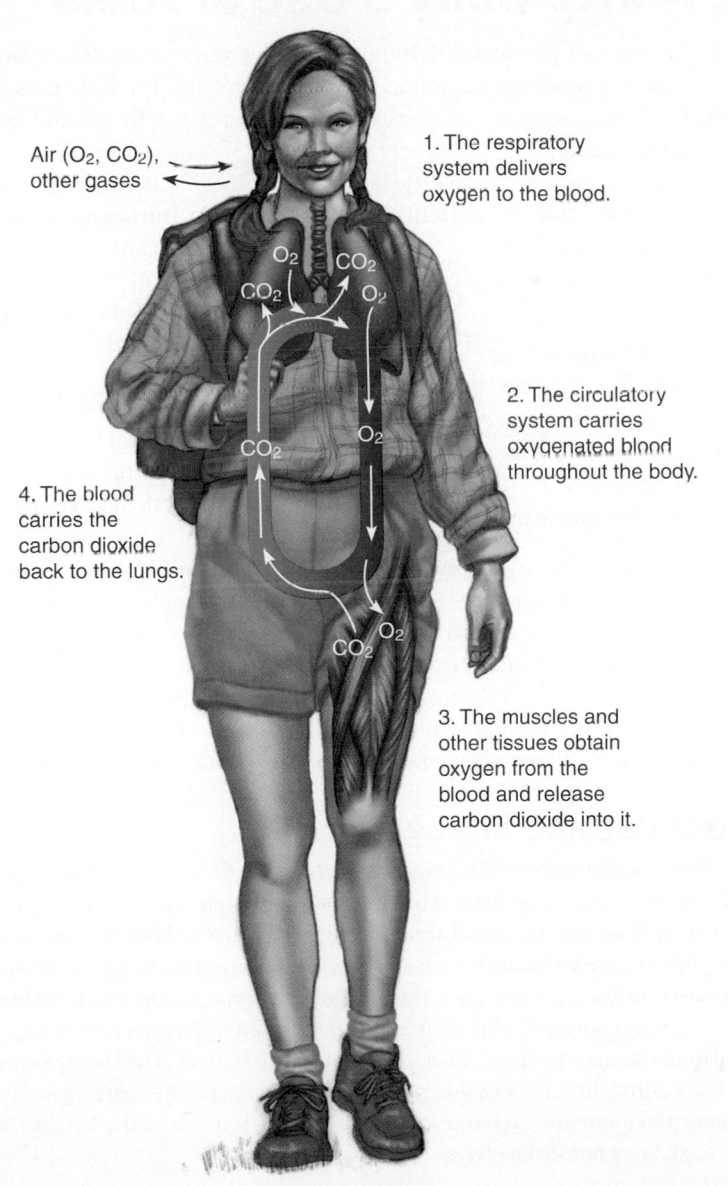

Air (O_2, CO_2), other gases

1. The respiratory system delivers oxygen to the blood.

2. The circulatory system carries oxygenated blood throughout the body.

3. The muscles and other tissues obtain oxygen from the blood and release carbon dioxide into it.

4. The blood carries the carbon dioxide back to the lungs.

cardiac output the volume of blood discharged by the heart each minute.

stroke volume the amount of oxygenated blood ejected from the heart toward body tissues at each beat.

Sit down and relax for five minutes before you begin. Using a watch or clock with a second hand, place your hand over your heart or your finger firmly over an artery at the underside of the wrist or side of the throat under the jawbone. Start counting your pulse at a convenient second and continue counting for 10 seconds. If a heartbeat occurs exactly on the tenth second, count it as one-half beat. Multiply by 6 to obtain the beats per minute. To ensure a true count:

- Use only fingers, not your thumb, on the pulse point (the thumb has a pulse of its own).
- Press just firmly enough to feel the pulse. Too much pressure can interfere with the pulse rhythm.

Which activities produce these beneficial changes? Effective activities elevate the heart rate, are sustained for longer than 20 minutes, and use most of the large-muscle groups of the body (legs, buttocks, and abdomen). Examples are swimming, cross-country skiing, rowing, fast walking, jogging, fast bicycling, soccer, hockey, basketball, in-line skating, lacrosse, and rugby.

An informal pulse check can give you some indication of how conditioned your heart is. The average resting pulse rate for adults is around 70 beats per minute. Active people can have resting pulse rates of 50 or even lower. To take your pulse, follow the directions in the margin.

KEY POINT

- Cardiorespiratory endurance training enhances the ability of the heart and lungs to deliver oxygen to the muscles. With cardiorespiratory endurance training, the heart becomes stronger, breathing becomes more efficient, and the health of the entire body improves.

The rest of this chapter describes the interactions between nutrients and physical activity. Nutrition alone cannot endow you with fitness or athletic ability, but along with the right mental attitude, it complements your effort to obtain them. Conversely, unwise food selections can stand in your way.

The Active Body's Use of Fuels

The fuels that support physical activity are glucose (from carbohydrate); fatty acids (from fat); and, to a small extent, amino acids (from protein). The body uses different mixtures of fuels depending on the intensity and duration of its activities and depending on its own prior training.

During rest, the body derives a little more than half of its energy from fatty acids, most of the rest from glucose, and a little from amino acids. During physical activity, the body adjusts its fuel mix to use the stored glucose of muscle glycogen. In the early minutes of an activity, muscle glycogen provides the majority of energy the muscles use to go into action. As activity continues, messenger molecules, including the hormone epinephrine, flow into the bloodstream to signal the liver and fat cells to liberate their stored energy nutrients, primarily glucose and fatty acids. Thus, hormones set the table for the muscles' energy feast, and the muscles help themselves to the fuels passing by in the blood.

> Epinephrine, discussed and defined in Chapter 3, is the major hormone that elicits the body's stress response, mobilizing fuels and readying the body for action.

The more fit a muscle is, the more oxygen it draws from the blood. This oxygen comes from the lungs, so a person with more fit muscles extracts oxygen from inhaled air more efficiently than a person with less fit muscles. The cardiovascular system responds to increased demand for oxygen by building up its capacity to deliver oxygen. Researchers can measure cardiovascular fitness by measuring the amount of oxygen a person consumes per minute while working out. This measure of fitness, which indicates the person's maximum rate of oxygen consumption, is called **VO$_2$ max**.

Glucose Use and Storage

Both the liver and the muscles store glucose as glycogen; the liver can also make glucose from fragments of other nutrients. Muscles hoard their glycogen stores—they do not release their glucose into the bloodstream to share with other body tissues, as the liver does. This hoarding is fortunate because a muscle that conserves its glycogen is prepared to act in emergencies, say, when running from danger, because muscle glucose fuels quick action. As activity continues, glucose from the liver's stored glycogen and dietary glucose absorbed from the digestive tract also become important sources of fuel for muscle activity.

The body constantly uses and replenishes its glycogen. The more carbohydrate a person eats, the more glycogen muscles store (up to a limit), and the longer the stores will last to support physical activity.

VO$_2$ max the maximum rate of oxygen consumption by an individual (measured at sea level).

A classic report compared fuel use during physical activity by three groups of runners, each on a different diet. For several days before testing, one of the groups ate a normal mixed diet (55 percent of Cal from carbohydrate); a second group ate a high-carbohydrate diet (83 percent of Cal from carbohydrate); and the third group ate a high-fat diet (94 percent of Cal from fat). As Figure 10–3 shows, the high-carbohydrate diet enabled the athletes to work longer before exhaustion. This study and many others established that a high-carbohydrate diet enhances an athlete's endurance by ensuring ample glycogen stores.

KEY POINT

- Glucose is supplied by dietary carbohydrate or made by the liver. It is stored in both liver and muscle tissue as glycogen. Total glycogen stores affect an athlete's endurance.

Activity Intensity, Glucose Use, and Glycogen Stores

The body's glycogen stores are much more limited than its fat stores. Glycogen supplies can easily support everyday activities but are limited to less than 2,000 Calories of energy.[26] Fat stores, however, can usually provide more than 70,000 Calories and fuel hours of activity without running out. How long a person's glycogen will last while exercising depends not only on diet but also on the intensity of the activity.

Anaerobic Use of Glucose   Intense activity—the kind that makes it difficult "to catch your breath," such as a 400-metre race— uses glycogen quickly. Muscles must begin to rely more heavily on glucose, which can be partially broken down by **anaerobic** metabolism. Thus, the muscles begin drawing more heavily on their limited glycogen supply.

As the upper portion of Figure 10–4 shows, glucose can yield energy quickly in anaerobic metabolism. Anaerobic breakdown of glycogen yields energy to muscle tissue when energy demands outstrip the body's ability to provide energy aerobically, but it does so by lavishly spending the muscles' glycogen reserves.

Aerobic Use of Glucose   In contrast, *moderate* physical activity, such as easy jogging, uses glycogen slowly. The individual breathes easily, and the heart beats at a faster pace than at rest but steadily—the activity is aerobic. As the bottom half of Figure 10–4

Figure 10–3

The Effect of Diet on Physical Endurance

A high-carbohydrate diet can increase an athlete's endurance. In this study, the high-fat diet provided 94 percent of Calories from fat and 6 percent from protein; the normal mixed diet provided 55 percent of Calories from carbohydrate; and the high-carbohydrate diet provided 83 percent of Calories from carbohydrate.

Maximum endurance time:

High-fat diet — 57 min

Normal mixed diet — 114 min

High-carbohydrate diet — 167 min

anaerobic (AN-air-ROH-bic) not requiring oxygen. Anaerobic activity may require strength but does not work the heart and lungs very hard for a sustained period.

The Active Body's Use of Fuels

Figure 10–4

Glucose and Fatty Acids in Their Energy-Releasing Pathways

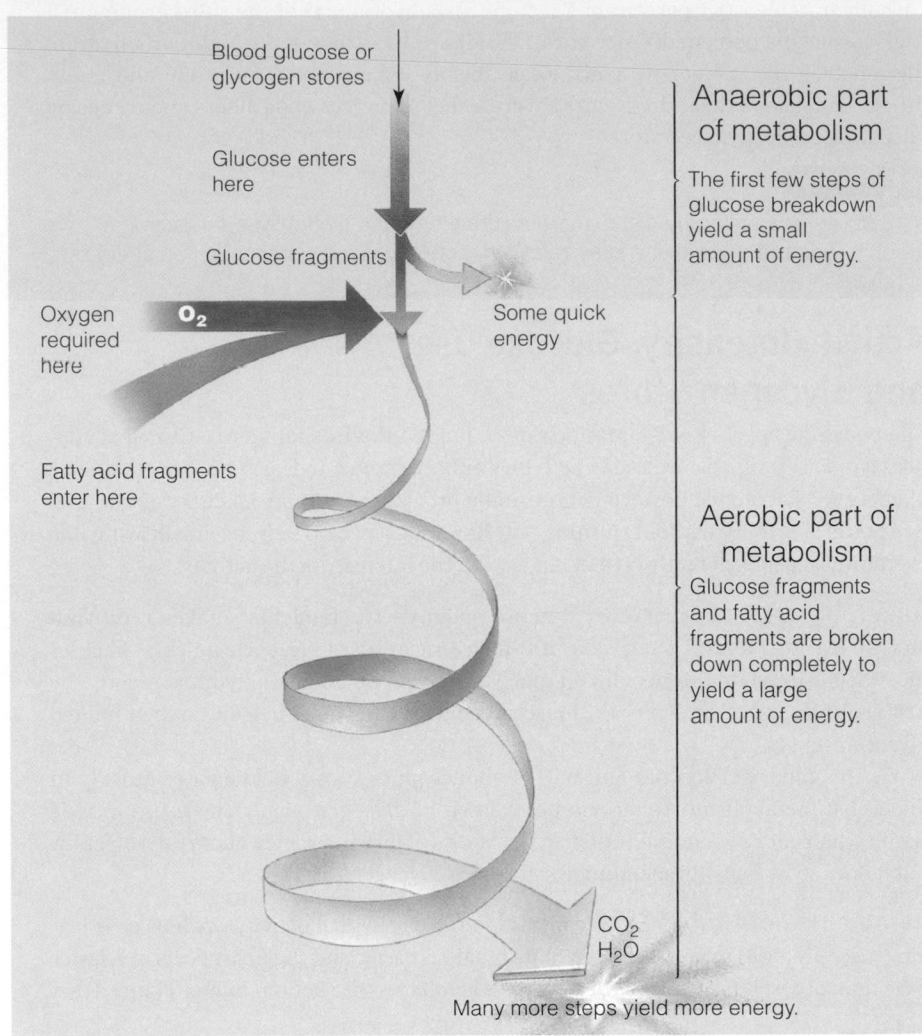

Blood glucose or glycogen stores

Glucose enters here

Glucose fragments

Oxygen required here

O₂

Some quick energy

Fatty acid fragments enter here

Anaerobic part of metabolism

The first few steps of glucose breakdown yield a small amount of energy.

Aerobic part of metabolism

Glucose fragments and fatty acid fragments are broken down completely to yield a large amount of energy.

CO_2
H_2O

Many more steps yield more energy.

shows, during aerobic metabolism, muscles extract their energy from both glucose and fatty acids. By depending partly on fatty acids, moderate aerobic activity conserves glycogen stores. Joggers still use glycogen, however, and eventually they can run out of it.

In the aerobic part of metabolism, glucose fragments and fatty acid fragments are broken down completely during metabolism in the Kreb's/TCA cycle to yield a large amount of energy with the help of the electron transport chain (ETC).

Lactic Acid   During intense activity, anaerobic breakdown of glucose produces **lactic acid**. When production of lactic acid exceeds the ability of the muscles to use it, they release it, and it travels in the blood to the liver. There liver enzymes convert the lactic acid back into glucose. Glucose can then return to the muscles to fuel additional activity.

At low intensities, lactic acid is readily cleared from the blood by the liver, but at higher intensities, lactic acid accumulates. When the rate of lactic acid production exceeds the rate of clearance, intense activity can be maintained for only one to three minutes (as in a 400- or 800-m race or a boxing match). Lactic acid was long blamed for a type of muscle fatigue, but recent thought disputes this idea. Muscles produce lactic acid during a type of fatigue, but the lactic acid does not cause the fatigue.[27]

KEY POINT

- The more intense an activity, the more glucose it demands. During anaerobic metabolism, the body spends glucose rapidly and accumulates lactic acid.

lactic acid a compound produced during the breakdown of glucose in anaerobic metabolism.

Activity Duration Affects Glucose Use

Glucose use during physical activity depends on the *duration* of the activity as well as its *intensity*. In the first 10 minutes or so of an activity, the active muscles rely almost entirely on their own stores of glycogen. Within the first 20 minutes or so of moderate activity, a person uses up about one-fifth of the available glycogen. As the muscles devour their own glycogen, they become ravenous for more glucose and increase their uptake of blood glucose dramatically. During moderate activity, blood glucose declines slightly, reflecting its use by the muscles.

A person who performs aerobic exercise at a moderate level for about one hour uses similar amounts of carbohydrate and fatty acids to fuel the muscles with the recruitment of fatty acids from adipose stores beginning almost immediately. Still, glucose use continues, and if the activity goes on longer and at higher intensity, muscle and liver glycogen stores will run out almost completely. Glycogen depletion generally occurs after about two hours of vigorous exercise.* Physical activity can continue for a short time thereafter only because the liver scrambles to produce some glucose from available lactic acid and certain amino acids. This minimum amount of glucose may briefly forestall exhaustion, but when hypoglycemia accompanies glycogen depletion, it brings nervous system function almost to a halt, making activity impossible. Marathon runners call this "hitting the wall."

> Hypoglycemia, which is abnormally low blood glucose, was discussed in Chapter 4.

Maintaining Blood Glucose for Activity
To postpone exhaustion, endurance athletes must maintain their blood glucose concentrations for as long as they can. Three dietary strategies and one training strategy can help maintain glucose concentrations. One diet strategy is to eat a high-carbohydrate diet on a daily basis (see this chapter's Food Feature). Another is to take in some glucose during the activity, usually in fluid (see the next section). The third is to eat carbohydrate-rich foods (approximately 60 g of carbohydrate) within a couple of hours after activity to boost the storage of glycogen. The training strategy involves training the muscles to store as much glycogen as they can while supplying enough dietary glucose to enable them to do so (called *carbohydrate loading*, described in a later section).

Glucose during Activity
Glucose ingested before and during exhausting endurance activities (lasting more than 45 min) makes its way from the digestive tract to

Four Strategies Can Help Maintain Blood Glucose to Support Sports Performance (for Endurance Athletes Only)

1. Eat a high-carbohydrate diet regularly.
2. Take glucose (usually in sports drinks) periodically during endurance activities.
3. Eat carbohydrate-rich foods after performance.
4. Train the muscles to maximize glycogen stores.

For Perspective, Snack Ideas Providing 60 g of Carbohydrate

- 480 mL sports drink and a small bagel
- 480 mL milk and four oatmeal-raisin cookies
- 240 mL pineapple juice and a granola bar

Those who compete in endurance activities require fluid and carbohydrate fuel.

© Warren Goldswain/Shutterstock

---

*Here "vigorous exercise" means exercise at 75 % of VO$_2$ max.

the working muscles, augmenting dwindling internal glucose supplies from the muscle and liver glycogen stores.[28] Especially during games such as soccer or hockey, which last for hours and demand repeated bursts of intense activity, athletes benefit from carbohydrate-containing drinks taken during the activity.[29]

Before concluding that sugar might be good for your own performance, consider first whether you engage in *endurance* activity. Do you run, swim, bike, or ski nonstop at a rapid pace for more than 45 minutes at a time, or do you compete in games lasting for hours? If not, the sugar picture changes. For an everyday jog or swim lasting less than 60 minutes, sugar probably won't help (or harm) performance. Even in athletes, extra carbohydrate does not benefit those who engage in sports in which fatigue is unrelated to blood glucose, such as 100-metre sprinting, baseball, casual basketball, and weightlifting. Further information about energy use when performing various activities can be found in Table 9–5 on page 384.

Carbohydrate Loading   Athletes whose sports routinely exhaust their glycogen stores sometimes use a technique called **carbohydrate loading** to trick their muscles into storing extra glycogen before competition. Carbohydrate loading can nearly double muscle glycogen concentrations. In general, the athlete tapers training during the week before the competition and then eats a high-carbohydrate diet during the three days just prior to the event.[30] See the carbohydrate-loading plan in Table 10–1.

In the carbohydrate-loading plan in Table 10–1, glycogen storage occurs slowly, and athletes must alter their training in the days just before the event. In contrast, a group of researchers designed a quick method of carbohydrate loading that has produced promising preliminary results. The researchers found that athletes could attain above-normal concentrations of muscle glycogen by eating a high-carbohydrate diet (10 g per kilogram of body weight) after a short (3 min) but very intense bout of exercise.[31] More studies are needed to confirm these findings and to answer such questions as whether an exercise session of lesser intensity and shorter duration would accomplish the same result.

Extra glycogen gained through carbohydrate loading can benefit an athlete who must keep going for 90 minutes or longer. Those who exercise for shorter times simply need a regular high-carbohydrate diet. In a hot climate, extra glycogen confers an additional advantage: as glycogen breaks down, it releases water (approximately 3 g of water for each gram of glycogen), which helps meet the athlete's fluid needs.

Glucose after Activity   Eating high-carbohydrate foods *after* physical activity also enlarges glycogen stores. Train normally; then, within two hours after physical activity, consume a high-carbohydrate meal, such as a glass of orange juice and some graham crackers, toast, or cereal. This method accelerates the rate of glycogen storage by 300 percent for a while. This is especially important to athletes who train hard more than once a day. Timing is important—eating the meal after two hours has passed

- To make glycogen, muscles need carbohydrate, but they also need rest. Vary daily activity routines to work different muscles on different days.

carbohydrate loading a regimen of moderate exercise, followed by eating a high-carbohydrate diet, that enables muscles to temporarily store glycogen beyond their normal capacity; also called *glycogen loading* or *glycogen supercompensation*.

Table 10–1			
Carbohydrate Loading			
Before the Event	Training Intensity	Training Duration	Dietary Carbohydrate
6 days	Moderate[a]	90 min	Normal (5 g/kg body weight)
5 days 4 days	Moderate[a]	40 min	Normal (5 g/kg body weight)
3 days 2 days	Moderate[a]	20 min	High-carbohydrate (10 g/kg body weight)
1 day	Rest	—	High-carbohydrate (10 g/kg body weight)

[a]Moderate intensity equals 70 % VO_2 max.

reduces the glycogen synthesis rate by almost half. For athletes who don't feel like eating right after exercise, **high-carbohydrate energy drinks** are available. These fruit-flavoured drinks are higher in Calories and carbohydrate than the regular sports drinks discussed in this chapter's Consumer Corner on pages 440–441.

Chapter 4 introduced the glycemic effect and discussed some possible health benefits of eating a diet ranking low on the glycemic index. For athletes wishing to maximize muscle glycogen synthesis after strenuous training, however, eating foods with a high glycemic index (see the margin) may restore glycogen most rapidly.[32]

Foods with a High Glycemic Index
- Cornflakes
- Mashed potatoes
- Short-grain rice
- Waffles
- Watermelon
- White bread

KEY POINT

- Physical activity of long duration places demands on the body's glycogen stores. Carbohydrate ingested before and during long-duration activity may help forestall hypoglycemia and fatigue. Carbohydrate loading is a regimen of physical activity and diet that enables an athlete's muscles to store larger-than-normal amounts of glycogen to extend endurance. After strenuous training, eating foods with a high glycemic index may help restore glycogen most rapidly.

Degree of Training Affects Glycogen Use

Training affects glycogen use during activity in at least two ways. First, muscles that deplete their glycogen stores through work adapt to store greater amounts of glycogen to support that work. Second, trained muscles burn more fat, and at higher intensities, than untrained muscles, so they require less glucose to perform the same amount of work.[33] A person attempting an activity for the first time uses up much more glucose per minute than an athlete trained to perform it. A trained person can work at high intensities for longer periods than an untrained person while using the same amount of glycogen.

People with diabetes should know how the moderating effect of physical training can influence their glucose metabolism. Those who must take insulin or insulin-eliciting drugs sometimes find that as their muscles adapt to physical activity, they can reduce their daily drug doses. Physical activity may also improve type 2 diabetes by helping the body lose excess fat.

Chapter 4 described the action of insulin on blood sugar.

Factors That Affect Glucose Use during Physical Activity
- Carbohydrate intake
- Intensity and duration of the activity
- Degree of training

KEY POINT

- Highly trained muscles use less glucose and more fat than do untrained muscles to perform the same work, so their glycogen lasts longer.

To Burn More Fat during Activity, Should Athletes Eat More Fat?

As Figure 10–3 showed, the importance of a high-carbohydrate diet for endurance has long been recognized. When endurance athletes "fat load" by consuming high-fat, low-carbohydrate diets for one to three days, their performance is impaired because their small glycogen stores are depleted quickly.[34] Endurance athletes who adhere to a high-fat, low-carbohydrate diet for more than a week, however, adapt by relying more on fat to fuel activity. Even with fat adaptation, however, performance benefits have not been consistently shown.[35] In some cases, athletes on high-fat diets experience greater fatigue and perceive the activity to be more strenuous than athletes on high-carbohydrate diets.[36]

High-fat diets carry risks of heart disease, too. Physical activity offers some protection against CVD, but even athletes can suffer heart attacks and strokes. Most nutrition experts agree that the potential for adverse health effects from prolonged high-fat diets makes them an unwise choice for athletes.

A diet that overly restricts fat is not recommended either. Athletes who restrict fat below 20 percent of total energy intake may fail to consume adequate energy and nutrients. Sports nutrition experts recommend that endurance athletes consume 20 to 30 percent of their energy from fat.[37] One expert says the message is "not

high-carbohydrate energy drinks fruit-flavoured commercial beverages used to restore muscle glycogen after exercise or as a pregame beverage.

that high-fat diets improve performance, but rather that very low-fat diets inhibit performance."*

As fuel for activity, body fat stores are more important than fat in the diet. Unlike the body's limited glycogen stores, fat stores can fuel hours of activity without running out; body fat is (theoretically) an unlimited source of energy. Even the lean bodies of elite runners carry enough fat to fuel several marathon runs.

Early in activity, muscles begin to draw on fatty acids from two sources—fats stored within the working muscles and fats from fat deposits such as the fat under the skin. Areas with the most fat to spare donate the greatest amounts of fatty acids to the blood (although they may not be the areas that one might choose to lose fat from). This is why "spot reducing" doesn't work: muscles do not own the fat that surrounds them. Fat cells release fatty acids into the blood for all of the muscles to share. Proof is found in a tennis player's arms: the fatfolds measure the same in both arms, even though one arm has better-developed muscles than the other.

Intensity and Duration Affect Fat Use   The *intensity* of physical activity also affects the percentage of energy contributed by fat because fat can be broken down for energy only by aerobic metabolism. When the intensity of activity becomes so great that energy demands surpass the ability to provide energy aerobically, the body cannot burn more fat. Instead, it burns more glucose.

The *duration* of activity also matters to fat use. At the start of activity, the blood fatty acid concentration falls, but a few minutes into an activity, the neurotransmitter norepinephrine signals the fat cells to break apart their stored triglycerides and to liberate fatty acids into the blood. After about 20 minutes of activity, the blood fatty acid concentration rises above the normal resting concentration. Only after the first 20 minutes, during this phase of sustained, submaximal activity, do the fat cells begin to shrink in size as they empty out their fat stores.

Degree of Training Affects Fat Use   Training—repeated aerobic activity— stimulates the muscles to develop more fat-burning enzymes. Aerobically trained muscles burn fat more readily than untrained muscles. With aerobic training, the heart and lungs also become stronger and better able to deliver oxygen to the muscles during high-intensity activities. This improved oxygen supply, in turn, enables the muscles to burn more fat. Intense, prolonged activity may also increase your basal metabolic rate (BMR), as the Think Fitness feature explains.

Factors That Affect Fat Use during Physical Activity

- Fat intake
- Intensity and duration of the activity
- Degree of training

KEY POINT

- Athletes who eat high-fat diets may burn more fat during endurance activity, but the risks to health outweigh any possible performance benefits. The intensity and duration of activity, as well as the degree of training, affect fat use.

---

*The quotation is attributed to David R. Pendergast, in Cutting fat may crimp performance in endurance athletes, *Nutrition and the M.D.*, December 2000, pp. 3–4.

Think Fitness   *move it!*

Can Physical Training Speed Up an Athlete's Metabolism?

Athletes in training, whether endurance athletes or power athletes, expend huge amounts of energy each day while practising. Common sense tells us that the harder an athlete works, the more energy the athlete spends. But what about *after* the work is done?

Does the athlete continue to spend more energy at rest than a sedentary person or a casual exerciser? Research suggests the answer may be yes, for a limited time after intense, prolonged activity.[38] For example, intense endurance activity (at greater than

70 % of VO_2 max) seems to increase BMR for anywhere from minutes to hours depending on the intensity and duration of the activity. The greater the intensity and the longer the duration of the activity, the longer the BMR remains elevated.

Using Protein and Amino Acids to Build Muscles and Fuel Activity

Athletes use protein to build and maintain muscle and other lean tissue structures and, to a small extent, to fuel activity. The body handles protein differently during activity than during rest.

Protein for Building Muscle Tissue In the hours of rest that follow physical activity, muscles speed up their rate of protein synthesis—they build more of the proteins they need to perform the activity. Research shows that just as eating high-carbohydrate foods immediately after exercise accelerates muscle glycogen storage, eating protein, together with carbohydrate, enhances muscle protein synthesis.[39] And whenever the body rebuilds a part of itself, it must tear down the old structures to make way for the new ones. Physical activity, with just a slight overload, calls into action both the protein-dismantling and the protein-synthesizing equipment of individual muscle cells that work together to remodel muscles.

Physical activity itself triggers the building of muscle proteins.

Dietary protein provides the needed amino acids for synthesis of new muscle proteins. As Chapter 6 pointed out, however, the true director of synthesis of muscle protein is physical activity itself. Repeated activity signals the muscle cells' genetic material to begin producing more of the proteins needed to perform the work at hand.

The genetic protein-making equipment inside the nuclei of muscle cells seems to "know" when proteins are needed. Furthermore, it knows *which* proteins are needed to support each type of physical activity. Apparently, the intensity and pattern of muscle contractions initiate signals that direct the muscles' genetic material to make particular proteins. For example, a weightlifter's workout sends the information that muscle fibres need added bulk for strength and more enzymes for making and using glycogen. A jogger's workout stimulates production of proteins needed for aerobic oxidation of fat and glucose. Muscle cells are exquisitely responsive to the need for proteins, and they build them conservatively only as needed.

Finally, after muscle cells have made all of the decisions about which proteins to build and when, protein nutrition comes into play. During active muscle-building phases of training, a weightlifter might add between 7 and 28 grams (1/4 oz. and 1 oz.) of protein to existing muscle mass each day. This extra protein comes from ordinary food.

Protein for Fuel Not only do athletes retain more protein, but they also use a little more protein as fuel. Studies of nitrogen balance show that the body speeds up its use of amino acids for energy during physical activity, just as it speeds up its use of glucose and fatty acids. Protein contributes about 10 percent of the total fuel used, both during activity and during rest.

Diet Affects Protein Use during Activity The factors that regulate how much protein is used during activity seem to be the same ones that regulate the use of glucose and fat. One factor is diet—a carbohydrate-rich diet spares protein from being used as fuel. Some amino acids can be converted into glucose when needed. If your diet is low in carbohydrate, much more protein will be used in place of glucose.

Intensity and Duration Affect Protein Use The intensity and duration of the activity also affect protein use. Endurance athletes who train for over an hour a day, engaging in aerobic activity of moderate intensity and long duration, may deplete their glycogen stores by the end of their training and become more dependent on body protein for energy. In contrast, anaerobic strength training does not use more protein for energy but does demand more protein to build muscle. Thus, the protein needs of both endurance and strength athletes are higher than those of sedentary people but not as high as the protein intakes many athletes consume.

Factors That Affect Protein Use during Physical Activity
- Carbohydrate intake
- Intensity and duration of the activity
- Degree of training

Degree of Training Affects Protein Use Finally, the extent of training also affects the use of protein. Particularly in strength athletes such as bodybuilders, the higher the degree of training, the less protein a person uses during activity at a given intensity.

KEY POINT

- Physical activity stimulates muscle cells to break down and synthesize protein, resulting in muscle adaptation to activity. Athletes use protein both for building muscle tissue and for energy. Diet, intensity and duration of activity, and training affect protein use during activity.

How Much Protein Should an Athlete Consume?

Although most athletes need somewhat more protein than do sedentary people, average protein intakes in Canada fall within the range of the needs for endurance athletes. Therefore, athletes in training should attend to protein needs but should back up the protein with ample carbohydrate. Otherwise, they will burn off as fuel the very protein they wish to retain in muscle.

The DRI committee does not recommend greater-than-normal protein intakes for athletes, but other authorities do.[40] A joint position paper from Dietitians of Canada (DC), the American College of Sports Medicine (ACSM), and the American Dietetic Association (ADA) recommends protein intakes somewhat higher than the 0.8 grams of protein per kilogram of body weight recommended for sedentary people.[41] Table 10–2 compares these recommendations with the DRI recommended intake and average Canadian intakes and translates them into daily intakes for athletes.

After considering these recommendations, you may wonder whether your diet provides the protein you need. This chapter's Food Feature and Controversy sections answer questions about choosing a performance diet. Meanwhile, relax. Athletes who eat a balanced, high-carbohydrate diet that provides enough total energy also consume enough protein that—provided this protein is high quality—they do not need special foods, protein shakes, or supplements.

KEY POINT

- Although athletes need more protein than sedentary people, a balanced, high-carbohydrate diet provides sufficient protein to cover an athlete's needs.

Table 10–2

Recommended Protein Intakes for Athletes

	Recommendations (g/kg/d)	Protein Intakes (g/d)	
		Males	Females
DRI recommended intake for adults	0.8	56	44
Recommended intake for power (strength or speed) athletes	1.6–1.7	112–119	88–94
Recommended intake for endurance athletes	1.2–1.6	84–112	66–88
Canadian average intake for young adults		107	73

NOTE: Daily protein intakes are based on a 70-kilogram (154-pound) man and a 55-kilogram (121-pound) woman.

Sources: Standing Committee on the Scientific Evaluation of Dietary Reference Intakes, Food and Nutrition Board, Institute of Medicine, Dietary Reference Intakes for Energy, Carbohydrate, Fibre, Fat, Fatty Acids, Cholesterol, Protein, and Amino Acids (Washington, D.C.: National Academies Press, 2002), pp. 10-52–10-53; Dietitians of Canada, American College of Sports Medicine, and American Dietetic Association, Joint Position Paper: Nutrition and Athletic Performance, 2008, available at http://www.dietitians.ca/news/highlights_positions .asp; K. Gray-Donald, L. Jacobs-Starkey, and L. Johnson-Down, Food habits of Canadians: Reduction in fat intake over a generation, Canadian Journal of Public Health, 91 (2000): 381–385.

Vitamins and Minerals—Keys to Performance

Many vitamins and minerals assist in releasing energy from fuels and transporting oxygen. In addition, vitamin C is needed for the formation of the protein collagen, the foundation material of bones and the cartilage that forms the linings of the joints and other connective tissues. Folate and vitamin B_{12} help build the red blood cells that carry oxygen to working muscles. Calcium and magnesium help make muscles contract, and so on. Do active people need extra nutrients to support their work? Do they need supplements?

Do Nutrient Supplements Benefit Athletic Performance?

Many athletes take supplements in the hope of improving their performance. A meta-analysis of more than 10,000 athletes involved in 15 sports at all levels found that about half of the athletes use vitamin–mineral supplements.[42] Elite athletes use supplements to a greater extent than university and college athletes, who, in turn, use supplements more than high school athletes. Supplement use by women exceeds that of men, and use by athletes exceeds that of the general population. One of the most common reasons athletes give for supplement use is "to improve performance."

Nutrient supplements do not enhance the performance of well-nourished athletes or active people. Deficiencies of vitamins and minerals, however, do impede performance. Regular, strenuous physical activity increases the demand for energy, but athletes and active people who eat enough nutrient-dense foods to meet energy needs also meet their vitamin and mineral needs. Active people eat more food; it stands to reason that with the right choices, they'll get more nutrients.

Some athletes believe that taking vitamin or mineral supplements just before competition will enhance performance. These beliefs are contrary to scientific reality. Most vitamins and minerals function as small parts of larger working units. After entering the blood, they have to wait for the cells to combine them with their appropriate other parts so that they can do their work. This takes time—hours or days. Vitamins or minerals taken right before an event do not improve performance, even if the person is actually suffering deficiencies of those nutrients.

Athletes who lose weight to meet low body-weight requirements, however, may consume so little food that they fail to obtain all of the nutrients they need.[43] The practice of "making weight" is opposed by many health and fitness organizations, but for athletes who choose this course of action, a single daily multivitamin–mineral tablet that provides no more than the DRI recommendations for nutrients can be beneficial.

Stringent weight requirements pose a risk of developing eating disorders. See Controversy 9.

In addition, some athletes do not eat enough food to maintain body weight during times of intense training or competition. For these athletes, too, a daily multivitamin–mineral supplement can be helpful.

Nutrients of Special Concern

In general, then, active people who eat well-balanced meals do not need vitamin or mineral supplements. Two nutrients, vitamin E and iron, do merit special attention, however, for different reasons. Vitamin E is addressed because so many athletes take supplements of it. Iron is discussed because some female athletes may be unaware that they need supplements.

Vitamin E During prolonged, high-intensity physical activity, the muscles' consumption of oxygen increases tenfold or more, enhancing the production of damaging free radicals in the body.[44] Vitamin E is a potent fat-soluble antioxidant that vigorously defends cell membranes against oxidative damage. Some athletes take megadoses of

- The Tolerable Upper Intake Level (UL) for vitamin E is 1,000 mg per day.

vitamin E in the hope of preventing such oxidative damage to muscles. Supplementation with vitamin E does seem to protect against exercise-induced oxidative stress (some of which is a normal response to exercise), but there is little evidence that vitamin E supplements can improve performance; Health Canada cautions those who have or are at risk for some chronic diseases to avoid taking high doses/megadoses (i.e., 400 IUs or more of supplemental Vitamin E).[45]

Some evidence of possible benefit of vitamin E comes from a study of sled dogs competing in an extreme endurance race in Alaska.[46] In this race, the winning dog team averages 192 kilometres per day for about 10 days. Researchers compared prerace blood vitamin E concentrations and performance in the dogs. Dogs with the highest vitamin E concentrations before the race were more likely to finish the race and had less risk of being withdrawn for every mile run than dogs with lower vitamin E concentrations. The vitamin E status of the dogs had no effect on speed, however. The authors speculated that vitamin E may have reduced fatigue in the dogs but stated that more research is needed to confirm their speculation. Clearly, more research is needed before drawing conclusions about vitamin E supplements for human athletes.

> Chapter 7 specified the risks of toxicity from vitamin pills and supplements.

Iron and Performance   Physically active young women, especially those who engage in endurance activities such as distance running, are prone to iron deficiency.[47] Physical activity can affect iron status in any of several ways. For one, iron losses in sweat may contribute to deficiency. For another, physical activity may cause small blood losses through the digestive tract, at least in some athletes. Perhaps more significant than these losses are the muscles' high demands for iron to make the iron-containing molecules of aerobic metabolism. Habitually low intakes of iron-rich foods, high iron losses through menstruation and through the other routes mentioned, and extra demands can contribute to iron deficiency in young female athletes.

In contrast, a type of red blood cell destruction associated with physical activity does not impair iron status. Blood cells are squashed when body tissues (such as the soles of the feet) make high-impact contact with an unyielding surface (such as the ground). The iron released from the bursting, or hemolysis, of these red blood cells is recycled, however, and is not lost in the urine. Thus, exertional hemolysis, as it is called, rarely, if ever, contributes to anemia in athletes.[48]

Vegetarian female athletes are particularly vulnerable to iron insufficiency.[49] The bioavailability of iron is often poor in plant-based diets because such diets are high in fibre and phytic acid and because the nonheme iron in plant foods is not absorbed as well as the heme iron in animal-derived foods. Vegetarian diets are usually rich in vitamin C, however, which enhances iron absorption. To protect against iron deficiency, vegetarian athletes need to pay close attention to their intake of good

Female athletes may be at special risk of iron deficiency.

AP Photo/The Canadian Press(Martin Meissner)

dietary sources of iron (fortified cereals, legumes, nuts, and seeds) and include vitamin C-rich foods with each meal.[50] As long as vegetarian athletes, like all athletes, consume enough nutrient-dense foods, they can perform as well as anyone.

Iron deficiency impairs performance because iron helps deliver the muscles' oxygen. Insufficient oxygen delivery reduces aerobic work capacity, so the person tires easily. Whether marginal deficiency without clinical signs of anemia hinders physical performance is less clear.[51]

Early in training, athletes may develop low blood hemoglobin. This condition, sometimes called "sports anemia," is not a true iron-deficiency condition. Strenuous training promotes destruction of the more fragile, older red blood cells, and the resulting cleanup work reduces the blood's iron content temporarily. Strenuous activity also promotes increases in the fluid of the blood; with more fluid, the red blood cell count in a unit of blood drops. Most researchers view sports anemia as an *adaptive*, temporary response to endurance training. True iron-deficiency anemia requires treatment with prescribed iron supplements, but sports anemia goes away by itself, even with continued training.

The best strategy concerning iron is to determine individual needs. Many menstruating women border on iron deficiency even without the additional iron demand and losses incurred by physical activity. Teens of both genders, because they are growing, have high iron needs, too. For women and teens, then, prescribed supplements may be needed to correct a deficiency of iron that is confirmed by tests. (Medical testing is needed to eliminate nondietary causes of anemia, such as internal bleeding or cancer.)

KEY POINT

- Vitamins are essential for releasing the energy trapped in energy-yielding nutrients and for other functions that support physical activity. Active people can meet their vitamin needs if they eat enough nutrient-dense foods to meet their energy needs. Vitamin E may protect against oxidative stress, but there is little evidence that it can improve performance. Iron-deficiency anemia impairs physical performance because iron is the blood's oxygen handler. Sports anemia is a harmless temporary adaptation to physical activity.

Foods like these are packed with the nutrients that active people need.

Fluids and Temperature Regulation in Physical Activity

The body's need for water far surpasses its need for any other nutrient. If the body loses too much water, its life-supporting chemistry is compromised.

The exercising body loses water primarily via sweat; second to that, breathing costs water, exhaled as vapour. During physical activity, both routes can be significant, and dehydration is a real threat. The first symptom of dehydration is fatigue. A water loss of even 1 to 2 percent of body weight can reduce a person's capacity to do muscular work.[52] A person with a water loss of about 7 percent is likely to collapse. The athlete who arrives at an event even slightly dehydrated starts out at a competitive disadvantage.

Temperature Regulation

As Chapter 8 pointed out, sweat cools the body. The conversion of water to vapour uses up a great deal of heat, so as sweat evaporates, it cools the skin's surface and the blood flowing beneath it.

In hot, humid weather, sweat may fail to evaporate because the surrounding air is already laden with water. Little cooling takes place, and body heat builds up. In such conditions, athletes must take precautions to avoid **heat stroke**. Heat stroke is an especially dangerous accumulation of body heat with accompanying loss of body fluid. Three measures to prevent heat stroke are to drink enough fluid before and during the activity, rest in the shade when tired, and wear lightweight clothing that

heat stroke an acute and life-threatening reaction to heat buildup in the body.

- Clumsiness
- Confusion or loss of consciousness
- Dizziness
- Headache
- Internal (rectal) temperature above 40° Celsius
- Nausea
- Stumbling
- Sudden cessation of sweating (hot, dry skin)

encourages evaporation.[53] The rubber or heavy suits sold with promises of weight loss during physical activity are dangerous because they promote profuse sweating, prevent sweat evaporation, and invite heat stroke. If you experience any of the symptoms of heat stroke listed in the margin, stop your activity, sip cold fluids, seek shade, and ask for help. The condition demands medical attention—it can kill.

In cold weather, **hypothermia**, or loss of body heat, can pose as serious a threat as heat stroke does in hot weather. Inexperienced runners participating in long races on cold or wet, chilly days are especially vulnerable to hypothermia. Slow runners can produce too little heat to keep warm, especially if their clothing is inadequate. Early symptoms of hypothermia include shivering and euphoria. As body temperature continues to fall, shivering stops, and weakness, disorientation, and apathy set in. People with these symptoms soon become helpless to protect themselves from further body heat losses. Even in cold weather, the body still sweats and needs fluids, but the fluids should be warm or at room temperature to help prevent hypothermia.

KEY POINT

- Evaporation of sweat cools the body. Heat stroke can be a threat to physically active people in hot, humid weather. Hypothermia threatens those who exercise in the cold.

Fluid Needs during Physical Activity

Endurance athletes can lose 2 or more litres of fluid in every hour of activity, but the digestive system can absorb only about a litre or so an hour. Hence, the athlete must hydrate before and rehydrate during and after activity to replace all of the lost fluid. In hot weather, the digestive tract may not be able to absorb enough water fast enough to keep up with an athlete's sweat losses, and some degree of dehydration becomes inevitable. Athletes who are preparing for competition are often advised to drink extra fluids in the last few days of training before the event. The extra fluid is not stored in the body, but drinking extra ensures maximum tissue hydration at the start of the event. Indeed, in the United States, any coach or athlete who withholds fluids during practice for any reason takes a great risk and is subject to sanctions by the American College of Sports Medicine.

 Athletes who rely on thirst to govern fluid intake can easily become dehydrated. During activity, thirst becomes detectable only *after* fluid stores are depleted. Don't wait to feel thirsty before drinking. Table 10–3 presents one schedule of hydration for physical activity. To find out how much water you need to replenish losses, weigh yourself before and after the activity. The difference is all water. Two cups (500 mL) of fluid weighs about half of a kilogram.

Table 10–3

Hydration Schedule for Physical Activity

When to Drink	Approximate Amount of Fluid
2 h before activity	2 to 3 c
15 min before activity	1 to 2 c
Every 15 min during activity	1 to 1½ c
After activity	2 c for each pound of body weight lost[a] (Drink enough to minimize loss of body weight, but don't overdrink.)

[a]Drinking 2 c of fluid every 20 to 30 min after exercise until the total amount required is consumed is more effective for rehydration than drinking the needed amount all at once. Rapid fluid replacement after exercise stimulates urine production and results in less body water retention.

Sources: R. Murray. Fluid, electrolytes, and exercise in Sports Nutrition: A Practice Manual for Professionals. 4th ed., M. Dunford (Chicago: The American Dietetic Association, 2005), pp. 94–115; D. J. Casa, P. M. Clarkson, and W. O. Roberts, American College of Sports Medicine Roundtable on Hydration and Physical Activity: Consensus statements, Current Sports Medicine Reports 4 (2005): 115–127. Sawka MN and co-authors. 2007. ACSM Position Stand: Exercise and Fluid Replacement. Med Sci Sports Exer 39(2): 377–390.

hypothermia a below-normal body temperature.

Water

What is the best fluid to support physical activity? The best drink for most active bodies is just plain cool water, for two reasons: (1) water rapidly leaves the digestive tract to enter the tissues, and (2) it cools the body from the inside out. Endurance athletes are an exception: they need more from their fluids than water alone. The first priority for endurance athletes should always be replacement of fluids to prevent life-threatening heat stroke. But endurance athletes also need carbohydrate to supplement their limited glycogen stores, so glucose is important, too. This chapter's Consumer Corner compares water and sports drinks as fluid sources for endurance athletes.

Electrolyte Losses and Replacement

During physical activity, the body loses electrolytes—the minerals sodium, potassium, and chloride—in sweat. Beginners lose these electrolytes to a much greater extent than do trained athletes. The body's adaptation to physical activity includes better conservation of these electrolytes. To replenish lost electrolytes, a person ordinarily needs only to eat a regular diet that meets energy and nutrient needs. In events lasting more than 45 minutes, sports drinks may be needed to replace fluids and electrolytes. Salt tablets can worsen dehydration and impair performance; they increase potassium losses, irritate the stomach, and cause vomiting. Athletes should avoid them.

Sodium Depletion

When athletes compete in endurance sports lasting longer than three hours, replenishing electrolytes becomes crucial. If athletes sweat profusely over a long period of time and do not replace lost sodium, a dangerous condition of sodium depletion, known as **hyponatremia**, may result. The symptoms of hyponatremia are similar to, but not the same as, those of dehydration (see the margin). Recent research shows that some athletes who sweat profusely may also lose more sodium in their sweat than others—and are prone to debilitating heat cramps.[54] These athletes lose twice as much sodium in sweat as athletes who don't cramp. Depending on individual variation, exercise intensity, and changes in ambient temperature and humidity, sweat rates can exceed 3 litres per hour.[55]

Table 8–1 on page 309 lists the symptoms of dehydration.

Hyponatremia may also occur when endurance athletes drink such large amounts of water over the course of a long event that they overhydrate, diluting the body's fluids to such an extent that the sodium concentration becomes extremely low.[56] During long competitions, when athletes lose sodium through heavy sweating *and* consume excessive amounts of liquids, especially water, hyponatremia becomes likely. Water intoxication, introduced in Chapter 8, can result in life-threatening hyponatremia.

Some athletes may be vulnerable to hyponatremia even when they drink sports drinks during an event.[57] Sports drinks do contain sodium, but as the Consumer Corner points out, their sodium content is low. In some cases, it is too low to replace sweat losses. Still, sports drinks do offer more sodium than plain water.

To prevent hyponatremia, endurance athletes need to replace sodium during prolonged events. They should favour sports drinks over water and eat pretzels in the

Active people need extra fluid, even in cold weather.

Fluid Replacement Tips

- To ensure adequate fluid intake without being distracted during an event, try this technique. Before the event, fill a 1 L water bottle and place two coloured rubber bands to mark the bottle into thirds. Finish off the first segment of the bottle in the first 30 min of activity; finish the next segment in the next 30 min and the remainder in the next. Have someone refill the bottle if activity lasts longer than 90 min.
- The urine of a person who is adequately hydrated is the colour of pale lemonade. Urine the colour of apple juice indicates slight dehydration.

Source: Based on J. Berning, nutrition professor and sports nutrition consultant, personal communication, 1999.

Symptoms of Hyponatremia

- Bloating, puffiness from water retention (shoes tight, rings tight)
- Confusion
- Seizure
- Severe headache
- Vomiting

hyponatremia (HIGH-poh-na-TREE-mee-ah) a decreased concentration of sodium in the blood [*hypo* means "below"; *natrium* means "sodium (Na)"; *emia* means "blood"].

last half of a long race.[58] Some may need beverages with higher sodium concentrations than commercial sports drinks. In the days before the event, especially an event in the heat, athletes should not restrict salt in their diets.

KEY POINT

- During events lasting longer than three hours, athletes need to pay special attention to replacing sodium losses to prevent hyponatremia.

Other Beverages

Some drinks, such as iced tea, deliver caffeine along with fluid. Moderate doses of caffeine (about the amount in 2 c of coffee) one hour prior to activity sometimes seem to assist athletic performance and other times seem to have no effect. Athletic competitions limit the amount of caffeine that can be consumed within two hours of an event. (More about caffeine's effects on performance can be found in this chapter's Controversy feature, and the amounts of caffeine in foods and beverages are listed in Controversy 14.)

Carbonated beverages are not a good choice for meeting an athlete's fluid needs. Although they are composed largely of water, the air bubbles from the carbonation make a person feel full quickly and so may limit fluid intake.

Athletes sometimes drink beverages that contain alcohol, but these beverages are inappropriate as fluid replacements. Alcohol is a diuretic. It promotes the excretion of water; of vitamins such as thiamin, riboflavin, and folate; and of minerals such as calcium, magnesium, and potassium—exactly the wrong effects for fluid balance and nutrition. It is hard to overstate alcohol's detrimental effects on physical activity. It impairs temperature regulation, making hypothermia or heat stroke much more likely. It alters perceptions and slows reaction time. It depletes strength and endurance and deprives people of their judgment, thereby compromising their safety in sports. Many sports-related fatalities and injuries each year involve alcohol.

> Read about alcohol's effects on the brain in Controversy 3.

KEY POINT

- Caffeine-containing drinks within limits may not impair performance, but water and fruit juice are preferred. Alcohol use can impair performance in many ways and is not recommended.

Beer Facts

- Beer is not carbohydrate-rich. Beer is Calorie-rich, but only one-third of its Calories are from carbohydrates. The other two-thirds are from alcohol.
- Beer is mineral-poor. Beer contains a few minerals, but to replace those lost in sweat, athletes need good sources such as fruit juices.
- Beer is vitamin-poor. Beer contains tiny traces of some B vitamins, but it cannot compete with rich food sources.
- Beer causes fluid losses. Beer is a fluid, but alcohol is a diuretic and causes the body to lose more fluid in urine than is provided by the beer.

---

use it! Consumer Corner

What Do Sports Drinks Have to Offer?

More than 20 **sports drinks** or **fluid replacers** (see Table 10–4) compete for their share of the $1 billion market. What do sports drinks offer? First, and most important, sports drinks offer fluids to help you offset the loss of fluids during physical activity, but plain water can do this, too.

Second, sports drinks supply glucose. A beverage that supplies glucose in some form can be useful during endurance activity lasting 45 minutes or more, during intense activity, or during prolonged competitive games that demand repeated intermittent activity.*,[1]

*Consumer Corner references are listed separately at the end of the chapter.

Table 10–4

Terms Related to Sport Drinks

- **fitness vitamin water** water that is lightly flavoured to enhance taste. Often contains small amounts of vitamins.
- **sports drinks (fluid replacers)** beverages specifically developed for athletes to replace fluids and electrolytes and to provide glucose before, during, and after physical activity, especially endurance activity.

Not just any sweet beverage can meet this need, however, because a carbohydrate concentration greater than 8 percent can delay fluid emptying from the stomach and thereby slow down the delivery of water to the tissues. Most sports drinks contain an appropriate amount to ensure water absorption—about 7 percent glucose (about half the sugar of ordinary soft drinks, or about 6 tsp in each 360 mL).

Chapter 10 Nutrients, Physical Activity, and the Body's Responses

NEL

Third, sports drinks offer sodium and other electrolytes to help replace those lost during physical activity. Sodium in sports drinks also helps improve palatability and fluid retention and maintains the osmotic drive for drinking fluid. This makes sense physiologically because the sensation of thirst is a function of changes in blood sodium concentration (and plasma osmolality).[2] Most sports drinks are relatively low in sodium (55–110 mg per serving), however, so healthy people who choose to use these beverages run little risk of excessive intake. Most athletes do not need to replace the other minerals lost in sweat immediately; a meal eaten within hours of competition replaces these minerals soon enough.

In addition, most sports drinks taste good. Manufacturers reason that if a drink tastes good, people will drink more, thereby ensuring adequate hydration. Fluids that are flavoured, sweetened, and cool stimulate fluid intake. Finally, sports drinks can also provide a psychological edge to people who associate them with success in sports.

Thus, for athletes who exercise intensely or for 45 minutes or more, sports drinks offer an advantage over water. **Fitness vitamin waters** and so-called energy drinks* do not provide the appropriate amounts of glucose and electrolytes that sports drinks do, but some active people may prefer their light flavour to plain water.

*Health Canada has provided guidance on the "Safe Use of Energy Drinks" and recommends that they not be mixed with alcohol (http://www.hc-sc.gc.ca/hl-vs/iyh-vsv/food-aliment/boissons-energ-drinks-eng.php) or used as a "fluid replacement," particularly if they contain caffeine (http://www.hc-sc.gc.ca/ahc-asc/media/nr-cp/_2011/2011-132bk-eng.php). Furthermore, hundreds of natural health products (more than 150 of which are caffeinated energy drinks) are being transitioned over to foods and will be labelled as foods (http://www.hc-sc.gc.ca/fn-an/prodnatur/transit-process-food-aliment-eng.php).

try it!
Food Feature

Choosing a Performance Diet

Many different diets can support an athlete's performance. Food choices must obey the rules for diet planning, however.

Nutrient Density

First, athletes need a diet composed mostly of nutrient-dense foods, the kind that supply a maximum of vitamins and minerals for the energy they provide. When athletes eat mostly refined, processed foods that have suffered nutrient losses and contain too much added sugar and solid fat, their nutrition status suffers. Even if foods are fortified or enriched, manufacturers cannot replace the whole range of nutrients and non-nutrients lost in refining. For example, manufacturers mill out much of a food's original magnesium and chromium but do not replace them. This doesn't mean that athletes can never choose a white bread, bologna, and mayonnaise sandwich but only that later they should eat a large salad or big portions of vegetables and whole grains and drink a glass of milk to compensate. The nutrient-dense foods will provide the magnesium and chromium; the bologna sandwich provides extra energy, mostly from fats.

Balance

Athletes must eat for energy, and their energy needs can be immense. Athletes need full glycogen stores, and they need to strive to prevent heart disease and cancer by limiting fat, especially saturated fat. To serve these special needs, a diet that is high in carbohydrate (60 to 70 percent of total Calories), moderate in fat (20 to 30 percent), and adequate in protein (10 to 20 percent) works best. Even if you do not compete in glycogen-depleting events, such a diet provides adequate fibre while supplying abundant nutrients and energy.

With these principles in mind, compare the two 500-Calorie sandwich meals in the margin. The trick to getting enough carbohydrate energy is easy, at least in theory: just reduce the amount of fat and meat in a meal and let carbohydrate-rich foods fill in for them.

Adding carbohydrate-rich foods is a sound and reasonable option for increasing energy intake, up to a point. It becomes unreasonable when the person cannot eat enough food to meet energy needs. At that point, the person can add more food energy into the diet by adding refined sugars, oils, or liquid meals. Still,

- Small daily choices, when made consistently, enhance an athlete's nutritional health.

Compare and Decide Which Best Meets Your Needs

- 1 sandwich of 2 slices bologna, 2 slices white bread, 2 tbs mayonnaise (525 Cal, 9% protein, 23% carbohydrate, 68% fat),

or

- 2 sandwiches of 2 slices lean ham, 4 slices whole-wheat bread, 2 tsp mayonnaise (503 Cal, 20% protein, 51% carbohydrate, 29% fat).

these energy-rich additions must be superimposed on nutrient-rich choices; energy alone is not enough.

Some athletes use commercial high-carbohydrate liquid supplements to obtain the carbohydrate and energy needed for heavy training and top performance. Most of these products contain **glucose polymers** and about 18 to 24 percent carbohydrate. These supplements do not replace regular food; they are meant to be used in addition to it. Unlike the sports drinks/beverages discussed in the Consumer Corner, these high-carbohydrate supplements are too concentrated in carbohydrate to be used for fluid replacement.

Protein

In addition to carbohydrate, athletes need protein. Meats and milk products head the list of protein-rich foods, but suggesting that athletes eat more than the recommended servings of meat would be shortsighted advice. Athletes must protect themselves from heart disease, and even lean meats contain saturated fat. Besides, the extra servings of carbohydrate-rich foods such as legumes, grains, and vegetables that an athlete needs to meet energy requirements also boost protein intakes.

Earlier in this chapter, Table 10–2 (page 434) showed recommended protein intakes for a 55-kilogram female athlete and a 70-kilogram male athlete. An athlete weighing 70 kilograms who engages in vigorous physical activity on a daily basis could require 3,000 to 5,000 Calories per day. As a general rule, endurance athletes should aim for an average intake of 50 Calories per kilogram (2.2 lb) of body weight (23 Cal per pound of body weight). Others may need more. To meet such an energy requirement, an athlete should select from a variety of nutrient-dense foods.

glucose polymers compounds that supply glucose, not as single molecules, but linked in chains somewhat like starch. The objective is to attract less water from the body into the digestive tract.

pregame meal a meal eaten three to four hours before athletic competition

Figure 10–5 provides an example of how foods that provide the extra nutrients athletes need can be added to a lower-Calorie eating pattern to attain a 3,300-Calorie diet. These meals supply about 125 grams of protein, equivalent to the highest recommended intake for an athlete weighing 70 kilograms (160 lb.). For those with reasonable diets, protein is rarely a problem.

The meals in Figure 10–5 provide 63 percent of their Calories from carbohydrate. Athletes who train exhaustively for endurance events may want to aim for somewhat higher carbohydrate levels—from 65 to 75 percent. Notice that breakfast, though low in saturated fat, is filling and hearty. Current thinking supports the idea that athletes benefit from such a morning start. If you train early in the morning, try splitting breakfast into two parts. An hour or so before training, eat some toast, juice, and fruit. Later, after your workout, come back for the cereal and milk.

Planning an Athlete's Meals

Table 10–5 (page 444) shows some sample eating patterns for athletes at various high-energy and high-carbohydrate intakes. These plans are effective only if the user chooses foods to provide nutrients (including a moderate amount of high-quality protein) as well as energy: extra milk for calcium and riboflavin; many servings of fruit for folate and vitamin C; energy-rich vegetables such as sweet potatoes, peas, and legumes; modest portions of lean meat for iron and other vitamins and minerals; and whole grains for B vitamins, magnesium, zinc, and chromium. In addition, these foods provide plenty of electrolytes.

A trick used by professional sports nutritionists to maximize athletes' intakes of energy and carbohydrates is to make sure that vegetable and fruit choices are as dense as possible in both nutrients and energy. A whole cupful of iceberg lettuce supplies few Calories or nutrients, but a half-cup portion of cooked sweet potatoes is a powerhouse of vitamins, minerals, and carbohydrate energy. Similarly, it takes a whole cup of

cubed melon to equal the Calories and carbohydrate in a half-cup of canned fruit. Small choices like these, made consistently, can contribute significantly to nutrient, energy, and carbohydrate intakes.

Before competition, athletes may eat particular foods or practise rituals that convey psychological advantages. One eats steak the night before; another spoons up honey at the start of the event. As long as these foods or rituals remain harmless, they should be respected. Still, science has recommendations for the **pregame meal**. The foods should be carbohydrate-rich and the meal light (300 to 800 Cal). It should be easy to digest and should contain fluids. Breads, potatoes, pasta, and fruit juices—carbohydrate-rich foods low in fat, protein, and fibre—form the basis of the pregame meal (see Figure 10–6, page 444, for some examples). Bulky, fibre-rich foods such as raw vegetables and high-fibre cereals, although usually desirable, are best avoided just before competition. Such foods can cause stomach discomfort during performance. The competitor should finish eating three to four hours before competition to allow time for the stomach to empty before exertion.

What about drinks or candylike sport bars claiming to provide "complete" nutrition? These mixtures of carbohydrate, protein (usually amino acids), fat, some fibre, and certain vitamins and minerals may taste good and provide additional food energy for a game or for weight gain. They fall short of providing "complete" nutrition, however, because they lack many of real food's nutrients and the nonnutrients that benefit health. These products may provide one single advantage for active people—they are easy to eat in the hours before competition. They are expensive, however.

As for "complete" drinks, Table 10–6 demonstrates that there is no point in paying high prices for fancy brand-name drinks. Homemade shakes are inexpensive and easy to prepare, and they perform every bit as well as commercial products. Don't drop a raw egg in the blender, though, because raw eggs often carry bacteria that cause food poisoning.

Figure 10–5

High-Carbohydrate Meals for Athletes

2,600 Calories

Breakfast:
1 c shredded wheat
1 c low-fat 1% milk
1 small banana
1 c orange juice

Lunch:
1 turkey sandwich on
  whole-wheat bread
1 c low-fat 1% milk

Snack:
2 c plain popcorn
A smoothie made from:
  1½ c apple juice
  1½ frozen banana

Dinner:
Salad:
  1 c spinach, carrots, and
  mushrooms
  ½ c garbanzo beans
  1 tbs sunflower seeds
  1 tbs ranch dressing
1 c spaghetti with meat sauce
1 c green beans
1 slice Italian bread
2 tsp soft margarine
1¼ c strawberries
1 c 1% low-fat milk

Modifications

The regular breakfast *plus*:
2 pieces whole-wheat toast
½ c orange juice
4 tsp jelly

3,300 Calories

The regular lunch *plus*:
1 turkey sandwich
½ c low-fat 1% milk
Large bunch of grapes

The regular snack *plus*:
1 c popcorn

The regular dinner *plus*:
1 corn on the cob
1 slice Italian bread
2 tsp soft margarine
1 piece angel food cake
1 tbs whipping cream

Total Cal: 2,600
62% Cal from carbohydrate
23% Cal from fat
15% Cal from protein

Total Cal: 3,300
63% Cal from carbohydrate
22% Cal from fat
15% Cal from protein

All vitamin and mineral intakes exceed the
recommendations for both men and women.

If you want to excel physically, apply the most accurate nutrition knowledge along with dedication to rigorous training. A diet that provides ample fluid and consists of a variety of nutrient-dense foods in quantities to meet energy needs will enhance not only athletic performance but overall health as well. Training and genetics being equal, who would win a competition—the person who habitually consumes less than the amounts of nutrients needed or the one who arrives at the event with a long history of full nutrient stores and well-met metabolic needs?*

*Dietitians of Canada's website provides weblinks to numerous reliable resources for physically active individuals including "What should I eat and drink before, during and after exercise?" "Energy Drinks," "Sports Drinks," and "Training Diets for Athletes," as well as responses to a number of frequently asked questions about sports nutrition: http://www.dietitians.ca/Your-Health/Nutrition-A-Z/Sports-Nutrition-(Adult).aspx?categoryID=48.

Table 10–5

High-Carbohydrate Eating Patterns for Athletes

Food Group	Number of Servings for a Daily Energy Intake of					
	1,500 Cal	2,000 Cal	2,500 Cal	3,000 Cal	3,500 Cal	4,000[a] Cal
Milk (c)	3	3	4	4	4	4
Fruit (c)	2½	3	3½	4½	5	6
Vegetable (c)	1½	2½	1½	2½	3	3½
Grain (g)	7	11	16	18	20	24
Oils (tsp)[b]	2	3	5	6	8	10
Meat (g)	5	5	5	5	6	6
Percent carbohydrate	58	58	63	64	60	62

[a]A way to add more energy to the diet without adding much bulk is to snack on milkshakes or "complete meal" liquid supplements (see the text).

[b]Soft margarine, oil, or the equivalent.

Figure 10–6

Examples of High-Carbohydrate Pregame Meals

Pregame meals should be eaten three to four hours before the event and provide 300 to 800 Calories, primarily from carbohydrate-rich foods. Each of these sample meals provides at least 65 percent of total Calories from carbohydrate.

300-Calorie meal
1 large apple
4 saltine crackers
1½ tbs reduced-fat
   peanut butter

500-Calorie meal
1 large whole-wheat bagel
2 tbs jelly
1½ c low-fat 1% milk

750-Calorie meal
1 large baked potato
2 tsp soft margarine
1 c steamed broccoli
1 c mixed carrots and green
   peas
5 vanilla wafers
1½ c apple or pineapple juice

Table 10–6

Commercial and Homemade Meal Replacers Compared

	Cost	Energy (Cal)	Protein (g)	Carbohydrate (g)	Fat (g)
360 mL commercial liquid meal replacer[a]	About $2 per serving	360	15 (17% of Calories)	55 (61%)	9 (22%)
360 mL homemade milkshake[b]	About 50¢ per serving	330	15 (18% of Calories)	53 (63%)	7 (19%)

[a]Average values for three commercial formulas.

[b]Home recipe: 250 mL skim milk, 125 mL ice milk, 3 heaping tsp malted milk powder. For even higher carbohydrate and Calorie values, blend in ½ mashed banana or ½ c other fruit. For athletes with lactose intolerance, use lactose-reduced milk or soy milk and chocolate or other flavoured syrup, with mashed banana or other fruit blended in.

Performance-Enhancing/ Ergogenic Aids: Breakthroughs, Gimmicks, or Dangers?

Athletes can be sitting ducks for quacks. Many are willing to try almost anything that is sold with promises of producing a winning edge as long as they perceive it to be safe.[*,1] Store shelves and the Internet abound with heavily advertised ergogenic aids, each striving to appeal to performance-conscious people: protein powders, amino acid supplements, caffeine pills, steroid replacers, "muscle-builders," vitamins, and more. Some athletes spend huge sums of money on these products, often heeding advice from a "voice of experience" such as a trusted coach or mentor. Table C10–1 defines the terms in boldface type in this section and lists many more substances promoted as ergogenic aids. Do these products work as advertised? And, most important, are they safe?

Table C10–1

Products Promoted as Ergogenic Aids

- **anabolic steroid hormones** chemical messengers related to the male sex hormone testosterone that stimulate building up of body tissues (anabolic means "promoting growth"; sterol refers to compounds chemically related to cholesterol).
- **androstenedione** (AN-droh-STEEN-dee-own) a precursor of testosterone that elevates both testosterone and estrogen in the blood of both males and females. Often called andro, it is sold with claims of producing increased muscle strength, but controlled studies disprove such claims.
- **arginine** a nonessential amino acid falsely promoted as enhancing the secretion of human growth hormone, the breakdown of fat, and the development of muscle.
- **bee pollen** a product consisting of bee saliva, plant nectar, and pollen that confers no benefit on athletes and may cause an allergic reaction in individuals sensitive to it.
- **boron** a nonessential mineral that is promoted as a "natural" steroid replacement.
- **branched-chain amino acids (BCAA)** the amino acids leucine, isoleucine, and valine, which are present in large amounts in skeletal muscle tissue; supplements are falsely promoted as necessary for exercising muscles.
- **brewer's yeast** a preparation of yeast cells, containing a concentrated amount of B vitamins and some minerals; falsely promoted as an energy booster.
- **caffeine** a stimulant that may produce alertness and reduced reaction time in small doses but creates fluid losses with a larger dose. Overdoses cause headaches, trembling, an abnormally fast heart rate, and other undesirable effects. More about caffeine appears in Controversy 11.
- **carnitine** a nitrogen-containing compound, formed in the body from lysine and methionine, that helps transport fatty acids across the mitochondrial membrane. Carnitine is claimed to "burn" fat and spare glycogen during endurance events, but it does neither.
- **cell salts** a mineral preparation supposedly prepared from living cells. No scientific evidence supports benefits from such preparations.
- **chaparral** a herb, promoted as an antioxidant (see also Table 11–8 on page 481 in Chapter 11).
- **chromium picolinate** a trace element supplement; falsely promoted to increase lean body mass, enhance energy, and burn fat.
- **coenzyme Q10** a cell constituent important to energy metabolism and shown to improve exercise performance in heart disease patients but not effective at improving performance in healthy athletes.
- **creatine** a nitrogen-containing compound that combines with phosphate to form a high-energy compound stored in muscle. Claims that creatine safely enhances energy during very high-intensity exercise have been well documented; however, there are still reports of digestive side effects.
- **desiccated liver** dehydrated liver powder that supposedly contains all of the nutrients found in liver in concentrated form; possibly not dangerous but has no particular nutritional merit and is considerably more expensive than fresh liver.

(continued)

*Controversy references are listed separately at the end of the chapter.

Products Promoted as Ergogenic Aids (continued)

- **DHEA (dehydroepiandrosterone)** a hormone made in the adrenal glands that serves as a precursor to the male hormone testosterone; banned by the FDA because it poses the risk of life-threatening diseases, including cancer. Falsely promoted to burn fat, build muscle, and slow aging.
- **DNA and RNA (deoxyribonucleic acid and ribonucleic acid)** the genetic materials of cells necessary in protein synthesis; falsely promoted as ergogenic aids.
- **energy drinks** sugar-sweetened beverages with supposedly ergogenic ingredients, such as vitamins, amino acids, caffeine, guarana, carnitine, ginseng, and others. While some are regulated as foods, others are regulated as natural health products.
- **Ephedra (ephedrine)** a dangerous and sometimes lethal herbal supplement previously sold for weight loss, muscle building, athletic performance, and other purposes. Although present in small doses in nasal decongestants, the addition of Ephedra to foods is not allowed in Canada, and it is now banned in the United States by the FDA.
- **epoetin** a drug derived from the human hormone erythropoietin and marketed under the trade name Epogen; illegally used to increase oxygen capacity.
- **ergogenic** (ER-go-JEN-ic) **aids** products that supposedly enhance performance, although none actually do so; the term *ergogenic* implies "energy giving" (*ergo* means "work"; *genic* means "give rise to").
- **gelatin** a soluble form of the protein collagen, used to thicken foods; sometimes falsely promoted as a strength enhancer.
- **ginseng** a root purported to increase work capacity through a number of mechanisms, none demonstrated by research. The bioavailability of the active constituent has been called into question and products vary widely in composition, often substituting other less costly stimulants for ginseng. (See Table 11–8 in Chapter 11.)
- **glandular products** extracts or preparations of raw animal glands and organs; sold with the false claim of boosting athletic performance but may present disease hazards if collected from infected animals.
- **glutamine** a conditionally indispensable amino acid, promoted as an ergogenic aid to assist in muscle cell repair after exercise and to maintain or boost immune function.
- **glycine** a nonessential amino acid, promoted as an ergogenic aid because it is a precursor of creatine.
- **growth hormone releasers** herbs or pills that supposedly regulate hormones; falsely promoted as enhancing athletic performance.
- **guarana** a reddish berry found in Brazil's Amazon basin that contains seven times as much caffeine as its relative, the coffee bean. It is used as an ingredient in carbonated sodas, and, taken in powder or tablet form, it supposedly enhances speed and endurance and serves as an aphrodisiac, a "cardiac tonic," an "intestinal disinfectant," and a "smart drug" touted to improve mental functions. High doses may stress the heart and can cause panic attacks.
- **herbal steroids** or **plant sterols** mixtures of compounds from herbs that supposedly enhance human hormone activity. Products marketed as herbal steroids include astragalus, damiana, dong quai, fo ti teng, ginseng root, licorice root, palmetto berries, sarsaparilla, schizardra, unicorn root, yohimbe bark, and yucca.
- **HMB (beta-hydroxy-beta-methylbutyrate)** a metabolite of the branched-chain amino acid leucine. Claims that HMB increases muscle mass and strength stem from "evidence" from the company that developed HMB as a supplement.
- **human growth hormone (HGH)** a hormone produced by the brain's pituitary gland that regulates normal growth and development (see text discussion); also called somatotropin.
- **inosine** an organic chemical that is falsely said to "activate cells, produce energy, and facilitate exercise." Studies have shown that it actually reduces the endurance of runners.
- **ma huang** a herbal preparation sold with promises of weight loss and increased energy but containing ephedrine, a banned cardiac stimulant with serious adverse effects (see Table C7–2 on page 293 in Controversy 7).
- **niacin** a B vitamin that when taken in excess rushes blood to the skin, producing vascularity and a red tint—physical attributes body-builders strive to attain prior to performance. These attributes do not enhance performance, and excess niacin can cause headaches and nausea.
- **octacosanol** an alcohol extracted from wheat germ, often falsely promoted as enhancing athletic performance.
- **ornithine** a nonessential amino acid falsely promoted as enhancing the secretion of human growth hormone, the breakdown of fat, and the development of muscle.
- **oryzanol** a plant sterol that supposedly provides the same physical responses as anabolic steroids without the adverse side effects; also known as ferulic acid, ferulate, or FRAC.
- **pangamic acid** also called vitamin B_{15} (but not a vitamin or even a specific compound—it can be anything with that label); falsely claimed to speed oxygen delivery.
- **phosphate salt** a product demonstrated to increase the levels of a metabolically important phosphate compound (diphosphoglycerate) in red blood cells and the potential of the cells to deliver oxygen to the body's muscle cells. However, it does not extend endurance or increase efficiency of aerobic metabolism, and it may cause calcium losses from the bones if taken in excess.

(*continued*)

Products Promoted as Ergogenic Aids (continued)

- **plant sterols** lipid extracts of plants, called ferulic acid, oryzanol, phytosterols, or "adaptogens," marketed with false claims that they contain hormones or enhance hormonal activity.
- **pyruvate** a 3-carbon compound derived during the metabolism of glucose, certain amino acids, and glycerol; falsely promoted as burning fat and enhancing endurance. Common side effects include intestinal gas and diarrhea and possibly reduced physical performance.
- **royal jelly** a substance produced by worker bees and fed to the queen bee; often falsely promoted as enhancing athletic performance.
- **sodium bicarbonate** baking soda; an alkaline salt believed to neutralize blood lactic acid and thereby reduce pain and enhance possible workload. "Soda loading" may cause intestinal bloating and diarrhea.
- **spirulina** a kind of alga ("blue-green manna") that supposedly contains large amounts of protein and vitamin B_{12}, suppresses appetite, and improves athletic performance. It does none of these things and is potentially toxic.
- **succinate** a compound synthesized in the body and involved in the TCA cycle; falsely promoted as a metabolic enhancer.
- **superoxide dismutase (SOD)** an enzyme that protects cells from oxidation. When it is taken orally, the body digests and inactivates this protein; it is useless to athletes.
- **tetrahydrogestrinone (THG)** an unapproved drug, once sold as an ergogenic aid, now banned by Health Canada.
- **wheat germ oil** the oil from the wheat kernel; often falsely promoted as an energy aid.
- **whey protein** a by-product of cheese production; falsely promoted as increasing muscle mass. As for whey, it is the liquid left when most solids are removed from milk.

This Controversy focuses on the scientific evidence for and against a few of the most common dietary supplements for athletes and exercisers. In light of the evidence, this section concludes with what most people already know: consistent training and sound nutrition serve an athlete better than any pill, powder, or other supplement.

 In Canada, many of the ergogenic aids described in this Controversy (Table C10–1) are regulated under the Natural Health Products regulations. To find out about ergogenic products and claims that are permitted in Canada, check the Natural Health Products Directorate website at http://www.hc-sc.gc.ca/ahc-asc/branch-dirgen/hpfb-dgpsa/nhpd-dpsn/index-eng.php.

Further Readings on Ergogenic Aids

- M. H. Williams and coauthors, *Nutrition for Health Fitness & Sport*, 10th ed., (Toronto, ON: McGraw-Hill, 2013).
- R. B. Kreider and B. Leutholtz, Optimizing nutrition for exercise and sport, in N. J. Temple, T. Wilson, and D. R. Jacobs Jr., eds., *Nutritional Health: Strategies for Disease Prevention*, 2nd ed. (Totowa, NJ: Humana Press, 2006), pp. 313–346.
- I. Wolinsky and J. A. Driskell, eds., *Nutritional Ergogenic Aids* (Boca Raton, FL: CRC Press, 2004).
- M. S. Bahrke and C. E. Yesalis, eds., *Performance Enhancing Substances in Sport and Exercise* (Windsor, ON: Human Kinetics, 2002).
- Dietitians of Canada, American College of Sports Medicine, and American Dietetic Association, Joint Position Paper: Nutrition and Athletic Performance, 2008, available at http://www.dietitians.ca/Downloadable Content/Public/noap-position-paper.aspx.
- Canadian Food Inspection Agency, information on sports nutrition products, July 2010, available at http://www.inspection.gc.ca/english/fssa/labeti/inform/sporte.shtml. (An inspection of sports nutrition meal replacements and nutritional supplements that involved 52 inspections in 31 cities across Canada between September and October was conducted in 2004.)
- The *British Journal of Sports Medicine* ran a series on dietary supplements and ergogenic aids between 2009 and 2013. Go to the journal's home page at bjsm.bmj.com and put "Dietary Supplements and Ergogenic Aids" in the Search window.

Paige and DJ

The story of two university roommates, Paige and DJ, demonstrates the decisions athletes face about their training regimens. After enjoying a first year when the first things on their agendas were parties and the last thing—the very last thing—was exercise, Paige and DJ have taken up running to shed the "freshman 15" pounds that have

Training serves an athlete better than any pills or powders.

© iStockphoto/Thinkstock

crept up on them. Their friendship, once defined by bonding over extra-cheese pizzas and fried chicken wing snacks, now focuses on 5-kilometre races. Both young athletes now compete to win.

Paige and DJ take their nutrition regimens and prerace preparations seriously, but they are as opposite as the sun and moon: DJ takes a traditional approach, sticking to the tried-and-true advice of her older brother, a national track and field star. He tells her to train hard, eat a nutritious diet, get enough sleep, drink plenty of fluid on race day, and warm up lightly for 10 minutes before the starting gun. He offers only one other bit of advice: buy the best-quality running shoes available every four months without fail, always on a Wednesday. Many an athlete admits laughingly to such superstitions as wearing "lucky socks" for the mental boost of a good luck charm.

Paige finds DJ's routine boring and woefully out of date. Paige surfs the Internet for the latest supplements and ergogenic aids advertised in her fitness magazines. She mixes carnitine and protein powders into her complete meal replacement drinks for the promised bonus muscle tissue to help at the weight bench, and she takes a handful of "ergogenic" supplements to get "pumped up" for a race. Her counter is cluttered with bottles of amino acids, caffeine pills, chromium picolinate, and even herbal steroid replacers. Sure, it takes money (a *lot* of money) to purchase the products and time to mix the potions and return the occasional wrong shipment—often cutting into her training time. And the high cost leaves little room in her budget for extras like new running shoes. Still, Paige feels smugly smart in her modern approach. Surely, she will win the most races.

• Looking for an amino acid supplement that rates a perfect score of 100 for protein quality? Try 30 g of chicken breast—it provides almost 10,000 mg of amino acids in perfect complement for use by the human body.

Ergogenic Aids

Is Paige right in thinking that she can gain an athletic edge from supplements? Is she safe in taking them? For the large majority of ergogenic aids, research findings do not support the claims made for them. Athletes who hear that a product is ergogenic should ask who is making the claim and who will profit from the sale. Sometimes, even with careful deliberations, savvy shoppers find it difficult to distinguish valid claims from bogus ones. It's easy to see why Paige is misled by advertisements in fitness magazines—they often appear to be informative articles, and they present a mixture of valid and invalid ideas that is hard to sort out. Colourful anatomical figures, graphs, and tables appear scientific. Such ads create the illusion of credibility to gain readers' trust. Keep in mind, however, that ads are created not to teach but to *sell* (the Controversy section in Chapter 1 addresses the sales tactics of quackery).

Also keep in mind that many substances are sold under the label of "dietary supplement" (see Controversy 7 for details). Aside from those regulated by Health Canada as Natural Health Products, athletes are on their own to evaluate them.

Amino Acid Supplements

Some athletes—particularly bodybuilders and weightlifters—believe that consuming large doses of amino acids will help build muscles. Amino acid supplements are unnecessary. Healthy athletes eating a well-balanced diet never need them, and in a few unfortunate cases, these supplements have proven dangerous (see the Consumer Corner feature in Chapter 6). Taking amino acid supplements puts the body in a too-much–too-little bind. Amino acids compete for carriers, and an overdose of one can limit the availability of some other needed amino acids. Supplements can also lead to digestive disturbances and excess water accumulation in the digestive tract.[2]

Specifically, **branched-chain amino acids (BCAA)** are advertised as a source of fuel for the exercising body. What the ads leave out is that compared with glucose and fatty acids, BCAA provide very little fuel to working muscles, and when they *are* needed, well-fed trained muscles have plenty on hand. No consistent research indicates a performance benefit from supplemental BCAA.[3] What is known, though, is that a diet too low in carbohydrates or energy triggers activity of an enzyme that breaks down BCAA for energy. Conversely, the athlete who consumes adequate carbohydrates and Calories conserves BCAA in the tissues. Perhaps more important, large doses of BCAA can raise plasma ammonia concentrations, causing fatigue—not an effect valued by endurance athletes.[4]

Paige's heavy use of amino acid supplements is unlikely to be helpful.[5] The supplements have not been scientifically demonstrated to be effective and may not even be safe. Her effort would be better spent on eating a nutritious diet adequate in carbohydrate, protein, and energy instead.

Caffeine

Many athletes find that, just as **caffeine** provides mental stimulation during late-night study sessions, the drug seems to provide a physical boost during endurance sports. Also, keep in mind that guarana is a source of caffeine as well, and many beverages labelled as "energy drinks" now contain it. Although some research supports this idea, the effectiveness of caffeine seems to depend on the activity.[6] For example, caffeine (3 to 6 mg per kilogram of body weight) has been demonstrated to improve endurance activities, such as cycling and rowing.[7] In contrast, sprinters, weightlifters, and other athletes performing high-intensity, short-duration activities derive little or no performance edge from caffeine.[8]

No one has yet shown exactly how caffeine benefits performance. One line of thinking, that caffeine could beneficially alter fuel use to spare glycogen, has not been supported by research.[9] Researchers conclude that while athletes may enjoy a "wake-up" effect from caffeine, it does not alter energy fuel use.[10]

Potential benefits from caffeine must be weighed against its known adverse

Chapter 10 Nutrients, Physical Activity, and the Body's Responses effects—stomach upset, nervousness, irritability, headaches, dehydration, and diarrhea. High doses of caffeine also constrict the arteries and raise blood pressure above normal, making the heart work harder to pump blood to the working muscles, an effect potentially detrimental to sports performance.

Competitors should be aware that university/college, national, and international athletic competitions prohibit the use of caffeine in amounts greater than the equivalent of 5 or 6 cups of coffee consumed in a two-hour period prior to competition. Athletes are disqualified if urine tests detect more than this amount. Table C14–4 in Controversy 14 lists caffeine doses in common foods, beverages, and pills.

Instead of taking caffeine pills to obtain a possible performance advantage, Paige might be better off engaging in some light activity before an event, as DJ does. Activity stimulates the release of fatty acids, and a little pregame exercise warms up the muscles and connective tissues, making them flexible and resistant to injury. Caffeine does not offer these benefits. And remember that caffeine is a diuretic. DJ enjoys a cup or two of coffee before her races, but she isn't likely to suffer dehydration from this small amount taken in beverages.

Carnitine

Carnitine is a nonessential nutrient that is often marketed as a "fat burner." In the body, carnitine does help transfer fatty acids across the membrane that encases the cell's mitochondria. (Recall from Figure 3–1 on page 77 of Chapter 3 that the mitochondria are structures in cells that release energy from fatty acids and other nutrients.) So carnitine marketers use this logic: "the more carnitine, the more fat burned, the more energy produced"—but the argument is not valid. In scientific studies, carnitine supplementation for 7 to 14 days neither raised muscle carnitine concentrations nor influenced fat or carbohydrate oxidation. (Paige found out the hard way that carnitine often produces diarrhea in those taking it, just the wrong effect for sports performance.) Nor do carnitine supplements enhance exercise performance.

For those concerned about obtaining adequate carnitine, milk and meat products are good sources, but, more important, carnitine is a *nonessential* nutrient. This means that the body makes plenty for itself when needed.

Chromium Picolinate

Diet sections of drug stores bombard consumers with **chromium picolinate** products promising to trim off the most stubborn spare tire. Photos of impossibly fit people, supposedly the "after" shots of those taking chromium picolinate supplements, tempt people despite their knowledge that fitness transformations never result from taking a pill.

Chromium is an essential trace mineral involved in carbohydrate and lipid metabolism. One or two initial studies reported that the supplements reduced body fatness and increased lean body mass in men who trained with weights.[11] A flurry of studies of chromium picolinate followed, but the great majority show no effects of chromium picolinate on body fatness; lean body mass; strength; or, for that matter, fatigue.[12]

The safety record of chromium picolinate is not unblemished. One athlete who ingested 1,200 micrograms of chromium picolinate over two days developed a dangerous condition of muscle degeneration, with the supplement strongly suspected as the cause. Chromium-sensitive people may have allergic reactions to chromium picolinate supplements.[13] Also, the release of chromium from chromium picolinate creates molecular free radicals that can, theoretically, contribute to potentially harmful levels of oxidative stress in body tissues.[14]

Creatine

Interest in—and use of—**creatine** supplements to enhance performance during intense activity have grown dramatically in the last few years. Power athletes such as weightlifters use creatine supplements in the belief that they enhance stores of the high-energy compound creatine phosphate (or phosphocreatine) in muscles. Theoretically, the more creatine phosphate in muscles, the higher the intensity at which an athlete can train.

The outcomes of some studies suggest that creatine supplementation may enhance performance of high-intensity strength activity such as weightlifting or repeated sprinting.[15] Other studies have found no effect of creatine supplements on strength performance, however, and the potential underlying mechanisms for such an effect remain obscure. Researchers tested creatine in U.S. Navy combat swimmers, SEALs, who need both strength and endurance to perform demanding physical tasks.* In a timed four-station obstacle course, no benefit from creatine over the placebo was evident.

More investigation of the effectiveness and safety of creatine supplements is required; in particular, appropriate long-term studies on creatine safety are lacking.[16] Immediate side effects such as cramping and gastrointestinal distress seem to occur with about the same dosages reported to benefit performance.[17] Even short-term (5–7 d) creatine supplementation may pose risks to athletes with kidney disease or other conditions. Medical and fitness experts voice concern that creatine is being taken in huge doses (5–30 g per day) and that children as young as nine years old are taking it with unknown consequences. Creatine levels from foods, even diets high in creatine-rich foods like red meat, do not approach the amount athletes take in supplement form.

Despite the uncertainties, creatine supplements are not illegal in international competition. The smart competitor, however, will pass up creatine until all of the important questions about its safety and effectiveness are answered.

Protein Powders

Like many other athletes, Paige is a big consumer of protein powders, especially **whey protein**.[18] Whey is one of nature's

*SEAL stands for Sea, Air, and Land combat teams of the U.S. Navy.

protein sources, and like lean meat, milk, and legumes, it can supply amino acids to the body, but it offers no special benefits beyond those provided by ordinary milk or yogurt.

This being the case, what do athletes hope to gain from added protein? Paige believes that because the body builds muscle protein from amino acids, eating extra protein will stimulate her muscles to grow, but this idea is false. She has been taken in by advertisements implying that "more is better." Muscle growth is stimulated by physically demanding activity, not by excess protein. Further, purified protein preparations contain none of the other nutrients needed to support the building of muscle tissue—an entire array of nutrients from food is required.

The body of an athlete who eats adequate food does not use the extra protein from supplements as such. Dutifully, the body dismantles the extra protein, removes the nitrogen from the amino acids, uses what it can for energy, and converts the rest to body fat for storage. The processing required to handle excess amino acids places an extra burden on the kidneys to excrete unused nitrogen.

Complete Meal Replacers

Specialty drinks and energy bars, packed with vitamins, minerals, and other healthy-sounding goodies, appeal to athletes by claiming to provide "complete" meals in convenient "to-go" packages. These bars and drinks usually taste good and provide extra food energy, largely as added fats and sugars, but unless they are labelled as a "meal replacement," they fall far short of providing "complete" nutrition.

What are they good for? A nutritionally "complete" drink may help a nervous athlete who cannot tolerate solid food on the day of an event. In that case, a liquid meal two or three hours before competition can supply some of the fluid and carbohydrate needed in a pregame meal. A shake of fat-free milk or juice (such as apple or papaya) and ice milk or frozen fruit (such as strawberries or bananas), however, can do the

same thing at a fraction of the cost (see Table 10–6, page 444). The bottom line is that this form of nutrition supplement can be useful as a pregame meal or a between-meal snack but is inferior to nutritious foods for meeting the high nutrient needs of athletes.

Recently, DJ, who never bothers with such products, placed ahead of Paige in 7 of their 10 shared competitions. In one of these races, Paige pulled out because of lightheadedness—perhaps a consequence of one or a combination of her ergogenic aids? Still, Paige remains convinced that, to win, she must have chemical help, and she is venturing over the danger line by considering hormone-related products. What she doesn't know is very likely to hurt her.

Hormone Preparations

The dietary supplements discussed so far are controversial in the sense that they may or may not enhance athletic performance. Although it is always wise to err on the side of caution when it comes to issues of health, most such supplements—in the doses commonly taken by healthy adults—probably pose little serious threat except to the pocketbook. The next group of substances, however, is clearly damaging to the body. Don't consider using these products—just steer clear.

Anabolic Steroid Hormones

Among the most dangerous and illegal ergogenic practices is the taking of **anabolic steroid hormones**. Often athletes take these drugs and related products without any medical supervision or testing, simply taking someone's word for their safety.[19]

The testes and adrenal glands in men and the adrenal glands in women make anabolic steroid hormones naturally. Synthetic versions of these natural hormones combine the masculinizing effects of male hormones and the adrenal steroid growth stimulation of female hormones. In the body, these steroids produce accelerated muscle bulking in response to physical activity in both men and women. Injections of

these "fake" hormones produce muscle size and strength far beyond that attainable by training alone, but at the price of great risks to health.

The list of adverse reactions to steroids is long and continues to grow amid only a slight decline in use of the drugs. Figure C10–1 lists the side effects of steroids. The Canadian Centre for Ethics and Sports (CCES), the American Academy of Pediatrics, and the American College of Sports Medicine condemn athletes' use of anabolic steroids, and the International Olympic Committee bans their use. Besides citing the known toxic side effects, these authorities maintain that taking these drugs is a form of cheating. Nevertheless, in professional circles where monetary rewards for excellence are high, steroid use is common. Athletes who lack superstar genetic material and who would normally never break into the ranks of the elite can, with the help of steroids, suddenly compete with true champions.

Steroid use has an unfortunate, domino effect on the entire athletic community. Other athletes are put in the difficult position of either conceding an unfair advantage to competitors who use steroids, or taking the drugs and accepting the risk of harmful side effects or discovery and banning from their sport. Young athletes should not be forced to make such a choice.

If swollen appearance, heart disease, or liver tumours are not frightening enough possibilities, add to the mix the urge to hurt oneself or someone else. Steroids produce changes in the brain that, in some people, bring on frightening exhibitions of overly aggressive behaviour, aptly nicknamed "roid rage."[20] Abusers of anabolic steroids with no previous history of mental illnesses are especially likely to die a violent death, when their impulsive, aggressive behaviour evokes an attack from others, or to die of suicide because of severe depression.[21] A number of bodybuilders, including a former Mr. Universe, are behind bars for the murders of their girlfriends, fiancées, and spouses, committed while under

Chapter 10 Nutrients, Physical Activity, and the Body's Responses

Mind
- Extreme aggression with hostility ("steroid rage"); mood swings; migraine headaches; anxiety; dizziness; drowsiness; unpredictability; insomnia; psychotic depression; personality changes; suicidal thoughts; epilepsy

Face and Hair
- Swollen appearance; greasy skin; severe, scarring acne; mouth and tongue soreness; yellowing of whites of eyes (jaundice)
- In females, male-pattern baldness and increased growth of facial and body hair; in males, baldness

Voice
- In females, irreversible deepening of voice

Chest
- In males, breathing difficulty; breast enlargement and development
- In females, breast atrophy; loss of female body contour

Heart
- Heart disease; elevated or reduced heart rate; heart attack; stroke; hypertension

Abdominal Organs
- Nausea; vomiting, bloody diarrhea; pain; edema; liver tumours (possibly cancerous); liver damage, disease, or rupture leading to fatal liver failure; kidney stones and damage; gallstones; frequent urination; possible rupture of aneurysm or hemorrhage

Blood
- Increased red blood cells; blood clots; increased LDL cholesterol; reduced HDL cholesterol; increased triglycerides; high risk of blood poisoning; those who share needles risk contracting diseases; septic shock (from injections); glucose intolerance

Reproductive System
- In males, permanent shrinkage of testes; early puberty in adolescents; prostate enlargement with increased risk of cancer; sexual dysfunction; loss of fertility; excessive and painful erections
- In females, loss of menstruation and fertility; increased libido; early puberty in adolescents; permanent enlargement of external genitalia; thickening of uterine lining; fetal damage, if pregnant

Muscles, Bones, and Connective Tissues
- Weight gain; altered body composition; increased susceptibility to injury with delayed recovery times; cramps; tremors; seizurelike movements; injury at injection site
- In adolescents, failure to grow to normal height

Other
- Fatigue; edema; increased risk of liver and uterine cancer; sleep, breathing disorders

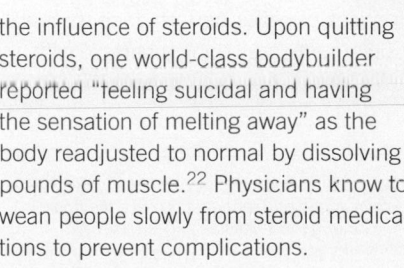

the influence of steroids. Upon quitting steroids, one world-class bodybuilder reported "feeling suicidal and having the sensation of melting away" as the body readjusted to normal by dissolving pounds of muscle.[22] Physicians know to wean people slowly from steroid medications to prevent complications.

In sum, steroids are not simple drugs that build bigger muscles but complex chemicals to which the body and mind react in many ways, particularly when bodybuilders and other athletes take them in large amounts. The safest, most effective way to build muscle has always been through consistent training and a sound diet, and—despite naive misconceptions—it still is.

Steroid Alternative Supplements

A substantial percentage of athletes, and particularly school-age athletes, have tried steroid "alternative" supplements such as banned "andro" (**androstenedione**) or **DHEA (dehydroepiandrosterone)** or a number of herbal preparations. Claims made for these substances—that they reduce fat, build muscle, slow aging, and other miracles—are unsupported by research.[23] In truth, these substances are converted to active hormones by body tissues, and users incur many of the same serious risks as for steroid drugs (listed in Figure C10–1).[24]

People respond unpredictably to these substances.[25] Generally, in males, estrogens increase linearly with increasing doses, while testosterone, the desired muscle-building hormone, elevates only a little.[26] Females may experience a greater proportional surge in testosterone along with increased estrogens.

Some rapidly occurring effects of steroid alternatives include oily skin, acne, body hair growth, liver enlargement, irreversible masculine changes in females, irreversible feminine changes in males, and aggressive behaviour. Long-term effects, such as serious liver damage, may occur after years of use. Particularly vulnerable to these effects are children and adolescent athletes, who may take steroid alternatives on the advice of misinformed parents or coaches.

Recently, Health Canada alerted Canadians about a voluntary recall of 17 products that may have contained androstenedione (see http://www .healthycanadians.gc.ca/recall-alert-rappel-avis/hc-sc/2010/13847a-eng. php). The National Collegiate Athletic Association, the National Football League, the International Olympic Committee, and Health Canada have banned the use of androstenedione and DHEA in competition. The American Academy of Pediatrics and many other medical professional groups have spoken out against the use of these and other "hormone replacement" substances.

As for the herbal or even insect sterols hawked as "natural" substitutes for steroid drugs, these are useless in sports. The body cannot convert them into human steroids, nor do they stimulate the body's own steroid production. These products may contain toxins, however. Remember: "natural" doesn't mean "harmless."

Human Growth Hormone

Although not a steroid, **human growth hormone (HGH)** can induce huge body size and is less readily detected in drug tests than steroids. Short or average-size athletes who are still growing sometimes use this hormone to build lean tissue and increase their height. Athletes in power sports such as weightlifting and judo are most likely to experiment with HGH, believing the injectable hormone will provide the benefits of anabolic steroids without the dangerous side effects. Alternatively, they may take growth hormone "stimulators," such as the amino acids **ornithine** and **arginine**.

Use of this hormone and related substances is a lose-lose proposition. The amino acids ornithine and arginine are useless in the form sold to athletes and do not stimulate growth hormone release. As for HGH itself, it causes the disease acromegaly, characterized by a widened jawline, widened nose, protruding brow, and buck teeth. The body of someone with acromegaly becomes huge, and the organs and bones enlarge abnormally. Other effects include diabetes, thyroid disorder, heart disease, menstrual irregularities, diminished sexual desire, and an increased likelihood of death before age 50.

Athletes who have paid the price of hormone abuse—even some for whom the drugs made careers in sports possible—have come forward to warn young athletes away from growth hormones. They say that even the rewards of sports success are not worth the side effects of the drugs. The U.S. Olympic Committee bans HGH use and maintains that it is a form of cheating, undermining the quest for physical excellence and seducing other athletes into joining the abuse. It is also on the Canadian Centre for Ethics in Sport (CCES) 2010 Prohibited Substances list.

A safe way to maximize the body's natural growth hormone production does exist: rest. Growth hormone is released during sleep, especially after physical activity, so make sure to get enough rest between periods of adequate training.

Drugs Posing as Supplements

Some ergogenic aids sold as dietary supplements turn out to be powerful drugs. A potent thyroid hormone known as TRIAC has been recalled by the U.S. FDA.[27] TRIAC interferes with normal thyroid functioning and has caused heart attack and stroke.* Another is **tetrahydrogestrinone (THG)**, a potentially harmful synthetic steroid.[28] The FDA has reclassified both TRIAC and THG as drugs, but products containing them are still making their way into the hands of athletes. Such synthetic steroid derivatives, or "designer steroids," are designed to sneak steroid use past detection tests in athletic events. Although the FDA has banned these two, others are likely to crop up to take their place because the demand is strong and profits are high.[29]

Conclusion

The general scientific response to ergogenic claims is "let the buyer beware." In a survey of advertisements in a dozen popular health and bodybuilding magazines, researchers identified over 300 products containing 235 different ingredients advertised as beneficial, mostly for muscle growth. None had been scientifically shown to be effective. What *has* weathered the test of time in priming athletes for success—from Little League players to Olympic-level gymnasts—is the basic combination of consistent training and sound nutrition.

Athletes like Paige who fall for the promises of better performance through supplements are taking a gamble with their money, their health, or both.

*Two of the products containing TRIAC (triiodothyroacetic acid, or tiratricol) have the trade names BioPharm T-Cuts and Triax Metabolic Accelerator.

They move from product to product, abandoning one after another when the promised performance miracles do not materialize. DJ, who takes the scientific approach reflected in this Controversy, faces a problem: How does she inform Paige of the hoaxes and still preserve their friendship?

Explaining to someone that a long-held belief is not true involves a risk: the person often becomes angry with the one delivering the truth rather than with the source of the misinformation. To avoid this painful outcome, DJ decides to mention only the supplements in Paige's routine that are most likely to cause harm—the chromium picolinate, the overdoses of caffeine, and the hormone replacers. As for the meal replacers, protein powders, and other supplements that are probably just a waste of money, DJ decides to keep her own counsel. Perhaps they may serve as harmless superstitions.

As for those occasions when Paige believes her performance was boosted by a new concoction, DJ understands that chances are the effect came from the power of the mind over the body. Don't discount that power—it is formidable. You don't have to rely on useless supplements for an extra edge because you already have a real one—your mind. And you can use the extra money you save to buy a great pair of running shoes—perhaps on a Wednesday.

Self-Check

Answers to these Self-Check questions are in Appendix D.

1. Which of the following provides most of the energy the muscles use in the early minutes of activity?
   a. fat
   b. protein
   c. glycogen
   d. b and c

2. Which diet has been shown to increase an athlete's endurance?
   a. high-fat diet
   b. normal mixed diet
   c. high-carbohydrate diet
   d. Diet has not been shown to have any effect.

3. Which of the following stimulates synthesis of muscle cell protein?
   a. physical activity
   b. a high-carbohydrate diet
   c. a high-protein diet
   d. amino acid supplementation

4. All of the following statements concerning beer are correct *except*
   a. beer is poor in minerals
   b. beer is poor in vitamins
   c. beer causes fluid losses
   d. beer gets most of its Calories from carbohydrates

5. A person who exercises moderately for longer than 20 minutes begins to
   a. use less glucose and more fat for fuel
   b. use less fat and more protein for fuel
   c. use less fat and more glucose for fuel
   d. use less protein and more glucose for fuel

6. Weight training to improve muscle strength and endurance has no effect on maintaining bone mass.
   T   F

7. The average resting pulse rate for adults is around 70 beats per minute, but the rate is higher in active people.
   T   F

8. An athlete should drink extra fluids in the last few days of training before an event in order to ensure proper hydration.
   T   F

9. Research does not support the idea that athletes need supplements of vitamins to enhance their performance.
   T   F

10. Aerobically trained muscles burn fat more readily than untrained muscles.
    T   F

Concepts in Action

Analyze Your Diet and Activities

The purpose of this exercise is to demonstrate the links between nutrients in the diet and physical activity.

1. The Canadian Physical Activity Guidelines (for adults 18–64 years) (Figure 10–1, page 422) recommend physical activity levels for health. From the Reports tab, select Energy Balance, and under the Nutrients heading select Day 1 of your 3-Day intake; include the entire day's food intake. Now, select the Track Activity tab, choose Day 1 and increase your physical activity by 30 min for this day. Select moderate physical activities that you enjoy. Include both aerobic and strengthening activities What changes did you notice?

2. Sweating causes a loss of electrolytes (e.g., the minerals sodium and potassium). From the Reports tab, select Day 1 and choose all meals and snacks. Under the Nutrients heading select Intake vs. Goals to see if your electrolyte (sodium and potassium) intake is inadequate, excessive, or within the DRI recommendations? What conditions might change your electrolyte needs? Discuss how and to what degree the requirements might change when you increase your activity level.

3. The Food Feature in this chapter demonstrates how to choose a performance diet with sufficient carbohydrate. Assume that you need such a diet. Modify your intake for all meals on Day 2 with the goal of increasing your carbohydrate intake. For help, use Figure 10–5 (page 443) as a guide. From the Reports tab, under the Nutrients heading select Macronutrient Ranges and then select Day 2; choose all meals and snacks). Did you obtain about 400 grams of carbohydrate? This amount would be sufficient for a 68 kg (150-pound) athlete in many activities (consult Table 10–5 on page 444).

4. A strategy for maintaining blood glucose levels during physical activity is to eat a carbohydrate-rich pregame meal a couple of hours beforehand. Add a high-carbohydrate snack to one of your food records. For ideas, look at the pregame meals in Figure 10–6 (page 444). Enter the new snack by selecting the Track Diet tab and selecting a new day. From the Reports tab, under the Advanced heading, select Source Analysis, and then select Carbohydrate from the drop-down pick-list. How did you do? Did your snack contribute an adequate amount of carbohydrate to help maintain blood glucose levels during physical activity?

5. Assume you are an endurance athlete, engaging in vigorous daily training. Calculate the recommended protein intake for an athlete of your weight using Table 10–2 (page 434). Now modify Day 2 of your diet records to increase the protein to the recommended level. To do this, select the Track Diet tab and select Day 2 from your food records. Hint: Use Figure 6–16 to find higher-protein foods for this day and include them in your food record. From the Reports tab, under the Nutrients heading, select Intake vs. Goals, and select Day 2. Did your modified diet provide enough protein for an endurance athlete of your size? Were you already consuming enough protein for an endurance athlete without making any changes?

6. Again, assume that you are an endurance athlete whose Caloric need is 50 Calories per kilogram (or 23 Calories per pound of body weight). Modify Day 2 of your diet in an attempt to reach the increased Calorie goal. From the Reports tab, under the Nutrients heading select Intake vs. Goals, and select Day 2, including all meals and snacks. Does this modified diet provide enough Calories to support the athlete's increased physical activity level? If not, which foods might you add to obtain adequate Calories, and why did you choose them and not others?

Endnotes

1. Y. A. Kesaniemi and coauthors, Dose-response issues concerning physical activity and health: An evidence-based symposium, *Medicine and Science in Sports and Exercise* 33 (2001): 351S–358S; I. M. Lee and R. S. Paffenbarger, Associations of light, moderate, and vigorous intensity physical activity with longevity: The Harvard Alumni Study, *American Journal of Epidemiology* 151 (2000): 293–299.

2. P. M. Barnes and C. A. Schoenborn, *Physical Activity among Adults: United States*, 2000, *Advance Data from Vital and Health Statistics*, Document no. 333 (2003), available at http://www.cdc.gov/nchs/data/ad/ad333.pdf.

3. K. R. Evenson and coauthors, The effect of cardiorespiratory fitness and obesity on cancer mortality in women and men, *Medicine and Science in Sports and Exercise* 35 (2003): 270–277; J. Dorn and coauthors, Lifetime physical activity and breast cancer risk in pre- and postmenopausal women, *Medicine and Science in Sports and Exercise*

35 (2003): 278–285; C. D. Lee and S. N. Blair, Cardiorespiratory fitness and stroke mortality in men, *Medicine and Science in Sports and Exercise* 34 (2002): 592–595; K. Moreau and coauthors, Increasing daily walking lowers blood pressure in post-menopausal women, *Medicine and Science in Sports and Exercise* 33 (2001): 1825–1831.

4. G. A. Colditz, Economic costs of obesity and inactivity, *Medicine and Science in Sports and Exercise* 31 (1999): 663S–667S.

5. Canadian Fitness and Lifestyle Research 2003 Physical Activity Monitor, available at http://72.10.49.94/pub_page/100.

6. U. G. Kyle and coauthors, Physical activity and fat-free and fat mass by bioelectrical impedance in 3853 adults, *Medicine and Science in Sports and Exercise* 33 (2001): 576–584.

7. L. Metcalfe and coauthors, Postmenopausal women and exercise for prevention of osteoporosis: The Bone, Estrogen, Strength Training (BEST) Study, *ACSM's Health & Fitness Journal*, May/June 2001, pp. 6–14.

8. C. E. Matthews and coauthors, Moderate to vigorous physical activity and risk of upper-respiratory tract infection, *Medicine and Science in Sports and Exercise* 34 (2002): 1242–1248.

9. C. M. Friedenreich, Physical activity and cancer: Lessons learned from nutritional epidemiology, *Nutrition Reviews* 59 (2001): 349–357.

10. American College of Sports Medicine, Position stand; Exercise and hypertension, *Medicine and Science in Sports and Exercise* 36 (2004): 533–553; M. R. Carnethon and coauthors, Cardiorespiratory fitness in young adulthood and the development of cardiovascular disease risk factors, *Journal of the American Medical Association* 290 (2003): 3092–3100; D. E. R. Warburton and coauthors, Health benefits of physical activity: The evidence, *Canadian Medical Association Journal* 176, 6 (2006): 801–809.

11. S. L. Wong and coauthors, Cardiorespiratory fitness is associated with lower abdominal fat independent of body mass index, *Medicine and Science in Sports and Exercise* 36 (2004): 286–291; A. Trichopoulou and coauthors, Physical activity and energy intake selectively predict the waist-to-hip ratio in men but not in women, *American Journal of Clinical Nutrition* 74 (2001): 574–578.

12. R. M. van Dam and coauthors, Physical activity and glucose tolerance in elderly men: The Zutphen Elderly Study, *Medicine and Science in Sports and Exercise* 34 (2002): 1132–1136; K. J. Stewart, Exercise training and the cardiovascular consequences of type 2 diabetes and hypertension: Plausible mechanisms for improving cardiovascular health, *Journal of the American Medical Association* 288 (2002): 1622–1631; D. E. R. Warburton and coauthors, 2006 [see reference 10].

13. G. Misciagna and coauthors, Diet, physical activity, and gallstones—A population-based, case-control study in southern Italy, *American Journal of Clinical Nutrition* 69 (1999): 120–126; M. F. Leitzmann and coauthors, Recreational physical activity and the risk of cholecystectomy in women, *New England Journal of Medicine* 341 (1999): 777–784.

14. W. J. Strawbridge and coauthors, Physical activity reduces the risk of subsequent depression for older adults, *American Journal of Epidemiology* 156 (2002): 328–334.

15. J. Myers and coauthors, Exercise capacity and mortality among men referred for exercise testing, *New England Journal of Medicine* 346 (2002): 793–801; I. M. Lee and R. S. Paffenbarger, 2000 [see reference 1].

16. T. Rantanen and coauthors, Midlife hand grip strength as a predictor of old age disability, *Journal of the American Medical Association* 281 (1999): 558–560.

17. J. Myers and coauthors, 2002 [see reference 15]; A. L. Dunn and coauthors, Comparison of lifestyle and structured interventions to increase physical activity and cardiorespiratory fitness, *Journal of the American Medical Association* 281 (1999): 327–334.

18. Public Health Agency of Canada, Why physical activity is important to you, Catalogue no. H39-429/1998-2E, available at http://www.phac-aspc.gc.ca/pau-uap/paguide/why.html.

19. Canadian Society for Exercise Physiology: Canadian Physical Activity Guidelines For Adults 18–64 Years, available at http://www.csep.ca/english/view.asp?x=804; American College of Sports Medicine, Position stand: Appropriate intervention strategies for weight loss and prevention of weight regain for adults, *Medicine and Science in Sports and Exercise* 33 (2001): 2145–2156; Standing Committee on the Scientific Evaluation of Dietary Reference Intakes, Food and Nutrition Board, Institute of Medicine, *Dietary Reference Intakes for Energy, Carbohydrate, Fiber, Fat, Fatty Acids, Cholesterol, Protein, and Amino Acids* (Washington, D.C.: National Academies Press, 2002), pp. 12-1–12-39.

20. M. Murphy and coauthors, Accumulating brisk walking for fitness, cardiovascular risk, and psychological health, *Medicine and Science in Sports and Exercise* 34 (2002): 1468–1474; W. D. Schmidt, C. J. Biwer, and L. K. Kalscheuer, Effects of long *versus* short bout exercise on fitness and weight loss in overweight females, *Journal of the American College of Nutrition* 20 (2001): 494–501.

21. C. D. Lee and S. N. Blair, 2002 [see reference 3].

22. American College of Sports Medicine, Position stand: Progression models in resistance training for healthy adults, *Medicine and Science in Sports and Exercise* 34 (2002): 364–380; M. L. Pollock and coauthors, AHA Science Advisory: Resistance exercise in individuals with and without cardiovascular disease: Benefits, rationale, safety, and prescription, *Circulation* 101 (2000): 828–833.

23. J. E. Layne and M. E. Nelson, The effects of progressive resistance training on bone density: A review, *Medicine and Science in Sports and Exercise* 31 (1999): 25–30.

24. E. C. Cussler and coauthors, Weight lifted in strength training predicts bone change in postmenopausal women, *Medicine and Science in Sports and Exercise* 35 (2003): 10–17.

25. W. J. Kraemer and coauthors, Physiological changes with periodized resistance training in women tennis players, *Medicine and Science in Sports and Exercise* 35 (2003): 157–168.

26. J. H. Wilmore and D. L. Costill, Physical energy: Fuel metabolism, *Nutrition Reviews* 59 (2001): S13–S16.

27. T. H. Pedersen and coauthors, Intracellular acidosis enhances the excitability of working muscle, *Science* 305 (2004): 1144–1147; D. Allen and H. Westerblad, Enhanced: Lactic acid—the latest performance-enhancing drug, *Science* 305 (2004): 1112–1113; R. A. Robergs, F. Ghiasvand, and D. Parker, Biochemistry of exercise-induced metabolic acidosis, *American Journal of Physiology—Regulatory, Integrative and Comparative Physiology* 287 (2004): R502–R516.

28. A. C. Utter and coauthors, Carbohydrate supplementation and perceived exertion during prolonged running, *Medicine and Science in Sports and Exercise* 36 (2004): 1036–1041.

29. R. S. Welsh and coauthors, Carbohydrates and physical/mental performance during intermittent exercise to fatigue, *Medicine and Science in Sports and Exercise* 34 (2002): 723–731.

30. E. Coleman, Carbohydrate and exercise, in C. A. Rosenbloom, ed., *Sports Nutrition: A Guide for the Professional Working with Active People*, 3rd ed. (Chicago, IL: The American Dietetic Association, 2000), pp. 13–31.

31. T. J. Fairchild and coauthors, Rapid carbohydrate loading after a short bout of near maximal-intensity exercise, *Medicine and Science in Sports and Exercise* 34 (2002): 980–986.

32. E. Coleman, 2000 [see reference 30].

33. J. Manetta and coauthors, Fuel oxidation during exercise in middle-aged men: Role of training and glucose disposal, *Medicine and Science in Sports and Exercise* 34 (2002): 423–429.

34. L. M. Burke and J. A. Hawley, Effects of short-term fat adaptation on metabolism and performance of prolonged exercise, *Medicine and Science in Sports and Exercise* 34 (2002): 1492–1498.

35. L. M. Burke and J. A. Hawley, 2002 [see reference 34]; L. M. Burke and coauthors, Adaptations to short-term high-fat diet persist during exercise despite high carbohydrate availability, *Medicine and Science in Sports and Exercise* 34 (2002): 83–91; A. L. Staudacher and coauthors, Effects of fat adaptation and carbohydrate restoration on prolonged endurance exercise, *Journal of Applied Physiology* 91 (2001): 115–122.

36. J. W. Helge, Long-term fat diet adaptation, effects on performance, training capacity, and fat utilization, *Medicine and Science in Sports and Exercise* 34 (2002): 1499–1504; N. D. Stepto and coauthors, Effect of short-term fat adaptation on high-intensity training, *Medicine and Science in Sports and Exercise* 34 (2002): 449–455.

37. E. Coleman, Does a low-fat diet impair nutrition and performance? *Sports Medicine Digest* 22 (2000): 41; Dietitians of Canada, American College of Sports Medicine, and American Dietetic Association, Joint position paper: Nutrition and athletic performance,

2008, available at http://www.dietitians.ca/Downloadable-Content/Public/noap-position-paper.aspx.

38. E. L. Melanson and coauthors, Resistance and aerobic exercise have similar effects on 24-hour nutrient oxidation, *Medicine and Science in Sports and Exercise* 34 (2002): 1793–1800; M. K. Thornton and J. A. Potteiger, Effects of resistance exercise bouts of different intensities but equal work on EPOC, *Medicine and Science in Sports and Exercise* 34 (2002): 715–722.

39. J. S. Volek, Influence of nutrition on response to resistance training, *Medicine and Science in Sports and Exercise* 36 (2004): 689–696; M. Suzuki, Glycemic carbohydrates consumed with amino acids or protein right after exercise enhance muscle formation, *Nutrition Reviews* 61 (2003): S88–S94; D. K. Levenhagen and coauthors, Postexercise protein intake enhances body and leg accretion in humans, *Medicine and Science in Sports and Exercise* 34 (2002): 828–837.

40. Standing Committee on the Scientific Evaluation of Dietary Reference Intakes, Food and Nutrition Board, Institute of Medicine, 2002, pp. 10-52–10-53 [see reference 19].

41. Dietitians of Canada, American College of Sports Medicine, and American Dietetic Association, 2008 [see reference 37].

42. T. L. Schwenk and C. D. Costley, When food becomes a drug: Nonanabolic nutritional supplement use in athletes, *American Journal of Sports Medicine* 30 (2002): 907–916.

43. Dietitians of Canada, American College of Sports Medicine, and American Dietetic Association, 2008 [see reference 37].

44. S. K. Powers, L. L. Ji, and C. Leeuwenburgh, Exercise training–induced alterations in skeletal muscle antioxidant capacity: A brief review, *Medicine and Science in Sports and Exercise* 31 (1999): 987–997.

45. M. L. Urso and P. M. Clarkson, Oxidative stress, exercise, and antioxidant supplementation, *Toxicology* 189 (2003): 41–54; H. Itoh and coauthors, Vitamin E supplementation attenuates leakage of enzymes following 6 successive days of running training, *International Journal of Sports Medicine* 21 (2000): 369–374; P. M. Clarkson and H. S. Thompson, Antioxidants: What role do they play in physical activity and health? *American Journal of Clinical Nutrition* 72 (2000): 637S–646S; Health Canada, *Healthy Living—The Safety of Vitamin E Supplements*, available at http://www.hc-sc.gc.ca/hl-vs/iyh-vsv/food-aliment/vitam-eng.php#vi.

46. R. J. Piercy and coauthors, Association between vitamin E and enhanced athletic performance in sled dogs, *Medicine and Science in Sports and Exercise* 33 (2001): 826–833.

47. J. Beard and B. Tobin, Iron status and exercise, *American Journal of Clinical Nutrition* 72 (2000): 594S–597S.

48. E. R. Eichner, Non-anemias in athletes—sports anemia and footstrike hemolysis: Friends not foes? *Sports Medicine Digest* 23 (2001): 53.

49. Dietitians of Canada, American College of Sports Medicine, and American Dietetic

Association, 2008 [see reference 37]; J. Beard and B. Tobin, 2000 [see reference 47].

50. Position of the American Dietetic Association and Dietitians of Canada: Vegetarian diets, *Journal of the American Dietetic Association* 103 (2003): 748–765; D. C. Nieman, Physical fitness and vegetarian diets: Is there a relation? *American Journal of Clinical Nutrition* 70 (1999): 570S–575S; M. N. Sawka and coauthors, ACSM position stand: Exercise and fluid replacement, *Medicine and Science in Sports and Exercise*, 39 (2007): 377–390; S. J. Whiting and W. A. Barabash, Dietary Reference Intakes for the micronutrients: Considerations for physical activity, *Applied Physiology, Nutrition, and Metabolism* 31 (2006): 80–85.

51. T. Brownlie and coauthors, Marginal iron deficiency without anemia impairs aerobic adaptation among previously untrained women, *American Journal of Clinical Nutrition* 75 (2002): 734–742; E. R. Eichner, Anemia in female athletes, *Sports Medicine Digest* 22 (2000): 42–43.

52. Standing Committee on the Scientific Evaluation of Dietary Reference Intakes, Food and Nutrition Board, Institute of Medicine, *Dietary Reference Intakes for Water, Potassium, Sodium, Chloride, and Sulfate* (Washington, D.C.: National Academies Press, 2004), pp. 4-31–4-36.

53. American College of Sports Medicine, Position stand: Heat and cold illness during distance running, *Medicine and Science in Sports and Exercise* 28 (1996): i–x.

54. J. R. Stofan and coauthors, Sweat and sodium losses in NCAA Division 1 football players with a history of whole-body muscle cramping, paper presented at the annual meeting of the American College of Sports Medicine, 2003.

55. N. J. Rehrer, Fluid and electrolyte balance in ultra-endurance sport, *Sports Medicine* 31 (2001):701–715.

56. J. W. Gardner, Death by water intoxication, *Military Medicine* 168 (2003): 432–434.

57. M. Hsieh and coauthors, Hyponatremia in runners requiring on-site medical treatment at a single marathon, *Medicine and Science in Sports and Exercise* 34 (2002): 185–189.

58. E. R. Eichner, Exertional hyponatremia: Why so many women? *Sports Medicine Digest* 24 (2002): 54, 56.

Consumer Corner 10

1. E. Coleman, Fluid replacement for athletes, *Sports Medicine Digest* 25 (2003): 76–77; Inter-Association Task Force on Exertional Heat Illness, Consensus statement, *NATA NEWS*, June 2003; Dietitians of Canada, Sports drinks: Their role in hydration for athletic performance, 2009, available at http://www.dietitians.ca/Dietitians-Views/Specific-Populations/Nutrition-and-Athletic-Performance.aspx.

2. R. Murray, Fluid and electrolytes, in C. A. Rosenbloom, ed., *Sports Nutrition: A Guide for the Professional Working with Active People*, 3rd ed. (Chicago, IL: The American Dietetic Association, 2000), pp. 95–106.

Controversy 10

1. T. L. Schwenk and C. D. Costley, When food becomes a drug: Nonanabolic nutritional supplement use in athletes, *American Journal of Sports Medicine* 30 (2002): 907–916.

2. T. L. Schwenk and C. D. Costley, 2002 [see reference 1].

3. E. Blomstrand, Amino acids and central fatigue, *Amino Acids* 20 (2001): 25–34.

4. M. J. Gibala, Regulation of skeletal muscle amino acid metabolism during exercise, *International Journal of Sports Nutrition and Exercise Metabolism* 11 (2001): 87–108.

5. M. J. Rennie and K. D. Tipton, Protein and amino acid metabolism during and after exercise and the effects of nutrition, *Annual Review of Nutrition* 20 (2000): 457–483; R. R. Wolfe, Protein supplements and exercise, *American Journal of Clinical Nutrition* 72 (2000): 551S–557S.

6. C. D. Paton, W. G. Hopkins, and L. Vollebregt, Little effect of caffeine ingestion on repeated sprints in team-sport athletes, *Medicine and Science in Sports and Exercise* 33 (2001): 822–825; C. J. Sinclair and J. D. Geiger, Caffeine use in sports: A pharmacological review, *Journal of Sports Medicine and Physical Fitness* 40 (2000): 71–79.

7. D. G. Bell and T. M. McLellan, Effect of repeated caffeine ingestion on repeated exhaustive exercise endurance, *Medicine and Science in Sports and Exercise* 35 (2003): 1348–1354; T. E. Graham, Caffeine and exercise: Metabolism, endurance and performance, *Sports Medicine* 31 (2001): 785–807; C. R. Bruce and coauthors, Enhancement of 2000-m rowing performance after caffeine ingestion, *Medicine and Science in Sports and Exercise* 32 (2000): 1958–1963; M. E. Anderson and coauthors, Improved 2000-meter rowing performance in competitive oarswomen after caffeine ingestion, *International Journal of Sports Nutrition and Exercise Metabolism* 10 (2000): 464–475.

8. I. Jacobs and coauthors, Effects of ephedrine, caffeine, and their combination on muscular endurance, *Medicine and Science in Sports and Exercise* 35 (2003): 987–997; C. D. Paton, W. G. Hopkins, and L. Vollebregt, 2001 [see reference 6].

9. T. E. Graham and coauthors, Caffeine ingestion does not alter carbohydrate or fat metabolism in human skeletal muscle during exercise, *Journal of Physiology* 529 (2000): 837–847.

10. D. Laurent and coauthors, Effects of caffeine on muscle glycogen utilization and the neuroendocrine axis during exercise, *Journal of Clinical Endocrinology and Metabolism* 85 (2000): 2170–2175.

11. G. W. Evans, The effect of chromium picolinate on insulin-controlled parameters in humans, *Journal of Biosocial Medicine Research* 11 (1989): 163–180.

12. J. M. Davis, R. S. Welsh, and N. A. Alerson, Effects of carbohydrate and chromium ingestion during intermittent high-intensity exercise to

fatigue, *International Journal of Sports Nutrition and Exercise Metabolism* 10 (2000): 476–485.

13. J. F. Fowler, Systemic contact dermatitis caused by oral chromium picolinate, *Cutis* 65 (2000): 116.

14. J. B. Vincent, The biochemistry of chromium, *Journal of Nutrition* 130 (2000): 715–718.

15. D. Preen and coauthors, Effect of creatine loading on long-term sprint exercise performance and metabolism, *Medicine and Science in Sports and Exercise* 33 (2001): 814–821.

16. E. B. Feldman, Creatine: A dietary supplement and ergogenic aid, *Nutrition Reviews* 57 (1999):45–50.

17. M. Greenwood and coauthors, Creatine supplementation patterns and perceived effects in select Division I collegiate athletes, *Clinical Journal of Sports Medicine* 10 (2000): 191–194.

18. E. Ha and M. B. Zemel, Functional properties of whey, whey components, and essential amino acids: Mechanisms underlying health benefits for active people (review), *Journal of Nutritional Biochemistry* 14 (2003): 251–258.

19. M. Freeman, Scientist fears athletes are using unsafe drugs, *New York Times Online*, October 21, 2003, available at http://www.nytimes .com/2003/10/21/sports/othersports/21STER.html.

20. R. C. Daly and coauthors, Cerebrospinal fluid and behavioral changes after methyltestosterone administration, *Archives of General Psychiatry* 58 (2001): 172–177.

21. I. Thiblin, O. Lindquist, and J. Rajs, Cause and manner of death among users of anabolic androgenic steroids, *Journal of Forensic Science* 45 (2000): 16–23.

22. Andrew Taber, Roid rage, *Salon.com*, November 18, 1999, available at http://www.salon .com/1999/11/18/steroids/.

23. B. B. Rasmussen and coauthors, Androstenedione does not stimulate muscle protein anabolism in young healthy men, *Journal of Clinical Endocrinology and Metabolism* 85 (2000): 55–59.

24. R. Skinner, E. Coleman, and C. A. Rosenbloom, Ergogenic aids, in C. A. Rosenbloom, ed., *Sports Nutrition: A Guide for the Professional Working with Active People*, 3rd ed. (Chicago, IL: The American Dietetic Association, 2000), pp. 107–146; E. Coleman, DHEA—An anabolic aid? *Sports Medicine Digest* 18 (1996): 140–141.

25. A. T. Kieman and coauthors, Effect of androstenedione ingestion on plasma testosterone in young women: A dietary supplement with potential health risks, *Clinical Chemistry* 49 (2002): 167–169; B. Z. Leder and coauthors, Oral androstenedione administration and serum testosterone concentrations in young men, *Journal of the American Medical Association* 283 (2000): 779–782; D. S. King and coauthors, Effect of oral androstenedione on serum testosterone and adaptations to resistance training in young men: A randomized controlled trial, *Journal of the American Medical Association* 281 (1999): 2020–2028.

26. Food and Drug Administration, Health effects of androstenedione, *FDA White Paper*, March 11, 2004, available at http://archive.is/ ELePm.

27. FDA warns against consuming dietary supplements containing tiratricol, *FDA Talk Paper*, November 2001, available at http://www.fda .gov/iceci/enforcementactions/enforcementstory/ enforcementstoryarchive/ucm107292.htm.

28. FDA Code of Federal Regulations (revised Apr 2013) Part 1300—Definitions, *anabolic steroids* includes (63) Tetrahydrogestrinone (THG), available at http://www.accessdata .fda.gov/scripts/cdrh/cfdocs/cfcfr/cfrsearch .cfm?fr=1300.01.

29. FDA statement on THG, 2003 [see reference 28].

11 Diet and Health

Do You Ever . . .

Wish that your diet could strengthen your immune system?

Wonder whether your food choices are damaging your heart?

Use herbs or alternative medicine to improve your health?

Choose "natural" foods without additives to avoid developing cancer?

Keep Reading . . .

Learning Objectives

After completing this chapter, you should be able to

LO 11.1 Describe relationships between immunity and nutrition, and explain how malnutrition and infection worsen each other.

LO 11.2 Compare and contrast the progression and the symptoms of heart disease in men and women.

LO 11.3 Describe what dietary and genetic factors may affect CVD risks and why higher LDL levels are a health concern.

LO 11.4 Develop a general eating plan for a person with hypertension.

LO 11.5 Speculate about possible mechanisms by which a diet high in red meat might increase the risk of colorectal cancer.

LO 11.6 Develop a healthy eating plan that reduces the intake of *trans* fats and saturated fats but maintains sufficient intakes of essential nutrients.

LO 11.7 Provide evidence to support or refute this statement: "Weight control is each individual's own responsibility."

LO 11.8 Develop a general plan to help a low-income family to choose an affordable, nutritious diet and to perform sufficient daily exercise.

Contents

Can your diet affect your risk of developing a disease? It depends on the disease. Two main kinds of diseases afflict people around the world: **infectious diseases** and **degenerative diseases**.* Infectious diseases, such as tuberculosis, smallpox, influenza, and polio, have been major killers of humankind since before the dawn of history. In any society not well defended against them, infectious diseases can cut life so short that the average person dies at 20, 30, or 40 years of age.

With the advent of vaccines and antibiotics, people in developed countries had become complacent about infectious diseases—until recently. Scientists now warn of growing infectious threats: **bioterrorism**, the emergence and rapid global spread of new diseases such as sudden acute respiratory syndrome (SARS), and a rising death toll from once-conquered diseases such as tuberculosis and foodborne infections that have become resistant to antibiotic drugs.[†,1] While scientists work to develop new controls for these perils, government and health agencies hasten to strengthen existing mechanisms for emergency preparedness and to protect our food and water supplies.

Individuals can take steps to protect themselves, too. Each of us encounters millions of microbes each day, and some of these can cause diseases. Although nutrition cannot directly prevent or cure infectious diseases, it can strengthen or weaken your body's defences against them.[2] One warning: many "immune-strengthening" foods, dietary supplements, and herbs are hoaxes. For healthy, well-fed people, supplements cannot trigger extra immune power to fend off dangerous infections. The best help you can provide to your immune system is to nourish it properly to ensure that it works to its capacity every day.

In developed nations such as Canada and the United States, degenerative diseases far outrank infections as the leading causes of death and illness.

> Chapter 12 will come back to the topic of the safety of Canada's food supply.

infectious diseases diseases that are caused by bacteria, viruses, parasites, and other microbes and can be transmitted from one person to another through air, water, or food; by contact; or through vector organisms such as mosquitoes and fleas.

degenerative diseases chronic, irreversible diseases characterized by degeneration of body organs due in part to such personal lifestyle elements as poor food choices, smoking, alcohol use, and a lack of physical activity. Also called lifestyle diseases, chronic diseases, or the diseases of old age.

bioterrorism the intentional spreading of disease-causing organisms or agricultural pests as a political weapon to produce fear and intimidate others.

---

*The term *disease* is also used to refer to conditions such as birth defects, alcoholism, obesity, and mental disorders.
†References are listed at the end of the chapter.

Figure 11–1

Leading Causes of Death in Canada, 2009

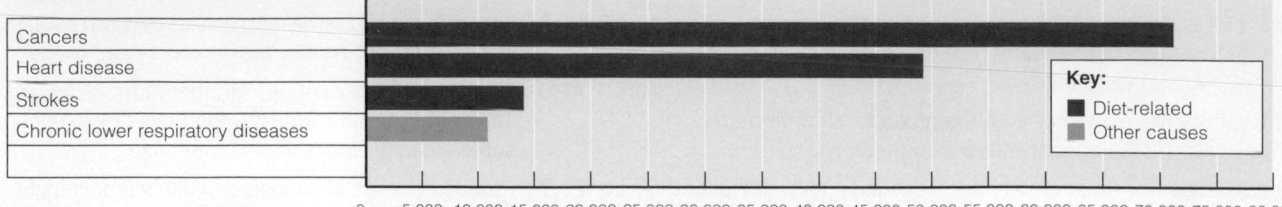

Cancers	
Heart disease	
Strokes	
Chronic lower respiratory diseases	

Key:
■ Diet-related
■ Other causes

0   5,000 10,000 15,000 20,000 25,000 30,000 35,000 40,000 45,000 50,000 55,000 60,000 65,000 70,000 75,000 80,000

Number of Deaths

Source: Adapted from Statistics Canada, Leading causes of death, by sex (Both sexes), CANSIM table 102-0561 and Catalogue no. 84-215-X, 2012. Reproduced and distributed on an "as is" basis with the permission of Statistics Canada.

Leading Causes of Death in Canada

The leading causes of death in Canada in 2009 are illustrated in Figure 11–1. Note that, while heart disease is the second-leading cause of premature death in Canada, heart disease and stroke together accounted for almost as many deaths as cancer.[3] Look for the most recent statistics for nutrition-related causes of mortality on the Statistics Canada website (http://www.statcan.gc.ca). The longer a person dodges life's other perils, the more likely that these diseases will take their toll.

Degenerative diseases do not arise from a straightforward cause such as infection but from a mixture of three factors: genetic predisposition, personal medical history, and lifestyle choices. The first two, inherited susceptibility and prior disease, people cannot control. Daily life choices that people control directly, however, can delay or prevent the onset of some diseases. Young people choose whether to nourish their bodies well, to smoke, to exercise, or to abuse alcohol. As people age, their bodies accumulate the effects of these choices, and in the later years, these impacts can make the difference between a life of health and one of chronic disability.[4] Thus, degenerative diseases are often called *chronic* diseases. After a discussion of nutrition's impact on the immune system, the rest of this chapter is devoted to the diet-related factors that affect the degenerative diseases that develop over a lifetime.

Nutrition and Immunity

Without your awareness, your immune system continuously stands guard against thousands of attacks mounted against you by microorganisms and cancer cells. If your immune system falters, you become vulnerable to disease-causing agents, and disease invariably follows.

These facts underscore nutrition's importance to immunity:

- Deficient intakes of many vitamins and minerals are associated with impaired disease resistance, as are some excessive intakes.[5]

- Immune tissues are among the first to be impaired in the course of a nutrient deficiency or toxicity.

- Some deficiencies are more immediately harmful to immunity than others; the speed of the impact is affected by whether another nutrient can perform some of the metabolic tasks of the missing nutrient, how severe the deficiency is, whether an infection has already taken hold, and the person's age.

Once a person becomes malnourished, malnutrition often worsens disease, which, in turn, worsens malnutrition. The cycle often begins when impaired immunity opens the way for disease; then disease impairs food assimilation, and nutrition status suffers further. Drugs become necessary, and many of them impair nutrition status (see Chapter 14's Controversy). Other treatments, such as surgery, take a further toll.[6]

- If there is any deficiency in food or exercise, the body will fall sick.
  —Hippocrates, a Greek physician, c. 400 BCE

- The term *immunonutrition* is used to describe the influence of nutrients on the functioning of the immune system, especially in medical nutrition therapies.

Thus, disease and poor nutrition together form a downward spiral that must be broken for recovery to occur (see Figure 11–2).

Certain groups of people are more likely than others to be caught in the downward spiral of malnutrition and weakened immunity. Among them are people who restrict their food intakes, whether because of a lack of appetite, eating disorders, desire for weight loss, or any other reason. Also susceptible are those who are one or more of the following: very young or old, poor, hospitalized, or malnourished. Rates of sickness and death increase dramatically when medical tests of a malnourished person indicate weakened immunity.

In protein-energy malnutrition (PEM), indispensable tissues and cells of the immune system dwindle in size and number, making the whole body vulnerable to infection. Table 11–1 shows PEM's effects on body defences. The skin and body linings, the first line of defence against infections, become thinner because their connective tissue is broken down, allowing agents of disease easy access to body tissues. For example, the digestive system normally musters a formidable defence—its linings are heavily laced with active immune tissues that work locally at the absorptive site and also form cells and antibodies that travel to protect other organs, such as the liver, pancreas, mammary glands, and uterus. When PEM sets in, the number of cells and antibodies present in secretions of the digestive tract diminishes. Thus, infectious agents that enter the body through linings weakened by PEM encounter diminished internal defensive responses and can easily cause illnesses of greater severity than would be possible in a well-nourished person.

Malnutrition can result not only from a lack of available food but also from diseases, such as **AIDS** and cancer, and their treatments. These alter the appetite and metabolism, causing a wasting away of the body's tissues similar to that seen in the last stages of starvation—the body uses its fat and protein reserves for survival. In people with AIDS, wasting or nutrient deficiencies can shorten survival, making medical nutrition therapy a critical need.[7] Nutrients cannot cure AIDS, of course, but an adequate diet may improve responses to drugs, shorten hospital stays, promote independence, and improve the quality of life. And exercise that strengthens muscles may hold wasting to a minimum.[8] In addition, food safety is paramount because common food bacteria and viruses can easily overwhelm a compromised immune system. Food safety rules are found in Chapter 12.

A deficiency or a toxicity of just a single nutrient can seriously weaken even a healthy person's immune defences. For example, in vitamin A deficiency, the body's skin and membranous linings become unhealthy and unable to ward off infectious organisms. A vitamin C deficiency robs white blood cells of their killing power. Too little vitamin E

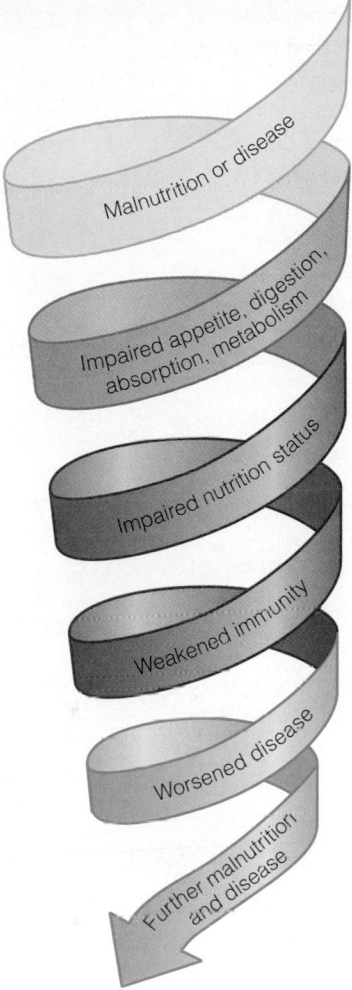

Figure 11–2

Malnutrition and Disease

- Malnutrition or disease
- Impaired appetite, digestion, absorption, metabolism
- Impaired nutrition status
- Weakened immunity
- Worsened disease
- Further malnutrition and disease

Table 11–1

Effects of Protein-Energy Malnutrition (PEM) on the Body's Defence Systems

System Component	Effects of PEM
Skin	Skin becomes thinner, with less connective tissue to serve as a barrier for protection of underlying tissues; skin sensitivity reaction to antigens is delayed.
Digestive tract membrane and other body linings	Antibody secretions and immune cell numbers are reduced.
Lymph tissues	Immune system organs[a] are reduced in size; cells of immune defence are depleted.
General response	Invader kill time is prolonged; circulating immune cells are reduced; immune response is impaired.

[a]Thymus gland, lymph nodes, and spleen.

AIDS acquired immune deficiency syndrome; caused by infection with human immunodeficiency virus (HIV), which is transmitted primarily by sexual contact, compromised epidermal layer coming in contact with infected blood, needles shared among drug users, or fluids transferred from an infected mother to her fetus or infant.

Deficiencies (↓) and Toxicities (↑) Known to Impair Immunity

- Protein (↓)
- Energy (↓)
- Vitamin A (↓)
- Vitamin E (↓)
- Vitamin D (↓)
- B vitamins (↓)
- Folate (↓)
- Vitamin C (↓)
- Iron (↓↑)
- Zinc (↓↑)
- Copper (↓)
- Magnesium (↓)
- Selenium (↓)

(a fat-soluble antioxidant) may impair several aspects of immunity, especially among the aged,[9] but Health Canada has also cautioned those over 55 years old with cardiovascular disease (CVD), diabetes, or cancer to consult a health-care practitioner before taking high doses/megadoses (i.e., 400 IU or more) of vitamin E (Health Canada: The Safety of Vitamin E Supplements, available at http://www.hc-sc.gc.ca/hl-vs/iyh-vsv/food-aliment/vitam-eng.php#th). Both deficient and excessive zinc impair immunity by reducing the number of effective white blood cells in the first case and impairing the immune response in the second.[10] The obvious conclusion is that a well-balanced diet is the cornerstone in building the best possible immune system defence.

As mentioned earlier, a *diet* of foods that supplies adequate nutrients ensures the proper functioning of the immune system, but extra daily doses of nutrients, herbs, or other substances do not enhance it. Furthermore, toxic doses clearly diminish it.

KEY POINT

- Adequate nutrition is a key component in maintaining a healthy immune system to defend against infectious diseases. Medical nutrition therapy can improve the course of wasting diseases. Both deficient and excessive nutrients can harm the immune system.

Lifestyle Choices and Risks of Degenerative Disease

In contrast to the infectious diseases, each of which has a distinct microbial cause such as a bacterium or virus, the degenerative diseases of adulthood have suspected contributors known as **risk factors**. Risk factors show a correlation with a disease, and although they are candidates for causes, they have not yet been voted in or out. We can say with confidence that a virus causes influenza, but we cannot name the cause of heart disease with such confidence.

An analogy may help clarify the concept of risk factors. A risk factor is like a person who is often seen lurking around the scene of a particular type of crime, say, arson. The police may suspect that person of setting fires, but it may very well be that another, sneakier individual who goes unnoticed is actually pouring the fuel and lighting the match. The evidence against the known suspect is only circumstantial. The police can be sure of guilt only when they observe the criminal in the act. Risk factors have not yet been caught in the act of causing diseases (the mechanisms are still largely unknown). The presence of risk factors often predicts the occurrence of diseases, however, and researchers are working on theories of how risk factors are related to disease causation.

Among the risk factors are environmental, behavioural, social, and genetic factors that tend to occur in clusters and interact with each other. For instance, food behaviours underlie many risk factors.[11] Choosing to eat a diet too high in saturated fat, salt, and Calories, for example, is choosing to risk becoming obese and contracting atherosclerosis, diabetes, diverticulosis, cancer, **hypertension**, or other diseases.[12] Figure 11–3 shows connections among some of the risk factors associated with today's major degenerative diseases and highlights the diet-related behaviours that contribute to them. Figure 11–3 also shows that in many cases, one disease or condition intensifies the risk of another.

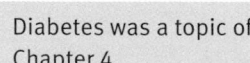

Diabetes was a topic of Chapter 4.

The exact contribution diet makes to each disease is hard to estimate. Many experts believe that diet accounts for about a third of all cases of coronary heart disease. The links between diet and cancer incidence are harder to pin down because cancer's different forms associate with different dietary factors. General trends, however, support many links between diet and cancer, and in some cases, the evidence is convincing.[13] Many other suspected causes of cancer, such as exposure to radiation or environmental contamination, are often beyond direct control by individuals, but people can control their own food choices. If a dietary change can't hurt and might help, why not make it?

risk factors factors known to be related to (or correlated with) diseases but not proven to be causal.

hypertension high blood pressure.

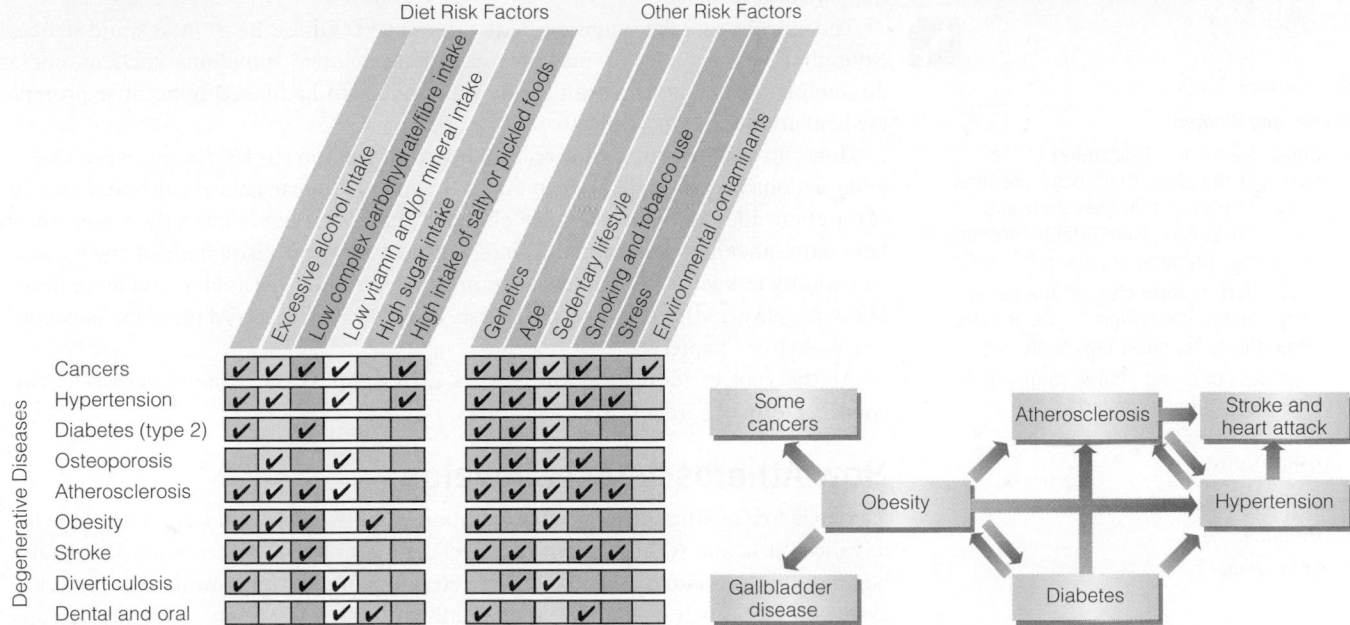

Figure 11–3

Diet/Lifestyle Risk Factors and Degenerative Diseases

This chart shows that the same risk factor can affect many degenerative diseases. Notice, for example, how many diseases have been linked to a sedentary lifestyle. The chart also shows that a particular disease, such as atherosclerosis, can have several risk factors.

This flowchart shows that many of these conditions are themselves risk factors for other degenerative diseases. For example, a person with diabetes is likely to develop atherosclerosis and hypertension. These two conditions, in turn, worsen each other. Notice how all of these degenerative diseases are linked to obesity.

Some choices, such as avoiding tobacco, are important to almost everyone's health. Other choices, such as those relating to diet, are more important for people who are genetically predisposed to certain diseases. To pinpoint your own areas of concern, search your family's medical history for diseases common to your forebears. Any condition that shows up in several close blood relatives may be a special concern for you.* Also, after your next physical examination, find out which test results are out of line. Family history and laboratory test results together are powerful predictors of disease.

Accepting that everyone has certain unchangeable "givens," an effective strategy is to look to the risk factors that can be changed and choose the most influential among them. For example, a person whose parents, grandparents, or other close blood relatives suffered from diabetes and heart disease is urgently advised to avoid becoming obese and not to smoke. The guidelines presented in later sections of this chapter can benefit most people.

Conditions in Parents, Grandparents, or Siblings, Especially Occurring Early in Life, That May Raise a Warning Flag for You

- Alcoholism
- Cancer
- Diabetes
- Heart and artery diseases
- Hypertension
- Liver disease (cirrhosis)
- Osteoporosis

KEY POINT

- The same diet and lifestyle risk factors may contribute to several degenerative diseases. A person's family history and laboratory test results can reveal strategies for disease prevention.

Cardiovascular Diseases

In 2007, 1.3 million Canadian men and women reported having CVD, and many die from it.[14] Worldwide, CVD accounts for more deaths among people of developed nations each year than any other single cause, mostly by way of heart attacks and strokes, with

---

*A free tool, "My Family Health Portrait," can help organize family health information; available at https://familyhistory.hhs.gov/fhh-web/home.action.

- Minutes and seconds count when heart attack or stroke strikes. Should any of the signs listed below occur, call for emergency medical help; in most areas, dial 911.

Heart Attack Symptoms

In Men and Women

- Chest discomfort. Discomfort in the centre of the chest that lasts more than a few minutes or that goes away and comes back. An uncomfortable pressure, squeezing, fullness, or pain in the chest.
- Discomfort in other areas of the upper body. Pain or discomfort in one or both arms, the back, neck, jaw, or stomach.
- Shortness of breath that accompanies or precedes chest discomfort.
- Other signs: cold sweat, nausea, or light-headedness.

Women May Instead Experience

- Breathlessness
- Cold sweat
- Dizziness
- Nausea
- Neck, shoulder, or abdominal pain
- Unusual fatigue
- Vomiting
- Weakness

Stroke Symptoms

- Sudden numbness or weakness of the face, arm, or leg, especially on one side of the body
- Sudden confusion, trouble speaking, or trouble understanding
- Sudden trouble seeing in one or both eyes
- Sudden trouble walking, dizziness, or loss of balance or coordination
- Sudden severe headache with no known cause

atherosclerosis (ath-er-oh-scler-OH-sis) the most common form of CVD; characterized by plaques along the inner walls of the arteries (*scleros* means "hard"; *osis* means "too much"). The term "arteriosclerosis" refers to all forms of hardening of the arteries and includes some rare diseases.

plaques (PLACKS) mounds of lipid material mixed with smooth muscle cells and calcium that develop in the artery walls in atherosclerosis (*placken* means "patch"). The same word is also used to describe the accumulation of a different kind of deposits on teeth, which promote dental caries.

macrophages (MACK-roh-fah-jes) large scavenger cells of the immune system that engulf debris and remove it (*macro* means "large"; *phagein* means "to eat").

almost 65,000 deaths from these causes in Canada alone in 2007.[15] A long-standing myth is that CVD is a men's disease; in fact, more women than men die of CVD in all of its forms each year. Men have more heart attacks than women do, but women still have them in large numbers.

The margin lists the symptoms of the major CVD killers, heart attack and stroke. Note that women may or may not experience classic symptoms such as chest discomfort. Learning to recognize the symptoms can be lifesaving because prompt medical attention is most effective.

How can you minimize your risks of heart attack and stroke? Or, more positively, what actions can you take to help maintain your cardiovascular health and vigour throughout life? Many people have changed their lifestyle to lower their risk: they have quit smoking or refrained from starting; they have also changed their diets, consuming less saturated fat, less sodium, more fruit and vegetables, and more fibre. Many people are still reluctant to exercise, however.[16] And record numbers of people are obese (see Chapter 9).

At the root of most forms of CVD is **atherosclerosis**. Atherosclerosis is the common form of hardening of the arteries.

How Atherosclerosis Develops

No one is free of atherosclerosis. The question is not whether you have it but how far advanced it is and what you can do to retard or reverse it. Atherosclerosis usually begins with the accumulation of soft, fatty streaks along the inner walls of the arteries, especially at branch points. These gradually enlarge and become hardened fibrous **plaques** that damage artery walls, making them inelastic and narrowing the passage through them (see Figure 11–4). Most people have well-developed plaques by the time they reach age 30.[17]

What causes the plaques to form? A diet high in saturated fat is a major contributor to the development of plaques and the progression of atherosclerosis.[18] But atherosclerosis is much more than the simple accumulation of lipids within the artery wall—it is a complex inflammatory response to tissue damage. Protein markers of inflammation and a host of other previously obscure compounds in the blood may one day help detect heart disease before a life-threatening event occurs.*

The damage may begin from a number of factors interacting with the cells that line the arteries: high LDL cholesterol, hypertension, toxins from cigarette smoking, elevated blood concentrations of the amino acid homocysteine, or some viral and bacterial infections.[19] Such damage produces an inflammatory response that provokes the immune system to send white blood cells to the site to try to repair the damage. Soon particles of LDL cholesterol become trapped in the blood vessel walls and become oxidized by free radicals produced during inflammatory responses.[20] The white blood cells—**macrophages**—flood the scene to remove the oxidized LDL, but to no avail. As the macrophages become engorged with oxidized LDL, they become known as foam cells, which themselves become sources of oxidation that attract more immune scavengers to the scene. Muscle cells of the arterial wall proliferate in an attempt to heal the oxidative damage, but they mix with the foam cells to form hardened areas of plaque. Mineralization increases hardening of the plaques. The process is repeated until many inner artery walls become virtually covered with disfiguring plaques.[21]

Normally, the arteries expand with each heartbeat to accommodate the pulses of blood that flow through them. Arteries hardened and narrowed by plaques cannot expand, however, so the blood pressure rises. The increased pressure damages the artery walls further and strains the heart. Because plaques are more likely to form at damage sites, the development of atherosclerosis becomes a self-accelerating process.

Homocysteine was defined in Chapter 7.

*Examples are C-reactive protein, adiponectin, interleukin-6, and tumour necrosis factor-alpha.

Figure 11–4

The Formation of Plaques in Atherosclerosis

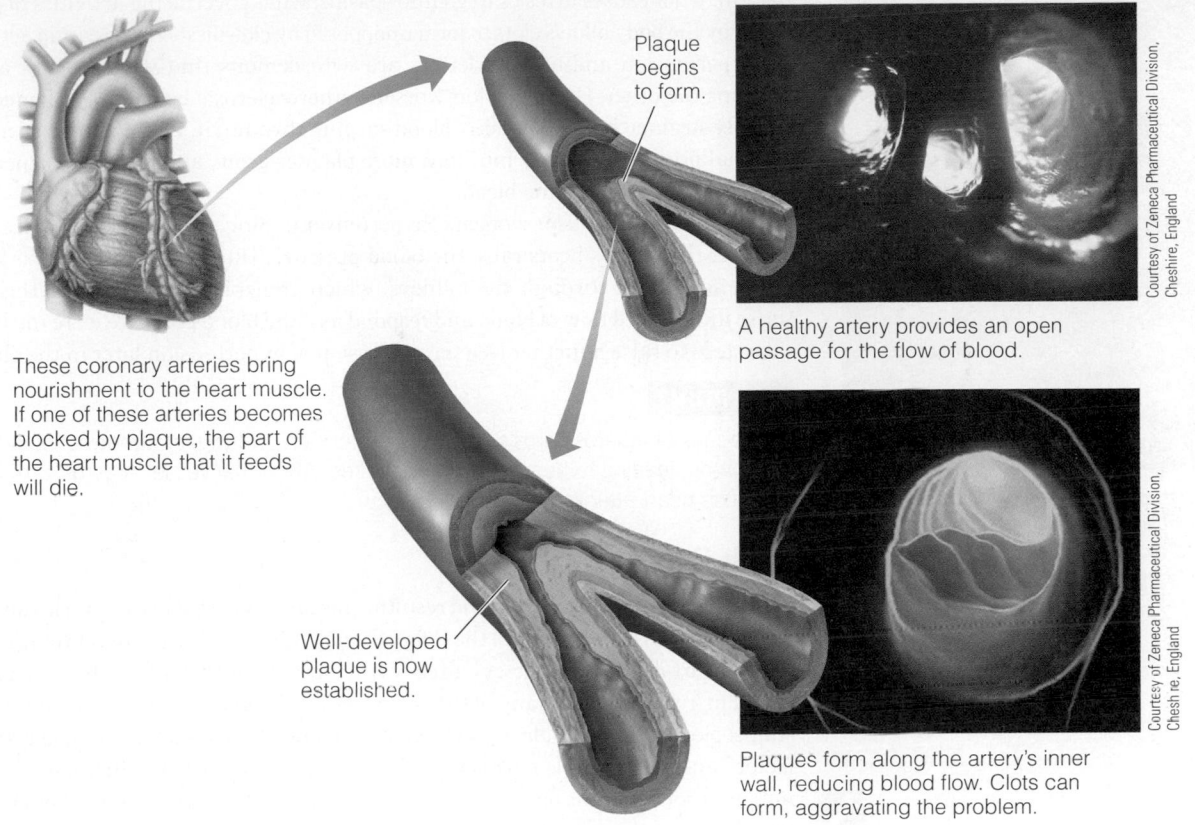

These coronary arteries bring nourishment to the heart muscle. If one of these arteries becomes blocked by plaque, the part of the heart muscle that it feeds will die.

Plaque begins to form.

Well-developed plaque is now established.

Courtesy of Zeneca Pharmaceutical Division, Cheshire, England

A healthy artery provides an open passage for the flow of blood.

Courtesy of Zeneca Pharmaceutical Division, Cheshire, England

Plaques form along the artery's inner wall, reducing blood flow. Clots can form, aggravating the problem.

As pressure builds up in an artery, the arterial wall may become weakened and balloon out, forming an **aneurysm**. An aneurysm can burst, and in a major artery such as the **aorta**, this leads to massive bleeding and death.

Abnormal blood clotting can also threaten life. Clots form and dissolve in the blood all the time, and when these processes are balanced, the clots do no harm. That balance is disturbed in atherosclerosis, however. Arterial damage, plaques in the arteries, and the inflammatory response favour the formation of blood clots. Small, cell-like bodies in the blood, known as **platelets**, normally cause clots to form when they encounter injuries in blood vessels. In atherosclerosis, when the platelets encounter hardened plaques, they respond to them as to an injury—by clotting the blood.

A clot, once formed, may remain attached to a plaque in an artery and grow until it shuts off the blood supply to the surrounding tissue. That tissue may die slowly and be replaced by nonfunctional scar tissue. The stationary clot is called a **thrombus**. When it has grown large enough to close off a blood vessel, it is a **thrombosis**. A clot can also break loose, becoming an **embolus**, and travel along the system until it reaches an artery too small to allow its passage. There the clot becomes stuck and is referred to as an **embolism**. The tissues fed by this artery will be robbed of oxygen and nutrients and will die suddenly. Such a clot can lodge in an artery of the heart, causing sudden death of part of the heart muscle, a **heart attack** (see margin photo on the next page). A clot may also lodge in an artery of the brain, killing a portion of brain tissue, a **stroke**.

Opposing the clot-forming actions of platelets are active products of omega-3 fatty acids, described in Chapter 5. A diet lacking the seafoods that contain these essential fatty acids may contribute to clot formation.[22]

aneurysm (AN-you-rism) the ballooning out of an artery wall at a point that is weakened by deterioration.

aorta (ay-OR-tuh) the large, primary artery that conducts blood from the heart to the body's smaller arteries.

platelets tiny cell-like fragments in the blood, important in blood clot formation (*platelet* means "little plate").

thrombus a stationary blood clot.

thrombosis a thrombus that has grown enough to close off a blood vessel. A *coronary thrombosis* closes off a vessel that feeds the heart muscle. A *cerebral thrombosis* closes off a vessel that feeds the brain (*coronary* means "crowning" [the heart]; *thrombo* means "clot"; the cerebrum is part of the brain).

embolus (EM-boh-luss) a thrombus that breaks loose and travels through the blood vessels (*embol* means "to insert").

embolism an embolus that causes sudden closure of a blood vessel.

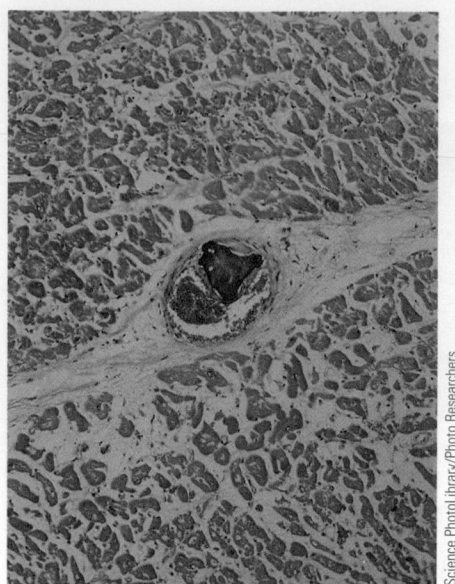

A blood clot in an artery, such as this fatal heart embolism, blocks the blood flow to tissues fed by that artery.

On many occasions, heart attacks and strokes occur with no apparent blockage. An artery may go into spasms, restricting or cutting off the blood supply to a portion of the heart muscle or brain. Much research today is devoted to finding out what causes plaques to form, what causes arteries to go into spasms, what governs the activities of platelets, and why the body allows clots to form unopposed by clot-dissolving cleanup activity.

Hypertension and atherosclerosis are twin demons that worsen CVD, and each worsens the other. Hypertension worsens atherosclerosis because a stiffened artery, already strained by each pulse of blood surging through it, is stressed further by high internal pressure. Injuries multiply, more plaques grow, and more weakened vessels become likely to burst and bleed.

Atherosclerosis also worsens hypertension. Since hardened arteries cannot expand, the heart's beats raise the blood pressure. Hardened arteries also fail to let blood flow freely through the kidneys, which control blood pressure. The kidneys sense the reduced flow of blood and respond as if the blood pressure were too low; they take steps to raise it further (see the discussion of hypertension later in the chapter).

KEY POINT

- Plaques of atherosclerosis induce hypertension and trigger abnormal blood clotting, leading to heart attacks or strokes. Abnormal vessel spasms can also cause heart attacks and strokes.

Risk Factors for CVD

Efforts to fight atherosclerosis and resulting diseases have led to discoveries about their prevention. An expert panel of the U.S. National Cholesterol Education Program defined major heart disease risk factors already listed briefly in Chapter 5; they are presented in full in Table 11–2.[23] Many of the same factors also predict the occurrence of stroke. All people reaching middle age exhibit at least one of these factors (middle age is a risk factor), and many people have several factors, silently increasing their risk.[24] It befits a nutrition book to focus on dietary strategies to reduce these risks, but Table 11–2 shows that diet is not the only, and perhaps not even the most important, factor in the development of heart disease or stroke. Age, gender, cigarette smoking, certain diseases, and

Table 11–2
Major Risk Factors for Heart Disease

See Figure 11–6 for standards by which to judge blood lipids, obesity, and blood pressure.

Risk factors that cannot be modified:

- Increasing age
- Male gender
- Family history of premature heart disease

Risk factors that can be modified:

- High blood LDL cholesterol
- Low blood HDL cholesterol
- High blood pressure (hypertension)
- Diabetes
- Obesity (especially central obesity)
- Physical inactivity
- Cigarette smoking
- An "atherogenic" diet (high in saturated fats including *trans* fats and low in vegetables, fruit, and whole grains)

Source: Expert Panel on Detection, Evaluation, and Treatment of High Blood Cholesterol in Adults (Adult Treatment Panel III) Third Report of the National Cholesterol Education Program (NCEP) NIH publication no 02–5215 (Bethesda, Md.: National Heart, Lung and Blood Institute, 2002) pp. II-15–II-20; R. J. Genest and coauthors, Canadian Cardiovascular Society/Canadian guidelines for the diagnosis and treatment of dyslipidemia and prevention of cardiovascular disease in the adult – 2009 recommendations, Canadian Journal of Cardiology 25,10 (2009): 567–579.

heart attack the event in which the vessels that feed the heart muscle become closed off by an embolism, thrombus, or other cause with resulting sudden tissue death. A heart attack is also called a *myocardial infarction* (*myo* means "muscle"; *cardial* means "of the heart"; *infarct* means "tissue death").

stroke the sudden shutting off of the blood flow to the brain by a thrombus, an embolism, or the bursting of a vessel (hemorrhage).

Chapter 11 Diet and Health

physical inactivity predict their development as well. The next few sections address these factors; discussions of diet and physical activity for CVD prevention follow.

Age, Gender, and Family History   Three of the major risk factors for CVD cannot be modified by lifestyle choices: age, gender, and family history. The increasing risk associated with growing older reflects the steady progression of atherosclerosis in most people as they age.[25]

In men, aging becomes a significant risk factor for heart disease at age 45 years or older; in women, the risk increases after age 55. Up to age 45, a woman's risk of developing heart disease is lower than a man's of the same age. But for women past menopause, rates of heart disease increase two to three times over premenopause rates.[26] Thus, CVD is not a men's disease—men die earlier of heart attacks than women, but women also die of them, especially in later life. In all of its forms, CVD kills more Canadian women than it does men.

As for family history, early heart disease in immediate family members (siblings or parents) is a major risk factor for developing it.[27] The more family members affected and the earlier the age at which they became ill, the greater the risk to the individual.[28] While these findings suggest a genetic component to CVD, scientists are encountering great complexities in trying to clarify these associations.[29]

High LDL and Low HDL Cholesterol   Low-density lipoprotein (LDL) cholesterol in the blood is strongly linked to a person's risk of developing atherosclerosis and heart disease—the higher the LDL, the greater the risk (see Figure 11–5). LDLs carry cholesterol to the cells, including the cells that line the arteries, where it can build up as part of the plaques of atherosclerosis described earlier. In clinical trials, lowering LDL greatly reduces the incidence of heart disease. By one estimate, for every percentage point drop in LDL cholesterol, the risk of heart disease falls proportionately (Figure C5–1 on page 198 demonstrated this effect). For this reason, both the LDL cholesterol goal for those at high risk for heart disease and the threshold LDL level at which to begin LDL-lowering medication have been significantly lowered.[30] Stroke is less consistently associated with elevated LDL cholesterol.[31] Figure 11–6 sums up the values considered a normal healthy level for blood lipids, body mass index (BMI), and blood pressure.

High-density lipoproteins (HDL) also carry cholesterol, but HDL carry cholesterol away from the cells to the liver for other uses or disposal. Elevated HDL indicates a reduced risk of atherosclerosis and heart attack, with growing evidence that it may prevent stroke as well.[32] High LDL and low HDL correlate *directly* with heart disease; low LDL and high HDL correlate *inversely* with risk. For this reason, heart disease risk assessment inventories, such as the one in Figure 11–7, give extra credit for having a high HDL value.

Exactly how elevated LDL increases the risk of heart disease remains unclear, but one mechanism may be through reducing plaque stability. As LDL cholesterol is incorporated into plaques, the plaques weaken and become unstable. When this happens, they can rupture, causing a heart attack. In advanced atherosclerosis, a goal of treatment is to lower LDL cholesterol to stabilize existing plaques while slowing the development of new ones.

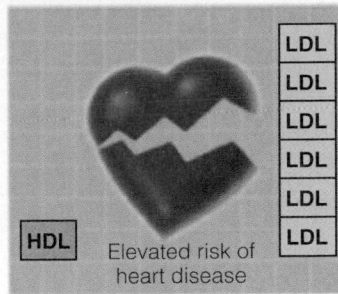

Figure 11–5

LDL, HDL, and Risk of Heart Disease

Low HDL relative to LDL increases risk

Elevated risk of heart disease

High HDL relative to LDL decreases risk

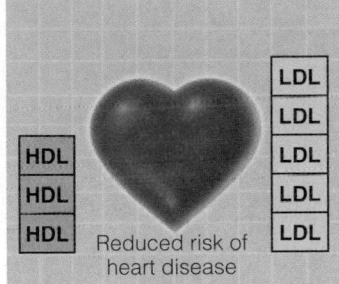

Reduced risk of heart disease

How to Remember LDL and HDL

- LDL = Low-density lipoproteins = Less healthy
- HDL = High-density lipoproteins = Healthy

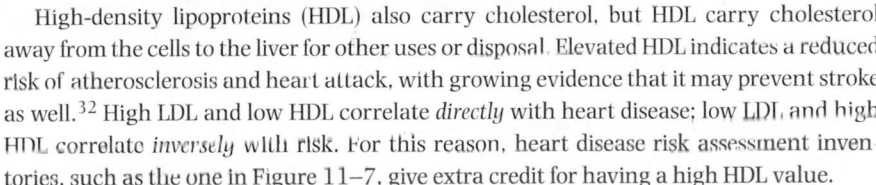

Figure 11–6

Adult Standards for Blood Lipids, Body Mass Index (BMI), and Blood Pressure

	Total blood cholesterol (mmol/L)	LDL cholesterol (mmol/L)	HDL cholesterol (mmol/L)	Total cholesterol to HDL cholesterol ratio	Triglycerides, fasting (mmol/L)	Body mass index (BMI)[a]	Blood pressure systolic / diastolic (mmHg)
Low risk	≤5.2	<3.5	>1.0 for males >1.3 for females	<5.0	<1.7	<25	<120/90

[a]Body mass index (BMI) was defined in Chapter 9; BMI standards are found on page Z at the back of the book.

Source: T. J. Anderson and coauthors, 2012 Update of the Canadian Cardiovascular Society Guidelines for the Diagnosis and Treatment of Dyslipidemia for the Prevention of Cardiovascular Disease in the Adult. Canadian Journal of Cardiology *29 (2) (2013): 157–167, available at http://www.onlinecjc.ca/article/ S0828-282X%2812%2901510-3/fulltext*

Figure 11–7

How to Assess Your Risk of Heart Disease

Do you know your heart disease risk score? This assessment estimates your 10-year risk for heart disease using charts from the Framingham Heart Study.* Be aware that a high score does not mean that you will develop heart disease, but it should warn you of the possibility and prompt you to consult a physician about your health. You will need to know your blood cholesterol (ideally, the average of at least two recent measurements) and blood pressure (ideally, the average of several recent measurements). With this information in hand, find yourself in the charts below and add the points for each risk factor.

Age (years)

	Points	
	Men	Women
30–34	0	0
35–39	2	2
40–44	5	4
45–49	(7)	5
50–54	8	7
55–59	10	8
60–64	11	9
65–69	13	10
70–74	14	11
75+	16	12

HDL Cholesterol Level (mmol/L)

	Points	
HDL-C (mmol/L)	Men	Women
>1.6	–2	–2
1.3–1.6	–1	–1
1.2–1.3	0	0
0.9–1.2	1	1
<0.9	(2)	2

Systolic Blood Pressure (mmHg)

	Points			
	Untreated		Treated	
	Men	Women	Men	Women
<120	–2	–3	0	–1
120–129	0	0	2	2
130–139	1	1	(3)	3
140–149	2	2	4	5
150–159	2	4	4	6
>160	3	5	5	7

Total Cholesterol (mmol/L)

	Points	
Total-C (mmol/L)	Men	Women
<4.1	0	0
4.1–5.2	1	1
5.2–6.2	2	3
6.2–7.2	(3)	4
>7.2	4	5

15

Cardiovascular Disease Risk

Total Points	Men (Risk, %)	Women (Risk, %)
–3 or less	<1	<1
–2	1.1	<1
–1	1.4	1.0
0	1.6	1.2
1	1.9	1.5
2	2.3	1.7
3	2.8	2.0
4	3.3	2.4
5	3.9	2.8
6	4.7	3.3
7	5.6	3.9
8	6.7	4.5
9	7.9	5.3
10	9.4	6.3
11	11.2	7.3
12	13.3	8.6
13	15.6	10.0
14	18.4	11.7
(15)	≈21.6	13.7
16	25.3	15.9
17	29.4	18.5
18	>30	21.5
19	>30	24.8
20	>30	27.5
21+	>30	>30

Scoring Your 10-Year Heart Disease Risk

From the four panels above, add up the total points for your gender: _____. Now find your 10-year risk score in the panel below.

- <10 = Low Risk
- 10–20 = Moderate Risk ✓
- >20 = High Risk ➖

*An electronic version of this assessment is available in the Supplementary Material for the 2012 Guidelines on the Canadian Journal of Cardiology website at http://www.ccsguidelineprograms.ca/index.php?option=com_content&view=article&id=185&Itemid=107. Another risk inventory is available from the Heart and Stroke Foundation of Canada at https://makehealthlast.ca/?gclid=CNaM5MPRp7gCFYo-MgodA24AKQ.

Source: Data from Genest, Jacques et al. "Canadian Guidelines for the Diagnosis and Treatment of Dyslipidemia and Prevention of Cardiovascular Disease in the Adult - 2009 Recommendations." Journal of the Canadian Cardiovascular Society, volume 25, issue 10, page 567.

Hypertension   Chronic hypertension worsens CVD. The higher the blood pressure above normal, the greater the risk of heart attack or stroke. The relationship between hypertension and disease risk holds for men and women, young and old. Hypertension injures the artery walls and accelerates plaque formation, thus initiating or worsening the progression of atherosclerosis. A later section gives details about hypertension because it constitutes a major threat to health on its own.

Diabetes   Diabetes constitutes a major independent risk factor for all forms of CVD, substantially increasing the risk of death from these causes.[33] In diabetes, atherosclerosis progresses rapidly, blocking blood vessels and diminishing circulation. For many people with diabetes, the risk of a future heart attack is roughly equal to that of a person with a confirmed diagnosis of heart disease—two to four times as high as that of a person without diabetes.[34] When heart disease occurs in conjunction with diabetes, the condition is likely to be severe.

Few people with diabetes recognize that, left uncontrolled, diabetes holds a grave threat of all forms of CVD.[35] Even insulin resistance without diabetes may elevate the risk. A symptomless type of insulin resistance may greatly increase the likelihood of a heart attack—*without* abnormal blood glucose or lipid values that might otherwise warn the person. Chapter 4 provided some details about minimizing the damage from diabetes and insulin resistance.

Insulin resistance was defined in Chapter 4.

Obesity and Physical Inactivity   Obesity, especially central obesity, and physical inactivity amplify a person's risk of CVD by elevating LDL cholesterol while lowering HDL cholesterol and worsening hypertension and diabetes.[36] Conversely, weight loss and physical activity lower LDL, raise HDL, improve insulin sensitivity, and lower blood pressure.[37]

Read more about central obesity and weight-loss diets in Chapter 9; the benefits of fitness are a topic of Chapter 10.

Routine physical activity strengthens muscles, including the muscles of the heart and arteries, and improves the heart's response to everyday demands.[38] Physical activity expands the volume of blood the heart can pump to the tissues at each beat, thereby reducing the heart's workload. It also stimulates development of new arteries to nourish the heart muscle, which may be a factor in the excellent recovery seen in some heart attack victims who exercise. In addition, physical activity favours lean over fat tissue for a healthy body composition. If pursued daily, even 30 minutes of light, balanced exercise, performed at intervals throughout the day, can improve the odds against heart disease considerably, and an hour a day, as recommended by the DRI committee, benefits the heart even more. This chapter's Think Fitness feature offers suggestions for incorporating physical activity into your daily routine.

Smoking   Cigarette smoking is a powerful risk factor for heart disease and other forms of CVD. The more a person smokes, the higher the CVD risk—a relationship that holds for both men and women. Smoking damages the heart directly with toxins and burdens it by raising the blood pressure. Body tissues starved for oxygen by smoke demand more heartbeats to deliver blood, thereby increasing the heart's workload. At the same time, smoking deprives the heart muscle itself of the oxygen it needs to maintain a steady beat. Smoking also damages platelets, making blood clots likely. Toxins in cigarette smoke directly damage the linings of the blood vessels, making atherosclerosis likely. When people quit smoking, their risk of heart disease begins to drop within a few months; a year later, their risk has dropped by half, and after 15 years of staying smoke-free, their risks equal those of lifetime nonsmokers.[39]

Atherogenic Diet   Diet influences the risk of CVD. An "atherogenic diet"—high in saturated fats, *trans* fats, and cholesterol—increases LDL cholesterol. Fortunately, a well-chosen diet often lowers the risk of CVD, and does so to a greater degree than might be expected from its effects on blood lipids alone. Any of a number of beneficial factors in such diets may take the credit, among them the vitamins, minerals, antioxidant phytochemicals, and omega-3 fatty acids. Strategies for choosing such a diet follow this section.

Ways to Include Physical Activity in a Day

The benefits of physical activity are compelling, so why not tie up your athletic shoes, head out the door, and get going? Here are some ideas to get you started:

- Coach a sport.
- Garden.
- Hike, bike, or walk to nearby stores or to classes.
- Mow, trim, and rake by hand.
- Park a block from your destination and walk.
- Play a sport.
- Play with children.

- Take classes for credit in dancing, sports, conditioning, or swimming.
- Take the stairs, not the elevator.
- Walk a dog.
- Walk 10,000 steps per day. This amounts to about 8 kilometres, enough to meet the daily activity level that defines an active person. An inexpensive pedometer can record your steps.
- Wash your car with extra vigour, or bend and stretch to wash your toes in the bath.
- Work out at a fitness club.

- Work out with friends to help one another stay fit.

Also, try these:

- Give two labour-saving devices to someone who wants them.
- Lift small hand weights while talking on the phone or watching TV.
- Stretch often during the day.
- If you have access to the Internet, check out the Public Health Agency of Canada's website for ways to become more active at home or in the workplace: http://www.phac-aspc.gc.ca/hp-ps/hl-mvs/pa-ap/index-eng.php.

Features of Metabolic Syndrome

- Central obesity
- Abnormal blood lipids: low HDL and high triglycerides
- Elevated blood pressure
- Elevated fasting blood glucose or insulin resistance
- People with elevated triglycerides should limit simple sugars and highly refined starchy foods, which often cause triglycerides to rise.

Metabolic Syndrome   People suffering from a characteristic cluster of CVD risk factors, including central obesity, high fasting blood glucose or insulin resistance, low blood HDL cholesterol, and hypertension, plus one other factor—elevated blood triglycerides—have an especially high risk of developing CVD.[40] Most of these factors elevate CVD risk independently, and when they occur together, they synergistically elevate the risk.[41] (On its own, an elevated triglyceride level is not a risk factor for CVD.) This deadly cluster, called **metabolic syndrome**, approaches the power of high LDL cholesterol in raising the risk of CVD.[42] Millions of people in North America face the threat of metabolic syndrome, but many remain unaware of it and thus do not seek treatment.[43]

Other Risk Factors   Factors other than the major ones listed earlier in Table 11–2 may also influence a person's risk. These factors, known as emerging risk factors, can help round out the assessment of an individual's risk of developing CVD. For example, research suggests emerging links among the B vitamins, homocysteine, and atherosclerosis, but authorities are not yet ready to declare homocysteine a risk factor for mortality due to CVD, and B vitamins have yet to prove themselves effective in heart disease prevention.[44] Also, in an effort to combine many existing and emerging factors that predict CVD and type 2 diabetes, a Canadian "cardiometabolic risk working group" recently proposed the term "global cardiometaboli risk" and released a position paper about the identification and management of cardiometabolic risk in Canada (http://www.onlinecjc.ca/article/S0828-282X%2811%2900138-3/abstract).

KEY POINT

- Major risk factors for CVD put forth by the U.S. National Cholesterol Education Program include age, gender, family history, high LDL cholesterol and low HDL cholesterol, hypertension, diabetes, obesity, physical inactivity, smoking, and an atherogenic diet. Other potential risk factors are under investigation.

Diet to Reduce CVD Risk

Now that you know which factors increase the risks of developing CVD, what role can diet play in minimizing your risks? The answer focuses primarily on how diet relates to high blood cholesterol. Diet's effects are felt in two opposing ways: first, a diet high in

metabolic syndrome a combination of characteristic factors—high fasting blood glucose or insulin resistance, central obesity, hypertension, low blood HDL cholesterol, and elevated blood triglycerides—that greatly increase a person's risk of developing CVD. Also called *insulin resistance syndrome* or *syndrome X*.

Table 11-3

How Much Does Changing the Diet Change LDL Cholesterol?[a]

Diet-Related Component	Modification	Possible LDL Reduction (%)
Saturated fat	<7% of Calories	8–10
Dietary cholesterol	<200 mg/day	3–5
Weight reduction (if overweight)	Lose 4.5 kg (10 lb)	5–8
Soluble, viscous fibre	5–10 g/day	3–5

[a]See Table 11–4, page 473, for other dietary changes believed to influence risk of CVD.

Source: Expert Panel on Detection, Evaluation, and Treatment of High Blood Cholesterol in Adults (Adult Treatment Panel III), Third Report of the National Cholesterol Education Program (NCEP), NIH publication no. 02-5215 (Bethesda, Md.: National Heart, Lung, and Blood Institute, 2002), p. V-21.

saturated fat and *trans* fatty acids contributes to high blood LDL cholesterol; second, reducing those fats in the diet lowers blood LDL cholesterol and may reduce the risk of CVD.[45] Table 11–3 demonstrates the power of diet-related factors to reduce LDL cholesterol.

Food sources of saturated fats and *trans* fatty acids were listed in Chapter 5; Controversy 5 distinguishes between fats that harm the heart and those thought to be safer.

Wherever in the world diets are high in saturated fat and low in fish, fruit, and vegetables, blood cholesterol is high, and heart disease takes a great toll on health and life.[46] Conversely, wherever dietary fat consists mostly of unsaturated fats with abundant fish, fruit, and vegetables, blood cholesterol and the rate of death from heart disease are low.

Controlling Dietary Lipids Nutrition authorities agree on this point: lowering intakes of saturated fat and *trans* fat lowers blood LDL cholesterol and reduces heart disease risks.[47] For healthy people living in Canada and the United States, saturated fat, including *trans* fatty acids, in the diet should account for no more than 10 percent of Calories. Based on the latest DRI reports, Health Canada recommends that the diet should also contain no more than 35 percent of Calories from total fat; other authorities recommend lower intakes of no more than 30 percent of Calories from fat.[48]

Health Canada, the World Health Organization, and many other experts also recommend that healthy people limit cholesterol intake to 300 milligrams a day in the context of a diet low in saturated fat and *trans* fatty acids. Although cholesterol plays a lesser role than saturated fat and *trans* fatty acids, it still elevates blood cholesterol. People with heart disease often consume diets rich in all three.[49]

Strictly limiting all kinds of dietary fats is probably not in the best interest of the health of the heart. In North America, healthy people choosing a diet moderate in fat—up to 35 percent of total Calories—do not necessarily invite heart disease as long as the diet is low in saturated fat and *trans* fat, controlled in energy (Calories), and ample in fish, fruit, vegetables, and milk products.[50] Many people in Canada, however, eat diets rich in meats and hydrogenated fats, so if they reduce their *total* fat intakes, their *saturated* fat and *trans* fatty acids will follow suit. Furthermore, Canada's Food Guide recommends we "Have meat alternatives such as beans, lentils and tofu often."

It matters, however, what people choose to eat instead of saturated fats. Simple carbohydrates (sugars) seem to elevate blood triglycerides and reduce HDL cholesterol—effects opposite of those desired. Choosing polyunsaturated or monounsaturated fats or complex carbohydrates from whole grains or vegetables improves the lipoprotein profile.[51]

Fish oils, rich in omega-3 polyunsaturated fatty acids, lower triglycerides, prevent blood clots, and may reduce the risk of sudden death associated with CVD.[52]

When diets are rich in vegetables and fruit, life expectancies are long.

For these reasons, Canada's Food Guide recommends two meals of fish per week.[53] Plant sources of essential fatty acids, which include flaxseed and flaxseed oil, canola oil, soybean oil, and nuts, also confer benefits on the heart.[54] Evidence leans against the use of fish oil supplements, however, which carry their own risks (see the Consumer Corner in Chapter 5, page 184).

Chapter 5, pages 177–179, explained mechanisms by which fish oils may affect heart health.

Effects of Fibre, Nutrients, and Phytochemicals   In addition to limiting fats, the heart-healthy diet encourages consumption of foods rich in complex carbohydrates, especially whole grains and other whole foods.[55] The viscous (soluble) fibre richly supplied by oats, barley, legumes, and pectin-rich fruit and vegetables helps improve blood lipids.[56] These fibres bind cholesterol and bile in the intestine, reducing their absorption. An extra 5 to 10 grams of viscous fibre daily lowers LDL cholesterol levels by about 5 percent.[57] Additionally, a high-fibre diet may reduce a blood marker of inflammation thought to indicate an elevated risk of having a heart attack.*,[58] Foods rich in viscous fibre also provide minerals to help control blood pressure (described later), antioxidants to help protect against LDL oxidation, and an array of vitamins and minerals, making them extraordinarily beneficial to health.

Diets rich in legumes, fruit, vegetables, and whole grains with their abundant fibres, nutrients, and phytochemicals correlate with low CVD rates. Some food constituents may help lower LDL cholesterol, protect LDL cholesterol from oxidation, or lower blood pressure, but these effects are observed consistently in the body only when whole foods supply the needed compounds. Supplements of nutrients or phytochemicals are ineffective for these purposes, as earlier chapters made clear. The Food Feature in this chapter provides details needed to help in choosing a protective diet.

Table 4–2 on page 120 lists fibres, characteristics, actions in the body, and health benefits. Controversy 2 gave details about phytochemicals.

Alcohol   People want to know whether moderate consumption of alcohol will reduce their CVD risk. Research on middle-aged and older people who drink one or two drinks a day with no binge drinking supports the idea.[59] For this group, moderate alcohol consumption has been reported to raise HDL cholesterol concentrations and reduce the risk of blood clots, thereby reducing the likelihood of heart attack.[60] The effect, however, cannot reverse the effects of other risk factors such as imprudent diet or physical inactivity.

Controversy 3 gave details about the health effects of alcohol.

Heavy alcohol use (more than three drinks a day) is known to elevate blood pressure, to damage the heart muscle, to elevate the risk of stroke, and to have many other deleterious effects on the body's organs.[61] Heart attacks among apparently healthy young people have been associated with alcohol intoxication from heavy weekend drinking. The bottom line for young people is that the risks from alcohol greatly outweigh any benefit to the heart.

Other Dietary Factors   Other dietary factors, such as soy products, also improve heart disease risk in various ways. Table 11–4 recounts them. A potentially helpful innovation is the sterol and stanol esters (introduced in Controversy 2) that have been added to foods such as margarine and orange juice. These compounds block absorption of cholesterol from the intestine, dropping blood cholesterol by about 7 to 10 percent. When these compounds accompany a diet low in saturated fats and high in ordinary plant foods, the effect may be as powerful as some medications in lowering blood LDL cholesterol.[62] Some foods, such as corn oil, naturally contain compounds related to sterol or stanol esters, but the amount present in a typical serving is too small to affect the health of the arteries. Sterol and stanol esters also reduce absorption of some

*The marker is C-reactive protein.

Alcohol Consumption among Students in 40 Canadian Universities (2004)

- 77% consumed alcohol the month prior to the study.
- Males reported drinking more and higher amounts than females.
- 18.5% consumed five or more drinks on a single occasion once every two weeks or more frequently.
- 6.6% consumed eight or more drinks on a single occasion once every two weeks or more frequently.
- Almost one-third of students reported at least one indicator of dependent drinking (e.g., being unable to stop).

Source: Adlaf, Edward M., Demers, Andrée, and Gliksman, Louis (Eds.) Canadian Campus Survey 2004. Toronto, Centre for Addiction and Mental Health. 2005 www.camh.net/Research/Areas_of_research/Population_Life_Course_Studies/CCS_2004_report.pdf

Table 11–4

Other Dietary Factors That May Protect against CVD

Dietary Factor	Protection against CVD
Omega-3 fatty acids (fish oils from two meals of fatty fish per week)	<ul><li>Limit clot formation</li><li>Prevent irregular heartbeats</li><li>Decrease blood triglycerides; slightly increase HDL cholesterol</li><li>Decrease inflammation</li><li>Relax the arteries, reducing blood pressure</li></ul>
Folate, vitamin B_6, vitamin B_{12} (DRI recommended intakes)	<ul><li>Reduce homocysteine but may not reduce the risk of death due to CVD</li></ul>
Vitamin E (DRI recommended intake)	<ul><li>Reduces arterial injuries and inflammation (but see text for cautionary statements regarding vitamin E and supplements of more than 400 IU per day)</li><li>Limits LDL oxidation</li></ul>
Soy foods including soy protein, soy "milk" products, and soybeans	<ul><li>Contain antioxidants</li><li>Lower LDL cholesterol</li></ul>
Ground flaxseed	<ul><li>Lower total and LDL cholesterol</li></ul>
Sterol esters, stanol esters	<ul><li>Reduce cholesterol absorption and lower blood cholesterol</li></ul>
Alcohol (for older adults, in moderation)	<ul><li>Raises HDL cholesterol</li><li>Limits clot formation</li></ul>

Controversy 6 discussed potential benefits of soybeans and soy products to heart health.

potentially beneficial phytochemicals, so their use may be best reserved for those who fail to lower their elevated cholesterol by other means.

More Strategies against CVD Periodically, the media repopularize the idea that the vitamin niacin can lower blood cholesterol. Experimentally, pharmaceutical doses of a specific form of niacin act like a drug in lowering blood cholesterol and prolonging life, but other drugs effective for this purpose probably have fewer side effects. Some of the most common of these drugs, the "statin" drugs, efficiently lower the blood LDL values of users. They work best in association with a cholesterol-lowering diet and exercise.[63] Ordinary niacin supplements are useless in lowering blood cholesterol.

Authors of some diet books claim that low-carbohydrate diets, with their high intakes of meats and saturated fats, lower blood cholesterol. Shifts in blood lipid values have been reported, especially reduced blood triglycerides and reduced HDL, but this profile is not known to benefit the heart.[64] When the diets are low enough in Calories to produce weight loss, blood cholesterol diminishes along with body fatness, but this occurs with weight loss achieved on any kind of diet. Standard cholesterol-lowering diets that are low in saturated fats improve or maintain the beneficial HDL, while lowering LDL cholesterol, and may produce beneficial weight loss if Calories are kept low.

Although diet and exercise are not the easy route to heart health that everyone hopes for, they form a powerful and safe combination for improving health. Needed weight loss often reduces blood pressure. So does eating a diet low in fat, restricted in cholesterol, and high in complex carbohydrates, whole grains, fruit, and vegetables. In a recent study of 15,000 male physicians, those consuming at least one and a half cups of dark green, deep yellow, or red vegetables daily had a 23 percent lower risk of heart disease than men who ate less than half a cup each day.[65] Indeed, agencies including Health Canada, the Heart and Stroke Foundation of Canada, and the Canadian Cardiology Society urge Canadians to consume a minimum of four to eight servings of vegetables and fruit per day to help prevent CVD. And even if such a diet does not lower cholesterol or blood pressure, it will help by normalizing blood glucose (diabetes). Remember, diabetes is a major risk factor for CVD. A meal or two of fish each week can help by favouring the right fatty-acid balance so that clot formation is unlikely.

The pattern of protection from the recommended diet and exercise regimen becomes clear—the effects of each small choice add to the beneficial whole. While you're at it, don't smoke. Relax. Meditate or pray. Control stress. Play. Relaxed, happy people have lower rates of heart attack.[66]

KEY POINT

- High blood cholesterol indicates a risk of heart disease, and diet can contribute to lowering blood cholesterol and thus the risk of heart disease. Dietary measures to lower LDL cholesterol include reducing intakes of saturated fat, *trans* fat, and cholesterol, along with obtaining the fibre, nutrients, and phytochemicals of fruit, vegetables, legumes, and whole grains. Even for people on prescription medication, diet and exercise are key.

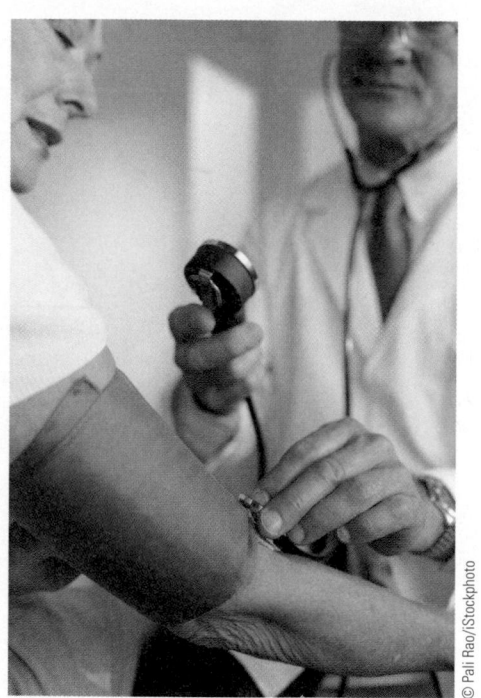

The most effective single step you can take against hypertension is to learn your own blood pressure.

systolic (sis-TOL-ik) pressure the first figure in a blood pressure reading (the "dupp" of the heartbeat is heard), which reflects arterial pressure caused by the contraction of the heart's left ventricle.

diastolic (dye-as-TOL-ik) pressure the second figure in a blood pressure reading (the "lubb" of the heartbeat is heard), which reflects the arterial pressure when the heart is between beats.

Nutrition and Hypertension

People with healthy low blood pressure generally enjoy a long life and suffer less often from heart disease. Chronic high blood pressure, or hypertension, remains one of the most prevalent forms of CVD, affecting 22 percent of Canadians 18 to 70 years old.[67] For people age 65 or older, the lifetime risk of developing it approaches 90 percent. Hypertension contributes to half a million strokes and over a million heart attacks each year in the United States, and its rate has been rising steadily.[68] The higher above normal the blood pressure, the greater the risk of heart disease. Hypertension is especially threatening when paired with atherosclerosis, as it often is.

You cannot tell if you have high blood pressure—it presents no symptoms you can feel. The most effective single step you can take to protect yourself from hypertension is to find out whether you have it. During a checkup, a health-care professional can take an accurate resting blood pressure reading. Self-test machines in drugstores and other public places are often inaccurate. If your resting blood pressure is above normal, the reading should be repeated before confirming the diagnosis of hypertension. Thereafter, blood pressure should be checked at regular intervals.

When blood pressure is measured, two numbers are important: the pressure during contraction of the heart's ventricles (large pumping chambers) and the pressure during their relaxation. The numbers are given as a fraction, with the first number representing the **systolic pressure** (ventricular contraction) and the second number the **diastolic pressure** (relaxation). Return to Figure 11–6 (page 467) to see how to interpret your resting blood pressure.

Canadian Recommendations for Hypertension

The Canadian Hypertension Education Program (CHEP) released its latest Canadian guidelines on hypertension in May 2013.[69] They include statements about the use of resistance and weight-training exercise in those with stage 1 hypertension, as well as higher targets for systolic blood pressure in elderly patients.

KEY POINT

- Atherosclerosis, obesity, insulin resistance, age, family background, and race contribute to hypertension risks. Prevention and treatment both deserve high-priority efforts.

How Does Blood Pressure Work in the Body, and What Makes It Too High?

Blood pressure is vital to life. It pushes the blood through the major arteries into smaller arteries and finally into tiny capillaries whose thin walls permit exchange of fluids between the blood and the tissues (see Figure 11–8). When the pressure is right, the cells receive a constant supply of nutrients and oxygen and can release their wastes.

The Role of the Kidneys   For the kidneys to filter waste materials out of the blood and into the urine, blood pressure has to be high enough to force the blood's fluid out of the capillaries and into the kidneys' filtering networks. If the blood pressure is too low, the kidneys act to increase it—they send hormones to constrict blood vessels and to retain water and salt in the body. Dehydration sets these actions in motion, and in this case, they are beneficial because when the blood volume is low, higher blood pressure is needed to deliver substances to the tissues. By constricting the blood vessels and conserving water and sodium, the kidneys ensure that normal blood pressure is maintained until the dehydrated person can drink water.

Atherosclerosis also sets this process in motion, however, and this is not beneficial. By obstructing blood vessels, atherosclerosis fools the kidneys, which react as if there were a water deficiency. The kidneys raise the blood pressure high enough to get

---

Figure 11–8

The Blood Pressure

Three major factors contribute to the pressure inside an artery. First, the heart pushes blood into the artery. Second, the small-diameter arteries and capillaries at the other end resist the blood's flow (peripheral resistance). Third, the volume of fluid in the circulatory system, which depends on the number of dissolved particles in that fluid, adds pressure.

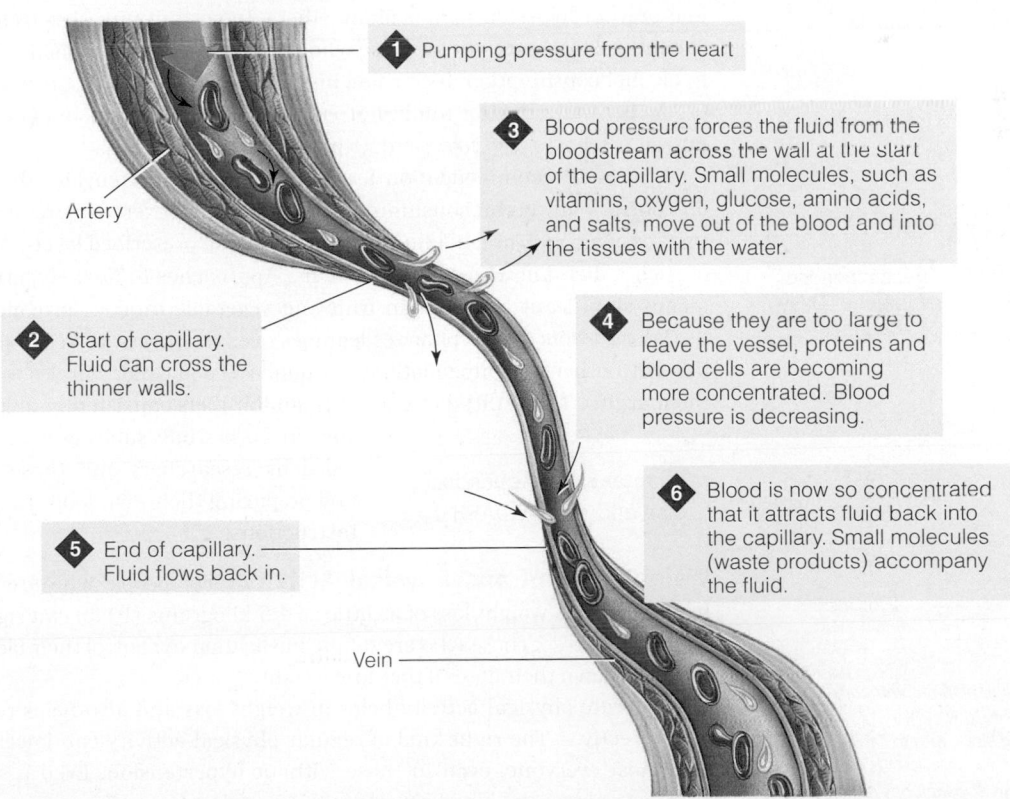

1 Pumping pressure from the heart

2 Start of capillary. Fluid can cross the thinner walls.

Artery

3 Blood pressure forces the fluid from the bloodstream across the wall at the start of the capillary. Small molecules, such as vitamins, oxygen, glucose, amino acids, and salts, move out of the blood and into the tissues with the water.

4 Because they are too large to leave the vessel, proteins and blood cells are becoming more concentrated. Blood pressure is decreasing.

5 End of capillary. Fluid flows back in.

6 Blood is now so concentrated that it attracts fluid back into the capillary. Small molecules (waste products) accompany the fluid.

Vein

the blood they need, but, in the process, they may make the pressure too high for the arteries and heart to withstand. Hypertension also aggravates atherosclerosis by mechanically injuring the artery linings, increasing the likelihood that plaques will form; plaques restrict blood flow to the kidneys, which may then raise the blood pressure still further, and the problem snowballs.

The Roles of Risk Factors Primary among the risk factors that precipitate or aggravate hypertension are atherosclerosis, obesity (particularly central obesity), and insulin resistance (which leads to type 2 diabetes). Excess fat means miles of extra capillaries through which the blood must be pumped.

Epidemiological studies have identified several other risk factors that predict hypertension. One is age: most people who develop hypertension do so in their 50s and 60s. Another is inherited genes, and researchers are working to identify the genetic determinants of hypertension.[70] A family history of hypertension and heart disease raises the risk of developing hypertension two to five times, and North Americans of African descent are likely to develop more severe hypertension earlier in life than those of European or Asian descent. Hypertension also bears some relation to insulin resistance, probably through a common genetic link, and some measures to prevent diabetes also protect against hypertension.

Environmental factors in Canada may also favour the development of hypertension, and the incidence of hypertension among some ethnic groups, for example, South Asians, Inuit, and Black Canadians, is higher than for other Canadians.

KEY POINT

- Hypertension is silent, progressively worsens atherosclerosis, and makes heart attacks and strokes likely. All adults should know their blood pressure.

How Does Nutrition Affect Hypertension?

Even mild hypertension can be dangerous, but individuals who adhere to treatment are less likely to suffer illness or early death. Some people need medications to bring their blood pressure down, but diet and exercise alone can bring improvements for many and prevent hypertension for many others. Important nutrition factors are lowering salt intake; losing weight for those who are overweight; using moderation with regard to alcohol consumption; increasing intakes of fruit, vegetables, fish, and low-fat dairy products; and reducing intakes of fat. Calcium, potassium, magnesium, and other nutrients seem to play roles, as does physical activity.

A blanket recommendation for prevention of hypertension, then, would centre on controlling weight, consuming a nutritious diet, exercising regularly, controlling intakes of alcohol, and holding sodium intakes to prescribed levels. A classic example of such a diet, known as DASH (Dietary Approaches to Stop Hypertension), recommends significant increases in fruit and vegetable intakes, provides 30 percent of its Calories from fat, emphasizes legumes over red meats, restricts sodium, and is in line with other recommendations of Canada's Food Guide besides (see Table 11–5 in the margin). The DASH diet and other similar diets consistently improve blood pressure in both study subjects whose diets are provided by researchers and those freely choosing and preparing their own foods in accordance with instructions.[71]

Chapter 8 and Appendix F also address the DASH diet.

Weight Control and Physical Activity For people who are overweight and hypertensive, a weight loss of as little as 4.5 kilograms (10 lb) can significantly lower blood pressure.[72] Those who are taking medication to control their blood pressure can often cut down their doses if they lose weight.

Moderate physical activity helps in weight loss and also helps reduce hypertension directly.[73] The right kind of regular physical activity can lower blood pressure in almost everyone, even in those without hypertension. Even a single session of exercise reduces the blood pressure, an effect that lasts 12 hours or more and intensifies as training improves physical condition.[74] The "right kind" of activity can be

Table 11–5

The DASH Eating Plan

Food Group	Recommended Number of Daily Servings[a]
Grains	7–8
Vegetables	4–5
Fruit	4–5
Milk (fat-free/low-fat)	2–3
Meat (lean)[b]	2 or less
Calories	2,000

NOTE: The DASH eating plan recommends that fats, oils, and sweets be used sparingly.

[a]For details on serving sizes, turn to Table F–2 of Appendix F.

[b]The DASH eating plan also includes recommended servings for nuts, seeds, and dry beans (4–5 per week).

walking, jogging, cycling, or others that also increase blood HDL and lower LDL.[75] The exercise need not be strenuous—even walking at any pace (about 10,000 steps) per day seems to be effective in bringing down high blood pressure.[76] The activity may even be broken up into manageable 10-minute segments throughout the day and still provide benefits.[77] Aerobic activity for cardiovascular fitness was described in Chapter 10.

Physical activity also changes the hormonal climate in which the body does its work. By reducing stress, physical activity reduces the secretion of stress hormones, and this lowers blood pressure. Physical activity also redistributes body water and eases transit of the blood through the peripheral arteries.

Salt, Sodium, and Blood Pressure

High dietary intakes of salt and sodium are associated with hypertension (also see section on sodium in Chapter 8 for information about the report from the multistakeholder "Working Group on Dietary Sodium Reduction"). As salt intakes decrease, blood pressure drops in a stepwise fashion.[78] This direct relationship is reported at all levels of intake, from very low to much higher than average. Although the benefit from reducing salt intake to prevent and treat hypertension is beyond question, some people respond to salt more sensitively, including those of African descent, people with a family history of hypertension, people with kidney problems or diabetes, and older people. People with hypertension often find that by lowering their salt (or sodium) intakes sufficiently, they can reduce or even eliminate blood pressure–reducing medication.[79] Increasing dietary potassium may also help heighten salt sensitivity in those who do not respond as vigorously to salt restriction alone.[80]

> Details concerning sodium, hypertension, and food sources of sodium were presented in Chapter 8.

The World Health Organization estimates that a significant reduction in sodium intake could reduce by half the number of people requiring therapy for hypertension and greatly reduce deaths from CVD. The recommendation of health professionals and agencies, based on available research, is that everyone should moderately restrict salt and sodium intake to a level not exceeding the DRI committee's Tolerable Upper Intake Level—that is, no more than 2,300 milligrams of sodium per day—and follow other standard dietary advice to help avoid hypertension.[81] In fact, the Canadian Stroke Network reminds us that an adequate intake of sodium for most adults is 1,500 mg or less per day (http://www.sodium101.ca/adultlimits). However, while there is still agreement among health professionals that dietary sodium levels need to be reduced, some controversy about the lower target levels for otherwise healthy individuals and those with various diseases has arisen since the release of the Institute of Medicine's (IOM) "Sodium Intake in Populations: Assessment of Evidence" (May 2013) report (http://www.iom.edu/~/media/Files/Report%20Files/2013/Sodium-Intake-Populations/SodiumIntakeinPopulations_RB.pdf). Thus, we will have to watch for further guidance from the various health agencies in this regard.

Alcohol

In moderate doses, alcohol initially relaxes the peripheral arteries and so reduces blood pressure, but high doses definitely raise blood pressure.[82] Hypertension is common among people with alcoholism and is apparently caused directly by the alcohol. Hypertension caused by alcohol leads to CVD, the same as hypertension caused by any other factor. Furthermore, alcohol may cause strokes—even *without* hypertension. Health Canada urges Canadians to take a sensible, moderate approach to alcohol consumption. *Moderation* means no more than one drink a day for women or two drinks a day for men, an amount that seems safe relative to blood pressure.

Calcium, Potassium, Magnesium, and Vitamin C

Other dietary factors may help regulate blood pressure. A diet providing enough calcium may be one such factor—increasing calcium often reduces blood pressure in both healthy people and those with hypertension. Indeed, leading North American researchers have suggested that an increase in milk consumption could significantly reduce hypertension and result in reduced health-care costs.[83] If you are concerned about your blood pressure, include more calcium-rich foods in your diet.

Adequate potassium and magnesium also appear to help prevent and treat hypertension in certain populations. Diets low in potassium-rich fruit and vegetables are often associated with hypertension, whereas diets adequate in such foods appear to both prevent and correct hypertension. Magnesium deficiency causes the walls of the arteries and capillaries to constrict and so may raise the blood pressure. Similarly, consuming a diet adequate in vitamin C (a water-soluble antioxidant) seems to help normalize blood pressure, while vitamin C deficiency may tend to raise it.[84]

Other dietary factors may also affect blood pressure; the roles of cadmium, selenium, lead, caffeine, protein, and fat are being studied. Vitamin supplements have not shown promise for lowering blood pressure in the long term.[85]

How can people be sure of getting all of the nutrients needed to keep blood pressure low? The best answer is to consume a low-fat diet with abundant fruit, vegetables, and low-fat dairy products that provide the needed nutrients while holding sodium intake in bounds. In addition to reducing blood pressure, a diet such as the DASH diet may also lower blood cholesterol values, providing a two-way benefit to the heart.[86]

The Food Feature in this chapter provides more details on dietary measures that help support normal blood pressure. Should diet and exercise fail to reduce blood pressure, drugs such as diuretics and other antihypertensive agents may be prescribed. Some of these work by increasing fluid loss in the urine, so they may also cause potassium losses. Chapter 8 specified foods that are rich in potassium, and people taking these drugs should make it a point to consume such foods daily.

People searching for an extra boost to health often combine nutrient supplements with herbs and other alternatives to mainstream medicine. The Consumer Corner in this chapter provides a look at some of these practices.

KEY POINT

- For most people, a healthy body weight, regular physical activity, consuming little sodium, moderation for those who use alcohol, and a diet high in fruit, vegetables, fish, and low-fat dairy products and low in fat work together to keep blood pressure normal.

use it! Consumer Corner

Alternative Therapies and Herbal Medicine

Where do you turn for help when illness strikes? Do you see a physician who offers treatment methods sanctioned by the established medical community? Or do you seek out a herbalist, an acupuncturist, or another practitioner of **alternative therapy**? As more people turn to alternative medicine, Canadian consumers are spending upward of $4 billion each year on such treatments.*,[1] Terms are defined in Table 11–6.

Some health-care professionals embrace certain helpful alternative therapies in their practices.[2] This open-minded approach, termed *complementary*

Consumer Corner references are listed separately at the end of the chapter.

medicine, often combines some humane elements of alternative therapies that fill emotional needs along with the best of proven scientific medicine, delivered by skilled physicians.

Unlike conventional therapies, alternative therapies have often been used for centuries but not all of them have been scientifically evaluated for safety or effectiveness.[3] Most medical schools in North America do not teach them, nor do most health insurance policies pay for them. Further, anyone can claim to be an expert in a "new" or "natural" therapy, and many practitioners act knowledgeable but are either misinformed or frauds (see Controversy 1).

Testimonials for mysterious "cures" by alternative therapies abound. The listener may think that unless the speaker is lying, the therapies really do cure diseases. But a third option also exists: remember from Chapter 1 that an ill person's belief in a treatment, even a placebo, often leads to physical healing.[4]

This is not to say that all alternative therapies are shams; several examples of effective therapies are described in this section. Nevertheless, the common belief that many of today's alternative therapies will become tomorrow's mainstream medicine is unfounded.

To tease apart potentially useful and safe alternative therapies from the

Table 11–6
Alternative Therapy Terms

- **acupuncture** (ak-you-punk-chur) a technique that involves piercing the skin with long, thin needles at specific anatomical points to relieve pain or illness. Acupuncture sometimes uses heat, pressure, friction, suction, or electromagnetic energy to stimulate the points.
- **alternative therapy** systems of theory and practice that have emerged independently of conventional biomedical approaches. Examples include acupuncture, biofeedback, chiropractic, faith healing, and many others. Also called alternative medical systems.
- **herbal medicine** use of herbs and other natural substances with the intention of preventing or curing diseases or relieving symptoms.

worthless or harmful, the Natural Health Products Directorate has regulations governing the content and claims for herbal and other supplements used in the practice of alternative medicine. Also, the prestigious U.S. National Institutes of Health established its National Center for Complementary and Alternative Medicine (NCCAM) and has found **acupuncture** useful for quelling nausea from surgery, cancer chemotherapy, and pregnancy and for relieving pain during dental procedures. Other potential uses include treating chronic headaches and migraines.[5] Acupuncture, when performed by skilled practitioners under sterile conditions, presents far less risk to the user than drugs used for these conditions.[6]

Dozens of **herbal medicines** contain effective natural drugs. For example, the resin called myrrh contains an analgesic (pain-killing) compound; white willow bark contains salicin, from which the acetylsalicylic acid in pain killers such as Aspirin is derived; the herb valerian contains a tranquillizing oil; senna leaves produce a powerful laxative. The World Health Organization currently recommends a herbal Chinese drug to developing nations of the tropics as an effective, important tool for combating malaria.*

*The herb is artemisinin (ar-TEM-is-in-in), derived from sweet wormwood.

Alternative Therapies and Herbal Medicine in Canada

Since the practice of health professions in Canada is regulated by the provinces, the regulation of groups that practise alternative therapies, such as naturopaths, varies from province to province. There is a growing trend to consider alternative practitioners, such as homeopaths, under health profession regulation to make them more accountable to the public. You can check the regulations for alternative therapists in your province or territory through its respective Ministry of Health website.

The federal Natural Health Products Directorate regulates the quality of natural health products and the claims that can be made for them. For current information about the regulations, check its website: http://www.hc-sc.gc.ca/dhp-mps/prodnatur/legislation/acts-lois/prodnatur/index_e.html.

Herbal medicines have several serious drawbacks, however. When analyzed, a majority of herb pills and supplements do not contain the species or the active ingredients stated on their labels.[7] Recently, researchers tested almost 900 samples of herbs and found that more often than not, the ingredients, potency, or variety differed significantly from the information on the labels.[†,8] Another example is *Aristolochia fangchi*, a herb that causes severe kidney damage and cancer. It was mistakenly included in Chinese herbal "weight reduction pills."[9] Some preparations may even include *Aristolochia* intentionally because no safety tests are required before herbs can be marketed.

Contamination can also be a problem. The heavy metal lead found in one herbal remedy reached

†The herbs tested included echinacea, St. John's wort, ginkgo biloba, garlic, saw palmetto, ginseng, goldenseal, aloe, Siberian ginseng, and valerian. For more information, see the website of the National Council Against Health Fraud at http://www.quackwatch.org.

toxic doses.[10] Mercury and arsenic detected in traditional Chinese herb balls for treating fever, rheumatism, and cataracts have exceeded the maximum allowable levels by 20,000 and 1,000 times, respectively. Interactions of herbs with medications are also common (see Chapter 14's Controversy).

Many people undergoing cancer treatments ask about the macrobiotic diet (see Controversy 6), a restrictive low-fat diet of grains, soy beans, and certain vegetables. The diet is promoted for curing diseases but has not been proven scientifically to be beneficial.[11] Indeed, research seems to weigh against its use, partly because this bulky, low-Calorie diet fails to provide the energy needed to battle cancer.[12]

To self-diagnose illnesses and then choose herbs for treatment is to invite problems. Few herbalists selling the pills base herbal therapy on botany, pharmacology, or human physiology but instead rely on hearsay and folklore to plan treatments. By delaying effective medical help, this dangerous choice may allow serious conditions time to worsen. Also, perilous mistakes with herbs are extraordinarily likely. For example, most mint is safe when brewed as tea, but some may contain highly toxic pennyroyal oil. Folk medicine urges parents to soothe a colicky baby with mint tea, but one concoction laden with pennyroyal was blamed for liver and neurological injuries to at least two infants, one of whom died. Table 11–7 lists some additional herbs and their potential actions.**

Intelligent, clear-minded people can fall for the allure of magical thinking when standard medical therapies fail. Many such consumers, loving life and desperate, fall prey to the worst kind of quackery on the feeblest promise of a cure.

**A reliable source of information about herbs is V. E. Tyler, Tyler's Honest Herbal: A Sensible Guide to the Use of Herbs and Related Remedies (New York: Pharmaceutical Products Press). Look for the latest edition.

Table 11–7

Selected Herbs: Their Effects and Hazards[a]

HAZARDOUS

- **belladonna** any part of the deadly nightshade plant; a fatal poison.
- **hemlock** any part of the hemlock plant, which causes severe pain, convulsions, and death within 15 minutes.
- **pennyroyal** relative of the mint family brewed as tea or extracted as oil; used as mosquito repellent, claimed to treat various conditions. Tea produced multiple organ failure in infants; 1/2 tsp of oil caused convulsions and coma; 2 tbs caused the death of an 18-year-old expectant mother within 2 h, despite hospitalization.

PROBABLY HAZARDOUS

- **chaparral** a herbal product made from ground leaves of the creosote bush and sold in tea or capsule form; supposedly, this herb has anti-oxidant effects, delays aging, "cleanses" the bloodstream, and treats skin conditions—all unproven claims. Chaparral has been found to cause acute toxic hepatitis, a severe liver illness. Deaths reported.
- **comfrey** leaves and roots of the comfrey plant; believed, but not proven, to promote cell proliferation. Toxic to the liver in doses ordinarily used. Deaths reported.
- **foxglove** a plant that contains a substance used in the heart medicine digoxin.
- **germander** an evergreen bush used in small quantities as a flavouring for alcoholic beverages. Recommended for gout and other ills, it causes often-irreversible liver damage and abnormalities. Deaths reported.
- **lobelia** (low-BEE-lee-uh) dried leaves and tops of lobelia ("Indian tobacco") plant used to induce vomiting or treat a cough; abused for a mild euphoria. Causes breathing difficulty, rapid pulse, low blood pressure, diarrhea, dizziness, and tremors. Possible deaths reported.
- **sassafras** root bark from the sassafras tree; once used in beverages but now banned as an ingredient in foods or beverages because it contains cancer-causing chemicals.

COULD BE HAZARDOUS

- **echinacea** (EK-eh-NAY-see-ah) a herb popular before the advent of antibiotics for its "anti-infectious" properties and as an all-purpose remedy, especially for colds and allergy and for healing of wounds. Research is mixed on these claims. An insecticidal property opens questions about safety. Also called coneflower.
- **ginkgo biloba** an extract of a tree of the same name, claimed to enhance mental alertness but not proven to be effective or safe.
- **ginseng** (JIN-seng) a plant root containing chemicals that have stimulant drug effects. Ginseng abuse syndrome is a group of symptoms associated with the overuse of ginseng, including high blood pressure, insomnia, nervousness, confusion, and depression.

- **kombucha** (KOM-boo-sha) a product of fermentation of sugar-sweetened tea by various yeasts and bacteria. Proclaimed as a treatment for everything from AIDS to cancer but lacking scientific evidence. Microorganisms in home-brewed kombucha have caused serious illnesses in people with weakened immunity. Also known as Manchurian tea, mushroom tea, or Kargasok tea.
- **skullcap** a native herb with no known medical uses but found in remedies. Other species may be harvested and sold as skullcap, so it has not been determined whether several deaths from liver toxicity reportedly from skullcap were, in fact, from another herb.

HAZARD UNDEFINED

- **aloe** a tropical plant with widely claimed value as a topical treatment for minor skin injury. Some scientific evidence supports this claim; evidence against its use in severe wounds also exists.
- **cat's claw** a herb from the rainforests of Brazil and Peru; claimed, but not proven, to be an "all-purpose" remedy.
- **chamomile** flowers that may provide some limited medical value in soothing menstrual, intestinal, and stomach discomforts.
- **feverfew** a herb sold as a migraine headache preventive. Some evidence exists to support this claim.
- **kava** the root of a tropical pepper plant, often brewed as a tea consumed for its calming effects. Limited scientific research supports use for anxiety relief. Adverse effects include skin rash, liver abnormalities, lethargy, and mental disorientation.
- **kudzu** a weedy vine, whose roots are harvested and used by Chinese herbalists as a treatment for alcoholism. Kudzu reportedly reduces alcohol absorption by up to 50% in rats.
- **saw palmetto** the ripe fruit or extracts of the saw palmetto plant. Claimed to relieve symptoms associated with enlarged prostate but reported as ineffective in research.
- **St. John's wort** a herb containing psychoactive substances that has been used for centuries to treat depression, insomnia, bedwetting, and "nervous conditions." Some scientific reports find St. John's wort equal in effectiveness to standard antidepressant medication for relief of depression. Long-term safety, however, has not been established.
- **valerian** a preparation of the root of a herb used as a sedative and sleep agent. Safety and effectiveness of valerian have not been scientifically established.
- **witch hazel** leaves or bark of a witch hazel tree; not proven to have healing powers.

[a]See also Table C7–2 of Controversy 7.

Sources: S. Foster and V. E. Tyler, Tyler's Honest Herbal: A Sensible Guide to the Use of Herbs and Related Remedies *(New York: Hawthorn Press, 2000); Twelve supplements you should avoid, Consumer Reports.org, May 2004, available at http://www.consumerreports.org; Boon, H. and Smith, M. 55 Most Common Medicinal Herbs, Second edition. Robert Roe Inc., Toronto, 2009.*

Nutrition and Cancer

cancer a disease in which cells multiply out of control and disrupt normal functioning of one or more organs.

Cancer ranks second only to heart disease and stroke as a leading cause of death and disability in Canada. Recent advances in early detection and treatment have transformed some potentially deadly cancers into curable diseases or treatable chronic illnes. The term *cancer survivor* has now all but replaced *cancer victim* when referring to a person with a diagnosis of cancer.[87]

Although the potential for cure is exciting, prevention of cancer remains far and away preferable. Can an individual's chosen behaviours affect the risk of contracting cancer? Probably. Inherited tendencies exert only a modest effect on most people's risk of cancer development.[88] Just a very few rare cancers are known to be caused by genetic inheritance alone and will appear in members of an affected family regardless of lifestyle choices. A few more are linked with viral infections, but far more often lifestyle and environmental factors come into play. For example, if everyone in Canada quit smoking right now and stayed quit, future total cancers would probably drop by a third. Another 15 percent may be preventable by preventing overweight and obesity.[89] Lack of physical activity almost certainly plays a role in the development of colon and breast cancer and probably contributes to others.[90]

Another 20 to 50 percent of total cancers are influenced by diet, and these relationships are the focus of this section. Dietary fat, meat, alcohol, excess Calories, and low intakes of fruit and vegetables have been the targets of much research with regard to the occurrence of cancer. Such constituents of the diet relate to cancer in several ways:

- Foods or their components may cause cancer.
- Foods or their components may promote cancer.
- Foods or their components may protect against cancer.

Also, for the person who has cancer, diet can make a crucial difference in recovery.

Research on diet and cancer remains challenging, and today's research methods are under scrutiny for refinement.[91] Some dietary and biological factors currently providing convincing or probable evidence of risk in relation to cancer causation or prevention are listed in Table 11–8.

- Environmental tobacco smoke (passive or secondhand smoke), overexposure to sun, infections, and exposure to water and air pollution or other toxic chemicals (possibly including pesticides that mimic estrogen in the body) are also responsible for a percentage of cancers.

Table 11–8

Factors Associated with Cancers at Specific Sites

	Convincing or Probable *Increased* Risk	Convincing or Probable *Decreased* Risk
Breast cancer (premenopausal)	Alcohol	Breastfeeding, body fatness
Breast cancer (postmenopausal)	Alcohol, body/abdominal fatness	Breastfeeding, physical activity
Colorectal cancer	Red and processed meat, body/abdominal fatness, alcohol	Foods containing dietary fibre, physical activity, garlic, diets high in calcium
Mouth and throat cancer	Alcohol	Fruit, nonstarchy vegetables
Esophagus cancer	Body, fatness, maté,* and alcohol	Fruit, nonstarchy vegetables
Liver cancer	Mould aflatoxin, alcohol	
Lung cancer	Beta carotene supplements (in smokers), arsenic in drinking water	Fruits
Pancreatic cancer	Body/abdominal fatness	Foods containing folate
Prostate cancer	Diets high in calcium	Foods containing lycopene, foods containing selenium
Stomach cancer	Salt, salted and salty foods	Fruit, nonstarchy vegetables, foods in the allium family (e.g., onion and garlic)

Source: This material has been adapted from the 2007 WCRF/AICR Report "Food, Nutrition, Physical Activity and the Prevention of Cancer: A Global Perspective." http://www.dietandcancerreport.org/ (accessed June 07, 2010). Please visit www.wcrf.org and www.aicr.org.

A herbal beverage in parts of South America that, while it is very hot, is drunk through a metal straw.

Nutrition and Cancer

Figure 11–9

Cancer Development

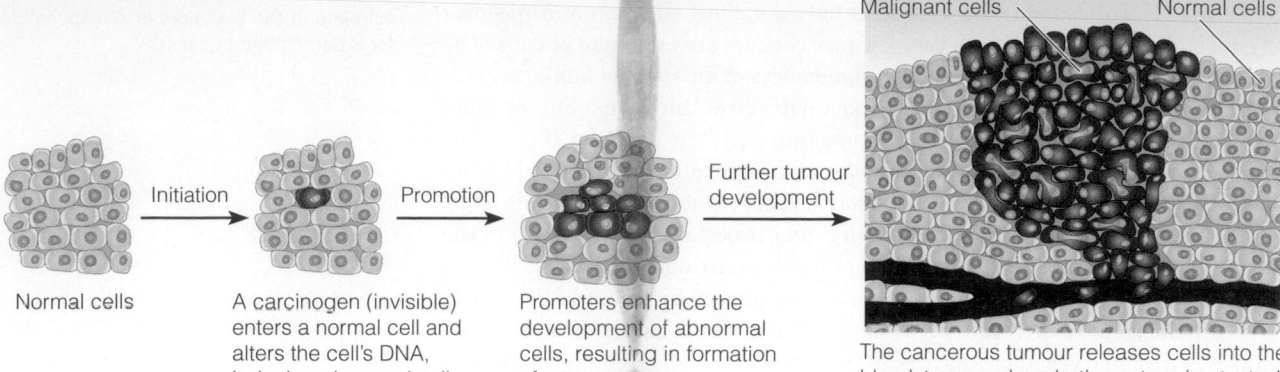

Normal cells → Initiation → A carcinogen (invisible) enters a normal cell and alters the cell's DNA, inducing abnormal cell division. → Promotion → Promoters enhance the development of abnormal cells, resulting in formation of a tumour. → Further tumour development → The cancerous tumour releases cells into the bloodstream or lymphatic system (metastasis).

Malignant cells   Normal cells

Some Selected Chemicals and Carcinogens That Occur Naturally in Breakfast Foods

- Coffee: acetaldehyde, acetic acid, acetone, atractylosides, butanol, cafestol palmitate, chlorogenic acid, dimethyl sulphide, ethanol, furan, furfural, guaiacol, hydrogen sulphide, isoprene, methanol, methyl butanol, methyl formate, methyl glyoxal, propionaldehyde, pyridine, 1,3,7,-trimethylxanthine

- Toast and coffee cake: acetic acid, acetone, butyric acid, caprionic acid, ethyl acetate, ethyl ketone, ethyl lactate, methyl ethyl ketone, propionic acid, valeric acid

Of course, consuming coffee, toast, and coffee cake does not elevate a person's risk of developing cancer because the body detoxifies small doses found in foods.

carcinogen (car-SIN-oh-jen) a cancer-causing substance (*carcin* means "cancer"; *gen* means "gives rise to").

initiation an event, probably occurring in a cell's genetic material, caused by radiation or by a chemical carcinogen that can give rise to cancer.

carcinogenesis the origination or beginning of cancer.

promoters factors that do not initiate cancer but speed up its development once initiation has taken place.

metastasis (meh-TASS-ta-sis) movement of cancer cells from one body part to another, usually by way of the body fluids.

How Does Cancer Develop?

Cancer arises as a disease of the genes.[92] It often begins when a cell's genetic material (DNA) sustains damage from a **carcinogen** such as a free-radical compound, radiation, or other influences. Such damage occurs every day, but most of the damage is quickly repaired. Sometimes DNA collects bits of damage here and there over time. Usually, if the damage cannot be repaired and the cell becomes unable to faithfully replicate its genome, the cell self-destructs, committing a sort of cellular suicide to avoid passing on the faulty genetic material to its progeny. Occasionally, a damaged cell loses its ability to self-destruct and also loses the ability to stop reproducing. It replicates uncontrollably, and the result is a mass of abnormal tissue—a tumour. Life-threatening cancer results when the tumour tissue overtakes the healthy organ in which it developed or disseminates its cells through the bloodstream to other parts of the body.

Simplified, cancer develops through the following steps (illustrated in Figure 11–9):

1. Exposure to a carcinogen

2. Entry of the carcinogen into a cell

3. **Initiation** of cancer as the carcinogen damages or changes the cell's genetic material **(carcinogenesis)**

4. Acceleration by other carcinogens, called **promoters**, so that the cell begins to multiply out of control—tumour formation

5. Often spreading of cancer cells via blood and lymph **(metastasis)**

6. Disruption of normal body functions

Researchers think that the first four steps, which culminate with tumour formation, are key to cancer prevention. On hearing this, many people mistakenly believe that they should avoid eating all foods that contain carcinogens. Doing so would be impossible, however, because most carcinogens occur naturally among thousands of other chemicals and nutrients the body needs. The body is well equipped to deal with the minute amounts of carcinogens occurring naturally in foods, such as those listed in the margin.

For those who suspect food additives of being carcinogenic, be assured that additives are held to strict standards, and no additive scientifically shown to cause cancer is approved for use in Canada. Contaminants that enter foods by accident or toxins that arise naturally, for example, when food becomes mouldy, may indeed be powerful carcinogens, or they may be converted to carcinogens during the body's attempts to metabolize them. Most such constituents are monitored in the Canadian food supply and are generally present, if at all, in amounts well below those that may pose significant cancer risks to consumers.

KEY POINT

- Cancer arises from genetic damage and develops in steps including initiation and promotion, which are thought to be influenced by diet. The body is equipped to handle tiny doses of carcinogens that occur naturally in foods.

Which Dietary Factors Most Influence a Person's Risk of Developing Cancer?

Almost certainly, diet substantially influences cancer development.[93] The cancer risk imposed by a food depends partly on the eater's genetic inheritance, and the relationships between the genes, foods, and cancer have yet to be clarified.[94] Studies of populations suggest that low rates of many, but not all, kinds of cancer correlate with intakes of fibre-rich fruit, vegetables, and whole grains, particularly whole wheat. Under study for possible effects regarding cancer are excess Calories, diets high in certain fats, daily use of alcohol, vitamins and minerals in foods and supplements, and diets in which meat plays a dominant role. The following sections explore current scientific thought on the effects of dietary constituents on cancer development.

Energy Balance Restricting energy intakes inhibits cancer formation. When Calorie intakes are reduced, cancer rates fall. In animal experiments, this **caloric effect** proves to be one of the most effective dietary interventions for cancer prevention. When researchers establish a cancer-causing condition and then restrict the energy in laboratory animals' feed, the onset of cancer in the restricted animals is delayed beyond the time when animals on normal feed have died. At the moment, no experimental evidence exists showing this effect in human subjects, but some population observations seem to imply that the effect seen in animals may hold true for human beings as well. This effect occurs only in cancer prevention; once started, cancer continues advancing even in a person who is starving.

It is also true that when Calorie intakes rise, cancer rates rise: excess Calories from carbohydrate, fat, and protein all raise cancer rates. The processes by which excess Calories may stimulate cancer development remain obscure. Obesity itself is clearly a risk factor for certain types of cancer (such as colon, breast in postmenopausal women, endometrial, kidney, and esophageal) and possibly other cancers (such as ovarian and prostate) as well.[95] The risk of cancer rises with BMI. In one study, cancer deaths among people with a BMI of 40 or above were more than 50 percent higher than among people with a BMI in the normal range.[96]

Physical activity to balance energy intake may lower the risk of developing some cancers.[97] People whose lifestyles include regular, vigorous physical activity have the lowest risk of colon cancer.[98] Physical activity may also protect against breast cancer by reducing body weight and by other mechanisms.[99]

Fat and Fatty Acids Laboratory studies using animals support the idea that high dietary fat intakes correlate with development of cancer. Simply feeding fat to experimental animals is not enough to get tumours started, however; an experimenter must also expose the animals to a known carcinogen. After that exposure, animals fed the high-fat diet develop more cancers faster than animals fed low-fat diets. Thus, fat appears to be a cancer promoter in animals.

In studies of human beings, however, evidence so far is mixed as to whether a diet high in fat promotes cancer.[100] Comparisons among world populations reveal that high-fat diets often, but not always, correlate with high cancer rates.[101] For example, early studies implicated a high-fat diet as a risk factor for breast cancer, but later studies seemed to reverse this idea. Today, scientific opinion is shifting back to probable culpability, particularly for saturated fat from red meats and high-fat dairy foods, in breast cancer causation.[102] The shift in opinion has come on the heels of a revelation that previous studies may have employed methods that failed to expose an existing link between saturated fats and breast cancer.[103]

Canadian Resources on Cancer

- Canadian Cancer Society website: http://www.cancer.ca
- Cancer Care Ontario, Insight on Cancer: News and information on nutrition and cancer prevention (e.g., practice guidelines and evidence-based summaries by disease), available at http://www.cancercare.on.ca

caloric effect the drop in cancer incidence seen whenever intake of food energy (Calories) is restricted.

Studying the effects of high fat intakes is complicated because an attribute of dietary fat is energy density—fat is extremely Calorie-dense. Because diets high in *Calories* do seem to promote cancer, especially in laboratory settings, researchers must untangle the effects of fat alone from those of the energy content of the diet.

Dietary fat also tends to oxidize when exposed to high cooking temperatures. When these oxidized fat compounds enter the body, they may set up a condition of oxidative stress that may trigger cancerous changes in the tissues of the colon and rectum. Finally, the type of fat in the diet may be important. Some laboratory evidence implicates omega-6 polyunsaturated fatty acids in cancer promotion while suggesting that omega-3 fatty acids from fish may protect against some cancers and may support recovery during treatment for cancer.[104] Moderation in fat intake and inclusion of several fish meals a week remain sound principles, if not for cancer protection then for the prevention of obesity and the protection of the heart.

Alcohol   Cancers of the head and neck correlate strongly with the combination of alcohol and tobacco use and with low intakes of green and yellow fruit and vegetables.

> Controversy 3 addressed the topic of alcoholic beverages and cancer risks.

Alcohol intake alone is associated with cancers of the mouth, throat, and breast, and alcoholism often damages the liver and precedes the development of liver cancer.

Smoked, Grilled, and Well-Done Meats   Evidence from population studies spanning the globe over a period of more than 20 years links diets high in red meat with a moderately elevated risk of developing cancer of the rectum and colon.[105] In particular, meats cooked to the crispy well-done stage may be at fault, especially in genetically susceptible men who smoke.[106]

Chemical reactions during browning of meat at high temperatures, which occurs in pan-frying, broiling, or grilling, form known carcinogens in the food. Meat drippings that fall and burn on hot coals also generate carcinogens that rise in smoke and stick to the food.* Eating smoked, grilled, charbroiled, or well-browned, well-cooked meats introduces carcinogens into the digestive system and may cause problems there. Once the chemicals are absorbed and enter the body, however, they are quickly captured and detoxified by the liver's competent detoxifying system.

Remember that correlation, even consistently evident in research, is not cause. Although certain foods may appear at the scene of the colon cancer crime, no one yet knows whether eating such foods actually causes cancer or whether some other feature of a meat-rich diet is at fault. Still, health-savvy diners replace most servings of red meats with poultry, fish, or legumes and choose well-done, grilled, fried, highly browned, and smoked meats only occasionally.

Acrylamide   Potatoes and other carbohydrate-rich foods develop a by-product, **acrylamide**, during high-temperature cooking, such as frying or conventional baking. Acrylamide results from a chemical reaction between the naturally occurring sugars and an amino acid in the food. High doses cause cancer in laboratory animals and are toxic to the human nervous system, but no one yet knows if acrylamide in amounts common in foods affects human beings. Health Canada is currently investigating exposure of Canadian consumers to acrylamide, while the World Health Organization urges consumers to take a cautious approach and limit their intakes of carbohydrate-rich foods cooked at excessively high temperatures, such as French fries and fried snack chips, and baked goods that are overly browned.[107]

Fibre and Fluid   Epidemiological studies often report links between eating plenty of fruit and vegetables (both good sources of fibre and fluid) and a low incidence of many cancers. While the reason for this association is not fully understood, Health Canada recently allowed the use of the following diet-related health claim linking vegetable and fruit consumption and cancer: "A healthy diet rich in a variety of vegetables and fruit may help reduce the risk of some types of cancer." One prominent theory is that

acrylamide (ah-KRILL-ah-mide) a chemical produced in carbohydrate-rich foods, such as potatoes and grains, when cooked at high temperatures. A known animal carcinogen, acrylamide is also toxic to the nervous system of both animals and humans. Also used in manufacturing and construction.

---

*The carcinogens of greatest concern are some of those called *heterocyclic amines*.

a fibre-rich diet may protect against some cancers by increasing stool weight, diluting the colon's contents, stimulating bacterial fermentation, and speeding up the transit time of materials through the colon, thus minimizing exposure of the colon walls to cancer-causing substances in the feces. Bacterial fermentation also produces fatty acids that nourish the cells that line the colon, improving their resistance to cancerous changes. Some well-designed studies have reported no effect of high-fibre diets against colon cancer, but more recent evidence from Europe vindicates fibre in this regard.[108] Over half a million people in European countries were studied for over six years. The researchers concluded that populations with lower-than-average fibre intakes were at a greatly increased risk of cancers of the colon and rectum and that they could reduce that risk by 40 percent by doubling their fibre intakes from fruit, vegetables, grain foods, and legumes. A respected medical group concurs that the majority of the evidence supports a role for fibre-rich diets as protective against colorectal cancer.[109]

Evidence weighs in favour of eating high-fibre, low-fat foods such as whole grains for many reasons. Such foods may not only reduce the risk of some cancers but also protect health in these ways:

- The breakdown of fibres of whole grains by digestive tract bacteria yields short-chain fatty acids thought to offer some protection against heart disease as well as cancers.

- High-fibre diets help regulate blood glucose and blood insulin, factors that may also play roles in cancer development.

- Whole grains are rich in antioxidants and other phytochemicals that reduce oxidative stress and promote overall health.[110]

If a meat-rich, Calorie-dense diet is implicated in causation of certain cancers and if a vegetable-rich, whole-grain-rich diet is associated with prevention, then shouldn't vegetarians have a lower incidence of those cancers? They do, as the many studies cited in Controversy 6 have shown.

One type of cancer, bladder cancer, may be related to intake of fluids. Men who drink about 10 cups of fluid a day have been reported to develop substantially less bladder cancer than those drinking only about half this amount.[111] The most probable explanation involves carcinogens that form naturally in urine. A greater fluid intake dilutes these carcinogens and causes more frequent urination, thus reducing the likelihood that carcinogens will interact with the tissues of the bladder. Plain water seems most beneficial in this regard, but almost any kind of fluid, save one kind, will do. The exception is alcoholic beverages, which increase the risks of many cancers.

Folate and Other Vitamins   Folate deficiency seems to make cancers of the cervix and colon more likely, and ample folate may ward off other cancers in certain populations.[112] Up to 10 percent of the Canadian population and a much larger percentage of people with low incomes consume a diet low enough in folate to cause breaks in DNA that make cancer likely to develop.[113] This reason alone is enough to warrant everyone attending to folate intake.

> Chapters 7 and 13 give other compelling reasons to attend to folate needs.

Vitamin A regulates aspects of cell division and communication that go awry in cancer, and it helps maintain the immune system. Immune system cells can often identify cancerous cells and destroy them before cancer can develop. Vitamin D and exposure to sunshine have long been suggested as protective against cancers other than skin cancer, but the relationship is not clearly defined.[114] Cancer-opposing roles have also been suggested for vitamin B_6, vitamin B_{12}, and pantothenic acid.

Vitamin E, vitamin C, and beta-carotene received attention in Controversy 7. Suffice it to say here that taking supplements has not been proven to prevent or cure cancer. In fact, once cancer is established, antioxidants may do more harm than good according to a current line of investigation. Immune system cells normally release oxidative free radicals in an oxidative burst to kill off potentially dangerous microorganisms and cancer cells. Research suggests that some cancer cells may selectively stockpile antioxidants to defend against oxidative assaults from the immune

Often whole foods like these, not individual chemicals, lower people's cancer rates.

system.[115] Researchers found that when mice with brain tumours were fed anti-oxidant-depleted chow, the tumour growth slowed and cancer cells died off at a rapid rate.[116] Whether this intriguing laboratory finding translates into useful information for fighting cancer in people remains to be seen.

Calcium and Other Minerals   Laboratory evidence suggests that a high-calcium diet may help prevent colon cancer. Supplemental calcium seems to suppress changes in the lining of the colon associated with the onset of cancerous changes. In laboratory experiments, human colon cancer cells replicate rapidly when deprived of calcium but slow their replication when calcium is restored.[117] The findings from epidemiological studies are mixed, but a recent review of the literature indicated that, overall, people who develop colon cancer consume less calcium than people who do not develop the cancer.[118] Together, these studies have not yet proven that one can avoid colon cancer by increasing calcium intake, but with all of the other points in calcium's favour, prudence dictates that everyone should arrange to meet calcium needs every day.

For years, iron has been the subject of research with regard to colon cancer. A recent review revealed that the majority of studies since 1990 confirm an association between colon cancer and both increased dietary iron intake and high body iron stores.[119] Whether iron increases a person's risk for colon cancer may depend on whether the person has inherited a tendency to store too much iron (a relatively common genetic trait), the person's gender (being female may be protective), and the degree of iron supplementation (higher intake poses greater risk).

How iron may facilitate cancer remains unanswered. Iron is a powerful oxidizing substance, and oxidation may damage DNA in ways that initiate cancer. Alternatively, iron supplements are constipating, and constipation also raises a person's risk of colon cancer. Also, meat is a generous supplier of iron in the diet, and high-meat diets often correlate with colon cancer. These findings have scientists questioning the wisdom of widespread enrichment of breads, cereals, and other grains with iron from a public health point of view. If the iron and cancer link holds up to further scrutiny, the benefits of enrichment to iron-deficient populations must be weighed against the harm to those prone to colorectal cancer.[120] Other minerals in foods, including zinc, copper, and selenium, are thought to play roles in cancer prevention, perhaps by helping antioxidant enzymes defend against its initiation.

Foods and Phytochemicals   In the end, whole foods and whole diets composed of them, not single nutrients, may be most influential on cancer development. For example, the phytochemicals of some fruit and vegetables are thought to be **anticarcinogens**. Some of these may protect against cancer by acting as mild toxins that force the body to build up its arsenal of carcinogen-destroying enzymes. Then, when a potent carcinogen arrives, the prepared body deals with it swiftly. Almost without exception, population studies find that diets lacking green and yellow fruit and vegetables and citrus fruit correlate with cancers of many types. Some evidence suggests that a number of antioxidant nutrients and phytochemicals from a diet rich in fruit, vegetables, and whole grains may be necessary to minimize DNA damage from certain types of radiation, at least in the laboratory.[121] A low intake of fruit and vegetables may also leave cells unprotected against DNA damage in the initiation of bladder and other cancers.[122] Infrequent use of **cruciferous vegetables**—broccoli, Brussels sprouts, cabbage, cauliflower, turnips, and the like—is common in colon cancer victims (see the margin).

One review of the literature found an almost unheard-of perfect association between reduced incidence of lung cancer and diets high in fruit and vegetables—every study included in the review reported a protective effect. The incidence of stomach cancer, too, correlates with too few vegetables in the diet: in one study, with vegetables in general; in another, with fresh vegetables; and in others, with lettuce and other fresh greens or vegetables containing vitamin C. Unfortunately, adults in Canada are slow to get the message (see Figure 11–10).

Foods that contain phytochemicals are believed to promote health and fight diseases. Such foods are often called *functional foods*, for which there is no universal definition; however, Health Canada defines them as "similar in appearance to, or may

● Cruciferous vegetables belong to the cabbage family: bok choy, broccoli, broccoli sprouts, Brussels sprouts, cabbages (all sorts), cauliflower, greens (collard, mustard, turnip), kale, kohlrabi, rutabaga, and turnip root.

anticarcinogens compounds in foods that act in any of several ways to oppose the formation of cancer.

cruciferous vegetables vegetables with cross-shaped blossoms—the cabbage family. Their intake is associated with low cancer rates in human populations. Examples include broccoli, Brussels sprouts, cabbage, cauliflower, rutabagas, and turnips.

be, a conventional food that is consumed as part of a usual diet, and is demonstrated to have physiological benefits and/or reduce the risk of chronic disease beyond basic nutritional functions." In addition, Agriculture and Agri-Food Canada provides more than a dozen examples of functional food components, such as lycopene, omega-3 fatty acids, probiotic organisms, and their potential benefits (see http://www4.agr .gc.ca/AAFC-AAC/display-afficher.do?id=1171305207040&lang=eng). Controversy 2 explored the state of the science concerning functional foods and their phytochemical constituents. This chapter's Food Feature lists dietary guidelines for cancer prevention.

- Diets high in certain fats and red meats are associated with cancer development. Foods containing ample fibre, folate, calcium, many other vitamins and minerals, and phytochemicals, along with an ample intake of fluid, are thought to be protective.

Conclusion

Nutrition is often associated with promoting health and medicine with fighting disease, but no clear line separates nutrition and medicine. Every major agency involved with health recommends a healthful diet as part of a lifestyle that provides the best possible chance for a long and healthy life.

This chapter has summarized the major forms of disease and their links with nutrition. You may have noticed a philosophical shift from previous chapters. There we could say that a deficiency of nutrient X causes disease Y. Here we could only cite theories and discuss research that illuminates current thinking. We can say with certainty, for example, that a diet lacking vitamin C causes scurvy, but to say that a low-fibre diet that lacks vegetables causes cancer would be inaccurate. We can, however, recommend behaviours that are prudent and increase your likelihood of a lifetime of good health. The Food Feature presents these recommendations.

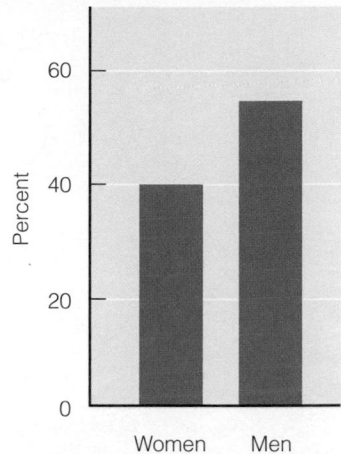

Figure 11–10

Percentage of Young Adults (Aged 19–30) Consuming Recommended Amounts of Fruit and Vegetables a Day

Source: Data from Statistics Canada, Garriguet, Didier; Nutrition: Findings from the Canadian Community Health Survey Catalogue no.: 82-620-MIE2006002, July 6, 2006. Reproduced and distributed on an "as is" basis with the permission of Statistics Canada.

---

try it!
Food Feature
Diet as Preventive Medicine

A remark by a former U.S. surgeon general is worth repeating: If you do not smoke or drink excessively, "your choice of diet can influence your long-term health prospects more than any other action you might take." Indeed, healthy young adults today are privileged to be the first generation in history with enough knowledge now to lay a foundation for healthy years ahead through a lifetime of proper nutrition. Figure 11–11 illustrates this point.

An early chapter of this book presented dietary guidelines for the prevention of diseases. Chapters that followed focused on the "whys" and "hows" of those guidelines. This Food Feature comes full circle to revisit the guidelines with a broader and deeper understanding to aid the reader in applying them meaningfully, as they were intended.

Dietary Guidelines for Disease Prevention

The more detailed our knowledge about nutrition science, it seems, the simpler the truth becomes: people who consume the moderate, adequate, balanced, Calorie-controlled diet recommended by Health Canada and health associations (see Table 11–9, page 489) may enjoy a longer, healthier life than those who do not.[123] They all offer suggestions for disease prevention. Table 11–9 presents guidelines from these sources and shows how similar they are, clinching the argument that it's time to get busy putting the recommendations into practice. The following paragraphs review the specifics.

Reduce Saturated Fat and *Trans* Fat Intake

Primary among the recommendations is to choose unsaturated fats in place of saturated fat and *trans* fat. To meet this goal requires people to limit such foods as high-fat milk and dairy products, stick margarine, high-fat baked goods and convenience foods, foods with high-fat creams and gravies, commercially fried foods, fat-marbled meat cuts, sausages, and fatty ground beef.

Conversely, foods such as nuts, olive oil, canola oil, and liquid margarines are

Figure 11–11

Proper Nutrition Shields against Diseases

A well-chosen diet can protect your health.

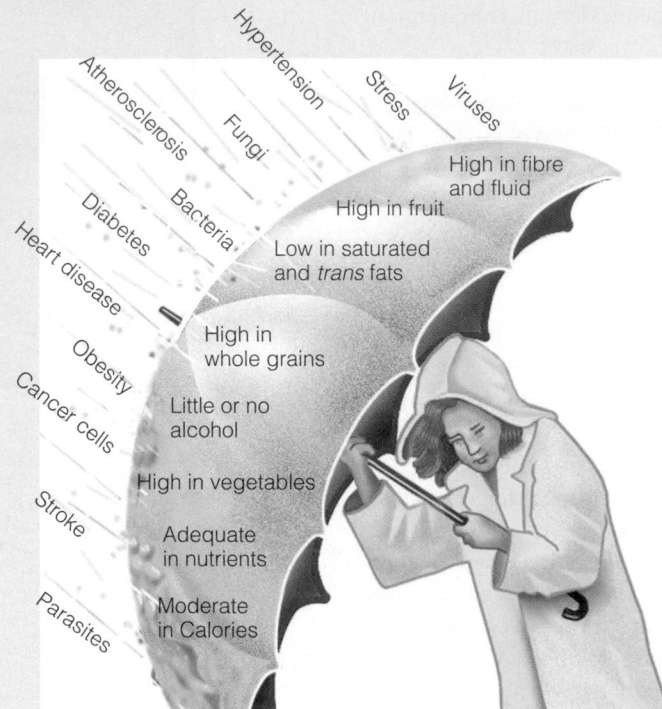

Who knows? Some of the foods still waiting for you on the produce shelves may become your favourites. An adventurous spirit is a plus in this regard.

As for whole grains, most guidelines call for their inclusion, but the authors of this book would go a step farther and ask that whole grains make up the majority of your grain choices. That way, the grain foods you consume daily will supply nutrients, fibre, and nonnutrients associated with good health.

Go for Variety

Eat foods high in potassium (fruit and vegetables), high in calcium and magnesium (milk products and appropriate substitutes), low in fat, high in fibre (whole grains, legumes, vegetables, and fruit), and ample in fluids. If you are prone to hypertension, experts advise that you eat fewer high-sodium foods and less salt.

Advice on varying your diet is based on an important concept in the prevention of cancer initiation—dilution. Whenever you switch from food to food, you are diluting whatever is in one food with what is in the others. It is safe to eat some salty foods or smoked or grilled meats, but don't eat them all the time.

Be Physically Active

Expend energy in daily physical activity that you enjoy. If the threat of CVD doesn't motivate you, then exercise to improve your self-image, to improve your morale, to control your body weight, to improve your complexion, or to make friends—but do exercise.

In the end, people's choices are their own. Whoever you are, we encourage you to take the time to work out ways of making your diet meet the guidelines you know will support your health. If you are healthy and of normal weight, if you are physically active, and if your diet on most days follows the guidelines just provided, then you can indulge occasionally in a cheesy pizza, marbled steak, a banana split, or even a greasy fast-food burger and fries without inflicting much damage on your health. (Once a week may be harmless, but the

high in polyunsaturated fats that supply the essential fatty acids and vitamin E. Because they are high in Calories, use them only within your daily energy budget. Regular meals of fish, particularly fatty fish such as salmon, help balance intakes of omega-6 and omega-3 fatty acids. For the type of fatty acids present in your favourite foods, visit the Canadian Nutrient File 2010 at http://www.hc-sc.gc.ca/fn-an/nutrition/fiche-nutri-data/index-eng.php.

Include Fruit, Vegetables, and Whole Grains

Every legitimate source of dietary advice urges people to include a variety of fruit and vegetables in the diet, not just for nutrients but also for the phytochemicals that combine synergistically to promote health.[124] The Canadian "Reach for It" program encourages consumers to eat enough fruit and vegetables to support health, and some tips for doing so appear in the margin.

Eating Well with Canada's Food Guide

- Five or more vegetable and fruit Food Guide servings per day are recommended for those four years and up.
- It is also recommended that Canadians two years and up "Eat at least one green and one orange vegetable per day" and "Have vegetables and fruit more often than juice."

Source: Eating Well with Canada's Food Guide. Health Canada, 2008 <http://www.hc-sc.gc.ca/fn-an/food-guide-aliment/choose-choix/fruit/index_e.html>

Table 11–9

Examples of Canadian Dietary Guidelines for Adults to Prevent/Reduce the Risk of Disease

Food Components	Health Canada[a]	H&SFC[b]	CDA[c]	CCS[d]
Carbohydrate energy	45–65% of total energy		45–60% of total energy	
Total/added sugars	Limit to <25% of total energy	25–35 g/day	10% of total energy	
Fibre	1 g/100 Cal (25–35 g/d)		25–50 g/d from a variety of sources	Choose high-fibre foods (≥4 g/serving)
Fat energy	20–35% of total energy	20–35% of total energy	<35% of total energy	"Limit added fat to 35–45 mL (2–3 tbs) of healthy fat/d"
SAFA[e] & *trans* fats	"Keep as low as possible while consuming a nutritionally adequate diet"	"Canadians consume a healthy balanced diet that includes: . . lower amounts of *trans* and saturated fat"; replace artificial *trans* fat with a healthier alternative	"Saturated and polyunsaturated fats should each provide <10% of daily energy requirements"; "Use of processed foods containing saturated fats and *trans*-fatty acids should be limited"	"Choose healthy fats . . . saturated fats and *trans* fats (hydrogenated fats) are potentially harmful fats"
Protein energy	10–35% of total energy	10–35% of Calories from protein	10–20% of total energy	
Fish	"Eat at least two Food Guide servings of fish each week"	"Canadians consume a healthy, balanced diet that includes . . . more polyunsaturated fat, especially omega-3 fatty acids (fatty fish, flaxseed, canola oil . . .)"	"Fish rich in omega-3 fatty acids should be recommended at least once weekly"	
Vegetables & fruit	7–10 Food Guide servings per day	5–10 servings each day	"Eat at least one dark green and one orange vegetable each day"; "Have vegetables and fruit more often than juice"	". . . a diet high in non-starchy vegetables may reduce your risk of some types of cancer . . ."
Alcohol	<5% of total energy intake	". . . limit yourself to one to two standard drinks per day . . ."	". . . no more than 5% of total energy intake or two drinks per day, whichever is less"	"Keep it to less than 1 drink per day for women and 2 drinks per day for men"

[a]*Health Canada, http://www.hc-sc.gc.ca/index-eng.php.*
[b]Heart and Stroke Foundation of Canada, *http://www.heartandstroke.com/site/c.ikIQLcMWJtE/b.2796497/k.BF8B/Home.htm?src=home.*
[c]*Canadian Diabetes Association, http://guidelines.diabetes.ca.*
[d]*Canadian Cancer Society, http://www.cancer.ca/Canada-wide.aspx?sc_lang=en.*
[e]*Saturated fatty acid.*

Sources: Health Canada, http://www.hc-sc.gc.ca/index-eng.php; Heart and Stroke Foundation of Canada, http://www.heartandstroke.com/site/c.ikIQLcMWJtE/b.2796497/k.BF8B/Home.htm?src=home; Canadian Diabetes Association, http://www.diabetes.ca; Canadian Cancer Society, http://www.cancer.ca/Canada-wide.aspx?sc_lang=en

less frequently the better.) Especially, take time to enjoy your meals: the sights, smells, and tastes of good foods are among life's greatest pleasures. Joy, even the simple joy of eating, contributes to a healthy life.

 Tips for Consuming More Fruit and Vegetables

- Vow to try a new fruit or vegetable once each month. Read some cookbooks for ideas.

- Eat a rainbow of fruit and vegetables: the more reds, oranges, yellows, greens, blues, and purples the better.
- Use the salad bar to buy ready-to-eat vegetables if you are in a hurry.

Exercise regularly, all of your life.

- Keep a fruit bowl in plain view, filled with fresh fruit, small raisin or dried cranberry packs, and shelf-stable fruit cups.

- Add dried fruit bits to salads, cereal, or yogurt.
- Place carrot and celery sticks in a glass of water like a bouquet and keep them in the refrigerator for crisp, healthy snacks.

- Try a grilled mushroom sandwich or "veggie burger" instead of a beef hamburger sandwich.

- Try using soy products in many ways. Soy drinks, ground and patty meat replacers, tofu, and soy snacks count as a vegetable and may offer unique benefits from soy protein, fibre, and phytochemicals.

- Drink 100 percent fruit or vegetable juices. Choose 100 percent juice bars for a frozen treat.

- Vegetable sauces count: 1/2 cup tomato spaghetti sauce or salsa counts as 1/2 cup "other vegetables" (see Chapter 2's Food Feature).

- Blend smoothies from bananas, fruit juice, and berries with ice or yogurt.

- Choose larger portions of lower-Calorie vegetables, such as cooked leafy greens or carrots.

- Add beans to salads, stews, and meat dishes. Beans soak up the flavour of meat and stretch the servings per pound.

CONTROVERSY 11

The Obesity Epidemic—How Can We Gain Control?

What if tomorrow's headlines read, "Overweight and obesity vanquished—population freed of overweight"? On that day, an estimated 14 million people would be freed from the threat of serious illness associated with obesity—heart disease, diabetes, arthritis, cancer, and others.[*,1] An estimate of the combined direct and indirect costs of obesity in Canada in 2008 was $4.8 billion.[2]

*Controversy references are listed separately at the end of the chapter.

Sadly, real headlines tell of rising rates of obesity (described in Chapter 9) that cost individuals and society dearly. How did we get into this predicament? And what can we do to get out of it?

Why Has Our Society Become Obesity-Prone?

A number of societal changes over the last 50 years have been suggested as factors driving the obesity epidemic in North America.[3] Together, these trends seem to add up to what has been called an "obesity-promoting/obesogenic environment" (see Figure C11–1).

Today, many people regularly overeat on large portions of inexpensive high-Calorie foods, consuming about 500 Calories per day more than in 1970.[4] At the same time, they have grown accustomed to leisure time in front of DVDs, videos, computers, or television sets; labour-saving devices such as automobiles and elevators; and jobs requiring more sitting than moving. Most do not exercise enough to maintain health and fitness (see Chapter 10), and, based on data from the 2007–2008 CCHS, about half (48%) of adult Canadians were considered moderately physically active.[5] Then, as they gain weight and lose fitness, stress and sleep disturbances creep into their lives, and they feel increasingly exhausted and less motivated to move.

The problem can worsen if a chronically tired person seeks relief by self-medicating with caffeine, medicines, weight-loss pills, high-Calorie "energy" foods and drinks, other inappropriate supplements, alcohol, tobacco, or other drugs. Although some of these drugs may provide some relief in the short term, none solve the problems of too little exercise and too many Calories from food.

As Chapter 9 made clear, some people's genetic inheritance lays the foundation for obesity, but such tendencies remain silent unless conditions are right to support weight gain.[6] Further, the obesity-prone individual makes free-will choices each day. Personal choices leading to overweight, however, may be so heavily influenced by societal conditions that such choices become less free than most people assume.

Changing Physical Activity

Throughout history, human beings have aspired to make physical work easier and increase leisure time. Over the years, technological advances have relieved people of much of the labour of planting and harvesting food; walking or running long distances, hauling water; and, in fact, performing most of life's basic physical tasks. One famous obesity researcher had this to say about our progress in making life easier: "The war on muscular work has been a remarkable success."[7] Some researchers assign the lion's share of blame for increasing national body weights on decreasing energy expenditure.[8]

Today, most people take labour-saving inventions for granted. Builders design automobile-dependent communities that feature efficient roadways but no sidewalks. Urban sprawl locates shopping malls and workplaces within commuting distances, but not within walking or biking distances, from residences. Relatives and friends may live at great distances. Buildings have conveniently located elevators but often hide stairwells from view. Consumers who choose to walk to work or use the stairs may find that these are inconvenient and unpleasant options. Roadways are often smelly, unattractive, and hazardous for pedestrians; stairwells are often stuffy and rarely cleaned. While labour-saving advances have no doubt liberated many human hours for intellectual and leisure

Figure C11–1

Obesity-Promoting/Obesogenic Environment

This environment promotes a sedentary lifestyle and overconsumption of high-energy foods.

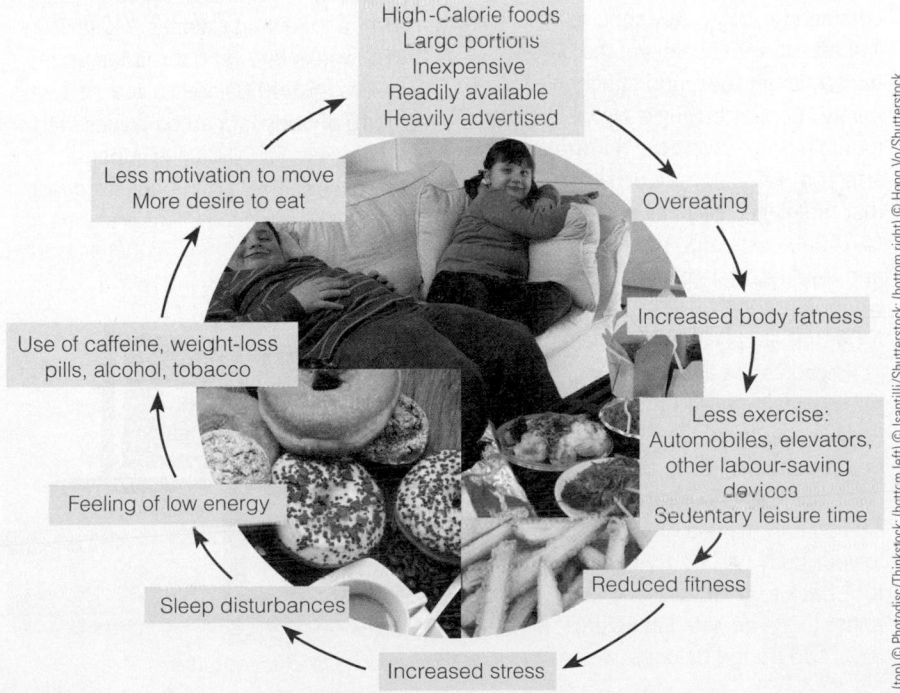

High-Calorie foods
Large portions
Inexpensive
Readily available
Heavily advertised

Overeating

Increased body fatness

Less exercise:
Automobiles, elevators,
other labour-saving
devices
Sedentary leisure time

Reduced fitness

Increased stress

Sleep disturbances

Feeling of low energy

Use of caffeine, weight-loss
pills, alcohol, tobacco

Less motivation to move
More desire to eat

pursuits, their costs in terms of human health are only now being counted in full.

Changing Home Life

Changes in the family structure have influenced people's food intakes over the past four decades. By one estimate, the diet changed more over the last half of the 20th century than in any other comparable period of human existence.[9] As more women have entered the workforce and as the hours worked by all wage earners have increased, families have less time for the traditional activities of homemaking, including meal planning, grocery shopping, and the labour-intensive preparation of meals of fresh foods. Consequently, more and more people rely on prepared or partially prepared foods to save time and effort at home. The enormous popularity of prepared foods speaks of the need for them.

Today's meals are often unplanned and are influenced more by which foods are familiar, readily available, moderately priced, and easy to prepare than by the nutrient needs of the purchasers. Chapter 1 pointed out that the farm-fresh foods consumed most often in the middle of the last century have largely been replaced by foods processed to some extent for convenience. Along with convenience, however, manufacturers often include flavourful ingredients such as salt, sugar, and fat and remove constituents such as fibre.

Thus, in exchange for convenience, the purchaser of prepared foods relinquishes to the food industry responsibility for the Calorie and nutrient content of the food. Whether the industry can be trusted to act in the consumer's best interest is a question worth considering.[10]

The Changing Food Supply

The majority of Canadians are still ordering takeout or home-delivered meals once or less per week (see Figure C11–2).[11] But with more and more of the Canadian diet originating with the food industry, nutritionists have

no doubt that this trend powerfully influences the health of the nation.

The "Buy More" Strategy

Everyone already eats some kind of food every day. To increase food sales, therefore, marketers must convince us to buy their brand over others or, if we already choose it, to buy more of it.[12] The fight for brand loyalty is fierce, and much of it is aimed at children, as a later section shows. A proven strategy for prodding consumers to buy more is to appeal to their economic sense.

Thanks largely to technological advances in agriculture, a restaurant often spends less on the food it serves than on most other expenses, such as personnel, facility, or monthly utilities. The strategy of offering more food for just a little more money at each selling opportunity therefore pays off in greater profits. To a consumer making choices at a food counter, a deal often seems sweeter if significantly more food can be obtained for only a few cents more—"for just an extra 99 cents, get the bigger burger, larger fries, and super cola." A thirsty shopper buying a big 591-millilitre fountain drink (twice the normal serving size and 300 Cal) for a dollar may find that the bigger 950-millilitre drink (470 Cal) costs only 10 cents more and that the best "bargain" is a whopping 1,370-millilitre drink (700 Cal) at only 19 cents more.

Portion sizes and obesity rates have increased proportionally over the years.[13] If you doubt that small daily decisions such as choosing a larger serving can make a difference to your body weight, try this: turn back to Chapter 2 and look at the foods depicted in Figure 2–9. Add up the Calories in a

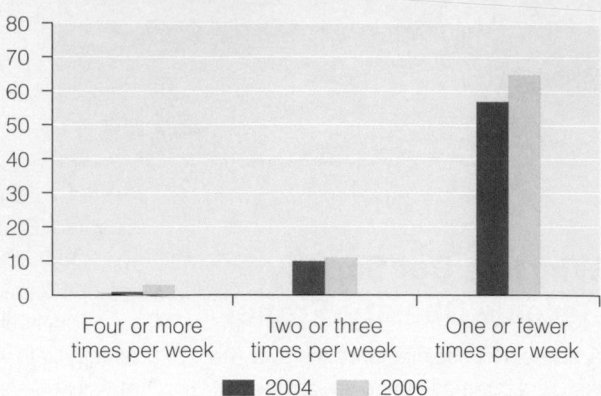

Figure C11–2

Percentage of Canadians Ordering Takeout or Home-Delivered Meals

Source: Data from Canadian Council of Food and Nutrition, Tracking Nutrition Trends VI *Woodbridge, Ontario, 2006.*

1970s hamburger, cola, and French fries (similar to today's "small" sizes). Do the same for the Calories in the "colossal" hamburger, cola, and French fries typical of today's meals.

Now find the Calorie difference between the two meals (subtract the smaller sum from the larger) and multiply the difference by 52 (for weeks in a year):

Today's Calorie total	=	2,020
–1970s Calorie total	=	925
Calorie difference	=	1,095

The difference between the two meals is over a thousand Calories. Multiplied by 52 weeks in a year, this adds up to an extra 56,940 Calories a year. If 1 kg (2.2 lb) of body fat can be gained with each excess 7,700 Calories, then a person who chooses a larger-sized fast-food meal *just once per week* stands to

A scientifically accurate food advertisement.

gain about 7.4 kilograms (16 lb) of body fat in a year's time. Many little daily decisions such as this add up over time.

Along with restaurant food, prepared food has also gotten larger, and most common servings exceed recommended portion sizes, sometimes by a huge margin,[14] for example, pasta, muffins, steaks, bagels, beer, and pizza. The single food reportedly still in compliance with its standard is a slice of white bread.

One source of this trend may be some recent initiatives by marketers to stimulate consumers to buy more food, thus increasing food company profits. An article with the headline "Can Package Size Accelerate Usage Volume?" outlines the strategy of increasing package sizes of pasta to increase sales.[15] A study reports that larger pasta packages prompt consumers to cook more pasta at a meal—a good result for those selling pasta. The probable fate of the extra cooked pasta was explained in Chapter 9: when presented with greater quantities of food, people eat more at a sitting.[16] Sales of candy and popcorn work the same way: the bigger the container, the larger the portion consumers will buy and eat and the higher the profits to the seller.[17]

Overall, food supersizing strategies seem to be a tremendous financial success wherever they are employed. And the effect is not all one sided: as consumers gradually adapt to larger portions, they put pressure on the food industry to supply more and more food per serving to remain competitive. All the while, obesity is skyrocketing.

Marketing to Children

In North America, the food industry spends over $10 billion annually promoting high-Calorie fast foods, fried snack foods, high-sugar cereals, candies, and soft drinks during children's television viewing hours and in other media.[18] The food industry vigorously pursues the attention of children, spurred by the influence of children on a huge portion of spending in the United States—up to $6 billion of their own pocket money each year and $132 billion more in annual family spending.[19]

A spokesperson for a commercial watchdog group speaking to the World Health Organization delineated the techniques used to sell foods and other products to youth.[20] These include manipulating children's emotional and physical needs, such as their needs for peer acceptance, love, safety, and security and their desire to be independent, to act older, and to develop an identity. Advertising agencies hire educated, talented, creative university graduates who draw on child psychology to develop effective ads. The speaker added this: "Advertisers are so successful at marketing to youth that they sometimes discuss it in terms of the battle over what they chillingly call 'mind share.'"

Some children are a captive audience for commercials brought into their classrooms in the United States by a media service that provides "free" programming to schools, paid for by selling children's classroom time to advertisers.[21] Such companies market fried snack food, fast food, and high-Calorie soft drinks to students, 8 million of whom are forced to watch two minutes of such ads each school day.[22]

Do the ads work? Yes, they do. Otherwise, the billions of dollars spent annually on advertising to children would be spent elsewhere. According to the Dietitians of Canada's recent publication "Advertising of Food and Beverages to Children: Position of Dietitians of Canada," "There is sufficient evidence to support the need for an integrated, multi-sectoral approach to reduce the negative impact of food and beverage advertising on children as one factor influencing the healthy growth and development of children and as a component of children's rights to adequate, safe and nutritious foods" (http://www.dietitians .ca/Downloadable-Content/Public/ Advertising-to-Children-position-paper .aspx; also, see "Advertising to Children in Canada: A Reference Guide," available at http://www.cab-acr .ca/english/social/advertisingchildren/ kids_reference_guide.pdf).

The Food Industry Speaks Out

The food industry has much to fear from accusations that its high-Calorie products and selling tactics are fuelling the obesity epidemic. Public sentiment that the industry is harming consumers for the sake of profits could direct consumer dollars elsewhere. Also, many food companies fear lawsuits that could force them to pay enormous settlements if, like tobacco firms, they are found culpable in causing harm to consumers. Finally, there is the matter of pride: many long-established food companies take pride in their traditions and products— providing the best pies and cookies, the finest steaks, or the most delicious doughnuts to consumers who are eager for them. Such companies hold that their primary goal is to meet the changing desires and demands of their customers.

Does the Food Industry Cause Obesity?

Is the food industry akin to tobacco companies in harming people's health? Products of both industries stand accused of causing illness. Both industries have marketed their wares to children. There is a difference, however. The evidence against tobacco smoke as a cause of such diseases as lung cancer and emphysema is ironclad, even when the products are used as intended. Individual foods, however, are unlikely to be found to cause obesity because many people eat them in moderation and remain lean. Tobacco smoke is a toxic, addictive, and unnecessary hazardous substance. Food is necessary for life, and even fast food provides some nutrients and seems tolerable by the healthy body when taken in moderation. Importantly, the food industry provides a service by preparing foods for today's families who cannot or choose not to prepare foods at home.

The arguments in defence of the food industry were summed up this way by the president of the U.S. national association representing restaurant owners: "Restaurants have a wide variety of choices on their menus, and people make the choice to eat what they want and when they want every day. This is all about personal responsibility and moderation."[23] Other spokespeople argue that the cause of obesity is North Americans' lack of exercise rather than the availability of certain food products or the prevalence of advertising.

New Menu of Choices

Many food companies have recently added lower-fat, lower-Calorie products to their lines, while a few others have eliminated the largest of the overlarge portion options, hoping to change the view that restaurant and convenience foods damage health. Fried chicken outlets now include baked chicken on the menu. Hamburger outlets now sport vegetarian burgers and salad options that cost no more than the standard chicken nuggets (made mostly of ground skin and breading) and fries. The food giant Kraft announced plans to offer more heart-healthy options in its food line. Still, consumer choices determine whether the new offerings translate into healthier meals. KFC's Double Down (bacon, processed cheese, and the Colonel's sauce "Sandwiched" between two seasoned chicken breasts) provides 540 Calories. A big or fancy hamburger can provide from 500 to 800 Calories, mostly from fat, with much of it saturated fat.* Plain, small, fast-food salads (no dressing) can be remarkably low in Calories, in the range of 100 to 300 Calories. A chef's salad without dressing provides 320 Calories. But served with toppings, such as bacon, cheese, chips, croutons, fried noodles, and sour cream, or drenched with the full one-third cup of oily dressing that comes with them, salads weigh in at 500 to 800 Calories—with enough fat and saturated fat to rival even the greasiest burgers.

*For a list of the restaurant chains participating in the Canadian Restaurant and Foodservices' Nutrition Information Program see http://www .crfa.ca/resources/nutritioninformationprogram/ participatingchains.asp.

Reasonable choices other than salads are available. One sandwich chain, Subway, has built its reputation on making available some low-Calorie sandwiches that can be used to support weight-loss efforts.[24] Other establishments, when asked, will omit fatty toppings from sandwiches and salads to produce a reasonably nutritious meal. The food industry states that such choices have always been available, but most people entering a fast-food restaurant associate these establishments with a chance to indulge. Only a few have the willpower to order slimmed-down offerings when familiar full-Calorie treats are within view and are the path of least resistance.

Can Government Actions Reverse Obesity Trends?

On learning of the obesity epidemic, people often respond by demanding that the government "do something" about it. Perhaps the current Food Guide is at fault, they say, or perhaps the *Dietary Guidelines* need a different focus. In truth, these documents and teaching tools are updated regularly and provide sound advice.

Many government resources and much private money are being spent on developing initiatives to reverse obesity in Canada.[25] However, in the United States, efforts to promote healthy weights are not too encouraging; for example, since 1950, at least 35 consumer education reports have specified sound weight-control practices as essential to maintenance of good health. Not one of these public health efforts has succeeded in slowing obesity rates in that country, however, so it seems unlikely that more reports and documents would be effective.[26] The U.S. Food and Drug Administration continues to make enhancements of food labels and in 2004 launched a "Calories Count" education campaign; the Obama administration launched the "Let's Move: America's Move to Raise a Healthier Generation of Kids" in February 2010.[27]

In the fall of 2005, the federal, provincial, and territorial ministers of health responsible for sport and recreation fitness approved "The Integrated Pan-Canadian Healthy Living Strategy," which includes a new set of targets for increases in healthy eating, physical activity, and healthy weights by 2015 (http://www.phac-aspc.gc.ca/hp-ps/ hl-mvs/ipchls-spimmvs). See the sidebar on page 420.

Previous initiatives that focused on individual responsibility failed to acknowledge the societal factors that erect barriers in the path of those who try to follow health-promoting advice. Individuals are ultimately responsible for their own behaviour, but in the current social environment, few people are prepared to choose behaviours that support health when doing so is difficult (review Figure C11–1).

Canada Relaunches ParticipACTION

According to a February 2007 news release, "Canada's new government recognizes the challenges facing Canada with regard to rising obesity levels and declining physical activity rates, and we know the ParticipACTION name continues to resonate with many Canadians as a motivator to be active," and had earmarked $5 million over the following two years to support the renewal of the program.[28] Thus, the ParticipACTION program has been revitalized. To obtain your ParticipACTION Toolkit, visit http:// www.participaction.com.

New Ideas for Change

When healthy foods cost less, people choose them more often.[29] Thus, policymakers and scientists have discussed how to make the healthiest choices also the most affordable and available.[30] One suggestion is to use monetary incentives to encourage both food producers and consumers to make healthier food and exercise choices.[31] This plan would raise taxes on high-Calorie, high-fat, high-salt

Fitness-Promoting Environment

This environment promotes sound nutrition and physical activity choices that lead to fitness.

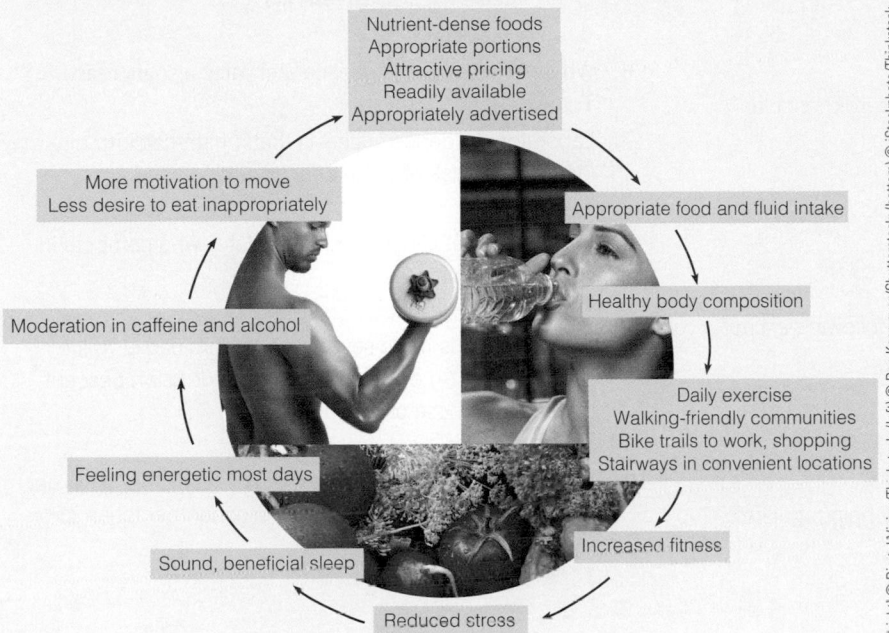

- Nutrient-dense foods
- Appropriate portions
- Attractive pricing
- Readily available
- Appropriately advertised

More motivation to move
Less desire to eat inappropriately

Appropriate food and fluid intake

Moderation in caffeine and alcohol

Healthy body composition

Daily exercise
Walking-friendly communities
Bike trails to work, shopping
Stairways in convenient locations

Feeling energetic most days

Increased fitness

Sound, beneficial sleep

Reduced stress

foods; sugary soft drinks and candies; and fried snack foods, potentially generating $40–100 million in extra tax revenue per year. These tax revenues could then subsidize purchases of health-promoting salads, low-fat chilli, whole-grain breads and buns, broiled chicken and fish, low-fat 1 percent milk, and fresh fruit and cooked vegetables. As consumers bought more and more of the less costly items, manufacturers would respond by making them available in greater varieties and by marketing them more heavily.

Why stop at foods? According to this construct, taxing automobiles and other labour-saving devices that rob people of the exercise they need could yield needed price incentives for purchasing and using bicycles, exercise equipment, and walking shoes. This could lead to a healthy restructuring of our whole society (see Figure C11–3) into one that promotes fitness rather than obesity. In such a society, physical activity would be a natural part of everyone's day, and

stress would be relieved as people interacted in small, centralized communities. They'd safely walk or bicycle to school, work, restaurants, libraries, and shops on pleasant paths in their own neighbourhoods with far less traffic and pollution.[32] In this society, buildings would be designed to invite most people to use attractive stairways while making elevators available for those with disabilities. Neighbours would meet neighbours, develop friendships, and look out for one another, making the community not only healthier but safer.

Conclusion

On hearing of economic plans such as the one just outlined, many people react with skepticism and resistance. They believe that in a free-market society, citizens are capable of making decisions in their own best interest and do not need the government to step in and restructure their lives. Consumers can choose to *live* right now, today, as

though such incentives were already in place. We can

- Turn off the television and take up a physically active recreation.
- Choose to live close enough to shopping, work, and school to allow walking as an option.
- Park farther away than usual and walk through the parking lot.
- Lobby for laws that require landscaping, trees, and walkways in parking lots to make them safe and inviting.
- Seek out and use stairways instead of elevators.
- Take walks and get to the know the neighbours.
- Write letters to building owners, asking them to improve stairwells and access to them.
- Obtain an inexpensive pedometer and vow to walk 10,000 steps each day.
- Choose to consistently follow the advice of the experts offered in Chapters 1 and 2 of this text, even if it means paying more for food and making time to prepare meals at home.
- Make a point to remember standard portion sizes (review Figure 2-4 in Chapter 2) and daily food amounts to decide how much to eat at a sitting.
- Take some of the food home for another meal when restaurant portions are too large.
- Save enticing fatty and sugary fast foods and snacks for special occasions while choosing healthier choices as staple, everyday foods.
- Teach the children in our lives to think differently about food.

People who consistently make personal choices that enhance their health often find that their body weights fall into line with recommendations almost automatically. A good place to start is to take the suggestions in all of the previous chapters to heart and to put in place a plan to eat wisely and exercise every day.

Self-Check

Answers to these Self-Check questions are in Appendix D.

1. By what age do most people have well-developed plaques in their arteries?
   a. 20 years
   b. 30 years
   c. 40 years
   d. 50 years

2. Which of the following is a risk factor for cardiovascular disease?
   a. high blood HDL cholesterol
   b. low blood pressure
   c. low LDL cholesterol
   d. diabetes

3. An "atherogenic diet" is high in all of the following *except*
   a. fibre
   b. cholesterol
   c. saturated fats
   d. *trans* fats

4. Which of the following dietary factors may help regulate blood pressure?
   a. calcium
   b. magnesium
   c. potassium
   d. all of the above

5. Which of the following have been associated with an increase in cancer?
   a. alcohol
   b. diets high in red meat
   c. high intakes of smoke-preserved foods
   d. all of the above

6. When Calorie intakes rise, cancer rates also increase.
   T   F

7. Laboratory evidence suggests that a high-calcium diet may increase the risk of colon cancer.
   T   F

8. The DASH diet is designed for athletes who compete in sprinting events.
   T   F

9. Hypertension is more severe and occurs earlier in life among North Americans of European or Asian descent than among those of African descent.
   T   F

10. Alternative therapies, such as herbal medicine, have not been well established by scientific experimentation to be safe and effective.
    T   F

Concepts in Action

Analyze Your Diet for Health Promotion

The purpose of this exercise is to increase your awareness of the characteristics of the diet recommended for disease prevention.

1. One way to lower your risk of heart attack is to keep your blood pressure in a normal range. Study Table 11–5 (page 476) and Table F–2, Dietary Approaches to Stop Hypertension (DASH), in Appendix F. This appendix provides an eating plan that supports normal blood pressure. Create a meal that follows the principles of the DASH diet. Select the Track Diet tab from the red navigation bar. Select a different date from that for your 3-Day food record and find the foods that you want to include in this meal. Once you're finished, select the Reports tab, go to Source Analysis under the Advanced heading for that meal, and select Sodium from the drop-down menu. How much sodium did your meal contain? Which foods contributed the most sodium to the meal? Also, go to the Reports tab, select Intake vs. Goals under the Nutrients heading, and select the same day that you used above; choose all meals and snacks. Locate sodium, and find the percentage of the DRI intake recommendation for sodium. If the sodium was higher than 33 percent (one-third) of your allowance, what can you change to bring it into compliance?

2. For people with compromised immune systems, malnutrition demands prompt medical nutrition therapy. Select the Track Diet tab from the red navigation bar. Select a new day, and find foods to create one meal that provides one-third of the day's recommendation for high-quality, easily digestible protein for an immune-compromised adult. Take into account a diminished appetite and food safety (you'll learn

more about this in Chapter 12), while making the food appealing and easy to eat and digest but also making sure it contains protein sources that are lower in saturated fat. From the Reports tab, select Source Analysis under the Advanced heading, choose the date for the meal that you entered, and select Protein from the drop-down menu. How many grams of protein did the meal provide?

Next, from the Reports Tab, select Intake vs. Goals under the Nutrients heading to see what percentage of the day's protein the meal supplied. Did it supply about a third of the day's need? If not, what adjustments can you make to better meet this person's need?

3. One diet characteristic recommended to reduce many chronic disease risks is reduced saturated fat intake. Create a meal low in saturated fat following the instructions in item 2 above. From the Reports tab, select Intake vs. Goals under the Nutrients heading for that meal. How much saturated fat did your meal supply? Was it less than 10 percent of total Calories for the meal? If not, what can you change to lower it?

4. Together, diet and exercise are a powerful and safe combination for improving heart health. Select the Track Diet tab and choose the day you used in item 3 above. Take a look at Table 11–9 (page 489) for examples of how to reduce disease risk; then, by adding foods for breakfast, lunch, and snacks, create a full day's menu that achieves the diet modifications listed for saturated fat. Now, from the Reports tab, select Intake vs. Goals under the Nutrients heading. Did your day's meals meet your saturated fat goals? If not, what modifications can you make to achieve your goal?

5. Research suggests that vegetarians have a lower rate of heart disease as well as a lower incidence of certain cancers. An ideal vegetarian diet is high in fibre, phytochemicals, whole grains, and vitamins, and it is low in saturated fat. Using Table 11–8 (page 481) and Table 11–9 (page 489) to guide you, create a vegetarian meal that includes foods associated with low cancer risks. Enter the data for a new day from the Track Diet tab. From the Reports Tab, select Intake vs. Goals under the Nutrients heading for that date and meal. What nutrients would be of interest when evaluating your vegetarian meal for adequacy (consult Figure C6–1 on page 235)? From the Reports Tab, select Intake vs. Goals under the Nutrients heading. Did the meal contain enough protein, vitamins, and minerals to meet your needs? How about fibre? Was it low enough in saturated fat?

Endnotes

1. Centers for Disease Control and Prevention, World TB Day—March 24, 2002, *Morbidity and Mortality Weekly Report* 51 (2002): 229; S. H. Gillespie, Antibiotic resistance in the absence of selective pressure, *International Journal of Antimicrobial Agents* 17 (2001): 171–176; D. K. Warren and V. J. Fraser, Infection control measures to limit antimicrobial resistance, *Critical Care Medicine* 29 (2001): N128–N134.

2. G. T. Keusch, The history of nutrition: Malnutrition, infection and immunity, *Journal of Nutrition* 133 (2003): 336S–340S; P. Bhaskaram, Micronutrient malnutrition, infection, and immunity: An overview, *Nutrition Reviews* 60 (2002): S40–S45.

3. Statistics Canada July 2012, Leading Causes of Death, by Sex for 2009, available at http://www.statcan.gc.ca/tables-tableaux/sum-som/l01/cst01/hlth36a-eng.htm.

4. M. J. Stampfer and coauthors, Primary prevention of coronary heart disease in women through diet and lifestyle, *New England Journal of Medicine* 343 (2000): 16–22; A. K. Kant and coauthors, A prospective study of diet quality and mortality in women, *Journal of the American Medical Association* 283 (2000): 2109–2115.

5. C. J. Field, I. R. Johnson, and P. D. Schley, Nutrients and their role in host resistance to infection, *Journal of Leukocyte Biology* 71 (2002): 16–32; P. Bhaskaram, 2002 [see reference 2].

6. P. C. Calder, Immunonutrition may have beneficial effects in surgical patients, editorial, *British Medical Journal* 327 (2003): 117–118.

7. W. W. Fawzi and coauthors, A randomized trial of multivitamin supplements and HIV disease progression and mortality, *New England Journal of Medicine* 351 (2004): 23–32.

8. Position of the American Dietetic Association and Dietitians of Canada: Nutrition intervention in the care of persons with human immunodeficiency virus infection, *Journal of the American Dietetic Association* 100 (2000): 708–717.

9. M. Serafini, Dietary vitamin E and T cell-mediated function in the elderly: Effectiveness and mechanism of action, *International Journal of Developmental Neuroscience* 18 (2000): 401–410; C. Y. Lee and J. Man-Fan Wan, Vitamin E supplementation improves cell-mediated immunity and oxidative stress of Asian men and women, *Journal of Nutrition* 130 (2000): 2932–2937.

10. Standing Committee on the Scientific Evaluation of Dietary Reference Intakes, Food and Nutrition Board, Institute of Medicine, *Dietary Reference Intakes for Vitamin A, Vitamin K, Arsenic, Boron, Chromium, Copper, Iodine, Iron, Manganese, Molybdenum, Nickel, Silicon, Vanadium, and Zinc*

(Washington, D.C.: National Academies Press, 2001), pp. 12–30; J. C. Fleet, Zinc, copper, and manganese, in M. H. Stipanuk, ed., *Biochemical and Physiological Aspects of Human Nutrition* (Philadelphia, PA: Saunders, 2000), p. 753.

11. Standing Committee on the Scientific Evaluation of Dietary Reference Intakes, Food and Nutrition Board, Institute of Medicine, *Dietary Reference Intakes for Energy, Carbohydrate, Fiber, Fat, Fatty Acids, Cholesterol, Protein, and Amino Acids* (Washington, D.C.: National Academies Press, 2005).

12. A. K. Kant, Dietary patterns and health outcomes, *Journal of the American Dietetic Association* 104 (2004): 615–635.

13. A. J. Blumenfeld and coauthors, Nutritional aspects of prostate cancer: A review, *Canadian Journal of Urology* 7 (2000): 927–935.

14. Public Health Agency of Canada, Tracking heart disease and stroke in Canada, 2009, available at http://www.phac-aspc.gc.ca/publicat/2009/cvd-avc/index-eng.php (accessed December 5, 2013).

15. Statistics Canada, Ranking and number of deaths for the 10 leading causes, Canada 2000 and 2007, available at http://www.statcan.gc.ca/pub/84-215-x/2010001/table-tableau/tbl001-eng.htm.

16. Centers for Disease Control and Prevention, State-specific prevalence of selected chronic disease-related characteristics—Behavioral risk factor surveillance system, 2001, *Morbidity and Mortality Weekly Report* 52 (2003): 4.

17. H. C. McGill and coauthors, Origin of atherosclerosis in childhood and adolescence, *American Journal of Clinical Nutrition* 72 (2000): 1307S–1325S.

18. F. B. Hu and W. C. Willett, Optimal diets for prevention of coronary heart disease, *Journal of the American Medical Association* 288 (2002): 2569–2578; R. P. Lauber and N. F. Sheard, The American Heart Association Dietary Guidelines for 2000: A summary report, *Nutrition Reviews* 59 (2001): 298–306.

19. F. Pellegatta and coauthors, Different short- and long-term effects of resveratrol on nuclear factor-kB phosphorylation and nuclear appearance in human endothelial cells, *American Journal of Clinical Nutrition* 77 (2003): 1220–1228; R. Ross, Atherosclerosis—An inflammatory disease, *New England Journal of Medicine* 340 (1999): 115–126.

20. G. A. A. Ferns and D. J. Lamb, What does the lipoprotein oxidation phenomenon mean? *Biochemical Society Transactions* 32 (2004): 160–163.

21. H. C. McGill and coauthors, 2000 [see reference 17].

22. Standing Committee on the Scientific Evaluation of Dietary Reference Intakes, Food and Nutrition Board, Institute of Medicine, 2005, pp. 11-40–11-43 [see reference 11]; H. Iso and coauthors, Intake of fish and omega-3 fatty acids and risk of stroke in women, *Journal of the American Medical Association* 285 (2001): 304–312.

23. R. McPherson and coauthors, Canadian Cardiovascular Society position statement—Recommendations for the diagnosis and treatment of dyslipidemia and prevention of cardiovascular disease, *Canadian Journal of Cardiology* 22 (2006): 913–927, available at http://www.ccs.ca/download/position_statements/lipids.pdf.

24. E. S. Ford, W. H. Giles, and W. H. Dietz, Prevalence of the metabolic syndrome among US adults: Findings from the Third National Health and Nutrition Examination Survey, *Journal of the American Medical Association* 287 (2002): 356–359.

25. Expert Panel on Detection, Evaluation, and Treatment of High Blood Cholesterol in Adults (Adult Treatment Panel III), *Third Report of the National Cholesterol Education Program (NCEP)*, NIH publication no. 02-5215 (Bethesda, MD: National Heart, Lung, and Blood Institute, 2002), p. II-18.

26. American Heart Association, Heart and Stroke Statistics—2012 Update: A Report from the American Heart Association. *Circulation* 125 (2012): e2–e220; originally published online December 15, 2011; doi: 10.1161/CIR.0b013e31823ac046.

27. D. M. Lloyd-Jones and coauthors, Parental cardiovascular disease as a risk factor for cardiovascular disease in middle-aged adults, *Journal of the American Medical Association* 291 (2004): 2204–2211.

28. Expert Panel on Detection, Evaluation, and Treatment of High Blood Cholesterol in Adults (Adult Treatment Panel III), 2002, p. II-19 [see reference 25].

29. J. M. Ordovas, Cardiovascular disease genetics: A long and winding road, *Current Opinion in Lipidology* 14 (2003): 47–54.

30. R. McPherson and coauthors, 2006 [see reference 23].

31. K. He and coauthors, Dietary fat intake and risk of stroke in male U.S. healthcare professionals: 14 year prospective cohort study, *British Medical Journal* 327 (2003): 777–783.

32. A. W. Weverling-Rijnsburger and coauthors, High-density vs low-density lipoprotein cholesterol as the risk factor for coronary artery disease and stroke in old age, *Archives of Internal Medicine* 163 (2003): 1549–1554; R. L. Sacco and coauthors, High-density lipoprotein cholesterol and ischemic stroke in the elderly: The Northern Manhattan Stroke Study, *Journal of the American Medical Association* 285 (2001): 2729–2735.

33. J. A. Beckman, M. A. Creager, and P. Libby, Diabetes and atherosclerosis: Epidemiology, pathophysiology, and management, *Journal of the American Medical Association* 287 (2002): 2570–2581.

34. Expert Panel on Detection, Evaluation, and Treatment of High Blood Cholesterol in Adults (Adult Treatment Panel III), 2002, pp. II-16, 11-50–11-53. *Third Report of the National Cholesterol Education Program* (NCEP), NIH publication no. 02-5215 (Bethesda, MD: National Heart, Lung and Blood Institute, 2002).

35. American Heart Association, 2002, p. 34 [see reference 26].

36. S. Bioletto and coauthors, Acute hyperinsulinemia and very-low-density and low-density lipoprotein subfractions in obese subjects, *American Journal of Clinical Nutrition* 71 (2000): 443–449.

37. P. T. Katzmaryzk and coauthors, Targeting the metabolic syndrome with exercise: Evidence from the HERITAGE Family Study, *Medicine and Science in Sports and Exercise* 35 (2003): 1703–1709.

38. M. L. Pollock and coauthors, Resistance exercise in individuals with and without cardiovascular disease, *Circulation* 101 (2000): 828–833.

39. American Heart Association, 2002, p. 26 [see reference 26]; Expert Panel on Detection, Evaluation, and Treatment of High Blood Cholesterol in Adults (Adult Treatment Panel III), 2002, p. II-16 [see reference 25].

40. G. A. Bray and C. M. Champagne, Obesity and the metabolic syndrome: Implications for dietetics practitioners, *Journal of the American Dietetic Association* 104 (2004): 86–89.

41. H. M. Lakka and coauthors, The metabolic syndrome and total and cardiovascular disease mortality in middle-aged men, *Journal of the American Medical Association* 288 (2002): 2709–2716; D. L. Sprecher and G. L. Pearce, How deadly is the "deadly quartet"? A post-CABG evaluation, *Journal of the American College of Cardiology* 36 (2000): 1159–1165.

42. National Institutes of Health, National Heart, Lung, and Blood Institute, NCEP issues major new cholesterol guidelines (press release), 2001, available at http://www.nhlbi.nih.gov/news/press-releases/2001/ncep-issues-major-new-cholesterol-guidelines.html.

43. E. S. Ford, W. H. Giles, and W. H. Dietz, 2002 [see reference 24].

44. J. W. Miller, Does lowering plasma homocysteine reduce vascular disease risk? *Nutrition Reviews* 59 (2001): 242–244.

45. A. Ascherio and coauthors, *Trans*-fatty acids and coronary heart disease, *New England Journal of Medicine* 340 (1999): 1994–1998.

46. S. Yusuf and coauthors, Effect of potentially modifiable risk factors associated with myocardial infarction in 52 countries (the INTERHEART study): Case-control study, *Lancet* 364 (2004): 937–952.

47. Standing Committee on the Scientific Evaluation of Dietary Reference Intakes, Food and Nutrition Board, Institute of Medicine, 2005, pp. 11–46 [see reference 11].

48. Joint WHO/FAO Expert Consultation, *Diet, Nutrition and the Prevention of Chronic Diseases* (Geneva, Switzerland: World Health Organization, 2003).

49. K. L. Herron and coauthors, Men classified as hypo- or hyperresponders to dietary cholesterol feeding exhibit differences in lipoprotein metabolism, *Journal of Nutrition* 133 (2003): 1036–1042.

50. Standing Committee on the Scientific Evaluation of Dietary Reference Intakes, Food and Nutrition Board, Institute of Medicine, 2005, pp. 11-3 [see reference 11].

51. P. M. Kris-Etherton, K. D. Hecker, and A. E. Binkoski, Polyunsaturated fatty acids and cardiovascular health, *Nutrition Reviews* 62 (2004): 414–426; M. Kanazawa and coauthors, Effects of a high-sucrose diet on body weight, plasma triglycerides, and stress tolerance, *Nutrition Reviews* 61 (2003): S27–S33; A. Raben and A. Astrup, Ad libitum intake of low-fat diets rich in either starchy foods or sucrose: Effects on blood lipids, factor VII coagulant activity, and fibrinogen, *Metabolism: Clinical and Experimental* 49 (2000): 731–735; J. P. Bantle and coauthors, Effects of dietary fructose on plasma lipids in healthy subjects, *American Journal of Clinical Nutrition* 72 (2000): 1128–1134.

52. R. N. Lemaitre and coauthors, n-3 polyunsaturated fatty acids, fatal ischemic heart disease, and nonfatal myocardial infarction in older adults: The Cardiovascular Health Study, *American Journal of Clinical Nutrition* 77 (2003): 319–325; C. M. Albert and coauthors, Blood levels of long chain n-3 polyunsaturated fatty acids and the risk of sudden death, *New England Journal of Medicine* 346 (2002): 1113–1118; P. Nestel and coauthors, The n-3 fatty acids eicosapentaenoic acid and docosahexaenoic acid increase systemic arterial compliance in humans, *American Journal of Clinical Nutrition* 76 (2002): 326–330; W. S. Harris, Cardioprotective effects

of ω-3 fatty acids, *Nutrition in Clinical Practice* 16 (2001): 6–12; C. R. Harper and T. A. Jacobson, The role of omega-3 fatty acids in the prevention of coronary heart disease, *Archives of Internal Medicine* 161 (2001): 2185–2192.

53. Eating Well with Canada's Food Guide—Meat & Alternatives, Catalogue no. H164-38/1-2007E (Ottawa, ON: Health Canada, 2007), available at http://www.hc-sc.gc.ca/fn-an/food-guide-aliment/choose-choix/meat-viande/index_e.html.

54. P. M. Kris-Etherton, K. D. Hecker, and A. E. Binkoski, 2004 [see reference 51]; L. Djousse and coauthors, Dietary linolenic acid and carotid atherosclerosis: The National Heart, Lung, and Blood Institute Family Heart Study, *American Journal of Clinical Nutrition* 77 (2003): 819–825; P. M. Kris-Etherton, W. S. Harris, and L. J. Appel, Fish consumption, fish oil, omega-3 fatty acids, and cardiovascular disease, *Circulation* 106 (2002): 2747–2757.

55. L. M. Steffen and coauthors, Associations of whole-grain, refined-grain, and fruit and vegetable consumption with risks of all-cause mortality and incident coronary artery disease and ischemic stroke: The Atherosclerosis Risk in Communities (ARIC) Study, *American Journal of Clinical Nutrition* 78 (2003): 383–390; S. Liu, Intake of refined carbohydrates and whole grain foods in relation to risk of type 2 diabetes mellitus and coronary heart disease, *Journal of the American College of Nutrition* 21 (2002): 298–306.

56. S. Liu and coauthors, Is intake of breakfast cereals related to total and cause-specific mortality in men? *American Journal of Clinical Nutrition* 77 (2003): 594–599; L. A. Bazzano and coauthors, Fruit and vegetable intake and risk of cardiovascular disease in US adults: The First National Health and Nutrition Examination Survey Epidemiologic Follow-up Study, *American Journal of Clinical Nutrition* 76 (2002): 93–99.

57. Expert Panel on Detection, Evaluation, and Treatment of High Blood Cholesterol in Adults (Adult Treatment Panel III), 2002, p. V-13 [see reference 34].

58. U. A. Ajani, E. S. Ford, and A. H. Mokdad, Dietary fiber and C-reactive protein: Findings from National Health and Nutrition Examination Survey data, *Journal of Nutrition* 134 (2004): 1181–1185.

59. C. T. Valmadrid and coauthors, Alcohol intake and the risk of coronary heart disease mortality in persons with older-onset diabetes mellitus, *Journal of the American Medical Association* 282 (1999): 239–246.

60. B.-H. Chung and coauthors, Alcohol-mediated enhancement of postprandial lipemia: A contributing factor to an increase in plasma HDL and a decrease in risk of cardiovascular disease, *American Journal of Clinical Nutrition* 78 (2003): 391–399; D. J. Baer and coauthors, Moderate alcohol consumption lowers risk factors for cardiovascular disease in postmenopausal women fed a controlled diet, *American Journal of Clinical Nutrition* 75 (2002): 593–599.

61. K. Reynolds and coauthors, Alcohol consumption and risk of stroke: A meta-analysis, *Journal of the American Medical Association* 289 (2003): 579–588.

62. D. J. A. Jenkins and coauthors, A dietary portfolio approach to cholesterol reduction: Combined effects of plant sterols, vegetable proteins, and viscous fibers in hyper-cholesterolemia, *Metabolism: Clinical and Experimental* 51 (2002): 1596–1604.

63. Expert Panel on Detection, Evaluation, and Treatment of High Blood Cholesterol in Adults (Adult Treatment Panel III), 2002 [see reference 34].

64. R. O. Bonow and R. H. Eckel, Diet, obesity and cardiovascular risk, *New England Journal of Medicine* 348 (2003): 2057–2058; D. M. Bravata and coauthors, Efficacy and safety of low-carbohydrate diets, *Journal of the American Medical Association* 289 (2003): 1837–1850.

65. S. Liu and coauthors, Intake of vegetables rich in carotenoids and risk of coronary heart disease in men: The Physicians' Health Study, *International Journal of Epidemiology* 30 (2001): 130–135.

66. A. Rosengren and coauthors, Association of psychosocial risk factors with risk of acute myocardial infarction in 11,119 cases and 13,648 controls from 52 countries (the INTERHEART study): Case-control study, *Lancet* 364 (2004): 953–962; L. A. Chaput and coauthors, Hostility predicts recurrent events among post-menopausal women with coronary heart disease, *American Journal of Epidemiology* 15 (2002): 1092–1099.

67. Canadian Hypertension Education Program (CHEP), 2013 Recommendations, available at http://www.hypertension.ca/chep.

68. I. Hajjar and T. A. Kotchen, Trends in prevalence, awareness, treatment, and control of hypertension in the United States, 1988–2000, *Journal of the American Medical Association* 290 (2003): 199–206.

69. Canadian Hypertension Education Program (CHEP), 2013 Recommendations, available at http://www.hypertension.ca/chep (accessed December 5, 2013).

70. J. M. Lalouel and A. Rohrwasser, Development of genetic hypotheses in essential hypertension, *Journal of Human Genetics* 46 (2001): 299–306; K.W. Sellers and coauthors, Gene therapy to control hypertension: Current studies and future perspectives, *American Journal of the Medical Sciences* 322 (2001): 1–6.

71. C. A. Nowson and coauthors, Blood pressure response to dietary modifications in free-living individuals, *Journal of Nutrition* 134 (2004): 2322–2329.

72. V. J. Stevens and coauthors, Long-term weight loss and changes in blood pressure: Results of the Trials of Hypertension Prevention, phase II, *Annals of Internal Medicine* 134 (2001): 1–11.

73. L. S. Pescatello and coauthors, American College of Sports Medicine position stand: Exercise and hypertension, *Medicine and Science in Sports and Exercise* 36 (2004): 533–553.

74. P. D. Thompson and coauthors, The acute versus the chronic response to exercise, *Medicine and Science in Sports and Exercise* 33 (2001): S452–S453.

75. P. D. Thompson and coauthors, 2001 [see reference 74].

76. M. Iwane and coauthors, Walking 10,000 steps/day or more reduces blood pressure and sympathetic nerve activity in mild essential hypertension, *Hypertension Research* 23 (2000): 573–580.

77. T. S. Altena and coauthors, Single sessions of intermittent and continuous exercise and postprandial lipemia, *Medicine and Science in Sports and Exercise* 36 (2004): 1364–1371.

78. U.S. Department of Agriculture and U.S. Department of Health and Human Services, Dietary Guidelines for Americans, 2010, available at http://health.gov/dietaryguidelines/2010.asp; Joint WHO/FAO Expert Consultation, 2003, pp. 85–86 [see reference 48].

79. L. Hooper and coauthors, Reduced dietary salt for prevention of cardiovascular disease, *Cochrane Database System Review* 3 (2003): CD003656.

80. U.S. Department of Agriculture and U.S. Department of Health and Human Services, 2010 [see reference 78]; Joint WHO/FAO Expert Consultation, 2003, pp. 85–86 [see reference 48].

81. Standing Committee on the Scientific Evaluation of Dietary Reference Intakes, Food and Nutrition Board, Institute of Medicine, *Dietary Reference Intakes for Water, Potassium, Sodium, Chloride, and Sulfate* (Washington, D.C.: National Academies Press, 2005); F. M. Sacks and coauthors, Effects on blood pressure of reduced dietary sodium and the Dietary Approaches to Stop Hypertension (DASH) diet, *New England Journal of Medicine* 344 (2001): 3–10.

82. F. D. Fuchs and coauthors, Alcohol consumption and the incidence of hypertension: The Atherosclerosis Risk in Communities Study, *Hypertension* 37 (2001): 1242–1250.

83. D. A. McCarron and R. P. Heaney, Estimated healthcare savings associated with adequate dairy food intake, *American Journal of Hypertension* 17 (2004): 88–97.

84. G. Block, Ascorbic acid, blood pressure, and the American diet, *Annals of the New York Academy of Sciences* 959 (2002): 180–187.

85. I. M. Hajjar and coauthors, A randomized, double-blind, controlled trial of vitamin C in the management of hypertension and lipids, *American Journal of Therapeutics* 10 (2003): 289–293; M. K. Kim and coauthors, Lack of long-term effect of vitamin C supplementation on blood pressure, *Hypertension* 40 (2002): 797–791.

86. E. Obarzanek and coauthors, Effects on blood lipids of a blood pressure-lowering diet: The Dietary Approaches to Stop Hypertension (DASH) trial, *American Journal of Clinical Nutrition* 74 (2001): 80–89.

87. Centers for Disease Control and Prevention, Cancer Survivors—United States, 2007, *Morbidity and Mortality Weekly Report* 60 (2011): 269–272. Available at http://www.cdc.gov/mmwr/preview/mmwrhtml/mm6009a1.htm.

88. P. Lichtenstein and coauthors, Environmental and heritable factors in the causation of cancer:

Analyses of cohorts of twins from Sweden, Denmark, and Finland, *New England Journal of Medicine* 343 (2000): 78–85.

89. E. E. Calle and coauthors, Overweight, obesity and mortality from cancer in a prospectively studied cohort of U.S. adults, *New England Journal of Medicine* 348 (2003): 1625–1638.

90. National Cancer Policy Board, Institute of Medicine, *Fulfilling the Potential of Cancer Prevention and Early Detection*, ed. S. J. Curry, T. Byers, and M. Hewitt (Washington, D.C.: National Academies Press, 2003), pp. 58–61.

91. M. R. Forman and coauthors, Nutrition and cancer prevention: A multidisciplinary perspective on human trials, *Annual Review of Nutrition* 24 (2004): 223–254.

92. Cell-cycle regulation and the genetics of cancer, in L. Hartwell and coauthors, *Genetics: From Genes to Genomes* (Boston, MA: McGraw-Hill, 2000), pp. 590–622.

93. Position of the American Dietetic Association and Dietitians of Canada: Nutrition and women's health, *Journal of the American Dietetic Association* 104 (2004): 984–1001.

94. S. A. Nowell, J. Ahn, and C. B. Ambrosone, Gene-nutrient interactions in cancer etiology, *Nutrition Reviews* 62 (2004): 427–438.

95. E. E. Calle and coauthors, 2003 [see reference 89]; National Cancer Policy Board, Institute of Medicine, 2003, pp. 61–66 [see reference 90].

96. E. E. Calle and coauthors, 2003 [see reference 89].

97. Y. Mao and coauthors, Physical inactivity, energy intake, obesity and the risk of rectal cancer in Canada, *International Journal of Cancer* 105 (2003): 831–837; A. S. Furberg and I. Thune, Metabolic abnormalities (hypertension, hyperglycemia and overweight), lifestyle (high energy intake and physical inactivity) and endometrial cancer risk in a Norwegian cohort, *International Journal of Cancer* 104 (2003): 669–676; E. Giovannucci, Diet, body weight, and colorectal cancer: A summary of the epidemiologic evidence, *Journal of Women's Health* 12 (2003): 173–182; H. Vainio, R. Kaaks, and F. Bianchini, Weight control and physical activity in cancer prevention: International evaluation of the evidence, *European Journal of Cancer Prevention* 2 (2002): S94–S100.

98. National Cancer Policy Board, Institute of Medicine, 2003, pp. 58–61 [see reference 90]; M. L. Slattery and coauthors, Lifestyle and colon cancer: An assessment of factors associated with risk, *American Journal of Epidemiology* 150 (1999): 869–877.

99. National Cancer Policy Board, Institute of Medicine, 2003, pp. 59–60 [see reference 90]; J. B. Barnett, The relationship between obesity and breast cancer risk and mortality, *Nutrition Reviews* 61 (2003): 73–76.

100. P. L. Zock, Dietary fats and cancer, *Current Opinions in Lipidology* 12 (2001): 5–10.

101. P. L. Zock, 2001 [see reference 100].

102. E. Cho and coauthors, Premenopausal fat intake and risk of breast cancer, *Journal of the National Cancer Institute* 95 (2003): 1079–1085.

103. S. A. Bingham and coauthors, Are imprecise methods obscuring a relation between fat and breast cancer? *Lancet* 362 (2003): 212–214.

104. S. C. Larsson and coauthors, Dietary long chain n-3 fatty acids for the prevention of cancer: A review of potential mechanisms, *American Journal of Clinical Nutrition* 79 (2004): 935–945; A. Nkondjock and coauthors, Specific fatty acids and human colorectal cancer: An overview, *Cancer Detection and Prevention* 27 (2003): 55–66; National Cancer Policy Board, Institute of Medicine, 2003, p. 77 [see reference 90]; P. D. Terry, T. E. Rohan, and A. Wolk, Intakes of fish and marine fatty acids and the risks of cancers of the breast and prostate and of other hormone-related cancers: A review of the epidemiologic evidence, *American Journal of Clinical Nutrition* 77 (2003): 532–543.

105. S. A. Nowell, J. Ahn, and C. B. Ambrosone, 2004 [see reference 94]; M. A. Murtaugh and coauthors, Meat consumption patterns and preparation, genetic variants of metabolic enzymes, and their association with rectal cancer in men and women, *Journal of Nutrition* 134 (2004): 776–784; L. M. Butler and coauthors, Heterocyclic amines, meat intake, and association with colon cancer in a population-based study, *American Journal of Epidemiology* 157 (2003): 434–445.

106. L. Le Marchand and coauthors, Well-done red meat, metabolic phenotypes and colorectal cancer in Hawaii, *Mutation Research* 506–507 (2002): 205–214.

107. Health Canada, Food and nutrition: Acrylamide, available at (accessed December 5, 2013); http://www.hc-sc.gc.ca/fn-an/securit/chem-chim/food-aliment/acrylamide/index-eng.php U.S. Food and Drug Administration, FDA action plan for acrylamide in food, March 2004, available at http://www.fda.gov/Food/FoodborneIllnessContaminants/ChemicalContaminants/ucm053519.htm.

108. S.A. Bingham and coauthors, Dietary fiber in food and protection against colorectal cancer in the European Prospective Investigation into Cancer and Nutrition (EPIC): An observational study, *Lancet* 361 (2003): 1496–1501; I. A. Schatzkin and coauthors, Lack of effect of a low-fat, high-fiber diet on the recurrence of colorectal adenomas, *New England Journal of Medicine* 342 (2000): 1149–1155.

109. American Gastroenterological Association, Medical position statement: Impact of dietary fiber on colon cancer occurrence, *Gastroenterology* 118 (2000): 1233–1234.

110. J. L. Slavin, Mechanisms for the impact of whole grain foods on cancer risk, *Journal of the American College of Nutrition* 19 (2000): S300–S307.

111. D. S. Michaud and coauthors, Fluid intake and the risk of bladder cancer in men, *New England Journal of Medicine* 340 (1999): 1390–1397.

112. S. W. Choi and J. B. Mason, Folate and carcinogenesis: An integrated scheme, *Journal of Nutrition* 130 (2000): 129–132; K.Young-In, Folate and cancer prevention: A new medical application for folate beyond hyperhomocysteinemia and neural tube defects, *Nutrition Reviews* 57 (1999): 314–324.

113. B. N. Ames, Micronutrient deficiencies: A major cause of DNA damage, *Annals of the New York Academy of Sciences* 889 (1999): 87–106.

114. K. Z. Guyton, T. W. Kensler, and G. H. Posner, Vitamin D and vitamin D analogs as cancer chemopreventive agents, *Nutrition Reviews* 61 (2003): 227–238; M. Chung and coauthors, The relationships of vitamin D and calcium intakes to nutrient status indicators and health outcomes. Evidence Report No. 183 (prepared by the Tufts Evidence-based Practice Center under Contract No. HHSA 290-2007-10055-I), AHRQ publication no. 09–E015 (Rockville, MD: Agency for Healthcare Research and Quality. June 2009), available at http://www.ahrq.gov/clinic/tp/vitadcaltp.htm (accessed December 5, 2013).

115. A. S. Vrablic and coauthors, Altered mitochondrial function and overgeneration of reactive oxygen species precede the induction of apoptosis by 1-O-octadecyl-2-methyl-rac-glycero-3-phophocholine in p53-defective hepatocytes, *FASEB Journal* 15 (2001): 1739–1744.

116. R. I. Salganik and coauthors, Dietary antioxidant depletion: Enhancement of tumor apoptosis and inhibition of brain tumor growth in transgenic mice, *Carcinogenesis* 21 (2000): 909–914.

117. E. Kallay and coauthors, Dietary calcium and growth modulation of human colon cancer cells: Role of the extracellular calcium-sensing receptor, *Cancer Detection and Prevention* 24 (2000): 127–136.

118. E. Kampman and coauthors, Calcium, vitamin D, sunshine exposure, dairy products and colon cancer risk (United States), *Cancer Causes and Control* 11 (2000): 459–466.

119. A.-L. M. Heath and S. J. Fairweather-Tait, Health implications of iron overloads: The role of diet and genotype, *Nutrition Reviews* 61 (2003): 45–62; R. L. Nelson, Iron and colorectal cancer risk: Human studies, *Nutrition Reviews* 59 (2001): 140–148.

120. R. L. Nelson, 2001 [see reference 119].

121. J. F. Weiss and M. R. Landauer, Protection against ionizing radiation by antioxidant nutrients and phytochemicals, *Toxicology* 189 (2003): 1–20.

122. M. Peluso and coauthors, White blood cell DNA adducts and fruit and vegetable consumption in bladder cancer, *Carcinogenesis* 21 (2000): 183–187.

123. Joint WHO/FAO Expert Consultation, 2003, pp. 30–53 [see reference 48]; A. K. Kant and coauthors, 2000 [see reference 4].

124. R. H. Liu, Health benefits of fruit and vegetables are from additive and synergistic combinations of phytochemicals, *American Journal of Clinical Nutrition* 78 (2003): 517S–520S.

Consumer Corner 11

1. C. Ramsey, Alternative medicine in Canada: Use and public attitudes, Fraser Institute, 1999, available at http://www.fraserinstitute.org.

2. M. A. Frenkel and J. M. Borkan, An approach for integrating complementary-alternative medicine into primary care, *Family Practice* 20 (2003): 324–332.

3. Mayo Clinic. Complementary and alternative medicine: Evaluate treatment claims: Don't take all CAM claims at face value. Do your homework when considering CAM therapies. October 2011, available at http://www.mayoclinic.com/health/alternative-medicine/SA00078/NSECTIONGROUP=2.

4. R. del la Fuente-Fernandez, M. Schultzer, and A. J. Stoessl, The placebo effect in neurological disorders, *Lancet Neurology* 1 (2002): 85–91.

5. A. J. Vickers and coauthors, Acupuncture for chronic headache in primary care: Large, pragmatic, randomised trial, *British Medical Journal* 328 (2004): 744–750; D. Wonderling and coauthors, Cost effectiveness analysis of a randomised trial of acupuncture for chronic headache in primary care, *British Medical Journal* 328 (2004): 747–752.

6. A. White and coauthors, Adverse events following acupuncture: Prospective survey of 32,000 consultations with doctors and physiotherapists, *British Medical Journal* 323 (2001): 485–486; H. MacPherson and coauthors, The York acupuncture safety study: Prospective survey of 34,000 treatments by traditional acupuncturists, *British Medical Journal* 323 (2001): 486–487.

7. C. M. Gilroy and coauthors, Echinacea and truth in labeling, *Archives of Internal Medicine* 163 (2003): 699–704; A. H. Feifer, N. E. Fleshner, and L. Klotz, Analytical accuracy and reliability of commonly used nutritional supplements in prostate disease, *Journal of Urology* 168 (2002): 150–154.

8. J. Garrard and coauthors, Varations in produce choices of frequently purchased herbs: caveat emptor, *Archives of Internal Medicine* 163 (2003): 2290–2295.

9. U.S. Food and Drug Administration, Letter to health professionals regarding safety concerns related to the use of botanical products containing aristolochic acid, April 2001, available at http://www.fda.gov/Food/RecallsOutbreaksEmergencies/SafetyAlertsAdvisories/ucm111200.htm.

10. Centers for Disease Control and Prevention, Lead poisoning associated with ayurvedic medications—five states, 2000–2003, *Morbidity and Mortality Weekly Report* 53 (2004): 582–584; G. Trochet, Warning! High levels of lead (a poisonous metal) have been found in an Ayurvedic pill taken to increase fertility, *Sacramento County Department of Health and Human Services*, available from Sacramento County Department of Health and Human Services, Childhood Illness and Injury Prevention Program at (916) 875-5869.

11. L. H. Kushi and coauthors, The macrobiotic diet in cancer, *Journal of Nutrition* 131 (2001): 3056S–3064S.

12. A. Nkondjock and coauthors, Specific fatty acids and human colorectal cancer: An overview, *Cancer Detection and Prevention* 27 (2003): 55–66;

Macrobiotic proponent dies of cancer, *Consumer Health Digest*, July 9, 2001, available at http://www.ncahf.org/digest/01-28.html.

Controversy 11

1. M. Tjepkema and M. Shields, Measured Obesity: Adult Obesity in Canada, Component of Statistics Canada, Catalogue no. 82-620-MWE2005001.

2. Public Health Agency of Canada. Obesity in Canada—A Joint Report from the Public Health Agency of Canada and the Canadian Institute for Health Information (2011), available at http://www.phac-aspc.gc.ca/hp-ps/hl-mvs/oic-oac/assets/pdf/oic-oac-eng.pdf.

3. J. Foreyt and G. K. Goodrick, Dieting and weight loss: The energy perspective, *Nutrition Reviews* 59 (2001): S25–S26.

4. J. J. Putnam and J. E. Allshouse, *Food Consumption, Prices, and Expenditures*, USDA Economic Research Service, 1999, Statistical Bulletin no. 965, available at http://www.ers.usda.gov/media/285994/sb965a_1_.pdf.

5. Canadian Fitness and Lifestyle Research Institute, 2008 Physical Activity Monitor, available at http://72.10.49.94/media/node/82/files/PAM2008FactsFigures_Bulletin02_PA_among_CanadiansEN.pdf.

6. L. Perusse and C. Bouchard, Gene-diet interactions in obesity, *American Journal of Clinical Nutrition* 72 (2000): 1285S–1290S; D. B. Allison and M. S. Faith, Genetic and environmental influences on human body weight: Implications for the behavior therapist, *Nutrition Today* 35 (2000): 18–21.

7. C. Bouchard, *Physical Activity and Obesity* (Champaign, IL: Human Kinetics Publishers, 2000), p. 14.

8. D. Lakdawalla and T. Philipson, The Growth of Obesity and Technological Change: A Theoretical and Empirical Examination, a paper from the National Bureau of Economic Research, October 8, 2001, available at http://papers.nber.org/papers/w8946.

9. E. Schlosser, *Fast Food Nation* (Boston, MA: Houghton Mifflin, 2001), p. 7.

10. M. Nestle, *Food Politics: How the Food Industry Influences Nutrition and Health* (Berkeley, CA: University of California Press, 2002).

11. Canadian Council of Food and Nutrition, *Tracking Nutrition Trends VI* (Woodbridge, ON: Author, 2006), available at http://www.cfdr.ca/Downloads/CCFN-docs/TNTVI---_TNS-C1062_-2006.aspx.

12. M. Nestle, 2002 [see reference 10].

13. B. J. Rolls, The supersizing of America: Portion size and the obesity epidemic, *Nutrition Today*, March/April, 2003, 42–53.

14. A. Clauson, Share of food spending for eating out reaches 47 percent, *Food Review* 22 (1999): 20–22, as cited by L. R.Young and M. Nestle, The contribution of expanding portion sizes to the US obesity epidemic, *American Journal of Public Health* 92 (2002): 246–249; USDA Baseline Projections, February 1999, available at http://www.usda.gov.

15. B. Wansink, Environmental factors that increase the food intake and consumption volume of unknowing consumers, *Annual Review of Nutrition* 24 (2004): 455–479.

16. B. J. Rolls, E. L. Morris, and L. S. Roe, Portion size of food affects energy intake in normal-weight and overweight men and women, *American Journal of Clinical Nutrition* 76 (2002): 1207–1213.

17. B. Wansink, 2004 [see reference 19].

18. G. Ruskin, Executive Director of Commercial Alert, to the World Health Organization Conference on Health Marketing and Youth, Treviso, Italy, April 17, 2002.

19. M. Nestle, 2002 [see reference 10].

20. G. Ruskin, 2002 [see reference 22].

21. R. Nader, Testimony on "Channel One" before the U.S. Senate Committee on Health, Education, Labor, and Pensions, 1999, available at http://www.commercialalert.org/news/featured-in/1999/05/ralph-naders-testimony-on-channel-one.

22. G. Ruskin, 2002 [see reference 22].

23. J Sommerfeld, Fat Suits: Who's to blame for flab? 2013 MSNBC.com, available at http://www.nbcnews.com/id/3076962/#.UrlTV7TtCZ9.

24. C. H. Powers and M. A. Hess, A message to the restaurant industry: It's time to "step up to the plate," *Journal of the American Dietetic Association* 103 (2003): 1136–1138.

25. K. D. Raine, *Overweight and Obesity in Canada: A Population Health Perspective*, Canadian Institute for Health Information, 2004; M. Tremblay, Major initiatives related to childhood obesity and physical activity in Canada—The year in review, *Canadian Journal of Public Health* 98, 6 (2007): 457–459.

26. M. Nestle and M. F. Jacobson, 2000 [see reference 14].

27. FDA Working Group on Obesity, *Calories Count: Report of the Working Group on Obesity*, March 2004, available at http://www.fda.gov/Food/FoodScienceResearch/ConsumerBehaviorResearch/ucm081696.htm; The White House: Office of the First Lady, Let's move: America's move to raise a healthier generation of kids, February 9, 2010, available at http://www.whitehouse.gov/the-press-office/first-lady-michelle-obama-launches-lets-move-americas-move-raise-a-healthier-genera.

28. Canadian Heritage, Government of Canada, Canada's New Government Re-Launches ParticipACTION, February 19, 2007, available at http://news.gc.ca/web/article-en.do?crtr.sj1D=&mthd=advSrch&crtr.mnthndVl=&nid=277549&crtr.dpt1D=&crtr.tp1D=&crtr.lc1D=&crtr.yrStrtVl=&crtr.kw=tax%2B&crtr.dyStrtVl=&crtr.aud1D=&crtr.mnthStrtVl=&crtr.yrndVl=&crtr.dyndVl=.

29. S. A. French, Pricing effects on food choices, *Journal of Nutrition* 133 (2003): 841S–843S.

30. F. Kuchler, A. Tegene, and J. M. Harris, Taxing snack foods: what to expect for diet and tax revenues, *Current Issues in Economics of Food Markets*, Agriculture Information Bulletin no.

747-08, August 2004, available at http://www.ers
.usda.gov/media/306707/aib74708_1_.pdf;
N. J. Temple and A. L. Balay-Karperien,
Nutrition in cancer prevention: An integrated
approach, *Journal of the American College of
Nutrition* 21 (2002): 79–83.

31. M. Nestle and M. F. Jacobson, Halting
the obesity epidemic: A public health policy
approach, *Public Health Reports* 115 (2000):
12–24.
32. C. E. Staunton, D. Hubsmith, and W.
Kallins, Promoting safe walking and biking

to school: The Marin County success story,
American Journal of Public Health 93 (2003):
1431–1434; K. E. Powell, I. M. Martin, and
P. P. Chowdhury, Places to walk: Convenience
and regular physical activity, *American Journal of
Public Health* 93 (2003): 1519–1521.

12 Food Safety and Food Technology

Do You Ever ...

Come down with digestive tract symptoms and maybe a headache that you attribute to a case of "stomach flu"?

Assume that foods from grocery stores and restaurants are free of harmful germs?

Refrigerate leftover party foods such as meatballs after the guests have gone home?

Eat raw sushi or raw cookie dough but avoid foods with additives to protect your health?

Keep Reading . . .

Learning Objectives

After completing this chapter, you should be able to

LO 12.1 Describe two ways in which foodborne micro-organisms can cause illness in the body, and give examples of each.

LO 12.2 Develop a plan, from purchase to table, by which consumers can reduce their risks of foodborne illnesses from seafood, meats, and produce.

LO 12.3 Name several recent advances aimed at reducing microbial food contamination, and describe their potential contribution to the safety of the Canadian food supply.

LO 12.4 Describe how pesticides enter the food supply, and suggest possible actions to reduce consumption of residues.

LO 12.5 Provide evidence to justify this statement: "Food additives used in Canada serve some important functions and are safe to consume."

LO 12.6 Compare and contrast the advantages and disadvantages of food production by way of genetic modification and conventional farming.

Contents

Consumers in Canada and the United States enjoy food supplies ranking among the safest (both ranked 4th out of 17 in the world in 2010), most pleasing, and most abundant in the world. With this benefit, though, comes the consumer's responsibility to distinguish between paths leading to food **safety** and those that pose a **hazard**. The agencies that regulate the safety of the Canadian food supply at the federal level are shown in Table 12–1. These agencies monitor all aspects of food safety (e.g., see list below), including the use of pesticides, which are primarily regulated by Agriculture and Agri-Food Canada. Provincial departments of health, agriculture, and the environment and municipal health departments also share responsibilities for the safety of the food and water supply.

1. *Microbial foodborne illness* affects many millions of people every year.

2. *Natural toxins in foods* constitute a hazard whenever people consume single foods either by choice (fad diets) or by necessity (poverty).

3. *Residues in food.*
   a. *Environmental contaminants* (other than pesticides) such as household and industrial chemicals are increasing yearly in number and concentration, and their impacts are hard to foresee and to forestall.

---

safety the practical certainty that injury will not result from the use of a substance.

hazard a state of danger; used to refer to any circumstance in which harm is possible under normal conditions of use.

Table 12–1

Agencies That Monitor the Canadian Food Supply

- **Health Canada**, Health Products and Food Branch: http://www.hc-sc.gc.ca/ahc-asc/branch-dirgen/hpfb-dgpsa/index-eng.php
- **Canadian Food Inspection Agency**: http://www.inspection.gc.ca/english/toce.shtml
- **Agriculture and Agri-Food Canada**: http://www.agr.gc.ca
- **Sustainable Development, Agriculture and Agri-Food Canada**: http://www.agr.gc.ca/eng/about-us/planning-and-reporting/sustainable-development/?id=1175526032952
- **Environment Canada**: http://www.ec.gc.ca

b. *Pesticides* are a subclass of environmental contaminants but are listed separately because they are applied intentionally to foods and, in theory, can be controlled.

c. *Animal drugs* include hormones and antibiotics that increase growth in food animals and arsenic compounds that enhance the growth of chickens.[*,1]

4. *Nutrients in foods* require close attention as more and more artificially constituted foods appear on the market.

5. *Intentional food additives* are of little concern because so much is known about them that they pose virtually no hazard to consumers and because their use is well regulated.

6. *Genetic modification of foods* is listed last because such foods undergo rigorous scrutiny before going to market.[2]

Microbial **foodborne illness**, commonly called *food poisoning*, is first on the list because episodes of food poisoning far outnumber any other kind of food contamination. The last items, food additives and genetic modification of foods, are of least concern. The others fall somewhere in between.

Canada has had a Foodborne Illness Outbreak Response Protocol (FIORP) in place since the summer of 2004, last updated in 2010,[3] a protocol undoubtedly affected by the events of September 11, 2001, and SARS. The Federal, Provincial, and Territorial Committee on Food Safety and Policy views it as a "key procedural document in national emergency preparedness." Many agencies are taking ongoing action to protect the food supply, and Canada[4] and the U.S. Food and Drug Administration (FDA) have developed broad strategies for countering bioterrorism.[5]

While the bioterrorism threat is serious, the immediate assault on health and life from foodborne illnesses is a current national problem that often yields to simple preventive tactics. This chapter focuses on actions that individuals can take to promote food safety. This chapter's Controversy section takes up the topic of genetic modification of foods.

Microbes and Food Safety

Some people brush off the threat from foodborne illnesses caused by **microbes** as less likely and less serious than the threat of flu, but they are misinformed—foodborne illnesses can be life-threatening and are increasingly unresponsive to standard antibiotics.[6] Even normally mild foodborne illnesses can be lethal for people who are ill or malnourished; have a compromised immune system; are in an institution; have liver or stomach illnesses; or are pregnant, very old, or very young.[7] Each year in Canada, there are an estimated 4 million domestic cases of foodborne illness.[8] The Canadian Food Inspection Agency (CFIA) provides information for consumers about the common bacteria, viruses, and parasites that cause foodborne illness.[9] To find food safety tips and fact sheets on how to prevent foodborne illness in the kitchen, visit the CFIA's website at http://www.inspection.gc.ca/english/fssa/concen/tipcone.shtml.

If digestive tract disturbances are the major or only symptoms of your next bout of "stomach flu," chances are excellent that what you really have is a foodborne illness. By learning something about these illnesses and taking a few preventive steps, you can minimize your chances of contracting a foodborne illness.

How Do Microbes in Food Cause Illness in the Body?

Microorganisms can cause foodborne illness either by infection or by intoxication. Infectious agents such as *Salmonella* bacteria or the virus that causes hepatitis A multiply and infect the tissues of the human body.[10] Other microorganisms in foods produce **enterotoxins** or **neurotoxins**, poisonous chemicals released as bacteria

---

Number of Domestic Cases of Foodborne Illnesses

"The Government of Canada estimates that there are about 4 million cases of foodborne illness in Canada every year."

Source: http://www.inspection.gc.ca/food/ information-for-consumers/fact-sheets/food-poisoning/eng/1331151916451/1331152055552.

Persons Especially Vulnerable to Foodborne Illnesses

- Pregnant women
- Newborns
- Older adults
- People with immune systems weakened by cancer treatments, AIDS, diabetes, and other causes

Symptoms That Require Medical Help

- Bloody stools
- Diarrhea of more than 3 days' duration
- Fever of longer than 24 hours' duration
- Headache accompanied by muscle stiffness and fever
- Numbness, muscle weakness, tingling sensations in the skin
- Rapid heart rate, fainting, dizziness

iStockphoto/Thinkstock

With the privilege of abundance comes the responsibility to choose and handle foods wisely.

foodborne illness illness transmitted to human beings through food and water; caused by an infectious agent (*foodborne infection*) or a poisonous substance (*food intoxication*). Also called *food poisoning.*

microbes a shortened name for *microorganisms;* minute organisms too small to observe without a microscope, including bacteria, viruses, and others.

enterotoxins poisons that act upon mucous membranes, such as those of the digestive tract.

neurotoxins poisons that act upon the cells of the nervous system.

multiply; once absorbed into the tissues, the poisons cause various kinds of harm ranging from mild stomach pain and headache to paralysis and death. The toxins may arise in food during improper preparation or storage or within the digestive tract after a person eats contaminated food. The sources and symptoms of foodborne illnesses are listed in Table 12–2.

Table 12–2
Foodborne Illnesses

Disease and Organism That Causes It	Most Frequent Food Sources	Onset and General Symptoms	Prevention Methods
Botulism Botulinum toxin (produced by the *Clostridium botulinum* bacterium)	Anaerobic environment of low acidity (canned corn, peppers, green beans, and other low-acid vegetables; canned meat, fish, and chicken; bottled garlic; packaged lunch meat, ham, and sausage; herb-flavoured oils; preserved fat or fish; baked potatoes in foil and other cooked foods held at warm temperature for more than 2 hr). In infants, honey may be a source.	Onset: 12 to 72 hr. Nervous system symptoms including blurred or double vision, inability to swallow, speech difficulty, and progressive paralysis of the respiratory system; often fatal; leaves prolonged symptoms in survivors.	Use proper canning methods for low-acid foods; avoid commercially prepared foods with leaky seals or with bent, bulging, or broken cans.
Campylobacteriosis *Campylobacter jejuni* bacterium	Raw poultry, beef, lamb, unpasteurized milk (foods of animal origin eaten raw or undercooked or recontaminated after cooking)	Onset: 2 to 5 days. Diarrhea, nausea, vomiting, abdominal cramps, fever; sometimes bloody stools; lasts 2 to 10 days; rarely, nervous system paralysis (Guillain-Barré syndrome).	Cook foods (especially poultry) thoroughly; use pasteurized milk; use sanitary food-handling methods.
Cryptosporidiosis *Cryptosporidium parvum* microscopic parasite	Commonly, contaminated swimming or drinking water, even from treated sources. Highly chlorine-resistant. Contaminated raw produce and unpasteurized juices and ciders.	Onset: 2 to 10 days. Diarrhea, loose or watery stools, stomach cramps, upset stomach, slight fever. Symptoms may come and go for weeks or months.	Wash all raw vegetables and fruits before peeling; choose pasteurized milk and juice. Do not swallow drops of water while using pools, hot tubs, ponds, lakes, rivers, or streams for recreation.
Cyclosporiasis *Cyclospora cayetanensis* single-cell parasite	Contaminated water; contaminated fresh produce.	Onset: average, 7 days. Watery diarrhea, loss of appetite, weight loss, stomach cramps, nausea, vomiting, muscle aches, fatigue. Symptoms may come and go for weeks or months.	In areas of uncertain sanitation, drink only treated or boiled water and eat only cooked hot foods or fruit you peel yourself.
Hemolytic-uremic syndrome *Escherichia coli (E. coli)* O157:H7 bacterium	Undercooked ground beef, unpasteurized milk and milk products, unpasteurized juices or cider, raw produce (especially sprouts), contaminated water, and person-to-person contact.	Onset: 1 to 8 days. Severe bloody diarrhea, abdominal pain, vomiting, acute kidney failure; death. Survivors may face kidney problems, hypertension, blindness, paralysis, and colon problems.	Cook ground beef thoroughly; avoid unpasteurized milk and juice products; use sanitary food-handling methods; use treated, boiled, or bottled water. Vulnerable people should avoid raw sprouts.
Hepatitis Hepatitis A virus	Undercooked or raw shellfish; raw or lightly cooked produce; contaminated water; baked goods or other ready-to-eat foods contaminated by infected food handlers.	Onset: 15 to 50 days (28 days average). Inflammation of the liver; fatigue; dark urine; headache; nausea, vomiting, or indigestion; jaundice (yellowed skin and eyes from buildup of wastes); muscle pain.	Cook foods thoroughly; test food handlers.

Table 12–2

Foodborne Illnesses (continued)

Disease and Organism That Causes It	Most Frequent Food Sources	Onset and General Symptoms	Prevention Methods
Listeriosis *Listeria monocytogenes* bacterium	Raw meat and seafood, luncheon meats, hot dogs, unpasteurized milk, and soft cheeses.	Onset: 7 to 70 days. Mimics flu; blood poisoning; meningitis (stiff neck, severe headache, and fever); miscarriage of pregnancy; severe illness or death of newborns; blood or brain infection in elderly or other vulnerable people.	Use sanitary food-handling methods; cook foods thoroughly; use pasteurized milk.
Salmonellosis *Salmonella* bacteria	Raw or undercooked eggs, meats, poultry, unpasteurized milk and other dairy products, shrimp, pasta, raw produce, unpasteurized juices, contaminated water.	Onset: 1 to 3 days. Nausea, fever, chills, vomiting, abdominal cramps, diarrhea, headache; severe cases can be fatal.	Use sanitary food-handling methods; use pasteurized milk and juice; cook foods thoroughly; refrigerate foods promptly and properly.
Shigellosis *Shigella* bacteria varieties	Contaminated food (may look and smell normal); raw produce and other foods contaminated by poor sanitation practices of infected farm workers or food handlers, human sewage fertilizer in growing fields, or exposure to flies. Contaminated drinking or swimming water.	Onset: 1 to 2 days. Diarrhea, fever, stomach cramps. The diarrhea is often bloody. In young children, high fever, seizures. Symptomless sufferers can spread the bacteria to others.	Frequent and careful hand washing with soap. In areas of uncertain sanitation, drink only treated or boiled water and eat only hot cooked foods or fruit you peel yourself. Do not swallow drops of water when swimming.
Staphylococcal food poisoning Staphylococcal toxin (produced by the *Staphylococcus aureus* bacterium)	Toxin produced in meat; poultry; egg products; tuna, potato, and macaroni salads; and cream-filled pastries.	Onset: 1/2 to 8 hr. Diarrhea, nausea, vomiting, abdominal cramps, fatigue; mimics flu; lasts 24 to 48 hr; rarely fatal.	Use sanitary food-handling methods; cook food thoroughly; refrigerate foods promptly and properly.
"Stomach flu"ᵃ (misnomer) Noroviruses	Foods, such as cookies, sandwiches, salads, and ice contaminated by infected food handlers; raw produce; shellfish from waters contaminated with human sewage, such as boat bilge.	Onset: 12 to 48 hr. Acute digestive illness, with pain, vomiting, possibly diarrhea, headache, and low-grade fever. Diarrhea more typical in adults; vomiting in children.	Choose restaurants that pass health department inspections and enforce worker sanitation. If uncertain, order cooked foods served steaming hot. Avoid raw shellfish.
"Stomach flu"ᵃ (misnomer) *Vibrio parahaemolyticus* and other *Vibrio* bacteria	Raw or undercooked shellfish, often oysters. Less commonly, skin infection when an open wound is exposed to warm seawater.	Onset: 24 hr. Watery diarrhea, abdominal cramping, nausea, vomiting, fever and chills.	Cook shellfish well, especially oysters. Purchase shellfish from reputable dealer. Avoid exposing wounds to warm seawater.
Traveller's diarrhea A variety of microorganisms including *Giardia* and other protozoa	Contaminated water, undercooked ground beef, raw foods, imported unpasteurized soft cheeses.	Onset: 2 days to several weeks. Loose and watery stools, nausea, vomiting, bloating, abdominal cramps.	Cook foods thoroughly; use safe, treated water and pasteurized milk; wash and peel raw fruit and vegetables or avoid them in areas of uncertain sanitation.
Trichinosis *Trichinella spiralis* parasite	Raw or undercooked pork or wild game (bear or moose); worms produce larvae that travel via the bloodstream to muscle tissue, producing cysts.	Onset: 1–2 days. Abdominal pain, nausea, vomiting, diarrhea, fatigue, and fever. Two to 8 weeks later, muscle pain, pain on breathing, edema (swelling), skin eruptions, loss of appetite, and weight loss.	Cook foods thoroughly.

Source: Data from Centers for Disease Control and Prevention, *Diagnosis and management of foodborne illnesses,* Morbidity and Mortality Weekly Report, supplement, 53 (2004): 7:12.

ᵃAlthough popularly called "stomach flu," the digestive disturbances caused by noroviruses and *Vibrio* organisms are unrelated to influenza.

For safety, when making flavoured oils, wash and dry the herbs before adding them to the oil and keep the oil refrigerated.

botulism an often-fatal food poisoning caused by botulinum toxin, a toxin produced by the *Clostridium botulinum* bacterium that grows without oxygen in nonacidic canned foods.

Although the most common source of food toxicity is the *Staphylococcus aureus* bacterium, the most infamous is undoubtedly *Clostridium botulinum*, an organism that produces a toxin so deadly that an amount as tiny as a single grain of salt can kill several people within an hour. In the fall of 2006, two confirmed cases of botulism in Toronto were associated with the consumption of carrot juice imported from California (see http://www.cbc.ca/news/canada/toxic-carrot-juice-paralyzes-2-in-toronto-1.578997). To reproduce and release the toxin, *C. botulinum* requires anaerobic conditions such as those found in improperly canned (especially home-canned) foods and homemade garlic or herb-flavoured oils stored at room temperature. **Botulism** quickly paralyzes muscles, making seeing, speaking, swallowing, and breathing difficult.[11] Because death can occur as soon as 24 hours later, botulism demands immediate medical attention (see the margin for warning signs). Even then, survivors may suffer the effects for months or years.

The botulinum toxin is destroyed by heat, so canned foods that contain the toxin can be rendered harmless by boiling them for 10 minutes. Food can be canned safely at home if proper canning techniques are followed to the letter.*

KEY POINT

- Public health experts estimate that each year in Canada millions of people suffer mild to life-threatening symptoms caused by foodborne illness. Although relatively rare, botulism is often deadly when it strikes.

As a result of the tragic events of the listeriosis outbreak during the summer of 2008 that affected more than 50 people (22 of whom died) in seven provinces across the country, (1) the prime minister appointed an independent investigator to study the reasons for the outbreak; (2) the federal government announced that it would invest $75 million more in food safety to further improve the ability to prevent, detect, and respond to future outbreaks; (3) the government stated that it will act on the 57 recommendations that subsequently arose from the independent investigator report (http://www.hc-sc.gc.ca/fn-an/pubs/securit/exec-listeriosis-res-eng.php); and (4) the government recently released (May 2013) its guidance document for the implementation of the "2011 Policy on *Listeria monocytogenes* in Ready-to-Eat Foods" (http://www.inspection.gc.ca/food/fish-and-seafood/communiques/2013-05-27/eng/13684690 48441/1368469119210). Also, in the fall of 2012, a total of 18 people in four provinces became sick from *Escherichia coli* 0157 after eating beef from a meat-processing plant in Alberta, leading to the largest beef recall in Canadian history. Since that time the government has (a) passed the Safe Foods for Canadians Act in November 2012 (http://www.inspection.gc.ca/about-the-cfia/acts-and-regulations/initiatives/sfca/ eng/1338796071420/1338796152395); (b) launched the "Safe Foods for Canadians Action Plan" in May 2013 (http://www.inspection.gc.ca/food/action-plan/eng/13669 21334607/1366921368545); (c) accepted the recommendations of the "Independent Review of XL Foods Inc. Beef Recall 2012" report (http://www.inspection.gc.ca/ about-the-cfia/newsroom/news-releases/2013-06-05/eng/1370364322344/13703 64337243); and (d) enhanced controls on *E. coli* in raw beef products (http://www .inspection.gc.ca/english/fssa/meavia/man/ch4/annexoe.shtml).

Food Safety from Farm to Table

Figure 12–1 shows that careful food handling is required to prevent microbes from becoming a problem—on the farm; in processing plants; during transportation; at supermarkets and restaurants; and by you, the consumer (for yourself and your family). The rapid globalization of the North American food supply has widened safety concerns in farming, processing, and transportation, especially because seafood and fresh produce lead the list of imported foods and both are common vectors of illness.[12] Equally critical to the chain of food safety, however, is the final handling of food by people who purchase it and consume it at home.

---

*Canadian Food Inspection Agency's Food Safety Facts on Botulism: http://healthycanadians.gc.ca/eating-nutrition/poisoning-intoxication/botulism-botulisme-eng.php.

Figure 12–1

Flow of Food Safety: From Farm to Table

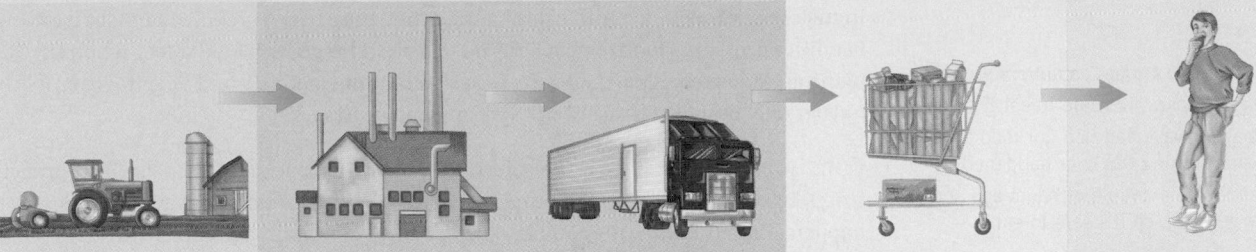

FARMS
Farmers and workers must use safe methods of growing, harvesting, sorting, packing, and storing food to minimize contamination hazards.

PROCESSING
Industries must monitor for safety at critical control points (use HACCP, see text).

TRANSPORTATION
Containers and vehicles transporting food must be clean. Cold food must be kept cold at all times.

RETAIL: GROCERY AND RESTAURANT SALES
Establishments must pass local health inspections and train staff in sanitation.

CONSUMER RESPONSIBILITY
Consumers must learn and use sound principles of food safety as taught in this chapter and stay mindful that foodborne illness is a real possibility.

The overwhelming majority of food-poisoning cases result from errors consumers make in handling foods *after* purchase. Commercially prepared food is usually safe, but rare accidents do occur and often affect many people at once. Dairy farmers, for example, rely on **pasteurization**, a process of heating milk to kill many disease-causing organisms and make the milk safe for consumption. When, as happened in Chicago in the mid-1980s or more recently in England, a major dairy develops flaws in its pasteurization system, many thousands of cases of foodborne illness result. Other types of farming require other safeguards. Growing food usually involves soil, and soil contains abundant bacterial colonies, making contamination of food likely. Additionally, farm workers who are ill can easily transfer disease-causing organisms to foods such as produce.

Attention on *E. coli* In the mid-1990s, a fast-food restaurant chain in the northwestern United States served undercooked hamburgers from meat that had been contaminated with the dangerous bacterium *E. coli* O157:H7. Four people died, and hundreds of other patrons were stricken with serious illness. News coverage focused the national spotlight on two important food-safety issues: raw meats routinely contain live, disease-causing organisms of many types, and thorough cooking is necessary to make animal-derived foods safe. Revelations about *E. coli* O157:H7 have led to a much-needed overhaul of many countries' mechanisms for ensuring meat safety.

Infections from *E. coli* O157:H7 cause bloody diarrhea, severe intestinal cramps, and dehydration, symptoms that set in a few days after eating tainted meat, unpasteurized milk, or even fresh berries or organic produce that has been contaminated. In the worst cases, *hemolytic-uremic syndrome* leads to abnormal blood clotting with kidney failure, damage to the central nervous system and other organs, and even death, especially among children.[13] Antibiotics and self-prescribed antidiarrhea medicines increase the absorption and retention of the toxin, worsening the condition.[14] Medical treatment consists of rest, fluids, and hospitalization should the kidneys fail or serious dehydration occur.

Industry Controls—Government Inspections and HACCP Under the mandatory Food Safety Enhancement Program (FSEP), all federally registered meat and poultry establishments and storage facilities are being encouraged to implement and maintain a **Hazard Analysis Critical Control Point (HACCP)** plan to help prevent foodborne illnesses at their source.[15] Each slaughterhouse, producer, packer, distributor, and transporter of susceptible foods must identify "critical control points" in its procedures where the risk of food contamination is high and then devise and implement ways of minimizing contamination.

Obtain Medical Help for These Symptoms
- Bloody diarrhea
- Severe intestinal cramps
- Dehydration

pasteurization the treatment of milk with heat sufficient to kill certain pathogens (disease-causing microbes) commonly transmitted through milk; not a sterilization process. Pasteurized milk retains bacteria that cause milk spoilage. Raw milk, even if labelled "certified," transmits many foodborne diseases to people each year and should be avoided.

Hazard Analysis Critical Control Point (HACCP) a systematic plan to identify and correct potential microbial hazards in the manufacturing, distribution, and commercial use of food products. *HACCP* may be pronounced "HASS-ip."

Since the development of the HACCP system, *Salmonella* contamination of U.S. poultry, ground beef, and pork, for example, has decreased by almost 50 percent, 40 percent, and 25 percent, respectively.[16] Illnesses from contamination in these industries are also declining, indicating that the HACCP requirement is working. Facilities providing food to people stand to benefit in terms of food safety when HACCP plans are followed. Soon dietitians in assisted-living facilities and hospitals across the nation may be called to assist in their implementation.[17]

Consumer Protection   The safety of canned and packaged foods sold in grocery stores is controlled through sound food technology practices, but rare accidents do happen. Batch numbering enables the recall of contaminated foods through public announcements via newspapers, websites, television, and radio, and Health Canada and other Canadian government agencies and the U.S. FDA monitor large food suppliers and importers. You can help protect yourself, too. Carefully inspect the seals and wrappers of packages. Reject open, leaking, or bulging cans, jars, and packages. Many jars have safety "buttons" on the lid, designed to pop up once the jar is opened; make sure that they have not "popped." If a package on the shelf looks ragged, soiled, or punctured, do not buy the product; turn it in to the store manager. A badly dented can or a mangled package is useless in protecting food from microorganisms, insects, spoilage, or even vandals. Frozen foods should be solidly frozen, and those in a chest-type freezer case should be stored below the frost line. See the margin for some food-safety myths that often make consumers sick.

> **KEY POINT**
> - Industry employs sound practices to safeguard the commercial food supply from microbial threats. Still, incidents of commercial foodborne illness have caused widespread harm to health.

Food Safety in the Kitchen

Large-scale commercial incidents make up only a fraction of the nation's total food-poisoning cases each year, although they are widely publicized. The vast majority of cases arise from one person's error in a small setting and affect just a few victims. Some people have come to accept a yearly bout or two of intestinal illness as inevitable, but these illnesses can and should be prevented. Just for fun, take the quiz in Table 12–3 to see how well you follow food-safety rules. Then read on to learn how you can do your part to make meals at home as safe as they can be.

Food can provide ideal conditions for bacteria to thrive or to produce toxins. Disease-causing bacteria require warmth (4–60°C), moisture, and nutrients. To defeat bacteria, deprive them of one of these conditions. Remember these four "keepers": keep hot food hot, keep cold food cold, keep raw foods separate, and keep your hands and the kitchen clean (see Figure 12–2).

Keep Hot Food Hot   Keeping hot food hot includes cooking foods long enough to reach an internal temperature that will kill microbes. To alert consumers to this fact, the U.S. Department of Agriculture (USDA) invented "Thermy," the cartoon character shown in the margin, who urges the use of a thermometer to test the temperatures of cooked foods. Figure 12–3 illustrates the safe internal temperatures of cooked foods and various types of thermometers. Table 12–4 is a glossary of thermometer terms.

After cooking, foods must be held at 60°C or higher until served because cooking does not destroy all bacterial toxins. Food registering 60°C on a thermometer feels hot, not just warm. Even hot cooked foods, if handled improperly prior to serving, can cause illness. Delicious-looking meatballs on a buffet may harbour bacteria unless they have been kept steaming hot. After the meal, cooked foods should be refrigerated immediately or within two hours at the maximum (one hour if room temperature approaches 32°C). If food has been left out longer than this, toss it out.

Keep Cold Food Cold   Keeping cold food cold starts when you leave the grocery store. If you are running errands, shop last so that the groceries do not stay in the car

---

Myths That Often Make Consumers Sick
- "If it tastes okay, it's safe to eat."
- "We have always handled our food this way, and nothing has ever happened."
- "I sampled it a couple of hours ago and didn't get sick, so it's safe to eat."

- Requirements of disease-causing bacteria: warmth, moisture, and nutrients.

Figure 12–2
Fight Bac!

Four ways to keep food safe: Clean, Separate, Cook, and Chill. The Fight Bac!® website is at http://www.fightbac.org.

The U.S. FDA's "Thermy" character was developed as a light-hearted appeal to consumers, encouraging them to use food thermometers.

Table 12–3

Can You Pass the Kitchen Food-Safety Quiz?

How food-safety savvy are you? Give yourself 2 points for each correct answer.

1. The temperature of the refrigerator in my home is
   A. 10°C
   B. 4°C
   C. I don't know; I don't own a refrigerator thermometer.

2. The last time we had leftover cooked stew or other meaty food, the food was
   A. cooled to room temperature and then put in the refrigerator.
   B. put in the refrigerator immediately after the food was served.
   C. left at room temperature overnight or longer.

3. If I use a cutting board to cut raw meat, poultry, or fish and it will be used to chop another food, the board is
   A. reused as is.
   B. wiped with a damp cloth or sponge.
   C. washed with soap and water.
   D. washed with soap and hot water and then sanitized.

4. The last time I had a hamburger, I ate it
   A. rare.
   B. medium.
   C. well-done.

5. The last time there was cookie dough where I lived, the dough was
   A. made with raw eggs, and I sampled some of it.
   B. store-bought, and I sampled some of it.
   C. not sampled until baked.

6. I clean my kitchen counters and food preparation areas with
   A. a damp sponge that I rinse and reuse.
   B. a clean sponge or cloth and water.
   C. a clean cloth with hot water and soap.
   D. the same as above, then a bleach solution or other sanitizer.

7. When dishes are washed in my home, they are
   A. cleaned by an automatic dishwasher and then air-dried.
   B. left to soak in the sink for several hours and then washed with soap in the same water.
   C. washed right away with hot water and soap in the sink and then air-dried.
   D. washed right away with hot water and soap in the sink and immediately towel-dried.

8. The last time I handled raw meat, poultry, or fish, I cleaned my hands afterward by
   A. wiping them on a towel.
   B. rinsing them under warm tap water.
   C. washing with soap and water.

9. Meat, poultry, and fish products are defrosted in my home by
   A. setting them on the counter.
   B. placing them in the refrigerator.
   C. microwaving and cooking promptly when thawed.
   D. soaking them in warm water.

10. I realize that eating raw seafood poses special problems for people with
    A. diabetes.
    B. HIV infection.
    C. cancer.
    D. liver disease.

Answers
1. Refrigerators should stay at 4°C or less, so if you chose answer B, give yourself two points; zero for other answers.
2. Answer B is the best practice; give yourself two points if you picked it; zero for other answers.
3. If answer D best describes your household's practice, give yourself two points; if C, one point.
4. Give yourself two points if you picked answer C; zero for other answers.
5. If you answered A, you may be putting yourself at risk for infection from bacteria in raw shell eggs. Answer C—eating the baked product—will earn you two points and so will answer B. Commercial products are made with pasteurized eggs.
6. Answer C or D will earn you two points each; answer B, one point; answer A, zero.
7. Answers A and C are worth two points each; other answers, zero.
8. The only correct practice is answer C. Give yourself two points if you picked it; zero for others.
9. Give yourself two points if you picked B or C; zero for others.
10. This is a tricky question: all of the answers apply. Give yourself two points for knowing one or more of the risky conditions.

Rating Your Home's Food Practices
20 points: Feel confident about the safety of foods served in your home.
12 to 19 points: Reexamine food-safety practices in your home. Some key rules are being violated.
11 points or below: Take steps immediately to correct food-handling, storage, and cooking techniques used in your home. Current practices are putting you and other members of your household in danger of foodborne illness.

Source: Adapted from U.S. Food and Drug Administration, Can your kitchen pass the food safety test? FDA Consumer, October 1998.

Table 12–4

Glossary of Thermometer Terms

- **appliance thermometer** a thermometer that verifies the temperature of an appliance. An *oven thermometer* verifies that the oven is heating properly; a *refrigerator/freezer thermometer* tests for proper refrigerator (<4°C) or freezer (–17°C) temperature.

- **fork thermometer** a utensil combining a meat fork and an instant-read food thermometer.

- **instant-read thermometer** (e.g., tip-sensitive digital thermometer) a thermometer that, when inserted into food, measures its temperature within seconds; designed to test temperature of food at intervals and not to be left in food during cooking.

- **oven-safe thermometer** a thermometer designed to remain in the food to give constant readings during cooking.

- **pop-up thermometer** a disposable timing device commonly used in turkeys. The centre of the device contains a stainless steel spring that "pops up" when food reaches the right temperature.

- **single-use temperature indicator** a type of instant-read thermometer that changes colour to indicate that the food has reached the desired temperature. Discarded after one use; they are often used in retail food markets to eliminate cross-contamination.

Figure 12–3

Food-Safety Temperatures and Household Thermometers

Different thermometers do different jobs. To choose the right one, pay attention to its temperature range: some have high temperature ranges intended to test the doneness of meats and other hot foods. Others have lower ranges for testing temperatures of refrigerators and freezers.

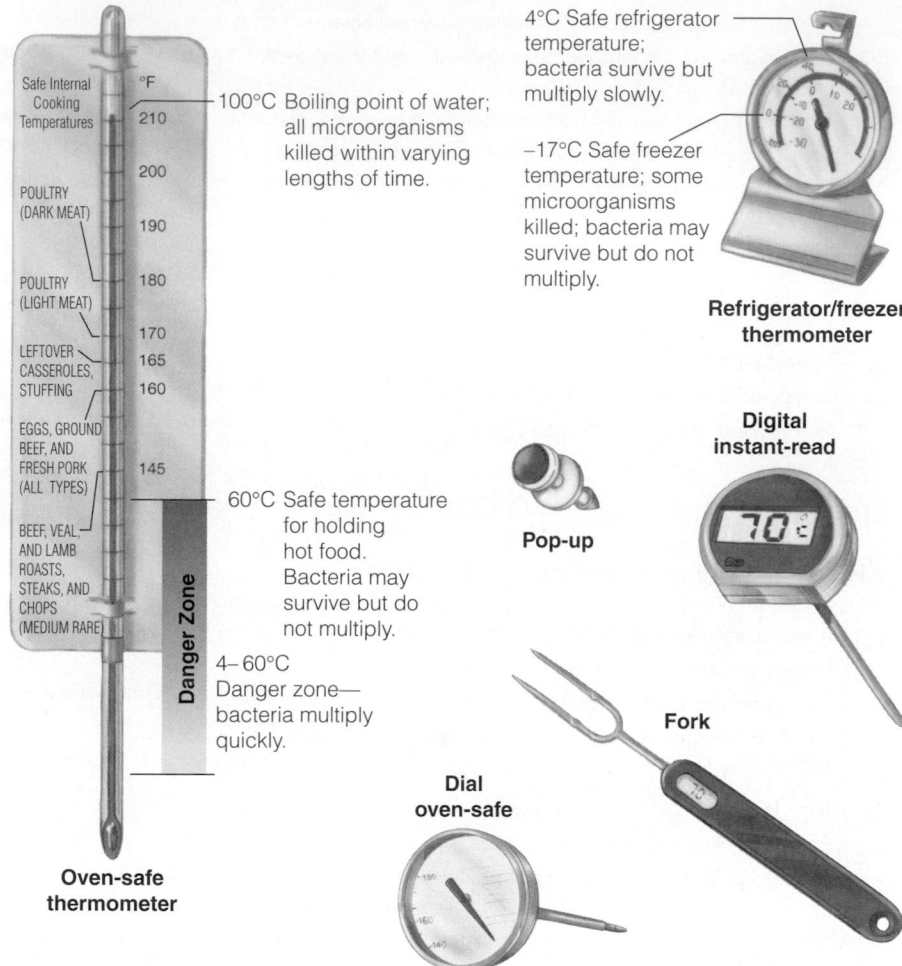

- For more on food-safety tips on how to handle foods in the kitchen, when barbecuing, etc., go to Health Canada's Web page "In Your Kitchen: Safe Food Handling Tips" at http://www.hc-sc.gc.ca/fn-an/securit/kitchen-cuisine/index-eng.php.

cross-contamination the contamination of a food through exposure to utensils, hands, or other surfaces that were previously in contact with a contaminated food.

too long. (If ice cream begins to melt, it has been too long.) Upon arrival home, load foods into the refrigerator or freezer immediately. Keeping foods cold applies to defrosting foods, too. Thaw meats or poultry in the refrigerator, not at room temperature, and marinate meats in the refrigerator, too. Table 12–5 lists some safe keeping times for foods stored at or below 4°C.

Any food with an "off" appearance or odour should not be used or even tasted. You cannot rely on your senses of smell and sight alone to warn you, however, because most hazards are not detectable by odour, taste, or appearance. As the old saying goes, "when in doubt, throw it out."

Keep Raw Food Separate   Keeping raw food separate means preventing **cross-contamination** of foods. Raw foods, especially meats, eggs, and seafood, are likely to contain bacteria. To prevent bacteria from spreading, keep the raw foods and their juices away from ready-to-eat foods. For example, if you take burgers out to the grill on a plate, wash that plate in hot, soapy water before using it to hold the cooked burgers. If you use a cutting board to cut raw meat, wash the board, the knife, and your hands thoroughly with soap before handling other foods and especially before making a salad or other foods that are eaten raw. Many cooks keep a separate cutting board just for raw meats.

Keep Your Hands and the Kitchen Clean Keeping your hands and the kitchen clean requires using freshly washed utensils and laundered towels and washing your hands properly, not just rinsing them, before and after handling raw food (see Figure 12–4). Normal, healthy skin is covered with bacteria, some of which may cause foodborne illness when deposited on moist, nutrient-rich food and allowed to multiply.[18] Remember to use a nailbrush to clean under fingernails when washing hands and tend to routine nail care—artificial nails, long nails, and chipped polish harbour more bacteria than do natural, clean, short nails.[19]

For most purposes, washing hands with ordinary soap and warm water is effective, but using an alcohol-based hand-sanitizing gel can provide additional killing power against many remaining bacteria and most viruses.[20] Using a hand sanitizer provides additional protection against spreading illnesses when someone in the house is ill or when preparing food for an infant, an elderly person, or someone with a compromised immune systems.*,[21] If you are ill or have open sores, stay away from food preparation.

In the kitchen, microbes love to nestle down in small, damp spaces such as the inner cells of sponges or the pores between the fibres of wooden cutting boards. Antibacterial cleaners, sponges, cloths, boards, and utensils possess a chemical additive intended to deter bacterial growth, but little science supports their use.[22] Disposable cutting sheets designed for cutting raw meats soak up raw juices and bacteria for disposal, but they are expensive and add to the environmental burden of garbage. You can ensure the safety of regular cutting boards and reduce the microbes in sponges by washing them in a dishwasher or by treating them as suggested in the next two paragraphs. Alternatively, save the sponges for car washing and other heavy cleaning chores and clean the kitchen with washable dishcloths that can be laundered often.

Figure 12–4

Proper Hand Washing Prevents Illness

Many people do not wash their hands at critical times or wash them without soap or for too short a time. You can avoid many illnesses by following these hand-washing procedures before, during, and after food preparation; before eating; after using the bathroom; after handling animals or their waste; or when hands are dirty. Wash hands more frequently when someone in the house is sick.

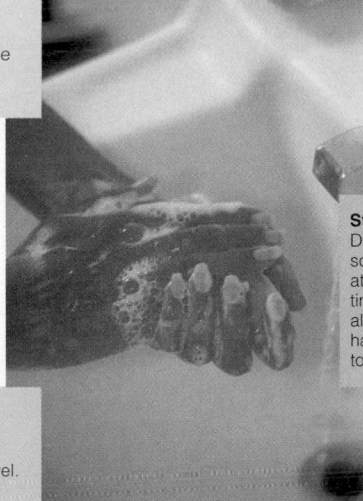

Step 1:
Wet hands and apply liquid or clean bar soap. Place bar soap on a rack to drain between uses.

Step 2:
Dislodge germs by scrubbing hands together for at least 20 seconds—about the time it takes to recite the alphabet. Scrub fingers, tops of hands, and palms; use a nailbrush to clean under fingernails.

Step 3:
Rinse hands in clean water and dry with a freshly laundered towel or paper towel.

Suza Scalora/Photodisc/Getty Images

Source: Centers for Disease Control and Prevention, An ounce of prevention keeps the gems away, *2002, http://www.cdc.gov/ounceofprevention/; Canadian Food Inspection Agency,* Kitchen Safety Tips - Preventing foodborne illness, *available at http://www.inspection.gc.ca/english/fssa/concen/tipcon/kitchene3.shtml*

---

*Effective hand sanitizers contain between 60% and 70% ethyl alcohol.

Table 12–5

Safe Food Storage Times: Refrigerator (≤4°C)

1 to 2 d

Raw ground meats, breakfast or other raw sausages, variety meats; raw fish or poultry; gravies

3 to 5 d

Raw steaks, roasts, or chops; cooked meats, vegetables, and mixed dishes; ham slices; mayonnaise salads (chicken, egg, pasta, tuna)

1 wk

Hard-cooked eggs, bacon or hot dogs (opened packages); whole or half hams; smoked sausages

2 to 4 wk

Raw eggs (in shells); bacon or hot dogs (packages unopened); dry sausages (pepperoni, hard salami); most aged and processed cheeses (Swiss, brick)

2 months

Mayonnaise (opened jar); most dry cheeses (parmesan, romano)

Remember These Four "Keepers"

- Keep hot food hot.
- Keep cold food cold.
- Keep raw foods separate.
- Keep your hands and the kitchen clean.

To eliminate microbes in your kitchen, you have four choices, each with benefits and drawbacks. One is to poison the microbes on cutting boards, sponges, and other equipment with toxic chemicals such as bleach (one teaspoon per litre of water). The benefit is that chlorine can kill even the hardiest organism. The drawback is that chlorine is toxic to handle, can ruin clothing, and washes down household drains into the water supply and forms chemicals that can harm waterways and fish.

A second option is to treat kitchen equipment with heat. Soapy water heated to 60°C kills most harmful organisms and washes most others away. This method takes effort, though, since the water must be truly scalding hot, well beyond the temperature of the tap. Third, an automatic dishwasher can combine both methods: it washes in water hotter than hands can tolerate, and most dishwasher detergents contain chlorine. Fourth, for sponges, place the wet sponge in a microwave oven and heat it until steaming hot (times vary). Pick one of these strategies to keep implements and surfaces safe for food preparation.

KEY POINT

- To prevent foodborne illness, always remember that it can happen. Keep hot foods hot, keep cold foods cold, keep raw foods separate, and keep your hands and the kitchen clean.

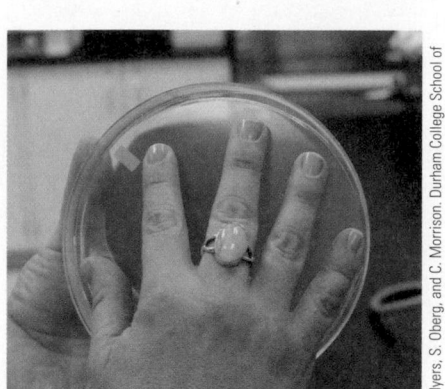

This person's clean-looking but unwashed hand is touching a sterile nutrient-rich gel.

Source: Courtesy of A. Estes Reynolds, George A. Schuler, James A. Christian, and William C. Hurst. Food, Hands and Bacteria. Cooperative Extension Service of the University of Georgia, Athens, GA. 2000. Extension Publication no. 693.

Which Foods Are Most Likely to Make People Sick?

Some foods are more hospitable to microbial growth than others. Foods that are high in moisture and nutrients and those that are chopped or ground are especially favourable hosts. These foods are likely to spoil quickly without proper refrigeration. Table 12–6 provides special tips for preserving food safely in the event of a power outage.

Meats and Poultry Raw meats and poultry require special handling, and packages bear labels to instruct consumers on meat safety (see Figure 12–5).* Meats in the grocery cooler often contain all sorts of bacteria, and they provide a moist, nutritious environment that is just right for microbial growth. Ground meat or poultry is handled more than meats left whole, and grinding exposes much more surface area for bacteria to land on, so experts advise cooking these foods to well-done. Use a thermometer to test

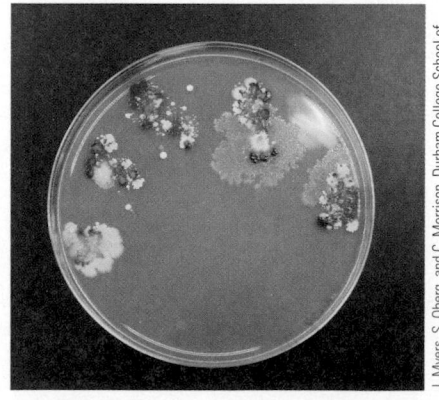

After 24 hours, these large colonies provide visible evidence of the microorganisms that were transferred from the hand to the gel.

Source: Courtesy of A. Estes Reynolds, George A. Schuler, James A. Christian, and William C. Hurst. Food, Hands and Bacteria. Cooperative Extension Service of the University of Georgia, Athens, GA. 2000. Extension Publication no. 693.

Table 12–6

Keeping Food Safe When the Power Goes Out

Keeping foods below 4°C during power outages can be challenging.

- Keep the refrigerator and freezer doors closed as much as possible to keep the cold in.
- Consume foods from the refrigerator first. Undisturbed, a full freezer will hold its temperature for about 48 hours; a refrigerator's temperature begins to rise in only 4 hours, even with the door closed.
- If available, place a block of ice or dry ice in the refrigerator; 50 pounds of dry ice can maintain the refrigerator temperature for about 2 days. Find out now where ice can be purchased in your neighbourhood. If the weather is cold, fill small containers with water and put them out to freeze; use them in refrigerators, freezers, or coolers.
- Keep a week's supply of shelf-stable items, such as canned goods, bottled water, dry cereals, dry or shelf-stable milk, and ready-to-serve infant or pet foods, as needed. Use and replace these items several times a year, and keep a hand-operated can opener in the cupboard.
- Place thermometers in the freezer and refrigerator now. Then, when the power is out, the thermometer will indicate when the temperature is no longer safe and perishable food must be discarded.
- If food partially thaws (still has ice crystals) during an outage, and the temperature in the freezer never rose above 4°C, the food can safely be refrozen for later use.

---

*If you have questions about meat and poultry safety: go to http://www.inspection.gc.ca/food/meat-and-poultry-products/eng/1300124955992/1300125034322 or call the Canadian Food Inspection Agency toll-free at 1-800-442-2342.

Figure 12–5

Safe Handling Instructions for Meat and Poultry

Never allow frozen meat to defrost at room temperature or in a bath of warm water. In both cases, meat thaws from outside in, and the outside meat layer can easily warm up to temperatures that permit bacterial growth before the core defrosts.

Safe Handling Instructions

THIS PRODUCT WAS PREPARED FROM INSPECTED AND PASSED MEAT AND/OR POULTRY. SOME FOOD PRODUCTS MAY CONTAIN BACTERIA THAT CAN CAUSE ILLNESS IF THE PRODUCT IS MISHANDLED OR COOKED IMPROPERLY. FOR YOUR PROTECTION, FOLLOW THESE SAFE HANDLING INSTRUCTIONS.

 KEEP REFRIGERATED OR FROZEN. THAW IN REFRIGERATOR OR MICROWAVE.

 KEEP RAW MEAT AND POULTRY SEPARATE FROM OTHER FOODS. WASH WORKING SURFACES (INCLUDING CUTTING BOARDS), UTENSILS, AND HANDS AFTER TOUCHING RAW MEAT OR POULTRY.

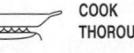 COOK THOROUGHLY. KEEP HOT FOODS HOT. REFRIGERATE LEFTOVERS IMMEDIATELY OR DISCARD.

Microwave cooking of meats requires special care. Large, thick, dense foods such as roasts or meat loaves may register "cooked" on an internal meat thermometer, but may harbour cool spots in which dangerous microorganisms, such as the *Trichinella spiralis* parasite, sometimes present in pork, can survive. Such foods are best cooked by another method or divided into thin individual portions to be microwaved.

Properly cooked food hot from the oven or stove is relatively free of bacteria, but as soon as it is taken out to serve, it is reinoculated. Kitchen utensils recontaminate the food, or bacteria from the air land on its surface. Promptly after serving, even while the food is still hot, refrigerate leftovers in shallow containers for quick, even chilling. Large amounts of food refrigerated in deep containers may take hours to cool through, allowing bacteria time to multiply in the warm internal portions.

Take care when preparing meats along with foods intended to be served raw, such as chopped salads or lettuce and tomato toppers for hamburgers. A grave error is to prepare raw foods on the same board or with the same utensils as were used to prepare raw meats for cooking.

the internal temperature of poultry and meats, even hamburgers, before declaring them done. Burgers often turn brown and appear cooked before their internal temperature is high enough to kill harmful bacteria.[23]

Bovine Spongiform Encephalopathy (BSE)   Although unrelated to sanitation, animal diseases such as "mad cow disease" or, more properly, **bovine spongiform encephalopathy (BSE)**, pose a worry for meat eaters. A disease of cattle, BSE is linked with a rare but invariably fatal human brain disorder observed in people who consume products from infected animals.* A similar condition is suspected to be linked to consuming wild game.[24] To date, about 215 people, most of them in the United Kingdom, have been diagnosed with or are suspected of having the disease.[25]

Scientists believe BSE to be among a handful of diseases caused by an oddly shaped protein known as a **prion**.[26] Ingested prions seem to lie dormant in the body for many years before their deadly symptoms arise. Unlike bacteria or viruses, prions are not living things and so cannot be killed or controlled through cooking or disinfecting. Also, the body's immune system fails to mount defensive actions against prions. So little is known about how prions cause diseases or how to treat them when they arise that prevention remains the only form of control.

The prion responsible for BSE concentrates in the nervous and digestive tissues of infected animals. People living in or travelling to areas reporting BSE should avoid such foods as sausages, ground meats, and chopped meat products that may contain these heavily infected parts. In cattle, the disease probably spreads by way of cattle feed enriched with nutrients derived from cattle brains, blood, or other tissues. Such feed is now banned from use in most countries.

A safe hamburger is cooked well-done, has juices that run clear, and has reached an internal temperature of 71°C (160°F). Place it on a clean plate when it's done.

bovine spongiform encephalopathy (BOW vinc SPON-jih-form en-SEH-fell-AH-path-ee) **(BSE)** an often-fatal illness of cattle affecting the nerves and brain. Also called *mad cow disease*.

prion (PREE-on) an infective agent consisting of an unusually folded protein that disrupts normal cell functioning, causing disease.

*The human disease is variant Creutzfeldt-Jakob disease (vCJD).

Since BSE emerged in the United Kingdom in the mid-1980s, tens of thousands of cattle have tested positive and four million animals have been destroyed.[27] In 2003, a single U.S. dairy cow in Washington, unable to walk at slaughter, was determined to have BSE. On hearing this news, many countries throughout the world instituted immediate bans on imports of U.S. beef and cattle. The cow, purchased from Canada, may have been fed old-style calf feed tainted with cattle parts. Since then, the U.S. Department of Agriculture has enacted protective measures, such as prohibiting the use of "downer" cattle (those unable to walk) for human consumption and increasing BSE testing of cattle at slaughter.[28] These and other safeguards (see the margin) minimize the risk to consumers of U.S. beef. One substantial risk remains, however: imported supplements made from glands of animals, often sold as hormone preparations, may be made in countries with lax BSE regulations.

For an overview of Canada's BSE safeguards, see http://www.inspection.gc.ca/ animals/terrestrial-animals/diseases/reportable/bse/safeguards/eng/1363896195473/ 1363896681768.

Eggs   Raw, unpasteurized eggs are likely to be contaminated by *Salmonella* bacteria. *Salmonella* of a most virulent type has been detected in blood from food-poisoning victims and samples of illness-causing foods that contained raw eggs. To reduce illnesses from *Salmonella*, the Canadian Food Inspection Agency requires egg cartons to carry instruction labels urging consumers to keep eggs refrigerated, but they may also indicate cooking eggs until yolks are firm, and cooking foods containing eggs thoroughly.[29]

Egg users may miss seeing these instructions, however, because they often appear in tiny type on the side of the egg carton. Healthy people can still safely enjoy favourite foods that call for raw or undercooked eggs, such as rich homemade ice cream, hollandaise sauce, or raw cookie dough, by preparing them with pasteurized egg substitute.[30] For Caesar or other salad dressings, hard-cooked eggs processed in a blender or food processor work well. Even raw pasteurized egg substitutes may contain a few live bacteria that escape the pasteurization process, however, so they may not be safe for pregnant women, the elderly, the very young, or those suffering from immune dysfunction.

Raw Produce   This book champions a diet with abundant fresh fruit and vegetables, yet these foods can present a microbial threat unless they are thoroughly rinsed in cold running water or commercial fruit and vegetable wash to remove microbes before peeling, chopping, or eating. Just 10 years ago, meats, eggs, and seafood posed the greatest foodborne illness threat by far, but today produce poses a similar threat.[31]

Especially troublesome are foods consumed raw, such as lettuce, tomatoes, scallions, and spinach. These foods grow close to the ground, making bacterial contamination from the soil and organic fertilizers likely. Also, much produce is imported from countries where farmers may not adhere to sanitary growing and harvesting procedures and where contagious diseases are widespread. Fields may be irrigated with contaminated water, crops may be fertilized with untreated animal or human manure, or produce may be picked by infected farm workers with poor hygiene practices. In 2003, more than 500 restaurant diners sickened and 3 died from hepatitis A transmitted by raw scallions that were harvested by infected farm workers in Mexico.[32]

Rough skins of melons such as cantaloupes provide crevices that harbour bacteria and so should be scrubbed with a brush under running water before peeling or cutting. Raspberries, other berries, and, in fact, all produce should be rinsed thoroughly under running water for at least 10 seconds (see Table 12–7). While commercial "veggie washes" are safe to use, it is still debatable whether they work any better than washing with clean water or a dilute vinegar solution for removing bacteria or chemical/pesticide residues. As depicted in Figure 12–1, you have to hope that everyone handling your produce from farm to table is following the appropriate regulations or recommendations to minimize bacterial, chemical, or other contamination. Unpasteurized or raw juices and ciders are not safe because microbes on the original fruit may multiply in the product. While all milk available for sale in Canada must be

Table 12–7

Produce Safety

Cleaning Fresh Fruit and Vegetables

1. Remove and discard the outer leaves from vegetables such as lettuce and cabbage before washing.
2. Wash all fruit and vegetables (including organically grown and homegrown, regardless of place of purchase) just before cooking or eating.
3. Wash under clean running water and scrub with a clean scrub brush or with your hands. Do not use soap, detergents, or bleach solutions; commercial vegetable washing products are safe to use.
4. Dry fruit and vegetables before cutting or eating.
5. Cut away damaged or bruised areas that may contain bacteria. Toss out mouldy fruit or vegetables.

Juice Safety

1. Choose chilled pasteurized juices or shelf-stable juices (canned or boxed) that have been treated with high temperature to kill microbes and check their seals to be sure no microbes have entered after processing.
2. Especially infants, children, the elderly, and people with weakened immune systems should never be given raw or unpasteurized juice products.

pasteurized, in 2000, Health Canada introduced a policy to encourage all producers of unpasteurized juices and ciders to voluntarily label them as "unpasteurized."

Raw sprouts (including alfalfa, clover, and radish), often eaten in salads, wraps, and other sandwiches, may not be safe.[33] Sprout seeds may harbour the dangerous *E. coli* O157:H7 bacteria, which cannot be washed away, making even homegrown raw sprouts a risky food. Some experts are calling for all consumers to avoid raw sprouts for safety's sake. Also, as mentioned, oils flavoured at home with fresh garlic or herbs may pose the threat of botulism unless the oils are refrigerated and used promptly.

Seafood   A variety of microbial dangers may lurk in even normal-appearing seafood: viral hepatitis; worms, flukes, and other parasites; viruses that can cause severe intestinal disorders; and naturally occurring toxins.* Hepatitis infection causes prolonged illness that persists for months or years; severely damages the liver; greatly increases the risk of developing liver cancer; and, once in the body, is transmissible to others. Many types of worms depend on the blood of their host for food and reproduction; they attack digestive membranes, sometimes causing life-threatening perforations. Flukes attack and damage the liver.

The dangers posed by seafood have grown in recent years. As population density increases along the seashores, the offshore waters are becoming more polluted, contaminating the seafood living there. Viruses that cause human diseases have been detected in some 90 percent of the waters off the U.S. coast.[34] Watchdog agencies monitor commercial fishing areas to keep harvesters out of unsafe waters, but unwholesome food can still reach the market. In a season, black-market dealers may sell millions of dollars worth of clams and oysters taken illegally from closed harvesting areas.

People who have enjoyed raw oysters and other raw seafood for years may be tempted to ignore these threats because they have never experienced serious illness. Some have heard that alcoholic beverages taken with raw seafood eliminate risks or that hot sauce kills the bacteria, but these assertions are not true. One study, long ago, did find a correlation between taking one drink of whiskey or wine and a reduced risk of disease after eating contaminated seafood, but this evidence is no guarantee of protection. Hot sauce is useless against the infectious agents that contaminate oysters. Experts unanimously agree that the risks of eating raw or lightly cooked seafood today are unacceptably high due to environmental contamination.

---

*To speak with an expert on seafood safety, call the CFIA at 1-800-442-2342.

Consequently, adults and children alike should refrain from eating raw **sushi** or lightly steamed seafood, even when the food is prepared by an expert master chef. Not all varieties of sushi are made from raw fish; sushi made with cooked crabmeat and vegetables, avocado, and other delicacies is safe. The rumour that freezing fish will make it safe to eat raw is only partly true. Freezing fish will kill mature parasitic worms, but only cooking can kill all worm eggs and other microorganisms that can cause illness.

Honey   Honey can contain dormant spores of *C. botulinum* that can awaken (germinate) in the human body to produce the deadly botulinum toxin. Mature healthy adults are usually protected against this threat, but infants under one year of age should never be fed honey, which can also be contaminated with environmental pollutants picked up by the bees. Honey has been implicated in several cases of sudden infant death.

Picnics, Lunch Bags, and Takeout Foods   For safe picnics and safe packed lunches, keep these precautions in mind. Choose foods that remain safe to eat without refrigeration, such as fresh uncut fruit and vegetables, breads and crackers, shelf-stable foods, and canned spreads and cheeses that you can open and use on the spot. Aged cheeses, such as cheddar and Swiss, do well at environmental temperatures for an hour or two, but for longer periods, carry them in a cooler or thermal lunch bag. Mayonnaise is somewhat resistant to spoilage because of its acid content, but when it is mixed with chopped ingredients in pasta, meat, or vegetable salads, the mixtures spoil easily. The chopped ingredients have extensive surface areas for bacteria to invade, and foods that have been in contact with cutting boards, hands, and kitchen utensils have picked up at least a few bacteria. Start with chilled ingredients and then chill chopped salads in shallow containers before, during, and after eating. Keep meat, egg, cheese, and seafood sandwiches cold until eaten.

To keep lunch bag foods chilled, choose a thermal lunch bag and freeze beverages (in appropriate containers, for example a Bisphenol A-free container) to pack in with the foods. As the beverages thaw in the hours before lunch, they keep the foods cold.

As for prepackaged single servings of cheese, cold cuts, and crackers promoted as lunch foods, these items keep well, but they can be extraordinarily high in saturated fat and sodium. They also often cost double or triple the price of the foods purchased separately and are excessively packaged, adding to a growing waste-disposal problem.

Many people rely on takeout foods—rotisserie chicken, pizza, Chinese dishes, and the like—for parties, picnics, or days too hectic to cook. Be certain that the food is safe when you buy it: hot foods should be steaming hot, and cold foods should be thoroughly chilled. Leftover portions of restaurant meals can make a convenient lunch or dinner later on. To be sure that these foods are also safe, reheat them thoroughly (to 60°C) before eating, and discard any portion held at room temperature for longer than two hours from the time it first appears at the restaurant table until you place it in your refrigerator at home.

Today, consumers bear much of the responsibility for staying safe from foodborne illnesses. They must cook meats and eggs to the well-done stage to kill dangerous microorganisms lurking in the raw products. They must scrub vegetables and fruit to remove bacteria, viruses, and pesticide residues. They must avoid foods like raw sprouts and raw seafood that may harbour disease-causing microorganisms. One proposal to help reduce the consumer's burden of responsibility is to expose foods to ionizing radiation in doses that kill microorganisms. This chapter's Consumer Corner on the next page provides some details.

KEY POINT

- Some foods pose special microbial threats and so require special handling. Raw seafood is especially likely to be contaminated. Honey is unsafe for infants. Almost all types of food poisoning can be prevented by safe food preparation, storage, and cleanliness.

- **Bisphenol A** (BPA): Canada was the first country in the world to add BPA to its "Toxic Substance" list. It is an industrial chemical used to make hard, clear plastic bottles and is used in the protective lining of food and beverage cans. While it has been banned from use in plastic baby bottles, we await further controls on its use in food containers (http://www.gazette .gc.ca/rp-pr/p2/2010/ 2010-10-13/html/ sor-dors194-eng.html).

sushi a Japanese dish that consists of vinegar-flavoured rice, seafood, and colourful vegetables, typically wrapped in seaweed. Some sushi is wrapped in raw fish; other sushi contains only cooked ingredients.

Irradiation and Food Safety

Food Irradiation

Food **irradiation** is not used as widely in Canada as it is in the United States. Canadian regulations allow for the irradiation of onions, potatoes, wheat, flour, whole-wheat flour, and whole or ground spices and dehydrated seasonings. A fact sheet on food irradiation from the Canadian Food Inspection Agency is available at http://www.inspection.gc.ca/english/fssa/concen/tipcon/irrade.shtml.

Health Canada has proposed adding the following to the list of irradiated foods permitted to be sold in Canada: fresh and frozen ground beef; fresh and frozen poultry; prepackaged fresh, frozen, prepared, and dried shrimp and prawns; and mangoes. Check the following Health Canada website for the status of this proposal: http://www.hc-sc.gc.ca/fn-an/securit/irridation/index-eng.php.

Scientists worldwide support the use of food irradiation (see Table 12–8). (Terms are defined in Table 12–9.) According to the American Dietetic Association, "Food irradiation enhances the safety and quality of the food supply and helps protect consumers from foodborne illness."*,1 The American Academy of Pediatrics states, "The science of food irradiation is mature and the scientific consensus on its efficacy and safety is strong."2 Rarely do so many scientists agree on a single issue.

Table 12–9

Irradiation Terms

- **irradiation** the application of ionizing radiation to foods to reduce insect infestation or microbial contamination or to slow the ripening or sprouting process. Also called *cold pasteurization.*
- **radiolytic products** chemicals formed in foods during the irradiation process; deemed harmless by experts.

*Consumer Corner references are listed separately at the end of the chapter.

Table 12–8

International Scientific Groups in Support of Food Irradiation

These groups and many others agree that irradiation, when used in conjunction with other safe food practices, can improve food safety in Canada and the rest of the world:

- American Academy of Pediatrics
- American Council on Science and Health
- American Dietetic Association
- American Medical Association
- American Veterinary Medical Association
- Canadian Food Inspection Agency
- Centers for Disease Control and Prevention
- Council for Agricultural Science and Technology
- Health Canada
- Institute of Food Technologists
- International Atomic Energy Agency
- Scientific Committee of the European Union
- United Nations Food and Agricultural Organization
- World Health Organization

 Health Canada has approved irradiation for controlling microbial contamination of many foods (see Table 12–10), but so far the process is little used.3 Can irradiation solve our food-safety and food-supply problems, and if so, why not use it?

Potential Benefits

Food irradiation's greatest potential benefit is its ability to kill almost all disease-producing microorganisms present in food, a characteristic that

Table 12–10

Food Approved for Irradiation in Canada

- Onions
- Potatoes
- Whole-wheat flour
- Whole and ground spices
- Dehydrated seasonings

Source: Modified from CFIA - Food Irradiation http://www.inspection.gc.ca/english/fssa/concen/tipcon/irrade.shtml [less than 5%]

has earned it the alternative name *cold pasteurization*. It has no effect on most toxins, prions, and microbial spores, however, and thus does not solve every contamination problem.*,4

Each year, the many millions of children, the elderly, and susceptible people worldwide who sicken or die from foodborne illnesses could be spared by the power of irradiation. Raw poultry, for example, emerges from irradiation treatment 99.9 percent free of disease-causing microorganisms. Thus, chicken is safer when purchased, and the threat of cross-contamination in home or industrial kitchens is reduced. Undercooking becomes less of a health threat, too.

Growers and marketers of fresh produce also stand to benefit. Irradiation eliminates the need to quarantine and spray fresh produce with pesticides before shipping to prevent the spread of plant diseases

*The spores of **Clostridium botulinum** are resistant to radiation.

or harmful insects and their eggs. Irradiation kills mould spores, replacing the fungicides now sprayed on harvested foods. Irradiation also slows decay in fruit and vegetables, making them last longer and appear fresher.

In addition to reducing the incidence of foodborne illness, irradiation greatly reduces the destruction of food by pests and decay. Up to half of the world's food bounty is lost each year to these problems. Irradiation facilities are expensive to build, however, placing them out of reach for the world's impoverished people who most need them—see Chapter 15 for more information on world hunger.

The Irradiation Process

Irradiation works by exposing foods to controlled doses of gamma rays from the radioactive compound cobalt 60. As radiation passes through living cells, it disrupts their internal structures and kills or deactivates the cells. Low doses can kill the growth cells in the "eyes" of potatoes and ends of onions, preventing them from sprouting. Low doses also delay ripening of bananas, avocados, and other fruits.[5] High doses can penetrate tough insect exoskeletons and mould or bacterial cell walls to destroy their life-maintaining DNA, proteins, and other molecules. Irradiation can kill most microbes even while food is in a frozen state, making irradiation uniquely useful in protecting foods such as whole turkeys that are ordinarily marketed frozen.

For perspective, compare the doses of radiation used on foods with the lethal human dose. The lowest doses of radiation needed to delay ripening and sprouting of fragile fruits and vegetables are 10 to 20 times as high as the doses that would kill human beings. The dose required to sterilize foods is many times higher still, but most foods are not completely sterilized because doses that high would destroy the food. Dried herbs and spices are notable exceptions—they can withstand sterilizing

IRRADIÉ

IRRADIATED

International radiation symbol

doses and are commonly irradiated before being purchased by consumers in the United States.

Labelling of Irradiated Foods

According to the Canadian Food Inspection Agency, "Pre-packaged foods that have been wholly irradiated display the international radiation symbol [i.e., the radura logo shown on this page], along with a statement that the product has been irradiated. Food that is not pre-packaged must have a sign with this information displayed beside the food. Pre-packaged foods that contain an irradiated ingredient which is more than 10 percent of the finished product must indicate in the list of ingredients that the component is irradiated."

If Irradiation Is So Great, Why Aren't More Foods Irradiated?

The answers to this question centre on cost, consumer acceptance, and fears about safety. Irradiated foods cost more to produce and package than conventionally processed foods, so the price to consumers is also higher. Irradiation also changes the flavour of foods somewhat, but most consumers have not tasted enough irradiated foods to know whether they like or dislike them.

People commonly give several reasons for fearing irradiation:

- Fear that the foods will become radioactive
- Fear that the foods will lose substantial nutrients during irradiation
- Fear that irradiated foods are not safe to eat
- Fear of harmful chemicals formed during irradiation
- Fear that the radioactive substances used to irradiate foods will endanger plant workers, the general population, and the environment

The first concern can immediately be put to rest—properly irradiated food does not become radioactive any more than teeth become radioactive after dental X-ray procedures. The use of radioactivity demands great care, though. Correct doses are of paramount importance to improve food safety while preserving nutrients.

Irradiation's Effects on Nutrients

Most nutrients, such as proteins, fats, carbohydrates, and minerals, survive irradiation intact or sustain only insignificant losses. Nutrients sensitive to heat treatment, such as the B vitamins and ascorbic acid, are sensitive to irradiation. Even so, substantial losses occur only with high doses of radiation well beyond those permitted in the treatment of food. In general, the nutrient losses sustained during properly administered irradiation are similar to those caused by canning or cooking. The U.S. FDA deems nutrient losses of less than 2 percent of the total as insignificant, and most losses incurred through irradiation fall within this limit.

Irradiation Safety

More than 40 years of research on animals has revealed no toxic effects from eating irradiated foods.[6] Decades ago, studies of human volunteers who ate a diet composed entirely of irradiated foods found no ill effects.* As for chemicals formed in foods during irradiation, this issue has been resolved to the scientific community's satisfaction. These **radiolytic products** have been identified as chemicals commonly formed in foods during many forms of processing. Among them are minuscule amounts of highly reactive free radicals that could, theoretically, be damaging to health. These tiny amounts, however, are unlikely to pose a hazard to the body, whose antioxidant systems are equipped to neutralize free radicals from many sources. After much scientific evaluation, the U.S. FDA has declared irradiation safe and effective for improving the microbial safety of foods.[7]

The irradiation process itself also arouses concerns. The process necessitates transporting radioactive materials, training workers to handle them safely,

and then disposing of the spent wastes, which remain radioactive for many years. Opponents of irradiation worry that workers could be exposed to nonlethal low doses of radiation that could conceivably cause ill effects. Their concerns are echoed by the food industry, which strives to safeguard both workers and consumers through strict operating standards and compliance with regulations.

Finally, some consumers worry that food manufacturers might use the technology unethically. An important point: irradiation is intended to complement other traditional food-safety methods, not to replace them. Even irradiation cannot entirely protect people from faulty food-safety practices and contamination due to poor sanitation on the farm, in the marketplace, or at home.

Consumers: The Final Authority

Only a few irradiated products are now available for use.[8] Although not currently allowed in Canada, irradiated ground

beef products are approved for U.S. school lunch programs, but the higher cost of these products discourages many schools from using them. Schools that do use them are encouraged to inform students and parents about the products.[9]

Whether more irradiated foods will appear in markets depends largely upon whether consumers choose to buy them. According to a U.S. survey of supermarket shoppers, the proportion of those who are willing to purchase irradiated foods declined during the past decade from 70 percent to about 50 percent.[10] Cost is a factor: people must be willing to pay a premium for irradiated meats, poultry, and seafood to cover the substantial expense of producing them.

In the end, acceptance may depend on taste. Flavour is high on most consumers' food priorities, and irradiation changes the taste of food slightly. Whether future refinements will positively influence consumer purchases of irradiated foods is for the future to tell.

*The USDA posts approximately 11,000 pages of research reports supported by the Office of the Surgeon General, Department of the Army, on the topic of wholesomeness of irradiated foods on its website: http://www.usda.gov/wps/portal/usda/usdahome?navid=FOOD_SAFETY.

How Can I Avoid Illness When Travelling?

People who travel to places where cleanliness standards are lacking have a 50–50 chance of contracting a foodborne illness—commonly known as traveller's diarrhea (see Table 12–2).[35] A bout of this illness can ruin a trip. To avoid foodborne illness while travelling:

- Before you travel, ask your physician which medicines to take with you in case you get sick.
- Wash your hands often with soap and water, especially before handling food or eating.
- Eat only cooked and canned foods. Eat raw fruit or vegetables only if you have washed them with your own clean hands in boiled water and peeled them yourself. Skip salads.
- Be aware that water, ice, and beverages made from water may be unsafe. Take along disinfecting tablets or an element that boils water in a cup. Drink only treated, boiled, canned, or bottled beverages and drink them without ice, even if they are not chilled to your liking.
- Avoid using the local water, even if you are just brushing your teeth, unless you boil or disinfect it first.
- Be aware that mad cow disease poses an extremely small risk (1 in 10 billion servings) to travellers to countries where BSE has been a problem.[36] To err on the safe side, avoid eating beef altogether or select solid pieces of muscle meat that are less likely to be contaminated. Avoid variety meats such as sweetbreads, brains, and tripe, as well as sausages and ground meats that may contain these cuts.

Don't let foodborne illness ruin your trip. Find information about risks in your destination at http://www.cdc.gov/travel/destinat.htm.

In general, remember these rules: boil it, cook it, peel it, or forget it. If you follow these recommendations, chances are excellent that you will remain well.

Natural Toxins in Foods

Some people think they can eliminate all poisons from their diets by eating only "natural" foods. On the contrary, nature has provided many plants with natural poisons to fend off diseases, insects, and other predators. Humans rarely suffer actual harm from such poisons, but the *potential* for harm does exist.

The herbs belladonna and hemlock have reputations as deadly poisons, but few people know that the herb sassafras contains a cancer-causing agent and is banned from use in commercially produced foods and beverages. Cabbage, turnips, mustard greens, and radishes all contain small quantities of harmful goitrogens, compounds that can enlarge the thyroid gland and aggravate thyroid problems. These effects show up only under extreme conditions when people have little but cabbage to eat. Ordinarily, cabbages and their relatives are celebrated for their nutrients and phytochemicals associated with low cancer rates.

Table 11–8 on page 481 in Chapter 11 provides more information on potentially harmful herbs.

Other natural poisons in *raw* lima beans, in the tropical root vegetable cassava, and in fruit seeds such as apricot pits are members of a group called *cyanogens*, which are precursors to the deadly poison cyanide. Many countries restrict commercial growers of lima beans to those varieties with the lowest cyanogen contents. Most cassava, a root vegetable eaten by hundreds of millions of people worldwide, contains just traces of cyanogens; the amount in bitter varieties, however, can be exceedingly high and poses a threat to hungry people who consume them in large quantities to escape starvation.[37] Fruit seeds are seldom deliberately eaten; an occasional swallowed seed or two presents no danger, but a couple of dozen seeds could be fatal to a small child. An infamous cyanogen is laetrile, a compound erroneously represented as a cancer cure. True, the poison laetrile kills cancer cells, but only at doses that kill the person, too. Research over the past 100 years has proven that laetrile is an ineffective cancer treatment and dangerous to the taker.

Potatoes contain many natural poisons, including solanine, a powerful, bitter, narcoticlike substance. The small amounts of solanine normally found in potatoes are harmless, but solanine can build up to toxic levels when potatoes are exposed to light during storage. Cooking does not destroy solanine, but because most of a potato's solanine is in a green layer that develops just beneath the skin, it can be peeled off, making the potato safe to eat. If the potato tastes bitter, however, throw it out.

At certain times of the year, seafood may become contaminated with the so-called *red tide toxin* that occurs during algae blooms. Eating seafood contaminated with red tide causes a form of food poisoning that paralyzes the eater. Fisheries and Oceans Canada monitors fishing waters and closes them to fishing when red tide algae appear (http://www.dfo-mpo.gc.ca/fm-gp/peches-fisheries/oc-of-eng.htm).

These examples of naturally occurring toxins serve as a reminder of three principles. First, any substance can be toxic when consumed in excess. Practice moderation in the use of all foods. Second, poisons are poisons, whether made by people or by nature. It is not the source of a chemical that makes it hazardous but its chemical structure. Third, by including a variety of foods in the diet, consumers ensure that toxins in foods are diluted by the volume of other foods eaten.

Residues and Contaminants in Foods

Nutrition-conscious consumers often wonder if our nation's foods are made unsafe by contamination. The next few sections address some of their concerns.

Pesticides

The use of **pesticides** helps ensure the survival of food crops, but the damage pesticides do to the environment is considerable and increasing. Moreover, there is some question about whether the widespread use of pesticides has really improved the overall yield of food. Even with extensive pesticide use, the world's farmers lose large quantities of their crops to pests every year.

Do Pesticides on Foods Pose a Hazard to Consumers? Many pesticides are broad-spectrum poisons that damage all living cells, not just those of pests. Their use poses hazards to the plants and animals in natural systems, and especially to workers involved with pesticide production, transport, and application. High doses of pesticides applied to laboratory animals cause birth defects, sterility, tumours, organ damage, and central nervous system impairment. Equivalent doses are extremely unlikely to occur in human beings, however, except through accidental spills. As Figure 12–6 demonstrates, pesticide **residues** on agricultural products can survive processing and may be present in and on foods served to people. Government agencies in Canada and the United States monitor pesticide safety and residues on foods to ensure minimal risk to the consumer.

Infants and children, however, may be more susceptible than adults to adverse effects from pesticides for several reasons.[38] The immature brain cannot exclude pesticides and other chemicals to the same extent as the adult brain. Many pesticides work by interfering with normal nerve and brain chemistry, and the effects of chronic, low-dose exposure to pesticides on the developing human brain are largely unknown. Children may be exposed to pesticides through normal behaviour such as playing outdoors on treated soil or lawns; handling sticks, rocks, and other potentially contaminated objects; crawling on treated carpets, furniture, and floors; placing fingers and other objects in the mouth; seldom washing their hands before eating; and using fingers instead of utensils to grasp foods. Further, children eat proportionally more food per pound of body weight than do adults, and traces of pesticides present on foods can build up quickly in their small bodies. Fortunately, compared with other sources of pesticides, the traces found on foods rarely exceed safe limits, and most of those present can be removed by washing produce thoroughly and following the other guidelines in Table 12–11.*

Regulation of Pesticides The regulation of pesticides focuses on the legal tolerance limit set for each pesticide. Safety factors of 100 to 1,000 are built in to the Acceptable Daily Intakes for pesticides and account for differences in response between adults and children.[39]

Possible Alternatives to Pesticides Ironically, some pesticides also promote the survival of the very pests they are intended to wipe out. A pesticide aimed at certain insects may kill *almost* 100 percent of them, but thanks to the genetic variability of large populations, a few hardy individuals are likely to survive exposure. These resistant insects can then multiply free of competition and soon will produce many offspring—offspring that have inherited resistance to the pesticide and can attack the crop with enhanced vigour. To control these resistant insects requires application of new and more powerful pesticides, which leads to the emergence of a population of still more resistant insects. The same effects arise from use of herbicides and fungicides. One

---

*For answers to questions about pesticides, go to http://www.hc-sc.gc.ca/cps-spc/pubs/pest/_fact-fiche/pesticide-food-alim/index-eng.php.

Pesticides
- Accumulate in the food chain.
- Kill pests' natural predators.
- Pollute the water, soil, and air.

Health Canada Assesses the Risk of Pesticides
- Companies wishing to sell a pesticide in Canada must submit information about the pesticide, including that it has been tested for its potential to cause cancer, damage chromosomes, etc.
- The control of pests in gardens is assessed.
- Maximum levels of pesticides in domestic and imported foods are assessed.
- Environmental risk of pesticide use is also assessed.

Source: See http://www.hc-sc.gc.ca/sr-sr/activ/environ/pesticides_e.html.

- Re-evaluations of current pesticide use occur on an ongoing basis, and stakeholders, including the public, are consulted before final decisions are made. To view current consultations and access reports on pesticides that cover almost 25 years, visit http://www.hc-sc.gc.ca/cps-spc/pest/part/consultations/index-eng.php.

pesticides chemicals used to control insects, diseases, weeds, fungi, and other pests on crops and around animals. Used broadly, the term includes *herbicides* (to kill weeds), *insecticides* (to kill insects), and *fungicides* (to kill fungi).

residues whatever remains. In the case of pesticides, those amounts that remain on or in foods when people buy and use them.

NEL · Residues and Contaminants in Foods · **523**

Figure 12–6

How Pesticide Residues Could End Up in a Fast-Food Meal

The red dots in the figure represent pesticide residues left on foods from field spraying or postharvest application. Notice that most pesticides follow fats in foods and that some processing methods, such as washing and peeling vegetables, reduce pesticide concentrations, while others tend to concentrate them.

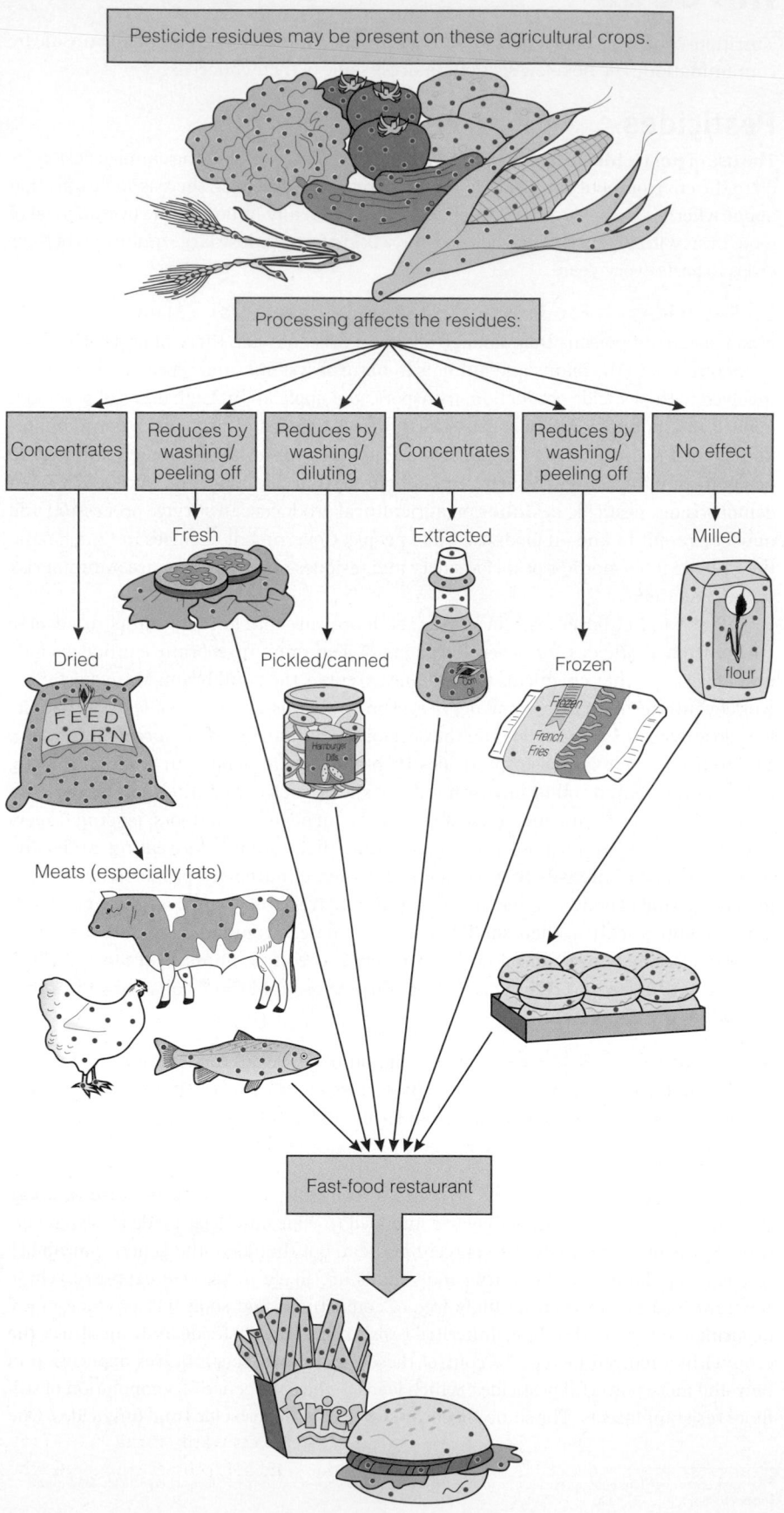

Pesticide residues may be present on these agricultural crops.

Processing affects the residues:

| Concentrates | Reduces by washing/peeling off | Reduces by washing/diluting | Concentrates | Reduces by washing/peeling off | No effect |

Fresh

Extracted

Milled

Dried

Pickled/canned

Frozen

flour

FEED CORN

Meats (especially fats)

Fast-food restaurant

Table 12-11

Ways to Reduce Pesticide Residue Intake

- Trim fat from meat and remove skin from poultry and fish; discard fats and oils in broths and pan drippings. (Pesticide residues concentrate in the animal's fat.)
- Vary meat, poultry, and fish choices from day to day and do not take fish oil capsules.
- Wash and trim fresh produce in water as instructed in Table 12–7, page 517.
- Use a knife to peel an orange or grapefruit; do not bite into the peel.
- Peel waxed fruit and vegetables. (Waxes don't wash off and can seal in pesticide residues.)
- Peel vegetables such as carrots and fruit such as apples when appropriate. (Peeling removes pesticides that remain in or on the peel but also removes some fibres, vitamins, and minerals.)

alternative to this destructive series of events is to manage pests using a combination of natural and biological controls, as discussed in Controversy 15.

Pesticides are not produced only in laboratories; they also occur in nature. The nicotine in tobacco and psoralens in celery are examples. A bacterium from soil yields a pesticide often used in organic gardening; the genetic blueprint for producing this bacterial pesticide has been transferred to vegetables, resulting in plants that grow their own pesticides in the field. Natural pesticides are less damaging to other living things and leave less persistent residues in the environment than most human-made ones. An ideal pesticide would destroy pests in the field but vanish long before consumers ate the food. Chemical companies are working to develop such safer pesticides, and advances in **biotechnology** have reduced the need for pesticide sprays on many crops. Another possibility for consumers who want fewer pesticides in their produce and meat is to choose **organic foods**; their pros and cons are also discussed in this chapter's Controversy section.

Foods imported from other countries may contain residues of pesticides that are banned from use here.

KEY POINT

- Pesticides can be part of a safe food production process but can also be hazardous if mishandled. Health Canada tests for pesticide residues in both domestic and imported foods. Consumers can take steps to minimize their ingestion of pesticide residues in foods.

Animal Drugs

Consumer groups express concern about drugs administered to livestock that produce food. Of particular concern to some consumers are hormones, antibiotics, and drugs that contain arsenic compounds.

Growth Hormone in Meat and Milk   The **growth hormone bovine somatotropin (bST)** is used to promote lean tissue growth and milk production in cattle in some countries, including the United States.

Canada and the European Union ban the use of bST for milk cows on the grounds that bST stimulates the release of another bovine hormone, insulinlike growth factor I (IGF-I), and some questions have been raised about its effects on human health.[40] IGF-I is produced naturally in people, with levels declining as they age. After a thorough review of the literature, the U.S. FDA concluded that IGF-I levels in milk from bST-treated cows are within the normal range of variation seen in milk from untreated cows and therefore that IGF-I from this source presents no additional risk.[41] Because all cows make bST, the U.S. FDA prohibits milk processors from stating "hormone-free" on milk labels.[42] The World Health Organization's expert committee on food additives concurs.

Antibiotics in Livestock   Ranchers and farmers often dose livestock with antibiotic drugs as part of a daily feeding regimen.[43] The drugs ward off infections that commonly afflict animals living in crowded conditions and help promote rapid growth. Thus, farms can produce more food at lower cost.

biotechnology the science of manipulating biological systems or organisms to modify their products or components or create new products; more properly called *genetic engineering* or *rDNA technology* (see the Controversy section).

organic foods products grown and processed without the use of synthetic chemicals such as pesticides, herbicides, fertilizers, and preservatives and without genetic engineering or irradiation.

growth hormone a hormone (somatotropin) that promotes growth and is produced naturally in the pituitary gland of the brain.

bovine somatotropin (so-MAT-ah-TROW-pin) **(bST)** growth hormone of cattle, which can be produced for agricultural use by genetic engineering. Also called *bovine growth hormone (bGH)*.

Both Canada and the United States prohibit livestock antibiotics from entering the food supply—ranchers and farmers must adhere to a drug-free waiting period before slaughter during which the drugs break down. Thus, North American consumers face little threat of ingesting antibiotic drugs in meats, milk, and eggs. Nevertheless, they run a substantial and increasing risk of illness from antibiotic-resistant bacteria wherever animals are treated with daily antibiotics.[44]

A limited number of antibiotic drugs exist—the same or related drugs used as growth promoters in livestock also treat illnesses in both animals and people. When the bacteria in an animal's intestinal tract encounter low daily doses of antibiotics, the bacteria adapt, losing their sensitivity to the drugs over time. Subsequently, such bacteria can infect consumers through food or by direct contact with ill persons. The result is a severe infectious disease that does not yield to standard antibiotic drug therapy, often ending in fatality. To safeguard the health of the world's people, the U.S. Centers for Disease Control and Prevention and the World Health Organization, along with other groups, support actions to stop the use of antibiotic drugs as animal growth promoters.

Chemical Contaminants of Concern in Foods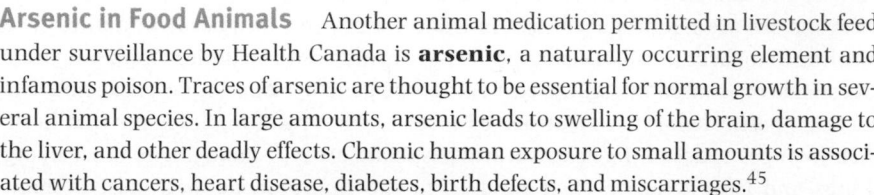

Heavy metals:
- Arsenic
- Cadmium
- Lead
- Mercury
- Selenium

Halogens and organic halogens:
- Chlorine
- Ethylene dichloride
- Iodine
- Polybrominated biphenyl (PBB)
- Polychlorinated biphenyls (PCBs)
- Trichloroethylene (TCE)
- Vinyl chloride

Others:
- Acrylamide
- Antibiotics (in animal feed)
- Asbestos
- Diethylstilbestrol (DES)
- Dioxins
- Heat-induced mutagens
- Lysinoalanine

Arsenic in Food Animals   Another animal medication permitted in livestock feed under surveillance by Health Canada is **arsenic**, a naturally occurring element and infamous poison. Traces of arsenic are thought to be essential for normal growth in several animal species. In large amounts, arsenic leads to swelling of the brain, damage to the liver, and other deadly effects. Chronic human exposure to small amounts is associated with cancers, heart disease, diabetes, birth defects, and miscarriages.[45]

Chicken and poultry farmers often give medicating ingredients (that contain tiny amounts of arsenic) to young flocks to control parasites that would otherwise inhibit their growth, thus acting as a growth promoter. Health Canada approves this use, but U.S. studies found that arsenic levels in grocery store chicken samples exceed expected levels by two to three times.[46] Arsenic is also present in other foods, such as fish, eggs, rice, milk products, and other meats to a lesser extent; drinking water and environmental exposure may be the chief sources in some areas.[47] Although the arsenic levels in chickens are higher than expected, healthy consumers run very little risk from ordinary portions (60–85 g) of chicken in the context of a varied diet.

KEY POINT

- Bovine somatotropin causes cattle to produce more meat and milk on less feed than untreated cattle. Although not allowed in Canada, the U.S. FDA has deemed the practice safe. Antibiotic overuse fosters antibiotic resistance in bacteria, threatening human health. Arsenic drugs are used to promote growth in chickens and other livestock.

Environmental Contaminants

As populations increase worldwide and nations become more industrialized, concerns grow about the environmental contamination of foods.[48] A food **contaminant** is anything that does not belong there.

Harmfulness of Contaminants   The potential harmfulness of a contaminant depends in part on the extent to which it lingers in the environment or in the human body—that is, on how **persistent** it is. Some contaminants are short-lived because microorganisms or agents such as sunlight or oxygen can break them down. Some contaminants linger in the body for only a short time because the body can rapidly excrete them or metabolize them to harmless compounds. These contaminants present little cause for concern. Some contaminants resist breakdown, however, and interact with the body's systems without being metabolized or excreted. These contaminants can pass from one species to the next and accumulate at higher concentrations in each level of the food chain, a process called **bioaccumulation**—see Figure 12–7.

How much of a threat do environmental contaminants pose to the food supply? It depends on the contaminant. In general, the threat remains small because Health

arsenic a poisonous metallic element. In trace amounts, arsenic is believed to be an essential nutrient in some animal species. Arsenic is often added to insecticides and weed killers and, in tiny amounts, to certain animal drugs.

contaminant any substance occurring in food by accident; any food constituent that is not normally present.

persistent of a stubborn or enduring nature; with respect to food contaminants, the quality of remaining unaltered and unexcreted in plant foods or in the bodies of animals and human beings.

bioaccumulation he accumulation of a contaminant in the tissues of living things at higher and higher concentrations along the food chain.

Figure 12–7

Bioaccumulation of Toxins in the Food Chain

If none of the chemicals are lost along the way, one person ultimately receives all of the toxic chemicals that were present in the original several tonnes of producer organisms.

❹ A person whose principal animal-protein source is fish may consume about 100 pounds of fish in a year.

❸ Larger fish consume a few tonnes of plankton-eating fish in the course of their lifetimes—and the toxic chemicals from the small fish become more concentrated in the flesh of the larger species.

❷ The toxic chemicals become more concentrated in the plankton-eating fish that consume several tonnes of producer organisms in their lifetimes.

❶ Producer organisms may become contaminated with toxic chemicals.

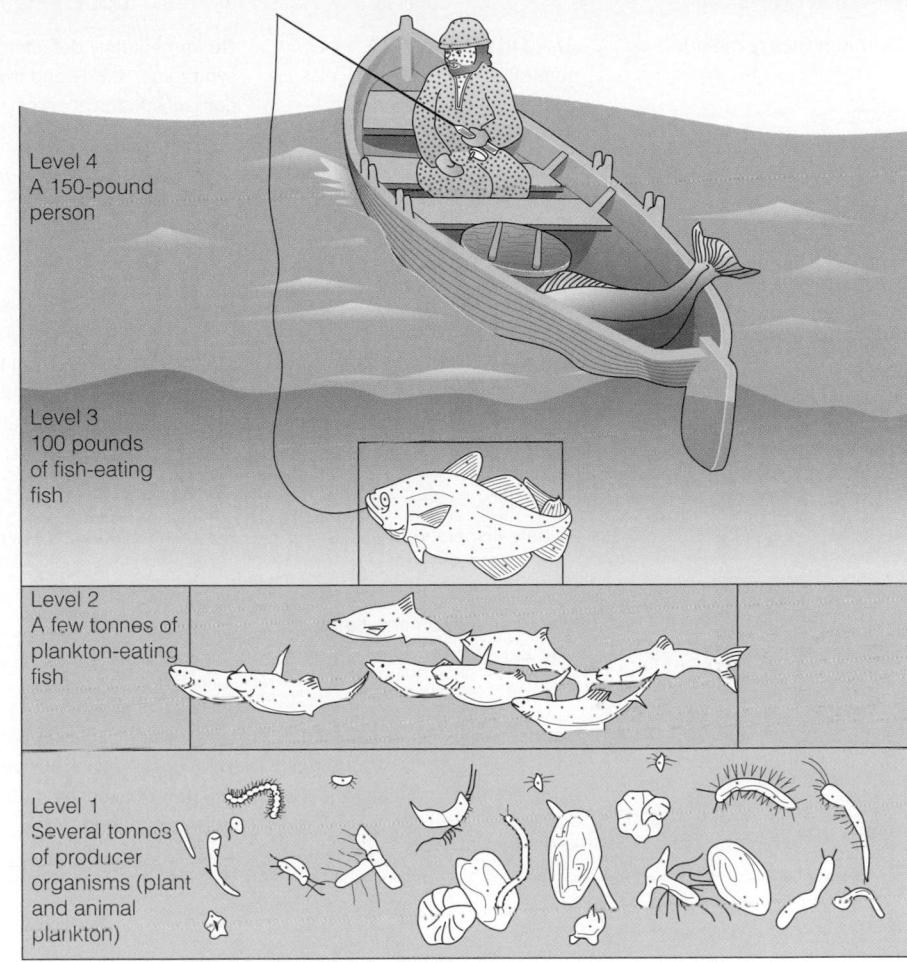

Level 4
A 150-pound person

Level 3
100 pounds of fish-eating fish

Level 2
A few tonnes of plankton-eating fish

Level 1
Several tonnes of producer organisms (plant and animal plankton)

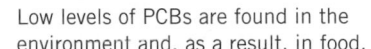 Toxic chemicals are represented by dots.

Canada monitors the presence of contaminants in foods and issues warnings when contaminated foods appear in the market. In the event of an industrial spill or a natural occurrence, such as a volcano's eruption, however, the hazard can suddenly become great.

Other contaminants build in the food supply more insidiously. For example, increasing levels of the **heavy metal** mercury expelled from industrial sites have been detected in Canadian lakes, rivers, and ocean fisheries. Virtually all fish have at least trace amounts of mercury (on average, 0.12 parts per million [ppm]). Mercury, polychlorinated biphenyls (PCBs), chlordane, dioxins, and DDT are the toxins most responsible for fish contamination, but mercury leads the list by threefold.[49] Table 12–12 selects a few contaminants of great concern in foods to show how pervasively a contaminant can affect the body.

When an environmental contaminant is detected in a person's blood or urine, it does not automatically mean that the chemical will cause disease.[50] The toxicity of a chemical depends upon its dose or concentration. Small amounts may be tolerable and of no consequence to health, while larger amounts may be dangerous. For some chemicals, such as mercury, the risks of increasing blood levels are well known; for other chemicals, such as certain pesticides, the health effects of varying blood levels are yet to be established.

Minimizing Your Risk of PCBs

- Low levels of PCBs are found in the environment and, as a result, in food.
- The highest amounts are found in animals at the top of the food web.
- According to Health Canada, "the average daily dietary intake of PCBs is thought to be less than half of one microgram (one microgram = one-millionth of a gram)."
- For more information, see http://www.hc-sc.gc.ca/hl-vs/iyh-vsv/environ/pcb-bpc-eng.php.

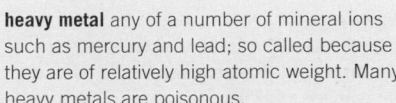

heavy metal any of a number of mineral ions such as mercury and lead; so called because they are of relatively high atomic weight. Many heavy metals are poisonous.

Table 12–12

Examples of Contaminants in Foods

Name and Description	Sources	Toxic Effects	Typical Route to Food Chain
Cadmium (heavy metal)	Used in industrial processes including electroplating, plastics, batteries, alloys, pigments, smelters, and burning fuels. Present in cigarette smoke and in smoke and ash from volcanic eruptions.	No immediately detectable symptoms; slowly and irreversibly damages kidneys and liver.	Enters air in smokestack emissions, settles on ground, absorbed into food plants, consumed by farm animals, and eaten in vegetables and meat by people. Sewage sludge and fertilizers leave large amounts in soil; runoff contaminates shellfish.
Lead[a] (heavy metal)	Lead crystal decanters and glassware, painted china, old house paint, batteries, pesticides, old plumbing, and some food-processing chemicals.	Displaces calcium, iron, zinc, and other minerals from their sites of action in the nervous system, bone marrow, kidneys, and liver, causing failure of function.	Originates from industrial plants and pollutes air, water, and soil. Still present in soil from many years of leaded gasoline use.
Mercury (heavy metal)	Widely dispersed in gases from earth's crust; local high concentrations from industry, electrical equipment, paints, and agriculture.	Poisons the nervous system, especially in fetuses.	Inorganic mercury released into waterways by industry and acid rain is converted to methylmercury by bacteria and ingested by food species of fish (tuna, swordfish, and others).
Polychlorinated biphenyls (PCBs) (organic compounds)	No natural source; produced for use in electrical equipment (transformers, capacitors).	Long-lasting skin eruptions, eye irritations, growth retardation in children of exposed mothers, anorexia, fatigue, others.	Discarded electrical equipment, accidental industrial leakage, or reuse of PCB containers for food.

[a]For answers to questions concerning lead, call CFIA national headquarters at 1-800-442-2342.

Mercury in Seafood Scientists learned of mercury's full potential for harm through tragedy. In 1953, a number of people in Minamata, Japan, became ill with a disease no one had seen before. By 1960, 121 cases had been reported, including 23 in infants. Mortality was high; 46 died, and the survivors suffered progressive, irreversible blindness, deafness, loss of coordination, and severely impaired mental function.* The cause of this misery was ultimately revealed: manufacturing plants in the region were discharging mercury into the waters of the bay, and bacteria in the water were converting the mercury into a more toxic form, **methylmercury**.[51] The fish in the bay were accumulating this poison in their bodies. Some of the poisoned people had been eating fish from the bay every day. The infants who contracted the disease had not eaten any fish, but their mothers had. The mothers were spared damage during their pregnancies because the poison had been concentrating in the tissues of the fetuses.

> Chapter 13 presents details about mercury and other threats during pregnancy. Chapter 5 explained the benefits of eating fish and the hazards of fish oil supplements.

• The fish highest in mercury are king mackerel, swordfish, shark, and tile fish.

Today, Health Canada warns of unacceptably high methylmercury levels in fish and other seafood. The department advises all pregnant women, women who may become pregnant, nursing mothers, and young children against eating fish species known to be high in methylmercury (Chapter 13 provides details of this warning).[52] Freshwater fish often contain PCBs and other industrial contaminants.[53]

methylmercury any toxic compound of mercury to which a characteristic chemical structure, a methyl group, has been added, usually by bacteria in aquatic sediments. Methylmercury is easily absorbed from the intestine and causes nerve damage in people.

*Minamata disease was named for the location of the disaster.

Chapter 12 Food Safety and Food Technology

No one expects the tragic results of 1953 to occur again, but lower doses of methylmercury cause headaches, fatigue, memory loss, impaired ability to concentrate, and muscle or joint pain in adults.[54] In children, the threats may be greater and long-lasting. Methylmercury is persistent in the environment, so efforts begun today to clean up Canadian and U.S. waters will take years to diminish this threat.

In an effort to limit exposure to pollutants, some consumers choose farm-raised fish. The "farms," however, are really giant ocean cages, exposed to whatever contaminants are in the water. Farm-raised salmon, especially from Europe, have tested high in certain industrial pollutants and pesticides that are banned from use in Canada and the United States.[55] Farm-raised fish do tend to collect less methylmercury in their flesh than wild fish do, and the levels of other harmful chemicals were far below the maximums set by the U.S. FDA. Nevertheless, the fact that methylmercury can be detected in farm-raised fish demonstrates that monitoring is essential. Such detection also serves as a reminder that our health is inextricably linked with the health of our planet (see Chapter 15).

Minamata disease. The effects of mercury contamination can be severe.

© Michael S. Yamashita/Corbis

KEY POINT

- Persistent environmental contaminants pose a significant, but generally small, threat to the safety of food. An accidental spill can create an extreme hazard. Mercury and other contaminants are of greatest concern during pregnancy, lactation, and childhood.

Effects of Food Processing on the Nutrients in Foods

Many consumers rely on packaged and processed foods for convenience and speed and so lose some control over exactly what their foods contain. What does processing do to foods and to their nutritional value? Food processing involves tradeoffs. It makes food safer, or it gives food a longer usable lifetime, or it cuts preparation time—but at the cost of some vitamin and mineral losses. A process such as pasteurization, which makes milk safe to drink, is clearly worth that cost. Boxes of milk that can be kept at room temperature have been treated with a process called **ultrahigh temperature (UHT)**. The milk is exposed to temperatures above those of pasteurization for just long enough to sterilize it. Irradiation, already discussed in this chapter's Consumer Corner, is a similar case: the price in terms of nutrient loss for gaining a safer food supply is probably trivial. Sometimes processed foods even gain a nutritional edge over their unprocessed counterparts, such as when fat is removed from milk or other foods.

Many forms of processing aim to extend the usable life of a food—that is, to preserve it. To preserve food, a process must prevent three kinds of events: (1) microbial growth, (2) oxidative changes, and (3) enzymatic destruction of food molecules. The first two have already been discussed—microbial growth earlier in this chapter and oxidative damage in Chapter 5. Enzymatic destruction occurs as active enzymes in food cells break down their internal molecular structures and cell membranes and walls. Processes involving heat denature the enzymes, and those applying cold slow enzyme activity. The next sections describe some of the most important preservation or processing techniques—modified atmosphere packaging (MAP), canning, freezing, drying, and extrusion—and their effects on nutrients.

KEY POINT

- Some nutrients are lost in food processing. Processing aims to protect food from microbial, oxidative, and enzymatic spoilage.

Extended Shelf Life

Today, in most grocery stores, shoppers can choose bags of washed, trimmed, fresh, chilled salads and chopped vegetables. Likewise, they can pick up fully prepared meats, chickens, and other main dishes whose shelf life has been extended through innovative

ultrahigh temperature (UHT) a process of sterilizing food by exposing it for a short time to temperatures above those normally used in processing.

packaging. The secret to these foods' long shelf life is vacuum packaging or **modified atmosphere packaging (MAP)**. These methods also preserve freshness and nutrients in soft pasta noodles, baked goods, prepared foods, fresh and cured meats, seafoods, dry beans and other dry products, ground and whole-bean coffee, and other foods. These convenient products are more expensive than comparable choices, but, unopened, they last much longer and so save on waste.

Food manufacturers using these techniques first package foods in plastic film or other wraps that oxygen cannot penetrate. Then they either remove the air inside the package, creating a vacuum, or replace the air with a mixture of oxygen-free gases, such as carbon dioxide and nitrogen. Excluding oxygen

- Slows ripening of fruit and vegetables.
- Reduces spoilage by mould and bacterial growth.
- Prevents discoloration of cut vegetables and fruit.
- Prevents spoilage of fats by rancidity.
- Slows development of "off" flavours from accelerated enzyme action that breaks down flavour and aroma molecules.
- Slows enzymatic breakdown of vitamins.

All foods packaged this way must be refrigerated to keep them fresh-tasting and safe.

 For safety, consumers must read labels to distinguish between shelf-stable foods and those that must be refrigerated. As with other foods, improper storage may allow growth of illness-causing bacteria. Consumers must also be able to identify foods too old to use; Table 12–13 provides a list of types of freshness dates printed on shelf-stable and other food packages.

Table 12–13

Glossary of Types of Freshness Dates on Labels

Food manufacturers voluntarily print the following kinds of dates on labels to inform both sellers and consumers of the products' freshness:[a]

- **Sell by:** Specifies the shelf life of the food. After this date, the food may still be safe for consumption if it has been handled and stored properly (check Table 12–5, p. 513, for safe storage times). Also called pull date.
- **Best if used by:** Specifies the last date the food will be of the highest quality. After this date, quality is expected to diminish, although the food may still be safe for consumption if it has been handled and stored properly (check Table 12–5 for safe storage times). Also called freshness date or quality assurance date.
- **Expiration date:** The last day the food should be consumed. All foods except eggs should be discarded after this date. For eggs, the expiration date refers to the last day the eggs may be sold as "fresh eggs." For safety, purchase eggs before the expiration date, keep them in their original carton in the refrigerator, and use them within 30 days.
- **Open dating:** A general term referring to label dates that are stated in ordinary language that consumers can understand, as opposed to closed dating, which refers to dates printed in codes decipherable only by manufacturers. Open dating is used primarily on perishable foods and closed dating on shelf-stable products such as canned goods.
- **Pack date:** The day the food was packaged or processed. When used on packages of fresh meats, pack dates can provide a general guide to freshness.
- **Durable life/Best before date:** "The anticipated amount of time that an unopened food product, when stored under appropriate conditions, will retain its freshness, taste, nutritional value, or any other qualities claimed by the manufacturer."

[a]Infant formula and some baby foods are required to bear a date.

Sources: U.S. Department of Agriculture, FOCUS ON: Food product dating, 2001, available at http://www.fsis.usda.gov/OA/pubs/dating; Canadian Food Inspection Agency. Date Labelling on Pre-packaged Foods, http://www.inspection.gc.ca/english/fssa/concen/tipcon/date.shtml.

---

modified atmosphere packaging (MAP) a preservation technique in which a perishable food is packaged in a gas-impermeable container from which air has been removed or to which another gas mixture has been added.

KEY POINT

- Modified atmosphere packaging (MAP) makes many fresh-packaged foods available to consumers. MAP foods compare well with fresh foods in terms of nutrient quality. MAP foods may pose a threat of foodborne illness if not properly stored. Consumers can judge the freshness of packaged foods by reading the dates on their labels.

Do Canned Foods Lose Nutrients?

Canning is one of the more effective methods of protecting food against the growth of microbes (bacteria, fungi, and yeasts) that might otherwise spoil it, but canned foods do have fewer nutrients. Like other heat treatments, the canning process is based on time and temperature. Each small increase in temperature has a major killing effect on microbes and only a minor effect on nutrients. In contrast, long heating times are costly in terms of nutrient losses. Therefore, food processors employ the **high-temperature–short-time (HTST) principle** for canning.

Which nutrients does canning affect, and how? The fat-soluble vitamins and most minerals are relatively stable and are not affected much by canning. Food scientists have thus paid particular attention to three vulnerable water-soluble vitamins: thiamin, riboflavin, and vitamin C.

Acid stabilizes thiamin, but heat rapidly destroys it; therefore, the foods that lose the most thiamin during canning are the low-acid foods such as lima beans, corn, and meat. Up to half, or even more, of the thiamin in these foods can be lost during canning. Unlike thiamin, riboflavin is stable to heat, but it is sensitive to light and so is most likely to be lost from glass-packed, not canned, foods. Vitamin C's special enemy is an enzyme (ascorbic acid oxidase) present in fruit and vegetables as well as in microorganisms. By destroying this enzyme, HTST processes such as canning actually help preserve at least some of the product's vitamin C.

Minerals are unaffected by heat, so they cannot be destroyed as vitamins can be. Both minerals and water-soluble vitamins can be lost, however, when they leach into canning or cooking water that the consumer then throws away. Losses are closely related to the extent to which a food's tissues have been broken, cut, or chopped and to the length of time the food is in the water.

> The Food Feature later in this chapter gives tips on preserving nutrients during cooking.

Some minerals are added when foods are canned. Important in this respect is sodium chloride, table salt, which is added for flavouring. Many food companies have begun making low-salt versions of their products, which may cost more because fewer low-salt batches are made.

KEY POINT

- Some water-soluble vitamins are destroyed by canning, but many more diffuse into the canning liquid. Fat-soluble vitamins and minerals are not affected by canning, but minerals also leach into canning liquid.

Freezing

Freezing preserves foods because it stops bacterial reproduction and dramatically slows enzymatic reactions. The nutrient contents of frozen foods are similar to those of fresh foods—losses are minimal. The freezing process itself does not destroy any nutrients, but some losses can occur during the steps before freezing, such as the quick dunking into boiling water (blanching), washing, trimming, or grinding. Vitamin C losses are especially likely because they occur whenever tissues are broken and exposed to air (oxygen destroys vitamin C). Uncut fruits, especially if they are acidic, do not lose their vitamin C; strawberries, for example, can be kept frozen for over a year without losing any vitamin C. Mineral contents of frozen foods are much the same as for fresh.

Frozen foods may even have a nutrient advantage over fresh. Fresh foods are often shipped long distances, and to ensure that they make the trip without bruising or spoiling, they are often harvested unripe. Frozen foods are shipped frozen, so produce

canning a method of preserving food by killing all microorganisms present in the food and then sealing out air. The food, container, and lid are heated until sterile; as the food cools, the lid makes an airtight seal, preventing contamination.

high-temperature–short-time (HTST) principle the rule that every 10°C (18°F) rise in processing temperature brings about an approximately tenfold increase in microbial destruction while only doubling nutrient losses.

freezing a method of preserving food by lowering the food's temperature to a point that halts life processes. Microorganisms do not die but remain dormant until the food is thawed.

is allowed to ripen in the field and to develop nutrients to their fullest potential. Foods frozen and stored under proper conditions will often contain more nutrients when served at the table than fresh fruit and vegetables that have stayed in the produce department of the grocery store for even a day.

Frozen foods have to be kept solidly frozen at −17°C if they are to be safe and retain their nutrients. Vitamin C converts to its inactive forms rapidly at warmer temperatures. Food may seem frozen even at 2°C, but much of it is actually unfrozen, and enzyme-mediated changes can occur fast enough to completely destroy the vitamin C in only two months. If foods defrost slightly but ice crystals remain, it is probably safe to refreeze the food for later use but at a cost of substantial loss of nutrients, texture, and flavour. In general, if a food is safe to eat, it is safe to refreeze, but it will lose both nutrients and appeal.

KEY POINT

- Foods frozen promptly and kept frozen lose few nutrients.

Drying

Dried or dehydrated foods offer several advantages. **Drying** eliminates microbial spoilage (because microbes need water to grow), and it greatly reduces the weight and volume of foods (because foods are mostly water). Commercial drying does not cause major nutrient losses. Foods dried in heated ovens at home, however, may sustain dramatic nutrient losses. Vacuum puff drying and freeze drying, which take place at cold temperatures, conserve nutrients especially well.

Sulphite additives are added during the drying of fruit such as peaches, grapes (raisins), and plums (prunes) to prevent browning. Some people suffer allergic reactions when they consume sulphites. Sulphur dioxide helps preserve vitamin C as well, but it destroys thiamin. This is of small concern, however, because most dehydrated products with added sulphur dioxide were not major sources of thiamin before processing.

KEY POINT

- Commercially dried foods retain most of their nutrients, but home-dried foods often sustain dramatic losses.

Extrusion

Some food products, particularly cereals and snack foods, have undergone a process known as **extrusion**. In this process, the food is heated, ground, and pushed through various kinds of screens to yield different shapes, such as breakfast "puffs," potato "crisps," the bacon-like "bits" you sprinkle on salad, and the so-called food novelties. Considerable nutrient losses occur during extrusion, and nutrients are usually added to compensate. But foods this far removed from the original fresh state are still lacking significant nutrients (notably, vitamin E) and fibre, and consumers should not rely on them as staple foods. Enjoy them as occasional snacks and as additions to enhance the appearance, taste, and variety of meals.

KEY POINT

- Extrusion involves heat and destroys nutrients.

Food Additives

What are **additives**, why are they there, and are they dangerous in any way? Food additives are regulated in Canada under the Food and Drugs Act and Regulations.[56] The approach and regulations are similar to those of the United States. The policy on the use of food additives in Canada is consistent with the FAO/WHO Joint Expert Committee on Food Additives.

The safety of food additives is a concern for individuals with allergies or hypersensitivities. The requirement that all ingredients and food additives be included

drying a method of preserving food by removing sufficient water from the food to inhibit microbial growth.

extrusion a process by which the form of a food is changed, such as changing corn to corn chips; not a preservation measure.

additives substances that are added to foods but are normally not consumed by themselves as foods.

on labels of prepackaged foods helps these individuals select foods that they can tolerate. Health Canada publishes warnings with product recalls; foods or beverages are recalled when nuts or other common allergens are found in them but are not listed as ingredients. Food recalls, health hazard alerts, safety alerts, and allergy alerts can be accessed from the CFIA's website at http://www.inspection.gc.ca/english/corpaffr/recarapp/recaltoce.shtml.

Manufacturers use food additives to give foods desirable characteristics: colour, flavour, texture, stability, enhanced nutrient composition, or resistance to spoilage. Additives, classed by their functions, are listed with their definitions in Table 12–14, and some are discussed in the following sections.

Regulations Governing Additives

The GRAS List   Many substances were exempted from complying with U.S. FDA procedure when they were first instituted because they had been used for a long time and their use entailed no known hazards. Some 700 substances in all were put on the **generally recognized as safe (GRAS) list**. When substantial scientific evidence or public outcry has questioned the safety of a GRAS list additive, however, its safety has been reevaluated. All substances about which any legitimate question was raised have been removed or reclassified.

The Margin of Safety   Decisions about an additive's safety are governed by the important distinction between **toxicity** and hazard associated with substances. Toxicity is a general property of all substances; hazard is the capacity of a substance to produce injury *under conditions of its use.** All substances can be toxic at some level of consumption, but they are called hazardous only if they are toxic in the amounts ordinarily consumed.

A food additive is supposed to have a wide **margin of safety**. Most additives that involve risk are allowed in foods only at levels 1/100 those at which the risk is still

---

Table 12–14

Food Additives by Function

- **antimicrobial agents** preservatives that prevent spoilage by mould or bacterial growth. Familiar examples are acetic acid (vinegar) and sodium chloride (salt). Others are benzoic, propionic, and sorbic acids; nitrites and nitrates; and sulphur dioxide.
- **antioxidants** preservatives that prevent rancidity of fats in foods and other damage to food caused by oxygen. Examples are vitamins E and C, BHA, BHT, propyl gallate, and sulphites.
- **artificial colours** certified food colours, added to enhance appearance. (*Certified* means approved by Health Canada.) Vegetable dyes, such as beta-carotene from carrots, are extracted from vegetables. Food colours are a mix of vegetable dyes and synthetic dyes approved by Health Canada for use in food.
- **artificial flavours, flavour enhancers** chemicals that mimic natural flavours and those that enhance flavour.
- **bleaching agents** substances used to whiten foods such as flour and cheese. Peroxides are examples.
- **chelating agents** defined in Chapter 4 as molecules that bind other molecules. As additives, they prevent discoloration, flavour changes, and rancidity that might occur because of processing. Examples are citric acid, malic acid, and tartaric acid (cream of tartar).
- **nutrient additives** vitamins and minerals added to improve nutritive value.
- **preservatives** antimicrobial agents, antioxidants, chelating agents, radiation, and other additives that retard spoilage or preserve desired qualities, such as softness in baked goods.
- **thickening and stabilizing agents** ingredients that maintain emulsions, foams, or suspensions or lend a desirable thick consistency to foods. Dextrins (short chains of glucose formed as a breakdown product of starch), starch, and pectin are examples. (Gums such as carrageenan, guar, locust bean, agar, and gum arabic are others.)

---

generally recognized as safe (GRAS) list a list, established by the U.S. FDA, of food additives long in use and believed to be safe.

toxicity the ability of a substance to harm living organisms. All substances are toxic if the concentration is high enough.

margin of safety in reference to food additives, a zone between the concentration normally used and that at which a hazard exists. For common table salt, for example, the margin of safety is 1/5 (five times the concentration normally used would be hazardous).

---

*In the United States, the Delaney Clause, a legal requirement of zero cancer risk for additives, was eliminated in 1996.

Food Additives

Without additives, bread would quickly mould and salad dressing would go rancid.

known to be zero. Experiments to determine the extent of risk involve feeding test animals the substance at different concentrations throughout their lifetimes. The additive is then permitted in foods at 1/100 the level that causes no harmful effect whatever in the animals. In many foods, *naturally* occurring toxins appear at levels that bring their margins of safety close to 1/10. Even nutrients, as you have seen, involve risks at high dosage levels. The margin of safety for vitamins A and D is 1/25 to 1/40; it may be less than 1/10 in infants. For some trace elements, it is about 1/5. People consume common table salt daily in amounts only 1/3 to 1/5 those that cause serious toxicity.

Most additives used in foods offer benefits that outweigh their risks or that make the risks worth taking. In the case of colour additives that only enhance the appearance of foods without improving their health value or safety, no amount of risk may be deemed worth taking.

Manufacturers must comply with other regulations as well. Additives must not be used

- In quantities larger than those necessary to achieve the needed effects.
- To disguise faulty or inferior products.
- To deceive the consumer.
- Where they significantly destroy nutrients.
- Where their effects can be otherwise achieved by economical, sound manufacturing processes.

The following sections focus on the food additives that receive the most publicity because people ask questions about them most often.

Antimicrobial Agents

Preservatives known as *antimicrobial agents* protect food from the growth of microbes that can spoil the food and cause foodborne illnesses. Three of these preservatives—salt, sugar, and nitrites—are commonly used.

Examples of Common Antimicrobial Additives
- Salt
- Sugar
- Nitrites

Two long-used preservatives.

Salt and Sugar The best-known, most widely used antimicrobial agents are two common substances—salt and sugar. Salt has been used since before recorded history to preserve meat and fish; sugar serves the same purpose in jams, jellies, and canned and frozen fruit. (Any jam or jelly that toots its "no preservatives" horn is exaggerating. There is no need to add extra preservatives, so most makers do not.) Both salt and sugar work by withdrawing water from the food; microbes cannot grow without water. Today, other additives, such as potassium sorbate and sodium propionate, are also used to extend the shelf life of baked goods, cheese, beverages, mayonnaise, margarine, and many other products.

Nitrites The *nitrites* are added to meats and meat products for three main purposes: to preserve their colour (especially the pink colour of hot dogs and other cured meats), to enhance their flavour by inhibiting rancidity (in cured meats), and to protect against bacterial growth. In particular, in amounts much smaller than needed to confer colour, nitrites prevent the growth of the bacterium that produces the deadly botulinum toxin.

Nitrites perform important jobs, but they have been the object of controversy because they can be converted in the human stomach to nitrosamines, which cause cancer in animals. Some cured meats are available without nitrites. Reducing nitrites consumed in meats, however, would hardly make a difference in a person's overall exposure to nitrosamine-related compounds. For example, an average cigarette smoker inhales 100 times the nitrosamines that the average bacon eater ingests. Likewise, a beer drinker imbibes up to roughly five times the amount that the bacon eater receives. Even the air inside automobiles delivers measurable nitrites.

● For more information on cancer risks from nitrites and other food constituents, go to the Canadian Cancer Society website at https://www.cancer.ca/en/cancer-information/cancer-101/what-is-a-risk-factor/diet.

KEY POINT

- Microbial food spoilage can be prevented by antimicrobial additives. Of these, sugar and salt have a long history of use. Nitrites added to meats have been associated with cancer in laboratory animals.

How Do Antioxidants Protect Food?

Food can also go bad when it undergoes changes in colour and flavour caused by exposure to oxygen in the air (oxidation). Often these changes involve little hazard to health, but they damage the food's appearance, taste, and nutritional quality. Antioxidants are often added to vulnerable foods to prevent the damage caused by oxidation. Familiar examples of oxidative changes are sliced apples or potatoes turning brown and oil going rancid. Antioxidant preservatives protect food from this kind of spoilage. Some 27 antioxidants, including vitamin C (ascorbate) and vitamin E (tocopherol), are approved for use in food.

Sulphites   The sulphites are another group of antioxidants used to prevent oxidation in many processed foods, in alcoholic beverages (especially wine), and in drugs. Sulphites were used to keep the raw fruit and vegetables in salad bars looking fresh, but this practice was banned after a few people experienced dangerous allergic reactions to the sulphites. Health Canada requires foods to list on their labels any sulphites that are present in quantities greater than 10 ppm (http://www.hc-sc.gc.ca/fn-an/label-etiquet/allergen/proj1220-revise-eng.php). For most people, sulphites do not pose a hazard in the amounts used in products, but they have one other drawback. Because sulphites can destroy a lot of thiamin in foods, you can't count on a food that contains sulphites to contribute to your daily thiamin intake.

> Chapter 7 describes how antioxidants break the destructive chain reactions of oxidation.

The ban on sulphites has stimulated a search for alternatives. Some producers now use honey to clarify browned apple juice. Agriculturists have created a hybrid apple that does not turn brown. A combination of four GRAS additives can also substitute for sulphites.*

Examples of Common Antioxidant Additives
- Vitamin C
- Vitamin E (tocopherol)
- Sulphites
- BHA and BHT

BHA and BHT   Two other antioxidants in wide use are BHA and BHT, which prevent rancidity in baked goods and snack foods. BHT provides a refreshing change from the many tales of woe and cancer scares associated with other additives. Among the many tests performed on BHT were several showing that animals fed large amounts of this substance developed *less* cancer when exposed to carcinogens and lived longer than controls. BHT apparently protects against cancer through an antioxidant effect similar to that of vitamin E. To obtain this effect, though, a much larger amount of BHT must be present in the diet than the Canadian average. A caution: used experimentally at very high levels of intake, the substance has *produced* cancer.

This discussion provides the opportunity to mention an important point about additives. No two additives are alike, so generalizations about them are meaningless. No single valid statement can apply to all of the 3,000-odd substances commonly added to foods. Questions about which additives are safe and under what conditions of use must be asked and answered item by item.

Raw grapes may be treated with sulphites. Wash them thoroughly before eating them.

KEY POINT
- Antioxidants prevent oxidative changes in foods that would lead to unacceptable discoloration and texture changes in the food. Ingestion of the antioxidant sulphites can cause problems for some people; BHT may offer antioxidant effects in the body.

Artificial Colours

As mentioned, only about 10 artificial colours are still on the GRAS list; this select group has survived considerable screening. Among the most intensively investigated of all additives, artificial colours are much better known than the *natural* pigments of plants,

Cancer Risks

According to a joint publication by the Canadian Cancer Society, Statistics Canada, the Public Health Agency of Canada, and Provincial/Territorial Cancer Registries, "In 2013, it is estimated that 187,600 Canadians will develop cancer and 75,500 will die of cancer" (http://www.cancer.ca/~/media/cancer.ca/CW/cancer%20information/cancer%20101/Canadian%20cancer%20statistics/canadian-cancer-statistics-2013-EN.pdf).

---

*The four GRAS additives are citric acid, ascorbic acid, sodium acid pyrophosphate, and calcium chloride.

Colour additives not only make foods attractive but identify flavours as well. Everyone agrees that yellow jellybeans should taste lemony and black ones like licorice.

and the limits on the safety of their use can be stated with greater certainty. Examples of natural pigments in common use are the caramel that tints cola beverages and baked goods and the carotenoids that colour margarine, cheeses, and pastas. Harmless food colourants added to the feed of farm-raised salmon give their flesh an orange-red colour that consumers find appealing.[57] Nevertheless, the food colours have been criticized more than almost any other group of additives. Simply stated, they only make foods pretty, whereas other additives, such as preservatives, make foods safe. Hence, with food colours, we can afford to require that their use entail no risk. With other food additives, we must weigh the risks of using them against the risks of *not* using them.

KEY POINT

- The addition of artificial colours is tightly controlled.

Artificial Flavours and MSG

Although only a few artificial colours are currently permitted in foods, close to 2,000 artificial flavours and flavour enhancers are approved, making them the largest single group of food additives. The safety evaluation of flavouring agents is somewhat problematic because so many flavouring agents are already in use, the flavours are strong and so are used in tiny amounts unlikely to impose risks, and they occur naturally in a wide variety of foods.

A well-known flavour enhancer is monosodium glutamate, or MSG (trade name Accent), the sodium salt of the common amino acid glutamic acid. MSG is used widely in restaurants, especially Asian restaurants. In addition to enhancing other flavours, MSG itself possesses a basic taste (termed *umami*) independent of the well-known sweet, salty, bitter, and sour tastes.

> The safety of another group of flavour additives, the artificial sweeteners, was discussed in Controversy 4.

In a few sensitive individuals, MSG produces adverse reactions known as the **MSG symptom complex**.[58] Symptoms may include burning sensations, chest and facial flushing or pain, and throbbing headaches. Plain broth with MSG seems most likely to bring on symptoms in sensitive people, while carbohydrate-rich meals seem to protect against them. When dining on Asian-style foods, potentially sensitive people should try ordering soups that contain noodles and eat plenty of plain rice, as do Asians themselves.

MSG has been investigated extensively enough to be deemed safe for adults to use, but it is kept out of foods for infants because very large doses have been shown to destroy brain cells in developing mice. Infants have not yet developed the capacity to fully exclude such substances from their brains. For other foods, the U.S. FDA requires that the ingredients list on the label itemize each additive by its full name, including MSG as *monosodium glutamate*.[59] Such changes to the Canadian "ingredients list" are also being considered by the Canadian Food Inspection Agency (see http://www.inspection.gc.ca/food/labelling/labelling-modernization-initiative/consultations/questionnaire/eng/1371096847742/1371096850664).

KEY POINT

- Among flavourings added to foods, the flavour enhancer MSG causes reactions in people with sensitivities to it.

Incidental Food Additives

Indirect or **incidental additives** are called *additives*, but they are really contaminants from some phase of production, processing, storage, packaging, or consumer preparation. Examples of incidental additives include tiny bits of plastic, glass, paper, tin, and the like from packages and chemicals from processing, such as the solvent used to decaffeinate some coffees.

Some microwave products are sold in "active packaging" that participates in cooking the food. Pizza, for example, may rest on a cardboard pan coated with a thin film of metal that absorbs microwave energy and may heat up to 260°C. During the intense heat, some particles of the packaging components migrate into the food. Regular

MSG symptom complex the acute, temporary, and self-limiting reactions experienced by sensitive people upon ingesting a large dose of MSG. The name *MSG symptom complex*, given by the U.S. FDA, replaces the former *Chinese restaurant syndrome*.

incidental additives substances that can get into food not through intentional introduction but as a result of contact with the food during growing, processing, packaging, storing, or some other stage before the food is consumed. Also called *accidental* or *indirect additives*.

plastic packages heat up less, but particles still migrate and may not be entirely safe for consumption. Avoid reusing disposable containers, such as margarine tubs or single-use trays from frozen microwavable meals, or ordinary plastic wraps for microwaving. Microwave-safe plastic wraps, waxed paper, cooking bags, parchment paper, and white microwave-safe paper towels are probably safe to use. The safest choice is to use only glass or ceramic containers or those plastic containers labelled as safe for microwaving.

Coffee filters, paper milk cartons, paper plates, and frozen food boxes can all be made of bleached paper and so can contaminate foods with trace amounts of compounds known as dioxins. Dioxins form during the chlorination step in making bleached paper. Dioxins can migrate into foods that come in contact with bleached paper, but the amounts entering food are infinitesimally small—one part per trillion, or the equivalent of one second in 32,000 years. Such amounts do not appear to present a health risk to people, and drinking milk from bleached cartons appears to be safe. Dioxins are persistent, however, and they leach into the environment by way of both paper mill effluent and discarded paper products in landfills, becoming more concentrated in land, water, and animals until they build up to hazardous levels.

You may have heard about the recent BPA (Bisphenol A) controversy (e.g., potential negative effects during neurological development and reproductive problems in animal studies). BPA is a chemical used in the production of polycarbonate plastic and epoxy resins. It is used in the production of infant feeding bottles (Health Canada banned the import and sale of polycarbonate baby bottles containing BPA in October 2008), beverage bottles, the protective linings of food containers, etc. While Health Canada's Food Directorate recently concluded that "the current dietary exposure to BPA through food packaging uses is not expected to pose a health risk to the general population, including newborns and infants," the Canadian government has recommended that ". . . the general principle of ALARA (as low as reasonably achievable) be applied to continue efforts on limiting BPA exposure from food packaging applications to infants and newborns . . ." (http://www.hc-sc.gc.ca/fn-an/securit/packag-emball/bpa/index-eng.php). Furthermore, Health Canada hosted an international meeting to review the toxicological and health aspects of BPA in late fall 2010.

Incidental additives sometimes find their way into foods, but adverse effects are rare. These additives are well regulated—all food packagers are required to test whether materials from packages are migrating into foods. If they are, their safety must be confirmed by strict procedures like those governing intentional additives.

KEY POINT

- Incidental additives are substances that get into food during processing. They are well regulated, and most present no hazard.

Nutrient Additives

Nutrients added to improve or to maintain the nutritional value of foods make up another class of additives. Among them are the enrichment nutrients added to refined grains; the iodine added to salt; vitamins A and D added to dairy products; and the nutrients used to fortify breakfast cereals, "energy" bars, liquid meal replacers, and the like. When nutrients are added to a nutrient-poor food, it may appear from its label to be nutrient rich. It is, but only in those nutrients chosen for addition. Nutrients are sometimes also added for other purposes. Vitamins C and E used as antioxidants and beta-carotene as a colourant are examples already mentioned.

To sum up the messages in this chapter, the Canadian and U.S. food supplies are safe and hazards are rare. Precautions against foodborne microbial illnesses are the most urgent measures for people to take to avoid food-related diseases. The Food Feature that follows offers pointers on the selection, storage, and cooking of foods to preserve their nutrients.

Examples of Common Nutrient Additives

- Thiamin, niacin, riboflavin, folate, and iron in grain products
- Iodine in salt
- Vitamins A and D in milk
- Vitamin C in fruit drinks
- Beta-carotene in cheeses

KEY POINT

- Nutrients are added to foods to enrich or to fortify them. These additives do not necessarily make the foods nutritious, only rich in the vitamins and minerals that have been added.

Preserving Nutrients in Foods

In general, the more heavily processed foods are, the less nutritious they become. Does that mean that you should avoid all processed food? The answer is not simple: in each case, it depends on the food and on the process. Consider the case of orange juice and vitamin C.

The Choice of Orange Juice

Orange juice is available in several forms, each processed a different way. Fresh juice is squeezed from the orange, a process that extracts the fluid juice from the fibrous structures that contain it. Each 100 Calories of the fresh-squeezed juice contains 98 milligrams of vitamin C. When this juice is condensed by heat, frozen, and then reconstituted, as is the juice from the freezer case of the grocery store, 100 Calories of the reconstituted juice contains just 85 milligrams of vitamin C because vitamin C is destroyed in the condensing process. Canning is even harder on vitamin C: 100 Calories of canned orange juice has 82 milligrams of vitamin C.

These figures seem to indicate that fresh juice is the superior food, but consider this: most people's recommended intake of vitamin C (75 mg for women or 90 mg for men) is fully or nearly met by 100 Calories of any of the above choices. Thus, for vitamin C, the losses due to processing are not a problem. Besides, processing confers enormous convenience and distribution advantages. Fresh orange juice spoils. Shipping fresh juice to distant places in refrigerated trucks costs much more than shipping frozen juice (which takes up less space) or canned juice (which requires no refrigeration). The fresh product still contains active enzymes that continue to degrade its compounds (including vitamin C) and so cannot be stored indefinitely without compromising nutrient quality. The savings gained from shipping and storing canned and frozen juices are passed on to consumers. Without canned or frozen juice, people with limited incomes or those with no access to fresh juice would be deprived of this excellent food. Vitamin C is readily destroyed by oxygen, so whatever the processing method, orange juice and other vitamin C-rich foods and juices should be stored properly and consumed within a week of opening.[60]

Processing Mischief

Some processing stories are not so rosy. In Chapter 8, for instance, you saw how processed foods are often loaded with sodium as their potassium is leached away, exactly the wrong effect for people with hypertension. A related mischief of processing is the addition of sugar and fat—palatable, high-Calorie additives that reduce nutrient density. For example, "natural yogurt"-coated nuts and raisins may sound like one healthy food being added to another, but the ingredients list shows that generous amounts of sugar and fat accompany the yogurt. About 75 percent of the weight of the product is sugar and fat; only 8 percent is yogurt. To pick one nutrient for an example, look at what happens to the iron density of the raisins: 100 Calories of raisins has 0.71 milligrams of iron; 100 Calories of "yogurt" raisins has 0.26 milligrams of iron. These foods taste so good that wishful thinking can take hold, but the reality is that sugar- and fat-coated food is candy. The word *yogurt* on the label means only that one of the ingredients of the candy coating is some small amount of yogurt.

Best Nutrient Buys

Here are two good general rules for making food choices:

- Choose whole foods to the greatest extent possible.

- Seek out among processed foods the ones that processing has improved nutritionally. For example, processing that removes saturated fat, as in skim milk, or pasteurization to improve the safety of juices is a benefit to the consumer.

Commercially prepared whole-grain breads, frozen cuts of meats, bags of frozen vegetables, and canned or frozen fruit juices do little disservice to nutrition and enable the consumer to eat a wide variety of foods at great savings in time and human energy. The nutrient density of processed foods exists on a continuum:

Whole-grain bread > refined white bread > sugared doughnuts
Milk > fruit-flavoured yogurt > canned chocolate pudding
Corn on the cob > canned creamed corn > caramel popcorn
Oranges > orange juice > orange-flavoured drink
Baked ham > devilled ham > fried bacon

The nutrient continuum is paralleled by another continuum—the nutrition status of the consumer. The closer to the farm the foods you eat, the better nourished you are, but that doesn't mean you have to live in the fields.

In terms of nutrient density, canned juice is almost as nutritious as fresh, but yogurt-covered raisins are not as nutritious as plain raisins.

Purchase mostly whole foods or those that processing has benefited nutritionally.

Steam vegetables or cook them in a microwave oven. Wrap foods tightly and refrigerate them. Space foods to allow chilled air to circulate around them.

Conserving Nutrients at Home

Wise food choices are half the story of smart nutrition self-care; skillful food preparation is the other half. In modern commercial processing, losses of vitamins seldom exceed 25 percent. In contrast, losses in the 60 to 75 percent range during food preparation at home are not unusual, and they can be close to 100 percent. The kinds of foods you buy make a difference, but what you do with them in your kitchen can make an even greater difference.

Preventing Enzymatic Destruction

Vitamins are organic compounds synthesized and broken down by enzymes found in the foods that contain them. Like all enzymes, the enzymes that break down nutrients in fruit and vegetables have a temperature optimum. They work best at the temperatures at which the plants grow, normally about

21°C (70°F), which is also the room temperature in most homes. Chilling fresh produce slows down enzymatic destruction of nutrients. To protect the vitamin content, most fruit and vegetables should be vine ripened (if possible), chilled immediately after picking, and kept cold until use.

Protecting from Light and Air

Besides being vulnerable to enzyme-mediated spoilage, the vitamin riboflavin is light sensitive. It can be destroyed by the ultraviolet rays of the sun or by fluorescent light. For this reason, milk is not sold (and should not be stored) in transparent glass containers. Cardboard or opaque plastic containers screen out light, protecting the riboflavin. Since grain products such as macaroni and rice are also important sources of riboflavin, cooks who store them in glass jars should stow the jars in closed cupboards.

Some vitamins are acids or anti-oxidants and so are most stable in an acid solution away from air. Citrus fruit, tomatoes, and many juices are acid—as long as the skin is uncut or the can unopened, their vitamins are protected from air. If you store a cut vegetable or fruit, cover it with an airtight wrapper; close an opened carton of juice tightly and store it in the refrigerator.

Refreezing

Labels on frozen foods tell you "Do not refreeze." As food freezes, the cellular water expands into long, spiky ice crystals that puncture cell membranes and disrupt tissue structures, changing the texture of the food. There is usually no danger in eating a twice-frozen food, although some nutrients are lost upon thawing and refreezing. Provided that it hasn't spoiled while it was thawed or wasn't thawed at a warm temperature, the main problems with a twice-frozen food may be its reduced nutrient value and loss of taste and texture.

Preventing Nutrient Losses in Water

Minerals and water-soluble vitamins in fresh-cut vegetables readily dissolve into the water in which they are washed, boiled, or canned. If the water is discarded, as much as half of the vitamins and minerals in foods go down the drain with it. A bit of southern U.S. folk wisdom is to serve the cooking liquid with the vegetables rather than throwing it away; this liquid is known as the "pot liquor" and may be used to moisten cornbread or to make gravies or soups.

Wash the intact food vigorously and briefly; don't soak it. Cut vegetables after washing except for those such as broccoli that you have to cut to wash adequately. For peeled vegetables, such as potatoes, add them to water that is vigorously boiling, not to cold water, to minimize the length of time the vegetables are exposed to nutrient-leaching water.

Another way to minimize cooking losses is to steam vegetables over water rather than boiling them in it. For example, boiled broccoli has been demonstrated to lose more than half of its original folate value, while steamed broccoli retains almost all of it even after 15 minutes of steaming[61] Likewise, stir-frying vegetables in small amounts of oil conserves nutrients. Microwave ovens are also excellent for nutrient retention. They cook fast without requiring fats or excess liquid. Some special microwaving concerns appear in the margin below.

During other types of cooking, minimize the destruction of vitamins by avoiding

- Take care when cooking in a microwave oven. Food can become extraordinarily hot or build up steam that can scald unprotected hands or face.
- Before cooking eggs, sausages, potatoes, or any food encased in a membrane, pierce the membrane to prevent explosion of the food.
- Never warm baby formula or baby food in a microwave oven because hot spots can form that can scald the baby.

high temperatures and long cooking times. Iron destroys vitamin C by catalyzing its oxidation, but perhaps the benefit of increasing the iron content of foods by cooking in iron utensils outweighs this disadvantage. Each of these tactics is small by itself, but saving a small percentage of the vitamins in foods each day can mean saving significant amounts in a year's time.

Meanwhile, however, a law of diminishing returns operates. Most vitamin losses under reasonable conditions are not catastrophic. You need not fret over small vitamin losses that occur in your kitchen; you may waste energy or time that is valuable to you in other ways. If you start with fresh, whole foods containing ample amounts of vitamins and are reasonably careful in their preparation, you will receive a bounty of the nutrients that they contain.

Organic Foods and Genetically Modified Foods: What Are the Pros and Cons?

Scientists and shoppers have strong opinions about groceries these days. Sales of all kinds of **certified organic foods** are skyrocketing, making organic foods one of the fastest growing segments of the Canadian food industry.[*,1] At the same time, many Canadian farms have shifted toward growing foods altered through **genetic engineering (GE)**. Today, more than 50 genetically modified (GM) foods have been approved for sale in Canada.[2]

The chapter addressed safety concerns surrounding conventional foods. This Controversy takes a scientific look at issues surrounding organic and **GE foods** to provide an understanding of the differences and similarities between these foods that will help you decide whether to choose either or both of them. Some terms relating to organic and GE foods are defined in Table C12–1. For a review of the workings of the genes, refer to Figure 3–2 and Figure 6–6.

*Controversy references are listed separately at the end of the chapter.

Genetically Modified Foods in Canada

Health Canada and the Canadian Food Inspection Agency (CFIA) are responsible for regulating products derived through biotechnology. Health Canada is responsible for assessing the human health and safety of products derived from biotechnology, including foods, drugs, cosmetics, medical devices, and pest-control products. CFIA is responsible for regulating products derived through biotechnology, including plants, animal feeds and animal feed ingredients, fertilizers, and veterinary biologics. For genetically modified crop plants, CFIA assesses the potential risk of adverse environmental effects and authorizes and oversees import permits, confined trials, unconfined release, and variety registration.

The Canadian General Standards Board approved standards for voluntary labelling and advertising of foods that are and are not products of genetic engineering. These standards were published in April 2004 and can be accessed via the Canadian General Standards Board website at http://www.tpsgc-pwgsc.gc.ca/ongc-cgsb/programme-program/normes-standards/internet/032-0315/index-eng.html. Note: It is mandatory to label all foods that have significant nutritional or compositional changes due to this technology or where health or safety risk exists, such as the presence of an allergen.

Issues Surrounding Organic Foods

A shopper picks up two fragrant, orange-yellow mangoes, one from a bin marked "organic" and another from a regular bin; both bear stickers identifying them as the Hayden variety. Both may be sweet and succulent. Both may have been kept in storage or shipped from faraway destinations. In fact, both may have been harvested from the same grove, separated by only a thin strip of land. The only obvious differences are the organic label and the cost: the organic mango costs more.

Organic Food and Food Technology Terms

- **certified organic foods** foods meeting strict Canadian production regulations, including prohibition of most synthetic pesticides, herbicides, fertilizers, drugs, and preservatives, as well as genetic engineering and irradiation.
- **clone** an individual created asexually from a single ancestor, such as a plant grown from a single stem cell; a group of genetically identical individuals descended from a single common ancestor, such as a colony of bacteria arising from a single bacterial cell; in genetics, a replica of a segment of DNA, such as a gene, produced by genetic engineering.
- **GE foods** genetically engineered foods; food plants and animals altered by way of rDNA technology.
- **genetic engineering (GE)** the direct, intentional manipulation of the genetic material of living things in order to obtain some desirable trait not present in the original organism. Also called *recombinant DNA technology and biotechnology.*
- **genetic modification** intentional changes to the genetic material of living things brought about through a range of methods, including rDNA technology, natural cross-breeding, and agricultural selective breeding.
- **outcrossing** the unintended breeding of a domestic crop with a related wild species.
- **plant pesticides** substances produced within plant tissues that kill or repel attacking organisms.
- **recombinant DNA (rDNA) technology** a technique of genetic modification whereby scientists directly manipulate the genes of living things; includes methods of removing genes, doubling genes, introducing foreign genes, and changing gene positions to influence the growth and development of organisms.
- **selective breeding** a technique of genetic modification whereby organisms are chosen for reproduction based on their desirability for human purposes, such as high growth rate, high food yield, or disease resistance, with the intention of retaining or enhancing these characteristics in their offspring.
- **stem cell** an undifferentiated cell that can mature into any of a number of specialized cell types. A stem cell of bone marrow may mature into one of many kinds of blood cells, for example.
- **transgenic organism** an organism resulting from the growth of an embryonic, stem, or germ cell into which a new gene has been inserted.

The not-so-obvious differences are the methods used to produce them.

 A farmer wishing to grow and market organic foods must receive certification by the CFIA. To be sold or labelled as organic, or to bear the Canada organic seal (see Figure C12–1), a food must be produced according to the procedures outlined in Table C12–2. Organic foods must be free of ingredients produced by way of

Table C12-2

General Principles of Organic Production

1. Protect the environment.
2. Maintain long-term soil fertility.
3. Maintain biological diversity.
4. Recycle and maintain resources to the greatest extent possible.
5. Provide attentive care to livestock.

Source: Adapted from Organic Production Systems General Principles and Management Standards, ICS 67.040, Canadian General Standards Board, CAN/CGSB‑32.310‑2006 http://www.pwgsc.gc.ca/cgsb/on_the_net/organic/032_0310_2006-e.pdf

Figure C12-1

Canada Organic Logo

Source: Courtesy of Canada Organic Office, Canadian Food Inspection Agency.

specified technologies, such as irradiation and genetic engineering. In contrast, foods bearing "natural" or "free-range" or other wholesome-sounding labels are not required to meet these standards.

Nutrient Composition

Supporters claim that foods produced the organic way contain more vitamins and minerals than conventional foods because organic compost fertilizes plants with more vitamins and trace minerals than those provided by synthetic chemical fertilizers. Biology tells us that plants do not take up vitamins from either compost or other fertilizers; they absorb only simple elements and water through their roots and use these substances to make complex organic molecules like vitamins that they need in their tissues. Trace minerals, on the other hand, are absorbed into plants, and some may be more abundant in organic compost than in synthetic fertilizers, which contain only the minerals that are added to the mix.

As yet, little research exists to support or refute whether organic foods are nutritionally superior to conventional foods.[3] The nutrient differences that have been reported are so small as to be explained by the seasonal nutrient variations that normally occur in crops.[4] For consumers, the nutrients in any packaged food are easily evaluated by reading the Nutrition Facts panel. Organic chocolate bars, frozen soy desserts, and fried snacks are no more nutritious than ordinary treats.

Standards for Organic Foods

The Canadian General Standards Board worked with the Canadian Organic Advisory Board to develop national standards for organic agriculture. For "Frequently Asked Questions" about where the Canadian General Standards Board sits regarding the proposed standards, go to the website at http://www.tpsgc-pwgsc.gc.ca/ongc-cgsb/programme-program/normes-standards/comm/32-20-agriculture-eng.html#a4. For links to the latest proposed documents on standards regarding Canadian Organic Production Systems, for example, the Canadian Organic Standards, visit the Organic Agriculture Centre of Canada at http://www.organi-cagcentre.ca/Standards/std_canadian.asp. For a list of links to various organic certification and inspection organizations in Canada, visit http://www.gov.mb.ca/agriculture/organic. Finally, Canada, like the United States and various European countries, has a "Canada organic" seal/symbol, which was published in the Canada Gazette in June 2009 (see Figure C12–1) (http://www.gazette.gc.ca/rp-pr/p2/2009/2009-06-24/html/sor-dors176-eng.html#REF1). According to information from Agriculture and Agri-Food Canada, there are just under 4,000 organic farms in Canada (http://www.agr.gc.ca/eng/industry-markets-and-trade/statistics-and-market-information/by-product-sector/organic-products/organic-production-canadian-industry/certified-organic-production-statistics-for-canada-2009/?id=1312385802597), and numerous certified "Canada Organic" products have appeared on store shelves since the Organic Product Regulations were released.

Pesticide Residues

Can consumers who pay more for organic foods trust that such foods are free of pesticide contamination? Tests have revealed pesticide residues in about three-quarters of conventionally grown foods and in about a quarter of organic food samples. Pesticides may persist in soils from previous applications, drift onto organic fields from nearby sprayed fields, or contaminate organic foods during shipping or marketing.

Federal standards for pesticide residues are set far below the threshold of any known threat to human health. Further, the human body is well equipped to handle tiny amounts of even poisonous substances without apparent harm—as long as the doses are small enough. Even if organic foods were completely pesticide free, it is unlikely that this would constitute a health advantage for healthy adults; pesticides are more of a concern for children, however, as the chapter made clear.

Regardless of how foods are grown, food-safety concerns dictate that consumers vigorously wash all fruit and vegetables for 10 seconds under running water. Doing so removes many harmful microbes as well as pesticide residues that may be present on conventional or organic foods.

Environmental Benefits

Farming the organic way, promoters say, will produce food without environmental harm indefinitely into the future. In general, organic foods are grown by using the techniques of *sustainable* agriculture (see Chapter 15). Vegetables and fruit are fertilized with composted animal manure or vegetable matter with no synthetic fertilizers that can run off into waterways and pollute them. No synthetic pesticides or disease-fighting agents are applied, so accidental spills and overuse are not a threat. Pests and diseases are battled by rotating crops each season, by introducing predatory insects to kill off pests, or by picking off large insects or diseased plant parts by hand. Only pesticides derived from natural sources, such as a pesticidal peptide toxin extracted from a bacterium that lives in soil, are allowed for use on organic fruit and vegetables.

Crop rotation and natural fertilizers not only minimize chemical impact on wildlife and human beings but also are beneficial to the soil. Such techniques curtail erosion and prevent

In some small gardens, handwork can take the place of pesticides.

contamination of drinking water from manure runoff, which is common on commercial farms.

To produce organic eggs, dairy products, and meats, farmers and ranchers raise food-producing animals in spacious, low-stress surroundings natural to their species with access to the outdoors. Animals raised this way can grow large and stay healthy without growth hormones, daily antibiotics, and other drugs that are required when animals are stressed in overcrowded pens that make diseases likely. Without overcrowding, the threat to the nation's waterways from waste runoff is also greatly reduced.

Potential Health Risks

Although proponents of organic foods believe that these foods are inherently safer for consumers than are conventional foods, this may not be the case. For example, the application of improperly composted animal manure fertilizer may expose consumers to dangerous microbial diseases, such as *E. coli* O157:H7. This chapter pointed out that organic sprouts and greens have caused many cases of serious food poisoning in recent years. Unpasteurized organic juices, milk, and cheeses may also constitute microbial hazards because pasteurization is required to kill disease-causing microorganisms in these foods. Furthermore, organic foods contain no preservatives and tend to spoil faster than other foods. Those purchasing organic foods are urged to buy only amounts that can be consumed within a few days, to store and cook the food properly, to wash raw produce vigorously, and to buy only pasteurized organic dairy products and juices.

Costs

A final factor to consider with regard to organically grown foods stems from the additional measures required to produce them—they cost more than conventional foods. Nevertheless, many people are willing to pay extra for foods they believe to be superior in nutrition, benevolent to the environment, produced with respect for animals, and low in pesticides. Some people also claim that organic fruit and vegetables taste better, and if perception of better taste encourages people to eat more fruit and vegetables, this is all to the good.

Like organic food production, another painstaking method of producing food, genetic engineering, carries its own potential set of risks and rewards. Unlike the tried and true organic foods, however, GE food varieties are new to the food supply.

Genetic Engineering

A shopper picks up two red, ripe tomatoes from two adjacent bins. Both may be delicious and nutrient-rich. Both may have been shipped a long distance. There are no obvious differences. Yet one may be a genetically altered tomato. The consumer may not be able to distinguish one from the other because genetically modified foods bear no special labels.

Food producers across the nation have welcomed **genetic modification** techniques, particularly **recombinant DNA (rDNA) technology**, to solve some age-old agricultural problems while boosting yields and profits. Many world governments and consumers, however,

These colourful carrots resulted from intensive selective breeding, not rDNA technology. Researchers bred carrots with high levels of colourful phytochemicals at each generation.

recoil from new genetic changes in basic foods without ironclad assurances of safety. Further, misinformation and urban legends abound on the Internet and other media and are often indistinguishable from fact to consumers unfamiliar with genetic sciences. Although genetic engineering technologies have only recently emerged from laboratories, their roots lie in genetic events taking place in nature and centuries-old selective breeding techniques that modify the genes of living things.

Natural Cross-Breeding and Selective Breeding

Eons ago, before being domesticated by humans, wild grains and other plants cross-pollinated randomly. Most of the resulting offspring failed to thrive, but occasionally a new plant formed with a biological advantage that ensured its survival. An example is the familiar wheat plant, which is the result of random crossing of wild grasses. Additionally, certain wild bacteria and viruses implant genetic material in host organism cells where it may blend into the host genome and be reproduced as native genes over generations.

Since the dawn of agriculture, season after season, farmers have been changing the genetic makeup of their

crop plants and farm animals through **selective breeding** to enhance traits desirable to human beings. Today's lush, hefty, healthy agricultural crops and animals, from cabbage and squash to pigs and cattle, all demonstrate the results of those efforts.

Take corn, for example. Today's large, full, sweet cobs and high yields bear little resemblance to the original wild, native corn with its sparse two or three kernels to a stalk. Modern-day breeders use improved methods to achieve dramatic results, such as those depicted to the left. Selective breeding works to genetically modify living things, but slowly and imprecisely.

Genetic Engineering Basics

In contrast to the lengthy process of cross-breeding in nature and selective breeding in agriculture, genetic engineering can change the genetic makeup of an organism in a year or two of work. A desirable gene from one organism can be inserted into another organism's DNA with great economy and precision. Genetic engineering can thus change one or more characteristics of a food. Figure C12–2 compares the genetic results of selective breeding and rDNA technology. Table C12–3 presents an overview of food-related genetic engineering research.

Improving Crops for Desirable Traits

Plant cells make likely candidates for genetic engineering because a single plant cell can often be coaxed into producing an entire new plant. Each cell of the resulting plant contains an exact replica of the genetic information contained in the original cell. If scientists introduce any DNA fragments into that first single cell, those fragments will be faithfully reproduced in all of the cell's offspring. All of the resulting cells are **clone** cells— exact genetic replicas of the original.

For example, by using rDNA technology, scientists can alter the DNA of an immature cell, known as a **stem cell**, from the "eye" of a potato plant. Into that

Comparing Traditional Breeding and Genetic Engineering

Traditional Breeding—DNA is a strand of genes, much like a strand of pearls. Traditional selective breeding combines many genes from two individuals of the same species.

Donor   +   Commercial variety   =   New variety (many genes are transferred)

Desired gene   Desired gene

rDNA Technology—Through rDNA technology, a single gene or several may be transferred to the receiving DNA from the same species or others.

Donor   +   Commercial variety   =   New variety (only desired gene is transferred)

Desired gene   Desired gene

Some Directions in Genetic Engineering Research

Research in genetic engineering is currently directed at creating:

- GE crops and animals with added desired traits, such as altered nutrient composition, extended shelf life, freedom from allergy-causing constituents, or resistance to diseases or insect pests.
- GE crops that survive harsh conditions, such as applications of herbicides, heavily polluted or salty soils, or drought conditions.
- GE microorganisms that produce needed substances, such as pharmaceuticals or other products, that do not occur in nature or occur only in small amounts.

stem cell, they can insert a gene snipped from the DNA of a virus that attacks potato plants (enzymes do the snipping). This gene codes for a harmless viral protein, not the infective part. The newly created stem cell is then stimulated to grow into a **transgenic organism**, in this case, a potato plant that makes a piece

of viral protein in each of its cells. The presence of the viral protein stimulates the potato plant to develop resistance and ready its defences against an attack from the real virus in the growing field.

In addition to transferring genes among organisms, scientists may also block or suppress a gene's activity to reduce or eliminate production of unwanted proteins. An example is provided by the first GE food to be approved: a long-lasting tomato. Tomatoes produce an enzyme that softens them after picking. Scientists introduced into a tomato plant an *antisense gene*, a mirror image of the native gene that coded for the "softening" enzyme. The antisense gene blocks production of the softener and produces otherwise normal tomatoes (see Figure C12–3). Whereas ordinary tomatoes must be harvested at the hard, green stage to withstand handling, a tomato with the antisense gene can be harvested and marketed at the most flavourful, nutritious, red-ripe stage and still last longer after purchase. Although such tomatoes turned out to be too expensive or troublesome to produce commercially, the technology that produced them is being applied to alter other foods in other ways.

Animals, too, may be modified for the benefit of human beings.[5] Thanks

How an Antisense Gene Can Block Formation of a Protein

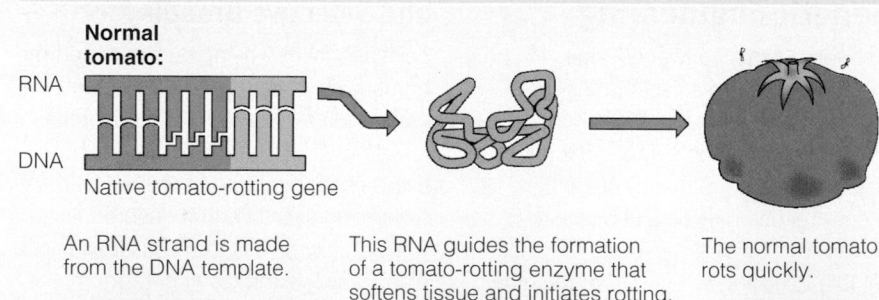

Normal tomato:
RNA
DNA
Native tomato-rotting gene

An RNA strand is made from the DNA template.

This RNA guides the formation of a tomato-rotting enzyme that softens tissue and initiates rotting.

The normal tomato rots quickly.

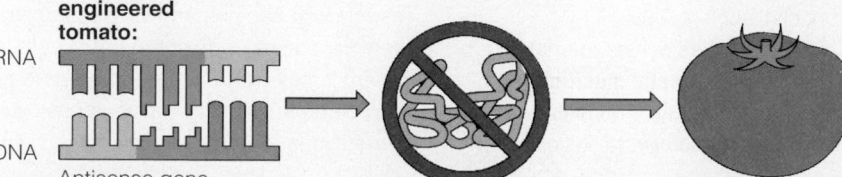

Genetically engineered tomato:
RNA
DNA
Antisense gene

Scientists insert a mirror image of the rotting gene (an antisense gene) into tomato DNA.

The antisense gene blocks the activity of the native gene, preventing production of the rotting enzyme.

The transgenic tomato lasts longer.

These salmon are all of the same age and type. The two largest fish received a growth-enhancing gene, greatly accelerating their growth rate.

to rDNA technology, larger salmon like those in the photo above grow at an astonishing rate and can be ready for market in far less time than it takes to grow an ordinary salmon. However, these genetically modified fish are not currently available to consumers.

The Promises of Genetic Engineering

Supporters hail genetic engineering as nothing short of a revolutionary means of overcoming many of the planet's pressing problems, such as food shortages, nutrient deficiencies, medicine shortages, dwindling farmland, and environmental degradation.[6] For example, animals and plants may one day join microorganisms as manufacturers of needed pharmaceutical products as well as extra nutrients and basic foods. Researchers have induced bananas and potatoes to make hepatitis vaccines and tobacco leaves to make AIDS drugs. Herds of animals that secrete vaccines into their milk could provide both nourishment and immunization to whole villages of people now suffering from the lack of both food and medical help. Many such projects hold promise for the future.

Rice, the staple food for half of the world's population, may become a source of supplemental nutrients in areas where deficiencies are common. Some GE rice produces beta-carotene to fight the world's most common cause of childhood

blindness: vitamin A deficiency. Other altered rice varieties, some offering 80 percent more iron and zinc than ordinary rice, could relieve much suffering from iron-deficiency anemia and zinc-deficiency diseases around the world.[7]

Other new crops can now resist insects without sprays, survive drought, or provide more complete sources of protein for people without access to animal products or adequate vegetable proteins. Still others may one day be safer for people with food allergies because scientists have successfully suppressed certain proteins that commonly cause allergy. Bananas may soon last many days longer than ordinary bananas. Vegetables may soon grow the fish oils EPA and DHA that most people's diets lack.[8] In areas where people cannot afford to lose a single morsel of food, plant disease can claim up to 80 percent of a season's sweet potatoes; GE sweet potatoes can resist disease and save the crop.[9]

Crops That Withstand Herbicides and Insects

Despite the almost unlimited potential, today's first generation of genetically engineered crops falls into two main categories: herbicide resistance and insect resistance.[10] Farmers planting fields of crops modified to withstand potent herbicides can more easily control weeds by spraying entire fields with weed killers. The weeds die, leaving only the desired chemical-resistant crop in the field.

Insect pests are also less troublesome to farmers planting crops that make what the U.S. Environmental Protection Agency (EPA) calls **plant pesticides**—pesticides made within the tissues of the plants. For example, a type of GE corn used for animal feed produces a pesticide that greatly reduces crop losses caused by a common corn-destroying worm. The technology isn't a panacea, however; farmers must still spray for attacking pests *not* killed by the plant pesticide. Also, the high cost of transgenic plants and the potential that insects will become resistant to the rDNA pesticide pose problems for researchers to solve.[11]

Modified Microorganisms

Genetically modified microorganisms are also currently at work. One bacterium, for example, was given the ability to make the enzyme rennin, a necessary enzyme in cheese production. Historically, rennin was harvested from the stomachs of calves, an expensive process. After a calf gene was spliced into the DNA of a bacterium, the resulting transgenic bacterial colony became a factory that mass-produces rennin. In the same way, another transgenic bacterial factory produces human growth hormone, so more children with growth hormone deficiency can grow normally. Still another manufactures the hormone insulin for use in treatment of people with diabetes.

Other Applications

The breadth of genetic engineering reaches far beyond applications in food production. Its techniques wield the awesome power to change the most basic patterns of life in ways never before possible. Its potential progeny are under development in fields as diverse as medicine, forestry, fuel production, environmental protection, and paper and plastics manufacturing. Its applications even extend to weapons of bioterrorism, such as treatment-resistant anthrax and other disease-causing organisms, and biodefences against them. Such uses and abuses lie beyond the scope of a nutrition text and must be left to ethical scientific minds to ponder and conquer.

The Future of Animal Cloning

Like plants, animals have stem cells and can therefore be cloned, as described earlier. The first and most famous barnyard clone, Dolly the sheep, developed from a single stem cell harvested from a ewe's udder. The path to useful cloning has not been smooth, however; many cloned animals were born with serious physical imperfections and often died early. Rats useful in medical experiments

● *Anthrax* is a bacterial disease associated with large-animal farming that has been altered to become a terrorist weapon but is not considered to be a foodborne threat.

have now been successfully cloned after many years of failures.[12]

Some cloned animals may prove useful as food, and Health Canada is currently assessing the potential risks associated with consuming meats from this source. Most likely, edible products from cloned cattle and pigs will be found to be as safe to eat as ordinary products for these reasons:

- Food animals, unlike many plants, do not produce toxins, so there is no threat of overproduction of toxins.
- Cloning does not involve gene transfer from other species, so cloned animals produce no foreign proteins.
- Malformed or otherwise imperfect animals would be destroyed and not used as food for people.

Nevertheless, until more certainty exists, Health Canada requires that food producers keep cloned animals out of the food supply.[13]

Issues Surrounding GE Foods

Consumers often question whether GE foods differ substantially from other foods in their nutrient contents or safety. The next sections address these questions.

Nutrient Composition

The *potential* ranges for nutrients in GE foods are virtually without limit. Except for the intentional variations, nutrients in GE foods are identical to those of comparable traditional foods. Therefore, eating the beta-carotene-enriched GE rice mentioned earlier would be the same from the body's point of view as eating plain rice and taking a beta-carotene supplement.

The current manufacturing practice of adding enrichment nutrients to wheat, rice, other grains, and milk products may one day become obsolete if rDNA plants and animals can make the extra nutrients in their tissues, thereby eliminating the possibility of human error. Consumers may also see favourite foods such as potatoes turned into "functional

foods" that sport heavy doses of disease-fighting phytochemicals made by genes borrowed from less familiar foods such as flaxseed or ginger. Thus, there is little need to worry about reduced nutrient contents of GE foods. Instead, consumers should stay alert to the possibility of nutrient or phytochemical overdoses.

Pesticide Residues

Industry scientists contend that rDNA technology could virtually eliminate pesticide residues on foods.[14] This is because both the nature of the pesticide and the amount present in the food are predetermined by the genetics of the plant, leaving no room for error or misuse by farmers.

Because plant pesticides produced by GE fruit and vegetables exist in the tissues of the food, consumers cannot wash or peel them off before eating the food. Nevertheless, it is unlikely that plant pesticides pose a danger to the body. The reason is that unlike synthetic pesticides, GE plant pesticides are made of protein. As Chapter 6 made clear, DNA governs the synthesis of protein. Plant pesticides are products of DNA activity—that is, they are peptide molecules. In the human body, peptide molecules are denatured and digested by digestive enzymes and so are rendered harmless. In addition, all pesticides are regulated as food additives by Health Canada and so must be proven safe for consumption before being sold to consumers, regardless of whether they are sprayed on the plants or made by them.

As mentioned, one of the few pesticides approved for use on organic foods is derived from a bacterium in soil. The extracted bacterial pesticide is a peptide chain that is lethal to insects that attack corn crops. The GE feed corn mentioned earlier received the bacterium's gene for producing this peptide. The corn expresses the gene and produces the plant pesticide internally. It's worth noting that the plant pesticide produced by GE corn is identical to the "natural" pesticide organic farmers spray on their crops to kill the same invading insects.

Unintended Health Effects

The possibility that genetic engineering of plants or animals may have unintended and therefore unpredictable effects on human consumers is a pressing concern for genetic scientists.[15] Such effects may arise with any sort of genetic modification, from the relatively rare cross-breeding in nature, to selective breeding in agriculture, to genetic engineering technology. Further, the results may be harmful, neutral, or even beneficial to consumers. Safety evaluations most appropriately focus on each new food itself rather than on the process used to create it.

Common celery provides an example of an unintended negative effect from genetic modification by selective breeding. Over the years, celery growers chose the most attractive celery plants for reproduction because consumers demand good-looking celery. Unknown to the growers, however, the celery stayed beautiful because it repelled pests with a natural plant pesticide whose concentrations increased with successive generations. This plant pesticide causes severe skin rashes in susceptible grocery and farm workers who handle the celery and are then exposed to sunlight.

An example of a positive, but still unintended, health effect of genetic engineering involves prevention of a cancer-causing fungus that contaminates corn.* Scientists conferred on a corn variety the ability to produce a plant pesticide that repels attacks by common worms. After several growing seasons, the scientists noted not only less destruction by worms but also far fewer attacks by the fungus than normal. No one knew previously that the worms repelled by the GE pesticide also infected the corn with the fungus as they burrowed.

By definition, intended changes to genetically modified foods are predictable, but *unintended* consequences are not. For this reason, Health Canada has

The fungus is of the mycoptoxin variety, including aflatoxin.

established a framework for evaluating unintended effects of genetically modified foods before they go to market.[16] Whether created by agricultural breeding or genetic engineering, a new food's composition can be chemically analyzed and studied for any variation from the original food. Except for the genetic manipulation, the two foods should be identical with regard to nutrients, phytochemicals, toxins, nutrient antagonists, and other constituents. If unintentional changes are detected, each variation must be evaluated for biological significance.

Unfortunately, even the most sophisticated chemical analysis cannot provide information about all possible health outcomes. Foods have complex compositions, and human interactions with food make safety assessments more difficult.

Factors such as the amount of the food commonly consumed and the nature of the alteration determine the degree of risk. For example, if the food is a GE spice ordinarily consumed in tiny quantities and the spice lacks a typical nutrient, little threat from this change would be predicted. People simply do not rely on spices to provide significant nutrients to the diet. If, however, the spice is heavily consumed by certain groups of people, the potential effect on the nutrient intakes of the heaviest consumers must be evaluated.

If, instead of a spice, the new food is a potato likely to be consumed in large quantities by most people, and the potato contains a constituent not typical of potatoes, the modified potato and the new constituent would require many more studies to determine their safety before marketing. Finally, postmarketing tracking systems for adverse events would be used confirm research findings.

Environmental Effects

Advances in rDNA technology promise bumper crops of food produced on far fewer hectares of land, with less loss of water and topsoil and less use of pesticides and herbicides to end up in foods and drinking water. By one estimate, genetic engineering has already led to an 80 percent reduction in insecticide use among U.S. transgenic cotton crops.[17] Other environmental worries have arisen, however.

One concern is the likelihood of **outcrossing**, the accidental cross-pollination of plant pesticide crops with related wild weeds. The failure to confine engineered genes may be irreversible—no cleanup strategy for "genetic pollution" has been developed.[18] If a weed inherited a pest-resistant trait from a neighbouring field of rDNA crops, it could gain an enormous survival advantage over other wild species and crowd them out.[19]

A solution to outcrossing is available, but it has spawned problems of its own. Scientists can ensure the destruction of all of a GE plant's offspring by using *terminator technology* to alter the plant's genetic material. Terminator technology keeps transgenic plants from passing their genes to wild weeds but makes it impossible for the world's farmers to save fertile seeds from their own harvests from year to year. Thus, even the poorest subsistence farmers would be forced to buy expensive new seeds each year. A possible alternative is to modify only the genetics of structures whose DNA passes through female lines because only male genes are carried by pollen.*,[20]

It is also possible that the new crops may directly damage wildlife. In the laboratory, monarch butterfly larvae die when they feed on pollen from pesticide-producing corn. In real life, wild butterflies do not seem to consume enough toxic corn pollen to be harmed, at least in the short term.[21] If butterflies remain safe in the long run, then the new technology may even protect monarchs and other harmless or beneficial insects that die when they dine on conventionally sprayed fields.[22] Still, long-term effects on butterflies and other species are unknown and require scientific vigilance.

The structures are chloroplasts.

Opposition to Biotechnology

Some fear that by tampering with the basic blueprint of life, genetic engineering will sooner or later unleash mayhem on an unsuspecting world. Opponents view biotechnology firms as naive and profit driven, lacking the necessary moral judgment or national laws to guide them.[23] They point out that while rDNA technology indisputably benefits biotechnology companies and giant industrial farms, it has produced no real benefits for consumers, and the risks are not defined. Others object to rDNA technology on religious grounds, holding that genetic decisions are best left to nature or a higher power. Table C12–4 summarizes some of the perceived strengths of and concerns about genetic engineering.

Some people envision a biotechnology run amok and used for frivolous, greedy purposes such as cloning animals for amusement. Others fear accidental doses of GE pharmaceuticals ending up in their children's cereal bowls at the breakfast table. Others are alarmed at the possibility of human beings cloned for certain traits and genetic "improvements." In the United States, government funds are withheld from any laboratory involved in human cloning experiments, but independent laboratories have stated their intent to move ahead with such research.

Proponents of genetic engineering respond that most of the world's people cannot afford the luxury of rejecting the potential benefits of biotechnology and accuse protesters of living in an elitist world of fertile lands with abundant food.[24] The world's poorest citizens suffer, they say, when protesters cause delays by destroying test crops and disrupting scientific meetings. Opponents of biotechnology counter that the scope of world hunger far exceeds simple solutions such as increasing food supplies and that the potential for harm to those most in need far outweighs any potential benefits to them.[25] Chapter 15 explores the tragedy of hunger in Canada and the world.

Genetic Engineering: Point, Counterpoint

Arguments in Opposition to Genetic Engineering	Arguments in Support of Genetic Engineering
1. **Ethical and moral issues.** It's immoral to "play God" by mixing genes from organisms unable to do so naturally. Religious and vegetarian groups object to genes from prohibited species occurring in their allowable foods.	1. **Ethical and moral issues.** Scientists throughout history have been persecuted and even put to death by fearful people who accuse them of playing God. Yet today many of the world's citizens enjoy a long and healthy life of comfort and convenience due to once-feared scientific advances put to practical use.
2. **Imperfect technology.** The technology is young and imperfect; genes rarely function in just one way, their placement is often imprecise, and potential effects are impossible to predict. Toxins are as likely to be produced as the desired trait.	2. **Advanced technology.** Recombinant DNA technology is precise and reliable. Many of the most exciting recent advances in medicine, agriculture, and technology were made possible by the application of this technology.
3. **Environmental concerns.** Environmental side effects are unknown. The power of a genetically modified organism to change the world's environments is unknown until such changes actually occur—then the "genie is out of the bottle." Once out, the genie cannot be put back in the bottle because insects, birds, and the wind distribute genetically altered seed and pollen to points unknown.	3. **Environmental protection.** Genetic engineering may be the only hope of saving rainforest and other habitats from destruction by impoverished people desperate for arable land. Through genetic engineering, farmers can make use of previously unproductive lands such as salt-rich soils and arid areas.
4. **"Genetic pollution."** Other kinds of pollution can often be cleaned up with money, time, and effort. Once genes are spliced into living things, those genes forever bear the imprint of human tampering.	4. **Genetic improvements.** Genetic side effects are more likely to benefit the environment than to harm it.
5. **Crop vulnerability.** Pests and disease can quickly adapt to overtake genetically identical plants or animals around the world. Diversity is key to defence.	5. **Improved crop resistance.** Pests and diseases can be specifically fought on a case-by-case basis. Biotechnology is the key to defence.
6. **Loss of gene pool.** Loss of genetic diversity threatens to deplete valuable gene banks from which scientists can develop new agricultural crops.	6. **Gene pool preserved.** Thanks to advances in genetics, laboratories around the world are able to stockpile the genetic material of millions of species that, without such advances, would have been lost forever.
7. **Profit motive**. Genetic engineering will profit industry more than the world's poor and hungry.	7. **Everyone profits.** Industries benefit from genetic engineering, and a thriving food industry benefits the nation and its people, as witnessed by countries lacking such industries. Genetic engineering promises to provide adequate nutritious food for millions who lack such food today. Developed nations gain cheaper, more attractive, more delicious foods with greater variety and availability year round.
8. **Unproven safety for people.** Human safety testing of genetically altered products is generally lacking. The population is an unwitting experimental group in a nationwide laboratory study for the benefit of industry.	8. **Safe for people.** Human safety testing of genetically altered products is unnecessary because the products are essentially the same as the original foodstuffs.
9. **Increased allergens.** Allergens can unwittingly be transferred into foods.	9. **Control of allergens.** A few allergens can be transferred into foods, but these are known, and foods likely to contain them are clearly labelled to warn consumers.
10. **Decreased nutrients.** A fresh-looking tomato or other produce held for several weeks may have lost substantial nutrients.	10. **Increased nutrients.** Genetic modifications can easily enhance the nutrients in foods.
11. **No product tracking.** Without labelling, the food industry cannot track problems to the source.	11. **Excellent product tracking.** The identity and location of genetically altered foodstuffs are known, and they can be tracked should problems arise.
12. **Overuse of herbicides.** Farmers, knowing that their crops resist herbicide effects, will use herbicides liberally.	12. **Conservative use of herbicides.** Farmers will not waste expensive herbicides in second or third applications when the prescribed amount gets the job done the first time.
13. **Increased consumption of pesticides.** When a pesticide is produced by the flesh of produce, consumers cannot wash it off the skin of the produce with running water as they can with most ordinary sprays.	13. **Reduced pesticides on foods.** Pesticides produced by produce in tiny amounts known to be safe for consumption are more predictable than applications by agricultural workers who make mistakes. Because other genetic manipulations will eliminate the need for postharvest spraying, fewer pesticides will reach the dinner table.
14. **Lack of oversight.** Government oversight is run by industry people for the benefit of industry—no one is watching out for the consumer.	14. **Sufficient regulation, oversight, and rapid response.** Health Canada and the U.S. National Academy of Sciences have established protocols for safety testing of GE foods. Government agencies are efficient in identifying and correcting problems as they occur in the industry.

This 5-tonne pile of corn is part of a Greenpeace protest demanding that GMO foods be labelled.

The Final Word

For those who would worry themselves into a diet of crackers and water, rest assured that eating more fruit and vegetables of any kind brings health advantages that far outweigh any slight risks. Many scientific organizations agree that rDNA technology can deliver on promises for an improved food supply if we give it a fair chance to do so. More information is available on the Internet (see Table C12–5). Table C12–6 sums up some pros and cons of all of the major food production methods. As presented in Controversy 6 and Chapter 11 of this book, the evidence is overwhelming: those who eat the recommended amounts of fruit and vegetables each day remain healthier than those who do not, regardless of the source of those foods. Furthermore, research has repeatedly shown that the great majority of all fruit and vegetables, both domestic and imported, test well within safety margins set for pesticide contamination. Consumers can best serve their health needs, then, by washing all produce thoroughly and by handling it properly before consumption but, most of all, by eating it in abundance every day.

Table C12–5

Genetic Engineering Internet Sites

Much more information (and misinformation) is available on the Internet. Here are some sites to explore.

1. For Canadian regulations of food derived from biotechnology, go to Health Canada's Science and Research website at http://www.hc-sc.gc.ca/sr-sr/pubs/biotech/reg_gen_mod-eng.php.

2. For policies, application, and research on biotechnology, go to Health Canada—Biotechnology at http://www.hc-sc.gc.ca/sr-sr/biotech/index_e.html.

3. Get a "pro" perspective from the Council for Biotechnology Information: http://gmoanswers.com.

4. A scientific view is available by searching for "biotechnology" or "genetic engineering" at the International Food Information Council: http://www.foodinsight.org.

5. Consider the opposing perspective at the Genetic Engineering section of Greenpeace, Canada: http://www.greenpeace.org/canada.

6. Another opposition view is available at the Union of Concerned Scientists: http://www.ucsusa.org.

Table C12–6

Food Production Methods Compared: Organic, Conventional, and Genetic Engineering

Soil Condition and Environment

- *Organic:* Improves soil condition through crop rotation and the addition of complex fertilizers such as manure; controls erosion; highly protective of waterways and wildlife. Uses sustainable agriculture techniques.
- *Conventional:* Depletes soil; adds synthetic chemical fertilizers containing only a few key elements; can create soil erosion problems. Runoff pollutes waterways, and sprays poison wildlife such as birds and beneficial insect predators.
- *Genetic engineering:* No direct effect on soil or erosion; may require fewer pesticide sprays, thus protecting waterways and wildlife, but may harm wildlife by exposing wild species to altered genes or plant pesticides; may soon make use of salty, dry, or other currently unusable lands. May produce "genetic pollution."

Nutrients in Foods

- *Organic:* Suggestive evidence of slightly increased content of trace minerals, vitamin C, and improved amino acid balance in produce over conventionally farmed produce.
- *Conventional:* Standards for nutrient composition of foods are set by analysis of conventionally produced foods.
- *Genetic engineering:* Potential for increasing nutrient and phytochemical content, at the will of the producer.

Benefits to Consumers

- *Organic:* Reduced exposure to pesticides and other sprays and animal medications and hormones. New standards define organic techniques, with regulatory oversight. Long history of safety for human consumption of food varieties. Ethical comfort of knowing that food-producing animals are well treated.
- *Conventional:* General safety and pesticide residues monitored regularly; many varieties of foods available at low cost.
- *Genetic engineering:* Greater food production at low cost, keeping consumer prices low and availability high. Particular products may meet particular consumer demands, such as better flavour, increased vitamin or phytochemical content, or improved freshness of foods. Potential exists for helping to ease world hunger. Crops may produce medicines needed in impoverished areas of the world.

(continued)

Self-Check

Answers to these Self-Check questions are in Appendix D.

1. Which of the following food hazards has Health Canada identified as its number one concern?

   a. pesticides in food

   b. microbial foodborne illnesses

   c. intentional food additives

   d. environmental contaminants

2. To prevent foodborne illnesses, the refrigerator's temperature should be less than

   a. 25°C

   b. 20°C

   c. 4°C

   d. −1°C

3. Which of the following may be contracted from normal-appearing raw seafood?

   a. hepatitis

   b. worms and flukes

   c. viral intestinal disorders

   d. all of the above

4. Which of the following is correct concerning fruits that have been irradiated?

   a. They decay and ripen more slowly.

   b. They lose substantial nutrients.

   c. They are not safe to eat.

   d. They become radioactive.

5. Which of the following organisms can cause *hemolytic-uremic syndrome?*

   a. *Listeria monocytogenes*

   b. *Campylobacter jejuni*

   c. *Escherichia coli O157:H7*

   d. *Salmonella*

6. It is possible to eliminate all poisons from your diet by eating only "natural" foods.
   T   F

7. Pregnant women are advised not to eat certain species of fish because Health Canada detected unacceptably high mercury levels in them.
   T   F

8. The canning industry chooses treatments that employ the low-temperature–long-time (LTLT) principle for canning.
   T   F

9. Artificial flavours and flavour enhancers are the largest single group of food additives.
   T   F

10. Infants under one year of age should never be fed honey because it can contain spores of *Clostridium botulinum.*
   T   F

Endnotes

1. Canadian Food Inspection Agency, Animal Health, available at http://www.inspection.gc.ca/english/toce.shtml.

2. Health Canada, Genetically Modified (GM) Foods and Other Novel Foods, available at http://www.hc-sc.gc.ca/fn-an/gmf-agm/index_e.html.

3. Canadian Food Inspection Agency, Foodborne Illness Outbreak Response Protocol (FIORP) 2010, available at http://www.inspection.gc.ca/food/safe-food-production-systems/food-recall-and-emergency-response/fiorp/eng/1337217904403/1337217972172.

4. Public Health Agency of Canada, Bioterrorism and Emergency Preparedness, available at http://www.phac-aspc.gc.ca/ep-mu/bioem-eng.php.

5. M. Meadows, The FDA and the fight against terrorism, *FDA Consumer*, January/February 2004, 20–27; Protecting the food supply: FDA actions on new bioterrorism legislation, May 2004, available at http://www.fda.gov/Food/GuidanceRegulation/AdministrativeDetention/ucm062177.htm.

6. Centers for Disease Control and Prevention, Preliminary FoodNet data on the incidence of foodborne illnesses—Selected sites, United States, *Morbidity and Mortality Weekly Report* 50 (2001): 241–246; R. G. Villar and coauthors, Investigation of multidrug-resistant *Salmonella* serotype *typhimurium* DT104 infections linked to raw-milk cheese in Washington state, *Journal of the American Medical Association* 281 (1999): 1811–1816.

7. Position of the American Dietetic Association: Food and water safety, *Journal of the American Dietetic Association* 103 (2003): 1203–1218.

8. Canadian Food Inspection Agency, Causes of Food Poisoning, available at http://www.inspection.gc.ca/english/fssa/concen/causee.shtml.

9. Canadian Food Inspection Agency, Causes of Food Poisoning [see reference 8].

10. Hepatitis A Outbreaks Associated with Green Onions at a Restaurant—Monaca, Pennsylvania 2003, November 21, 2003, available at http://www.cdc.gov/mmwr/preview/mmwrhtml/mm52d1121a1.htm.

11. E. A. Coleman and M. E. Yergler, Botulism, *American Journal of Nursing* 102 (2002): 44–47.

12. Position of the American Dietetic Association, 2003 [see reference 7].

13. W. L. Chandler and coauthors, Prothrombotic coagulation abnormalities preceding the hemolytic-uremic syndrome, *New England Journal of Medicine* 346 (2002): 23–32; E. F. Grabowski, The hemolytic-uremic syndrome: Toxin, thrombin, and thrombosis, *New England Journal of Medicine* 346 (2002): 58–61.

14. L. B. Zimmerhackl, *E. coli*, antibiotics, and the hemolytic-uremic syndrome, *New England Journal of Medicine* 342 (2000): 1990–1991.

15. Canadian Food Inspection Agency, Meat Hygiene Manual of Procedures (March 2011), available at http://www.inspection.gc.ca/food/meat-and-poultry-products/manual-of-procedures/eng/1300125426052/1300125482318.

16. USDA, Second progress report on *Salmonella* testing for raw meat and poultry products, *FSIS Backgrounder*, January 21, 1999.

17. J. Sneed, C. Strohbehn, and S. H. Gilmore, Food safety practices and readiness to implement HACCP programs in assisted-living facilities in Iowa, *Journal of the American Dietetic Association* 104 (2004): 1678–1683; C. Strohbehn, S. H. Gilmore, and J. Sneed, Food safety practices and HACCP implementation: Perceptions of registered dietitians and dietary managers, *Journal of the American Dietetic Association* 104 (2004): 1693–1699.

18. J. M. Boyd and D. Pittet, Centers for Disease Control and Prevention, Guideline for hand hygiene in health-care settings, *Morbidity and Mortality Weekly Report* 51 (2002): 1–44.

19. J. M. Boyd and D. Pittet, 2002 [see reference 18].

20. B. Hammond and coauthors, Effect of hand sanitizer use on elementary school absenteeism, *American Journal of Infection Control* 28 (2000): 340–346.

21. W. Picheansathian, A systematic review on the effectiveness of alcohol-based solutions for hand hygiene, *International Journal of Nursing Practice* 10 (2004): 3–9; C. M. Lin and coauthors, A comparison of hand washing techniques to remove *Escherichia coli* and caliciviruses under natural or artificial fingernails, *Journal of Food Protection* 66 (2003): 2296–2301; D. J.Weber and coauthors, Efficacy of selected hand hygiene agents used to remove *Bacillus atrophaeus* (a surrogate of *Bacillus anthracis*) from contaminated hands, *Journal of the American Medical Association* 289 (2003): 1274–1277; J. M. Boyce, Using alcohol for hand antisepsis: Dispelling old myths, *Infection Control and Hospital Epidemiology* 21 (2000): 438–442.

22. E. Larson and coauthors, Effect of antibacterial home cleaning and handwashing products on infectious disease symptoms, *Annals of Internal Medicine* 140 (2004): 321–329.

23. J. Henkel, "Thermy" promotes thorough food cooking, *FDA Consumer*, September/October 2000, p. 35.

24. Centers for Disease Control and Prevention, Fatal degenerative neurologic illnesses in men who participated in wild game feasts—Wisconsin, 2002, *Morbidity and Mortality Weekly Report* 52 (2003): 125–127.

25. G. Legname and coauthors, Synthetic mammalian prions, *Science* 305 (2004): 673–676; Centers for Disease Control and Prevention, Probable variant Creutzfeldt-Jakob disease in a U.S. resident—Florida, 2002, *Morbidity and Mortality Weekly Report* 51 (2002): 927–929; Department of Health and Human Services, Centers for Disease Control and Prevention, vCJD (Variant Creutzfeldt-Jakob Disease), available at http://cdc.gov/ncidod/dvrd/vcjd/factsheet_nvcjd.htm.

26. Executive summary, *Advancing Prion Research: Guidance for the National Prion Research Program*

(Washington, D.C.: National Academies Press, 2004).

27. C. A. Donnelly, Bovine spongiform encephalopathy in the United States—An epidemiologist's view, *New England Journal of Medicine* 350 (2004): 539–542.

28. L. Bren, Agencies work to corral mad cow disease, *FDA Consumer*, May/June 2004, pp. 29–35.

29. Canadian Food Inspection Agency. *Eggs and Egg Products*, available at http://www.inspection.gc.ca/food/eggs-and-egg-products/eng/1299796526271/1299796885258.

30. L. Bren, Homemade ice cream: A safe summertime treat? *FDA Consumer Magazine*, July/August 2004, available at http://permanent.access.gpo.gov/lps1609/www.fda.gov/fdac/features/2004/404_summer.html.

31. U.S. Food and Drug Administration, Center for Food Safety and Applied Nutrition, *Produce Safety from Production to Consumption: 2004 Action Plan to Minimize Foodborne Illness Associated with Fresh Produce Consumption*, October 2004, available at http://www.fda.gov/Food/FoodborneIllnessContaminants/BuyStoreServeSafeFood/ucm129487.htm; FDA issues alert on foodborne illness associated with certain basil and mesculin/spring mix salad products, *FDA News*, May 21, 2004, available at http://www.fda.gov/NewsEvents/Newsroom/PressAnnouncements/2004/ucm108304.htm.

32. FDA update on recent hepatitis A outbreaks associated with green onions from Mexico, *FDA Statement*, December 9, 2003, available at http://www.cdc.gov/mmwr/preview/mmwrhtml/mm5247a5.htm.

33. U.S. Food and Drug Administration, Urgent Nationwide Alfalfa Sprout Recall, May 2010, available at http://www.fda.gov/newsevents/newsroom/pressannouncements/2010/ucm213136.htm.

34. Viruses—just a flush away? *Science News* 155 (1999): 107.

35. E. T. Ryan, M. E. Wilson, and K. C. Kain, Illness after international travel, *New England Journal of Medicine* 347 (2002): 505–516.

36. CDC National Center for Infectious Diseases, Creutzfeldt-Jakob disease (nvCJD), Risk for Travelers, February 2013, available at http://www.cdc.gov/ncidod/dvrd/vcjd/risk_travelers.htm

37. M. Sheffer, ed., *Hydrogen Cyanide and Cyanides: Human Health Aspects* (Geneva, Switzerland: World Health Organization, 2004), pp. 4–9.

38. B. Weiss, S. Amler, and R.W. Amler, Pesticides, *Pediatrics* 113 (2004): 1030–1036.

39. Health Canada, Assessing Human Health Risks During Pesticide Review in Canada, available at http://www.hc-sc.gc.ca/cps-spc/pubs/pest/_fact-fiche/assess-health-eval-sante/index-eng.php.

40. J. Ma and coauthors, Milk intake, circulating levels of insulin-like growth factor-I, and risk of colorectal cancer in men, *Journal of the National Cancer Institute* 93 (2001): 1330–1336.

41. FDA Center for Veterinary Medicine, Report on the Food and Drug Administration's review of the safety of recombinant bovine somatotropin, available at http://www.fda.gov/animalveterinary/safetyhealth/productsafetyinformation/ucm130321.htm.

42. National Council Against Health Fraud. Milk processors warned to remove "hormone free" claims from the labeling of dairy products, September 12, 2003, available at http://www.ncahf.org/digest03/03-46.html.

43. K. H. Mathews Jr. and coauthors, USDA Economic Research Service, Livestock drugs: More questions than answers? *Agricultural Outlook*, September 2001, 18–21.

44. No more antibiotics says WHO, *Nutrition Today* 38 (2003): 163.

45. Health Canada, *Food and Nutrition: Arsenic*, available at http://www.hc-sc.gc.ca/fn-an/securit/chem-chim/environ/arsenic-eng.php.

46. T. Lasky and coauthors, Mean total arsenic concentrations in chicken 1989–2000 and estimated exposures for consumers of chicken, *Environmental Health Perspectives* 112 (2004): 18–21.

10. Standing Committee on the Scientific Evaluation of Dietary Reference Intakes, Food and Nutrition Board, Institute of Medicine, *Dietary Reference Intakes for Vitamin A, Vitamin K, Arsenic, Boron, Chromium, Copper, Iodine, Iron, Manganese, Molybdenum, Nickel, Silicon, Vanadium, and Zinc* (Washington, D.C.: National Academies Press, 2001).

48. C. P. Dougherty and coauthors, Dietary exposures to food contaminants across the United States, *Environmental Research* 84 (2000): 170–185.

49. EPA Fact Sheet, Update: National listing of fish and wildlife advisories, December 2013, available at http://www.epa.gov/ost/fish.

50. Centers for Disease Control and Prevention, *Fourth National Report on Human Exposure to Environmental Chemicals*, September 2013, available at http://www.cdc.gov/exposurereport/index.html.

51. K. M. Smith and N. R. Sahyoun, Fish consumption: Recommendations versus advisories, can they be reconciled? *Nutrition Reviews* 63 (2005): 39–46.

52. Health Canada, *It's Your Health—Mercury and Human Health*, available at http://www.hc-sc.gc.ca/hl-vs/iyh-vsv/environ/merc-eng.php.

53. EPA national advice on mercury in fish caught by family and friends for women who are or may become pregnant, nursing mothers, and young children, *EPA National Advisory*, 2004, available at http://water.epa.gov/scitech/swguidance/fish-shellfish/outreach/advice_index.cfm.

54. J. M. Hightower and D. Moore, Mercury levels in high-end consumers of fish, *Environmental Health Perspectives* 111 (2003): 604–608.

55. R. A. Hites and coauthors, Global assessment of organic contaminants in farmed salmon, *Science* 303 (2004): 226–229.

56. Health Canada, Food Additives, available at http://www.hc-sc.gc.ca/fn-an/securit/addit/index-eng.php.

57. Canadian Aquaculture Industry Alliance, *Your Quick Guide to Canadian Farmed Salmon*, available at http://www.aquaculture.ca/files/GuidetoCanadianFarmedSalmon.pdf.

58. M. Meadows, MSG: A common flavor enhancer, *FDA Consumer* 37 (2003): 35.

59. International Food Information Council, Glutamate and monosodium glutamate: Examining the myths, *IFIC Review*, November 2001, available at http://www.foodinsight.org/Content/76/Glutamate-and-Monosodium-Glutamate.pdf.

60. C. S. Johnston and D. L. Bowling, Stability of ascorbic acid in commercially available orange juices, *Journal of the American Dietetic Association* 102 (2002): 525–529.

61. D. J. McKillop and coauthors, The effect of different cooking methods on folate retention in various foods that are amongst the major contributors to folate intake in the UK diet, *British Journal of Nutrition* 88 (2002): 681–688.

Consumer Corner 12

1. Position of the American Dietetic Association: Food irradiation, *Journal of the American Dietetic Association* 100 (2000): 246–253.

2. K. M. Shea, Technical report: Irradiation of food, *Pediatrics* 106 (2000): 1505–1510.

3. Canadian Food Inspection Agency, Food Irradiation, available at http://www.inspection.gc.ca/food/information-for-consumers/fact-sheets/labelling-food-packaging-and-storage/irradiation/eng/1332358607968/1332358680017.

4. M. T. Osterholm and A. P. Norgan, The role of irradiation in food safety, *New England Journal of Medicine* 350 (2004): 1898–1901.

5. P. Loaharanu, Irradiated Foods (New York: American Council on Science and Health, 2003).

6. Position of the American Dietetic Association: Food and water safety, *Journal of the American Dietetic Association* 103 (2003): 1203–1218.

7. Canadian Food Inspection Agency [see reference 3].

8. A. L. Young, Food irradiation: After 35 years, have we made progress? A government perspective, *Environmental Science and Pollution Research International* 10 (2003): 82–88.

9. J. Daniels and M. Abrams, USDA releases specifications for the purchase of irradiated ground beef in the national school lunch program, USDA News Release, May 29, 2003.

10. P. D. Frenzen and coauthors, Consumer acceptance of irradiated meat and poultry in the United States, *Journal of Food Protection* 64 (2001): 2020–2026.

Controversy 12

1. Agriculture and Agri-Food Canada, *Canada's Organic Industry at a Glance 2009*, available at http://www.agr.gc.ca/eng/industry-markets-and-trade/statistics-and-market-information/by-product-sector/organic-products/organic-production-canadian-industry/canada-s-organic-industry-at-a-glance-2009/?id=1276292934938.

2. Government of Canada, *Genetically Modified (GM) Foods and Other Novel Foods—Approved Products*, available at http://www.hc-sc.gc.ca/fn-an/gmf-agm/index-eng.php.

3. C. M. Williams, Nutritional quality of organic food: Shades of grey or shades of green? *Proceedings of the Nutrition Society* 61 (2002): 19–34.

4. Organic foods: More nutritious? *Nutrition and the MD*, August 2002, pp. 6–7.

5. C. Lewis, A new kind of fish story: The coming of biotech animals, *FDA Consumer*, January/February 2001, pp. 15–20.

6. P. W. Phillips, Biotechnology in the global agri-food system, *Trends in Biotechnology* 20 (2002): 376–381.

7. G. Khush, Productivity improvements in rice, *Nutrition Reviews* 61 (2003): S114–S116.

8. B. Qi and coauthors, Production of very long chain polyunsaturated omega-3 and omega-6 fatty acids in plants, *Nature Biotechnology* 10 (May 16, 2004), available at http://www.nature.com/nbt/journal/v22/n6/abs/nbt972.html.

9. F. M. Wambugu, Development and transfer of genetically modified virus-resistant sweet potato for subsistence farmers in Kenya, *Nutrition Reviews* 61 (2003): S110–S113.

10. A. Pollack, Narrow path for new biotech food crops, *New York Times*, May 20, 2004, available at http://www.nytimes.com/2004/05/20/business/narrow-path-for-new-biotech-food-crops.html?pagewanted=all&src=pm.

11. H. C. Sharma and coauthors, Prospects for using transgenic resistance to insects in crop improvement, *EJB Electronic Journal of Biotechnology* 3, no. 2 (2000), available at http://www.ejbiotechnology.info/index.php/ejbiotechnology/article/view/v3n2-3/847.

12. J. Travis, Rats join the roster of clones, *Science News* 164 (2003): 237.

13. Health Canada, Food Directorate Interim Policy on Foods from Cloned Animals, available at http://www.hc-sc.gc.ca/fn-an/legislation/pol/pol-cloned_animal-clones_animaux-eng.php.

14. J. Huang, C. Pray, and S. Rozelle, Enhancing the crops to feed the poor, *Nature* 418 (2002): 678–684.

15. National Research Council and Institute of Medicine, *Safety of Genetically Engineered Foods: Approaches to Assessing Unintended Health Effects* (Washington, D.C.: National Academies Press, 2004), pp. 1–15.

16. Health Canada, Food Directorate Interim Policy on Foods from Cloned Animals [see reference 13].

17. Amy Ridenour, director of the National Center for Public Policy Research in Washington, D.C.

18. Committee on Biological Confinement of Genetically Engineered Organisms of the National Research Council, *Biological Confinement of Genetically Engineered Organisms* (Washington, D.C.: National Academies Press, 2004), pp. 10–13.

19. S. Milius, When genes escape: Does it matter to crops and weeds? *Science News* 164 (2003): 232–233.

20. H. C. Sharma and coauthors, 2000 [see reference 11].

21. M. K. Sears and coauthors, Impact of BT corn pollen on monarch butterfly populations: A risk

assessment, *Proceedings of the National Academy of Sciences* 98 (2001): 11937–11942.

22. D. E. Stanley-Horn and coauthors, Assessing the impact of Cry1Ab-expressing corn pollen on monarch butterfly larvae in field studies, *Proceedings of the National Academy of Sciences* 98 (2001): 11931–11936.

23. J. Walsh, Brave new farm, *Time*, January 11, 1999, pp. 86–88.

24. H. Adamu, Nigeria's minister of agriculture and rural development, "Hungry Africans want biotech crops, so get out of the way," *International Herald Tribune*, September 12, 2000, p. 8.

25. A. Bakshi, Potential adverse health effects of genetically modified crops, *Journal of Toxicology and Environmental Health. Part B, Critical Reviews* 6 (2003): 211–215; B. C. Babcock and C. A. Francis, Solving global nutrition challenges requires more than new biotechnologies, *Journal of the American Dietetic Association* 100 (2000): 1308–1311.

13 Life Cycle Nutrition: Mother and Infant

Do You Ever . . .

Think that men's lifestyle habits are of no consequence to a future pregnancy?

Wonder how much alcohol it takes to harm a developing unborn child?

Consider breastfeeding to be about the same as formula feeding for babies?

Wonder how young infants can thrive for months on only breast milk or formula without other foods?

Keep Reading . . .

Learning Objectives

After completing this chapter, you should be able to

LO 13.1 Explain why a nutritionally adequate diet is important long before a pregnancy is established.

LO 13.2 Identify the special nutritional needs of a pregnant teenager as compared to a pregnant adult.

LO 13.3 Evaluate the statement that "no level of alcoholic beverage intake is safe or advisable during pregnancy."

LO 13.4 Describe the impacts of gestational diabetes and preeclampsia on the health of a mother and of her unborn child.

LO 13.5 Discuss the nutrition and health benefits of breast-feeding to both the mother and the child.

LO 13.6 Discuss some relationships between childhood obesity and chronic diseases.

LO 13.7 Develop a healthy eating and activity plan to help an obese child improve his or her short- and long-term health overall.

Contents

All people need the same nutrients, but the amounts we need change as we move through life. This chapter is the first of two on life's changing nutrient needs. It focuses on the two life stages that might be the most important to an individual's life-long health—pregnancy and infancy.

Pregnancy: The Impact of Nutrition on the Future

We normally think of our nutrition as personal, affecting only our own lives. The woman who is pregnant, or who soon will be, must understand that her nutrition today is critical to the health of her future child throughout life. The nutrient demands of pregnancy are extraordinary.

Preparing for Pregnancy

Before she becomes pregnant, a woman must establish eating habits that will optimally nourish both the growing **fetus** and herself. She must be well nourished at the outset because early in pregnancy the **embryo** undergoes rapid and significant developmental changes that depend on good nutrition.

Fathers-to-be are also wise to examine their eating and drinking habits. For example, a sedentary lifestyle and consuming too few fruit and vegetables may affect men's **fertility** (and the fertility of their children), and men who drink too much alcohol or encounter other toxins in the weeks before conception can sustain damage to their sperm's genetic material.*,[1] When both partners adopt healthy habits, they will be better prepared to meet the demands of parenting that lie ahead.

---

*References are listed at the end of the chapter.

Both parents can prepare in advance for a healthy pregnancy.

fetus (FEET-us) the stage of human gestation from eight weeks after conception until the birth of an infant.

embryo (EM-bree-oh) the stage of human gestation from the third to the eighth week after conception.

fertility the capacity of a woman to produce a normal ovum periodically and of a man to produce normal sperm; the ability to reproduce.

Prepregnancy Weight   Before pregnancy, all women, but underweight women in particular, should strive for appropriate body weights. A woman who starts out underweight and who fails to gain sufficiently during pregnancy is very likely to bear a baby with a dangerously low birthweight.[2] A later section comes back to the needed gains in pregnancy. Infant birthweight is the most potent single indicator of an infant's future health. A **low-birthweight** baby, defined as one who weighs less than 2,500 grams (5½ lb), is nearly 40 times as likely to die in the first year of life as a normal-weight baby. To prevent low birthweight, underweight women are advised to gain weight before becoming pregnant and to strive to gain adequately thereafter.

Underweight is defined as BMI < 18.5. *Overweight* is defined as BMI > 25 (see Table 13–4 on page 565).

When nutrient supplies during pregnancy fail to meet demands, the fetus may adapt to the sparse conditions in ways that may make obesity or chronic diseases more likely in later life (see Controversy 13 in this chapter).[3] Low birthweight is also associated with lower adult IQ and other brain impairments, short stature, and educational disadvantages.[4] Nutrient deficiency coupled with low birthweight is the underlying cause of more than half of all the deaths worldwide of children under five years of age.

The infant mortality rate in Canada tends to be lower than that in the United States (6.4 in 1,000 live births), with a rate of 4.8 deaths per 1,000 in 2011—a decrease from 6.5 deaths per 1,000 in 1995.[5] This low rate has remained about the same over the last 15 years and is a tribute to public health efforts aimed at reducing infant deaths (see Figure 13–1).

You can find perinatal statistics and other information about perinatal health behaviours by province in the Perinatal Health Indicators for Canada—2011 Edition (http://www.phac-aspc.gc.ca/rhs-ssg/phi-isp-2011-eng.php). Information about infant and child health from the Canadian Paediatric Surveillance Program is also available at http://www.cpsp.cps.ca/publications. Not all cases of low birthweight reflect poor nutrition. Heredity, disease conditions, smoking, and drug (including alcohol) use during pregnancy all contribute.[6] Even with optimal nutrition and health during pregnancy, some women give birth to small infants for unknown reasons. But poor nutrition is the major factor in low birthweight—and an avoidable one, as later sections make clear.[7]

Obese women are also urged to strive for healthy weights before pregnancy. The infant of an obese mother may be larger than normal and may be large even if born prematurely. The large early baby may not be recognized as premature and thus may not receive the special medical care required. The baby of an obese mother may be twice as likely to be born with a neural tube defect (NTD) than others, but the reasons for this are not known.[8] Obese women are more likely to require drugs to induce labour or to require surgical intervention for the birth, and they suffer gestational diabetes, hypertension, and infections after the birth more often than do women of healthy weight.[9] In addition, obese women have a greater risk of giving birth to infants with heart defects.[10] An appropriate goal for the obese woman who wishes to become pregnant is to strive to attain a healthy prepregnancy body weight in order to minimize her medical risks and those of her future child.

A Healthy Placenta and Other Organs   A major reason the mother's nutrition before pregnancy is so crucial is that it determines whether her **uterus** will be able to support the growth of a healthy **placenta** during the first month of **gestation**. The placenta is both a supply depot and a waste-removal system for the fetus. If the placenta works perfectly, the fetus wants for nothing; if it doesn't, no alternative source of sustenance is available, and the fetus will fail to thrive. Figure 13–2 shows the placenta, a mass of tissue in which maternal and fetal blood vessels intertwine and exchange materials. The two bloods never mix, but the barrier between them is notably thin. To grasp how thin, picture your hands encased in skintight surgical gloves and immersed in water. Your hands represent the fetal blood vessels, the water is the pool of maternal blood, and the gloves are the tissue-thin placenta separating them. Across this thin barrier, nutrients and oxygen move from the mother's blood into the fetus's blood, and wastes move out of the fetal blood, to be excreted

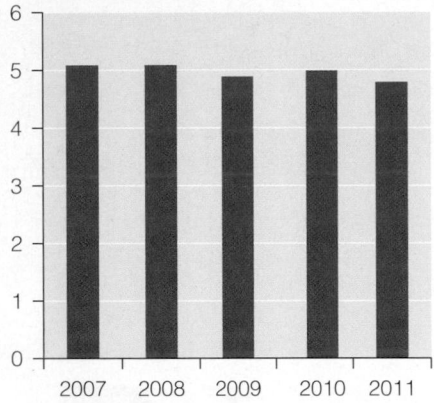

Figure 13–1

Canadian Infant Mortality Rates (2007–2011)

Source: Statistics Canada, Infant mortality rates, by province and territory (Both sexes), *CANSIM, table 102-0504. 2013. Reproduced and distributed on an "as is" basis with the permission of Statistics Canada.*

low birthweight a birthweight of less than 2,500 g (5½ lb); used as a predictor of probable health problems in the newborn and as a probable indicator of poor nutrition status of the mother before and/or during pregnancy. Low-birthweight infants are of two different types. Some are *premature infants*; they are born early and are the right size for their gestational age. Other low-birthweight infants have suffered growth failure in the uterus; they are small for gestational age (small for date) and may or may not be premature.

uterus (YOO-ter-us) the womb, the muscular organ within which the infant develops before birth.

placenta (pla-SEN-tuh) the organ of pregnancy in which maternal and fetal blood circulate in close proximity and exchange nutrients and oxygen (flowing into the fetus) and wastes (picked up by the mother's blood).

gestation the period of about 40 weeks (three trimesters) from conception to birth; the term of a pregnancy.

Figure 13–2

The Placenta

The placenta is composed of spongy tissue in which fetal blood and maternal blood flow side by side, each in its own vessels. The maternal blood transfers oxygen and nutrients to the fetus's blood and picks up fetal wastes to be excreted by the mother. Thus, the placenta performs the nutritive, respiratory, and excretory functions that the fetus's digestive system, lungs, and kidneys will provide after birth.

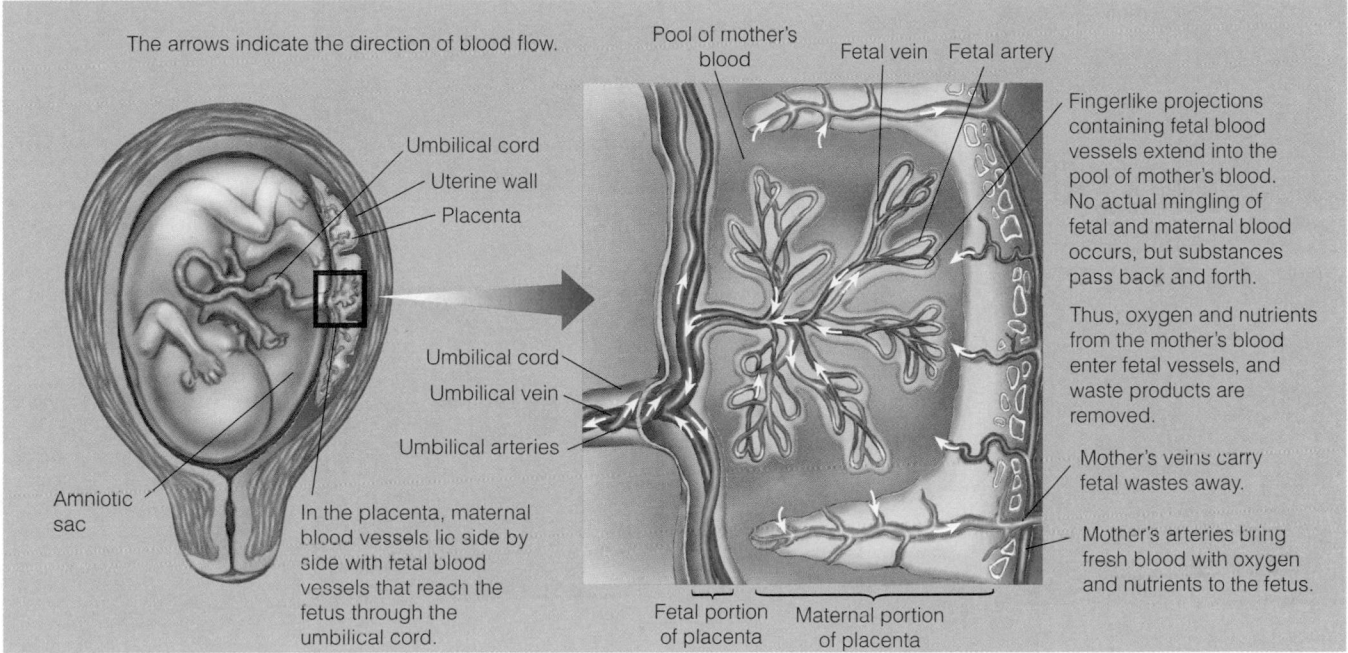

The arrows indicate the direction of blood flow.

Pool of mother's blood

Fetal vein   Fetal artery

Umbilical cord
Uterine wall
Placenta

Fingerlike projections containing fetal blood vessels extend into the pool of mother's blood. No actual mingling of fetal and maternal blood occurs, but substances pass back and forth.

Thus, oxygen and nutrients from the mother's blood enter fetal vessels, and waste products are removed.

Umbilical cord
Umbilical vein
Umbilical arteries

Mother's veins carry fetal wastes away.

Amniotic sac

In the placenta, maternal blood vessels lie side by side with fetal blood vessels that reach the fetus through the umbilical cord.

Mother's arteries bring fresh blood with oxygen and nutrients to the fetus.

Fetal portion of placenta   Maternal portion of placenta

by the mother. The umbilical cord is the pipeline from the placenta to the fetus. The **amniotic sac** surrounds and cradles the fetus, cushioning it with fluids.

The placenta is an active metabolic organ with many responsibilities of its own. It actively gathers up hormones, nutrients, and protein molecules such as antibodies and transfers them into the fetal bloodstream. The placenta also produces a broad range of hormones that act in many ways to maintain pregnancy and prepare the mother's breasts for **lactation**.[11]

If the mother's nutrient stores are inadequate during the period when her body is developing the placenta, then the placenta will never form and function properly. As a consequence, no matter how well the mother eats later, her fetus will not receive optimal nourishment, and a low-birthweight baby with all of the associated risks is likely. After getting such a poor start on life, the child may be ill equipped, even as an adult, to store sufficient nutrients, and a girl may later be unable to grow an adequate placenta or bear healthy full-term infants. Thus, a woman's poor nutrition during her early pregnancy could affect her grandchild as well as her child.[12]

KEY POINT

- Adequate nutrition before pregnancy establishes physical readiness and nutrient stores to support fetal growth. Both underweight and overweight women should strive for appropriate body weights before pregnancy. Newborns who weigh less than 2.5 kilograms (5½ lb) face greater health risks than normal-weight babies. The healthy development of the placenta depends on adequate nutrition before pregnancy.

The Events of Pregnancy

The newly fertilized **ovum**, called a **zygote**, begins as a single cell and divides into many cells during the days after fertilization. Within two weeks, the zygote embeds itself in the uterine wall in a process known as **implantation**, and the placenta

amniotic (AM-nee-OTT-ic) **sac** the "bag of waters" in the uterus in which the fetus floats.

lactation production and secretion of breast milk for the purpose of nourishing an infant.

ovum the egg, produced by the mother, that unites with a sperm from the father to produce a new individual.

zygote (ZYE-goat) the term that describes the product of the union of ovum and sperm during the first two weeks after fertilization.

implantation the stage of development, during the first two weeks after conception, in which the fertilized egg (fertilized ovum or zygote) embeds itself in the wall of the uterus and begins to develop.

Figure 13–3

Stages of Embryonic and Fetal Development

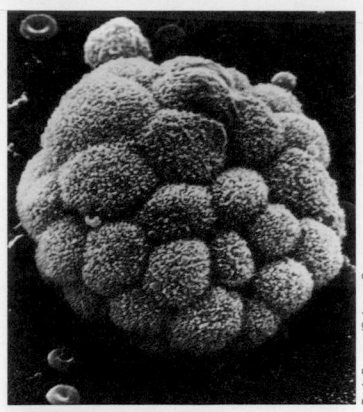

(1) A newly fertilized ovum is about the size of the period at the end of this sentence. This zygote at less than one week after fertilization is not much bigger and is ready for implantation.

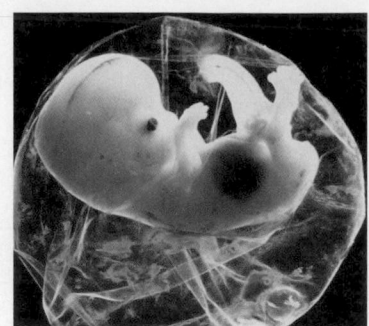

(2) After implantation, the placenta develops and begins to provide nourishment to the developing embryo. An embryo five weeks after fertilization is about 1.25 cm long.

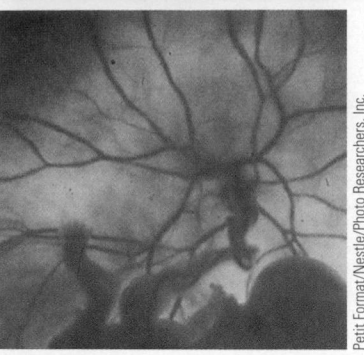

(3) A fetus after 11 weeks of development is just over 2.5 cm long. Notice the umbilical cord and blood vessels connecting the fetus with the placenta.

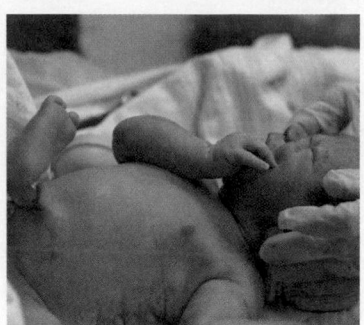

(4) A newborn infant after nine months of development measures close to 50 cm in length. The average birthweight is about 3.5 kg (7½ lb). From eight weeks to term, this infant grew 20 times as long and 50 times as heavy.

begins to grow inside the uterus. Minimal growth in size takes place at this time, but it is a crucial period in development. Adverse influences such as smoking, drug abuse, and malnutrition at this time lead to failure to implant or to abnormalities such as NTDs that can cause loss of the zygote, possibly before the woman knows she is pregnant.

The Embryo and Fetus During the next six weeks, the embryo registers astonishing physical changes (see Figure 13–3). At eight weeks, the fetus has a complete central nervous system, a beating heart, a fully formed digestive system, well-defined fingers and toes, and the beginnings of facial features.

In the last seven months of pregnancy, the fetal period, the fetus grows 50 times as heavy and 20 times as long. Critical periods of cell division and development occur in organ after organ. The amniotic sac fills with fluid, and the mother's body changes. The uterus and its supporting muscles increase in size, the breasts may become tender and full, the nipples may darken in preparation for lactation, and the mother's blood volume increases by half to accommodate the added load of materials it must carry. Gestation lasts approximately 40 weeks and ends with the birth of the infant. The 40 or so weeks of pregnancy are divided into thirds, each of which is called a **trimester**.

A Note about Critical Periods Each organ and tissue type grows with its own characteristic pattern and timing. The development of each takes place only at a certain time—the **critical period**. Whatever nutrients and other environmental conditions are necessary during this period must be supplied on time if the organ is to reach its full potential. If the development of an organ is limited during a critical period, recovery is impossible. For example, the fetus's heart and brain are well developed at 14 weeks and the lungs 10 weeks later. Therefore, early malnutrition impairs the heart and brain; later malnutrition impairs the lungs.

trimester a period representing gestation. A trimester is about 13 to 14 weeks.

critical period a finite period during development in which certain events may occur that will have irreversible effects on later developmental stages. A critical period is usually a period of cell division in a body organ.

The effects of malnutrition during critical periods of pregnancy are seen in defects of the nervous system of the embryo (explained later); in the child's poor dental health; and in the adolescent's and adult's vulnerability to infections and possibly higher risks of diabetes, hypertension, stroke, or heart disease.[13] The effects of malnutrition during critical periods are irreversible: abundant and nourishing food, fed after the critical time, cannot remedy harm already done.

Table 13–1 provides a list of factors that make nutrient deficiencies and complications likely during pregnancy. Notice that young age heads the list; a later section explains why pregnant adolescents are especially prone to malnutrition.

KEY POINT

- Implantation, fetal development, and early critical periods depend on maternal nutrition before and during pregnancy.

Increased Need for Nutrients

During pregnancy, a woman's nutrient needs increase more for certain nutrients than for others. Figure 13–4 shows the percentage increase in nutrient intakes recommended for pregnant women compared with nonpregnant women. To meet the high nutrient demands of pregnancy, a woman must make careful food choices, but her body will also do its part by maximizing nutrient absorption and minimizing losses.[14]

Energy, Carbohydrate, Protein, and Fat   Energy needs vary with the progression of pregnancy. In the first trimester, the pregnant woman needs no additional energy, but her energy needs rise as pregnancy progresses. She requires an additional 340 daily Calories during the second trimester and an extra 450 Calories each day during the third trimester.[15] Well-nourished pregnant women meet these demands for more energy in several ways: some eat more food, some reduce their activity, and some store less of their food energy as fat.[16] A woman can easily meet the need for extra Calories by selecting more nutrient-dense foods from the four food groups. Table 2–3 (on page 47) provides suggested eating patterns for several Calorie levels, and Table 13–2 offers a sample menu for pregnant and lactating women.

If a woman chooses less nutritious options such as sugary soft drinks or fatty snack foods to meet energy needs, she will undoubtedly come up short on nutrients. The increase in the need for nutrients is even greater than for energy, so the mother-to-be should choose nutrient-dense foods such as whole-grain breads and cereals; legumes; dark green vegetables; citrus fruit; low-fat milk and milk products; and lean meats, fish, poultry, and eggs.

Ample carbohydrate (ideally, 175 g or more per day and certainly no less than 135 g) is necessary to fuel the fetal brain and spare the protein needed for fetal growth. Fibre in carbohydrate-rich foods such as whole grains, vegetables, and fruit can help alleviate the constipation that many pregnant women experience.

The Dietary Reference Intake (DRI) committee's protein recommendation for pregnancy is higher than for nonpregnant women by 25 grams per day. Most women in Canada, however, need not add protein-rich foods to their diets because they already exceed the recommended protein intake for pregnancy. Excess protein may also have adverse effects, as Chapter 6 explained.

Some vegetarian women limit or omit protein-rich meats, eggs, and dairy products from their diets. For them, meeting the recommendation for food energy each day and including several generous servings of plant-protein foods such as legumes, tofu, whole grains, nuts, and seeds are imperative. Protein supplements during pregnancy can be harmful, and their use is discouraged.

The high nutrient requirements of pregnancy leave little room in the diet for excess energy from solid fats such as butter. The essential fatty acids, however, are particularly important to the growth and development of the fetus.[17] The brain is composed mainly of lipid material and depends heavily on long-chain omega-3 and omega-6 fatty acids for its growth, function, and structure. (See Table 5–5 on page 178 for a list of good food sources of the essential fatty acids.)

Table 13–1

Factors Placing Pregnant Women at Nutritional Risk

Women likely to develop nutrient deficiencies and pregnancy complications include those who

- Are young (adolescents).
- Have had many previous pregnancies (3 or more to mothers under age 20; 4 or more to mothers age 20 or older).
- Have short intervals between pregnancies (<18 months).
- Have a history of poor pregnancy outcomes.
- Lack nutrition knowledge, have too little money to purchase adequate food, or have too little family support.
- Consume an inadequate diet due to food faddism, preferences, weight-loss "dieting," uninformed vegetarianism, or eating disorders.
- Smoke cigarettes or use alcohol or illicit drugs.
- Are lactose intolerant or suffer chronic health conditions requiring special diets.
- Are underweight or overweight at conception.
- Are carrying twins or triplets.
- Gain insufficient or excessive weight during pregnancy.
- Have a low level of education.

● DRI nutrient and energy intake recommendations for pregnant women are listed on the inside front cover.

Pregnancy: The Impact of Nutrition on the Future

Figure 13–4

Comparison of Nutrient Recommendations for Nonpregnant, Pregnant, and Lactating Women

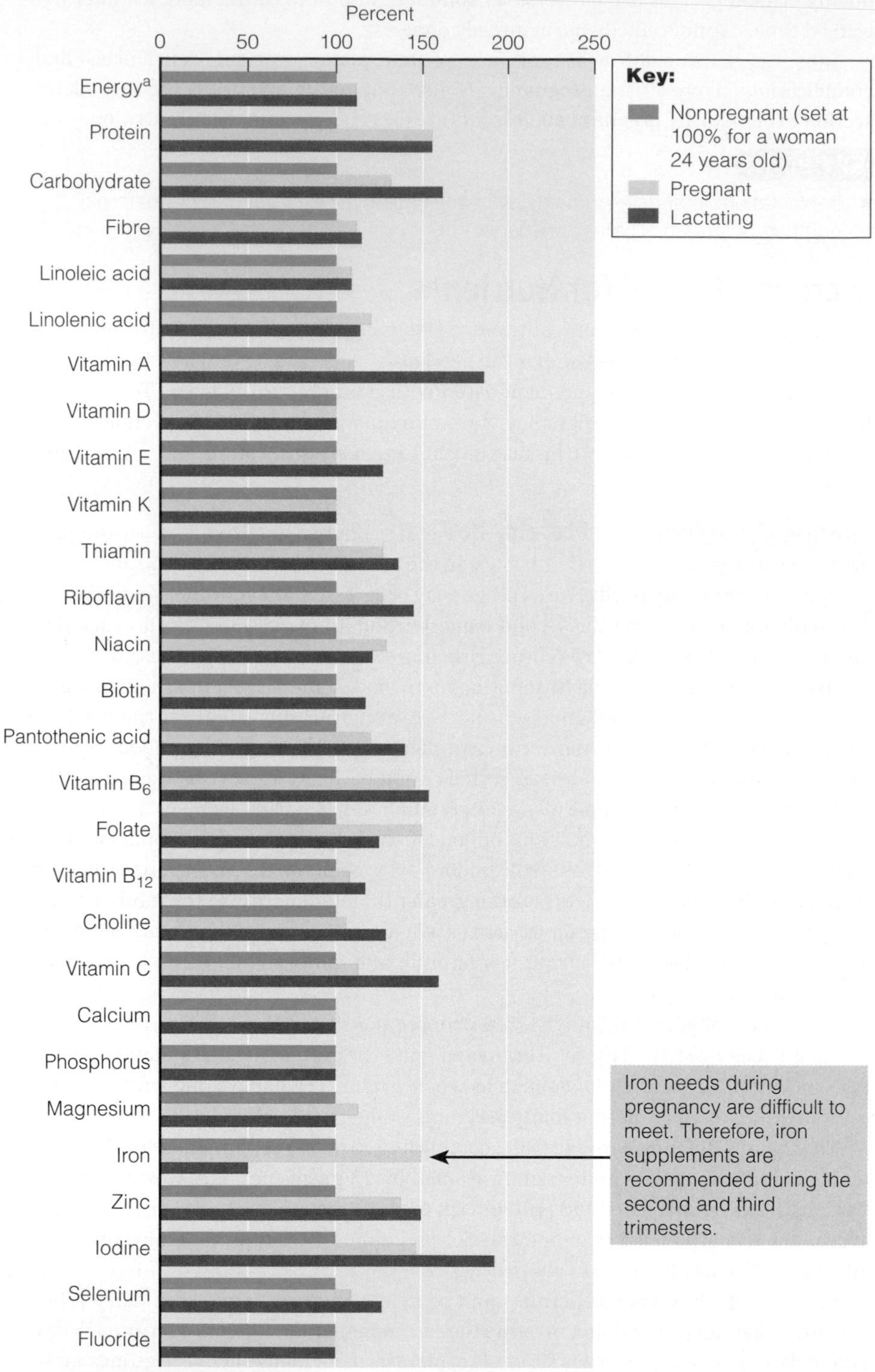

Percent

Key:

■ Nonpregnant (set at 100% for a woman 24 years old)

■ Pregnant

■ Lactating

Energy[a]
Protein
Carbohydrate
Fibre
Linoleic acid
Linolenic acid
Vitamin A
Vitamin D
Vitamin E
Vitamin K
Thiamin
Riboflavin
Niacin
Biotin
Pantothenic acid
Vitamin B_6
Folate
Vitamin B_{12}
Choline
Vitamin C
Calcium
Phosphorus
Magnesium
Iron
Zinc
Iodine
Selenium
Fluoride

Iron needs during pregnancy are difficult to meet. Therefore, iron supplements are recommended during the second and third trimesters.

[a]*Energy allowance during pregnancy is for the 2nd trimester; energy allowance during the 3rd trimester is slightly higher; no additional allowance is provided during the 1st trimester. Energy allowance during lactation is for the first 6 months; energy allowance during the second 6 months is slightly higher.*

KEY POINT

■ Pregnancy brings physiological adjustments that demand increased intakes of energy and nutrients. A balanced diet that includes more nutrient-dense foods from the five food groups can help meet these needs.

Table 13–2

Food Choices for Pregnant and Lactating Women

SAMPLE MENU

Breakfast

1 whole-wheat English muffin
2 tbs peanut butter
1 c low-fat vanilla yogurt
½ c fresh strawberries
1 c orange juice

Mid-morning snack

½ c cranberry juice
30 g pretzels

Lunch

Sandwich (tuna salad on whole-wheat bread, but limit canned albacore tuna to
no more than 300 g/wk)
½ carrot (sticks)
1 c low-fat milk

Dinner

Chicken cacciatore
    90 g chicken
    ½ c stewed tomatoes
1 c rice
½ c summer squash
1½ c salad (spinach, mushrooms, carrots)
1 tbs salad dressing
1 slice Italian bread
2 tsp soft margarine
1 c low-fat 1% milk

NOTE. This sample meal plan provides about 2,500 Cal (55% from carbohydrate, 20% from protein, and 25% from fat) and meets most of the vitamin and mineral needs of pregnant and lactating women.

Of Special Interest: Folate and Vitamin B_{12}   The vitamins famous for their roles in cell reproduction—folate and vitamin B_{12}—are needed in large amounts during pregnancy. New cells are laid down at a tremendous pace as the fetus grows and develops. At the same time, the number of the mother's red blood cells must rise because her blood volume increases, a function requiring more cell division and therefore more vitamins. To accommodate these needs, the recommendation for folate during pregnancy increases from 400 to 600 micrograms a day (Health Canada, Prenatal Nutrition: Folate, http://www.hc-sc.gc.ca/fn-an/pubs/nutrition/folate-eng.php).

As described in Chapter 7, folate plays an important role in preventing NTDs. To review, the early weeks of pregnancy are a critical period for the formation and closure of the **neural tube** that will later develop to form the brain and spinal cord. By the time a woman suspects she is pregnant, usually around the sixth week of pregnancy, the embryo's neural tube normally has closed. A **neural tube defect (NTD)** occurs when the tube fails to close properly (some risk factors for neural tube defects are listed in the margin). In Canada, about 260 newborns are born each year with an NTD.[18] When the neural tube fails to close properly and brain development fails, a rare but lethal defect known as **anencephaly** occurs. All infants with anencephaly die shortly after birth.

In a more common NTD, the spinal cord and backbone do not develop normally—and the result is **spina bifida** (see Figure 13–5). The membranes covering the spinal cord often protrude from the spine as a sac, and sometimes a portion of the spinal cord is contained in the sac. Spina bifida is often accompanied by varying degrees of paralysis, depending on the extent of spinal cord damage. Mild cases may not be noticed. Moderate cases may involve curvature of the spine, muscle weakness, mental handicaps, and other ills; severe cases can lead to death.

A Pregnancy Affected by an NTD Can Occur in Any Woman, but These Factors Make It More Likely

- A previous pregnancy affected by an NTD
- Exposure to high temperatures early in pregnancy (prolonged fever or hot-tub use)
- Inadequate folate intake
- Low socioeconomic status
- Maternal diabetes (type 1)
- Maternal obesity
- Maternal use of antiseizure medications
- Race/ethnicity (NTDs are more common among whites and Hispanics than among others)

neural tube the embryonic tissue that later forms the brain and spinal cord.

neural tube defect (NTD) a group of nervous system abnormalities caused by interruption of the normal early development of the neural tube.

anencephaly (an-en-SEFF-ah-lee) an uncommon and always fatal NTD in which the brain fails to form.

spina bifida (SPY-na BIFF-ih-duh) one of the most common types of NTDs in which gaps occur in the bones of the spine. Often the spinal cord bulges and protrudes through the gaps, resulting in a number of motor and other impairments.

Figure 13–5
Spina Bifida—An NTD

Normally, the bony central chamber closes fully to encase the spinal cord and its surrounding membranes and fluid. In spina bifida, the two halves of the slender bones that should complete the casement of the cord fail to join.

In the serious form shown here, membranes and fluid have bulged through the gap and nerves are exposed, invariably leading to some degree of paralysis and often to mental retardation.

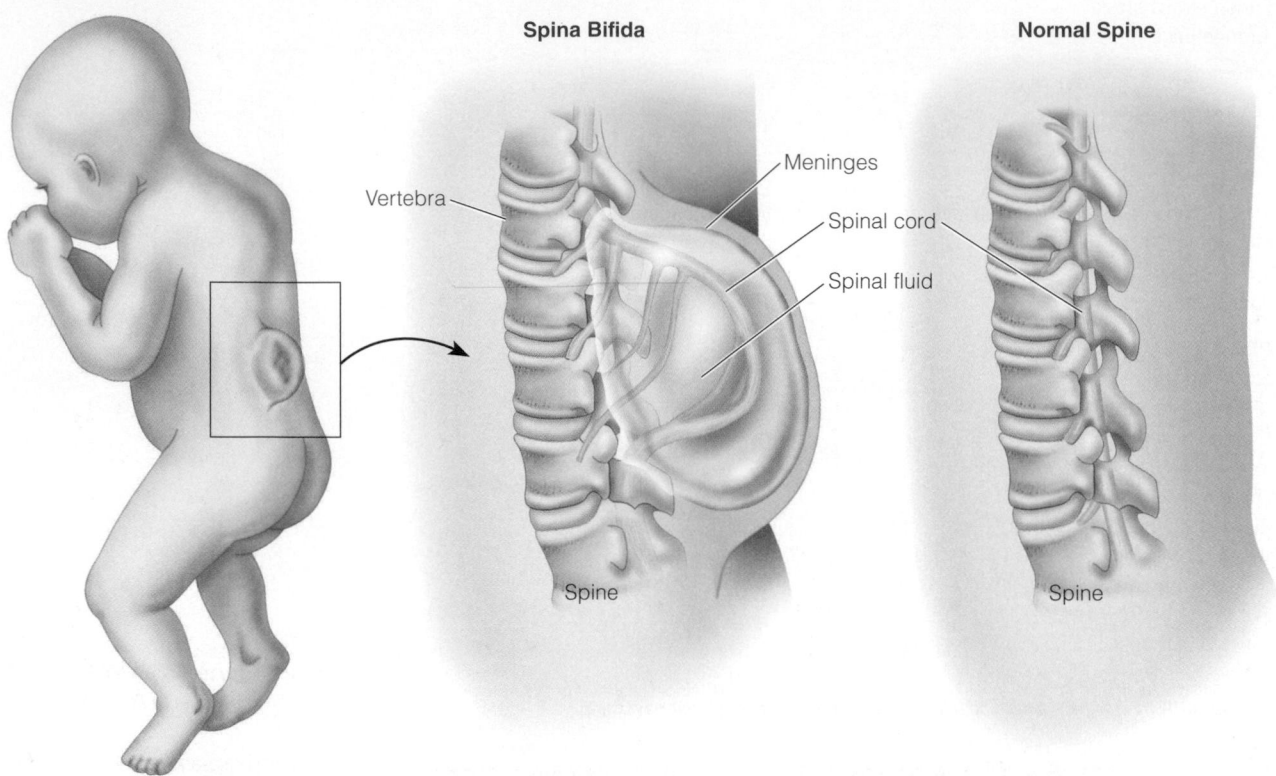

Spina Bifida **Normal Spine**

Meninges

Vertebra

Spinal cord

Spinal fluid

Spine Spine

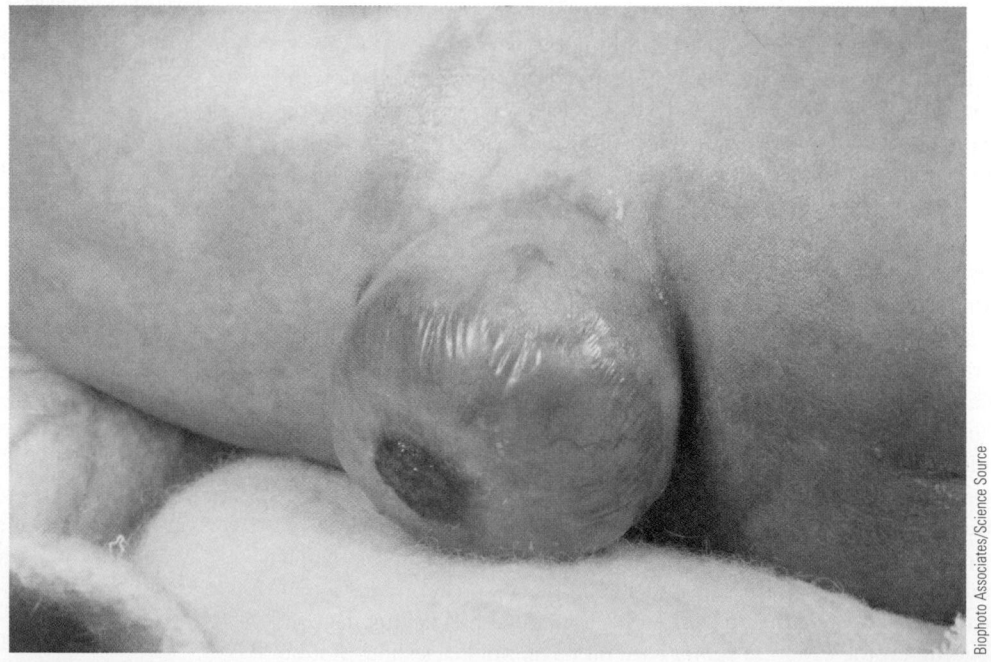

Biophoto Associates/Science Source

To reduce the risk of NTDs, women who are capable of becoming pregnant should obtain 400 micrograms of folic acid daily from supplements, fortified foods, or both, in addition to eating folate-rich foods (see Table 13–3).[19] The DRI committee recommends intake of synthetic folate, called folic acid, in supplements and fortified foods because it is absorbed better than the folate naturally present in foods.[20] Foods that naturally contain folate are still important, however, because they contribute to folate intakes while providing other needed vitamins, minerals, fibre, and phytochemicals.

All enriched grain products containing bleached wheat flour (cereal, pasta, rice, bread, and the like) sold commercially in Canada and the United States are fortified with folic acid. This measure has improved folate status in women of childbearing age and lowered the number of NTDs that occur each year.[21] Folate fortification does raise one safety concern, however. The pregnant woman needs a greater amount of vitamin B_{12} to assist folate in the manufacture of new cells. High intakes of folate complicate the diagnosis of a vitamin B_{12} deficiency. For this reason, folate intakes should not exceed 1 milligram per day.[22]

Chapter 7 describes how excessive folate intakes can mask symptoms of vitamin B_{12} deficiency.

People who eat meat, eggs, or dairy products receive all of the vitamin B_{12} they need, even for pregnancy. Those who exclude all animal products from the diet need vitamin B_{12}-fortified foods or supplements.

KEY POINT

- Due to their key roles in cell reproduction, folate and vitamin B_{12} are needed in large amounts during pregnancy. Folate plays an important role in preventing NTDs.

Calcium, Magnesium, Iron, and Zinc Among the minerals, calcium, phosphorus, and magnesium are in great demand during pregnancy because they are necessary for normal development of the bones and teeth. Intestinal absorption of calcium doubles early in pregnancy, and the mineral is stored in the mother's bones. Later, when fetal bones begin to calcify, the mother's bone calcium stores are mobilized, and there is a dramatic shift of calcium across the placenta. In the final weeks of pregnancy, more than 300 milligrams of calcium a day are transferred to the fetus. Efforts to ensure an adequate calcium intake during pregnancy are aimed at conserving the mother's bone mass while supplying fetal needs.

Most women do not meet the DRI recommendations for calcium and should increase their intakes.[23] In particular, pregnant women under age 25, whose own bones are still actively depositing minerals, should strive to meet the DRI recommendation for calcium by increasing their intakes of milk, cheese, yogurt, and other calcium-rich foods. Less preferred, but still acceptable, is a daily supplement of

---

Table 13–3

Rich Folate Sources[a]

Natural Folate Sources	Fortified Folate Sources
Liver (90 g) 221 µg	Multi-Grain Cheerios Plus cereal (1 c) 400 µg[b]
Lentils (½ c) 179 µg	Raisin Bran (1 c) 42 µg[b]
Chickpeas or pinto beans (½ c) 145 µg	Shreddies (1 c) 33 µg[b]
Asparagus (½ c) 131 µg	Pasta, cooked (1 c) 110 µg
Spinach (1 c raw) 131 µg	Rice, cooked (1 c) 134 µg
Avocado (½ c) 45 µg	Bagel (1 small whole) 75 µg
Orange juice (1 c) 74 µg	Waffles, frozen (2) 36 µg
Beets (½ c) 68 µg	Bread, white (1 slice) 28 µg

[a]For the amount of folate in other foods, visit the Canadian Nutrient File 2010 at http://www.hc-sc.gc.ca/fn-an/nutrition/fiche-nutri-data/cnf_aboutus-aproposdenous_fcen-eng.php.

[b]Folate in cereals varies; read the Nutrition Facts panel of the label.

600 milligrams of calcium. The DRI recommendation for calcium intake is the same for nonpregnant and pregnant women in the same age group. The mineral magnesium is also essential for bone and tissue growth, and pregnancy slightly increases the need for magnesium in the diet.

During pregnancy, the body avidly conserves iron—menstruation ceases and absorption of iron increases up to threefold. Despite these conservation measures, iron stores dwindle because the developing fetus draws heavily on its mother's iron to store up a supply sufficient to carry it through the first three to six months of life. Even women with inadequate iron stores transfer significant amounts of iron to the fetus, suggesting that the iron needs of the fetus have priority over those of the mother.[24] Maternal blood losses are also inevitable at birth, especially during a delivery by **cesarean section**, further draining the mother's iron supply. Few women enter pregnancy with adequate stores to meet pregnancy demands, so a daily iron supplement containing 16–20 milligrams is recommended during the second and third trimesters for all pregnant women (Health Canada, Prenatal Nutrition: Iron, http://www.hc-sc.gc.ca/fn-an/pubs/nutrition/iron-fer-eng.php). When a low hemoglobin or hematocrit is confirmed by a repeat test, more than 30 milligrams of iron may be prescribed. To enhance iron absorption, the supplement should be taken between meals and with liquids other than milk, coffee, or tea, which inhibit iron absorption.

Zinc, required for protein synthesis and cell development, is vital during pregnancy. Severe zinc deficiency during pregnancy predicts low birthweight.[25] Zinc is provided abundantly by protein-rich foods such as shellfish, meat, and nuts, but its absorption may be hindered by other trace elements or fibre in foods. For example, iron interferes with the body's absorption and use of zinc, so women taking iron supplements in excess of 30 milligrams per day may also need zinc supplements to prevent zinc deficiency.[26] Most supplements for pregnancy provide about 15–60 milligrams of iron a day.

Fish

While Health Canada also recommends that women continue to eat fish during pregnancy, 150 grams of cooked fish per week as recommended in Canada's Food Guide, they also mention that women pay special attention to the types of fish they consume during this time. For example, it is recommended that they choose the types of fish generally known to have low levels of contaminants, such as salmon, trout, and canned light tuna (Health Canada, Prenatal Nutrition: Fish and Omega-3 Fatty Acids, http://www.hc-sc.gc.ca/fn-an/pubs/nutrition/omega3-eng.php).

KEY POINT

- All pregnant women, but especially those who are less than 25 years of age, need to pay special attention to ensure adequate calcium intakes. A daily iron supplement is recommended for all pregnant women during the second and third trimesters.

Prenatal Supplements   Physicians often recommend daily multivitamin–mineral supplements for pregnant women. These **prenatal** supplements typically provide more folate, iron, and calcium than regular supplements (see Figure 13–6). Prenatal supplements are especially beneficial for women who do not eat adequately and for those in high-risk groups: women carrying twins or triplets, cigarette smokers, and alcohol and drug abusers.[27] For these women, prenatal supplements may be of some help in reducing the risks of preterm delivery, low birthweights, and birth defects.[28] Supplements cannot prevent the vast majority of destruction from tobacco, alcohol, and drugs, however, as later sections explain.

KEY POINT

- Women most likely to benefit from multivitamin–mineral supplements during pregnancy include those who do not eat adequately, those carrying twins or triplets, and those who smoke cigarettes or are alcohol or drug abusers.

Figure 13–6

Example of a Prenatal Supplement Label

Notice that vitamin A is reduced to guard against birth defects, while extra amounts of folate, iron, and other nutrients are provided to meet the specific needs of pregnant women.

Prenatal Vitamins

Supplement Facts
Serving Size 1 Tablet

Amount Per Tablet	% Daily Value for Pregnant/ Lactating Women
Vitamin A 4000 IU	50
Vitamin C 100 mg	167
Vitamin D 400 IU	100
Vitamin E 11 IU	37
Thiamin 1.84 mg	108
Riboflavin 1.7 mg	85
Niacin 18 mg	90
Vitamin B$_6$ 2.6 mg	104
Folate 800 mcg	100
Vitamin B$_{12}$ 4 mcg	50
Calcium 200 mg	15
Iron 27 mg	150
Zinc 25 mg	167

INGREDIENTS: calcium carbonate, microcrystalline cellulose, dicalcium phosphate, ascorbic acid, ferrous fumarate, zinc oxide, acacia, sucrose ester, niacinamide, modified cellulose gum, di-alpha tocopheryl acetate, hydroxypropyl methylcellulose, hydroxypropyl cellulose, artificial colours (FD&C blue no. 1 lake, FD&C red no. 40 lake, FD&C yellow no. 6 lake, titanium dioxide), polyethylene glycol, starch, pyridoxine hydrochloride, vitamin A acetate, riboflavin, thiamin mononitrate, folic acid, beta carotene, cholecalciferol, maltodextrin, gluten, cyanocobalamin, sodium bisulphite.

---

cesarean (see-ZAIR-ee-un) **section** surgical childbirth, in which the infant is taken through an incision in the woman's abdomen.

prenatal (pree-NAY-tal) before birth.

Canadian Prenatal Programs

Although Canada does not have a single national nutrition program for pregnant women, supportive nutrition programs are available to them. The **Canada Prenatal Nutrition Program (CPNP)**, first announced by Health Canada in 1994, is now available from the Public Health Agency of Canada's website for the Division of Childhood and Adolescence. The CPNP provides food supplementation, nutrition counselling, support, education, referral, and counselling on lifestyle issues for women who are most likely to have unhealthy babies. The program also supports community-based services by funding local community groups to establish and deliver services according to the local population needs and build on existing prenatal programs. The women targeted by this program include pregnant adolescents, youth at risk of becoming pregnant, pregnant women who abuse alcohol or other substances, pregnant women living in violent situations, off-reserve Aboriginal and Inuit women, refugees, and pregnant women living in isolation or not having access to services. The CPNP is jointly managed by the federal government and provincial/territorial governments. In 2002, 350 CPNP projects were funded by the Public and Population Health Branch, serving over 2,000 communities across Canada.[29] In addition, over 550 CPNP projects were funded by the First Nations and Inuit Health Branch in Inuit and on-reserve First Nations communities. You can obtain the most current information about the CPNP from the website (http://www.phac-aspc.gc.ca/hp-ps/dca-dea/prog-ini/cpnp-pcnp/), or check with your local public health department to find the CPNP in your community.

Many public health departments or community health agencies offer prenatal and postnatal education programs to interested members of the community.[30] To find out about programs for pregnant women at nutritional risk in your locality, contact your local or provincial public health department.

KEY POINT

- Supportive nutrition programs available through the Public Health Agency of Canada's website can provide nutritious food for pregnant women of limited financial means.

How Much Weight Should a Woman Gain during Pregnancy?

Women must gain weight during pregnancy—fetal and maternal well-being depend on it. Ideally, a woman will have begun her pregnancy at a healthy weight, but even more important, she will gain within the recommended weight range based on her prepregnancy body mass index (BMI). Table 13–4 presents recommended weight gains for pregnancy. For the normal-weight woman, the ideal pattern is about 1.5 kilograms (3½ lb) total during the first trimester and 0.5 kilogram (1 lb) per week thereafter. Pregnancy weight gains within the recommended ranges are associated with fewer surgical births, a greater number of healthy birthweights, and other positive outcomes for both mothers and infants, but many women do not gain within these ranges.[31]

Dieting during pregnancy is not recommended. Even an obese woman should gain about 6.8 kilograms (15 lb) for the best chance of delivering a healthy infant.[32] Weight gain for a pregnant teenager must be adequate to accommodate her own growth and that of her fetus. Women who are carrying twins must gain more still. A sudden, large weight gain is a danger signal, however, because it may indicate the onset of preeclampsia (see the section entitled "Troubleshooting").

The weight the pregnant woman puts on is nearly all lean tissue: placenta, uterus, blood, milk-producing glands, and the fetus itself (see Figure 13–7). The fat she gains is needed later for lactation. Physical activity can help a pregnant woman cope with the extra weight, as the next section explains. Some weight is lost at delivery, but many women retain a few pounds with each pregnancy.

Table 13–4

Canadian Gestational Weight Gain Recommendations

Prepregnancy BMI Category	Recommended Range of Total Weight Gain	
	kg	lb
BMI <18.5 Underweight	12.5–18	28–40
BMI 18.5–24.9 Normal weight	11.5–16	25–35
BMI 25.0–29.9 Overweight	7–11.5	15–25
BMI >30 Obese	5–9	11–20

Source: Canadian Gestational Weight Gain Recommendations. *Health Canada, 2010. Reproduced with permission from Her Majesty the Queen in Right of Canada, represented by the Minister of Health, 2013.*

Canada Prenatal Nutrition Program (CPNP) The women targeted by this program include pregnant adolescents, youth at risk of becoming pregnant, pregnant women who abuse alcohol or other substances, pregnant women living in violent situations, off-reserve Aboriginal and Inuit women, refugees, and pregnant women living in isolation or not having access to services; visit http://www.phac-aspc.gc.ca/hp-ps/dca-dea/prog-ini/cpnp-pcnp.

Figure 13–7

Components of Weight Gain during Pregnancy

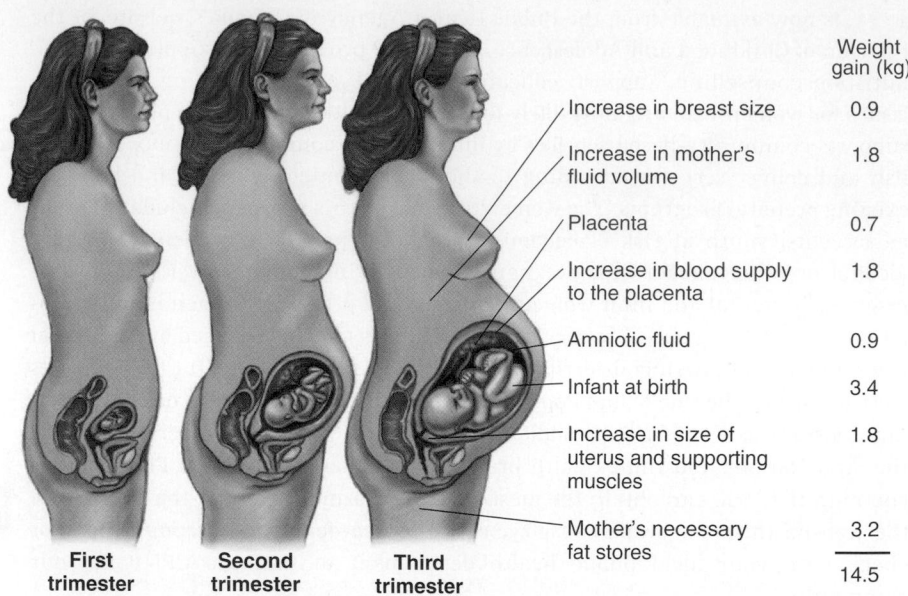

	Weight gain (kg)
Increase in breast size	0.9
Increase in mother's fluid volume	1.8
Placenta	0.7
Increase in blood supply to the placenta	1.8
Amniotic fluid	0.9
Infant at birth	3.4
Increase in size of uterus and supporting muscles	1.8
Mother's necessary fat stores	3.2
	14.5

First trimester Second trimester Third trimester

KEY POINT

- Weight gain is essential for a healthy pregnancy. A woman's prepregnancy BMI, her own nutrient needs, and the number of fetuses she is carrying help determine appropriate weight gain.

Should Pregnant Women Be Physically Active?

An active, physically fit woman experiencing a normal pregnancy can and should continue to exercise throughout pregnancy, adjusting the intensity and duration as the pregnancy progresses. Staying active during the course of a normal, healthy pregnancy improves the fitness of the mother-to-be, facilitates labour, helps prevent or manage gestational diabetes, and reduces psychological stress.[33] Women who remain active during pregnancy report fewer discomforts throughout their pregnancies and retain habits that help in losing excess weight and regaining fitness after the birth.

Women who become pregnant and plan to either become or remain active during pregnancy should fill out the four-page "PARmed-X for Pregnancy" screening tool (which can be found at http://www.csep.ca/english/view.asp?x=698, along with a weblink to a DVD on this topic, *Move for Two*, by a leading Canadian expert in this field) and let their health-care professional know about their intentions. Pregnant women should take care in choosing their physical activities, however, participating in "low-impact" activities and avoiding sports in which they might fall or be hit by other people or objects (for some suggestions, see the Think Fitness feature in this chapter). Pregnant women with medical conditions or pregnancy complications should undergo a thorough evaluation by their health-care professional before engaging in physical activity. A few guidelines are offered in Figure 13–8.[34] Several of the guidelines are aimed at preventing excessively high internal body temperature and dehydration, both of which can harm fetal development. To this end, pregnant women should also stay out of saunas, steam rooms, and hot whirlpools.

KEY POINT

- Physically fit women can continue to be physically active throughout pregnancy. Pregnant women should be cautious in their choice of activities.

Figure 13–8

Guidelines for Physical Activity during Pregnancy

DO		DON'T
Do exercise regularly (at least three times a week). Do warm up with 5 to 10 minutes of light activity. Do exercise for 20 to 30 minutes at your target heart rate. Do cool down with 5 to 10 minutes of slow activity and gentle stretching. Do drink water before, after, and during exercise. Do eat enough to support the additional needs of pregnancy plus exercise.	 Pregnant women can enjoy the benefits of physical activity.	Don't exercise vigorously after long periods of inactivity. Don't exercise in hot, humid weather. Don't exercise when sick with fever. Don't exercise while lying on your back after the first trimester of pregnancy. Don't stand motionless for prolonged periods. Don't exercise if you experience any pain or discomfort. Don't participate in activities that may harm the abdomen or involve jerky, bouncy movements. Don't scuba dive.

© Silvrshootr/iStockphoto

Think Fitness  Physical Activities for the Pregnant Woman

Is there an ideal physical activity for the pregnant woman? There might be. Swimming and water aerobics offer advantages over other activities during pregnancy. Water cools and supports the body; provides natural resistance; and lessens the impact of the body's movement, especially in the later months.[35] Research shows that water aerobics can reduce the intensity of back pain during pregnancy.[36] Other activities considered safe and comfortable for pregnant women include walking, light strength training, rowing, and climbing stairs.

Teen Pregnancy

According to the Society of Obstetricians and Gynaecologists of Canada, in 2006 there were 27.9 pregnancies per 1,000 15- to 19-year-olds, down by more than one-third from the mid-1990s.[37] A pregnant adolescent presents a special case of intense nutrient needs. Young teenage girls have a hard enough time meeting nutrient needs for their own rapid growth and development, let alone those of pregnancy. Many teens enter pregnancy deficient in vitamins A and D, folate, iron, calcium, and zinc—deficiencies that place both mother and fetus at risk. Smoking also presents risks, and teens are more likely to smoke while pregnant than older women. Pregnant teenagers have more miscarriages, premature births, stillbirths, and low-birthweight infants than do pregnant adult women.[38] The greatest risk, though, is death of the infant: mothers under age 16 bear more infants who die within the first year than do women in any other age group. These factors combine to make teenage pregnancy a major public health problem.

Adequate nutrition is an indispensable component of prenatal care for teenagers and can substantially improve the outlook for both mother and infant. To support the needs of both mother and fetus, a pregnant teenager with a BMI in the normal range is encouraged to gain about 15 kilograms (35 lb) to reduce the likelihood of a low-birthweight infant.[39] Pregnant and lactating teenagers would do well to follow the eating pattern presented in Table 2–3 on page 47, making sure to choose a Calorie level high enough to support weight gain.

- Of all the population groups, pregnant teenage girls have the highest nutrient needs and an increased likelihood of having problem pregnancies.

Why Do Some Women Crave Pickles and Ice Cream While Others Can't Keep Anything Down?

Does pregnancy give a woman the right to demand pickles and ice cream at 2 a.m.? Perhaps so, but not for nutrition's sake. Food cravings and aversions during pregnancy are common but do not seem to reflect real physiological needs. In other words, a woman who craves pickles is not in need of salt. Food cravings and aversions are due to changes in taste and smell sensitivities, and they quickly disappear after the birth.

Sometimes strange cravings may occur in women with nutrient-poor diets. A pregnant woman who is deficient in iron, zinc, or other nutrients may crave and eat soil, clay, ice, cornstarch, and other nonnutritious substances (pica, first mentioned in Chapter 8). Such cravings are not adaptive; the substances the woman craves do not deliver the nutrients she needs. In fact, clay and other substances can cling to the intestinal wall and form a barrier that interferes with normal nutrient absorption. Furthermore, if the soil or clay contains environmental contaminants such as lead or parasites, health and nutrition suffer.

The nausea of "morning" (actually, anytime) sickness seems unavoidable and may even be a welcome sign of a healthy pregnancy because it arises from the hormonal changes of early pregnancy. Many women complain that smells, especially cooking smells, make them sick. Thus, minimizing odours can alleviate morning sickness. Sipping carbonated drinks and nibbling soda crackers or other salty snack foods before getting out of bed can sometimes prevent nausea. Some women do best by simply eating what they desire whenever they feel hungry. Table 13–5 offers some other tips for relieving common discomforts of pregnancy, but morning sickness can be persistent. If morning sickness interferes with normal eating for more than a week or two, the woman should seek medical advice to prevent nutrient deficiencies.

As the hormones of pregnancy alter her muscle tone and the thriving fetus crowds her intestinal organs, an expectant mother may complain of heartburn or

---

Table 13–5

Tips for Relieving Common Discomforts of Pregnancy

To alleviate the nausea of pregnancy:

- On waking, get up slowly.
- Eat dry toast or crackers.
- Chew gum or suck hard candies.
- Eat small, frequent meals whenever hunger strikes.
- Avoid foods with offensive odours.
- When nauseated, do not drink citrus juice, water, milk, coffee, or tea.

To prevent or alleviate constipation:

- Eat foods high in fibre.
- Exercise daily.
- Drink at least 8 glasses of liquids a day.
- Respond promptly to the urge to defecate.
- Use laxatives only as prescribed by a physician; avoid mineral oil—it carries needed fat-soluble vitamins out of the body.

To prevent or relieve heartburn:

- Relax and eat slowly.
- Eat small, frequent meals.
- Drink liquids between meals.
- Avoid spicy or greasy foods.
- Sit up while eating.
- Wait an hour after eating before lying down.
- Wait 2 hours after eating before exercising.

constipation. Raising the head of the bed with two or three pillows can help relieve nighttime heartburn. A high-fibre diet, physical activity, and a plentiful water intake will help relieve constipation. The pregnant woman should use laxatives or heartburn medications only if her physician prescribes them.

KEY POINT

- Food cravings usually do not reflect physiological needs, and some may interfere with nutrition. Nausea arises from normal hormonal changes of pregnancy.

Some Cautions for the Pregnant Woman

Some choices that pregnant women make or substances they encounter can harm the fetus, sometimes severely. Among these threats, smoking, medications, herbal supplements, illegal drugs, environmental contaminants, foodborne illness, vitamin–mineral megadoses, dieting, sugar substitutes, and caffeine deserve consideration. Alcohol constitutes a major threat to fetal health and is given a section of its own.

Cigarette Smoking   Constituents of cigarette smoke, such as nicotine and cyanide, are toxic to a fetus. Smoking restricts the blood supply to the growing fetus and so limits the delivery of oxygen and nutrients and the removal of wastes. It slows growth, thus retarding physical development of the fetus, and it may cause behavioural or intellectual problems later. Cigarette (and cigar) smoking also impairs fetal nutrition and development by adversely affecting the pregnant woman's nutrition status. Smokers tend to have lower intakes of dietary fibre, vitamin A, beta-carotene, folate, and vitamin C.

A mother who smokes is more likely to have a complicated birth, and her infant is more likely to be of low birthweight.[40] The more a mother smokes, the smaller her baby will be. Of all preventable causes of low birthweight in Canada, smoking has the greatest impact. Sudden infant death syndrome (SIDS), the unexplained deaths that sometimes occur in otherwise healthy infants, has been linked to the mother's cigarette smoking during pregnancy.[41] Research suggests that even in women who do not smoke, exposure to **environmental tobacco smoke** (**ETS**, or secondhand smoke) during pregnancy increases the risk of low birthweight and the likelihood of SIDS.[42] Unfortunately, an estimated one in eight pregnant women smokes, and rates are even higher for unmarried women and those who have not graduated from high school.[43]

Medicinal Drugs and Herbal Supplements   Medicinal drugs taken during pregnancy can cause serious birth defects. Pregnant women should not take over-the-counter drugs or any medications not prescribed by a physician. Drug labels warn: "As with any drug, if you are pregnant or nursing a baby, seek the advice of a health professional before using this product." For aspirin and ibuprofen, there is an additional warning: "It is especially important not to use aspirin (or ibuprofen) during the last three months of pregnancy unless specifically directed to do so by a doctor because it may cause problems in the unborn child or excessive bleeding during delivery." Such warnings should be taken seriously.

Some pregnant women mistakenly consider herbal supplements to be safe alternatives to medicinal drugs and take them to relieve nausea, promote water loss, alleviate depression, aid sleep, or for other reasons. Some herbal products may be safe, but almost none have been tested for safety or effectiveness during pregnancy. Pregnant women should stay away from herbal supplements, teas, or other products unless their safety during pregnancy has been ascertained.[44] The Society of Obstetricians and Gynecologists of Canada website lists herbal supplements that may or may not be safe to use during pregnancy.* Chapter 11's Consumer Corner offers more information about herbal supplements and other alternative therapies.

Abuse of Drugs   Research shows that women who abuse drugs such as marijuana and cocaine during pregnancy inflict serious health consequences, including nervous

---

*Go to Society of Obstetricians and Gynaecologists of Canada at http://sogc.org/publications/medications-and-drugs-before-and-during-pregnancy.

environmental tobacco smoke (ETS) the combination of exhaled smoke (mainstream smoke) and smoke from lighted cigarettes, pipes, or cigars (sidestream smoke) that enters the air and may be inhaled by other people.

- Amphetamines: Suspected nervous system damage; behavioural abnormalities
- Barbiturates: Drug withdrawal symptoms in the newborn, lasting up to six months
- Cocaine: Uncontrolled jerking motions; paralysis; permanent mental and physical damage
- Marijuana: Short-term irritability at birth
- Opiates (including heroin): Drug withdrawal symptoms in the newborn; permanent learning disability (attention deficit hyperactivity disorder)

To Protect Their Fetuses and Newborns from Listeriosis, Pregnant Women Should

- Avoid the following Mexican soft cheeses: queso blanco, queso fresco, queso de hoja, queso de crema, and asadero. Also avoid feta cheese, brie, Camembert, and blue-veined cheeses like Roquefort.
- Use only pasteurized dairy products.
- Eat only thoroughly cooked meat, poultry, and seafood.
- Before eating hot dogs and luncheon or deli meats, including cured meats like salami, thoroughly reheat them until steaming hot.
- Wash all fruit and vegetables.
- Do not eat refrigerated smoked seafood, such as salmon or trout, or any fish labelled "nova-style," "lox," or "kippered," unless it is an ingredient in a cooked dish.
- Do not eat refrigerated pâté or meat spreads. Canned or shelf-stable pâté and meat spreads are safer.

listeriosis a serious foodborne infection that can cause severe brain infection or death in a fetus or a newborn; caused by the bacterium *Listeria monocytogenes*, which is found in soil and water.

system disorders, on their fetuses.[45] Drugs of abuse such as cocaine easily cross the placenta and impair fetal growth and development.[46] Infants born to mothers who abuse crack and other forms of cocaine face low birthweight, heartbeat abnormalities, the pain of withdrawal, or even death as they first experience life outside the womb. Some effects on the fetus of other abused drugs are listed in the margin.

Environmental Contaminants   Infants and young children whose mothers were exposed to environmental contaminants such as lead and mercury during pregnancy show signs of impaired cognitive development. During pregnancy, lead and mercury readily move across the placenta, inflicting severe damage on the developing fetal nervous system.[47]

- Unacceptably high concentrations of mercury in fish have prompted Health Canada to warn all pregnant women and young children against eating large ocean fish, such as shark, swordfish, and fresh or frozen tuna more than once per month.[48] It is prudent for the same groups of people to

- Eat up to 340 grams a week of a variety of safer fish and shellfish such as canned light tuna, salmon, pollock, catfish, and shrimp; children should be given smaller portions. Albacore "white" tuna has more mercury than canned light tuna and so should be limited to 170 grams or less per week.

- Check local advisories about the safety of fish caught by family and friends in lakes, rivers, and coastal areas. If no advice is available, eat up to 170 grams per week of fish from local waters, but don't eat any other fish during that week. Chapter 12 offers more details on contaminants in foods.

Foodborne Illness   The vomiting and diarrhea caused by many foodborne illnesses (see Chapter 12) can leave a pregnant woman exhausted and dangerously dehydrated. Particularly threatening, however, is **listeriosis**, which can cause miscarriage, stillbirth, or severe brain or other infections to fetuses and newborns. According to the U.S. Centers for Disease Control and Prevention, pregnant women are "about 20 times more likely than other healthy adults to get listeriosis."[49] A woman with listeriosis may develop symptoms such as fever, vomiting, and diarrhea about 12 hours after eating a contaminated food; serious symptoms may develop a week to six weeks later. A blood test can reliably detect listeriosis, and antibiotics given promptly to the pregnant sufferer can often prevent infection of the fetus or newborn. The margin lists preventive measures pregnant women can take to avoid contracting listeriosis.

Vitamin–Mineral Megadoses   Many vitamins are toxic when taken in excess, and minerals are even more so. A single massive dose of preformed vitamin A (100 times the recommended intake) has caused birth defects. Chronic use of lower doses of vitamin A supplements (three to four times the recommended intake) may also cause birth defects. Intakes before the seventh week of pregnancy appear to be the most damaging. For this reason, additional vitamin A is not recommended during pregnancy, and the vitamin is prescribed in the first trimester of pregnancy only upon evidence of deficiency, which is rare.

Dieting   Dieting, even for short periods, is hazardous during pregnancy. Low-carbohydrate diets or fasts that cause ketosis deprive the growing fetal brain of needed glucose and may impair its development. Such diets are also likely to be deficient in other nutrients vital to fetal growth. Energy restriction during pregnancy is dangerous, regardless of the woman's prepregnancy weight or the amount of weight gained in the previous month.

Ketosis was defined in Chapter 4. Also see the Glossary.

Sugar Substitutes   According to Health Canada, "pregnant women should be cautioned against excessive amounts of products containing aspartame and other artificial sweeteners since such foods could replace nutrient-dense, energy-yielding foods." They should also carefully read the labels of table-top sweeteners containing either cyclamates or saccharin and use them only on the advice of their physician (see Controversy 4).[50] Still, pregnant women would be prudent to use sweeteners in

Figure 13–9

Recommended Maximum Caffeine Intake Levels for Pregnant or Lactating Women and for Children 4 to 12 Years of Age

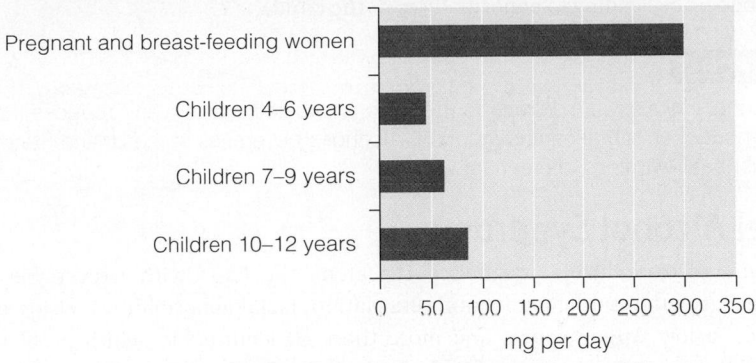

Source: It's Your Health: Caffeine. *Health Canada, Original: February 2006; Updated: March 2010. Reproduced with permission from Her Majesty the Queen in Right of Canada, represented by the Minister of Health, 2013.*

moderation and within an otherwise nutritious and well-balanced diet. Women with phenylketonuria should not use aspartame, as Controversy 4 explains.

 Caffeine   Caffeine crosses the placenta, and the fetus has only a limited ability to metabolize it. The recommended maximum amounts of caffeine for women of child-bearing age, those who are pregnant or lactating, and children are listed in Figure 13–9.[51] The most sensible course is to limit caffeine consumption to the equivalent of one cup of coffee or two 355-milligram cola beverages a day. Caffeine amounts in food and beverages are listed in Controversy 14 on page 640.

KEY POINT

- Abstaining from smoking and other drugs, limiting intake of foods known to contain unsafe levels of contaminants such as mercury, taking precautions against foodborne illness, avoiding large doses of nutrients, refraining from dieting, using artificial sweeteners in moderation, and limiting caffeine use are recommended during pregnancy.

Drinking during Pregnancy

Alcohol is arguably the most hazardous drug to future generations because it is legally available, heavily promoted, and widely abused. Society sends mixed messages concerning alcohol. Beverage companies promote an image of drinkers as healthy and active. Opposing this image, health authorities warn that alcohol can be injurious to health, especially during pregnancy. Every container of beer, wine, or liquor for sale in the United States is required to warn pregnant women of the dangers of drinking during pregnancy, but Canada is still awaiting similar legislation.

Alcohol's Effects

Women of childbearing age need to know about alcohol's harmful effects on a fetus. Alcohol crosses the placenta freely and is directly toxic:[52]

- A sudden dose of alcohol can halt the delivery of oxygen through the umbilical cord. Oxygen is indispensable on a minute-to-minute basis to the development of the fetus's central nervous system.
- Alcohol slows cell division, reducing the number of cells produced and inflicting abnormalities on those that are produced and all of their progeny.
- During the first month of pregnancy, the fetal brain is growing at a rate of 100,000 new brain cells a minute. Even a few minutes of alcohol exposure during this critical period can exert a major detrimental effect.

- Alcohol interferes with placental transport of nutrients to the fetus and can cause malnutrition in the mother; all of malnutrition's harmful effects compound the effects of the alcohol.
- Before fertilization, alcohol can damage the ovum or sperm in the mother- or father-to-be, leading to abnormalities in the child.

KEY POINT

- Alcohol limits oxygen delivery to the fetus, slows cell division, and reduces the number of cells that organs produce. Alcoholic beverages in the United States must bear warnings to pregnant women.

Fetal Alcohol Syndrome

Drinking alcohol during pregnancy threatens the fetus with irreversible brain damage, growth retardation, mental retardation, facial abnormalities, vision abnormalities, a low **Apgar score**, and more than 40 identifiable health problems—a cluster of symptoms known as **fetal alcohol syndrome (FAS)**. The fetal brain is extremely vulnerable to a glucose or oxygen deficit, and alcohol causes both by disrupting placental functioning. The lifelong mental retardation and other tragedies of FAS can be prevented by abstaining from drinking alcohol during pregnancy. Once the damage is done, however, the child remains impaired.

 Figure 13–10 shows the facial abnormalities of FAS, which are easy to depict. A visual picture of the internal harm is impossible, but that damage seals the fate of the child.

"A Drink" as Defined in Controversy 3
- 150 mL wine (12% alcohol)
- 300 mL wine cooler
- 355 mL beer
- 45 mL (1½ oz) hard liquor (80 proof)

Figure 13–10

Typical Facial Characteristics of FAS

The severe facial abnormalities shown here are just outward signs of severe mental impairments and internal organ damage. These defects, though hidden, may create major health problems later.

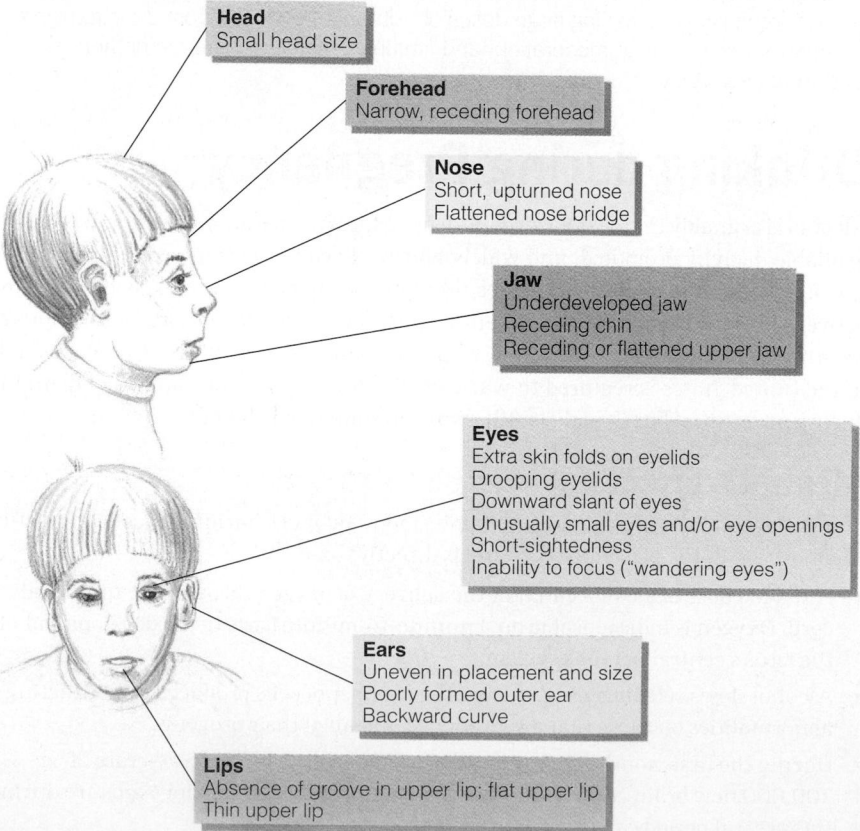

Head
Small head size

Forehead
Narrow, receding forehead

Nose
Short, upturned nose
Flattened nose bridge

Jaw
Underdeveloped jaw
Receding chin
Receding or flattened upper jaw

Eyes
Extra skin folds on eyelids
Drooping eyelids
Downward slant of eyes
Unusually small eyes and/or eye openings
Short-sightedness
Inability to focus ("wandering eyes")

Ears
Uneven in placement and size
Poorly formed outer ear
Backward curve

Lips
Absence of groove in upper lip; flat upper lip
Thin upper lip

Apgar score a system of scoring an infant's physical condition right after birth. Heart rate, respiration, muscle tone, response to stimuli, and colour are ranked 0, 1, or 2. A low score indicates that medical attention is required to facilitate survival.

fetal alcohol syndrome (FAS) the cluster of symptoms including brain damage, growth retardation, mental retardation, and facial abnormalities seen in an infant or child whose mother consumed alcohol during her pregnancy.

It is estimated that 9 in 1,000 children in Canada are born with fetal alcohol spectrum disorder (see *Fetal Alcohol Spectrum Disorder (FASD): A Framework for Action* at http://www .phac-aspc.gc.ca/publicat/fasd-fw-etcaf-ca/index-eng.php). The report recommends that health professionals inform pregnant women that both mother and fetus will benefit if the mother stops drinking alcohol at any time during the pregnancy. They should also inform those who have consumed small amounts of alcohol occasionally that the risk is minimal. Client education related to preventing fetal alcohol syndrome is part of the CPNP.

In December 2003, the Public Health Agency of Canada announced *Fetal Alcohol Spectrum Disorder (FASD): A Framework for Action* in an effort to help frontline health workers prevent it and improve outcomes for those with FASD (approximately 9 in every 1,000 children are born with FASD).[53] Education materials include a brochure and a poster (http://www.phac-aspc.gc.ca/hp-ps/dca-dea/prog-ini/fasd-etcaf/index-eng.php). These and other materials can also be accessed through the Public Health Agency of Canada's website for the Division of Childhood and Adolescence (http://www.phac-aspc.gc.ca/hp-ps/dca-dea).

Even when a child does not develop full FAS, prenatal exposure to alcohol can lead to less severe, but nonetheless serious, mental and physical problems. The cluster of mental problems associated with prenatal alcohol exposure is known as **alcohol-related neurodevelopmental disorder (ARND)**, and the physical malformations are referred to as **alcohol-related birth defects (ARBD)**. Some ARND and ARBD children show no outward sign of impairment, but others are short in stature or display subtle facial abnormalities. Most perform poorly in school and in social interactions and suffer a subtle form of brain damage. Mood disorders and problem behaviours, such as aggression, are common.[54]

For every child diagnosed with FAS, three or four with ARND or ARBD go undiagnosed. Anyone exposed to alcohol before birth may always respond differently to it, and also to certain drugs, than if no exposure had occurred, making addictions likely.

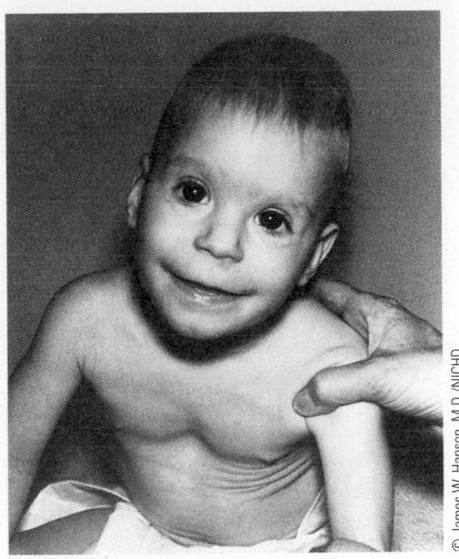

A child with FAS.

© James W. Hanson, M.D./NICHD

KEY POINT

- The birth defects of fetal alcohol syndrome arise from severe damage to the fetus caused by alcohol. Lesser conditions, ARND and ARBD, may be harder to diagnose but also rob the child of a normal life.

Experts' Advice

Despite alcohol's potential for harm, 12 percent of pregnant women drink alcohol sometime during pregnancy, more than 3 percent report "frequent" drinking (seven or more drinks per week), and more than 2 percent admit to binge drinking (five or more drinks on one occasion).[55] Almost half of all pregnancies are unintended, and many are conceived during a binge drinking episode.[56]

For women who know they are pregnant and wonder how much alcohol is too much, some research findings may be of interest. Research using animals shows that one-fifth of the amount of alcohol needed to produce major visible defects will produce learning impairments or other defects in the offspring.[57] Compared with women who drink less than one drink *per week*, a sizable and significant increase in stillbirths occurs in women who drink five or more drinks per week.[58] Low birthweight is reported among infants born to women who have two drinks per day during pregnancy, and FAS is also known to occur with as few as two drinks a day. Birth defects have been reliably observed among the children of women who have four drinks of alcohol daily during pregnancy. The most severe impact is likely to occur in the first two months, when the woman may not even be aware that she is pregnant.

Given such evidence, Health Canada and the Canadian Paediatric Society take the position that women should stop drinking as soon as they *plan* to become pregnant (see margin).[59] This step is important for fathers-to-be as well. Researchers have looked for a "safe" alcohol intake limit during pregnancy and have found none. Their conclusion: abstinence from alcohol is the best policy for pregnant women. The authors of this book recommend this choice, too. After the birth of a healthy baby, celebrate with one glass of champagne, if you choose to drink.

- The joint statement from Health Canada and the Canadian Paediatric Society regarding the recommendations for alcohol and pregnancy is that "the prudent choice for women who are or may become pregnant is to abstain from alcohol."

alcohol-related neurodevelopmental disorder (ARND) behavioural, cognitive, or central nervous system abnormalities associated with prenatal alcohol exposure.

alcohol-related birth defects (ARBD) malformations in the skeletal and organ systems (heart, kidneys, eyes, ears) associated with prenatal alcohol exposure.

For a pregnant woman who has already been drinking alcohol, the advice is "stop now." A woman who has drunk heavily during the first two-thirds of her pregnancy can still prevent some organ damage by stopping heavy drinking during the third trimester.

KEY POINT

- Abstinence from alcohol is critical to prevent irreversible damage to the fetus.

Troubleshooting

Disease during pregnancy can endanger the health of the mother and the health and growth of the fetus. If discovered early, many diseases can be controlled—another reason early prenatal care is recommended.

Gestational Diabetes   Some women are prone to develop a pregnancy-related form of diabetes, **gestational diabetes**. Gestational diabetes usually resolves after the infant is born, but some women go on to develop diabetes (usually type 2) later in life, especially if they are overweight.[60] Gestational diabetes can lead to fetal or infant sickness or death. If it is identified early and managed properly, however, the most serious risks fall dramatically.[61] More commonly, gestational diabetes leads to surgical birth and high infant birthweight.[62] The Canadian Diabetes Association Clinical Practice Guidelines Expert Committee recommends that all pregnant women be screened for gestational diabetes mellitus between 24 and 28 weeks' gestation.[63]

Preeclampsia   A certain degree of **edema** is to be expected in late pregnancy, and some women also develop hypertension during that time. If a rise in blood pressure is mild, it may subside after childbirth and cause no harm. In some cases, however, hypertension may signal the onset of **preeclampsia**, a condition characterized not only by high blood pressure but also by protein in the urine and fluid retention (edema). The edema of preeclampsia is a severe, whole-body edema, distinct from the localized fluid retention women normally experience late in pregnancy. The normal edema of pregnancy is a response to gravity; fluid from blood pools in the ankles. The edema of preeclampsia causes swelling of the face and hands as well as of the feet and ankles.

Preeclampsia afflicts 1 in 20 pregnancies, usually first pregnancies, and most often during the final trimester.[64] Both men and women who were born of pregnancies complicated by preeclampsia are more likely to have a child born of a pregnancy complicated by preeclampsia, suggesting a genetic predisposition.[65] Black women have a much greater risk of preeclampsia than white women.

Preeclampsia affects almost all of the mother's organs—the circulatory system, liver, kidneys, and brain. If the condition progresses and she experiences convulsions, the condition is called eclampsia. Maternal mortality during pregnancy is rare in developed countries, but eclampsia is the most common cause. Preeclampsia demands prompt medical attention. Dietary factors have been studied over the years, but so far none convincingly prevent preeclampsia.[66] Calcium supplementation may reduce the incidence of preeclampsia in some women, however.[67]

KEY POINT

- Gestational diabetes and preeclampsia are common medical problems associated with pregnancy. These should be managed to minimize associated risks.

Lactation

As the time of childbirth nears, a woman must decide whether she will feed her baby breast milk, infant formula, or both. These options are the only foods recommended for an infant during the first four to six months of life. A woman who plans to breastfeed her baby should begin to prepare toward the end of her pregnancy. No elaborate or expensive preparations are needed, but the expectant mother can read one

---

Risk Factors for Gestational Diabetes
- Glucose in the urine
- Obesity
- Personal history of gestational diabetes
- Strong family history of diabetes

Reproductive Females of These Racial and Ethnic Groups Are More Prone to Gestational Diabetes
- Aboriginal descent
- Hispanic descent
- Asian descent
- African descent

Warning Signs of Preeclampsia
- Blurred vision
- Dizziness
- Headaches
- Persistent abdominal pain
- Sudden weight gain
- Swelling, especially facial swelling

gestational diabetes abnormal glucose tolerance appearing during pregnancy.

edema (eh-DEE-mah) accumulation of fluid in the tissues (also defined in Chapter 6).

preeclampsia (PRE-ee-CLAMP-see-uh) a potentially dangerous condition during pregnancy characterized by edema, hypertension, and protein in the urine.

of the many handbooks available on breastfeeding or consult a **certified lactation consultant**, available through the "baby hospital" in your area or through the local Health Unit.* Part of the preparation involves learning what dietary changes are needed because adequate nutrition is essential to successful lactation.

In rare cases, women produce too little milk to nourish their infants adequately. Severe consequences, including infant dehydration, malnutrition, and brain damage, can occur should the condition go undetected for long. Early warning signs of insufficient milk are dry diapers (a well-fed infant wets about six diapers a day) and infrequent bowel movements.

Nutrition during Lactation

A nursing mother produces about 750 millilitres of milk a day, with considerable variation from woman to woman and in the same woman from time to time, depending primarily on the infant's demand for milk. Producing this milk costs a woman almost 500 Calories per day above her regular need during the first six months of lactation. To meet this energy need, the woman is advised to eat an extra 330 Calories of food each day. The other 170 Calories can be drawn from the fat stores she accumulated during pregnancy. The food energy consumed by the nursing mother should carry with it abundant nutrients. Look back at Figure 13–4 (page 560) for a lactating woman's nutrient recommendations and at Table 13–2 on page 561 for a sample menu.

The volume of breast milk produced depends on how much milk the baby demands, not on how much fluid the mother drinks. The nursing mother is nevertheless advised to drink plenty of liquids each day (about 13 cups) to protect herself from dehydration. To help themselves remember to drink enough liquid, many women make a habit of drinking a glass of milk, juice, or water each time the baby nurses as well as at mealtimes.

A common question is whether a mother's milk may lack a nutrient if she fails to get enough in her diet. The answer differs from one nutrient to the next, but in general, the effect of nutritional deprivation of the mother is to reduce the *quantity*, not the *quality*, of her milk. Women can produce milk with adequate protein, carbohydrate, fat, folate, and most minerals, even when their own supplies are limited. For these nutrients, milk quality is maintained at the expense of maternal stores. This is most evident in the case of calcium: dietary calcium has no effect on the calcium concentration of breast milk, but maternal bones lose some of their density during lactation. Such losses are generally made up quickly when lactation ends, and breastfeeding has no long-term harmful effects on women's bones.[68]

Any excess water-soluble vitamins the mother takes in are excreted in the urine; the body does not release them into the milk. The amounts of some vitamins in human milk, however, are affected by the mother's excessive or deficient intakes. For example, large doses of vitamin A raise the concentration of this vitamin in breast milk.

Some infants may be sensitive to foods such as cow's milk, onions, or garlic in the mother's diet and become uncomfortable when she eats them. Nursing mothers are advised to eat whatever nutritious foods they choose. If a particular food seems to cause an infant discomfort, the mother can eliminate that food from her diet for a few days and see if the problem goes away.

Another common question is whether breastfeeding promotes a more rapid loss of the extra body fat accumulated during pregnancy. Studies on this question have not provided a definitive answer. When breastfeeding continues for three months or longer, lactation does seem to accelerate a woman's weight loss, but factors such as percentage of body fat and weight gain during pregnancy also play a role.[69] This does not mean that a breastfeeding woman can eat unlimited food and return to prepregnancy weight. Breastfeeding costs energy, true, but diet and physical activity are still the cornerstones of weight control. Physical activity in particular helps reduce body fatness and improve fitness while having little effect on a woman's milk production or her infant's weight gain. A gradual weight loss of about 0.5 kilogram (1 lb) per week

● The DRI recommendation for *total* water intake during lactation is 3.8 L/day. This includes 3.1 L or about 13 c as total beverages, including drinking water.

certified lactation consultant a health-care provider, often a registered nurse or a registered dietitian, with specialized training and certification in breast and infant anatomy and physiology who teaches the mechanics of breastfeeding to new mothers.

---

*La Leche League is an international organization that helps women with breastfeeding concerns. See Appendix G, available online at http://www.nelson.com/nutrition3ce, for its address and website.

is safe and does not reduce milk output.[70] Too large an energy deficit, especially soon after birth, will inhibit lactation.

■ The lactating woman needs extra fluid and enough energy and nutrients to make sufficient milk each day. Malnutrition most often diminishes the quantity of the milk produced without altering quality. Lactation may facilitate loss of the extra fat gained during pregnancy.

Breastfeeding: Other Important Factors to Keep in Mind*

Some substances impair maternal milk production or enter breast milk and interfere with infant development, making breastfeeding an unwise choice. Some medical conditions also prohibit breastfeeding.

Alcohol, Nicotine, and Other Drugs Alcohol enters breast milk and can adversely affect production, volume, composition, and ejection of breast milk as well as overwhelm an infant's immature alcohol-degrading system. Alcohol concentration peaks within one hour after ingestion of even moderate amounts (equivalent to a can of beer). This amount may alter the taste of the milk to the disapproval of the nursing infant, who may, in protest, drink less milk than normal. While it is not advisable to consume alcohol if your baby is being exclusively breastfed, those moms who do intend to consume small amounts should consider expressing and discarding some breast milk between feedings.

Drug addicts, including alcohol abusers, can take such high doses that their infants become addicts by way of breast milk. In these cases, breastfeeding is contraindicated. As for cigarette smoking, research shows that lactating women who smoke produce less milk, and milk with a lower fat content, than mothers who do not smoke. Thus, their infants gain less weight than infants of nonsmokers. A lactating woman who smokes not only transfers nicotine and other chemicals to her infant via her breast milk but also exposes the infant to secondhand smoke. Babies who are "smoked over" experience a wide array of health problems—poor growth, hearing impairment, vomiting, breathing difficulties, and even unexplained death. For those breastfeeding moms who do smoke, according to the Canadian Public Health Association "even if you cannot stop smoking, breastfeeding is still the best choice for your baby. Try not to smoke an hour or two before nursing. And never expose your baby to second-hand smoke" (http://you-and-your-baby.cpha.ca/healthy-mom/smoking.html). This website also has additional information about the negative effects of secondhand smoke.

Excess caffeine can make an infant jittery and wakeful. Caffeine consumption should be moderate when breastfeeding.

Many medicines pose no danger during breastfeeding, but others cannot be used because they suppress lactation or are secreted into breast milk and can harm the infant.[71] If a nursing mother must take medication that is secreted in breast milk and is known to affect the infant, then breastfeeding must be put off for the duration of treatment. Meanwhile, the flow of milk can be sustained by pumping the breasts and discarding the milk. A nursing mother should consult with her physician before taking medicines or herbal supplements.

Many women wonder about using oral contraceptives during lactation. One type that combines the hormones estrogen and progestin seems to suppress milk output, lower the nitrogen content of the milk, and shorten the duration of breastfeeding. In contrast, progestin-only pills have no effect on breast milk or breastfeeding and are considered appropriate for lactating women.

Environmental Contaminants A woman sometimes hesitates to breastfeed because she has heard warnings that contaminants in fish, water, and other foods

---

*An excellent, credible and up-to-date online resource that provides information about the topics in this section is http://www.motherisk.org/women/index.jsp.

(see page 570) may enter breast milk and harm her infant. Although some contaminants do enter breast milk, others may be filtered out. Because formula is made with water, formula-fed infants consume any contaminants that may be in the water supply. Any woman who is concerned about breastfeeding on this basis can consult with a physician or dietitian familiar with the local circumstances. With the exception of rare, massive exposure to a contaminant, the many benefits of breastfeeding far outweigh the risk associated with environmental hazards in North America.[72]

Maternal Illness   If a woman has an ordinary cold, she can continue nursing without worry. The infant will probably catch it from her anyway, and thanks to immunological protection, a breastfed baby may be less susceptible than a formula-fed baby. With appropriate treatment, a woman who has an infectious disease such as hepatitis or tuberculosis can breastfeed; transmission is rare.[73]

The human immunodeficiency virus (HIV), responsible for causing AIDS, can be passed from an infected mother to her infant during pregnancy, at birth, or through breast milk, especially during the early months of breastfeeding.[74] In the case of HIV-infected women, when the mother is known to be HIV antibody positive, alternatives to breastfeeding are indicated.[75] Where safe alternatives are available, women who have tested positive for HIV should not breastfeed their infants.

In developing countries, where feeding inappropriate or contaminated formulas causes 1.5 million infant deaths each year, breastfeeding can be critical to infant survival. This advantage, however, must be weighed against the 200,000 to 300,000 infants who become infected with HIV each year by way of breastfeeding.[76] Whether HIV-infected women in developing countries should breastfeed comes down to a delicate decision between risks and benefits. For HIV-positive women in developing countries who are literate, have access to safe water, and have an uninterrupted supply of infant formula, replacement feeding may reduce the risk of infant illness and death by AIDS. For those without those assets, interventions to decrease the risk of breastfeeding transmission of HIV are urgently needed.

KEY POINT

- Breastfeeding is not advised if the mother's milk is contaminated with alcohol, drugs, or environmental pollutants. Most ordinary infections such as colds have no effect on breastfeeding. Where safe alternatives are available, HIV-infected women should not breastfeed their infants.

Feeding the Infant

Early nutrition affects later development, and early feedings establish eating habits that influence nutrition throughout life. Trends change, and experts may argue the fine points, but nourishing a baby is relatively simple. Common sense and a nurturing, relaxed environment go far to promote the infant's well-being.

Nutrient Needs

A baby grows faster during the first year of life than ever again, as Figure 13–11 shows. Pediatricians carefully monitor the growth of infants and children because growth directly reflects their nutrition status. An infant's birthweight doubles by about five months of age and triples by the age of one year. If a 68-kilogram (150-lb) adult were to grow like this, the person would weigh 205 kilograms (450 lb) after a single year. The infant's length changes more slowly than weight, increasing about 25 centimetres from birth to one year. By the end of the first year, the growth rate slows considerably; an infant typically gains less than 4.5 kilograms (10 lb) during the second year and grows about 12.5 centimetres in height.

Not only do infants grow rapidly, but their basal metabolic rate is remarkably high—about twice that of an adult's, based on body weight. The rapid growth and metabolism of the infant demand an ample supply of all nutrients. Of special importance during infancy are the energy nutrients and the vitamins and minerals critical to the growth process, such as vitamin A, vitamin D, and calcium.

Figure 13–11

Weight Gain of Human Infants and Children in the First Five Years of Life

The coloured vertical bars show how the yearly increase in weight gain slows its pace over the years.

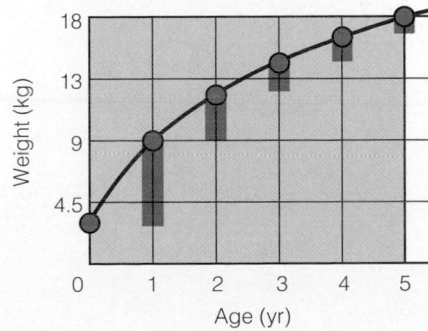

Because they are small, babies need smaller *total* amounts of these nutrients than adults do, but as a percentage of body weight, babies need more than twice as much of most nutrients. Infants require about 100 Calories per kilogram of body weight per day; most adults require fewer than 40 (see Table 13–6). Figure 13–12 compares a five-month-old baby's needs (per unit of body weight) with those of an adult man. You can see that differences in vitamin D and iodine, for instance, are extraordinary.

Figure 13–12

Nutrient Recommendations for a Five-Month-Old Infant and Adult Male Compared on the Basis of Body Weight

Infants may be relatively small and inactive, but they use large amounts of energy and nutrients in proportion to their body size to keep all their metabolic processes going.

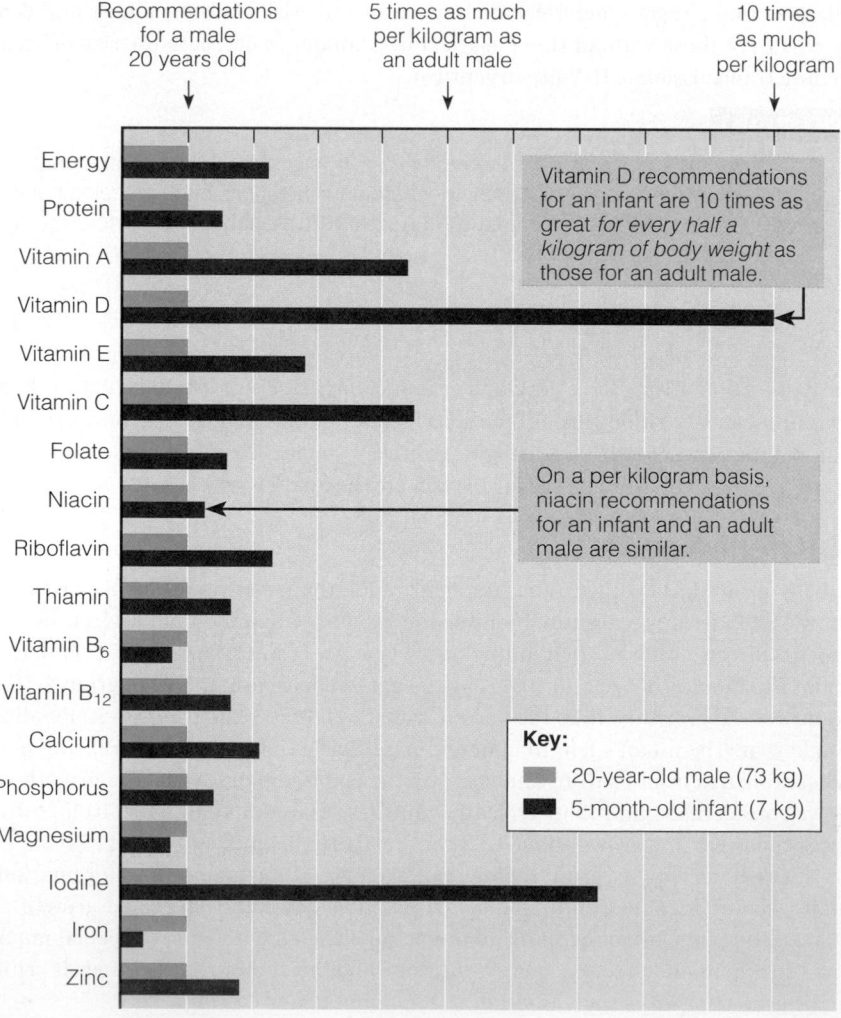

Around six months of age, energy needs begin to increase less rapidly as the growth rate begins to slow down, but some of the energy saved by slower growth is spent in increased activity. When their growth slows, infants spontaneously reduce their energy intakes. Parents should expect their babies to adjust their food intakes downward when appropriate and should not force or coax them to eat more.

Vitamin K nutrition for newborns presents a unique case. A newborn's digestive tract is sterile, and vitamin K–producing bacteria take weeks to establish themselves in the baby's intestines. To prevent bleeding in the newborn, the Canadian Paediatric Society and College of Family Physicians of Canada recommend that a single dose of vitamin K be given at birth.[77]

One of the most important nutrients for infants, as for everyone, is water. The younger a child is, the more of its body weight is water. Breast milk or infant formula normally provides enough water to replace fluid losses in a healthy infant. Even in hot, dry climates, neither breastfed nor bottle-fed infants need supplemental water.[78] Because proportionately more of an infant's body water than an adult's is between the cells and in the vascular space, this water is easy to lose. Conditions that cause rapid fluid loss, such as vomiting or diarrhea, require an electrolyte solution designed for infants.

After six months of age, the energy saved by slower growth is spent on increased activity.

KEY POINT

- Infants' rapid growth and development depend on adequate nutrient supplies, including water from breast milk or formula.

Why Is Breast Milk So Good for Babies?

Both the Canadian Paediatric Society and the American Academy of Pediatrics (AAP) stand behind this statement: "Breast-feeding is strongly recommended for full-term infants, except in the few instances where specific contraindications exist." Health Canada advocates exclusive breastfeeding for at least six months for the nutritional health it confers on the infant as well as for the physiological, social, economic, and other benefits it gives to the mother (see Table 13–7).[79] It is well recognized that exclusive breastfeeding for 6 months, and breastfeeding with complementary foods for at least 12 months, is an optimal feeding pattern for infants.[80] All legitimate

Table 13–7

Benefits of Breastfeeding

For infants:

- Provides the appropriate composition and balance of nutrients with high bioavailability
- Provides hormones that promote physiological development
- Improves cognitive development
- Protects against a variety of infections
- May protect against some chronic diseases, such as diabetes (type 1) and hypertension, later in life
- Protects against food allergies

For mothers:

- Contracts the uterus
- Delays the return of regular ovulation, thus lengthening birth intervals (it is not, however, a dependable method of contraception)
- Conserves iron stores (by prolonging amenorrhea)
- May protect against breast and ovarian cancer

Other:

- Provides cost savings from not needing medical treatment for childhood illnesses or time off work to care for sick children
- Provides cost savings from not needing to purchase formula (even after adjusting for added foods in the diet of a lactating mother)[a]
- Provides environmental savings to society from not needing to manufacture, package, and ship formula or dispose of packaging

[a]A nursing mother produces approximately 140 litres of milk during the first six months, saving her roughly $450 in formula costs.

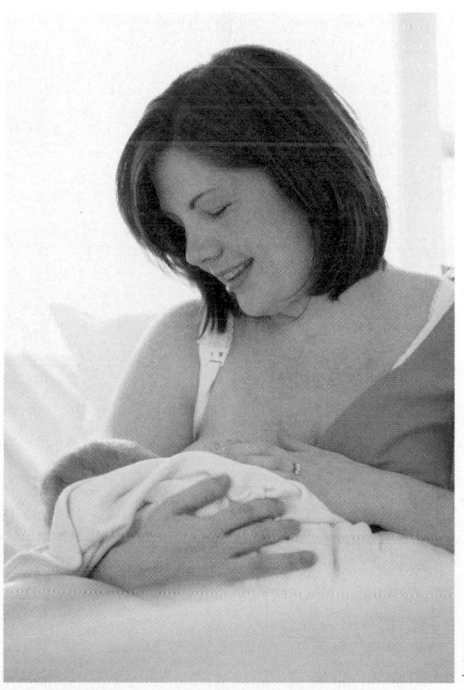

Breastfeeding is a natural extension of pregnancy—the mother's body continues to nourish the infant.

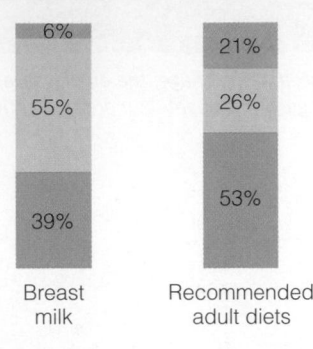
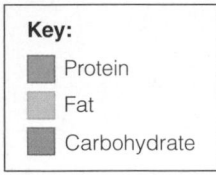
alpha-lactalbumin (lact-AL-byoo-min) the chief protein in human breast milk. The chief protein in cow's milk is *casein* (CAY-seen).

lactoferrin (lack-toe-FERR-in) a factor in breast milk that binds iron and keeps it from supporting the growth of the infant's intestinal bacteria.

nutrition authorities share this view, but some makers of baby formula try to convince women otherwise—see the Consumer Corner on pages 583–584.

Breast milk excels as a source of nutrients for the young infant. With the exception of vitamin D (discussed later), breast milk provides all of the nutrients a healthy infant needs for the first six months of life.[81] Breast milk also conveys immune factors, which both protect an infant against infection and inform its body about the outside environment.

Energy Nutrients in Breast Milk   The energy–nutrient balance of breast milk differs dramatically from that recommended for adults (see Figure 13–13). Yet, for infants, breast milk is the most nearly perfect food, affirming that people at different stages of life have different nutrient needs.

The carbohydrate in breast milk (and standard infant formula) is lactose. Besides being easily digested, lactose enhances calcium absorption.

The lipids in breast milk—and infant formula—provide the main source of energy in the infant's diet. Breast milk contains a generous proportion of the essential fatty acids linoleic acid and linolenic acid, as well as their longer-chain derivatives, arachidonic acid and DHA (defined in Chapter 5). Formula makers are now adding arachidonic acid and DHA to formulas.[82] Infants can produce some arachidonic acid and DHA from linoleic and linolenic acid, but some infants may need more than they can make.

Arachidonic acid and DHA are found abundantly in the brain and the retina of the eye.[83] Breastfed infants generally score higher on tests of mental development than formula-fed infants do, and researchers are investigating whether this difference can be attributed to DHA and arachidonic acid in breast milk and whether adding these lipids to infant formula will close the gap.[84]

The protein in breast milk is largely **alpha-lactalbumin**, a protein the human infant can easily digest. Another breast milk protein, **lactoferrin**, is an iron-gathering compound that helps absorb iron into the infant's bloodstream, keeps intestinal bacteria from getting enough iron to grow out of control, and kills certain bacteria.[85]

Vitamins and Minerals in Breast Milk   With the exception of vitamin D, the vitamin content of the breast milk of a well-nourished mother is ample. Even vitamin C, for which cow's milk is a poor source, is supplied generously. The concentration of vitamin D in breast milk is low, however, and vitamin D deficiency impairs bone mineralization. Vitamin D deficiency is most likely in infants who are not exposed to sunlight daily, have darkly pigmented skin, and live at Canada's geographical latitude. During the first 18 months of the Canadian Paediatric Society's 2002 surveillance of childhood illness campaign, 69 cases of vitamin D-deficiency rickets in infants were confirmed.[86] Health Canada continues to recommend "that all breast-fed, healthy term infants in Canada receive a daily vitamin D supplement of 10 µg (400 IU)."[87]

As for minerals, the calcium content of breast milk is ideal for infant bone growth, and the calcium is well absorbed. Breast milk is also low in sodium. The limited amount of iron in breast milk is highly absorbable, and its zinc, too, is absorbed better than from cow's milk, thanks to the presence of a zinc-binding protein.

After four to six months, an exclusively breastfed baby needs iron. Before four months, supplemental iron is unnecessary. Most babies are born with enough iron in their livers to last about half a year, and iron deficiency is rarely seen in very young infants. As lactation progresses, the iron in breast milk dwindles, making iron a concern for the four- to six-month-old. By six months, feeding the breastfed infant iron-fortified cereals is desirable. If the water supply is severely deficient in fluoride, both breastfed and formula-fed infants require fluoride supplementation after six months of age.

Immune Factors in Breast Milk   Breast milk offers an infant unsurpassed protection against infection by providing antiviral agents, antibacterial agents, and infection inhibitors.[88] For example, immune factors in breast milk interfere with the growth of bacteria that could otherwise attack the infant's vulnerable digestive tract linings. Breastfed babies are less prone to develop stomach and intestinal disorders during the first few months of life and so experience less vomiting and diarrhea than formula-fed babies.[89] Breast milk contains antibodies and other factors against the most common cause of diarrhea in infants and young children (rotavirus).* Breastfeeding reduces the severity and duration of symptoms associated with this infection.

Breastfeeding also protects against other common illnesses of infancy, such as middle ear infection and respiratory illness.[90] Breast milk may also offer protection against the development of cardiovascular disease. Compared with formula-fed infants, breastfed infants have lower blood cholesterol as adults.[91]

During the first two or three days of lactation, the breasts produce **colostrum**, a premilk substance containing antibodies and white cells from the mother's blood. Because it contains immunity factors, colostrum helps protect the newborn infant from those infections against which the mother has developed immunity—precisely those in the environment likely to infect the infant. Maternal antibodies from colostrum inactivate harmful bacteria within the infant's digestive tract. Later, breast milk also delivers antibodies, although not as many as colostrum.

In addition to their protective features, colostrum and breast milk contain hormones and other factors that stimulate the development of the infant's digestive tract. Clearly, breast milk is a very special substance.

Other Potential Benefits   Researchers are investigating whether breastfeeding may also help protect against obesity in childhood and later years. This promising research is described in the Controversy section in this chapter.

As suggested earlier, breastfeeding may also have a positive effect on later intelligence.[92] In one study, young adults who had been breastfed as long as nine months scored higher on two different intelligence tests than those who had been breastfed less than one month. Many other studies suggest a beneficial effect of breastfeeding on intelligence, but when subjected to strict standards of methodology (e.g., large sample size and appropriate intelligence testing), the evidence is less convincing.[93] Nevertheless, the possibility that breastfeeding may positively affect later intelligence is intriguing. It may be that some specific component of breast milk, such as DHA, contributes to brain development or that certain factors associated with the feeding process itself promote intellect.

KEY POINT

- Breast milk is the ideal food for infants because it provides the needed nutrients in the right proportions, as well as protective factors.

Formula Feeding

The substitution of formula feeding for breastfeeding involves striving to copy nature as closely as possible. Human milk and cow's milk differ; cow's milk is significantly higher in protein, calcium, and phosphorus, for example, to support the calf's faster growth rate. Thus, to prepare a formula from cow's milk, the formula makers must first dilute the milk and then add carbohydrate and nutrients to make the proportions comparable to those of human milk (see Table 13–8 for a comparison of human milk and standard formulas).

Standard formulas are inappropriate for some infants. For example, premature babies require special formulas, and infants allergic to milk protein can drink special **hypoallergenic formulas** or formulas based on soy protein.[94] Soy formulas are lactose-free and so can be used for infants with lactose intolerance; they are also useful as an alternative to milk-based formulas for vegetarian families. For infants with other special needs, many other variations are available.

The 2007 update of Nutrition for Healthy Term Infants from the joint working group of the Canadian Paediatric Society, Dietitians of Canada, Breastfeeding

*More children are hospitalized for rotavirus infection than for any other single cause.

Formula Options

- Liquid concentrate (inexpensive, relatively easy)—mix with equal part water.
- Powdered formula (cheapest, lightest for travel)—follow label directions.
- Ready-to-feed (easiest, most expensive)—pour directly into clean bottles.

Never an option—whole cow's milk before 12 months of age.

colostrum (co-LAHS-trum) a milklike secretion from the breasts during the first day or so after delivery before milk appears; rich in protective factors.

hypoallergenic formulas clinically tested infant formulas that do not provoke reactions in 90% of infants or children with confirmed cow's milk allergy.

Table 13–8

Human Milk Compared with Infant Formula for Selected Nutrients

Content	Mature Human Milk	Fortified Infant Formula*
Energy (Cal/L)	680	680
Protein (g)	9	15
Fat (g)	35	35
Carbohydrate (g)	80	75
Iron (mg/L)	0.5	10
Vitamin A (µg/L)	450	350
Niacin (mg/L)	4	7
Vitamin D (µg/L)	3	10

Some may also contain added arachidonic acid and DHA.

Source: Data from Committee on Nutrition, American Academy of Pediatrics, Pediatric Nutrition Handbook, 5th ed. Ed R. E. Kleinman (Elk Grove III: American Academy of Pediatrics, 2004) Appendix E. ISBN 1581101096

Committee for Canada, and Health Canada recommends iron-fortified formulas for all formula-fed infants.[95] Low-iron formulas have no role in infant feeding. Use of iron-fortified formulas has risen in recent decades and is credited with the decline of iron-deficiency anemia in infants.[96]

Formula feeding offers an acceptable alternative to breastfeeding. Nourishment for an infant from formula is adequate, and parents can choose this course with confidence. One advantage is that parents can see how much milk the infant drinks during feedings. Another is that other family members can participate in feeding sessions, giving them a chance to develop the special closeness that feeding fosters. Mothers who return to work early after giving birth may choose formula for their infants, but they have another option. Breast milk can be pumped into bottles and given to the baby by the father or other caregiver. At home, mothers may breastfeed as usual. Many mothers use both methods—they breastfeed at first but wean to formula later on.

For as long as breast milk or formula is the baby's major food (until the first birthday), unmodified cow's milk is an inappropriate replacement because milk provides little iron and vitamin C. If an infant's digestive tract is sensitive to the protein

The infant thrives on formula offered with affection.

With the first birthday comes the possibility of tasting whole, unmodified cow's milk for the first time.

content of cow's milk, it may bleed and worsen iron deficiency. Thus, plain cow's milk both causes iron loss and fails to replace iron. Also, the infant's immature kidneys are stressed by plain cow's milk. Once the baby is obtaining at least two-thirds of total daily food energy from a balanced mixture of cereals, vegetables, fruit, and other foods (usually after 12 months of age), whole cow's milk, fortified with vitamins A and D, is an acceptable accompanying beverage. Reduced-fat 1 percent or 2 percent milk is not recommended before the age of two years.

KEY POINT

- Infant formulas are designed to resemble breast milk and must meet Health Canada's standards for nutrient composition. Special formulas are available for premature infants, allergic infants, and others. Formula should be replaced with milk only after the baby's first birthday.

use it! Consumer Corner

Formula's Advertising Advantage

Most women are free to choose whatever feeding method best suits their needs. For only a few is breastfeeding either prohibited for medical reasons or medically indicated for special needs of the infant. With the strong scientific consensus that breastfeeding is preferable for most infants, why do women who could breastfeed their infants choose formula? Some women find the time and logistics of breastfeeding burdensome. For many women, though, the decision to forgo breastfeeding is influenced by advertising of formulas.

In early 2007, in a "Letter to Industry," the Canadian Food Inspection Agency reminded industry about nutrition claims on infant formula, stating:

The International Code of Marketing of Breastmilk Substitutes, to which Canada is a signatory, outlines labelling principles that promote clear labelling regarding the appropriate use of an infant formula while promoting breast-feeding. Comparing infant formula to breast milk, including comparisons of the levels of a nutrient in infant for-mula to the levels of the same nutrient in breast milk, is contrary to the mes sage embodied in the Code. While the Code has not been incorporated into Canadian domestic legislation, the infant formula industry is encouraged not to make a reference to breast milk on a label or advertising of infant for-mula, other than a statement regarding

the superiority of breastfeeding or that breast milk is the optimal method of feeding infants.*,[1]

Marketing tactics can undermine a woman's confidence concerning her breastfeeding choice, and lack of confidence has a significant influence on early discontinuation of breastfeeding.[2]

National efforts to promote breast-feeding seem to be working to some

*Consumer Corner references are listed separately at the end of the chapter.

extent.[3] Many hospitals employ certified lactation consultants, who specialize in helping new mothers establish a healthy breastfeeding relationship with their newborns. Table 13–9 lists 10 steps hospitals and birth centres can take to promote successful long-term breastfeeding. An encouraging trend of breastfeeding initiation is emerging, with 65 percent of women initiating breast-feeding today, up from 50 percent in 1990. Despite this trend toward increasing breastfeeding, the percentage of women breastfeeding their infants still

Table 13–9

10 Steps to Successful Breastfeeding

To promote breastfeeding, every maternity facility should

- Develop a written breastfeeding policy that is routinely communicated to all health-care staff.
- Train all health-care staff in the skills necessary to implement the breastfeeding policy.
- Inform all pregnant women about the benefits and management of breastfeeding.
- Help mothers initiate breastfeeding within ½ hour of birth.
- Show mothers how to breastfeed and how to maintain lactation, even if they need to be separated from their infants.
- Give newborn infants no food or drink other than breast milk, unless medically indicated.
- Practise rooming-in, allowing mothers and infants to remain together 24 hours a day.
- Encourage breastfeeding on demand.
- Give no artificial nipples or pacifiers to breastfeeding infants.[a]
- Foster the establishment of breastfeeding support groups, and refer mothers to them at discharge from the facility.

[a]Compared with nonusers, infants who use pacifiers breastfeed less frequently and stop breastfeeding at a younger age.

Source: Reproduced, with the permission of the publisher, from The World Health report: Health Systems Financing: The Path to Universal Coverage. Geneva, World Health Organization, 2010 (Fig. 5.1, http://whqlibdoc.who.int/whr/2010/9789241564021_eng.pdf)

falls short of the goal of *Healthy People 2010*. Lagging even further behind national goals are the number of infants breastfed beyond about two months of age.[4]

Formula-fed infants in developed nations are healthy and grow normally, but they miss out on the breastfeeding advantages described in the text. In developing nations, however, the consequence of choosing not to breast-feed can be tragic. Feeding formula is often fatal to the infant in nations where poverty limits access to formula mixes, clean water is unavailable for safe formula preparation, and medical help is limited. The World Health Organization (WHO) strongly supports breastfeeding for the world's infants in its "baby-friendly" initiative and opposes the marketing of infant formulas to new mothers.

Women are free to choose between breast and bottle, but the decision should be made by weighing valid factual information and not being influenced by sophisticated advertising ploys.

An Infant's First Foods

Foods can be introduced into the diet as the infant becomes physically ready to handle them. This readiness develops in stages. A newborn can swallow only liquids that are well back in the throat. Later (at four months or so), the tongue can move against the palate to swallow semisolid food such as cooked cereal. The stomach and intestines are immature at first; they can digest milk sugar (lactose) but not starch. Still later, the first teeth erupt, but not until some time during the second year can a baby begin to handle chewy food.

When to Introduce Solid Food   Health Canada recommends exclusive breast-feeding for the first six months (Nutrition for Healthy Term Infants: Recommendations from Birth to Six Months, http://www.hc-sc.gc.ca/fn-an/nutrition/infant-nourisson/recom/index-eng.php), and infants who are ready for solid foods thrive on receiving them and develop new skills through handling the foods. Indications of readiness for solid foods include

- The infant can sit with support and can control its head movements.
- The infant is six months or older.

Infants develop according to their own schedules, and although Table 13–10 presents a suggested sequence, individuality is important. Three considerations are relevant: the baby's nutrient needs, the baby's physical readiness to handle different forms of foods, and the need to detect and control allergic reactions. With respect to nutrient needs, the nutrient needed most is iron and then vitamin C.

Foods to Provide Iron and Vitamin C   Iron ranks highest on the list of nutrients most needing attention in infant nutrition. An infant's stored iron supply from before birth runs out after the birthweight doubles, long before the end of the first year. Iron deficiency is prevalent in children between the ages of six months and three years due to their rapid growth rate and the significant place that milk has in their diets. Excessive milk consumption (more than 875 mL or 3½ c a day) can displace iron-rich foods and lead to iron-deficiency anemia, popularly called **milk anemia**.

To prevent iron deficiency, breast milk or iron-fortified formula, then iron-rich foods, such as iron-fortified cereals, and meat or meat alternatives such as legumes are recommended. Once infants are eating these iron-rich foods, parents or caregivers should begin selecting vitamin C-rich foods to go with meals to enhance absorption. The best sources of vitamin C are fruit and vegetables.

Many fruit juices are naturally rich in vitamin C, and others may be fortified. A danger lies in overfeeding juice, however: some babies and young children may fail to grow and thrive when juice displaces other nutrient- and energy-dense foods from their diets. The Canadian Paediatric Society recommends no more than 60–120 millilitres of fruit juice per day when mothers are weaning their baby from the breast and suggests that more than this amount could interfere with the intake of breast milk or its substitiute.[97] Fruit juices should be served in a cup, not a bottle, and not before the infant is six months of age.

Foods such as iron-fortified cereals and formulas, mashed legumes, and strained meats provide iron.

David Strand

milk anemia iron-deficiency anemia caused by drinking so much milk that iron-rich foods are displaced from the diet.

Chapter 13 Life Cycle Nutrition: Mother and Infant

Table 13-10

Infant Development and Recommended Foods

Age (mo)	Feeding Skill	Foods Introduced into the Diet
0–4	Turns head toward any object that brushes cheek. Initially swallows using back of tongue; gradually begins to swallow using front of tongue as well. Strong reflex (extrusion) to push food out during first 2 to 3 months.	Feed breast milk or infant formula.
4–6[a]	Extrusion reflex diminishes, and the ability to swallow nonliquid foods develops. Indicates desire for food by opening mouth and leaning forward. Indicates satiety or disinterest by turning away and leaning back. Sits erect with support at 6 months. Begins chewing action. Brings hand to mouth. Grasps objects with palm of hand.	Begin iron-fortified cereal mixed with breast milk, formula, or water. Begin pureed vegetables and fruit and meat.
6–8	Able to feed self with fingers. Develops pincher (finger to thumb) grasp. Begins to drink from cup.	Begin mashed vegetables and fruit. Begin plain baby food meats. Begin plain, unsweetened fruit juices from cup.
8–10	Begins to hold own bottle. Reaches for and grabs food and spoon. Sits unsupported.	Begin breads and cereals from table. Begin yogurt. Begin pieces of soft, cooked vegetables and fruit from table. Gradually begin finely cut meats, fish, casseroles, cheese, eggs, and legumes.
10–12	Begins to master spoon but still spills some.	Include breads and cereals from table, in addition to infant cereal; soft or cooked fruit and vegetables; and finely chopped or ground meat, fish, or poultry; eggs; and mashed legumes.[b]

[a]*Health Canada recommends exclusive breastfeeding for the first six months of life for healthy term infants. See* Nutrition for Health Term Infants: Recommendations from Birth to Six Months, *available at http://www.hc-sc.gc.ca/fn-an/nutrition/infant-nourisson/recom/index_eng.php.*

[b]*Portions of foods for infants and young children are smaller than those for an adult. For example, a grain serving might be ½ slice of bread instead of 1 slice, or ¼ cup rice instead of ½ cup.*

Source: Adapted in part from Committee on Nutrition, American Academy of Pediatrics, Pediatric Nutrition Handbook, *5th ed, ed. R. E. Kleinman (Elk Village, Ill.: American Academy of Pediatrics, 2004) p 103–115.*

NOTE: Because each stage of development builds on the previous stage, the foods from an earlier stage continue to be included in all later stages.

Physical Readiness for Solid Foods

Foods introduced at the right times contribute to an infant's physical development. When the baby can sit up, can handle finger foods, and is teething, hard crackers and other finger foods may be introduced under the watchful eye of an adult. These foods promote the development of manual dexterity and control of the jaw muscles, but the caregiver must be careful that the infant does not choke on them. Babies and young children cannot safely chew and swallow any of the foods listed in the margin; they can easily choke on these foods, a risk not worth taking. Nonfood items of small size should always be kept out of the infant's reach to prevent choking.[98]

Some parents want to feed solids as early as possible on the theory that "stuffing the baby" at bedtime will promote sleeping through the night. There is no proof for this theory. Babies start to sleep through the night when they are ready, no matter when solid foods are introduced.

Food Allergies

New foods should be introduced one at a time so that allergies or other sensitivities can be detected. For example, when fortified baby cereals are introduced, try rice cereal first for several days; it causes allergy least often. Try wheat-containing cereal last; it is a common offender. Introduce egg whites, soy products, cow's milk, and citrus fruit still later for the same reason. If a food causes an allergic reaction (irritability due to skin rash, digestive upset, or respiratory discomfort), discontinue its use before going on to the next food. About 9 times out of 10, the allergy won't be evident immediately but will manifest itself in vague symptoms occurring up to five

To Prevent Choking, Do Not Give Infants or Young Children Any of the Following

- Carrots
- Cherries
- Gum
- Hard or gel-type candies
- Hot dog slices
- Marshmallows
- Nuts
- Peanut butter
- Popcorn
- Raw celery
- Whole beans
- Whole grapes

Keep These Nonfood Items Out of Their Reach:

- Balloons
- Coins
- Pen tops
- Small balls
- Other items of similar size

days after the offending food is eaten. Wait a month or two to try the food again; many sensitivities disappear with maturity. If your family history indicates allergies, apply extra caution in introducing new foods. Parents or caregivers who detect allergies early in an infant's life can spare the whole family much grief.

> Chapter 14 offers more information on allergies.

Choice of Infant Foods Commercial baby foods in Canada and the United States are safe, and except for mixed dinners with added starch fillers and heavily sweetened desserts, they have high nutrient density. Brands vary in their use of starch and sugar—check the ingredients lists. Parents or caregivers should not feed directly from the jar—remove portions to a dish for feeding in order not to contaminate the leftovers that will be stored in the jar.

An alternative to commercial baby food is to process a small portion of the family's table food in a blender, food processor, or baby food grinder. This necessitates cooking without salt or sugar, though, as the best baby food manufacturers do. Adults can season their own food after taking out the baby's portion. Pureed food can be frozen in an ice cube tray to yield a dozen or so servings that can be quickly thawed, heated, and served on a busy day.

Foods to Omit Sweets of any kind (including baby food "desserts") have no place in a baby's diet. The added food energy can promote obesity, and they convey few or no nutrients to support growth. Products containing sugar alcohols such as sorbitol should also be limited as these may cause diarrhea. Canned vegetables are inappropriate for babies because they often contain too much salt. Awareness of foodborne illness and precautions against it are imperative. Honey should never be fed to infants because of the risk of botulism.

> Chapter 12 provides details about botulism.

Foods at One Year For the infant weaned to whole milk after one year of age, whole milk can supply most of the needed nutrients: 500–875 mL (2–3½ c) a day meet those needs. A variety of other foods—meat and meat alternatives, iron-fortified cereal, enriched or whole-grain bread, fruit, and vegetables—should be supplied in amounts sufficient to round out total energy needs. Ideally, the one-year-old sits at the table, eats many of the same foods everyone else eats, and drinks liquids from a cup, not a bottle. A meal plan that meets the requirements for a one-year-old is shown in Table 13–11.

KEY POINT

- Solid food additions to an infant's diet should begin at about six months and should be governed by the infant's nutrient needs and readiness to eat. By one year, the baby should be receiving foods from all food groups.

Children love to eat what their families eat.

- For the nutrient content of commercial baby foods, visit the Canadian Nutrient File 2010 at http://www.hc-sc.gc.ca/fn-an/nutrition/fiche-nutri-data/index-eng.php.

Table 13–11

Meal Plan for a One-Year-Old

Breakfast	Afternoon Snack
½ c whole milk	½ c whole milk
½ c iron-fortified cereal	½ slice toast
½ c orange juice	1 tbs apple butter
Morning snack	**Dinner**
½ c yogurt	1 c whole milk
½ c fruit[a]	55 g chopped meat or well-cooked mashed legumes
Lunch	¼ c potato, rice, or pasta
½ c whole milk	½ c vegetables[b]
½ c vegetables[b]	½ c fruit[a]
1 egg or ¼ c tofu	
½ c noodles	

[a]Include citrus fruit, melons, and berries.
[b]Include dark green, leafy, and deep yellow vegetables.

Looking Ahead

The first year of life is the time to lay the foundation for future health. From the nutrition standpoint, the problems most common in later years are obesity and dental disease. Prevention of obesity may also help prevent the obesity-related diseases: atherosclerosis, diabetes, and cancer.

The most important single measure to undertake during the first year is to encourage eating habits that will support continued normal weight as the child grows. This means introducing a variety of nutritious foods in an inviting way, not forcing the baby to finish the bottle or baby food jar, avoiding concentrated sweets and empty-Calorie foods, and encouraging physical activity. Parents should not teach babies to seek food as a reward, to expect food as comfort for unhappiness, or to associate food deprivation with punishment. If they cry because they're thirsty, give them water, not milk or juice. If they cry for companionship, pick them up—don't feed them. If they are hungry, by all means, feed them appropriately. More pointers are offered in this chapter's Food Feature.

An irrational fear of obesity leads some parents to underfeed their infants, depriving them of the energy and nutrients they need to grow. Others wonder if they should feed their infants a low-fat diet to reduce heart disease risk, but Health Canada's document "Nutrition for Healthy Term Infants" does not recommend restricting fat intake during the first two years. A diet too low in fat hinders growth and development even when energy from carbohydrate and protein is ample. With rare exceptions, to be identified by physicians, babies from age one to two years need the food energy and fat of whole milk. They also need frequent servings of food containing the essential fatty acids.

The same strategies promote normal dental development: supply nutritious foods, avoid sweets, and discourage the association of food with reward or comfort. Dentists strongly discourage the practice of giving a baby a bottle as a pacifier. Sucking for long periods of time pushes the normal jawline out of shape and causes a bucktoothed profile: protruding upper and receding lower teeth. Prolonged sucking on a bottle of milk or juice also bathes the upper teeth in a carbohydrate-rich fluid that favours the growth of bacteria that produce acid that dissolves tooth material. Babies regularly put to bed with a bottle sometimes have teeth decayed all the way to the gum line, a condition known as early childhood caries/nursing bottle syndrome, shown in the photos below and on the next page.

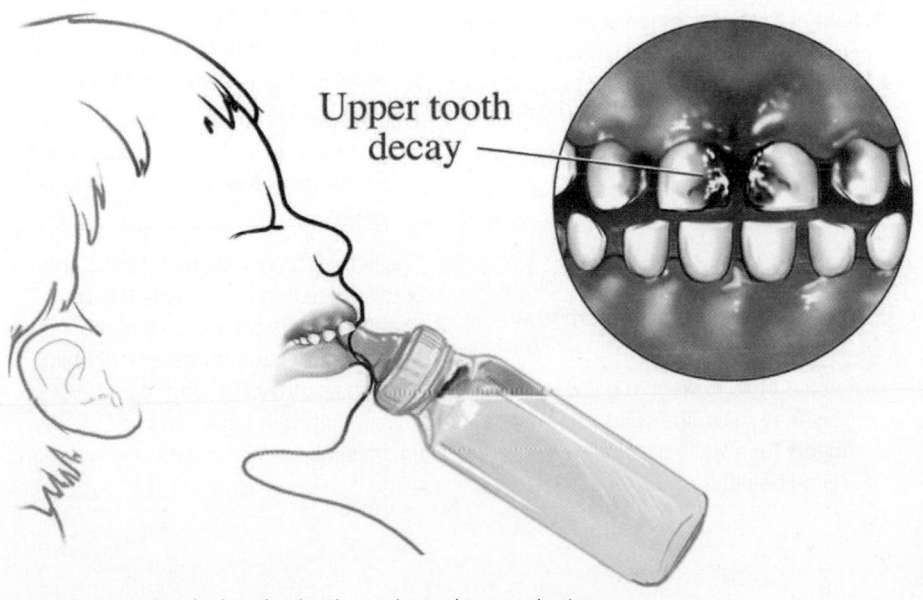

Upper tooth decay

Early childhood caries/nursing bottle syndrome in an early stage.

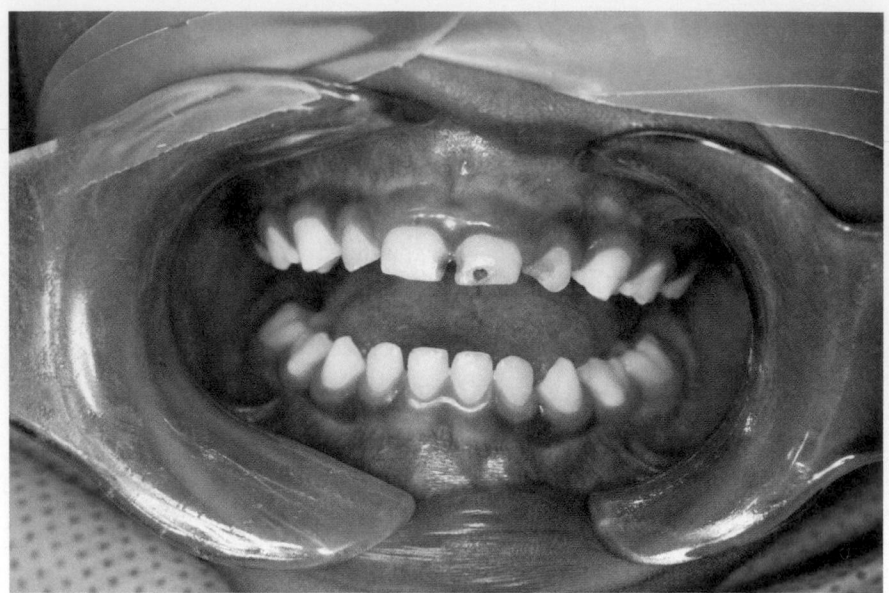

Early childhood caries/nursing bottle syndrome, an extreme example. The upper teeth have decayed all the way to the gum line.

Custom Medical Stock Photos

KEY POINT

- The early feeding of the infant lays the foundation for lifelong eating habits. It is desirable to foster preferences that will support normal development and health throughout life.

Mealtimes with Infants

The wise parent or caregiver of a one-year-old offers nutrition and affection together. "Feeding with love" produces better growth in both weight and height than feeding the same food in an emotionally negative climate.

Foster a Sense of Autonomy

The person feeding a one-year-old has to be aware that the child's exploring and experimenting are normal and desirable behaviours. The child is developing a sense of autonomy that, if allowed to develop, will provide the foundation for later assertiveness in choosing when and how much to eat and when to stop eating. The child's self-direction, if consistently overridden, can later turn into shame and self-doubt.

Some Feeding Guidelines

In light of the developmental and nutrient needs of one-year-olds and in the face of their often contrary and willful behaviour, a few feeding guidelines may be helpful:

- Discourage unacceptable behaviour (such as standing at the table or throwing food) by removing the child from the table to wait until later to eat. Be consistent and firm, not punitive. The child will soon learn to sit and eat.

- Let the child explore and enjoy food. This may mean the child eats with fingers for a while. Use of the spoon will come in time.

- Don't force food on children. Provide children with nutritious foods and let them choose which ones and how much they will eat. Gradually, they will acquire a taste for different foods. If children refuse milk, provide cheese, cream soups, and yogurt.

- Limit sweets strictly. Infants have little room in their 1,000-Calorie daily energy allowance for empty-Calorie sweets.

These recommendations reflect a spirit of tolerance that best serves the emotional and physical interests of the infant. This attitude, carried throughout childhood, helps the child develop a healthy relationship with food. The next chapter finishes the story of growth and nutrition.

Childhood Obesity and Early Development of Chronic Diseases

When people think of health problems in children and adolescents, they most often think of measles and acne, not type 2 diabetes and hypertension. Today, however, unprecedented numbers of Canadian children are being diagnosed with obesity.[*,1] Canadian children are not alone—galloping rates of obesity are injuring the health of an alarming number of children around the globe.[2]

This trend bodes ill for some 60 million children who, without immediate intervention, are destined to suffer type 2 diabetes and hypertension in childhood followed by cardiovascular disease (CVD) in young adulthood. Most overweight children become overweight adolescents and adults and face increased risks of many chronic diseases.[3] Without preventive measures, many will die young of their disease.

For the sake of today's children and of future societies, prevention or treatment of childhood obesity is of critical importance. Yet, despite numerous advances in the prevention and cure of other childhood diseases, such as measles and even some forms of leukemia, reversing obesity remains an unanswered challenge.[4]

The Childhood Obesity Problem

Obesity, high blood cholesterol, and hypertension stand with diabetes at the top of the list of factors associated with the development of CVD (recall from Chapter 11). When these conditions appear in childhood, CVD may set in soon afterward—and much sooner than most people expect. Education is

urgently needed in this regard. Most overweight children and their parents discount these deadly threats, focusing instead on appearance and the social costs of obesity.[5]

Characteristics of Childhood Obesity

Children are heavier today than they were 30 or so years ago. Since the late 1970s, the prevalence of overweight has doubled for children and shows no sign of slowing (see Figure C13–1). Typically, obese children

- Are female.
- Have a family history of type 2 diabetes.
- Are of non-European descent.
- Were born to mothers who had diabetes while pregnant with them.

Figure C13–1

Prevalence of Overweight among Children and Adolescents

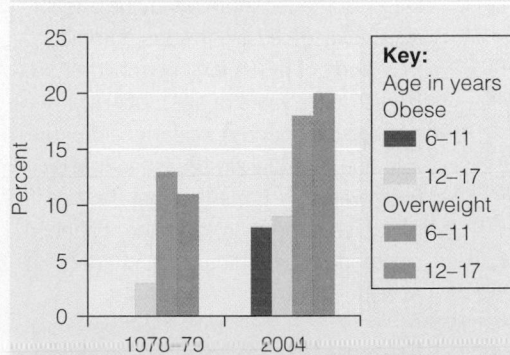

*There is a large coefficient of variation for the "obese" data for children 6–11 years old from 1978–79; therefore, data are unreliable.

Source: Data from Statistics Canada. Shields, M., Measured Obesity - Overweight Canadian Children and Adolescents. Nutrition: Findings from the CCHS Issue No 1. Cat No. 82-620 MWE2005001 www.statcan.ca/english/research/82-620-MIE/2005001/pdf/cobesity.pdf. Reproduced and distributed on an "as is" basis with the permission of Statistics Canada.

- Have metabolic syndrome, including hypertension, impaired glucose tolerance, elevated blood triglycerides, and reduced HDL cholesterol.[6]
- Have a low family income.
- Are more sedentary than their peers.[7]

Additionally, parental obesity predicts excessive weight gain during childhood and more than doubles the chance that a child will become an obese adult.

Influence of Genetics

For obesity, as well as for heart disease, hypertension, and type 2 diabetes, genetics does not appear to play a *determining* role; that is, most people are not simply destined at birth to develop them. Instead, genetics appears to play a largely *permissive role—the potential is inherited and will then develop if* given a push by factors in the environment such as poor diet, sedentary lifestyle, or cigarette smoking.

Genes help govern the complex system of appetite control (described in Chapter 9).[8] If the tendency to consume lesser or greater amounts of food is inherited through the genes, then such genes may influence who among the population stays lean and who becomes obese. Other genes may influence whether an individual spends more or less energy in metabolism. Enzymes (proteins, produced by the genes) determine the body's ability to conserve its energy and store body fat. Such metabolic tendencies are probably in place from birth, but some researchers believe that genes alone are insufficient to explain such tendencies and are exploring whether events before and shortly after birth may affect their expression.

Fetal Theories of Obesity Development

A theory called *fetal programming* or *fetal origins of disease* states that maternal malnutrition or other harmful conditions at a critical period of fetal development could have lifelong effects on an individual's pattern of genetic expression and therefore on the tendency to develop obesity and certain diseases.[9]

An infant born with a high birthweight is likely to remain heavy into adulthood.[10] According to the fetal programming theory, *overnutrition* during fetal life may be to blame. A fetus with a rich supply of energy nutrients may adapt to its energy-rich environment by producing more of the enzyme systems active in forming and storing body fat. Later, when the fetus emerges as an independent individual, this overabundance of fat-storing enzymes makes weight gain likely. This theory may also explain why infants born to women with uncontrolled diabetes during pregnancy generally have high birthweights— diabetes causes a buildup of energy fuels in the mother's bloodstream, thereby providing an energy-rich environment for the fetus.

A twist on the fetal obesity theory states that *underfed* fetuses may also adapt to their environment by becoming adept at conserving energy, but for reasons different from the overfed fetus.[11] An underfed fetus must maximize every molecule of energy nutrient it receives in order to grow and develop, so it becomes predominantly "thrifty" in its energy metabolism. Such a thrifty fetus would have an advantage if born into a famine environment, but when the newborn instead emerges into a food-rich world, the child faces a greatly increased risk for obesity and the many diseases it foreshadows.[12] When a female child who was starved in the womb then grows up to bear children of her own, they may

also carry the thrifty traits, making the consequences of nutrition deprivation during pregnancy known across several generations.[13]

A related hypothesis also attributes chronic diseases to fetal origins and adverse circumstances shortly after birth.* Investigations into English birth records from the early 20th century revealed that, as a group, people who were born small for date or who failed to thrive as infants suffered in later life from higher blood pressure, lower bone density, and higher rates of type 2 diabetes than other people. They were also more likely to have altered blood lipids; thicker left heart walls, indicating circulatory difficulties; less elastic arteries; and even greater stress responses.[14] More studies are needed to confirm or refute these ideas.

Breastfeeding

Researchers are also exploring whether infant feeding methods influence later body fatness, but the findings are not yet clear on this point. In a well-controlled survey of over 15,000 adolescent children and their mothers, infants who were mostly breastfed for the first six months of life were less likely to be overweight than infants fed mostly formula.[15] An explanation may be that most breastfed infants spontaneously take in just enough energy to meet their needs and thus learn self-regulation of food intake at the earliest stage of life.[16] Bottle-fed infants may be encouraged to overfeed by anxious parents. In a study of much younger children (three to five years of age), however, researchers found no clear effect of the duration of exclusive breastfeeding on body weight.[17] It may be that the effect becomes evident only in later childhood, or perhaps some other factors are at work.

Energy Intake and Sedentary Behaviour

Children learn food behaviours largely from their families, and entire

This theory is named the Barker hypothesis after its originator.

families may be eating too much, dieting inappropriately, and exercising too little, a pattern often noted among mothers and daughters.[18] When researchers ask, "Are today's children consuming significantly more Calories than those of 30 years ago?" the answer comes back, "Yes." Some researchers report an increase of 100 to 200 Calories a day for all age groups, enough to account for significant weight gain.[19] The answer to another popular question, "Are children eating too many carbohydrates?" is a qualified "no"—children with the highest carbohydrate intakes, with the exception of added sugars, are leaner than other children.[20]

Research links added sugars, and especially high-fructose corn syrup—the easily consumed, energy-dense liquid sugar added to soft drinks—with excess body fatness in children. Controversy 4 pointed out that just over two cans of sugary soft drinks—an amount consumed every day by many adolescents— provide 400 Calories.[21] According to one estimate, the risk of obesity increases by 60 percent with each daily sugary drink consumed by overweight children.[22]

Although the tremendous increase in soft drink consumption may play some role in the obesity epidemic, much of the epidemic can be explained by lack of exercise. Children have grown more sedentary, and sedentary children are more often overweight. A child who spends more than an hour or two in front of a television, computer monitor, or other media can become obese and develop unhealthy blood lipids even while eating fewer Calories than a more active child (Figure C13–2).[23] Physically active children have higher HDL, lower LDL, and lower blood pressure than sedentary children, and these positive findings often persist into adulthood.

Early Development of Type 2 Diabetes

An estimated 85 percent of the children diagnosed with type 2 diabetes are obese.[24] Most are diagnosed during puberty, but as children become more obese and less active, the trend is

Figure C13–2

Prevalence of Overweight and Obesity of Adolescents 12–17 Years of Age by Hours of Screen Time*

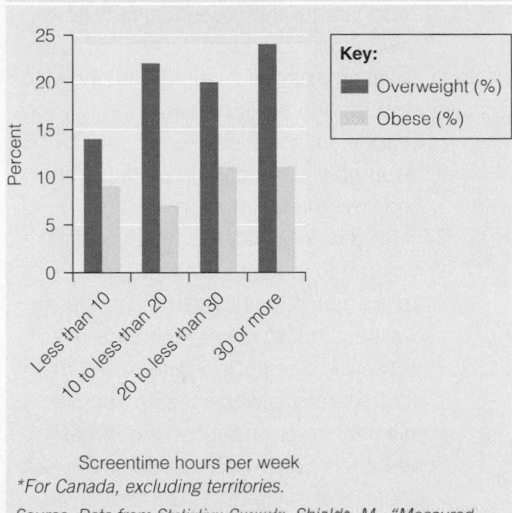

Screentime hours per week

*For Canada, excluding territories.

Source: Data from Statistics Canada. Shields, M., "Measured Obesity - Overweight Canadian Children and Adolescents." Nutrition: Findings from the CCHS Issue No 1.Cat No. 82-620 MWF2005001 http://www.statcan.gc.ca/pub/82-620-m/2005001/pdf/4193660-eng.pdf. Reproduced and distributed on an "as is" basis with the permission of Statistics Canada.

shifting toward younger and younger children. Type 2 diabetes is most likely to attack those who are obese and sedentary and have a family history of diabetes.

In type 2 diabetes, the cells become insulin resistant—that is, insulin can no longer escort glucose from the blood into the cells. The combination of obesity and insulin resistance produces a cluster of symptoms, including high blood lipids and high blood pressure, which, in turn, promotes the development of atherosclerosis and the early development of heart disease.[25] Other common problems evident by early adulthood include kidney disease, blindness, and

More and more children with obesity are being diagnosed with type 2 diabetes.

miscarriages. Details about diabetes are in Chapter 4.

Determining exactly how many children suffer from type 2 diabetes is tricky. For one thing, the symptoms of type 2 and type 1 diabetes differ only subtly in children. The child with type 2 diabetes may lack classic telltale diabetes symptoms, such as glucose in the urine, ketones in the blood, weight loss, and excessive thirst and urination, so the condition often advances undetected. Weight loss is particularly difficult to detect because childhood type 2 diabetes is associated with overweight, and the child's obesity may mask any weight loss caused by the diabetes. Also, children's physicians expect to find type 1 diabetes (once called *juvenile-onset* diabetes) and not type 2 in children, making misdiagnosis likely when signs of type 2 diabetes present themselves. Undiagnosed diabetes means that children suffering with the condition are left undefended against its ravages.

Prevention and treatment of type 2 diabetes depend on weight management, which can be particularly difficult in a youngster's world of food advertising, video games, and pocket money for junk food. The activity and dietary suggestions to help defend against heart disease later in this Controversy section apply to type 2 diabetes as well.

Early Development of Heart Disease

By adolescence, most children have formed fatty streaks in their coronary arteries. By early adulthood, the fibrous plaques may begin to calcify and become raised lesions, causing arterial damage and blockage that make heart attacks and strokes likely. In short, the consequences of atherosclerosis, which become apparent only in adulthood, have their beginnings in the first decades of life.[26]

Children with the highest risks of developing heart disease are sedentary

and obese, with diabetes, high blood pressure, and high blood cholesterol.[27] In contrast, children with the lowest risks of heart disease are physically active and of normal weight, with low blood pressure and favourable lipid profiles.

Blood Cholesterol

As blood cholesterol rises, atherosclerosis increases. Cholesterol values at birth are similar in all populations, but differences emerge in early childhood.

In general, blood cholesterol tends to rise as dietary saturated fat intakes increase. In recent years, for example, Japanese children have adopted a diet more like that of North America—higher in saturated fat—and their blood cholesterol has increased.[28]

Blood cholesterol also correlates with childhood obesity, especially central obesity.[29] LDL cholesterol rises with obesity, and HDL declines. These relationships are apparent in childhood and increase in magnitude with age.

Children who are both overweight and have high blood cholesterol are likely to have parents who develop heart disease early.[30] For this reason, screening is recommended for children and adolescents whose parents (or grandparents) have heart disease, whose parents have elevated blood cholesterol, and whose family history is unavailable, especially if other risk factors are evident.[31] Because blood cholesterol in children is a good predictor of their adult cholesterol, some experts recommend universal cholesterol screening for all children, particularly for those who are overweight, smoke, are sedentary, or consume diets high in saturated fat.[32] Early—but not advanced—artery lesions are reversible, making screening and education a high priority.

Blood Pressure

Pediatricians routinely monitor blood pressure in children and adolescents. High blood pressure may signal an underlying disease or the early onset of hypertension. Hypertension may develop in the first decades of life, especially among obese children, and worsen with time.[33] Hypertension accelerates the development of atherosclerosis.

Breastfeeding and Hypertension

Every authority making recommendations for infants promotes breast milk as the ideal food for normal, healthy infants. A 2001 report ran counter to this wisdom, however, by reporting increased stiffness of the arteries in 20-year-old subjects who as infants had been exclusively breastfed for more than four months.[34] Less flexible arteries can lead to hypertension, elevating heart disease risk (see Chapter 11). Another report linked elevated blood cholesterol with breastfeeding for more than a year and also with bottle feeding alone.[35] No practical meaning can be derived from these findings, and parents should be assured that the benefits of breastfeeding far outweigh any suggestion of risk.

Controlling Hypertension

Children with hypertension can often make dramatic improvements by participating in regular aerobic activity and by losing weight or maintaining their weight as they grow taller. Evidence is needed to clarify whether restricting sodium in children's and adolescents' diets lowers blood pressure. It may be worth watching caffeine intakes, however. In one recent study, teens, and particularly African Americans, who drank two to four cans of caffeinated soft drinks each day had higher blood pressure readings than those drinking mostly other beverages.[36] No one yet knows if caffeine, soft drinks, or other factors in a lifestyle that includes such choices bear responsibility for this effect.

Prevention of hypertension may be of special urgency for adolescents because their response to blood pressure-lowering medication may be less consistently favourable than in adults.[37]

Lifestyle Recommendations for Children

Because their health is imperilled, the most critical efforts to modify lifestyles focus on children who are already overweight.[38] Children with high blood cholesterol should first be treated with diet and physical activity. If blood cholesterol remains high in children 10 years and older after 6–12 months of lifestyle intervention, then drugs can lower blood cholesterol without threatening growth or development.[39] First, though, an honest evaluation of the lifestyle choices affecting the child can be of help in planning necessary changes.

Diet Moderation, Not Deprivation

All children should eat a variety of foods and maintain a desirable weight, that much is clear. There is less agreement as to whether it is wise to restrict fat in a healthy child's diet, but most experts recommend that children over age two receive at least 25 percent and no more than 35 percent of total energy from fat.[40] Restricting saturated fat and *trans* fat may be especially beneficial. Such measures appear to improve blood lipids without compromising nutrient adequacy, physical growth, or neurological development.[41] Pediatricians warn parents and caregivers to avoid extremes, though; they caution that while intentions may be good, excessive fat restriction may create nutrient deficiencies, impair growth, and spark unnecessary battles about food.

Healthy children over age two can continue eating age-appropriate portion sizes, with low-fat choices and more fruit and vegetables replacing some high-fat foods.[42] Healthy meals should occasionally include moderate portions of a child's favourite foods, even if they are high-fat treats such as French fries or ice cream. A steady diet of offerings from some "children's menus" in restaurants, such as commercially fried chicken nuggets, hot dogs, and French fries, easily exceeds a prudent intake of saturated fat, *trans* fat, and Calories, however, and invites both nutrient shortages and gains of body fat.[43] Many major restaurant chains are changing children's menus to include lower-Calorie, lower-fat, and lower-sodium items—additions welcomed by busy parents who often dine out or purchase takeout foods.[44]

Other fatty foods, such as nuts; vegetable oils; and safer varieties of fish, such as light canned tuna or salmon, are important for their essential fatty acids. Low-fat milk products deserve special attention in a child's diet for the needed calcium and other nutrients they supply; in addition, some evidence supports a favourable effect of milk products on body weights of children.[45]

In Britain, educators taught schoolchildren to reduce their soft-drink consumption, resulting in lower rates of overweight at several school locations.[46] In Hawaii, researchers determined that adolescent girls who consumed more milk had lower measures of body fatness than girls drinking more sugary soft drinks and punches.[47] The best beverage choice for dense bones, adequate nutrients, and perhaps even lean body composition is low-fat 1 percent or 2 percent milk. Sugary soft drinks and punches are best limited to occasional treats.[48]

Physical Activity

Active children have a better lipid profile and lower blood pressure than more sedentary children. Additionally, the effects of combining a nutritious Calorie-controlled diet with exercise can be seen in observable improvements in children's outer measures of health, such as reduced waist circumference and increased muscle strength, along with the inner benefits of greatly improved condition of the heart and arteries.[49]

Just as blood cholesterol and obesity track over the years, so does a youngster's level of physical activity. Inactive children are likely to grow up to be inactive adults. Similarly, those who are physically active now tend to remain so. Compared with inactive teens, those who are physically active weigh less, smoke less, eat diets lower in saturated fats, and have better blood lipid profiles. Conversely, teens who pass their spare time watching television or playing video games have higher rates of obesity and more atherogenic blood cholesterol. The message is clear: physical activity offers numerous health benefits, and children who are active today are most likely to be active for years to come.

Smoking*

Smoking poses so serious a threat to children and adults that it deserves attention, even in a nutrition text. Each day, 3,000 children light up for the first time—typically in *grade* school. Almost two out of three high school students have tried smoking, and one in seven smokes regularly.[50] Approximately 80 percent of all adult smokers began smoking before the age of 18.[51]

Of those teenagers who continue smoking, half will eventually die of smoking-related causes. Efforts to teach children about the dangers of smoking seem most effective when they focus on immediate health consequences, such as shortness of breath when playing sports, or other consequences, such as ruined clothing, spent pocket money, and bad breath. Whatever the context, the message to all children and teens should be clear: "Don't start smoking. If you've already started, quit now."

Moving toward Solutions

Treatment of established obesity is notoriously unsuccessful, making prevention of childhood obesity and the diseases it engenders a high national priority.[52] Exactly how to proceed in this regard remains uncertain, however.[53] Education is clearly needed. Classroom lessons that are reinforced by lunchroom offerings and other school policies often help children change their eating habits for the better.[54] When school nutrition policy conflicts with classroom teachings and adults set poor examples, however, children are likely to follow their taste buds, not nutrition teachings. Table C13–1 offers some provincial and territorial healthy living strategies in place across the country designed to

improve the health of Canadians through the promotion of healthy eating, physical activity, and healthy weights. Many of these strategies are in keeping with "The Integrated Pan-Canadian Healthy Living Strategy 2005" prepared by The Secretariat for the Intersectoral Healthy Living Network in partnership with the F/P/T Healthy Living Task Group and the F/P/T Advisory Committee on Population Health and Health Security (ACPHHS) (http://www.phac-aspc.gc.ca/hp-ps/hl-mvs/ipchls-spimmvs).

Children are an appropriate focus of national obesity concerns, but to help them, help must also reach the adults in their lives who are growing fatter and sicker themselves. Adults not only feed this and future generations of children but also set examples that children almost invariably follow.[55]

To tackle the problem in earnest may require looking honestly at global

trends, such as greater accessibility to large portions of inexpensive, highly palatable, high-Calorie foods (especially in schools); greater use of automobiles; and diminishing incentives to be physically active (Controversy 11 sheds light

Courtesy Health Nexus/Nexus Santé

Table C13–1

Provincial and Territorial Healthy Living Strategies

Strategies include one or more of the following: healthy eating, physical activity, and healthy weights.

- Alberta—Framework for a Healthy Alberta: An Integrated Approach, http://www.health.alberta.ca/documents/Framework-For-Health.2003.pdf
- British Columbia—ActNowBC, http://www.phac-aspc.gc.ca/publicat/2009/ActNowBC/index-eng.php
- Manitoba—The goal is a 10% increase in the population who are physically active by 2010.
- New Brunswick—Wellness Strategy Action Plan 2013-2014, http://www2.gnb.ca/content/gnb/en/departments/dhic/wellness.html
- Newfoundland and Labrador—Achieving Health and Wellness: Provincial Wellness Plan for Newfoundland and Labrador, http://www.health.gov.nl.ca/health/wellnesshealthyliving/nlprovincialwellnessplan.pdf
- Northwest Territories—The goal is a 10% increase in the population who are physically active by 2010.
- Nova Scotia—Active, Healthy Living, http://www.gov.ns.ca/hpp/physicalactivity/activehealthyliving.asp
- Nunavut—The goal is a 10% increase in the population who are physically active by 2010.
- Ontario—Healthy Eating and Active Living (HEAL) Action Plan, http://www.mhp.gov.on.ca/en/heal/default.asp
- PEI Government—Prince Edward Island Healthy Living Strategy, http://www.gov.pe.ca/health/index.php3?number=1020884&lang=E
- Québec—Défi Santé, http://www.defisante.ca/fr/accueil
- Saskatchewan—Saskatchewan Promotes Healthy Living, http://www.health.gov.sk.ca/healthy-living
- Yukon—The goal is a 10% increase in the population who are physically active by 2010.

Source: Based on The Integrated Pan Canadian Healthy Living Strategy 2005, The Secretariat for the Intersectoral Healthy Living Network in partnership with the F/P/T Healthy Living Task Group and the F/P/T Advisory Committee on Population Health and Health Security (ACPHHS), Cat. N° HP10-1/2005 http://www.phac-aspc.gc.ca/hl-vs-strat/pdf/hls_e.pdf

*According to the Canadian Lung Association, "Smoking is the biggest threat to the lung health of Canadians. Every year, 45,000 Canadians die from smoking and hundreds of thousands struggle with smoking-related diseases."

on these issues). Schools would also do well to provide sound nutrition and physical education for every able child in their care.[56]

It is tempting to look for simple answers to complex problems, but in truth, if everyone today would take the advice of every legitimate health agency worldwide, many of these problems would disappear. Today, the best advice remains the easiest to give and perhaps the most difficult to follow: don't smoke, choose a diet in accordance with the nutrition recommendations for Canadians, follow Canada's Food Guide (Chapter 2), and make it a habit to be physically active each day. In the end, parents and other significant adults can help mould children's behaviours by the examples they set.[57]

Self-Check

Answers to these Self-Check questions are in Appendix D.

1. A pregnant woman needs an extra 450 Calories above the allowance for nonpregnant women during which trimester(s)?
   a. first
   b. second
   c. third
   d. first, second, and third

2. A deficiency of which nutrient appears to be related to an increased risk of NTDs in the newborn?
   a. vitamin B$_6$
   b. folate
   c. calcium
   d. niacin

3. Which of the following preventive measures should a pregnant woman take to avoid contracting listeriosis?
   a. avoid feta cheese
   b. avoid pasteurized milk
   c. thoroughly heat hot dogs
   d. (a) and (c)

4. Breastfed infants may need supplements of
   a. iron and vitamin D
   b. zinc, iron, and vitamin C
   c. vitamin E, calcium, and fluoride
   d. vitamin K, magnesium, and potassium

5. Which of the following foods poses a choking hazard to infants and small children?
   a. pudding
   b. marshmallows
   c. hot dog slices
   d. b and c

6. Sweets of any kind (including baby food "desserts") have no place in a baby's diet.
   T   F

7. A major reason why a woman's nutrition before pregnancy is crucial is that it determines whether her uterus will support the growth of a normal placenta.
   T   F

8. Fetal alcohol syndrome (FAS) is the leading known cause of mental retardation in the world.
   T   F

9. In general, the effect of nutritional deprivation on a breast-feeding mother is to reduce the quality of her milk.
   T   F

10. A sure way to get a baby to sleep through the night is to feed solid foods as soon as the baby can swallow them.
    T   F

track it!

Diet Analysis
PLUS ✚ Concepts in Action

start now! ┄┄▷ Ready to make a change? If you weren't exercising regularly before you became pregnant, see the Physical Activity Readiness Medical Examination for Pregnancy Guidelines (PARmed-X for Pregnancy; see http://www.csep .ca/english/view.asp?x=698) and talk to your doctor before undertaking an activity. Track your activity daily using the Diet Analysis Plus Activity Tracker.

Analyze the Adequacy of a Diet for Pregnancy

The purpose of this exercise is to reinforce the importance of good food choices to provide nutrients to support health during pregnancy, lactation, and growth.

1. To reduce the risk for neural tube defects in infants, women of child-bearing age are urged to obtain 400 micrograms (expressed as Dietary Folate Equivalents, DFE) of folic acid daily in addition to a varied diet. Find folic acid among many vegetables and fruit and enriched grains and other fortified foods. Select the Track Diet tab from the red navigation bar. Select a new date, and enter foods to create a meal that provides folic acid from the following resources: Snapshot 7–9, Figure 7–17, and Table 1 below. (Hint: A good meal to choose is breakfast.) Select the Reports tab, and select Source Analysis under the Advanced heading. Select Folate from the drop-down menu and generate a report. How close did your meal come to providing one-third of the needed 400 micrograms/DFE for folic acid?

2. A pregnant teenager's need for calcium is 1,300 milligrams a day. Many teenagers fail to meet their calcium needs, even before pregnancy. From the DA+ Home tab, select Create New Profile and enter demographic data appropriate for a pregnant teenager. Select the Track Diet tab, and select a new day. Add foods to create a high-calcium meal for a pregnant teen. (For tips, see Snapshot 8–1 on page 318.) Select the Reports tab. Then, under the Advanced heading, select Source Analysis. Select Calcium from the drop-down menu and generate a report. How much calcium was provided by the foods in this meal? What did you take into consideration when choosing the foods high in calcium? How can you increase the likelihood that the teenager will consume this meal?

3. During lactation, a woman needs an additional 330 Calories per day more than her regular need. From the DA+ Home tab, select Create New Profile, making it similar to your own but selecting Female and 0–19 Weeks Pregnant from the Profile drop-down menu. To meet this woman's need, choose among nutrient-dense foods (refer to Table 2), and using the Track Diet tab, create a one-day diet to meet her increased energy need. Select the Reports tab, and, under the Nutrients heading, select Energy Balance and then select all meals. Did your food choices help this woman to meet her increased energy need? Was a minimum of "330" listed in the "Net kcal" column?

4. Zinc is required for protein synthesis and cell development. Obtaining zinc poses a challenge to vegetarians. Create a vegetarian meal that includes zinc-rich foods (see Snapshot 8–6, page 338). Select the profile for the pregnant woman, if you haven't already, and then click the Track Diet tab. Select a new date. Choose some zinc-rich foods to create a meal. Select Reports and then select Source Analysis under the Nutrients heading. Select Zinc from the drop-down menu. What zinc-rich foods would you advise for a pregnant vegan?

Table 1

Rich Folate Sources[a]

Natural Folate Sources	Fortified Folate Sources
Liver (3 oz) 221 μg DFE	Highly enriched ready-to-eat cereals (¾ c) 680 μg DFE[b]
Lentils (½ c) 179 μg DFE	Pasta, cooked (1 c) 154 (average value) μg DFE
Chickpeas or pinto beans (½ c) 145 μg DFE	Rice, cooked (1 c) 153 μg DFE
Asparagus (½ c) 134 μg DFE	Bagel (1 small whole) 156 μg DFE
Spinach (1 c raw) 58 μg DFE	Waffles, frozen (2) 78 μg DFE
Avocado (½ c) 61 μg DFE	Bread, white (1 slice) 48 μg DFE
Orange juice (1 c) 74 μg DFE	
Beets (½ c) 68 μg DFE	

[a]Folate amounts for these and thousands of other foods are listed in the Table of Food Composition in Appendix A.

[b]Folate in cereals varies; read the Nutrition Facts panel of the label.

Table 2

Daily Food Choices for Pregnancy (2nd and 3rd Trimesters) and Lactation

Food Group	Amounts	SAMPLE MENU	
Fruits	2 c	**Breakfast** 1 whole-wheat English muffin 2 tbs peanut butter 1 c low-fat vanilla yogurt ½ c fresh strawberries 1 c orange juice	**Dinner** Chicken cacciatore 90 g chicken ½ c stewed tomatoes 1 c rice ½ c summer squash 1½ c salad (spinach, mushrooms, carrots) 1 tbs salad dressing 1 slice Italian bread 2 tsp soft margarine 1 c low-fat milk
Vegetables	3 c		
Grains	240 g	**Midmorning snack** ½ c cranberry juice 1 oz pretzels	
Protein Foods	195 g	**Lunch** Sandwich (tuna salad on whole-wheat bread) ½ carrot (sticks) 1 c low-fat milk	
Milk	3 c		

NOTE: This sample meal plan provides about 2,500 Calories (55% from carbohydrate, 20% from protein, and 25% from fat) and meets most of the vitamin and mineral needs of pregnant and lactating women.

5. An infant just beginning to eat solid foods needs iron and vitamin C in particular. From the DA+ Home tab page, select Create New Profile and create a profile for a 75-centimetre (2 ft. 6 in.), 11-kilogram (24-pound) 1-year-old child. Select the Track Diet tab, and create a breakfast and snack that include foods that are good sources of iron and vitamin C (see Snapshots 7–5, page 265, and 8–5, page 333). Select the Reports tab, then select Source Analysis under the Advanced heading, and finally Iron from the drop-down menu. What were the top sources of iron? Do the same for vitamin C, and name the top sources. Did your food choices supply more than a third of the child's iron and vitamin C recommendations? If not, what other foods might you select?

Endnotes

1. W. Y. Wong and coauthors, New evidence of the influence of exogenous and endogenous factors on sperm count in man, *European Journal of Obstetrics, Gynecology, and Reproductive Biology* 110 (2003): 49–54; R. M. Sharpe and S. Franks, Environment, lifestyle, and infertility—An inter-generational issue, *Nature Cell Biology* 4 (2002): S33–S40.

2. M. S. Kramer, The epidemiology of adverse pregnancy outcomes: An overview, *Journal of Nutrition* 133 (2003): 1592S–1596S.

3. C. M. Law and coauthors, Fetal, infant, and childhood growth and adult blood pressure: A longitudinal study from birth to 22 years of age, *Circulation* 105 (2002): 1088–1092; K. M. Rasmussen, The "fetal origins" hypothesis: Challenges and opportunities for maternal and child nutrition, *Annual Review of Nutrition* 21 (2001): 73–95.

4. M. Hack and coauthors, Outcomes in young adulthood for very-low-birth-weight infants, *New England Journal of Medicine* 346 (2002): 149–157.

5. Statistics Canada, Health status indicators—Infant mortality rates by province and territory, available at http://www.statcan.gc.ca/tables-tableaux/sum-som/l01/cst01/health21a-eng.htm.

6. M. S. Kramer, 2003 [see reference 2].

7. U. Ramakrishnan, Nutrition and low birth weight: From research to practice, *American Journal of Clinical Nutrition* 79 (2004): 17–21.

8. M. L. Watkins and coauthors, Maternal obesity and risk for birth defects, *Pediatrics* 111 (2003): 1152–1158; F. Galtier-Dereure, C. Boegner, and J. Bringer, Obesity and pregnancy: Complications and cost, *American Journal of Clinical Nutrition* 71 (2000): 1242S–1248S.

9. Position of the American Dietetic Association: Nutrition and lifestyle for a healthy pregnancy outcome, *Journal of the American Dietetic Association* 102 (2002): 1479–1490; J. M. Baeten, E. A. Bukusi, and M. Lambe, Pregnancy complications and outcomes among overweight and obese nulliparous women, *American Journal of Public Health* 91 (2001): 436–440.

10. National Institutes of Health, Risk of newborn heart defects increases with maternal obesity, April 2010, available at http://www.nichd.nih.gov/news/resources/links/Pages/transcript040710.aspx.

11. M. C. Lacroix and coauthors, Placental growth hormones, *Endocrine* 1 (2002): 73–79.

12. A. J. Drake and B. R. Walker, The intergenerational effects of fetal programming: Non-genomic mechanisms for the inheritance of low birth weight and cardiovascular risk, *Journal of Endocrinology* 180 (2004): 1–16.

13. A. Singhal and coauthors, Programming of lean body mass: A link between birth weight, obesity, and cardiovascular disease? *American Journal of Clinical Nutrition* 77 (2003): 726–730; B. E. Birgisdottir and coauthors, Size at birth and glucose intolerance in a relatively genetically homogeneous, high-birth weight population, *American Journal of Clinical Nutrition* 76 (2002): 399–403.

14. M. F. Picciano, Pregnancy and lactation: Physiological adjustments, nutritional requirements and the role of dietary supplements, *Journal of Nutrition* 133 (2003): 1997S–2002S; J. C. King, Physiology of pregnancy and nutrient metabolism, *American Journal of Clinical Nutrition* 71 (2000): 1218S–1225S.

15. Standing Committee on the Scientific Evaluation of Dietary Reference Intakes, Food and Nutrition Board, Institute of Medicine, *Dietary Reference Intakes for Energy, Carbohydrate, Fiber, Fat, Fatty Acids, Cholesterol, Protein, and Amino Acids* (Washington, D.C.: National Academies Press, 2002), pp. 5-59–5-64.

16. R. M. Pitkin, Energy in pregnancy, *American Journal of Clinical Nutrition* 69 (1999): 583; L. E. Kopp-Hoolihan and coauthors, Longitudinal assessment of energy balance in well-nourished, pregnant women, *American Journal of Clinical Nutrition* 69 (1999): 697–704.

17. S. J. Otto and coauthors, Changes in the maternal essential fatty acid profile during early pregnancy and the relation of the profile to diet, *American Journal of Clinical Nutrition* 73 (2001): 302–307; G. Hornstra, Essential fatty acids in mothers and their neonates, *American Journal of Clinical Nutrition* 71 (2000): 1262S–1269S.

18. Health Canada, *It's Your Health—Folic Acid and Birth Defects*, available at http://www.hc-sc.gc.ca/hl-vs/iyh-vsv/med/folic-folique-eng.php.

19. Standing Committee on the Scientific Evaluation of Dietary Reference Intakes, Food and Nutrition Board, Institute of Medicine, *Dietary Reference Intakes for Thiamin, Riboflavin, Niacin, Vitamin B6, Folate, Vitamin B12, Pantothenic Acid, Biotin, and Choline* (Washington, D.C.: National Academies Press, 1998), pp. 196–305.

20. H. McNulty, G. J. Cuskelly, and M. Ward, Response of red blood cell folate to intervention: Implications for folate recommendations for the prevention of neural tube defects, *American Journal of Clinical Nutrition* 71 (2000): 1308S–1311S.

21. J. G. Ray and coauthors, Association of neural tube defects and folic acid fortification in Canada, *Lancet* 360 (2002): 2047–2048.

22. Standing Committee on the Scientific Evaluation of Dietary Reference Intakes, Food and Nutrition Board, Institute of Medicine, 1998 [see reference 19].

23. A. Prentice, Maternal calcium metabolism and bone mineral status, *American Journal of Clinical Nutrition* 71 (2000): 1312S–1316S.

24. K. O. O'Brien and coauthors, Maternal iron status influences iron transfer to the fetus during the third trimester of pregnancy, *American Journal of Clinical Nutrition* 77 (2003): 924–930.

25. J. C. King, Determinants of maternal zinc status during pregnancy, *American Journal of Clinical Nutrition* 71 (2000): 1334S–1343S.

26. C. S. Chung and coauthors, A single 60-mg iron dose decreases zinc absorption in lactating women, *Journal of Nutrition* 132 (2002): 1903–1905; J. C. King, 2000 [see reference 25].

27. Position of the American Dietetic Association, 2002 [see reference 9].

28. M. M. Werler and coauthors, Multivitamin supplementation and risk of birth defects, *American Journal of Epidemiology* 150 (1999): 675–682.

29. Public Health Agency of Canada, Canada Prenatal Nutrition Program (CPNP), available at http://www.phac-aspc.gc.ca/hp-ps/dca-dea/prog-ini/cpnp-pcnp/.

30. Public Health Agency of Canada, Canadian Prenatal Nutrition Program Projects Online, available at http://cpnp-pcnp.phac-aspc.gc.ca/index-eng.php.

31. B. Abrams, S. L. Altman, and K. E. Pickett, Pregnancy weight gain: Still controversial, *American Journal of Clinical Nutrition* 71 (2000): 1233S–1241S.

32. Position of the American Dietetic Association, 2002 [see reference 9].

33. R. Artal and M. O'Toole, Guidelines of the American College of Obstetricians and Gynecologists for exercise during pregnancy and the postpartum period, *British Journal of Sports Medicine* 37 (2003): 6–12; American College of Obstetricians and Gynecologists, Exercise during pregnancy and postpartum period, ACOG

Committee Opinion no. 267, *Obstetrics and Gynecology* 99 (2002): 171–173.

34. American College of Obstetricians and Gynecologists, 2002 [see reference 33].

35. K. Kullick and L. Dugan, Exercise and pregnancy, in C. A. Rosenbloom, ed., *Sports Nutrition: A Guide for the Professional Working with Active People*, 3rd ed. (Chicago: The American Dietetic Association, 2000), pp. 463–476.

36. M. Kihlstrand and coauthors, Water-gymnastics reduced the intensity of back/low back pain in pregnant women, *Acta Obstetrica Gynecologica Scandinavica* 78 (1999): 180–185.

37. Society of Obstetricians and Gynaecologists of Canada, *Statistics on Canadian Teen Pregnancies*, available at http://www .sexualityandu.ca/sexual-health/statistics1/ statistics-on-canadian-teen-pregnancies.

38. D. S. Elfenbein and M. E. Felice, Adolescent pregnancy, *Pediatric Clinics of North America* 50 (2003): 781–800, viii; R. J. Trissler, The child within: A guide to nutrition counseling for pregnant teens, *Journal of the American Dietetic Association* 99 (1999): 916–917.

39. D. J. Hunt and coauthors, Effects of nutrition education programs on anthropometric measurements and pregnancy outcomes of adolescents, *Journal of the American Dietetic Association* 102 (2002): S100–S102.

40. J. M. Lightwood, C. S. Phibbs, and S. A. Glantz, Short-term health and economic benefits of smoking cessation: Low birth weight, *Pediatrics* 104 (1999): 1312–1320.

41. American Academy of Pediatrics, Task Force on Infant Sleep Position and Sudden Infant Death Syndrome, Changing concepts of sudden infant death syndrome: Implication for infant sleeping environment and sleep position, *Pediatrics* 105 (2000): 650–656.

42. J. R. DiFranza, C. A. Aligne, and M. Weitzman, Prenatal and postnatal environmental tobacco smoke exposure and children's health, *Pediatrics* 113 (2004): 1007–1015; K. I. McMartin and coauthors, Lung tissue concentrations of nicotine in sudden infant death syndrome (SIDS), *Journal of Pediatrics* 140 (2002): 205–209.

43. S. J. Ventura and coauthors, Trends and variations in smoking during pregnancy and low birth weight: Evidence from the birth certificate, 1990–2000, *Pediatrics* 111 (2003): 1176–1180.

44. Position of the American Dietetic Association, 2002 [see reference 9].

45. M. S. Scher, G. A. Richardson, and N. L. Day, Effects of prenatal cocaine/crack and other drug exposure on electroencephalographic sleep studies at birth and one year, *Pediatrics* 105 (2000): 39–48.

46. L. T. Singer and coauthors, Cognitive and motor outcomes of cocaine-exposed infants, *Journal of the American Medical Association* 287 (2002): 1952–1960; E. S. Bandstra and coauthors, Intrauterine growth of full-term infants: Impact of prenatal cocaine exposure, *Pediatrics* 108 (2001): 1309–1319.

47. S. E. Schober and coauthors, Blood mercury levels in US children and women of childbearing age, 1999–2000, *Journal of the American Medical Association* 289 (2003): 1667–1674; A. Gomaa and coauthors, Maternal bone lead as an independent risk factor for fetal neurotoxicity: A prospective study, *Pediatrics* 110 (2002): 110–118.

48. Environment Canada, *Mercury and the Environment: Environment and Health—Health Concerns*, available at http://www .ec.gc.ca/mercure-mercury/default .asp?lang=En&n=0EB35C98-1.

49. Centers for Disease Control. Preventing Foodborne Illness: Listeriosis. available at http:// wonder.cdc.gov/wonder/prevguid/p0000005/ p0000005.asp.

50. Health Canada. Prenatal Nutrition Guidelines for Health Professionals—Background on Canada's Food Guide, available at http:// www.hc-sc.gc.ca/fn-an/pubs/nutrition/guide-prenatal-eng.php.

51. Health Canada, *Fact Sheet—Caffeine and Your Health*, available at http://www.hc-sc.gc.ca/hl-vs/ iyh-vsv/food-aliment/caffeine-eng.php.

52. J. W. Olney and coauthors, The enigma of fetal alcohol neurotoxicity, *Annals of Medicine* 34 (2002): 109–119; C. Ikonomidou and coauthors, Ethanol-induced apoptotic neurodegeneration and fetal alcohol syndrome, *Science* 287 (5455) (2000): 947–948.

53. Public Health Agency of Canada, *Fetal Alcohol Spectrum Disorder (FASD): A Framework for Action (2003)*, available at http://www.phac-aspc.gc.ca/ publicat/fasd-fw-etcaf-ca/index-eng.php.

54. M. J. O'Connor and coauthors, Psychiatric illness in a clinical sample of children with prenatal alcohol exposure, *American Journal of Drug and Alcohol Abuse* 28 (2002): 743–754; B. Sooc and coauthors, Prenatal alcohol exposure and childhood behavior at age 6 to 7 years: Dose-response effect, *Pediatrics* 108 (2001): e34.

55. Alcohol use among women of childbearing age—United States 1991–1999, *Morbidity and Mortality Weekly Report* 51 (2002): 273–276.

56. T. S. Naimi and coauthors, Binge drinking in the preconception period and the risk of unintended pregnancy: Implications for women and their children, *Pediatrics* 111 (2003): 1136–1141.

57. Committee on Substance Abuse and Committee on Children with Disabilities, American Academy of Pediatrics, Fetal alcohol syndrome and alcohol-related neuro-developmental disorders, *Pediatrics* 106 (2000): 358–361.

58. U. Kesmodel and coauthors, Moderate alcohol intake during pregnancy and the risk of stillbirth and death in the first year of life, *American Journal of Epidemiology* 155 (2002): 305–312.

59. Committee on Substance Abuse and Committee on Children with Disabilities, 2000 [see reference 57].

60. Position statement from the American Diabetes Association: Gestational diabetes mellitus, *Diabetes Care* 26 (2003): S103–S105.

61. Report of the Expert Committee on the Diagnosis and Classification of Diabetes Mellitus, *Diabetes Care* 26 (2003): S5–S20.

62. Position statement from the American Diabetes Association, 2003 [see reference 60].

63. Canadian Diabetes Association Clinical Practice Guidelines Expert Committee, Gestational diabetes mellitus, in Canadian Diabetes Association 2003 Clinical Practice Guidelines for the Prevention and Management of Diabetes in Canada, *Journal of the Canadian Diabetes Association* 27 (Suppl. 2) (2003): s99–s105.

64. B. M. Sibai, Diagnosis and management of gestational hypertension and preeclampsia, *Obstetrics and Gynecology* 102 (2003): 181–192; R. Skjaerven, A. J. Wilcox, and R. T. Lie, The interval between pregnancies and the risk of preeclampsia, *New England Journal of Medicine* 346 (2002): 33–38.

65. M. S. Esplin and coauthors, Paternal and maternal components of the predisposition to preeclampsia, *New England Journal of Medicine* 344 (2001): 867–872.

66. D. Maine, Role of nutrition in the prevention of toxemia, *American Journal of Clinical Nutrition* 72 (2000): 298S–300S.

67. J. Villar and coauthors, Nutritional interventions during pregnancy for the prevention or treatment of maternal morbidity and preterm delivery: An overview of randomized controlled trials, *Journal of Nutrition* 133 (2003): 1606S–1625S.

68. L. M. Paton and coauthors, Pregnancy and lactation have no long-term deleterious effect on measures of bone mineral in healthy women: A twin study, *American Journal of Clinical Nutrition* 77 (2003): 707–714.

69. G. Kac and coauthors, Breast feeding and postpartum weight retention in a cohort of Brazilian women, *American Journal of Clinical Nutrition* 79 (2004): 487–493; L. N. Haiek and coauthors, Postpartum weight loss and infant feeding, *Journal of the American Board of Family Practice* 14 (2001): 85–94.

70. M. A. McCrory, Does dieting during lactation put infant growth at risk? *Nutrition Reviews* 59 (2001): 18–27; C. A. Lovelady and coauthors, The effect of weight loss in overweight, lactating women on the growth of their infants, *New England Journal of Medicine* 342 (2000): 449–453.

71. S. Ito and A. Lee, Drug excretion into breast milk—Overview, *Advanced Drug Delivery Reviews* 55 (2003): 617–627; Committee on Drugs, American Academy of Pediatrics, The transfer of drugs and other chemicals into human milk, *Pediatrics* 108 (2001): 776–789.

72. R. M. Lawrence and R. A. Lawrence, Given the benefit of breastfeeding, what contraindications exist? *Pediatric Clinics of North America* 48 (2001): 235–251.

73. J. S. Wang, Q. R. Zhu, and X. H. Wang, Breastfeeding does not pose any additional risk of immunoprophylaxis failure on infants of HBV carrier mothers, *International Journal of Clinical Practice* 57 (2003): 100–102; J. B. Hill and coauthors, Risk of hepatitis B transmission in breast-fed infants of chronic hepatitis B carriers, *Obstetrics and Gynecology* 99 (2002): 1049–1052; P. Ormrod, Tuberculosis in pregnancy and the puerperium, *Thorax* 56 (2001): 494–499.

74. R. Nduati and coauthors, Effect of breastfeeding and formula feeding on transmission of HIV-1: A randomized clinical trial, *Journal of the American Medical Association* 283 (2000): 1167–1174.

75. Canadian Paediatric Society, Dietitians of Canada, and Health Canada, *Nutrition for Healthy Term Infants* (Ottawa, ON: Minister of Public Works and Government Services, 2005).

76. J. Humphrey and P. Iliff, Is breast not best? Feeding babies born to HIV-positive mothers: Bringing balance to a complex issue, *Nutrition Reviews* 59 (2001): 119–127.

77. Canadian Paediatric Society, Routine administration of vitamin K to newborns, available at http://www.cps.ca/ENGLISH/statements/FN/fn97-01.htm.

78. Committee on Nutrition, American Academy of Pediatrics, *Pediatric Nutrition Handbook*, 5th ed., ed. R. E. Kleinman (Elk Grove, IL: American Academy of Pediatrics, 2004), pp. 110–111.

79. Health Canada, *Exclusive Breastfeeding Duration—2004 Health Canada Recommendation*, available at http://www.hc-sc.gc.ca/fn-an/nutrition/infant-nourisson/recom/index-eng.php.

80. Position of the American Dietetic Association: Breaking the barriers to breastfeeding, *Journal of the American Dietetic Association* 101 (2001): 1213–1220; Committee on Nutrition, American Academy of Pediatrics, Hypoallergenic infant formulas, *Pediatrics* 106 (2000): 346–349.

81. M. S. Kramer and R. Kakuma, Optimal duration of exclusive breastfeeding, *Cochrane Database of Systematic Reviews* 1 (2002): CD003517.

82. Health Canada, *Novel Food Information— DHASCO® and ARASCO® as Sources of Docosahexaenoic Acid and Arachidonic Acid in Infant Formulas*, available at http://www.hc-sc.gc.ca/fn-an/gmf-agm/appro/dhasco_arasco_e.html.

83. I. B. Helland and coauthors, Maternal supplementation with very-long-chain n-3 fatty acids during pregnancy and lactation augments children's IQ at 4 years of age, *Pediatrics* 111 (2003): e39; N. Auestad and coauthors, Growth and development in term infants fed long-chain polyunsaturated fatty acids: A double-masked, randomized, parallel, prospective, multivariate study, *Pediatrics* 108 (2001): 372–381; J. W. Anderson, B. M. Johnstone, and D. T. Remley, Breast-feeding and cognitive development: A meta-analysis, *American Journal of Clinical Nutrition* 70 (1999): 525–535.

84. W. W. Koo, Efficacy and safety of docosahexaenoic acid and arachidonic acid addition to infant formulas: Can one buy better vision and intelligence? *Journal of the American College of Nutrition* 22 (2003): 101–107; E. E. Birch and coauthors, A randomized controlled trial of long-chain polyunsaturated fatty acid supplementation of formula in term infants after weaning at 6 wk of age, *American Journal of Clinical Nutrition* 75 (2002): 570–580.

85. B. Lonnerdal, Nutritional and physiologic significance of human milk proteins, *American Journal of Clinical Nutrition* 77 (2003): 1537S–1543S.

86. Canadian Paediatric Society, Canadian Paediatric Surveillance Program—2012 Results, available at http://www.cpsp.cps.ca/publications.

87. Health Canada, *Vitamin D recommendation for Breastfed Infants—2004 Health Canada Recommendation*, publication no. 4828, available at http://www.hc-sc.gc.ca/fn-an/nutrition/infant-nourisson/recom/index-eng.php.

88. Position of the American Dietetic Association, 2001 [see reference 80].

89. J. Raisler and coauthors, Breast-feeding and infant illness: A dose-response relationship? *American Journal of Public Health* 89 (1999): 25–30.

90. M. Gdalevich, D. Mimouni, and M. Mimouni, Breastfeeding and the risk of bronchial asthma in childhood: A systematic review with meta-analysis of prospective studies, *Journal of Pediatrics* 139 (2001): 261–266; S. Arifeen and coauthors, Exclusive breastfeeding reduces acute respiratory infection and diarrhea deaths among infants in Dhaka slums, *Pediatrics* 108 (2001): 309–320.

91. C. G. Owen and coauthors, Infant feeding and blood cholesterol: A study in adolescents and a systematic review, *Pediatrics* 110 (2002): 597–608.

92. E. L. Mortensen and coauthors, The association between duration of breastfeeding and adult intelligence, *Journal of the American Medical Association* 287 (2002): 2365–2371.

93. A. Jain, J. Concato, and J. M. Leventhal, How good is the evidence linking breastfeeding and intelligence? *Pediatrics* 109 (2002): 1044–1053.

94. Committee on Nutrition, American Academy of Pediatrics, 2004 [see reference 78].

95. Health Canada, *Nutrition for Healthy Term Infants—Statement of the Joint Working Group: Canadian Paediatric Society, Dietitians of Canada and Health Canada*, available at http://www.hc-sc.gc.ca/fn-an/nutrition/infant-nourisson/recom/index-eng.php.

96. Committee on Nutrition, American Academy of Pediatrics, Iron fortification of infant formulas, *Pediatrics* 104 (1999): 119–123.

97. Canadian Paediatric Society, Weaning from the breast, *Paediatrics & Child Health* 9 (2004): 249–253, available at http://www.cps.ca/english/statements/CP/cp04-01.htm.

98. Centers for Disease Control and Prevention, Nonfatal choking-related episodes among children—United States, 2001, *Morbidity and Mortality Weekly Report* 51 (2002): 945–948.

Consumer Corner 13

1. Canadian Food Inspection Agency, *Letter to Industry: Requirements Related to Nutrition Information and Nutrition and Health Claims for Infant Formula*, January 8, 2007, available at http://www.inspection.gc.ca/english/fssa/labeti/inform/20070112e.shtml.

2. I. Ozturk, N. Votto, and J. M. Leventhal, The timing and predictors of the early termination of breastfeeding, *Pediatrics* 107 (2001): 543–548.

3. B. L. Phillip and coauthors, Baby-friendly hospital initiative improves breastfeeding initiation rates in a U.S. hospital setting, *Pediatrics* 108 (2001): 677–681.

4. R. Li and coauthors, Prevalence of breastfeeding in the United States: The 2001 National Immunization Survey, *Pediatrics* 111 (2003): 1198–1201.

Controversy 13

1. M. Shields, *Measured Obesity—Overweight Canadian Children and Adolescents. Nutrition: Findings from the CCHS Issue no. 1*, Statistics Canada, Catalogue no. 82620 MWE2005001, available at http://www.statcan.gc.ca/pub/82-620-m/2005001/pdf/4193660-eng.pdf.

2. M. Kohn and M. Booth, The worldwide epidemic of obesity in adolescents, *Adolescent Medicine* 14 (2003): 1–9; L. S. Lieberman, Dietary, evolutionary, and modernizing influences on the prevalence of type 2 diabetes, *Annual Review of Nutrition* 23 (2003): 345–377.

3. A. Must, Does overweight in childhood have an impact on adult health? *Nutrition Reviews* 61 (2003): 139–142; D. S. Freedman, Clustering of coronary heart disease risk factors among obese children, *Journal of Pediatric Endocrinology and Metabolism* 15 (2002): 1099–1108.

4. J. P. Kaplan, C. T. Liverman, and V. I. Kraak, eds., *Preventing Childhood Obesity: Health in the Balance* (Washington, D.C.: National Academies Press, 2005), available at http://www.nap.edu/openbook.php?isbn=0309091969; M. I. Goran, Metabolic precursors and effects of obesity in children: A decade of progress, 1990–1999, *American Journal of Clinical Nutrition* 73 (2001): 158–171.

5. A. N. Jeffery and coauthors, Parents' awareness of overweight in themselves and their children: Cross-sectional study within a cohort (EarlyBird 21), *British Medical Journal* 330 (2005): 23–24; S. T. Borra and coauthors, Developing health messages: Qualitative studies with children, parents, and teachers help identify communications opportunities for healthful lifestyles and the prevention of obesity, *Journal of the American Dietetic Association* 103 (2003): 721–728.

6. R. Weiss and coauthors, Obesity and the metabolic syndrome in children and adolescents, *New England Journal of Medicine* 350 (2004): 2362–2374.

7. M. L. Story and coauthors, Demographic and lifestyle factors associated with body mass index among children and adolescents, *International Journal of Food Sciences and Nutrition* 54 (2003): 491–503.

8. J. M. de Castro, Genes, the environment, and the control of food intake, *British Journal of Nutrition* 92 (2004): S59–S62.

9. G. Wu and coauthors, Maternal nutrition and fetal development, *Journal of Nutrition* 134 (2004): 2169–2172.

10. R. Martorell, A. D. Stein, and D. G. Schroeder, Early nutrition and later adiposity, *Journal of Nutrition* 131 (2001): 874S–880S.

11. A. J. Drake and B. R. Walker, The intergenerational effects of fetal programming: Non-genomic mechanisms for the inheritance of low birth weight and cardiovascular risk, *Journal of Endocrinology* 189 (2004): 1–16.

12. M. Hanson and coauthors, Report on the 2nd World Congress on Fetal Origins of Adult Disease, Brighton, U.K., *Pediatric Research* 55 (2004): 894–897; J. V. Neel, The "thrifty genotype" in 1998, *Nutrition Reviews* 57 (1999): S2–S9.

13. A. J. Drake and B. R. Walker, 2004 [see reference 11].

14. D. Barker, The midwife, the coincidence, and the hypothesis, *British Medical Journal* 327 (2003): 1428–1430.

15. M. W. Gillman and coauthors, Risk of overweight among adolescents who were breastfed as infants, *Journal of the American Medical Association* 285 (2001): 2461–2467.

16. K. G. Dewey, Is breastfeeding protective against childhood obesity? *Journal of Human Lactation* 19 (2004): 9–18.

17. M. L. Hediger and coauthors, Association between infant breastfeeding and overweight in young children, *Journal of the American Medical Association* 285 (2001): 2453–2460.

18. T. M. Cutting and coauthors, Like mother, like daughter: Familial patterns of overweight are mediated by mothers' dietary disinhibition, *American Journal of Clinical Nutrition* 69 (1999): 608–613.

19. S. Kranz, A. M. Siega-Riz, and A. H. Herring, Changes in diet quality of American preschoolers between 1977 and 1998, *American Journal of Public Health* 94 (2004): 1525–1530; S. J. Nielsen, A. M. Siega-Riz, and B. M. Popkin, Trends in energy intake in U.S. between 1977 and 1996: Similar shifts seen across age groups, *Obesity Research* 10 (2002): 370–378.

20. M. L. Story and coauthors, 2003 [see reference 7].

21. L. Harnack, J. Stang, and M. Story, Soft drink consumption among U.S. children and adolescents: Nutritional consequences, *Journal of the American Dietetic Association* 99 (1999): 436–441.

22. D. S. Ludwig, K. E. Peterson, and L. S. Gortmaker, Relation between consumption of sugar-sweetened drinks and childhood obesity: A prospective, observational analysis, *Lancet* 357 (2001): 505–508; R. P. Troiano and coauthors, Energy and fat intakes of children and adolescents in the United States: Data from the National Health and Nutrition Examination Surveys, *American Journal of Clinical Nutrition* 72 (2000): 1343S–1353S.

23. M. H. Proctor and coauthors, Television viewing and change in body fat from preschool to early adolescence: The Framingham Children's Study, *International Journal of Obesity and Related Metabolic Disorders* 27 (2003): 827–833.

24. D. S. Ludwig and C. B. Ebbeling, Type 2 diabetes mellitus in children: Primary care and public health considerations, *Journal of the American Medical Association* 286 (2001): 1427–1430; American Diabetes Association, Type 2 diabetes in children and adolescents, *Pediatrics* 105 (2000): 671–680.

25. R. Kohen-Avramoglu, A. Theriault, and K. Adeli, Emergence of the metabolic syndrome in childhood: An epidemiological overview and mechanistic link to dyslipidemia, *Clinical Biochemistry* 36 (2003): 413–420.

26. S. Li and coauthors, Childhood cardiovascular risk factors and carotid vascular changes in adulthood: The Bogalusa Heart Study, *Journal of the American Medical Association* 290 (2003): 2271–2276; K. B. Keller and L. Lemberg, Obesity and the metabolic syndrome, *American Journal of Clinical Care* 12 (2003): 167–170; H. C. McGill Jr. and coauthors, Origin of atherosclerosis in childhood and adolescence, *American Journal of Clinical Nutrition* 72 (2000): 1307S–1315S.

27. V. N. Muratova and coauthors, The relation of obesity to cardiovascular risk factors among children: The CARDIAC project, *West Virginia Medical Journal* 98 (2002): 263–267.

28. S. C. Couch and coauthors, Rapid westernization of children's blood cholesterol in 3 countries: Evidence for nutrient-gene interactions? *American Journal of Clinical Nutrition* 72 (2000): 1266S–1274S.

29. O. Fiedland and coauthors, Obesity and lipid profiles in children and adolescents, *Journal of Pediatric Endocrinology and Metabolism* 15 (2002): 1011–1016; T. Dwyer and coauthors, Syndrome X in 8-y-old Australian children: Stronger associations with current body fatness than with infant size or growth, *International Journal of Obesity and Related Metabolic Disorders* 26 (2002): 1301–1309.

30. B. Glowinska, M. Urban, and A. Koput, Cardiovascular risk factors in children with obesity, hypertension and diabetes: Lipoprotein (a) levels and body mass index correlate with family history of cardiovascular disease, *European Journal of Pediatrics* 161 (2002): 511–518.

31. A. Wiegman and coauthors, Family history and cardiovascular risk in familial hypercholesterolemia: Data in more than 1000 children, *Circulation* 107 (2003): 1473–1478.

32. American Academy of Pediatrics, Physicians Recommend All Children, Ages 9–11, Be Screened for Cholesterol (November 2011), available at http://www.aap.org/en-us/about-the-aap/aap-press-room/pages/Physicians-Recommend-all-Children,-Ages-9-11,-Be-Screened-for-Cholesterol.aspx.

33. T. Dwyer and coauthors, 2002 [see reference 29].

34. C. P. M. Leeson and coauthors, Duration of breast feeding and arterial distensibility in early adult life: Population based study, *British Medical Journal* 322 (2001): 643–647.

35. C. H. Fall and coauthors, Relation of infant feeding to adult serum cholesterol concentration and death from ischaemic heart disease, *British Medical Journal* 304 (1992): 427–431, as cited by Y. S. Chong; Human milk is still best, letter, *British Medical Journal* 327 (2003): 683.

36. M. R. Savoca and coauthors, The association of caffeinated beverages with blood pressure in adolescents, *Archives of Pediatrics and Adolescent Medicine* 158 (2004): 473–477.

37. U. S. Sieber and coauthors, How good is blood pressure control among treated hypertensive children and adolescents? *Journal of Hypertension* 21 (2003): 633–637.

38. Committee on Nutrition, American Academy of Pediatrics, 2003 [see reference 11].

39. S. de Jongh and coauthors, Efficacy and safety of statin therapy in children with familial hypercholesterolemia: A randomized, double-blind, placebo-controlled trial with simvastatin, *Circulation* 106 (2002): 2231–2237.

40. R. E. Olson, Is it wise to restrict fat in the diets of children? *Journal of the American Dietetic Association* 100 (2000): 28–32; E. Satter, A moderate view on fat restriction, *Journal of the American Dietetic Association* 100 (2000): 32–36; L. A. Lytle, In defense of a low-fat diet for healthy children, *Journal of the American Dietetic Association* 100 (2000): 39–41.

41. E. Obarzanek and coauthors, Long-term safety and efficacy of a cholesterol-lowering diet in children with elevated low-density lipoprotein cholesterol: Seven-year results of the Dietary Intervention Study in Children (DISC), *Pediatrics* 107 (2001): 256–264; L. Rask-Nissila and coauthors, Neurological development of 5-year-old children receiving a low-saturated fat, low cholesterol diet since infancy: A randomized controlled study, *Journal of the American Medical Association* 284 (2000): 993–1000; R. M. Lauer and coauthors, Efficacy and safety of lowering dietary intake of total fat, saturated fat, and cholesterol in children with elevated LDL cholesterol: The Dietary Intervention Study in Children, *American Journal of Clinical Nutrition* 72 (2000): 1332S–1342S.

42. J. Orlet Fisher, B. J. Rolls, and L. L. Birch, Children's bite size and intake of an entree are far greater with large portions than with age-appropriate or self-selected portions, *American Journal of Clinical Nutrition* 77 (2003): 1164–1170.

43. J. Hurley and B. Liebman, Kids' cuisine: "What would you like with your fries?" *Nutrition Action Healthletter* 31 (2004): 12–15.

44. E. Hobin and coauthors, Nutritional quality of food items on fast-food 'kids' menus': Comparisons across Countries and Companies, Public Health Nutrition, published online October 22, 2013, doi:10.1017/S1368980013002498, available at http://journals.cambridge.org/download.php?file=%2FPHN%2FS1368980013002498a.pdf&code=09b982e618b4a25a1e3a1a9fe14560df; N. Hellmich, Children's menus hold the fries, dish up broccoli, *USA Today*, May 26, 2004, available at http://www.usatoday.com/news/health/2004-05-26-kids-menus_x.htm.

45. S. M. Phillips and coauthors, Dairy food consumption and body weight and fatness studied longitudinally over the adolescent period, *International Journal of Obesity and Related Metabolic Disorders* 27 (2003): 1106–1113; C. M. Weaver and C. J. Boushey, Milk—Good for bones, good for reducing childhood obesity? *Journal of the American Dietetic Association* 103 (2003): 1598–1599; J. D. Skinner and coauthors, Longitudinal calcium intake is negatively related to children's body fat indexes, *Journal of the American Dietetic Association* 103 (2003): 1626–1631.

46. J. A. Welsh and coauthors, Overweight among low income preschool children associated with the consumption of sweet drinks: Missouri, 1999–2002, *Pediatrics* 115 (2005): 223–229; J. James and coauthors, Preventing childhood obesity by reducing consumption of carbonated drinks: Cluster randomised controlled trial, *British Medical Journal* 328 (2004): 1236.

47. R. Novotny and coauthors, Dairy intake is associated with lower body fat and soda intake

with greater weight in adolescent girls, *Journal of Nutrition* 134 (2004): 1905–1909.

48. G. A. Bray, S. J. Nielsen, and B. M. Popkin, Consumption of high-fructose corn syrup in beverages may play a role in the epidemic of obesity, *American Journal of Clinical Nutrition* 79 (2004): 537–543.

49. K. S. Woo and coauthors, Effects of diet and exercise on obesity-related vascular dysfunction in children, *Circulation* 109 (2004): 1981–1986.

50. Trends in cigarette smoking among high school students—United States, 1991–2001, *Morbidity and Mortality Weekly Report* 51 (2002): 409–412.

51. Youth tobacco surveillance—United States, 2000, *Morbidity and Mortality Weekly Report* 50 (2001): entire supplement.

52. A. J. Drake and B. R. Walker [see reference 11].

53. P. Wilson and coauthors, The prevention and treatment of childhood obesity, *Quality and Safety in Health Care* 12 (2003): 65–74.

54. S. M. Gross and B. Cinelli, Coordinated school health program and dietetics professionals: Partners in promoting healthful eating, *Journal of the American Dietetic Association* 104 (2004): 793–798.

55. J. O. Fisher and coauthors, Parental influences on young girls' fruit and vegetable, micronutrient, and fat intakes, *Journal of the American Dietetic Association* 102 (2002): 58–64.

56. R. Lowry and coauthors, Recent trends in participation in physical education among U.S. high school students, *Journal of School Health* 71 (2001): 145–152; Committee on Sports Medicine and Fitness and Committee on School Health, Physical fitness and activity in schools, *Pediatrics* 105 (2000): 1156–1157.

57. A. Moag-Stahlberg, A. Miles, and M. Marcello, What kids say they do and what parents think kids are doing: The ADAF/Knowledge Networks 2003 Family Nutrition and Physical Activity Study, *Journal of the American Dietetic Association* 103 (2003): 1541–1546.

14 Child, Teen, and Older Adult

Do You Ever . . .

Or will you ever provide nourishment to children?

Suspect that symptoms you feel may be from a food allergy?

Think that teenagers are old enough to decide for themselves what to eat?

Wonder whether nutrition can help you live longer?

Keep Reading . . .

Learning Objectives

After completing this chapter, you should be able to

LO 14.1 Discuss how a toddler's nutritional needs differ from an adult's needs.

LO 14.2 Distinguish among a food allergy, a food intolerance, and a food aversion, and describe how they can impact the diet.

LO 14.3 Explain ways in which a teenager's choice of soft drinks/energy drinks/sports beverages over milk or soy milk may jeopardize nutritional health.

LO 14.4 Discuss the importance of physical activity in the later years.

LO 14.5 Outline food-related factors that can predict malnutrition in older adults.

LO 14.6 Describe several specific drug–nutrient interactions, and name some herbs that may interfere with medication.

LO 14.7 Design a healthy meal plan for an elderly widower with a fixed income.

Contents

To grow and to function well in the adult world, children need a firm background of sound eating habits, which begin during babyhood with the introduction of solid foods. At that point, the person's nutrition story has just begun; the plot thickens. Nutrient needs change throughout life into old age, depending on the rate of growth, gender, activities, and many other factors. Nutrient needs also vary from individual to individual, but generalizations are possible and useful.

Seven out of 10 children aged 4 to 8 years in Canada do not meet the minimum recommendation of five servings of vegetables and fruit per day, and 37 percent aged 4 to 9 years do not obtain the recommended two to three servings of milk products each day.*, [1] The consequences of such diets may not be evident to the casual observer, but nutritionists know that nutrient deficiencies during growth often have far-reaching effects on physical and mental development. Anyone who cares about the children in their lives, now or in the future, would profit from knowing how to provide the nutrients children require to reach their potential.

Early and Middle Childhood

Imagine growing 25 centimetres (10 in.) taller in just one year, as the average healthy infant does during the first dramatic year of life. At age 1, infants have just learned to stand and toddle, and growth has slowed by half; by age 2, they can take long strides with solid confidence and are learning to run, jump, and climb. These new accomplishments reflect the accumulation of a larger mass, greater density of bone and muscle tissue, and refinement of nervous system coordination. These same growth trends, a lengthening of the long bones and an increase in musculature, continue until adolescence, but unevenly and more slowly. To support healthy growth and development, there are now "Canadian Physical Activity Guidelines for the Early

---

*References are listed at the end of the chapter.

Years—0–4 Years" and "Canadian Physical Activity Guidelines for Children—5–11 Years" (see http://www.csep.ca/english/view.asp?x=804).

Mentally, too, the child is making rapid advances, and proper nutrition is critical to normal brain development. The child malnourished at age 3 often demonstrates diminished mental capacities at age 11, even when other life circumstances are comparable to those of peers.[2]

Feeding a Healthy Young Child

At no time in life does the human diet change faster than during the second year.[3] From 12 to 24 months, a child's diet changes from infant foods consisting of mostly formula or breast milk to mostly modified adult foods. This doesn't mean, of course, that milk loses its importance in the toddler's diet—it remains a central source of calcium, vitamin D, protein, and other nutrients. Nevertheless, the rapid growth and changing body composition (see Figure 14–1) during this remarkable period demand more nutrients than can be provided by milk alone. Further, the toddling years are marked by bustling activity made possible by new muscle tissue and refined neuromuscular coordination. To support both their activity and growth, toddlers need nutrients and plenty of them. Note that Health Canada conducted an open consultation on the draft statement *Nutrition for Healthy Term Infants—Recommendations from Six to 24 Months* in the spring of 2013 (http://www.hc-sc.gc.ca/fn-an/consult/infant-nourrisson6-24/recommendations/index-eng.php), with expected updated guidance for this growth period in 2014.

Energy and Protein   An infant's appetite decreases markedly near the first birthday and fluctuates thereafter. At times children seem to be insatiable, and at other times they seem to live on air and water. Parents and other caregivers need not worry: given a selection of nutritious foods and limited treats, internal appetite regulation in children of normal weight guarantees that their overall energy intakes will be right for each stage of growth. This ideal situation depends upon the restriction

Figure 14–1

Composition of Weight Gain: Infants and Toddlers

These graphs demonstrate that a young infant deposits much more fat than lean tissue, but a toddler deposits more lean than fat. Water follows lean tissue, demonstrated by the water gains in the toddler. You can see that the body shape of a one-year-old (left photo) changes dramatically by age 2 (right photo). The two-year-old has lost much baby fat; the muscles (especially in the back, buttocks, and legs) have firmed and strengthened; and the leg bones have lengthened.

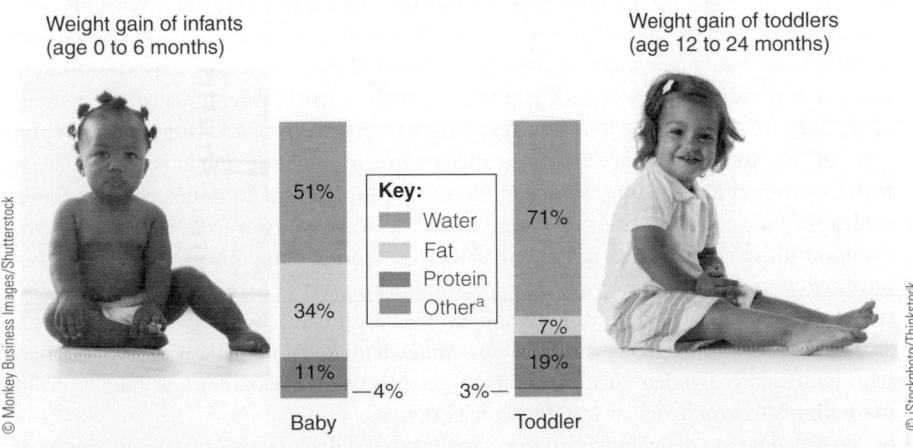

Weight gain of infants (age 0 to 6 months)

Weight gain of toddlers (age 12 to 24 months)

Key:
Water
Fat
Protein
Other[a]

51%
34%
11%
—4%
Baby

71%
7%
19%
3%—
Toddler

[a]"Other" consists of carbohydrate and minerals.

Source: Date from K.L McConahy and M.F. Picciano, How to grow a healthy toddler—12 to 24 months, Nutrition Today *38 (2003): 156–163.*

Details about appetite are found in Chapter 9.

of treats, however. Today's children too often consume foods high in added sugars, saturated fat, and Calories.[4] Faced with a tempting array of such foods, children may disregard internal satiety signals and overconsume Calories, inviting obesity. *Eating Well with Canada's Food Guide* provides safe and appropriate goals for the diets of healthy children two years of age and older and does not compromise nutrient intakes or growth.[5]

Individual children's energy needs vary widely, depending on their growth and physical activity. A one-year-old child needs about 800 Calories a day; at age 6, the child needs about 800 Calories more. By age 10, about 2,000 Calories a day supports normal growth and activity without causing excess storage of body fat. As children age, the total number of Calories needed increases, but per kilogram of body weight, the need declines from the extraordinarily high demand of infancy.

As for protein, total needs increase slightly as a child grows larger. On a kilogram-for-kilogram basis, however, the older child's need for protein is actually slightly lower than the younger child's (see the DRI values, inside front cover). Children's protein needs are well covered by a typical Canadian diet.

Carbohydrate and Fibre

Carbohydrate recommendations are based on glucose use by the brain. A one-year-old's brain is large for the size of the body, so the 130 grams of glucose demanded by the one-year-old falls in the adult range (see inside front cover).[6] Fibre recommendations derive from adult intakes and should be adjusted downward for children who are picky eaters and take in little energy.[7] The recommended fibre intake of one- to three-year-olds is about 19 grams/day and for four- to eight-year-olds it is 25 grams/day. Health Canada recently announced that "Canadian children may not be meeting their needs for fibre" (http://www.hc-sc.gc.ca/fn-an/surveill/nutrition/commun/art-nutr-child-enf-eng.php).[8]

Fat and Fatty Acids

Keeping fat intake within bounds helps control saturated fat and *trans* fatty acids and so may help protect children from developing early signs of adult diseases. Taken to extremes, however, a low-fat diet can lack essential nutrients and energy needed for growth. Children's small stomachs can hold only so much food, and fat provides a concentrated source of food energy needed for growth. In addition, essential fatty acids (i.e., essential omega-6 and omega-3 polyunsaturated fatty acids) are critical to proper growth and development of nerve, eye, and other tissues. The Dietary Recommended Intake (DRI) recommended ranges for total fat for children (see margin) and the specific fatty acids, linoleic and linolenic acids, in a child's diet assume that energy is sufficient.[9] Specific DRI recommendations for the various types of fat and fatty acids for all age groups, including children, are on the inside front cover.

Vitamins and Minerals

As a child grows larger, so does the demand for vitamins and minerals. On a kilogram-for-kilogram basis, a five-year-old's need for, say, vitamin A is about double the need of an adult man (see the margin). A balanced diet of nutritious foods can meet children's needs for these nutrients, with the notable exception of iron. Iron deficiency is a major problem worldwide; it occurs in a small percentage of toddlers one to two years of age in North America.[10] During the second year of life, toddlers progress from a diet of iron-rich infant foods such as breast milk, iron-fortified formula, and iron-fortified infant cereal to a diet of adult foods and iron-poor cow's milk. At the same time, the stores of iron from birth diminish. Compounding the problem is the variability in toddlers' appetites; some two-year-olds are finicky, while others prefer milk and juice and reject solid foods for a time.[11] All of these factors—switching to whole milk and unfortified foods, diminished iron stores, and unreliable food consumption—make iron deficiency likely at a time when iron is critically needed for normal brain growth and development. A later section comes back to iron deficiency and its consequences.

To prevent iron deficiency, children's foods must deliver from 7 to 10 milligrams of iron per day. To achieve this goal, snacks and meals should include iron-rich foods. Milk intake, though critical for the calcium needed for dense, healthy bones, should

The DRI Range for Total Fat Intakes for Children

- 30–40% of energy for children 1 to 3 years of age
- 25–35% of energy for children 4 to 18 years of age

• An 80-kg (175-lb) adult male needs 900 mg of vitamin A, or 11.25 mg/kg (5.2 mg per pound). A 20-kg (44-lb) five-year-old needs 500 mg of vitamin A, or 25 mg/kg (11.4 mg per pound).

not exceed daily recommendations to avoid displacing lean meats, fish, poultry, eggs, legumes, and whole-grain or enriched-grain products from the diet. Table 14–1 in the margin lists some iron-rich foods that many children like to eat.

Health Canada recently announced that based on Canadian Community Health Survey (CCHS) (2004) data for food and beverage intake (i.e., not including supplements), "The diets of children provide adequate amounts of most vitamins and minerals." However, they also added that the recommended intake of potassium for one- to three-year-olds is 3,000 milligrams/day and for four- to eight-year-olds it is 3,800 milligrams/day, stating "Canadian children may not be meeting their needs for potassium. . . ." In addition, it stated, "Canadian children's sodium intakes are associated with an increased risk of adverse health effects" (http://www.hc-sc.gc.ca/fn-an/surveill/nutrition/commun/art-nutr-child-enf-eng.php).

Recommended Number of Food Guide Servings for Young Children   The recommendations for preschool children, shown in Table 14–2, display one means of providing the needed nutrients to children. This plan designates a set number of servings from each food group rather than amounts in cups and grams as for adults (see Chapter 2). Children two to six years old need at least the specified number of Food Guide servings, but the serving sizes should vary according to age to keep Calorie intakes moderate.[12] Older children and adolescents need additional Food Guide servings. Children and adolescents derive the majority of their daily energy (55 percent of Calories) from carbohydrates, with most of their Calories (31 percent) coming from grain products.[13] Still, intakes of nutrients such as calcium and zinc often fall far below recommendations.[14]

Active, normal-weight children may enjoy occasional treats of high-Calorie but nutritious foods. From the milk group, ice cream or pudding is good now and then; from the grains group, whole-grain or enriched cakes, cookies, or doughnuts are an acceptable occasional addition to a balanced diet. These foods encourage a child to learn that pleasure in eating is important. Too many of these treats, however, can only lead to nutrient deficiencies, obesity, or both.

KEY POINT
- Children's nutrient needs reflect their stage of growth. For a healthy child, the DRI recommended intakes and Canada's Food Guide are intended to establish food patterns that provide adequate nourishment for growth while defending against obesity and chronic diseases.

Mealtimes and Snacking

The childhood years are the parents' last chance to influence their child's food choices. Appropriate eating habits and attitudes toward food, set in place by parents, can help future adults emerge with healthy eating habits that reduce risks of degenerative diseases in later life.

Children's Preferences   Children naturally like nutritious foods in all food groups, with one exception—vegetables, which some young children refuse. Here presentation and variety may be the key. The more nutritious choices presented to a child, the more likely the child will choose adequately.

Many children prefer vegetables that are mild flavoured, slightly undercooked and crunchy, bright coloured, and easy to eat. Cooked foods should be served warm, not hot, because a child's mouth is much more sensitive than an adult's. The mild flavours of carrots, peas, and corn are often preferred over sharper-tasting broccoli or turnips because a child has more taste buds. Smooth foods such as oatmeal, mashed potatoes, and pea soup are often well received.

Fear of new foods is practically universal among children. Suggesting, rather than commanding, that a child try small amounts of new foods at the beginning of a meal when the child is hungry seems to work best. Offering the child samples of new foods that adults are enjoying can stimulate the child's natural curiosity and often produces the desired result: the child tastes the new food. Forcing or bribing a child to eat certain foods, for example, by allowing extra television time as a reward for

---

Table 14–1

Iron-Rich Foods Kids Like[a]

Breads, Cereals, and Grains

Canned macaroni (½ c)
Canned spaghetti (½ c)
Cream of wheat (½ c)
Fortified dry cereals (30 g)[b]
Noodles, rice, or barley (½ c)
Tortillas (1 flour or whole wheat, 2 corn)
Whole-wheat, enriched, or fortified bread (1 slice)

Vegetables

Baked flavoured potato skins (½ skin)
Cooked mung bean sprouts or snow peas (½ c)[c]
Cooked mushrooms (½ c)
Green peas (½ c)
Mixed vegetable juice (1 c)

Fruit

Canned plums (3 plums)
Cooked dried apricots (¼ c)
Dried peaches (4 halves)
Raisins (1 tbs)

Meat and Legumes

Bean dip (¼ c)
Canned pork and beans (⅓)
Lean chopped roast beef or cooked ground beef (30 g)
Liverwurst on crackers (15 g)
Meat casseroles (½ c)
Mild chilli or other bean/meat dishes (¼ c)
Peanut butter and jam sandwich (½ sandwich)
Sloppy joes (½ sandwich)

[a]Each serving provides at least 1 mg iron, or one-tenth of a child's iron recommendation. Vitamin C–rich foods included with these snacks increase iron absorption.

[b]Some fortified breakfast cereals contain more than 10 mg iron per half-cup serving (read the labels).

[c]Raw sprouts may pose a bacterial hazard to young children.

Table 14–2

Recommended Number of Food Guide Servings for Children 2–3 Years of Age

Food Group	Number of Food Guide Servings	Examples of One Child-Size Serving
Vegetables and Fruit	4 ■ Eat at least one dark green and one orange vegetable each day ■ Choose vegetables and fruit prepared with little or no added fat ■ Have vegetables and fruit more often than juice	½ cup fresh, frozen, or canned vegetables ½ cup cooked or 1 cup raw leaf vegetables 1 fruit or ½ cup fresh, frozen, or canned fruit ½ cup 100% juice
Grain Products	3 ■ Make at least half of your grain products whole grain each day ■ Choose grain products that are lower in fat, sugar, or salt	1 slice bread ½ bagel ½ pita or tortilla ½ cup cooked rice, bulgur, or quinoa ¾ cup hot cereal or 30 g cold cereal ½ cup cooked pasta or couscous
Milk and Alternatives	2 ■ Drink skim, 1%, or 2% milk each day ■ Select lower-fat milk alternatives	1 cup milk or powdered milk (reconstituted) ½ cup canned milk (evaporated) 1 cup fortified soy beverage ¾ cup yogurt
Meat and Alternatives	1 ■ Have meat alternatives such as beans, lentils, and tofu often ■ Eat at least two Food Guide servings of fish each week ■ Select lean meat and alternatives prepared with little or no added fat	1½ cup or 2½ oz cooked fish, shellfish, poultry, lean meat ¾ cup legumes ¾ cup tofu 2 eggs 2 tbs peanut or nut butter ¼ cup shelled nuts and seeds

Source: Eating Well with Canada's Food Guide. *Health Canada, 2011. Reproduced with permission from Her Majesty the Queen in Right of Canada, represented by the Minister of Health, 2013.*

Little children like to eat small portions of food at little tables.

eating vegetables, produces the opposite of the desired effect: the child will likely not develop a preference for those foods.[15] Likewise, when children are forbidden to eat favourite foods, they yearn for them more—the reverse of the well-meaning caretaker's goal.[16]

Little children prefer small portions of food served at little tables. If offered large portions, children may fill up on favourite foods, ignoring others. Toddlers often go on food jags—consecutive days of eating only one or two favoured foods. For food jags lasting a week or so, make no response because two-year-olds regard any form of attention as a reward. After two weeks of serving the favoured foods, try serving tiny portions of many foods, including the favoured items. Invite the child's friends to occasional meals and make other foods as attractive as possible.

Just as parents are entitled to their likes and dislikes, a child who genuinely and consistently rejects a food should be allowed the same privilege. Children should be believed when they say they are full: the "clean-your-plate" dictum should be stamped out for all time. Children who are forced to override their own satiety signals are in training for obesity. Honouring preferences does not mean that children should dictate the diet, however, because many children will choose an abundance of heavily advertised snack chips, crackers, sugary cereals, fast foods, and sugary drinks if allowed to do so.[17] Today's rushed parents may be tempted to abdicate food decisions to a child's taste buds, but a hungry child offered between-meal sweets and fatty treats will reliably fill up on them rather than on nutritious foods served at mealtimes. The parent is responsible for *what* the child is offered to eat, but the child should decide *how much* and even *whether* to eat.

Choking A child who is choking may make no sound, so an adult should keep an eye on children when they are eating. A child who is coughing most often dislodges the food and recovers without help. To prevent choking, encourage the child to sit when eating—choking is more likely when children are running or reclining.

Chapter 3 describes actions to prevent choking and those to take should choking occur.

Round foods such as grapes, nuts, hard candies, and pieces of hot dog can become lodged in a child's small windpipe. Other potentially dangerous foods include tough meat, popcorn, chips, and peanut butter eaten by the spoonful.

Snacking and Other Healthy Habits Parents today often find that their children snack so much that they are not hungry at mealtimes. This is not a problem if children are taught how to snack—nutritious snacks are just as health promoting as small meals. Keep snack foods simple and available: milk, cheese, crackers, fruit, vegetable sticks, yogurt, peanut butter sandwiches, and whole-grain cereal.

A bright, unhurried atmosphere free of conflict is conducive to good appetite and provides a climate in which a child can learn to enjoy eating. Parents who beg, cajole, and demand that their children eat make power struggles inevitable. A child may find mealtimes unbearable if they are accompanied by a barrage of accusations—"Susie, your hands are filthy . . . your report card . . . and clean your plate!" The child's stomach recoils as both body and mind react to stress of this kind.

Children love to be included in meal preparation, and they like to eat foods they helped prepare (see Table 14–3 in the margin). A positive experience is most likely when tasks match developmental abilities and are undertaken in a spirit of enthusiasm and enjoyment, not criticism or drudgery. Praise for a job well done (or at least well attempted) expands a child's sense of pride and helps develop skills and positive feelings toward healthy foods.

Many parents overlook perhaps the single most important influence on their child's food habits—their own habits.[18] Parents who don't prepare, serve, and eat carrots shouldn't be surprised when their child refuses to eat carrots.

KEY POINT

- Healthy eating habits and positive relationships with food are learned in childhood. Parents teach children best by example. Choking can often be avoided by supervision during meals and avoiding hazardous foods.

Can Nutrient Deficiencies Impair a Child's Thinking or Cause Misbehaviour?

A child who suffers from nutrient deficiencies exhibits physical and behavioural symptoms: the child feels sick and out of sorts. Diet–behaviour connections are of keen interest to caretakers who both feed children and live with them.

Deficiencies of protein, energy, vitamin A, iron, and zinc plague children the world over. In developing nations, such deficiencies cause or contribute to nearly half the deaths of children under four and inflict blindness, stunted growth, and vulnerability to infections on millions more.

In developed countries such as Canada and the United States, most deficiencies have subtle, even unnoticeable, effects. A study of seemingly healthy British children revealed that about 40 percent of them had intakes of less than half the recommended amounts of folate, vitamin D, calcium, iron, magnesium, selenium, zinc, and other minerals. The researchers gave multinutrient supplements to some of these children and later administered intelligence tests to all of them. Those who had received the supplements scored significantly higher on the tests than the others did. The researchers interpreted the findings to mean that brain function may be sensitive to borderline deficiencies of some nutrients, even in children who are well nourished with protein and some vitamins. This conclusion has been supported by other findings.[19]

Iron deficiency remains common among children and adolescents despite iron fortification of foods and other programs to combat this deficiency. Besides carrying

Table 14–3

Food Skills of Preschoolers[a]

Age 1–2 years, when large muscles develop, the child
- uses short-shanked spoon.
- helps feed self.
- lifts and drinks from cup.
- helps scrub, tear, break, or dip foods.

Age 3 years, when medium hand muscles develop, the child
- spears food with fork.
- feeds self independently.
- helps wrap, pour, mix, shake, or spread foods.
- helps crack nuts with supervision.

Age 4 years, when small finger muscles develop, the child
- uses all utensils and napkin.
- helps roll, juice, mash, or peel foods.
- cracks egg shells.

Age 5 years, when fine coordination of fingers and hands develops, the child
- helps measure, grind, grate, and cut (soft foods with dull knife).
- uses hand-cranked egg beater with supervision.

[a]These ages are approximate. Healthy, normal children develop at their own pace.

Sources: Adapted from M. Sigman-Grant, Feeding preschoolers: Balancing nutrition and developmental needs, Nutrition Today, July/August 1992, pp. 13:17; A. A. Hertzler, Preschoolers: Food handling skills: Motor development, Journal of Nutrition Education 21 (1989): 100B:100C.

oxygen in the blood, iron works as part of large molecules to release energy within cells and plays key roles in many molecules of the brain and nervous system. A lack of iron not only causes an energy crisis but also affects behaviour, mood, attention span, and learning ability.

Iron deficiency is diagnosed by a deficit of iron in the *blood*, after anemia has developed. A child's *brain*, however, is sensitive to slightly lowered iron concentrations long before the blood effects appear. Distinguishing the effects of iron deficiency from those of other factors in children's lives is difficult, but studies have found connections between iron deficiency and behaviour. Iron deficiency may lessen the motivation to persist at intellectually challenging tasks, shorten the attention span, and reduce overall intellectual performance. Iron-deficient children may be irritable, aggressive, and disagreeable or sad and withdrawn. They may be labelled "hyperactive," "depressed," or "unlikable." Furthermore, a child who had iron-deficiency anemia *as an infant* may continue to perform poorly as he or she grows older, even with improvement in iron status.[20] No one knows whether the poverty and poor health often associated with early iron deficiency or some lingering effect of the deficiency itself is to blame for the later cognition and behaviour problems.[21]

The diet of a disruptive or apathetic child should be examined by a registered dietitian who can identify problems and suggest actions to correct them. Only a health-care provider should make the decision to give iron supplements, and supplements should be kept out of children's reach. Iron toxicity is a leading cause of poisoning each year in toddlers and other children who accidentally ingest iron pills.[22]

> Earlier, Table 14–1 listed some iron-rich foods that children will often accept.

KEY POINT

- The detrimental effects of nutrient deficiencies in children in developed nations can be subtle. Iron deficiency is the most widespread nutrition problem of children and causes abnormalities in both physical health and behaviour. Iron toxicity is a major form of poisoning in children.

The Problem of Lead

Another form of metal poisoning arises from ingestion of lead. Lead poisoning often occurs because babies love to explore and put everything into their mouths, including things that may harm them, such as chips of old paint, pieces of metal, and other unlikely substances. Lead may also leach into a home's water supply from old lead pipes. Recently, the water flowing into older homes in London, Ontario, was found to contain elevated levels of lead, and since this is a matter of concern to everyone, especially pregnant women and children, the chief drinking water inspector for Ontario ordered three dozen municipalities from across the province "to conduct immediate drinking water tests for lead in older homes." The results of testing during 2008–2009 revealed that, of the 70,000 samples tested, 98 percent met the provincial standard of less than 10 milligrams/litre.[23] Also, recent analysis from the 2009–2011 CHMS survey revealed that average blood lead concentrations for children 3–11 years was less than 1 microgram/decilitre, far below the 10 micrograms/decilitre intervention level.

Lead is an indestructible metal element; the body cannot alter it. Lead can build up so silently in a child's body that caretakers will not notice unusual symptoms until much later, after toxicity has set in. Tragically, once symptoms set in, even today most effective medical treatments may not reverse all of the functional damage.[24] Impaired thinking, reasoning, perception, and other academic skills, as well as hearing impairments and decreased growth, are associated with even very low levels of lead toxicity.[25]

As lead toxicity slowly injures the kidneys, nerves, brain, bone marrow, and other organs, the child may slip into coma, have convulsions, and possibly even die if an accurate diagnosis is not made in time to prevent it.[26] Older children with high blood lead may be suffering physical consequences but be mislabelled as delinquent, aggressive, or learning disabled.

Old paint is the main source of lead in most children's lives.

© C. McGregor

Infants and young children absorb 5 to 10 times as much lead as adults do. Malnutrition makes lead poisoning more likely because children absorb more lead if they have empty stomachs or if they lack calcium, zinc, vitamin C, vitamin D, or iron.[27] A child with iron-deficiency anemia is three times as likely to have elevated blood lead as a child with normal iron status. The chemical properties of lead are similar to those of nutrient minerals like iron, calcium, and zinc, and lead displaces these minerals from their sites of action in body cells but cannot perform their biological functions.

Bans on leaded gasoline, leaded house paint, and lead-soldered food cans have dramatically reduced the amount of lead in the North American environment in recent years and have produced a steady decline in children's average blood lead concentrations (see Figure 14–2).[28] Lead still threatens children, however, especially in low-income families who live in older houses that still contain lead-based paint.[29] Even chips of such paint mixed into neighbourhood soil can be a problem. By one estimate in the United States, more than 400,000 children—most of them under age 6—currently have enough lead in their blood to cause mental, behavioural, and other health problems.[30] Some tips for avoiding lead toxicity are offered in Table 14–4.

KEY POINT

- Lead poisoning has declined dramatically over the past two decades, but when it occurs it can inflict severe, irreparable damage on growing children. Higher awareness of the remaining sources of lead poisoning can help reduce its present rate of occurrence.

Food Allergy, Intolerance, and Aversion

Food **allergy** is frequently blamed for physical and behavioural abnormalities in children, but just 3–5 percent of children are diagnosed with true food allergies.[31] Children sometimes "grow out" of their food allergies (notably, allergy to peanuts may fade with time) until in adulthood food allergies affect only about 1 or 2 percent of the population.[32]

A true food allergy occurs when a food protein or other large molecule enters body tissues. Recall that most proteins from food are dismantled to smaller fragments in the digestive tract before absorption. Some, however, enter the bloodstream before being fully digested. Once inside the body of an allergic person, the foreign molecules trigger a reaction from the immune system similar to the defence it launches against any other **antigen**: it releases **antibodies**, **histamine**, or other defensive agents

- To access a fact sheet on the effects of lead on human health, go to Health Canada's website at http://www.hc-sc.gc.ca/iyh-vsv/environ/lead-plomb_e.html.

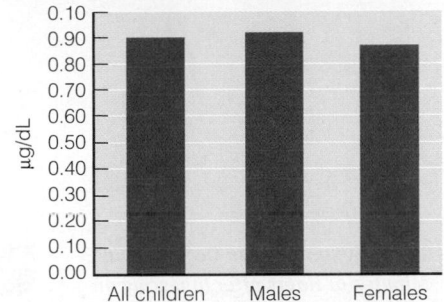

Figure 14–2

Blood Lead in Children, Based on CHMS Data for 2007–2009

Source: Statistics Canada, http://www.statcan.gc.ca/pub/82-625-x/2013001/figureicle/11779-eng.htm. Reproduced and distributed on an "as is" basis with the permission of Statistics Canada.

Table 14–4

Steps to Prevent Lead Poisoning

To protect children:
- If your home was built before 1978, wash floors, windowsills, and other surfaces weekly with warm water and detergent to remove dust released by old lead paint; clean up flaking paint chips immediately.
- Feed children balanced, timely meals with ample iron and calcium.
- Prevent children from chewing on old painted surfaces.
- Wash children's hands, bottles, and toys often.
- Wipe soil off shoes before entering the home.
- Ask a pediatrician whether your child should be tested for lead.

To safeguard yourself:
- Avoid daily use of handmade, imported, or old ceramic mugs or pitchers for hot or acidic beverages, such as juices, coffee, or tea. In 2008, Health Canada set a "Leachable lead limit" for glazed ceramic foodware sold in Canada (see http://www.hc-sc.gc.ca/cps-spc/pubs/indust/ceramics-ceramiques/index-eng.php). If ceramic dishes or cups become chalky, use them for decorative purposes only.
- Do not use lead crystal decanters for storing alcoholic or other beverages.
- If your home is old and may have lead pipes, run the water for a minute before using, especially before the first use in the morning.
- Remove lead foil from wine bottles and wipe the mouth of the bottle before pouring.

allergy an immune reaction to a foreign substance, such as a component of food. Also called *hypersensitivity* by researchers.

antigen a substance foreign to the body that elicits the formation of antibodies or an inflammation reaction from immune system cells. Food antigens are usually large proteins. Also defined in Chapter 3.

antibodies large protein molecules that are produced in response to the presence of antigens and then help inactivate the antigens. Also defined in Chapters 3 and 6.

histamine a substance that participates in causing inflammation; produced by cells of the immune system as part of a local immune reaction to an antigen.

to attack the invaders. In some people, the result is the life-threatening food allergy reaction of **anaphylactic shock**. Peanuts, tree nuts, milk, eggs, wheat, soybeans, fish, and shellfish are the substances most likely to trigger this extreme reaction.[33]

Managing Food Allergies   If a child reacts to allergens with a life-threatening response, the family and school must guard against any exposure to the allergen.[34] Parents must teach the child which foods to avoid, but avoiding allergens can be tricky because they often sneak into foods in unexpected ways. For example, a pork chop (an innocent food) may be breaded (wheat allergy) and dipped in egg (egg allergy) before being fried in peanut oil (peanut allergy), a chocolate cookie may contain hydrogenated soybean oil shortening (soybean allergy), marshmallow candies contain eggs, lunch meat may contain milk protein binders, and so forth.

Most caretakers of allergic children must pack safe lunches and snacks at home and ask school officials to strictly enforce a "no swapping" policy in the lunchroom. To prevent nutrient deficiencies, caretakers must also provide adequate substitutes that supply the essential nutrients in the omitted foods.[35] For example, a child allergic to milk must be supplied with calcium from fortified foods, such as calcium-rich orange juice.

The allergic child must learn to recognize the symptoms of impending anaphylactic shock, such as a tingling of the tongue, throat, or skin or difficulty breathing (see the margin). Finally, the child and the school staff should be prepared to administer injections of **epinephrine**, which prevents anaphylaxis after exposure to the allergen.[36] Too many preventable deaths occur each year among people with food allergies who accidentally ingest the allergen but have no access to epinephrine.[37]

Health Canada provides weblinks to pamphlets on the priority list of the most common allergy-causing items in foods (see margin note).[38] For example, a food containing "textured vegetable protein" must say "soy" on its label. Similarly, "casein" must be identified as "milk protein." Food producers must also prevent cross-contamination during production and clearly label the foods in which it is likely to occur. When cross-contamination happens, the affected foods are recalled and Allergy Alerts are announced.[39] Equipment used for making peanut butter must be scrupulously clean before being used to pulverize cashew nuts for cashew butter to protect unsuspecting cashew butter consumers from peanut allergens. Note: Health Canada recently included *mustard*, *gluten*, and *sulphites* in the list of priority food allergies/food sensitivities (see the margin on this page, as well as http://www.hc-sc.gc.ca/fn-an/securit/allerg/fa-aa/index-eng.php), and Canada's new food allergy labelling regulations came into effect in August 2012.

Technology may soon offer new solutions. Drugs under development may interfere with the immune response that causes allergic reactions.[40] Through genetic engineering, scientists may one day banish allergens from peanuts, soybeans, and other foods to make them safer.

Detecting a Food Allergy   Allergies have one or two components. They *always* involve antibodies; they *sometimes* involve symptoms. Therefore, allergies cannot be diagnosed from symptoms alone. A starting point for diagnosis may entail eliminating suspected foods from the diet for a week or two and reintroducing them one at a time. If the symptoms disappear and then recur with reintroduction of a food, medical tests can then confirm the allergy. (Anyone who has suffered anaphylaxis or other severe symptoms should not reintroduce suspected foods but should go instead for medical testing.) A positive result from a blood test for antibodies can confirm a diagnosis.[41] So can a skin-prick test in which a clinician applies droplets of food extracts to the skin and then lightly pricks or scratches the skin. When a food allergy exists, raised, red, itchy bumps appear within minutes.

Identifying a food that causes an immediate allergic reaction is easy because symptoms correlate with the time of eating the food. Sometimes the reaction is delayed up to 24 hours, however, making identification of the offending food more difficult because other foods will have been eaten by the time the symptoms appear.

Quick and easy scientific-sounding allergy quackery abounds on the market and may deceive people seeking relief from everything from itchy skin to mental

These Symptoms Can Occur within Minutes or Hours after Ingesting an Allergen*

- Tingling sensation in the mouth
- Swelling of the tongue and throat
- Irritated, reddened eyes
- Difficulty breathing, wheezing, asthma
- Hives, swelling, rashes
- Vomiting, abdominal cramps, diarrhea
- Drop in blood pressure
- Loss of consciousness
- Death

*For additional information, see the Allergy/Asthma Information Association at http://aaia.ca/en/index.htm.

Health Canada's List of Priority Food Allergies

- Eggs
- Milk
- Mustard
- Peanuts
- Seafood (Fish, Crustaceans and Shellfish)
- Sesame seeds
- Soy
- Sulphites
- Tree nuts
- Wheat

Source: Health Canada, Food Allergies *(2013). http://www.hc-sc.gc.ca/fn-an/securit/allerg/fa-aa/index-eng.php*

anaphylactic (an-ah-feh-LACK-tick) **shock** a life-threatening whole-body allergic reaction to an offending substance.

epinephrine (epp-eh-NEFF-rin) a hormone of the adrenal gland that counteracts anaphylactic shock by opening the airways and maintaining heartbeat and blood pressure.

These eight normally wholesome foods—milk, shellfish, fish, peanuts, tree nuts, eggs, wheat, and soybeans (and soy products)—may cause life-threatening symptoms in people with allergies.

depression. Beware of "food sensitivity testing." It involves fake blood or other body fluid tests that supposedly determine appropriate dietary changes and indicate which expensive supplements the "patient" should buy from the test giver to relieve the "allergy."[42]

Food Intolerance and Food Aversion A **food intolerance** is characterized by unpleasant symptoms that reliably occur after consumption of certain foods—lactose intolerance is an example. Unlike allergy, a food intolerance does not involve an immune response. A **food aversion** is an intense dislike of a food that may be a biological response to a food that once caused trouble. Parents are advised to watch for signs of food aversion and to take them seriously. Such a dislike may turn out to be a whim or fancy, but it may turn out to be an allergy or other valid reason to avoid a certain food. Don't prejudge. Test. Then, if an important staple food must be excluded from the diet, find other foods to provide the omitted nutrients.

> Chapter 4 provides details about lactose intolerance.

Foods are often unjustly blamed when behaviour problems arise, but children who are sick from any cause are likely to be cranky. The next section singles out one such type of misbehaviour.

KEY POINT

- Food allergies can cause serious illness. Diagnosis is based on the presence of antibodies, and tests are imperative to determine whether allergy exists. Food aversions can be related to food allergies or to adverse reactions to food.

food intolerance an adverse reaction to a food or food additive not involving an immune response.

food aversion an intense dislike of a food, biological or psychological in nature, resulting from an illness or other negative experience associated with that food.

Does Diet Affect Hyperactivity?

Hyperactivity, or attention-deficit/hyperactivity disorder (ADHD), is a **learning disability** that occurs in 3–5 percent of young, school-aged children—at least 1 in every classroom of 30 children. ADHD is characterized by the chronic inability to pay attention, along with overly active behaviour and poor impulse control (see the margin). It can delay growth, lead to academic failure, and cause major behavioural problems. Although some children improve with age, many reach the college or university years or adulthood before they receive a diagnosis and with it the possibility of treatment.

Food allergies have been blamed for ADHD, but research to date has shown no connection. Research has also all but dismissed the idea that sugar makes children hyperactive (see Controversy 4 for details). About 20 years ago, one study did find an association between doses of the food colorant tartrazine and increased irritability, restlessness, and sleep disturbances in a small percentage of hyperactive children.[43] Parents who wish to avoid tartrazine can find it listed with the ingredients on food labels.

Parents hope that a new diet or some other simple solution may improve children's behaviour. Unfounded dietary "treatments" may seem to help for a while due to the placebo effect, but they fail to provide lasting cures.

Common sense says that all children get unruly and "hyper" at times. A child who often fills up on caffeine-containing colas and chocolate, misses lunch, becomes too cranky to nap, misses out on outdoor play, and spends hours in front of a television suffers stresses that can trigger chronic patterns of crankiness (see margin note). This cycle of tension and fatigue resolves itself when the caretakers begin insisting on regular hours of sleep, regular mealtimes, a nutritious diet, and regular outdoor exercise.

Living with chronic hunger is a cause of misbehaviour in some children; simply lifting the children from poverty often significantly improves their behaviour.[44] In the United States, for example, an estimated 12 million children are hungry at least some of the time. Such children often lack iron, and a link between iron deficiency and ADHD may be emerging.[45] Hunger issues are many; see Chapter 15. Once the obvious causes of misbehaviour are eliminated, a physician can recommend other strategies, such as special educational programs or psychological counselling and, in many cases, prescription medication.[46]

> Controversy 14 presents a table of the caffeine in common foods and beverages.

KEY POINT

- Hyperactivity, properly named *attention-deficit/hyperactivity disorder* (ADHD), is not caused by food allergies; temporary "hyper" behaviour may reflect excess caffeine consumption or inconsistent care. A wise parent will limit children's caffeine intakes and meet their needs for structure. Poverty may cause behavioural problems.

Time Use, Television, and Children's Nutrition Problems

The average child in Canada watches many hours of television each week. In addition, video and computer games and other media add significantly to children's passive viewing time, while active free play time decreases substantially, facts about which parents, school principals, and teachers are very concerned.[47]

Television exerts four major adverse impacts on children's nutrition. First, television viewing requires no energy. It seems to reduce the metabolic rate below the resting level, requiring even less energy than daydreaming. Second, it consumes time that could be spent in energetic play. An inactive child can become obese even while eating less food than an active child.[48] Third, more television watching correlates with more between-meal snacking and with eating the high-Calorie fatty and sugary foods most heavily advertised on children's programs, increasing the risk of dental caries. Fourth, children who watch more than four hours of television a day, or watch during meals, are least likely to eat fruit and vegetables and most likely to be obese.[49] Children's intakes of sugary foods and soft drinks and fatty treats have soared in recent years, while intakes of other, more nutritious foods have fallen off.[50] To oppose the effects of marketing on children's appetites, it often helps to talk with children so that they recognize the motivations and marketing techniques of advertisements.

Some blame a sedentary lifestyle for the upswing in obesity in children and adults. Fewer and fewer children actively participate in physical education classes.[51] At home, limiting television watching, other screen use (thus, a less "screenogenic" environment), and other sedentary activities is probably a good idea.[52] Healthy children should never have television sets in their bedrooms—a recent U.S. study revealed that the many who do (up to 65 percent of 8- to 18-year-olds) spend even more time watching television and are very likely to be overweight.[53]

The Problem of Childhood Obesity

Obesity is increasing among the world's children and poses hazards to the health of children both now and in the future (Controversy 13 provides details). Meanwhile, medical science has little to offer in the way of a cure.[54] A few obese children may remain untouched by the adverse effects of being overweight, but the majority must cope with health problems and altered physical and psychological development. Early in adolescence, an obese child's high blood pressure, insulin resistance, and blood lipid profile may warn of impending cardiovascular disease (CVD; Chapter 11 provides details about these connections). More often than thinner children, obese children develop diseases such as diabetes and asthma.[55]

Obese children often mature and develop earlier than their peers and develop the greater bone and muscle mass needed to carry their extra weight. Consequently, they tend to remain "stocky" even after losing their excess body fatness.

Obese children also suffer psychologically.[56] Adults may discriminate against them, and peers may make thoughtless comments or reject them. An obese child may develop a poor self-image, a sense of failure, and a passive approach to life. Television shows, a major influence on children, stereotype the fat person as a misfit. Children have few defences against these unfair portrayals and may internalize an unfavourable, negative attitude toward bulky body sizes.

Prevention and Treatment of Childhood Obesity

An integrated approach involving diet, physical activity, psychological support, and behavioural changes can help the overweight child.[57] Consulting a professional, such as a registered dietitian who specializes in childhood nutrition and weight management, can be useful. Overweight in children must be sensitively addressed, however. Children are impressionable and may come to believe that their worth or lovability is somehow tied to their weight.

> Concern is growing for the future health of children worldwide. See Controversy 13.

The best solutions usually involve the whole family and, in fact, the whole community.* Parents are among the most influential forces in shaping the self-concept, weight concerns, and dieting practices of children.[58] Thus, they play key roles in preventing or managing obesity and in helping the overweight child make appropriate lifestyle changes. Beyond this, parents can be powerful tools in helping to instill healthy habits and a strong sense of self-worth that can benefit a child through a lifetime. In addition, community efforts can support the lessons learned at home.

An initial goal is to slow the obese child's rate of gain—that is, to hold weight steady while the child grows taller. Weight loss is ordinarily not recommended because diet restriction can easily interfere with normal growth.[59] By feeding the whole family balanced meals, offering appropriate portion sizes, restricting treats, and boosting physical activity, the goal is often accomplished, and the child does not feel singled out.[60] See the margin for family lifestyle choices list that often prove effective in helping the overweight child. Furthermore, a collaborative public policy statement that involved the Dietitians of Canada, Canadian Paediatric Society, College of Family Physicians of Canada, and Community Health Nurses of Canada was released in early 2010 entitled

Family Lifestyle Choices to Help the Overweight Child

- Do not use foods to reward or punish behaviours.
- Have fun and play vigorously outdoors every day, as a family or with friends.
- Involve children in shopping for and preparing family meals.
- Learn and use appropriate food portions.
- Limit high-sugar, high-fat foods, including sugar-sweetened soft drinks.
- Provide an appropriate nutritious breakfast every day.
- Provide a wide variety of nutritious snacks that are low in fat and sugar.
- Provide fruit juices in the amounts recommended in guidelines, such as Canada's Food Guide, but no more than this amount.
- Serve family meals that control both the Calorie density of the foods and the portions offered.
- Set a good example and demonstrate positive behaviours for children to imitate.
- Slow down eating and pause to enjoy table companions; stop eating when full.

Community Actions to Help Correct and Prevent Obesity

- Provide safe walking and biking routes to school.
- Make fruit and vegetables available and affordable.
- Provide recreational facilities with planned physical activities.
- Increase opportunities for physical activity.
- Advertise to promote energy balance and healthy body weight.
- Change governing policies to promote energy balance.

---

*An informative reference is Food and Nutrition Board, Institute of Medicine, Preventing Childhood Obesity: Health in the Balance (Washington, D.C.: National Academies Press, 2005).

Promoting Optimal Monitoring of Growth in Canada: Using the New WHO Growth Charts. Hopefully, this resource will support the efforts mentioned here and be used by health-care professionals as the authors intended: "The desired outcome is the promotion of consistent practices in monitoring growth and assessing patterns of linear growth and weight gain in infants, children and adolescents to support healthy child growth and development" (see http://www.cps.ca/tools-outils/who-growth-charts). Furthermore, a number of efforts to make childhood overweight and obesity a collective priority and to curb childhood obesity are underway in Canada, including the recent release of "Curbing Childhood Obesity: A Federal, Provincial and Territorial Framework for Action to Promote Healthy Weights" by the Public Health Agency of Canada (see http://www.phac-aspc.gc.ca/hp-ps/hl-mvs/framework-cadre/index-eng.php). This document calls for a sustained multisectoral approach of joint and complementary actions in order to effectively address this complex issue.

Dental Caries   Sticky, high-carbohydrate snack foods cling to the teeth and provide an ideal environment for the growth of mouth bacteria that cause caries. Parents can help prevent tooth damage by helping children to

- Limit between-meal snacking.
- Brush and floss daily, and brush or rinse after eating meals and snacks.
- Choose foods that don't stick to teeth and are swallowed quickly.
- Snack on crisp or fibrous foods to stimulate the release and rinsing action of saliva.

Table 14–5 lists foods that promote dental health and those that require speedy removal from the teeth.

Health Canada recently allowed food manufacturers to use a diet-related health claim on foods that links very small amounts of carbohydrates in foods with statements such as "won't cause cavities" [see http://www.inspection.gc.ca/english/fssa/labeti/guide/ch8e.shtml#a8_4_5 on the Canadian Food Inspection Agency (CFIA) website].

KEY POINT

- The nation's children are growing fatter and face advancing risks of diseases. Childhood obesity demands careful family-centred management. Television viewing can contribute to obesity through lack of exercise and by promoting overconsumption of Calorie-dense snacks. The sugary snacks advertised on children's TV programs also contribute to dental caries.

Is Breakfast Really the Most Important Meal of the Day for Children?

Our elders have long held that breakfast is the most important meal of the day, and for children, this bit of wisdom is now backed by science. A nutritious breakfast is a central feature of a child's diet that supports healthy growth and development. When a child consistently skips breakfast or is allowed to choose sugary foods (candy or marshmallows) in place of nourishing ones (whole-grain cereals), the child will fail to get enough of several nutrients. Nutrients missed from a skipped breakfast won't be "made up" at lunch and dinner but will be left out completely that day.[61]

Children who eat no breakfast are more likely to be overweight, perform poorly in tasks requiring concentration, have shorter attention spans, achieve lower test scores, and be tardy or absent more often than their well-fed peers.[62] Common sense tells us that it is unreasonable to expect anyone to study and learn when no fuel has been provided. Even children who have eaten breakfast suffer from distracting hunger by late morning. Chronically underfed children suffer more intensely.

Although the Canadian government does not have a national school feeding program, the U.S. government funds several programs to provide nutritious, high-quality meals, including breakfast, to children at school. Children who eat school breakfast consume less fat and more magnesium during the day and are more replete with vitamin C and folate.[63] Schools that participate in the U.S. federal school meal programs observe improved academic, behavioural, emotional, and social functioning of students along with lower tardiness and absentee rates.[64]

Table 14–5

The Caries Potential of Foods

Low Caries Potential

These foods are less damaging to teeth:

- Eggs, legumes
- Fresh fruit, fruit packed in water
- Lean meat, fish, poultry
- Milk, cheese, plain yogurt
- Most cooked and raw vegetables
- Pizza
- Popcorn, pretzels
- Sugarless gum and candy,[a] diet soft drinks
- Toast, hard rolls, bagels

High Caries Potential

Brush teeth after eating these foods:

- Cakes, muffins, doughnuts, pies
- Candied sweet potatoes
- Chocolate milk
- Cookies, granola or "energy" bars, crackers
- Dried fruits (raisins, figs, dates)
- Frozen or flavoured yogurt
- Fruit juices or drinks
- Fruit in syrup
- Ice cream or ice milk
- Jams, jellies, preserves
- Lunch meat with added sugar
- Meat or vegetables with sugary glazes
- Oatmeal, oat cereals, oatmeal baked goods[b]
- Peanut butter with added sugar
- Potato and other snack chips
- Ready-to-eat sugared cereals
- Sugared gum, soft drinks, candies, honey, sugar, molasses, syrups
- Toaster pastries

[a]Cariogenic bacteria cannot efficiently metabolize the sugar alcohols in these products, so they do not contribute to dental caries.

[b]The soluble fibre in oats makes this grain particularly sticky and therefore cariogenic.

■ Breakfast is critical to school performance. Not all children start the day with an adequate breakfast, but school breakfast programs help fill the need.

- Make ahead and freeze sandwiches to thaw and serve with juice. Fillings may include peanut butter, low-fat cream cheese, other cheeses, jams, fruit slices, or meat. Or use flour tortillas with cheese; roll up, wrap, and freeze for later heating in a toaster oven or microwave oven.

- Teach school-aged children to help themselves to dry cereals, milk, and juice. Keep unbreakable bowls and cups in low cupboards and keep milk and juice in small, unbreakable pitchers on a low refrigerator shelf.

- Keep a bowl of fresh fruit and small containers of shelled nuts, trail mix (the kind without candy), or roasted peanuts for grabbing. Granola or other grain cereal poured into a 250-mL yogurt tub is easy to eat on the run. So are plain, toasted whole-grain frozen waffles—no syrup needed.

- Nontraditional choices are often acceptable. Purchase or make ahead enough carrot sticks to divide among several containers; serve with yogurt or bean dip. Leftover casseroles, stews, or pasta dishes are nutritious choices that children can eat hot or cold.

School Food Policy

Canada is the only developed country in the world that has no national policy or program for feeding schoolchildren. Some provinces or local boards of education, often in collaboration with public health departments, are developing school food policies to address the availability and quality of food in schools and the nutrition curriculum. Teacher associations are showing great concern for the hungry children in classrooms, and many schools have developed some type of feeding program. If interested, check with your local board of education to get details on local programs and policies for foods in schools. In Canada, a resolution by the Alberta Public Health Association[65] and the Ontario Ministry of Education[66] issued guidelines for food and beverages that can be sold in vending machines in elementary schools in the hope of reducing childhood obesity. Details on the latter guidelines can be found at http://www.edu.gov.on.ca/eng/document/reports/healthyschools/report.pdf. The Ontario guidelines were based largely on reports from the Ontario Society of Nutrition Professionals in Public Health (OSNPPH) Nutrition Workgroup Steering Committee and Dietitians of Canada. Furthermore, The Ontario Ministry of Children and Youth Services recently announced plans to expand its Student Nutrition Program to include the creation of 700 new breakfast programs which includes the expansion of 300 existing programs with the highest need (see http://www.children.gov.on.ca/htdocs/English/topics/schoolsnacks/index.aspx).

School feeding programs are often looking for student volunteers. The Canadian Living Foundation: Breakfast for Learning provides resources for breakfast programs for children (http://www.breakfastforlearning.ca). This nonprofit organization is helping out in over 6,900 communities in every province and territory in Canada. You might also have heard that Shania Twain, an internationally recognized Canadian singer, has promoted and fundraised for this national organization, which is solely dedicated to supporting child nutrition.

How Nourishing Are the Lunches Served at School?

For over 50 years, school lunches have been meeting the midday nutrient needs of the children in the United States; however, no such program currently exists in Canada, although there are lobbying efforts to develop one. The U.S. nationally prescribed school lunches provide servings of milk, protein-rich foods (meat, poultry, fish, cheese, eggs, legumes, or peanut butter), vegetables, fruit, and breads or other grain foods each day.[67] The lunches are designed to meet at least a third of the recommended intake for specified nutrients and are often more nutritious than typical lunches brought from home.[68] Students who regularly eat school lunches have higher intakes of many nutrients and fibre than students who do not.[69] Even children's ability to learn seems to benefit from participating in national school food programs.[70] Table 14–6 shows school lunch patterns for different ages.

Children don't always like what they are served, so school lunch programs must strike a balance between what children want to eat and what will nourish them and guard their health. Additionally, short lunch periods and long waiting lines prevent some students from eating a school lunch and leave others with too little time to complete their meal.[71]

To help reduce cardiovascular risk, government-funded meals served at U.S. schools must follow the *Dietary Guidelines for Americans*. Often, however, private vendors offer unregulated meals, even heavily advertised fast foods, that compete side by side with the nutritious school lunches.[72] Children develop a taste for such foods early in life and may reject nutritious school meals when offered a choice of meals higher in fat, sugar, and salt.[73] Those who do so consume fewer fruit and vegetables not only at lunchtime but later on at supper as well.[74] Children receive a mixed message when they are left on their own to choose between the health-supporting school lunch and the less optimal foods that their taste buds may prefer.

Table 14-6

School Lunch Patterns for Different Ages

Food Group Serving	4–8 Years Old	9–13 Years Old
Milk and Alternatives, 1	1 cup milk (white or chocolate) or ¾ cup plain or fruit-bottom yogurt or 50 g cheese	1 cup milk (white or chocolate) or ¾ cup plain or fruit-bottom yogurt or 50 g cheese
Meat and Alternatives, ½–1	30 g (lean meat, poultry, or fish), an egg, 30 g seeds	30–60 g (lean meat, poultry, or fish), an egg, 30 g seeds
Vegetables and Fruit, 2	½ cup of fresh vegetables or juice* and a medium-sized fruit or juice	½–1 cup fresh vegetables or juice and a medium-sized fruit or juice
Grain Products, 2	Whole-grain bagel or 2 slices of whole-grain bread	Whole grain bagel or 2 slices of whole-grain bread

*Keep in mind that Canada's Food Guide recommends that we "have vegetables and fruit more often than juice" (i.e., for both fruit and vegetable juices).

Source: Based on Health Canada, Eating Well with Canada's Food Guide, Catalogue no. H164-38/1-2007E (Ottawa, Ont.: Minister of Health, 2007).

● The nutritive values of selected fast foods can be viewed by visiting the Canadian Nutrient File, 2010, at http://www.hc-sc.gc.ca/fn-an/nutrition/fiche-nutri-data/index-eng.php.

Students in some high schools also face the additional temptations of soft drinks, frozen confections, candies, and other low-nutrient treats from school snack bars, vending machines, or stores. Health professionals and administrators of the U.S. school lunch program have proposed limiting or banishing such treat sales from school grounds, but they face opposition from the food industries and individual school districts that profit from students' pocket money.[75] In the United States, nutrition professionals advocate that all foods available on school grounds or at school functions, even those from vending machines or school stores, be chosen to help meet the *Dietary Guidelines* standards.[76] Reducing the prices of nutritious foods greatly increases the likelihood that students will purchase them.[77]

A word about juice: authorities recommend limiting fruit juices in children's diets to about half a cup a day because juices are high in Calories and natural sugars and so could contribute to obesity or dental caries.[78] Indeed, the Canadian Paediatric Society recommends the following: "Offer water instead of juice. Limit juice to one serving, 125 to 175 mL (4 to 6 ounces) per day. If you do offer juice, be sure it is 100% fruit juice (with no added sugar)." See more at http://www.caringforkids.cps.ca/handouts/healthy_snacks_for_children#sthash.W92FqOnU.dpuf. Of course, consuming too much of any high-Calorie food could lead to weight gain, but evidence is mixed on whether juice intakes are linked with obesity.[79] Taken in moderation, juice is a nutritious food and may even crowd sugary soft drinks out of the diet—and soft drinks *are* associated with childhood obesity.[80] Frequent exposure of the teeth to the sugars in fruit juice increases the likelihood of dental caries, however, so children should be taught to brush their teeth after consuming juice.

Meeting the nutrition and education needs of children is critical to supporting their healthy growth and development.[81] The most effective education plans involve whole families and focus on changing behaviours to improve food choices at home as well as at school.[82]

KEY POINT

■ In the United States, school lunches are designed to provide at least a third of the nutrients needed daily by growing children and to stay within limits set by the *Dietary Guidelines for Americans*. Soft drink and snack vending machines, fast-food and snack bars, and school stores tempt students with foods high in fats and sugars. Fruit juice is a healthy food but may cause dental problems if used to excess.

The Teen Years

Teenagers are not fed; they eat. Nutrient needs are high during adolescence, and choices made during the teen years profoundly affect health, both now and in the future. Teens need reliable nutrition information to enable them to make healthy food choices. In the face of many demands on their time, including after-school jobs, social activities, and home responsibilities, they easily fall into irregular eating habits, relying on quick snacks or fast foods for meals.[83] The 2004 CCHS 2.2 survey revealed that on the day before their interview, one-third of adolescents (14–18 years) "consumed something that was prepared in a fast-food outlet."[84] The adolescent who does eat at home with family members consumes more nutritious fruit, vegetables, grains, and calcium-rich foods and fewer soft drinks than others.[85]

The teen years bring a search for identity, acquired largely through trial and error. Among influences shaping a teenager's self-concept, the most important are parents, peers, and the media.[86] Teens face tremendous pressures regarding body image, and many adopt fads and scams offering promises of slenderness, good-looking muscles, freedom from acne, or control over symptoms that may accompany menstruation. A negative self-assessment may open the door to taking risks such as using alcohol, tobacco, and drugs of abuse such as marijuana.

> Food sources of iron are listed in Chapter 8 (Snapshot 8–5, page–333).
>
> See Controversy 3 for details concerning alcohol and nutrition.

Growth and Nutrient Needs of Teenagers

Needs for vitamins, minerals, the energy-yielding nutrients, and, in fact, all nutrients are greater during adolescence than at any other time of life except pregnancy and lactation (see the DRI table on the inside front cover). The need for iron is particularly high as all teenagers gain lean body mass and girls begin menstruation (see margin note). Calcium needs are high to support the development of peak bone mass.

The Special Case of Iron The increase in need for iron during adolescence occurs across the genders, but for different reasons. A boy needs more iron at this time to develop extra lean body mass, whereas a girl needs extra not only to gain lean body mass but also to support menstruation. Because menstruation continues throughout a woman's childbearing years, her need stays high until older age. As boys become men, their iron needs drop back to the preadolescent value during early adulthood.

An interesting detail about adolescent iron requirements is that the need increases during the **growth spurt**, regardless of the age of the adolescent.[87] This shifting requirement makes pinpointing an adolescent's need tricky, as the margin list demonstrates.

Iron intakes often fail to keep pace with increasing needs, especially for girls, who typically consume less iron-rich foods such as meat and fewer total Calories than boys. Not surprisingly, iron deficiency is most prevalent among adolescent girls, and their performance on standardized tests often suffers.[88]

KEY POINT

- The need for iron increases during adolescence for males and females. Women's iron needs remain higher as long as they continue to menstruate.

Other Vitamins and Minerals

Health Canada recently announced that based on CCHS (2004) data for food and beverage intake (i.e., does not include supplements), "Many adolescents have inadequate intakes of magnesium, vitamin A and phosphorous" and that "there is a concern that adolescents may not be meeting their needs for potassium, calcium, and fibre." In addition, it also stated, "Canadian adolescents' sodium intakes are associated with an increased risk of adverse health effects" (http://www.hc-sc.gc.ca/fn-an/surveill/nutrition/commun/art-nutr-adol-eng.php).

Adolescence and the Bones Adolescence is a crucial time for bone development. The bones are growing longer at a rapid rate (see Figure 14–3), thanks to a special bone structure, the **epiphyseal plate**, that disappears as a teenager reaches adult height. At the same time, the bones are gaining density, laying down the calcium needed later in life. Low calcium intakes have reached crisis proportions: 85 percent of girls and 64

The Tragedy of Drug or Alcohol Abuse Often Begins in Adolescence and Causes Multiple Nutrition Problems

- Money is spent on drugs or alcohol instead of food.
- Substance-induced euphoria depresses the appetite.
- A drug- or alcohol-focused lifestyle does not include nutrition.
- Infections from sharing needles raise nutrient needs.
- Medical treatment for drug abuse may alter nutrition needs.

Iron DRI Intake Goals for Adolescent Boys

- 9–13 years: 8 mg/d
  If in growth spurt, 10.9 mg/d.
- 14–18 years: 11 mg/d
  If in growth spurt, 13.9 mg/d.

Iron DRI Intake Goals for Adolescent Girls

- 9–13 years: 8 mg/d
  If menstruating, 10.5 mg/d.
  If menstruating and in growth spurt, 11.6 mg/d.
- 14–18 years: 15 mg/d
  If in growth spurt, 16.1 mg/d.

Nutritious snacks play an important role in an active teen's diet.

growth spurt the marked rapid gain in physical size usually evident around the onset of adolescence.

epiphyseal (eh-PIFF-ih-seal) **plate** a thick, cartilagelike layer that forms new cells that are eventually calcified, lengthening the bone (*epiphysis* means "growing" in Greek).

Figure 14–3

Growth of Long Bones

Bones grow longer as new cartilage cells accumulate at the top portion of the epiphyseal plate and older cartilage cells at the bottom of the plate are calcified.

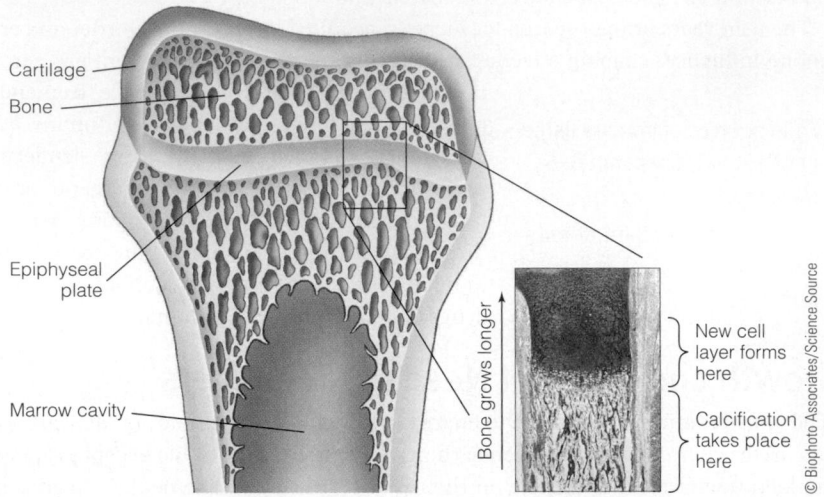

Cartilage

Bone

Epiphyseal plate

Marrow cavity

Bone grows longer

New cell layer forms here

Calcification takes place here

© Biophoto Associates/Science Source

percent of boys ages 12 to 19 years have too-low intakes. Paired with lack of physical activity, low calcium intakes can compromise the development of peak bone mass, greatly increasing the risk of osteoporosis and other bone diseases later on.[89]

Teens often choose soft drinks as one of their main beverages (see Figure 14–4), a choice that displaces calcium-rich milk from the diet.[90] Conversely, increasing milk products to meet calcium needs increases bone density.[91] In teenage girls especially, soft-drink intake soars while milk intake—and therefore calcium—declines sharply just when calcium needs are greatest (see Figure 14–5).[92] Regular soft-drink consumption is also linked in some but not all cases with overweight in adolescents.[93] There is growing concern about the amount of caffeine being consumed by older children and adolescents; thus, it is important to remind them and their parents to look for the amount of caffeine in the beverages they consume on a regular basis. This is especially true now that Health Canada has transitioned numerous natural health products, such as caffeine-containing energy drinks, over to foods. These products must now list on their labels the amount of caffeine in them from all sources,

Figure 14–4

Average Daily Consumption of Regular Soft Drinks (in grams) by Household Population Aged 1–18, Canada excluding Territories, 2004

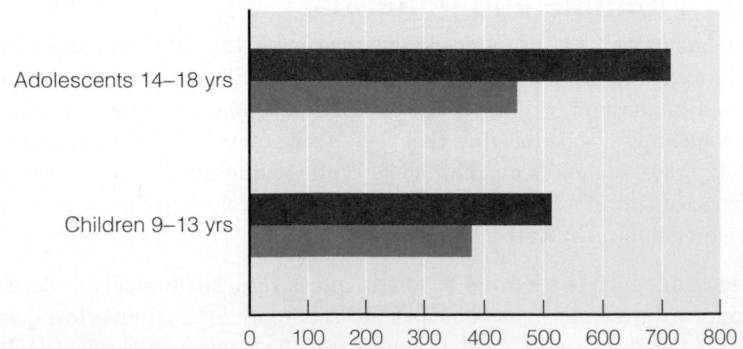

Adolescents 14–18 yrs

Children 9–13 yrs

0 100 200 300 400 500 600 700 800

Source: Statistics Canada. Average daily consumption (in grams) of selected beverages, by gender and age group, household population aged 1 to 18, Canada excluding territories, 2004, 2004 Canadian Community Health Survey – Nutrition. Reproduced and distributed on an "as is" basis with the permission of Statistics Canada.

that is, the amount of added caffeine plus the amount present in the guarana that was added, and so on. Indeed, a reminder about the importance of managing caffeine consumption by various subgroups of Canadians, including children and pregnant women, was released in June 2013 (see http://healthycanadians.gc.ca/recall-alert-rappel-avis/hc-sc/2013/34021a-eng.php).

In addition to needing dietary calcium, bones grow stronger with physical activity, but few high schools require students to attend physical activity classes (see Figure 14–6), so most teenagers must make a point to be physically active during leisure hours. Attainment of maximal bone mass during youth and adolescence is the best protection against age-related bone loss and fractures in later life.

KEY POINT

- Sufficient calcium intake is crucial during adolescence to support normal bone growth and density. When teens choose soft drinks and abandon milk, they increase their chances of bone disease later on in life.

The Body Changes of Adolescence   The adolescent growth spurt brings rapid growth and hormonal changes that affect every organ of the body, including the brain. An average girl's growth spurt begins at 10 or 11 years of age and peaks at about 12 years. Boys' growth spurts begin at 12 or 13 years and peak at about 14 years, slowing down at about 19. Two boys of the same age may vary in height by a foot, but if growing steadily, then each is fulfilling his genetic destiny according to an inborn schedule of events. Weight standards meant for adults are useless for adolescents. Parents should watch only for smooth progress and guard against comparisons that can diminish the child's self-image.

The energy needs of adolescents vary tremendously depending on growth rate, gender, body composition, and physical activity.[94] Energy balance is often difficult to regulate in this society—an estimated 18 percent of Canadian children and adolescents 2 to 17 years of age are overweight.[95] An active, growing boy of 15 may need 3,500 Calories or more a day just to maintain his weight, but an inactive girl of the same age whose growth has slowed may need fewer than 1,700 Calories to keep from becoming obese.

Girls normally develop a somewhat higher percentage of body fat than boys do, a fact that causes much needless worry about becoming overweight. Healthy, normal-weight teenagers are often "on diets" and make all sorts of unhealthy weight-loss attempts—even taking up smoking.[96] Some teens may benefit from lower-Calorie diets that increase fruit, vegetables, (skim) milk, and other nutritious foods while limiting cookies, cakes, soft drinks, fried snacks, and other less healthy choices. A few teens without diagnosable eating disorders have been reported to "diet" so severely that they stunted their own growth. Most weight-loss dieting undertaken by adolescents,

> Eating disorders may arise during the teen years and often prevent the adolescent from obtaining not only energy but also sufficient calcium and a number of other needed nutrients. Controversy 9 presents details.

Figure 14–5

Milk and Alternatives Consumption among Older Children and Younger Adolescents

The majority of girls (83%) and boys (61%) 10 to 16 years of age "do not meet their recommended minimum of three daily servings."

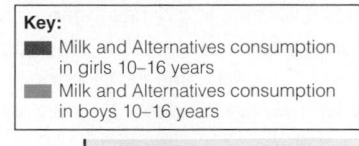

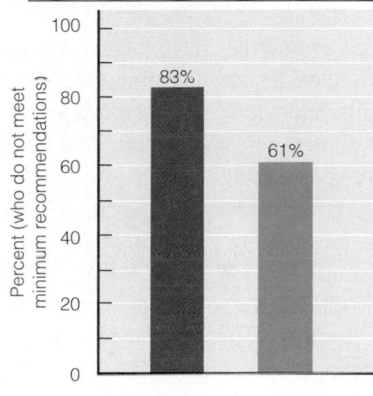

Source: Statistics Canada. Data from D. Garriguet, Nutrition: Findings from the CCHS: Overview of Canadians' Eating Habits, Catalogue no. 82-620-MIE-No. 2, 2006.

Figure 14–6

U.S. High School Students Attending Daily Physical Education Classes, 1991–2001

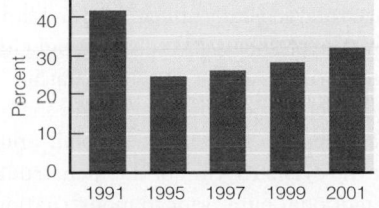

Source: Data from Centers for Disease Control and Prevention, National Youth Risk Behaviour Surveillance—United States, 2001, available at http://www.cdc.gov.

Nutrition and PMS

PMS affects up to 85 percent of menstruating women and adolescent girls.*,[1] The symptoms can include any or all of these: cramps and aches in the abdomen; back pain; headache; acne; swelling of the face and limbs associated with water retention; food cravings (especially for chocolate and other sweets); abnormal thirst; pain and lumps in the breasts; diarrhea; and mood changes, including both nervousness and depression. In a small number of severe cases, diagnosed as *premenstrual dysphoric disorder*, uncontrollable irritability, anxiety, and even panic can cause misery.[2]

An official diagnosis of ordinary PMS requires that such symptoms impair some facet of a woman's life. This is true for about 5 to 10 percent of menstruating women.[3] The timing and pattern of symptoms are also important, and women who seek help must keep daily records.

The cause of PMS is unknown. One proposed mechanism is an altered response to the two major regulatory hormones of the menstrual cycle: estrogen and progesterone.[4] In particular, the hormone estrogen can affect the brain's neurotransmitters and thereby alter mood. Adequate serotonin in the brain buoys a person's mood, but a serotonin deficiency creates a depressed mood and is related to major depressive disorders. In PMS, the natural rise and fall of estrogen levels in the blood may affect

*Consumer Corner references are listed separately at the end of the chapter.

the activities of serotonin in the brain during the last half of each menstrual cycle. Taking oral contraceptives, which supply estrogen, often improves mood by eliminating hormonal peaks and valleys. Taking antidepressant drugs that magnify the effects of serotonin may help in some cases, too.[5]

The major connections between PMS and nutrition concern energy metabolism and intakes of vitamin B_6 and calcium. Scientists believe that during the two weeks prior to menstruation, two events affect a woman's metabolism:

- The basal metabolic rate during sleep speeds up.
- Appetite and Calorie intakes increase.[6]

Most studies indicate that women take in an average of 300 Calories a day more during the 10 days prior to menstruation than during the 10 days after it. As a consequence, a woman who wishes to control her weight may find it easier to restrict Calories during the two weeks following menstruation. Limiting Calories may be harder during the two weeks before the next menstruation, however, because she is fighting a natural, hormone-governed increase in appetite.

A link with calcium is intriguing: in a few studies, calcium intakes of 1,000 to 1,300 milligrams per day significantly improved the irritability, cramping, and other symptoms of PMS.[7] Another review concluded that high-dose supplements of vitamin B_6 (100 mg/d) may alleviate some PMS symptoms, but this amount is also the DRI Tolerable

Upper Intake Level, indicating that, over the long term, such supplements may harm health. The following have not proven consistently useful in research: taking multivitamins, magnesium, or manganese supplements; cutting down on alcohol or sodium; or taking diuretics to relieve water retention.[8] If women retain sodium and water just before menstruation, that effect may be normal and desirable; diuretic drugs eliminate sodium and water but also cause a loss of potassium, potentially worsening PMS.

Consumption of black tea has been positively linked with PMS. Which component of tea—the caffeine, pigments, or other substances—may worsen PMS is not known, but evidence indicates a potential role for caffeine. Data from questionnaires administered to more than 800 women correlated caffeine intakes with PMS in a linear fashion: the more caffeine-containing beverages the women reported drinking, up to 10 cups per day, the more symptoms of PMS they reported suffering. Thus, a woman who finds menstrual symptoms troublesome might try a caffeine-free lifestyle for a while and see if her symptoms improve.

The woman with PMS should examine her total lifestyle, of which diet is only a part. Adequate sleep and physical activity help, and controlling stress may be important. She should also be on guard against bogus, possibly hazardous, PMS "cures" that abound in the marketplace.

---

particularly girls, is self-prescribed and generally unhealthful and can easily lead to nutrient deficiencies.[97] Such dieting may even promote *gain* of excess weight in the long run.[98]

Girls face a major change with the onset of menstruation. The hormones that regulate the menstrual cycle affect not just the uterus and the ovaries but the metabolic rate, glucose tolerance, appetite, food intake, mood, and behaviour as well. Most women live easily with the cyclic rhythm of the menstrual cycle, but some are afflicted with physical and emotional pain prior to menstruation, a condition called **premenstrual syndrome (PMS)** (see this chapter's Consumer Corner). Many teens struggle with outbreaks of acne.

premenstrual syndrome (PMS) a cluster of symptoms that some women experience prior to and during menstruation. They include, among others, abdominal cramps, back pain, swelling, headache, painful breasts, and mood changes.

- The adolescent growth spurt increases the need for energy and nutrients. The normal gain of body fat during adolescence may be mistaken for obesity, particularly in girls. Some self-prescribed diets are detrimental to health and growth.

Acne No one knows why some people get **acne** while others do not, but heredity plays a role—acne runs in families. The hormones of adolescence also play a role by stimulating the oil glands in the skin. The skin's natural oil is made in deep glands and is supposed to flow out through tiny ducts to the skin's surface. In acne, the ducts become clogged, and oily secretions build up in the ducts, causing irritation, inflammation, and breakouts of acne.

Various foods are often charged with aggravating acne, but research has demonstrated that two often-accused foods, chocolate and sugar, do *not* worsen acne. Evidence is less conclusive for cola beverages, fatty or greasy foods, milk, nuts, and foods or salt containing iodine, but research has not shown that any of these is an aggravating factor. Psychological stress, though, clearly worsens acne. Vacations from school often bring acne relief. Sun and swimming also help, perhaps because they are relaxing, the sun's rays kill bacteria, and water cleanses the skin. Prescribed antibiotic pills and ointments work for some.

The oral prescription medicine Accutane, made from vitamin A, is effective against deep lesions from a severe form of acne. Accutane is highly toxic, though, and causes serious birth defects if taken during pregnancy. Although medicines made from vitamin A are successful in treating acne, vitamin A itself has no effect, and supplements of the vitamin can be toxic. Quacks, undaunted by these facts, market potentially toxic vitamin A and related compounds as supplements to young people who hope to cure acne.

One remedy always works: time. While waiting, attend to basic needs. Petal-smooth, healthy skin reflects a tended, cared-for body whose owner provides it with nutrients and fluids to sustain it, exercise to stimulate it, and rest to restore its cells.

KEY POINT

- Although no foods have been proven to aggravate acne, stress can worsen it. Supplements are useless against acne, but sunlight, proven medications, and relief from stress can help.

Eating Patterns and Nutrient Intakes

During adolescence, food habits change for the worse, and teenagers often miss out on nutrients they need. Teens may begin to skip breakfast; choose less milk, fruit, juices, and vegetables; and consume more soft drinks each day.[99] Ideally, the adult becomes a **gatekeeper**, controlling the type and availability of food in the teenager's environment. Teenage sons and daughters and their friends should find plenty of nutritious, easy-to-grab food in the refrigerator (meat for sandwiches, raw vegetables, milk, fruit, and fruit juices) and more in the cupboards (breads, peanut butter, nuts, popcorn, cereals). In reality, in many households today, all of the adults work outside the home, and teens perform some of the gatekeeper's roles, such as shopping for groceries or choosing fast foods or prepared foods.

On average, about a fourth of a teenager's total daily energy intake comes from snacks, which, if chosen carefully, can contribute some of the needed nutrients. Often, however, teens choose foods that are too high in saturated fat and sodium and too low in fibre to support the future health of their arteries. Their calcium intakes often fall short unless they snack on dairy products, and they often fail to obtain enough iron and vitamin A. For iron and other nutrients, a teen could snack on iron-containing meat sandwiches, low-fat bran muffins, or tortillas with spicy bean spread along with a glass of orange juice to help maximize the iron's absorption.

Teenagers love fast food, and, fortunately, some fast-food establishments are offering more nutritious choices than the standard hamburger meal. The gatekeeper can help the teenager choose wisely by delivering nutrition information in a way that is meaningful to

acne chronic inflammation of the skin's follicles and oil-producing glands, which leads to an accumulation of oils inside the ducts that surround hairs; usually associated with the maturation of young adults.

gatekeeper with respect to nutrition, a key person who controls other people's access to foods and thereby affects their nutrition profoundly. Examples are the spouse who buys and cooks the food, the parent who feeds the children, and the caretaker in a daycare centre.

How Will You Age?

- In what ways do you expect your appearance to change as you age?
- What physical activities do you see yourself enjoying at age 70?
- What will be your financial status? Will you be independent?
- What will your sex life be like? Will others see you as sexy?
- How many friends will you have? What will you do together?
- Will you be happy? Cheerful? Curious? Depressed? Uninterested in life or new things?

Tips for Productive Aging

1. Simplify your life; identify priorities and trim the superfluous.
2. Pay attention to yourself—body, mind, and spirit.
3. Continue to teach and learn; take up leisure activities (painting, woodwork, nature).
4. Be flexible; learn to navigate change.
5. Be charitable; make it a practice to give (wisdom, experience, money, time, yourself).
6. Be financially astute; invest early for retirement.
7. Find and participate in activities that interest you; you'll live better in retirement if you do.
8. Commit to good nutrition and exercise, no matter what.
9. Think about your past and future; deal with your mortality.
10. Be involved; be positive; link with others.

Source: Reprinted from Productive Aging: A Quality of Life Agenda by KERSCHNER HELEN and PEGUES JO ANN M. Journal of the American Dietetic Association Elsevier Limited December 1998 pp. 1445–1448 with permission from Elsevier [from Figure 2].

- The DRI nutrient intake reports provide separate recommendations for those 51–70 years and for those 70 and older. See the inside front cover.

life expectancy the average number of years lived by people in a given society.

life span the maximum number of years of life attainable by a member of a species.

longevity long duration of life.

the individual teen. Those who are prone to gain weight will often open their ears to news about Calories in fast foods. Others attend best to information about the negative effects of an ill-chosen diet on sport performance. Still others are fascinated to learn of the skin's need for vitamins. Rather than dictating a list of dos and don'ts, the wise gatekeeper does more listening than talking.[100] When asked, teens often identify for themselves the factors blocking healthy behaviours, and acknowledging such factors is the first step in eliminating them.

The gatekeeper can set a good example, provide an environment with plenty of nutritious foods, keep lines of communication open, and stand by with reliable nutrition information and advice, but the rest is up to the teens themselves. Ultimately, they make the choices.

KEY POINT

- With planning, the gatekeeper can encourage teens to meet nutrient requirements by providing nutritious snacks.

The Later Years

The title may imply a section about older people, but it is relevant even if you are only 20 years old. How you live and think at 20 years of age affects the quality of your life at 60 or 80 years. According to an old saying, "as the twig is bent, so grows the tree." Unlike a tree, however, you can bend your own twig.

Before you will adopt nutrition behaviours to enhance your health in old age, you must accept on a personal level that you yourself are aging. To learn what negative and positive views you hold about aging, try answering the questions in the margin. Your answers reveal not only what you think of older people now but also what will probably become of you. When older adults were asked to give tips to younger people on how to live life fully in the later years, they offered 10 suggestions, also listed in the margin.

The "greying" of North America is evident. Since 1950, the population over age 65 has doubled, and people over 85 years old are the fastest-growing age group.[101] People reaching and exceeding age 100 have doubled in number in the last decade, and many of the world's populations have followed similar trends.

In Canada, the **life expectancy** is 83 years for women and 79 years for men.[102] Once a person survives the perils of youth and middle age to reach age 80, women can expect to survive an additional nine years, on average; men survive an additional seven. One expert opinion estimates that 70–80 percent of the average person's life expectancy may depend on individual health-related behaviours, with genes determining the remaining 20–30 percent.[103]

The biological schedule that we call aging cuts off life at a genetically fixed point in time. The **life span** (the maximum length of life possible for a species) of human beings is believed to be 130 years. Even this limit may one day be challenged with advances in medical and genetic technologies. One caution: to date, scientists who study the aging process have found no specific diet or nutrient supplement that will increase **longevity**, although there are hundreds of dubious claims to the contrary.

KEY POINT

- Life expectancy for Canadian adults increased in the 20th century. Life choices can greatly affect how long a person lives and the quality of life in the later years. No diet or supplement can extend life.

Nutrition in the Later Years

Nutrient needs become more individual with age, depending on genetics and individual medical history. For example, one person's stomach acid secretion, which helps in iron absorption, may decline, so that person may need more iron. Another person may excrete more folate due to past liver disease and thus need a higher dose. Table 14–7 lists some changes of aging that can affect nutrition.

Table 14–7

Physical Changes of Aging That Affect Nutrition

Digestive tract	Intestines lose muscle strength, resulting in sluggish motility that leads to constipation. Stomach inflammation, abnormal bacterial growth, and greatly reduced acid output impair digestion and absorption. Pain and fear of choking may cause food avoidance or reduced intake.
Hormones	For example, the pancreas secretes less insulin and cells become less responsive, causing abnormal glucose metabolism.
Mouth	Tooth loss, gum disease, and reduced salivary output impede chewing and swallowing. Choking may become likely; pain may cause avoidance of hard-to-chew foods.
Sensory organs	Diminished sight can make food shopping and preparation difficult; diminished senses of smell and taste may reduce appetite, although research is needed to clarify this effect.
Body composition	Weight loss and decline in lean body mass lead to lowered energy requirements. May be preventable or reversible through physical activity.

Energy and Activity

Energy needs often decrease with advancing age. One reason is that the number of active cells in each organ decreases, reducing the body's overall metabolic rate, although much of this loss may not be inevitable. Another reason is that older people often reduce their physical activity, and their lean tissue diminishes.

After about the age of 50, the intake recommendation for energy assumes about a 5 percent reduction in energy output per decade. As in other groups, obesity is increasingly a problem. For those who must limit energy intake, there is little leeway in the diet for foods of low nutrient density such as sugars, fats, and alcohol.

Current thinking refutes the idea that declining energy needs are unavoidable, however. Physical activity and a diet adequate in nutrients and rich in phytochemicals are key not only to maintaining energy needs but also to upholding other functions, such as a healthy immune response and mental functioning.[104] Physical activity and diet also oppose a destructive spiral of sedentary behaviour and mental and physical losses in the elderly, sometimes called the "dwindles."[105] The "dwindles" refers to a complex of interacting failures in the elderly including

- Decreased physical ability to function
- Diminished mental function
- Malnutrition
- Social withdrawal
- Weight loss

Involuntary weight loss deserves immediate attention in the older person. It could be the result of some easily treatable condition, such as ulcers.[106] For people older than 70 years, the best health and lowest risk of death have been observed in those who maintain a body mass index (BMI) between 25 and 32, which is higher than the optimal BMI for younger people (18.5 to 25) (also see the BMI Nomogram on page Z at the back of the book and the Canadian Guidelines for Body Weight Classification in Adults, http://www .hc-sc.gc.ca/fn-an/nutrition/weights-poids/guide-ld-adult/index-eng.php, with particular attention to those 65 years and older).

Body mass index was discussed in Chapter 9.

The Integrated Pan-Canadian Healthy Living Strategy 2005 *(Physical Activity Goal)*

- "By 2015, increase by 20% the proportion of Canadians who participate in regular physical activity based on 30 minutes/day of moderate to vigorous activity."

Source: The Integrated Pan-Canadian Healthy Living Strategy 2005 *The Secretariat for the Intersectoral Healthy Living Network in partnership with the F/P/T Healthy Living Task Group and the F/P/T Advisory Committee on Population Health and Health Security (ACPHHS) Cat. No. HP10-1/2005 ISBN 0-662-69384-1 http://www.phac-aspc.gc.ca/hl-vs-strat/pdf/ hls_e.pdf.*

This chapter's Think Fitness feature emphasizes the importance of physical activity to maintaining body tissue integrity throughout life.[107] An expert in the nutrition of aging phrases it this way:

> We now know that physically active elders can build and rebuild muscle mass. Even the frail elderly can improve function by a remarkable 200 percent on a short, focused exercise regimen. No single feature of aging can more dramatically affect basal metabolism, insulin sensitivity, Calorie intake, appetite, breathing, ambulation, mobility, and independence than muscle mass.[108]

Some people in their *nineties* have gained muscle mass, regained or improved their balance, and added pep to their walking steps and regained some precious independence after just eight weeks of weight training. People spending energy in physical activity can also eat more food (and/or nutritional supplements), gaining important nutrients including high-quality protein to maintain and possibly build muscle tissue. Sadly, over 90 percent of older U.S. adults fail to meet national exercise objectives and miss the opportunity for more robust health and fitness in their later years.[109]

The photos below dramatize this point: they compare cross-sections of the thigh of a young woman and of an older woman to demonstrate the muscle loss typical of sedentary aging, which brings with it destructive weakness, poor balance, and deterioration of health and vigour.[110] Strength training helps prevent at least some of this muscle loss.

Some unscrupulous practitioners try to sell elderly people a shortcut to muscle and bone tissue retention in the form of growth hormone (GH) "therapy." Although secretion of GH does decline with age, science does not yet support its usefulness or safety in reversing the tissue loss of aging.

KEY POINT

- Energy needs decrease with age, but exercise burns off excess fuel, maintains lean tissue, and brings health benefits.

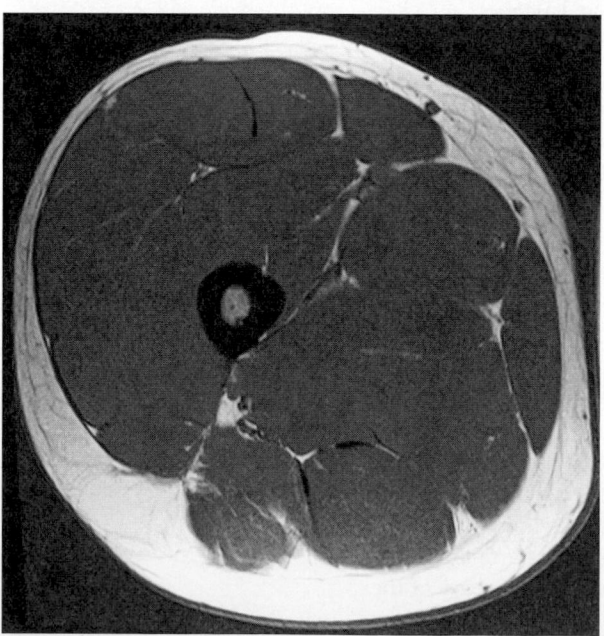 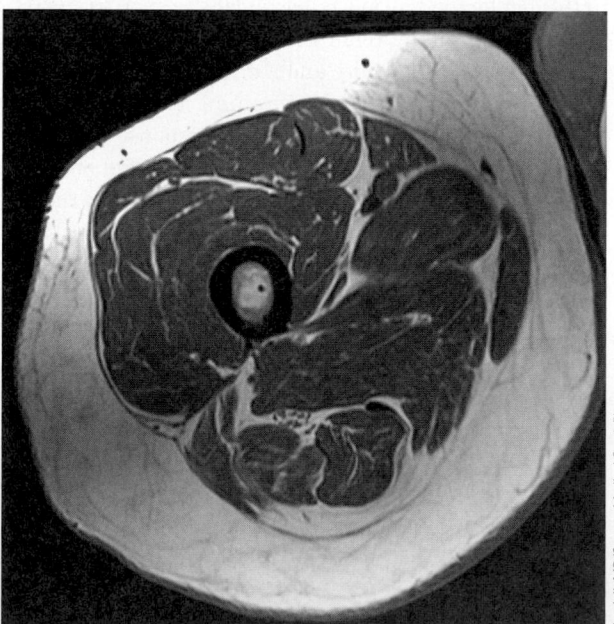

Cross-sections of two thighs. These two women's thighs may appear to be about the same size from the outside, but the 20-year-old woman's thigh (left) is dense with muscle tissue (dark areas). The 64-year-old woman's thigh (right) has lost muscle and gained fat, changes that may be largely preventable with strength-building physical activities.

Think Fitness move it! Benefits of Physical Activity for the Older Adult

Physically active older adults have more flexibility and endurance, more lean body mass, a better sense of balance, greater blood flow to the brain, and stronger immune systems; they suffer fewer falls and broken bones; experience fewer symptoms of arthritis, better retain cognitive abilities, enjoy better overall health; and even live longer than their less-fit peers. Older people should feel free to exercise in their own way (as outlined in Canadian Physical Activity Guidelines for Older Adults 65 Years and Older, at http://www.csep.ca/english/view.asp?x=804), at their own pace, and should attend to fluid and nutrient needs to support activity. Any exercise, even a 10-minute walk a day or strength and flexibility training while seated, provides progressive benefits. Great achievements are possible, and improvements are inevitable. In fact, older runners, especially women, have logged better personal time improvements than younger runners in the New York City Marathon over the past two decades.[111] An aging person unavoidably loses some capacity to perform exercise, however, so routines should be tailored to abilities.

Protein Needs

Protein needs remain about the same for older people as for young adults, although emerging data is beginning to challenge protein needs for both groups, that is, recommend higher protein levels. Adequate daily protein is needed to replace losses, but too much protein can be hard on the ailing kidneys of older adults because of the extra burden of excreting its nitrogen. Which protein-rich foods elders choose to eat takes on extra importance, too. For older people who have lost their teeth, chewing tough foods is next to impossible, and they need soft cooked beans or meat or chopped foods. Individuals with chronic constipation, heart disease, or diabetes may benefit from fibre-rich low-fat legumes and grains as sources of protein. Should a flagging appetite reduce food intake, liquid nutritional formulas between meals can supply needed energy, protein, and other nutrients.[112]

These chair volleyball players are working their upper bodies and having fun, while remaining safely seated.

KEY POINT

- Protein needs remain about the same through adult life, but choosing low-fat fibre-rich protein foods may help control other health problems.

Carbohydrates and Fibre

The recommendation to obtain ample amounts of mostly whole-grain breads, cereals, rice, and pasta holds true for older people. As for younger people, a steady supply of carbohydrate is essential for optimal brain functioning.[113] With age, fibre takes on extra importance for its role against constipation, a common complaint among older adults and among nursing home residents in particular. Fruit and vegetables supply viscous (soluble) fibres thought to help ward off diseases of aging, but factors such as transportation problems, limited cooking facilities, and chewing problems limit some elderly people's intakes of fresh fruit and vegetables.[114] Most older adults do not obtain the recommended daily 25 or more grams of fibre (14 g per 1,000 Cal).[115] When low fibre intakes are combined with low fluid intakes, inadequate exercise, and constipating medications, constipation becomes inevitable.

KEY POINT

- Generous carbohydrate intakes are recommended for older adults. Including fibre in the diet is important to avoid constipation.

Bogus or Unproven Arthritis Treatments
- Alfalfa tea
- Aloe vera liquid
- Any of the amino acids
- Burdock root
- Calcium
- Celery juice
- Copper or copper complexes
- Dimethyl sulphoxide (DMSO)
- Fasting
- Fresh fruit
- Honey
- Inositol
- Kelp
- Lecithin
- Melatonin
- Para-aminobenzoic acid (PABA)
- Raw liver
- Selenium
- Superoxide dismutase (SOD)
- Vitamin or mineral supplements
- Watercress
- Yeast
- Zinc
- 100 other substances

Fats and Arthritis

Older adults must attend to fat intakes for several reasons. Consuming enough of the essential fatty acids supports continued good health, and limiting intakes of saturated and *trans* fats is a priority to minimize the risk of heart disease. Many of the foods lowest in saturated fat are richest in vitamins, minerals, and phytochemicals. In addition, certain fats may affect one type of **arthritis**, a painful deterioration and swelling of the joints. High-fat diets also correlate with obesity, an arthritis risk factor.

Two kinds of arthritis attack the joints: osteoarthritis and rheumatoid arthritis. The more common type, osteoarthritis, affects upward of 40 percent of adults; it results from being overweight or from unknown causes as people age.[116] During movement, the ends of healthy bones are protected by small sacs of fluid that act as lubricants. With arthritis, the sacs erode, cartilage and bone ends disintegrate, and joints become malformed and painful to move. Nutrition does not seem to play a role in the causation of osteoarthritis. High intakes of vitamins E and C, in particular, do not slow progression or ease pain.[117] Low intake of vitamin D may speed its progression, however. Loss of body weight often brings relief, particularly in the knees.

Rheumatoid arthritis can strike at any age. It probably arises from a malfunction of the immune system—the immune system mistakenly attacks the bone coverings as if they were foreign tissue. One positive nutrition link centres around Mediterranean-style diets rich in antioxidants and the omega-3 fatty acid, EPA, found in fish oil.[118] EPA may interfere with activities of hormonelike chemicals involved in inflammation. The antioxidants in vegetables, fruit, nuts, and olive oil may also interfere with inflammation by reducing oxidative stress in the joints.[119] Supplemental doses of vitamin C may worsen the condition, if the results of animal studies also prove true for people.[120] The same diet recommended for heart health—one low in saturated fats and high in fruit, vegetables, whole grains, and oils from fish—may help prevent or reduce the inflammation in the joints that makes arthritis so painful.[121]

No one universally effective diet for arthritis relief is known. Weight loss helps those who are overweight; strength training may help others.[122] Many *ineffective* or unproven "cures" are sold, however, as the margin list shows. Traditional medical interventions for arthritis include medication and surgery. Two popular supplements—glucosamine and chondroitin—may indeed relieve pain and improve mobility, and they may even slow the progression of osteoarthritis if substantial additional research bears out preliminary findings.[123]

> Medical drugs used to relieve arthritis can impose nutrition risks. Controversy 14 in this chapter explains.

KEY POINT

- A diet high in fruit and vegetables and low in fats of meat and dairy products may improve some symptoms of arthritis. Omega-3 fatty acids may also have a positive effect.

Vitamin Needs

Vitamin A stands alone among the vitamins in that its absorption appears to increase with aging. For this reason, some researchers have proposed lowering the vitamin A requirement for aged populations. Others resist this proposal because foods containing vitamin A and its precursor beta-carotene are under study for preventing oxidative damage to body tissues, an effect described in Chapter 7.

As people age, vitamin D synthesis declines fourfold, setting the stage for deficiency. Many older adults drink little or no vitamin D-fortified milk and get little or no exposure to sunlight. Thus, the Recommended Dietary Allowance (RDA) for vitamin D for everyone from 1 to 70 years old is 15 micrograms (600 IU) and rises to 20 micrograms (800 IU) for those 71 and over. Every elderly person should obtain this amount of vitamin D and get outside more often (or sit by a sunny open window for a while).[124] Furthermore, Health Canada recommends, "In addition to following Canada's Food Guide, everyone over the age of 50 should take a daily vitamin D supplement of 10 µg (400 IU)" (http://www.hc-sc.gc.ca/fn-an/food-guide-aliment/choose-choix/index-eng.php; click on "Advice for different ages and stages").

arthritis a usually painful inflammation of joints caused by many conditions, including infections, metabolic disturbances, or injury; usually results in altered joint structure and loss of function.

The DRI committee has recommended that adults aged 51 years and older obtain 2.4 micrograms of vitamin B_{12} daily *and* that vitamin B_{12}-fortified foods (such as fortified cereals) or supplements be used to meet much of this intake.[125] The committee's recommendation reflects the finding that many people older than 50 years lose the ability to produce enough stomach acid to make the protein-bound form of vitamin B_{12} available for absorption. Vitamin B_{12} may be a problem for 10–15 percent of those over 60 who may suffer a serious deficiency that goes unrecognized and so untreated.[126] Synthetic vitamin B_{12} is reliably absorbed, however, and much misery can be averted by preventing deficiencies of vitamin B_{12} in elderly people.[127] In addition to other functions, a sufficiency of vitamin B_{12} along with two other B vitamins, folate and vitamin B_6, may prevent some loss of mental ability that commonly occurs among older people.[128] Other nutrients, including antioxidants such as vitamin E, may also play roles in conserving immunity, mental functions, and eyesight in the aged.[129]

Several links have emerged between the nutrients and phytochemicals in foods and age-related changes in the eyes. One theory concerns the leading cause of permanent blindness in people over age 60—macular degeneration, described in Chapter 7.[130] People with lifelong high intakes of vegetables, particularly the carotenoid-rich dark green leafy vegetables such as spinach and collard greens, rarely suffer from macular degeneration. These vegetables are rich in certain carotenoid phytochemicals that

The macula of the eye was described in Chapter 7.

may protect the eyes from this destructive disease.*,[131] Diets high in fat may also pose a risk for macular degeneration, but the fatty acids of fish oils may be protective.[132]

Another problem facing older people is **cataracts**. A cataract is a clouding of the lens that impairs vision and leads to blindness. Only 5 percent of people younger than 50 years have cataracts; by age 65, the percentage jumps to over 50 percent.

The lens of the eye is easily oxidized. People who shun fruit and green vegetables obtain too few antioxidants that may protect against both macular degeneration and cataracts. Some studies suggest that a diet providing ample carotenoids, vitamin C, and vitamin E may be especially important for preventing early onset of cataracts.[133] Also, cataracts can occur even in well-nourished individuals due to injury, sun exposure, or other trauma.[134] Most cataracts are vaguely called *senile cataracts*, meaning "caused by aging."

Water and the Minerals

Dehydration is a major risk for older adults: the thirst mechanism may become imprecise, and older people may go for long periods without drinking fluids. The kidneys also become less efficient in recapturing water before it is lost as urine. This water loss causes some problems and worsens others, such as constipation and bladder problems. In a person with asthma, dehydration thickens mucus in the lungs, which may then block airways. To prevent dehydration, older adults need to drink at least 6 cups of fluids each day to provide the needed water.[135]

A person we know uses this trick to ensure getting enough water: he keeps six inexpensive 250-millilitre cups in the cupboard. Through the day he uses each to drink one cup of fluid, including juices and other beverages, collecting the used cups in the dish drain. (For clear soups and other hot beverages, he simply moves one of his cups for each 250 mL consumed from his bowl or mug.) In the afternoon he checks the cupboard and drinks from any remaining cups. For him, drinking enough fluid has become a habit, and seldom are any cups left in the cupboard after supper.

*The carotenoids are lutein and zeaxanthin, which help form pigments of the macula of the eye.

Water Recommendation for Adults
- Total water intake women ~2.5 L/d, men ~3.5 L/d

Adults of all ages need 6–8 glasses of fluid each day.

© Rob Marmion/Shutterstock

cataracts (CAT-uh-racts) clouding of the lens of the eye that can lead to blindness. Cataracts can be caused by injury, viral infection, toxic substances, genetic disorders, and, possibly, some nutrient deficiencies or imbalances.

- These foods provide iron and zinc together: meat, poultry, liver, oysters, whole grains, fortified breakfast cereals,* and legumes.

*Cereals fortified with iron and zinc may not be available in Canada.

Iron Iron status generally improves in later life, especially in women after menstruation ceases and in those who take iron supplements, eat red meat regularly, and include vitamin C-rich fruits in their daily diet.[136] When iron-deficiency anemia does occur, diminished appetite with low food intake is often the cause. Aside from diet, other factors make iron deficiency likely in older people:

- Chronic blood loss from ulcers or hemorrhoids
- Poor iron absorption due to reduced stomach acid secretion
- Antacid use, which interferes with iron absorption
- Use of medicines that cause blood loss, including anticoagulants, aspirin, and arthritis medicines

Older people take more medicines than others, and drug and nutrient interactions are common.

Zinc Zinc deficiencies are also common in older people. Zinc deficiency can depress the appetite and blunt the sense of taste, thereby leading to low food intakes and worsening of zinc status. Many medications interfere with the body's absorption or use of zinc, and older adults' medicine load can worsen zinc deficiency.

Research on zinc supplements demonstrates that nutrient supplements taken by the elderly can bring unexpected results. Researchers studying the immune response of elderly people sometimes observe a reduced immune response, sometimes an enhanced response, and sometimes no effect in those given supplements of zinc.[137]

Calcium-rich foods are listed in Chapter 8 (Snapshot 8–1, page 318), and Controversy 8 discusses the threat to the bones from osteoporosis.

Calcium With aging, calcium absorption declines; at the same time, many adult women in Canada fail to obtain enough calcium, and many men do, too.[138] If fresh milk causes stomach discomfort, as the majority of older people report, then lactose-reduced milk or other calcium-rich foods should take its place.

KEY POINT

- Aging alters vitamin and mineral needs. Some needs rise, while others decline.

 Elderly people often benefit from a balanced low-dose vitamin and mineral supplement.[139] Older people taking such supplements suffer fewer sicknesses caused by infection. Vitamin A has been seen to depress the immunity of elders, while vitamin E may enhance it. A summary of the effects of aging on nutrient needs appears in Table 14–8.

Can Nutrition Help People Live Longer?

The evidence concerning nutrition and longevity is intriguing. In a classic study, researchers in California observed nearly 7,000 adults and noticed that some were young for their ages, while others were old for their ages.[140] To uncover what made the difference, the researchers focused on health habits and identified six factors that affect physiological age. Three of the six factors were related to nutrition:

- Abstinence from, or moderation in, alcohol use
- Regular nutritious meals
- Weight control

The other three were regular adequate sleep, abstinence from smoking, and regular physical activity. The physical health of those who engaged in all six positive health practices was comparable to that of people 30 years younger who engaged in few or none. Numerous studies have confirmed the benefits of such lifestyle factors that people can control.[141] These findings suggest that even though people cannot alter the year of their birth, they can alter the probable length and quality of their lives. Table 14–9 in the margin on the next page and Table 14–10 on page 630 list some changes of aging that are beyond control and some that may yield to lifestyle influences.

Table 14–8

Summary of Nutrient Concerns in Aging

Nutrient	Effects of Aging	Comments
Energy	Need decreases.	Physical activity moderates the decline.
Fibre	Low intakes make constipation likely.	Inadequate water intakes and physical inactivity compound constipation.
Protein	Needs stay the same.	Low-fat, high-fibre legumes and grains meet both protein and other needs.
Vitamin A	Absorption increases.	Supplements normally not needed.
Vitamin D	Increased likelihood of inadequate intake; skin synthesis declines.	Daily moderate exposure to sunlight may be of benefit.
Vitamin B$_{12}$	Malabsorption of some forms.	Foods fortified with synthetic vitamin B$_{12}$ or a low-dose supplement may be of benefit in addition to a balanced diet.
Water	Lack of thirst and increased urine output make dehydration likely.	Mild dehydration is a common cause of confusion.
Iron	In women, status improves after menopause; deficiencies linked to chronic blood losses and low stomach acid output.	Stomach acid required for absorption; antacid or other medicine use may aggravate iron deficiency; vitamin C and meat enhance absorption.
Zinc	Intakes are often inadequate and absorption may be poor, but needs may also increase.	Medications interfere with absorption; deficiency may depress appetite and sense of taste.
Calcium	Intakes may be low; osteoporosis becomes common.	Lactose intolerance commonly prevents milk intake; substitutes are needed.

Evidence that diet might influence life span emerged more than a half-century ago from experiments on rats. Researchers fed a group of young rats diets extremely low in energy, while control rats ate normally. The starved rats stopped growing while the control rats grew normally; when the researchers increased food energy, growth resumed. Many of the starved group died young from malnutrition. The few survivors, though permanently deformed from their ordeal, remained alive far beyond the normal life span for such animals and developed diseases of aging much later than normal.

Present-day studies have repeated these findings with more moderate diets that mildly restrict energy and provide adequate nutrients and do not inflict physical malformations. Restricted animals retain youthfulness longer and develop fewer of the factors associated with chronic diseases, such as high blood pressure, changes in immune functions, and glucose intolerance.[142] News from an ongoing study of energy-restricted monkeys reports that as the animals age, the restricted group has retained healthy blood glucose and insulin responses and has healthier blood lipid profiles than the freely fed controls.[143] Even occasional fasting or energy restriction without lifetime restriction may provide benefits, at least in laboratory mice.[144] Evidence from other species (see the margin) suggests that this effect spans many biological systems.

As for whether such animal findings can be applied to human beings, the answer may be yes. Human beings share a significant portion of their genome with other species, making human beings more or less metabolically similar to them (see the margin on the next page). Many of the physiological responses seen in rats during energy restriction are also observed in human beings who moderately restrict energy

Table 14–9

Changes with Age You Probably Must Accept

These changes are probably beyond your control:
- ✔ Greying of hair
- ✔ Balding
- ✔ Some drying and wrinkling of skin
- ✔ Impairment of near vision
- ✔ Some loss of hearing
- ✔ Reduced taste and smell sensitivity
- ✔ Reduced touch sensitivity
- ✔ Slowed reactions (reflexes)
- ✔ Slowed mental function
- ✔ Diminished visual memory
- ✔ Menopause (women)
- ✔ Loss of fertility (men)
- ✔ Loss of joint elasticity

Table 14–10

Changes with Age You Probably Can Slow or Prevent

By exercising, eating an adequate diet, reducing stress, and planning ahead, you may be able to slow or prevent:

- Wrinkling of skin due to sun damage
- Some forms of mental confusion
- Elevated blood pressure
- Accelerated resting heart rate
- Reduced lung capacity and oxygen uptake
- Increased body fatness
- Elevated blood cholesterol
- Slowed energy metabolism
- Decreased maximum work rate
- Loss of sexual functioning
- Loss of joint flexibility
- Diminished oral health: loss of teeth, gum disease
- Bone loss
- Digestive problems, constipation

Differences in Maximum Life Span between Animals Eating Normally and Those That Are Energy-Restricted

- Rats:
  Normal diet, 33 months
  Restricted diet, 47 months
- Spiders:
  Normal diet, 100 days
  Restricted diet, 139 days
- Single-celled animals (protozoans):
  Normal diet, 13 days
  Restricted diet, 25 days

According to the U.S. National Institutes of Health, the Human Genome Is

- 30% similar to yeast
- 40% similar to a worm
- 50% similar to a banana
- 60% similar to a housefly
- 90% similar to a mouse
- 98.4% similar to a monkey
- 99.9% similar to other human beings (except for identical twins who share an identical genome)

- Some degree of memory loss is often simply a function of aging and is termed *benign* (meaning "harmless") *senescent* (meaning "of aging") *forgetfulness*. Occasional forgetful moments generally do not forecast the development of Alzheimer's disease in an older person.

senile dementia the loss of brain function beyond the normal loss of physical adeptness and memory that occurs with aging.

intakes. Researchers recently measured blood pressure, blood LDL concentration, and other atherosclerosis risk factors in a group of 18 people who have for years voluntarily reduced their caloric intakes by 1,100 to 1,900 Calories a day. The researchers concluded that Calorie restriction "results in profound and sustained beneficial effects on the major atherosclerosis risk factors. . . ."[145] Much more evidence must be collected, however, before such findings can be applied to the general population.

Investigators have proposed several mechanisms to explain how energy restriction prolongs life in rats, but none have been proven. A delay in the onset of age-related diseases has already been mentioned. Genetics may play a role: genes that modulate the aging process seem to become less active when food energy is scarce.[146] Current research is focused on the genetic response of both young and old rats to energy restriction in the hope of identifying genes that play key roles in aging. Some predict that future drugs and treatments may one day mimic the effects of energy restriction at the genetic level and so confer its life-extending effects without the drawbacks of Calorie restriction.[147]

A free-radical hypothesis blames damage from oxidative stress for the physical deterioration associated with aging. The body's internal antioxidant enzymes diminish with age. Many "age-related" degenerative diseases are linked to free-radical damage, while the antioxidant-rich Mediterranean diet is linked with longevity.[148] However, the storm of "life-extending" pills, supplements, and treatments on the market is worthless. Research proves that it's better to spend money on fresh fruit and green and yellow vegetables, which are naturally rich sources of antioxidants and are linked with many health benefits (see Controversy 2).

KEY POINT

- Lifestyle factors can make a difference in aging. In rats and other species, food energy deprivation may lengthen the lives of individuals. Claims for life extension through antioxidants or other supplements are common hoaxes.

Can Foods or Supplements Affect the Course of Alzheimer's Disease?

Today, Alzheimer's disease affects around 500,000 Canadians over 65 years old, and an estimated 1,000,000 in this age group are expected to develop Alzheimer's or a related disease by 2031.[149] In Alzheimer's disease, the most prevalent form of **senile dementia**, abnormal deterioration occurs in the areas of the brain that coordinate memory and cognition. In Alzheimer's disease, the brain is littered with clumps of abnormal protein fragments that clog the brain and damage or kill certain nerve cells.* The defining symptom of Alzheimer's is impairment of memory and reasoning powers, but it may be accompanied by loss of the ability to communicate; loss of physical capabilities; anxiety; delusions; depression; inappropriate behaviour; irritability; sleep disturbance; and, eventually, loss of life itself.[150] Once the destruction begins, the outlook for its reversal is most often bleak.[151] More research is needed, quickly, to perfect a drug or vaccine to block the destructive progression of the disease and to further investigate the positive effects of high-dose vitamin E on functional decline in mild to moderate Alzheimer's disease.[152]

Research has revealed only weak links between nutrition and Alzheimer's disease (see Table 14–11). For example, a causal connection with a buildup of the mineral aluminum seems unlikely. There is conflicting evidence as to whether supplements of zinc or other trace minerals worsen Alzheimer's disease, so to err on the safe side, food sources, not concentrated supplements, of trace minerals are advisable for people with the disease.[153] Also, supplements of choline and lecithin (first mentioned in Chapter 5), once investigated as potential treatments, have had no consistent effect on memory, mental functioning, or the progression of Alzheimer's. Fish oils may hold promise, however—learning and memory depend on DHA, an omega-3 fatty acid. Diets deficient in omega-3 fatty acids produce degeneration of certain brain proteins

*The protein fragments are called *beta-amyloid*.

Table 14-11

Possible Links between Nutrition and Alzheimer's Disease

Researchers are exploring the following links between nutrition and Alzheimer's disease:

- *Aluminum in the brain tissues.* Brain aluminum exceeds normal brain aluminum by some 10–30 times, but blood and hair aluminum remains normal, indicating that the accumulation is caused by something in the brain itself, not by high aluminum in the diet.
- *Elevated levels of copper, iron, and zinc in the brain tissues.* Such elements may accelerate the progression of the disease, possibly by increasing the formation of free radicals that produce oxidative stress.[a] Their accumulation, however, may simply be a result of the disease process.
- *Low antioxidant nutrient intake.* Free radicals may attack brain tissue, damaging DNA, cell membranes, and proteins. This effect could plausibly be worsened by a diet low in fruit and vegetables, antioxidant nutrients, or soy foods.[b]
- *Low fish oil and fish intakes.* A number of observations suggest that low fish intake is often linked with Alzheimer's disease incidence. A recent study of over 800 elderly people concludes that intake of omega-3 fatty acids and weekly meals of fish may reduce the risk.
- *Obesity and overweight.* In one study, the effect of body weight in the elderly on development of Alzheimer's disease, particularly among women, was dramatic—disease risk increased 36 percent for each 1-point increase in BMI (see inside back cover).[c]
- *Fats and saturated fats.* No clear consensus exists on whether a high intake of saturated or *trans* fat may increase risk or whether unsaturated and unhydrogenated fats may reduce it.[d]
- *Gene and diet interactions.* Several genes responsible for rare, inherited Alzheimer's disease account for about 5 percent of cases, but investigations into the roles of other genes suggest they may increase susceptibility. Dietary factors, such as a high-Calorie diet or folate deficiency, may foster the expression of the disease in those with a genetic predisposition to develop it.[e]

[a]M. J. Engelhart and coauthors, Dietary intake of antioxidants and risk of Alzheimer disease, Journal of the American Medical Association 287 (2002): 3223–3229; M. C. Morris, Dietary intake of antioxidant nutrients and the risk of incident Alzheimer disease in a biracial community study, Journal of the American Medical Association 287 (2002): 3230–3237; Y. Christen, Oxidative stress and Alzheimer disease, American Journal of Clinical Nutrition 71 (2000): 621S–629S.

[b]R. H. Liu, Health benefits of fruit and vegetables are from additive and synergistic combinations of phytochemicals, American Journal of Clinical Nutrition 78 (2003): 517S–520S; A. Martin, Antioxidant vitamins E and C and risk of Alzheimer's disease, Nutrition Reviews 61 (2003): 69–73; J. A. Joseph and coauthors, Blueberry supplementation enhances signaling and prevents behavioural deficits in an Alzheimer disease model, Nutritional Neuroscience 6 (2003): 153–162; S. E. File, New studies: Soy appears to benefit cognitive function, The Soy Connection, July 2003, pp. 1–2; L. R. White and coauthors, Brain aging and midlife tofu consumption, Journal of the American College of Nutrition 19 (2000): 207–209; M. Grundman, Vitamin E and Alzheimer disease: The basis for additional clinical trials, American Journal of Clinical Nutrition 71 (2000): 630S–636S.

[c]D. Gustafson and coauthors, An 18-year follow-up of overweight and risk of Alzheimer disease, Archives of Internal Medicine 163 (2003): 1524–1528.

[d]M. C. Morris and coauthors, Dietary fats and the risk of incident Alzheimer disease, Archives of Neurology 60 (2003): 194–200; M. J. Engelhart and coauthors, Diet and risk of dementia: Does fat matter? The Rotterdam Study, Neurology 59 (2002): 1915–1921.

[e]A. Rocchi and coauthors, Causative and susceptibility genes for Alzheimer's disease: A review, Brain Research Bulletin 61 (2003): 1–24; M. P. Mattson, Gene-diet interactions in brain aging and neurodegenerative disorders, Annals of Internal Medicine 139 (2003): 441–444.

in mice, a finding researchers hope will yield treatments to avert some Alzheimer's damage in people.[154]

The results of one small study seemed to indicate a modest benefit from the medicinal herb ginkgo biloba in cognitive and social functioning in Alzheimer's patients. More recent results from well-controlled studies do not support this result, however.[155] To date, no proven benefits are available from herbs or other remedies, but claims from quacks are all too common.

Preventing weight loss is an important nutrition concern for the person suffering with Alzheimer's disease.[156] Depression and forgetfulness can lead to skipped meals and poor food choices. Caregivers can help by providing well-liked, well-balanced, and well-tolerated meals and snacks served in a cheerful, peaceful atmosphere.

- "Smart" drugs, drinks, and supplements, sold with promises of brainpower enhancement, are generally useless except for the caffeine or other stimulant "wake-up" effects.

KEY POINT

- Alzheimer's disease causes some degree of brain deterioration in many people past age 65. Current treatment helps only marginally; dietary aluminum is probably unrelated. The importance of nutrition care increases as the disease progresses.

Food Choices of Older Adults

Most older people are independent, socially sophisticated, mentally lucid, fully participating members of society who report themselves to be happy and healthy. The quality of life among the 85 and older group has improved, and their chronic disabilities have declined dramatically in recent years.[157] Results of national surveys indicate that many older people have heard and heeded nutrition messages: they have cut down on saturated fats in dairy foods and meats and are eating slightly more vegetables and whole-grain breads. However, using an abbreviated version of

The DETERMINE Predictors of Malnutrition in the Elderly Are as Follows

- Disease
- Eating poorly
- Tooth loss or oral pain
- Economic hardship
- Reduced social contact
- Multiple medications
- Involuntary weight loss or gain
- Need of assistance with self-care
- Elderly person older than 80 years

Federal Sources of Support for the Elderly

- Canada Pension Plan (CPP)
- Old Age Security (OAS)
- Guaranteed Income Supplement (GIS)
- Allowance for the Survivor Program (ASP)

Shared meals can be the high point of the day.

Dr. H. Keller's SCREEN II tool (SCREEN II-AB), the 2008–2009 Healthy Aging arm of the Canadian Community Health Survey (CCHS-HA) revealed that 34 percent of seniors (more women than men), 65 and older, who were living in their own homes were considered to be at nutritional risk (Statistics Canada, *Nutritional Risk among Older Canadians*, http://www.statcan.gc.ca/pub/82-003-x/2013003/article/11773-eng.htm). Thus, following such awareness, targeted programs to aid this vulnerable group are anticipated in the near future.

Those who choose a wide variety of foods are found to have better nutrient status than those who eat monotonous diets.[158] Grocers assist the elderly by prominently displaying good-tasting, low-fat, nutritious foods in easy-to-open, single-serving packages with labels that are easy to read. Furthermore, while a Canadian Malnutrition Task Force has been established and continues efforts to close the gaps between research and practice in terms of prevention, detection, and treatment of malnutrition in Canadians through hospital-based research (see http://nutritioncareincanada.ca), more research on the nutritional status of older Canadians living in long-term care and retirement home settings is also being conducted.

Many nutrient and other supplements are marketed to older adults. Whether to take a supplement is a personal choice, but evidence supports the idea that a single low-dose multivitamin–mineral tablet a day, that is, one containing vitamins and minerals for which DRI values are set (see the inside front cover), can improve resistance to disease in older people.

Obstacles to Adequacy Many factors affect the food choices and eating habits of older people, including whether they live alone or with others, at home or in an institution. Men living alone, for example, are likely to consume poorer-quality diets than those living with spouses. Older people who have difficulty chewing because of tooth loss or loss of taste sensitivity may no longer seek a wide variety of foods. Medical conditions and functional losses can also adversely affect food choices and nutrition.[159] Many older people become weak when unintentional reductions in food intake result in weight loss and loss of muscle tissue, events often followed by illness or death.[160] It may be that some of these outcomes could have been prevented or delayed if the person had consumed an adequate diet.[161]

Two other factors seem to make older people vulnerable to malnutrition: use of multiple medications and abuse of alcohol. People over age 65 take about a fourth of all of the medications, both prescription and over-the-counter, sold in North America. Although these medications enable people with health problems to live longer and more comfortably, they also pose a threat to nutrition status because they may interact with nutrients, depress the appetite, or alter the perception of taste (see the Controversy feature in this chapter).

The incidence of alcoholism, alcohol abuse, or problem drinking among the elderly in North America is estimated at between 2 and 10 percent. Evidence is mounting that loneliness, isolation, and depression in the elderly accompany overuse of alcohol. It isn't possible to say whether the depression or the alcohol abuse comes first, for each worsens the other, and both detract from nutrient intakes. Table 14–12 and the margin notes on this page provide means of identifying seniors who might be at risk for malnutrition.

Programs That Help Federal programs can provide help for older people.[162] The Canada Pension Plan provides income to retired people over age 62 who paid into the system during their working years, and the Old Age Security pension scheme was set up to guarantee a fixed minimum income for Canadian residents over 65 years old. For the homebound, Meals on Wheels volunteers deliver meals to the door, a benefit even though the recipients miss out on the social atmosphere of the congregate meals. Nutritionists are wise not to focus solely on nutrient and food intakes of the elderly because enjoyment and social interactions may be as important as food itself.[163]

Many older people, even able-bodied ones with financial resources, find themselves unable to perform cooking, cleaning, and shopping tasks. For anyone living alone and particularly for those of advanced age, it is important to work through the problems that food preparation presents. This chapter's Food Feature presents some ideas.

Table 14–12

Nutrition Screening Initiative Checklist for Older Americans

Circle the number to the right if the statement applies to you.

Statement	Yes
I have an illness or condition that makes me eat different kinds and/or amounts of food.	2
I eat fewer than 2 meals per day.	3
I eat few fruits or vegetables and use few milk products.	2
I have 3 or more drinks of beer, liquor, or wine almost every day.	2
I have tooth or mouth problems that make it hard for me to eat.	2
I don't always have enough money to buy the food I need.	4
I eat alone most of the time.	1
I take 3 or more different prescribed or over-the-counter drugs a day.	1
Without wanting to, I have lost or gained 10 pounds in the last six months.	2
I am not always physically able to shop, cook, and/or feed myself.	2
	Total

NOTE: The Nutrition Screening Initiative is part of a U.S. effort to identify and treat nutrition problems in older Americans. American Journal of Public Health, Nutrition and health risks in the elderly: the nutrition screening initiative (see http://www.ncbi.nlm.nih.gov/pmc/articles/PMC1694757).

Score: 0–2: Good. Recheck your score in six months. 3–5: Moderate nutritional risk. Visit your local office on aging, senior nutrition program, senior citizens centre, or health department for tips on improving eating habits. 6 or more: High nutritional risk. See your doctor, dietitian, or other health-care professional for help in improving your nutrition status.

KEY POINT

- Food choices of the elderly are affected by aging, altered health status, and changed life circumstances. Assistance programs can help by providing nutritious meals, offering opportunities for social interaction, and easing financial problems.

try it!

Food Feature

Single Survival and Nutrition on the Run

When it comes to feeding themselves wisely, singles of all ages face problems ranging from selection of restaurant foods to the purchasing, storing, and preparing of food from the grocery store. Whether the single person is a busy student in a campus dormitory, an elderly person in a retirement apartment, or a professional in an efficiency suite, the problems of preparing nourishing meals are often the same. People who live in places without kitchens and freezers find storing foods problematic. Following is a collection of ideas gathered from single people who have devised answers to some of these problems.

Is Eating in Restaurants the Answer?

For the single person as for others, restaurants mean convenience. When asked about the foods consumed the day before the CCHS interview that were prepared in fast-food outlets, one-quarter of Canadians indicated that such foods were consumed that day. Restaurant foods may be the quickest, easiest, and least taxing way to satisfy hunger at mealtime, but can they meet your body's nutrient needs or support health as well as homemade foods? The answer is "perhaps," if the diner makes the effort to meet nutritional needs.[164]

A few chefs and restaurant owners are concerned with the nutritional health of their patrons, but more often chefs strive to please the palate and leave nutrition-conscious diners on their own. Restaurant foods are often overly endowed with Calories, fat, saturated fat, and salt yet not overly generous with needed constituents such as fibre, iron, or calcium.[165] Meat portions may exceed a whole day's allowance in Canada's Food Guide. Nevertheless, restaurants can provide both convenience and nutrition if you follow these suggestions: restrict your portions to sizes that do not exceed your energy needs, ask that excess portions be placed in takeout containers, and make judicious choices of foods that stay within intake guidelines for fat and salt. The Food Feature in Chapter 5 offered specific suggestions for ordering fast food and other foods with an eye to keeping fat intakes within bounds, and Chapter 8 presented a list of high-sodium foods.

Grocery Store Takeout Choices

Takeout delicatessen-style foods offer convenience—they can be purchased while shopping for other items—and a modicum of control over their nutrient contents. They also often cost substantially less than similar foods from restaurants. Another bonus is control: you can specify the amount you need and portion it onto your plate at home.

Grocery store takeout can be an excellent bargain in terms of nutrient density, too. Choose from among roast chicken, smoked seafood, pasta with tomato sauce, steamed vegetables, precut salads and fruit without dressings, cooked beans, and plain baked potatoes for convenient nutrient bargains. Table 14–13 offers additional tips for using grocery store foods to best advantage. Be aware that stuffing, macaroni and cheese, meat loaf and gravy, vegetables with creamy sauces, mayonnaise-dressed mixed salads, and fried chicken and fish can be as laden with saturated fat and Calories as any traditional fast food.

Keep in mind that ready-to-eat takeout foods can spoil. Transport them home quickly and refrigerate them or reheat them within two hours

Chapter 12 has more about preventing foodborne illnesses.

Table 14–13

Time-Saving Tips to Turn Convenience Foods into Nutritious Meals

- Add extra nutrients and a fresh flavour to canned stews and soups by tossing in some frozen ready-to-use mixed vegetables. Choose vegetables frozen without salty, fatty sauces—prepared foods generally contain enough salt to season the whole dish including added vegetables.
- Buy frozen vegetables in a bag, toss in a variety of herbs, and use as needed. Vary your choices to prevent boredom.
- When grilling burgers, wrap a mixture of frozen broccoli, onion, and carrots in a foil packet with a tablespoon of Italian dressing and grill alongside the meat for seasoned grilled vegetables.
- Use canned fruit in their own juices as desserts. Toss in some frozen berries or peach slices and top with flavoured yogurt for an instant fruit salad.
- Prepared rice or noodle dishes are convenient, but those claiming to contain broccoli, spinach, or other vegetables really contain just a trifle—not nearly enough to contribute meaningfully to the day's need for vegetables. Pump up the nutrient value by adding a half-cup of your frozen vegetables per serving of pasta or rice just before cooking.
- Purchase frozen onion, mushroom, and pepper mixtures to embellish jarred spaghetti sauce or small frozen pizzas. Top with Parmesan cheese.
- Use frozen shredded potatoes, sold for hash browns, in soups or stews or mix with a handful of shredded reduced-fat cheese or a can of fat-free "cream of anything" soup and bake for a quick and hearty casserole.

of purchase (within an hour if the temperature is above 33°C).[166] Reheat the foods to an internal temperature of 70°C and bring soups, gravies, and sauces to a boil to prevent foodborne illness.

More Grocery Store Know-How

Singles often face the quantity problem in the grocery store. Large packages of meat and vegetables, whether fresh or frozen, are suitable for a family of four or more, and even a head of lettuce can spoil before one person can use it all.

Buy only what you will use. Don't be timid about asking the grocer to break open a family-size package of wrapped meat or fresh vegetables. Look for bags of prepared salad greens to take the place of lettuce in both salads and sandwiches. Purchasing prepared salads and other small containers of food may be expensive, but it is also expensive to let the unused portion of a large container spoil. Buy only three pieces of each kind of fresh fruit: a ripe one, a medium-ripe one, and a green one. Eat the first right away and the second soon, and let the last one ripen to eat days later.

Think up ways to use a vegetable that you must buy in large quantity. For example, you can divide a head of cauliflower into thirds. Cook one-third and eat it as a hot vegetable. Toss another third into a salad dressing marinade for use as an appetizer. Blend up the rest, cooked, in a creamy soup.

Buy fresh milk in the size you can best use. If your grocer doesn't carry 500–1,000 millilitres sizes of milk, try a convenience store. If you eat lunch in a cafeteria, buy two 500 millilitres of milk—one to drink and one to take home and store. Buy a loaf of bread and immediately store half, well wrapped, in the freezer (not the refrigerator, which will make it stale).

Food Preparation Hints

A wise person once said, "An hour spent organizing can save three hours later on."* This holds true in food preparation. For shelf-stable items, prepare a space for rows of glass jars (jars from spaghetti sauce, applesauce, or other foods work well). Use the jars to store

*That wise person was the late Eva May Hamilton, one of the original authors of this textbook.

pasta, rice, lentils, other dry beans, flour, cornbread or biscuit mix, powdered skim milk, and cereal. Light destroys riboflavin, so use opaque jars for enriched pasta and powdered milk. Cut the directions-for-use label from the package of each item and attach it to the jar. Place each jar, tightly sealed, in the freezer for a few days to kill any eggs or organisms before storing it on the shelf. Then the jars will keep bugs out of the foods indefinitely. The jars are also pretty to look at and will remind you of possibilities for variety in your menus.

Experiment with stir-fried foods. A large fry pan works well to stir-fry a variety of vegetables and meats. Inexpensive vegetables such as cabbage and celery are delicious when crisp cooked in a little oil with soy sauce or lemon juice. Interesting frozen vegetable mixtures are available, or cooked leftover vegetables can be dropped into a stir-fry at the last minute. A bonus of a stir-fried meal is that you have only one pan to wash.

Make mixtures using what you have on hand. A thick stew prepared from any leftover vegetables and bits of meat, with some added frozen onions, peppers, celery, and potatoes, makes a complete and balanced meal, except for milk. If you like creamed gravy, add some powdered skim milk to your stew.

If you can afford a microwave oven, buy one. Cooking times are quick, and you'll use fewer pots and pans. Be sure to use containers designed for microwaving, however. Margarine tubs, plastic bowls, and storage bags and containers can release potentially harmful chemicals into food when they are heated in the microwave oven. Use glass or buy plastic containers that are labelled as safe for microwaving.

Depending on your freezer space, make a regular-size recipe of a dish that takes time to prepare: a casserole, vegetable pie, or meat loaf. Freeze individual portions in containers that can be heated later. Date these so you will use the oldest first.

Dealing with Loneliness

For nutrition's sake, it is important to attend to loneliness at mealtimes. The person who is living alone must learn to connect food with socializing. Invite guests and make enough food so that you can enjoy the leftovers later on. If you know an older person who eats alone, you can bet that person would love to join you for a meal now and then.

Nutrient–Drug Interactions: Who Should Be Concerned?

A 45-year-old business executive attempts to give up smoking with the help of nicotine gum. She replaces smoking breaks with beverage breaks, drinking frequent servings of tomato juice, coffee, and colas. She is discouraged when her stomach becomes upset and her craving for tobacco continues unabated despite the nicotine gum. **Problem:** Nutrient–drug interaction.

A 14-year-old girl develops frequent and prolonged respiratory infections. Over the past six months, she has suffered constant fatigue despite adequate sleep, has had trouble completing school assignments, and has given up playing volleyball because she runs out of energy on the court. During the same six months, she has been taking huge doses of antacid pills each day because she heard this was a sure way to lose weight. Her pediatrician has diagnosed iron-deficiency anemia. **Problem:** Nutrient–drug interaction.

A 30-year-old schoolteacher who benefits from antidepressant medication attends a faculty wine and cheese party. After sampling the cheese with a glass or two of red wine, his face becomes flushed. His behaviour prompts others to drive him home. In the early morning hours, he awakens with severe dizziness, a migraine headache, vomiting, and trembling. An ambulance delivers him to an emergency room where a physician takes swift action to save his life. **Problem:** Nutrient–drug interaction.

Medicines and Nutrition

People sometimes think that medical drugs do only good, not harm. As the opening stories illustrate, however, both prescription and over-the-counter (OTC) medicines can have unintended consequences, causing harm when they interact with the body's normal use of nutrients.[*,1] As Figure C14–1 shows, drugs can interact with nutrients in the following ways:

- Foods or nutrients can enhance, delay, or prevent drug absorption.
- Drugs can enhance, delay, or prevent nutrient absorption.

*Controversy references are listed separately at the end of the chapter.

- Nutrients can alter the distribution of a drug among body tissues or interfere with its metabolism, transport, or elimination from the body.
- Drugs can alter the distribution of a nutrient among body tissues or interfere with its metabolism, transport, or excretion.[2]
- Drugs also often modify taste, appetite, or food intake.
- Herbs can also modify drug effects.

These interactions do not occur every time a person takes a drug. Some people are more vulnerable than others to nutrient–drug interactions. The potential for undesirable nutrient–drug interactions is greatest for those who

- Take drugs (or medicines) for long times.
- Take two or more drugs at the same time.
- Are poorly nourished to begin with or are not eating well.

Alcohol is also infamous for its interactions with nutrients (see Controversy 3).

Many people seeking the healing power of medicines also turn to herbs, but few inform their physicians. Some known herb–drug interactions are found in Table C14–1. For example, many herbs, including ginkgo biloba, feverfew, and willow, have the potential to increase the anti-blood-clotting effect of OTC pain and fever reducers, especially aspirin and its relatives.[3]

Absorption of Drugs and Nutrients

The business executive described earlier felt the effects of the first type of interaction in the list above. Acid from the tomato juice, coffee, and colas she drank before chewing the nicotine gum kept the nicotine from being absorbed into the bloodstream through the lining of her mouth. With absorption blocked, the nicotine could not quell her craving but instead travelled to her stomach and caused nausea (see Table C14–2 for other interactions with nicotine gum).

An interaction that can have serious consequences occurs when dairy products or calcium-fortified juices interfere with the absorption of certain antibiotics.[4] Without absorption of the proper dose, the antibiotics fail to do their jobs, and dangerous infectious diseases can worsen. Even the stomach acid normally secreted in response to eating can destroy some antibiotics, thereby reducing the dose.

Drug labels include instructions for avoiding most such interactions, such as "Take on an empty stomach" or "Do not combine with dairy products."

Drugs can also interfere with the small intestine's absorption of nutrients, particularly minerals. This interaction explains the experience of the tired 14-year-old. Her overuse of antacids eliminated the stomach's normal acidity, on which iron absorption depends. The medicine bound tightly to the iron molecules, forming an insoluble, unabsorbable complex. Her iron stores already bordered on deficiency, as iron stores for young girls typically do, so her misuse of antacids pushed her over the edge into outright deficiency.

Chronic laxative use can also lead to malnutrition. Laxatives can carry nutrients through the intestines so rapidly that many vitamins have no time to be absorbed. Mineral oil, a laxative the body cannot absorb, can rob a person of fat-soluble vitamins. Vitamin D deficiencies can occur this way; calcium can also be excreted with the oil, potentially accelerating adult bone loss.

Metabolic Interactions and Nutrient Excretion

The teacher who landed in the emergency room was taking an antidepressant medicine, one of the monoamine oxidase inhibitors (MAOI). At the party, he suffered a dangerous chemical interaction between the medicine and the compound tyramine

Figure C14–1

Food, Drug, and Herb Interactions

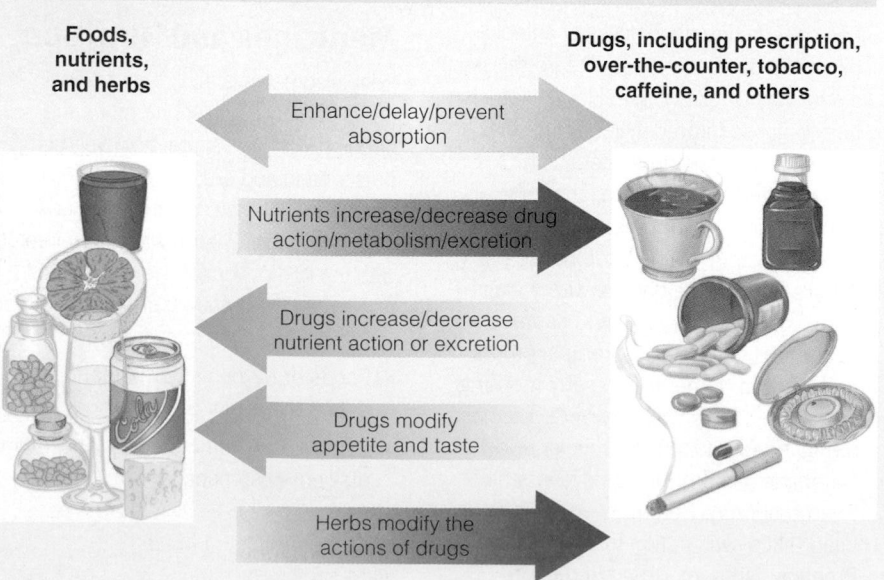

Foods, nutrients, and herbs		Drugs, including prescription, over-the-counter, tobacco, caffeine, and others

Enhance/delay/prevent absorption

Nutrients increase/decrease drug action/metabolism/excretion

Drugs increase/decrease nutrient action or excretion

Drugs modify appetite and taste

Herbs modify the actions of drugs

Table C14–1

Herb and Drug Interactions

Herb	Drug	Interaction
Bilberry, dong quai, feverfew, garlic, ginger, gingko biloba, ginseng, meadowsweet, St. John's wort, turmeric, and willow	Warfarin, coumarin (anticlotting drugs, "blood thinners"); aspirin, ibuprofen, and other nonsteroidal anti-inflammatory drugs	Prolonged bleeding time; danger of hemorrhage
Black tea, St. John's wort, saw palmetto	Iron supplement; antianxiety drug	Tannins in herbs inhibit iron absorption; St. John's wort speeds antianxiety drug clearance.
Borage, evening primrose oil	Anticonvulsants	Seizures
Chinese herbs (*xaio chai hu tang*)	Prednisone (steroid drug)	Decreased blood concentrations of the drug
Echinacea (possible immunostimulant)	Cyclosporine and corticosteroids (immunosuppressants)	May reduce drug effectiveness
Feverfew	Aspirin, ibuprofen, and other nonsteroidal anti-inflammatory drugs	Drugs negate the effect of the herb for headaches.
Garlic supplements	Protease inhibitors (HIV-AIDS[a] drugs)	Decreased blood concentrations of the drug
Ginseng	Estrogens, corticosteroids	Enhanced hormonal response
Ginseng, hawthorn, kyushin, licorice, plantain, St. John's wort, uzara root	Digoxin (cardiac antiarrhythmic drug derived from the herb foxglove)	Herbs interfere with drug action and monitoring.
Ginseng, karela	Blood glucose regulators	Herbs affect blood glucose levels.
Kelp (iodine source)	Synthroid or other thyroid hormone replacers	Herb may interfere with drug action.
Licorice	Corticosteroids (oral and topical ointments)	Overreaction to drug (potentiation)
Panax ginseng	Antidepressants	Overexcitability, mania
St. John's wort	Increased enzymatic destruction of many drugs; cyclosporine (immunosuppressant); antiretroviral drugs (HIV[a] drugs), warfarin (anticoagulant, used to reduce blood clotting) MAOIs (used to treat depression, tuberculosis, or high blood pressure)[b]	Decreased drug effectiveness; increased organ transplant rejection; reduced effectiveness of drugs to treat AIDS;[a] reduced anticoagulant effect Potentiation, with serotonin syndrome (mild): sweating, chills, blood pressure spike, nausea, abnormal heartbeat, muscle tremors, seizures
Valerian	Barbiturates (sedatives)	Enhanced sedation

[a]Acquired immune deficiency syndrome, caused by HIV (human immunodeficiency virus) infection.

[b]MAOI stands for monoamine oxidase inhibitors.

NOTE: Canada's Natural Health Products Directorate has approved hundreds of natural health products, including many herbal preparations; some, such as St. John's wort, are well known for their interactions with medications (for a list of available monographs for these products, including potential interactions with other medications, see http://www.hc-sc.gc.ca/dhp-mps/prodnatur/applications/licen-prod/monograph/index-eng.php). Valuable free resources for reliable online information about herbs are offered by the Memorial Sloan-Kettering Cancer Center at http://www.mskcc.org/aboutherbs, and Canada's Natural Health Product Directorate monographs for herb–drug/herb–nutrient interactions at http://webprod.hc-sc.gc.ca/nhpid-bdipsn/monosReq.do?lang_eng.

in his cheese and wine. Tyramine is produced during the fermenting process in cheese and wine manufacturing.

The MAOI medication works by depressing the activity of enzymes that destroy the brain neurotransmitter dopamine. With less enzyme activity, more dopamine is left, and depression lifts. At the same time, the drug also depresses enzymes in the liver that destroy tyramine. Ordinarily, the man's liver would have quickly destroyed the tyramine from the cheese and wine. But due to the MAOI medication, tyramine built up too high in the man's body and caused the potentially fatal reaction.

Other culprits that affect the metabolism of medication include grapefruit juice; soy milk; and one of the most popular herbal supplements in North America, ginkgo biloba. A chemical constituent of grapefruit juice suppresses an enzyme responsible for breaking down more than 20 kinds of medical drugs. With less drug breakdown, doses build up in the blood to levels that can have undesirable effects on the body. For example, in a drinker of grapefruit juice, a normal dosage of the blood-thinning drug coumarin can lead to dangerously prolonged bleeding and delayed clotting of blood. Soy milk seems to have the opposite effect: it reduces blood levels of a related blood-thinning drug.[5] As for ginkgo, people take it as a supplement in the hope of improving memory, but this effect is unproven. Takers may not know that it has been found to stimulate the activity of liver enzymes responsible for metabolizing many medications and so may diminish their effects.

Drugs often cause nutrient losses, too. Many people take large quantities of aspirin (10–12 tablets each day) to relieve the pain of arthritis, backaches, and headaches. This much aspirin can speed up blood loss from the stomach by as much as 10 times, enough to cause iron-deficiency anemia in some people. People who take aspirin regularly should eat iron-rich foods regularly as well. Table C14–3 lists some examples of other possible nutrient–drug interactions, including both prescription and OTC medications. Details on some common interactions follow.

Oral Contraceptives

Millions of women use oral contraceptives, daily doses of hormones that prevent pregnancy. Oral contraceptive interactions with nutrients illustrate the complexity of nutrient–drug interactions.

Each nutrient responds differently to oral contraceptive use (see Table C14–3). The vitamin B_{12} status of oral contraceptive users may be slightly lower than in others. Beta-carotene values may also be reduced, leading researchers to wonder whether the lower levels of this antioxidant might influence some disease risks. Vitamin D levels, on the other hand, may be higher in oral contraceptive users, with unknown effects. At first glance, these findings seem to indicate that women using oral contraceptives are on their way to suffering deficiencies of some nutrients and have somehow enlarged their body stores of others. Research has yielded conflicting results, however, so any such assumptions are premature.

Significantly, oral contraceptives alter blood lipids, possibly increasing the risk of CVD for menstruating women.[6] Especially in women older than about 35 years, most oral contraceptives raise total cholesterol and triglyceride concentrations and lower HDL, amplifying the risk of stroke and heart disease. A few women using oral contraceptives also experience mild hypertension.

Some women lose weight when taking oral contraceptives, but others may gain as much as 10 kilograms or more from fat deposited in the hips, thighs, and breasts or from retained fluid. Some lean tissue is also deposited in response to an androgenic (steroid) effect of the pills. Sometimes a switch to another form of pill can normalize body weight.

As with oral contraceptives, women's responses to estrogen replacement drugs must be assessed individually. Some women suffer edema because estrogen promotes sodium conservation by the kidneys; dietary sodium restriction can correct this condition. Others develop low blood folate or vitamin B_6, indicating a need to include more vitamin-rich, nutrient-dense foods in the diet. All women taking estrogen either in oral contraceptives or in hormone replacement therapy should be aware that vitamin C doses of a gram or more may elevate serum estrogen and falsely suggest that a lower dose is needed.

If a woman taking any form of estrogen thinks she may have a nutrient deficiency, she should refrain from taking individual supplements and seek testing and a diagnosis from a health-care professional to rule out other causes of her symptoms. For most women, a nutritious diet is all that is needed. If a woman feels compelled to take a supplement, however, a standard multivitamin–mineral supplement is probably harmless, as long as it accompanies a well-balanced diet.

Caffeine

The well-known "wake-up" effect of caffeine is the primary reason people in every society use it in some form. Compared with the drugs discussed so far, though, caffeine's interactions with foods and nutrients are subtle. Yet caffeine's relationship to nutrition is important because caffeine is so widespread that people may be unaware that they are consuming it—see Table C14–4 for the caffeine contents of many beverages and foods. Many OTC cold and headache remedies contain caffeine because, in addition to being a mild pain reliever in its own right, caffeine remedies the headache caused by caffeine withdrawal that no other pain reliever can touch. Caffeine is present in chocolate bars, colas, and other foods children favour, and children are more sensitive to caffeine's effects because they are small and, at first, not adapted to its use.

Caffeine is among the most popular and widely consumed drugs in North America. Note that for adult Canadians, about 60 percent of caffeine intake comes from coffee, but the number of products containing guarana (another source of caffeine) has increased, and Health Canada has set new maximum daily intake recommendations for caffeine intake for children and pregnant and lactating women.[7] Many people's intake patterns fulfill some of the accepted criteria for a diagnosis of drug dependence.

Table C14-3

Nutrition Effects of a Few Commonly Used Medical Drugs

Medicines and Caffeine	Effects on Absorption	Effects on Excretion	Effects on Metabolism
Antacids (aluminum-containing)	Reduce iron absorption	Increase calcium and phosphorus excretion	May accelerate destruction of thiamin
Antibiotics (long-term use)	Reduce absorption of fats, amino acids, folate, fat-soluble vitamins, vitamin B$_{12}$, calcium, copper, iron, magnesium, potassium, phosphate, zinc	Increase excretion of folate, niacin, potassium, riboflavin, vitamin C	Destroy vitamin K–producing bacteria and reduce vitamin K production
Antidepressants (monoamine oxidase inhibitors, MAOI)			Slow breakdown of tyramine, with dangerous blood pressure spike and other symptoms on consuming tyramine-rich foods or drinks: *alcoholic beverages* (sherry, vermouth, red wines, some beers); *cheeses* (aged and processed); *some meats* (caviar, pickled herring, liver, smoked and cured sausages, lunch meat); *fermented products* (soy sauce, miso, sauerkraut); *others* (brewer's yeast, yeast supplements, yeast paste [baked goods made with baker's yeast are safe]; foods past their expiration date)
Aspirin (large doses, long-term use)	Lowers blood concentration of folate	Increases excretion of thiamin, vitamin C, vitamin K; causes iron and potassium losses through gastric blood loss	
Caffeine		Increases secretion of small amounts of calcium and magnesium	Stimulates release of fatty acids into the blood
Cholesterol-lowering "statin" drugs (Zocor, Lipitor)			Grapefruit juice slows drug metabolism, causing buildup of high drug levels; potentially life-threatening muscle toxicity can result
Diuretics		Raise blood calcium and zinc; lower blood folate, chloride, magnesium, phosphorus, potassium, vitamin B$_{12}$; increase excretion of calcium, sodium, thiamin, potassium, chloride, magnesium	Interfere with storage of zinc
Estrogen replacement therapy	May reduce absorption of folate	Causes sodium retention	May raise blood glucose, triglycerides, vitamin A, vitamin E, copper, and iron; may lower blood vitamin C, folate, vitamin B$_6$, riboflavin, calcium, magnesium, and zinc
Laxatives (effects vary with type)	Reduce absorption of glucose, fat, carotene, vitamin D, other fat-soluble vitamins, calcium, phosphate, potassium	Increase excretion of all unabsorbed nutrients	
Oral contraceptives	Reduce absorption of folate, may improve absorption of calcium	Cause sodium retention	Raise blood vitamin A, vitamin D, copper, iron; may lower blood beta-carotene, riboflavin, vitamin B$_6$, vitamin B$_{12}$, vitamin C; may elevate requirements for riboflavin and vitamin B$_6$; alter blood lipids, elevating risk of heart disease in smokers and older women

Table C14–4

Caffeine Content of Beverages and Foods

Most labels of caffeinated foods or beverages fail to list caffeine among their ingredients because it occurs naturally in the food or beverage; however, numerous brands of energy drinks have recently been transitioned from Natural Health Products to Foods and must list the amount of caffeine from all sources.

Drinks and Foods	Average (mg)	Range (mg)
Coffee (150-mL cup)		
Brewed, drip method	130	110–150
Brewed, percolator	94	64–124
Instant	74	40–108
Instant "lite"	30	no data
Decaffeinated, brewed or instant	3	1–5
Tea (150-mL cup)		
Brewed, major Canadian brands	40	20–90
Brewed, imported brands	60	25–110
Instant	30	25–50
Iced (355-mL glass)	70	67–76
Herb teas (caffeine-free)	0	0
Soft drinks (355-mL can)		
Dr. Pepper		40
Colas and cherry colas		
Regular		30–46
Diet		50 (average)
Clear and caffeine free		0–trace
Extra caffeine (Jolt)		75–100
Fresca, 7-Up, Sprite, Sunkist Orange, seltzers, root beers		0
Cocoa beverage (150-mL cup)	4	2–20
Chocolate milk beverage (240 mL)	5	2–7
Milk chocolate candy (30 g)	6	1–15
Dark chocolate, semisweet (30 g)	20	5–35
Baking chocolate (30 g)	26	26
Chocolate-flavoured syrup (30 g)	4	4
Carob	0	0

NOTE: Many OTC medications, such as pain relievers and cold medicines, also contain caffeine. Their labels must list the milligram amounts of caffeine per dose of medicine. Read medicine labels carefully.

© Thomas Northcut/Lifesize/Thinkstock

Many studies indicate that a 200-milligram dose of caffeine significantly improves the ability to pay attention, especially if subjects are sleepy, but more caffeine is probably not better.[8] A single dose of 500 milligrams has been shown to worsen thinking abilities in almost everyone, and more than this may present some risk to health through its actions as a stimulant.

An individual's reaction to caffeine may depend in part on daily caffeine habits. In a regular user, deprivation of caffeine often causes headache and fatigue and worsens mental performance and mood; restoration of the drug greatly improves these measures.[9] When deprived regular users were restored to ordinary intakes and then given an additional dose, their performance and mood did not benefit.[10]

Caffeine is a true stimulant drug. Like all stimulants, it increases the respiratory rate, heart rate, blood pressure, and secretion of stress and other hormones. A moderate dose of caffeine may speed up metabolic energy expenditures for several hours, and it stimulates the digestive tract, promoting efficient elimination. Because caffeine is a diuretic, it promotes some water loss from the body as well (see Chapter 8 for details).

Despite caffeine's tremendous popularity, many people today are consuming less because they fear possible harm to their health. Research in the last decade has yielded sporadic reports linking caffeine to health problems such as cancer, birth defects, and hypertension. Much other research, however, refutes any links between caffeine and cancer or birth defects and finds a weak link between caffeine and elevated blood pressure, an effect that may be significant for those with diagnosed hypertension.[11] Coffee and tea contain phytochemicals other than caffeine, some of which may reduce heart disease risk, while others may increase it.[12] Also, there is emerging evidence that genetic background may be a factor in whether coffee has potentially protective (e.g., type 2 diabetes) or adverse (e.g., cardiovascular) effects on health.

Caffeine seems relatively harmless when used in moderation (two cups of coffee a day). One study reports that men consuming two to three cups of coffee a day run a 40 percent lower risk of developing active gallstone disease than men who avoid coffee.[13] Cola consumption, however, may increase the risk.[14] In higher doses, caffeine can cause symptoms associated with anxiety: sweating, tenseness, and inability to concentrate. High doses may also accelerate bone loss in women past midlife, and caffeine may contribute to painful but benign fibrocystic breast disease. More controlled studies are needed to determine whether eliminating caffeine can help reverse breast disease.[15]

If you like caffeine-containing foods or beverages, the most reasonable approach is to limit your intake to the equivalent of 300 millilitres of coffee per day. For most people, this is enough to reduce drowsiness and sharpen awareness without paying too high a price. Pregnant women should exercise moderation in using caffeine, and parents should monitor and control their children's intakes.

Tobacco

Cigarette and other tobacco use causes thousands of people to suffer from cancer and other diseases of the cardiovascular, digestive, and respiratory systems. These effects are beyond nutrition's scope, but smoking does depress hunger and body fatness and change nutrient status, and the nutrition effects are also linked to lung cancer. Chapter 9 provided details on smoking and body fatness.

Nutrient intakes of smokers and nonsmokers differ. Smokers have lower intakes of dietary fibre, vitamins, and minerals, even when their energy intakes are quite similar to those of nonsmokers. The association between smoking and low vitamin intake may be important because studies have shown that smoking alters the metabolism of vitamin C. (Research has just begun on other nutrients.)

Research shows that the vitamin C requirement of smokers exceeds that of nonsmokers. Smokers break down vitamin C faster and so must take in more vitamin C-containing foods to achieve steady body pools comparable to those of nonsmokers. The effect is apparently related to an increase in oxidative stress produced by smoking and is not related to the tobacco drug nicotine.[16] The evidence is so strong that the vitamin C recommendation is set higher for smokers—smokers require an extra 35 milligrams of vitamin C per day.

Illicit Drugs

People know that illicit drugs are harmful, but many choose to abuse them anyway in spite of the risks. Like OTC and prescription drugs, illegal drugs modify body functions. Unlike medicines, however, no watchdog agency such as Health Canada monitors them for safety, effectiveness, or even purity.

Smoking a marijuana cigarette affects several senses including the sense of taste. It produces an enhanced enjoyment of eating, especially of sweets. Why or how this effect occurs is not known. Despite higher food intakes, marijuana abusers often consume fewer nutrients than do nonabusers because the extra foods they choose tend to be high-Calorie, low-nutrient snack foods. Besides the nutrition effects, regular marijuana users face the same risk of lung cancer as people who smoke a pack of cigarettes a day.

Many other drugs of abuse elicit effects such as intense euphoria, restlessness, heightened self-confidence, irritability, insomnia, and loss of appetite. Weight loss is a common side effect, and unlike marijuana, most other drugs of abuse cause serious malnutrition. The stronger the craving for the drug, the less a drug abuser wants nutritious food. Rats given unlimited access to cocaine will choose the drug over food until they die of starvation. The effects of addictive drugs vary somewhat, but many are similar to the effects of cocaine, listed in Table C14–5. Drug abusers face multiple nutrition problems, and an important aspect of addiction recovery is the identification and correction of nutrition problems.

Personal Strategy

In conclusion, when you need to take a medicine, do so wisely. Ask your physician, pharmacist, or other health-care provider for specific instructions about the doses, the times, and how to take the medication—for example, with meals or on an empty stomach. If you notice new symptoms or if a drug seems not to be working well, consult your physician. The only instruction people need about illicit drugs is to avoid them altogether for countless reasons. As for smoking and chewing tobacco, the same advice applies: don't take these habits up, or if you already have, take steps to quit. For drugs with lesser consequences to health, such as caffeine, use moderation.

Try to live life in a way that requires less chemical assistance. If you are sleepy, try a 15-minute nap or stretching exercises instead of a 15-minute coffee break. The coffee will stimulate your nerves for an hour, but the alternatives will refresh your attitude for the rest of the day. If you suffer constipation, try getting enough exercise, fibre, and water for a few days. Chances are that a laxative will be unnecessary. The strategy being suggested here is to take control of your body, allowing your reliable, self-healing nature to make fine adjustments that you need not force with chemicals. Bodies have few requests: adequate nutrition, rest, exercise, and hygiene. Give your body what it asks for and let it function naturally, day to day, without interference from drugs.

Table C14–5

Nutrition Effects of Four Nonmedical Drugs

Drug of Abuse	Possible Effects on Nutrition Status
Cocaine	Reduces intakes of nutritious foods; increases intakes of alcohol, coffee, and fat; may induce or aggravate eating disorders
Heroin	Heightens and delays insulin response to glucose; reduces intakes of nutritious foods
Marijuana	Increases intakes of foods, especially sweets; may cause weight gain
Nicotine[a]	Reduces intake of sweet foods and water; increases intakes of fat; reduces fetal weight; lowers blood concentration of beta-carotene

[a]Other effects of smoking include increased vitamin C requirements.

Sources: Data from M. E. Mohs, R. R. Watson, and T. Leonard-Green, Nutritional effects of marijuana, heroin, cocaine, and nicotine, Journal of the American Dietetic Association 90 (1990): 1261:1267; G. van Poppel, S. Spanhaak, and T. Ockhuizen, Effects of beta carotene on immunological indexes in healthy male smokers, American Journal of Clinical Nutrition 57 (1993): 402:407.

Self-Check

Answers to these Self-Check questions are in Appendix D.

1. Children naturally like nutritious foods in all food groups, *except*
   a. dairy
   b. meat
   c. vegetables
   d. fruit

2. Which of the following can contribute to choking in children?
   a. peanut butter eaten by the spoonful
   b. hot dogs and tough meat
   c. grapes and hard candy
   d. all of the above

3. Which of the following is most commonly deficient in children and adolescents?
   a. folate
   b. zinc
   c. iron
   d. vitamin D

4. Which of the following may worsen symptoms of PMS?
   a. adequate vitamin B_6
   b. physical activity
   c. caffeine
   d. calcium

5. Which of the following have been shown to improve acne?
   a. avoiding chocolate and fatty foods
   b. Accutane
   c. vitamin A supplements
   d. stress

6. Physical changes of aging that can affect nutrition include
   a. reduced stomach acid
   b. increased saliva output
   c. tooth loss and gum disease
   d. a and c

7. Research to date supports the idea that food allergies or intolerances are common causes of hyperactivity in children.
   T   F

8. Nutrition does not seem to play a role in the causation of osteoarthritis.
   T   F

9. Vitamin A absorption decreases with age.
   T   F

10. Herbal supplements have been shown to slow down the progression of Alzheimer's disease.
   T   F

track it!

Diet Analysis PLUS+

Concepts in Action

start now! ····> Ready to make a change? If you are an older person, or if you care for an older person, devise a sensible exercise plan and track your/their activity using Diet Analysis Plus for one week. At the end of that week, look at your/their total physical activity, and compare it to the Canadian Physical Activity Guidelines (65 years and older, see http://www.csep.ca/english/view.asp?x=949) and decide if you/they meet these guidelines or if you/they need to increase your/their level of activity.

Analyze Three Diets

The purpose of this exercise is to explore food choices and the potential for nutrient deficiencies among young children, teens, and older adults, using three new profiles: a 2-year-old, a 14-year-old, and a 70-year-old.

1. Iron nutrition is required for normal development. From the DA+ Home tab, select Create New Profile and create a profile for a 2-year-old toddler with a reasonable height and weight. Select the Track Diet tab; choose a new day, and then, using Table 14–1, choose foods to create a balanced iron-rich meal for a 2-year-old toddler. Once you've entered the foods, select the Reports tab, and under the Nutrients heading, select Intake vs. Goals for that meal. Did the meal supply a third of the iron this toddler needs? Now select the Reports tab and select Intake Spreadsheet under the Spreadsheets heading

to find out which foods contributed most of the iron.

2. For nutrient adequacy, children's diets should include a variety of foods from each food group (see Figure 2–4, pages 38–43). Modify your child's meals to provide the recommended number of Food Guide servings (for the child's age group) according to Canada's Food Guide (also see Table 14–2 for examples), keeping in mind that children eat small portions and often like colourful, crunchy vegetables and smooth bland foods. Did your choices provide the right number of Food Guide servings for a variety of foods from each food group? Do you need to improve this child's food intake? If so, how can you do it?

3. Nutrients missed at breakfast often cannot be made up at lunch or dinner. Create a nutritious breakfast for your 2-year-old from the above activities, using the ideas for a rushed morning provided in Table 1. Enter the data via the Track Diet tab. From the Reports tab, under the Nutrients heading, select Intake vs. Goals for that date and meal. Did the breakfast meet a significant portion of the child's nutrient needs? If not, what foods or beverages might improve it?

4. Teens' diets often lack calcium, iron, and vitamin A. From the DA+ Home tab, select Create New Profile and create a new profile for a 14-year-old girl of reasonable height and weight. Select the Track Diet tab, and choose foods that are excellent sources of calcium, iron, and vitamin A for a lunch meal (see Snapshot 8–1, page 318, Snapshot 8 5, page 333, and Snapshot 7–1, page 252). Recall that vitamin C helps maximize iron absorption from nonheme (nonmeat) sources of iron. Select the Reports tab and then, under the Advanced heading, select Source Analysis from the drop-down menu for Calcium, Iron, Vitamin A, and Vitamin C. Did the meal meet the teen's needs for calcium and iron? Did meat or nonheme sources of iron predominate? Which foods also supplied vitamin A and vitamin C?

5. Teens often make snack choices with taste and convenience in mind, but nutritious snacks better suit their nutrient needs. Select the teen's profile (via the DA+ Home tab) created in item 4 above, and select the Track Diet tab. Consult Table 1 for help in choosing foods to include in a nutritious snack for the morning and afternoon. Make each snack supply about 150 Calories of nutritious foods. From the Reports tab, under the Nutrients heading, select Intake vs. Goals and then select Snacks. Did any of the snacks provide about 20 percent of the significant nutrients for teens? Which ones? How much saturated fat and sodium did these snacks provide?

6. For older people, nutritious meals help to maintain good health. From the DA+ Home tab, select Create New Profile and create a new profile for a 70-year-old single adult of reasonable height and weight. Select the Track Diet tab, and choose foods to create a nutritious, convenient, easy-to-eat dinner for this person. Select the Reports tab and then, under the Nutrients heading, select Intake vs. Goals for that meal. Did the meal supply enough zinc, protein, vitamin B_{12}, and calcium to meet one-third of the person's need without excessive Calories? Did it supply omega-3 fatty acids? If not, suggest ways of improving it.

Table 1

Breakfast Ideas for Rushed Mornings

With some planning, even a rushed morning can include a nutritious breakfast.
- Make ahead sandwiches or tortilla wraps. Freeze, thaw or heat, and serve with juice. Fillings may include peanut butter, low-fat cream cheese or other cheeses, jams, fruit slices, refried beans, or meats.
- Teach school-aged children to help themselves to dry cereals, milk, and juice. Keep unbreakable bowls and cups in low cabinets, and keep milk and juice in small, covered, plastic pitchers on a low refrigerator shelf.
- Keep a bowl of fresh fruit and small containers of shelled nuts, trail mix (the kind without candy), or roasted peanuts for grabbing.
- Mix granola or other grain cereal into 8-oz. tubs of yogurt.
- Toast whole-grain frozen waffles—no syrup needed—to grab and go.
- *Nontraditional choices*: Divide carrot sticks among several containers; serve with yogurt or bean dip. Leftover casseroles, stews, or pasta dishes are nutritious choices that children can eat hot or cold.

Endnotes

1. D. Garriguet, Nutrition: Findings from the CCHS—Overview of Canadians' Eating Habits, Statistics Canada, Cat. no. 82-620-MIE-No. 2 (2006).

2. J. Liu and coauthors, Malnutrition at age 3 years and lower cognitive ability at age 11 years: Independence from psychosocial adversity, *Archives of Pediatrics and Adolescent Medicine* 157 (2003): 593–600.

3. K. L. McConahy and M. F. Picciano, How to grow a healthy toddler—12 to 24 months, *Nutrition Today* 38 (2003): 156–163.

4. S. Kranz, A. M. Siega-Riz, and A. H. Herring, Changes in diet quality of American preschoolers between 1977 and 1998, *American Journal of Public Health* 94 (2004): 1525–1530; S. J. Nielsen, A. M. Siega-Riz, and B. M. Popkin, Trends in energy intake in U.S. between 1977 and 1996: Similar shifts seen across age groups, *Obesity Research* 10 (2002): 370–378.

5. Health Canada, Eating Well with Canada's Food Guide, Catalogue no. H164-38/1-2007E (Ottawa, ON: Minister of Health, 2007).

6. Committee on the Scientific Evaluation of Dietary Reference Intakes, Food and Nutrition Board, Institute of Medicine, Dietary Reference Intakes for Energy, Carbohydrate, Fiber, Fat, Fatty Acids, Cholesterol, Protein, and Amino Acids (Washington, D.C.: National Academies Press, 2002), Chapter 6.

7. Committee on the Scientific Evaluation of Dietary Reference Intakes, Food and Nutrition Board, Institute of Medicine, 2002, Chapter 7 [see reference 6].

8. Health Canada, Food and Nutrition: Do Canadian Children Meet Their Nutrient Requirements through Food Alone? available at http://www.hc-sc.gc.ca/fn-an/surveill/nutrition/commun/art-nutr-child-enf-eng.php (accessed December 13, 2013).

9. Position of the American Dietetic Association, 2004, Dietary guidance for healthy children ages 2 to 11 years, *Journal of the American Dietetic Association* 104 (2004): 660–667; Committee on the Scientific Evaluation of Dietary Reference Intakes, Food and Nutrition Board, Institute of Medicine, 2002, Chapter 8 [see reference 6].

10. Centers for Disease Control and Prevention, Iron deficiency—United States, 1999–2000, *Morbidity and Mortality Weekly Report* 51 (2002): 897–899; A. N. Eden, Iron deficiency and the toddler: An ongoing dilemma, Nutrition & the M.D. 27 (2001): 1–3.

11. S. L. Johnson, Children's food acceptance patterns: The interface of ontogeny and nutrition needs, *Nutrition Reviews* 60 (2002): S91–S94; A. N. Eden, 2001 [see reference 10].

12. K. L. McConahy and coauthors, Portion size of common foods predicts energy intake among preschool-aged children, *Journal of the American Dietetic Association* (2004): 975–979.

13. D. Garriguet, 2006 [see reference 1].

14. S. B. Roberts and M. B. Heyman, Micronutrient shortfalls in young children's diets: Common, and owing to inadequate intakes both at home and at child care centers, *Nutrition Reviews* 58 (2000): 27–29.

15. L. L. Birch, Development of food preferences, *Annual Review of Nutrition* 19 (1999): 41–62.

16. J. O. Fisher and L. L. Birch, Restricting access to palatable foods affects children's behavioral response, food selection, and intake, *American Journal of Clinical Nutrition* 69 (1999): 1264–1272.

17. J. D. Skinner and coauthors, Meal and snack patterns of infants and toddlers, *Journal of the American Dietetic Association* 104 (2004): S65–S70.

18. J. O. Fisher and coauthors, Parental influences on young girls' fruit and vegetable, micronutrient, and fat intakes, *Journal of the American Dietetic Association* 102 (2002): 58–64.

19. J. Bryan and coauthors, Nutrients for cognitive development in school-aged children, *Nutrition Reviews* 62 (2004): 295–306; M. Singh, Role of micronutrients for physical growth and mental development, *Indian Journal of Pediatrics* 71 (2004): 59–62.

20. E. K. Hurtado, A. H. Claussen, and K. G. Scott, Early childhood anemia and mild or moderate mental retardation, *American Journal of Clinical Nutrition* 69 (1999): 115–119.

21. J. Liu and coauthors, Malnutrition at age 3 years and externalizing behavior problems at ages 8, 11, and 17 years, *American Journal of Psychiatry* 161 (2004): 2005–2013; D. Pinero, B. Jones, and J. Beard, Variations in dietary iron alter behavior in developing rats, *Journal of Nutrition* 131 (2001): 311–318; S. M. Grantham-McGregor, S. P. Walker, and S. Chang, Nutritional deficiencies and later behavioral development, *Proceedings of the Nutrition Society* 59 (2000): 47–54.

22. B. D. Anderson and coauthors, Retrospective analysis of ingestions of iron containing products in the United States: Are there differences between chewable vitamins and adult preparations? *Journal of Emergency Medicine* 19 (2000): 255–258; C. C. Morris, Pediatric iron poisonings in the United States, *Southern Medical Journal* 93 (2000): 352–358.

23. Province of Ontario: Drinking water Ontario—Drinking Water Reports, available at http://www.ene.gov.on.ca/environment/dwo/en/story/STDPROD_095729.html.

24. K. Kalia and S. J. Flora, Strategies for safe and effective therapeutic measures for chronic arsenic and lead poisoning, *Journal of Occupational Health* 47 (2005): 1–21; X. Liu and coauthors, Do children with falling blood lead levels have improved cognition? *Pediatrics* 110 (2002): 787–791.

25. W. J. Rogan and coauthors, The effect of chelation therapy with succimer on neuropsychological development in children exposed to lead, *New England Journal of Medicine* 344 (2001): 1421–1426; J. F. Rosen and P. Mushak, Primary prevention of childhood lead poisoning—the only

solution, *New England Journal of Medicine* 344 (2001): 1470–1471.

26. Fatal pediatric lead poisoning—New Hampshire, 2000, *Morbidity and Mortality Weekly Report* 50 (2001): 457–459.

27. T. D. Matte, Reducing blood lead levels: Benefits and strategies, Journal of the American Medical Association 281 (1999): 2340–2342; J. A. Simon and E. S. Hudes, Relationship of ascorbic acid to blood lead levels, Journal of the American Medical Association 281 (1999): 2289–2293.

28. P. A. Meyer and coauthors, Surveillance for elevated blood lead levels among children—United States, 1997–2001, *Morbidity and Mortality Weekly Report* 52 (2003): 1–21; M. J. Brown and coauthors, The effectiveness of housing policies in reducing children's lead exposure, *American Journal of Public Health* 91 (2001): 621–624.

29. Advisory Committee on Childhood Lead Poisoning Prevention, Recommendations for blood lead screening of young children enrolled in Medicaid: Targeting a high-risk group, *Morbidity and Mortality Weekly Report* 49 (2000): 1–13.

30. Centers for Disease Control and Prevention, Lead, available at http://www.cdc.gov/nceh/lead/.

31. National Institute of Allergy and Infectious Diseases, Food Allergy, available at http://www.niaid.nih.gov/topics/foodallergy/Pages/default.aspx; R. Formanek Jr., Food allergies: When food becomes the enemy, FDA Consumer, July/August 2001, pp. 10–16.

32. H. S. Skolnick and coauthors, The natural history of peanut allergy, Journal of Allergy and Clinical Immunology 107 (2001): 367–374.

33. K. J. Falci, K. L. Gombas, and E. L. Elliot, Food allergen awareness: An FDA priority, Food Safety Magazine, February/March, 2001, available at http://www.foodsafetymagazine.com/magazine-archive1/februarymarch-2001/food-allergen-awareness-an-fda-priority/.

34. B. Wuthrich, Lethal or life-threatening allergic reactions to food, *Journal of Investigational Allergology and Clinical Immunology* 10 (2000): 59–65.

35. L. Christie and coauthors, Food allergies in children affect nutrient intake and growth, *Journal of the American Dietetic Association* 102 (2002): 1648–1651.

36. G. S. Rhim and M. S. McMorris, School readiness for children with food allergies, *Annals of Allergy, Asthma and Immunololgy* 86 (2001): 172–176.

37. S. A. Bock, S. Munoz-Furlong, and H. A. Sampson, Fatalities due to anaphylactic reactions to foods, *Journal of Allergy and Clinical Immunology* 107 (2001): 191–193.

38. Health Canada—Food and Nutrition: Food Allergies, available at http://www.hc-sc.gc.ca/fn-an/securit/allerg/fa-aa/index-eng.php.

39. Canadian Food Inspection Agency, Food Recalls and Allergy Alerts, available at http://

www.inspection.gc.ca/english/corpaffr/recarapp/recaltoce.shtml.

40. B. Merz, Studying peanut anaphylaxis, *New England Journal of Medicine* 348 (2003): 975–976; H. Metzger, Two approaches to peanut allergy, *New England Journal of Medicine* 348 (2003): 1046–1048; X. M. Li and coauthors, Persistent protective effect of heat-killed Escherichia coli producing "engineered," recombinant peanut proteins in a murine model of peanut allergy, *Journal of Allergy and Clinical Immunology* 112 (2003): 159–167.

41. K. Beyer, Characterization of allergenic food proteins for improved diagnostic methods, *Current Opinion in Allergy and Clinical Immunology* 3 (2003): 189–197.

42. S. Barrett, Allergies: Dubious diagnosis and treatment, August 23, 2003, available at http://www.quackwatch.com/01QuackeryRelatedTopics/Tests/allergytests.html.

43. K. S. Rowe and K. J. Rowe, Synthetic food coloring and behavior: A dose response effect in a double-blind, placebo-controlled, repeated measure study, *Journal of Pediatrics* 125 (1994): 691–698.

44. E. J. Costello and coauthors, Relationships between poverty and psychopathology: A natural experiment, Journal of the American Medical Association 290 (2003): 2023–2029.

45. E. Konofal and coauthors, Iron deficiency in children with attention-deficit/hyperactivity disorder, *Archives of Pediatric and Adolescent Medicine* 158 (2004): 1113–1115; Child Stats.gov, Welcome to America's Children: Key National Indicators of Well-Being, 2013, available at http://www.child-stats.gov.

46. S. Parmet, C. Lynm, and R. M. Glass, Attention-deficit/hyperactivity disorder, Journal of the American Medical Association 288 (2002): 1804.

47. R. Sturm, Childhood obesity—what we can learn from existing data on societal trends, part 1, Preventing Chronic Disease: Public Health Research, Practice, and Policy, January 2005, available at http://www.ncbi.nlm.nih.gov/pmc/articles/PMC1323315/; Committee on Public Education, American Academy of Pediatrics, Policy statement: Children, adolescents, and television, *Pediatrics* 107 (2001): 423–426; M. He and coauthors, Screen-related sedentary behaviors: Children's and parents' attitudes, motivations and practices, *Journal of Nutrition Education and Behavior* 42 (2010): 17–25; M. He and coauthors, Screen-related sedentary behaviors of school-aged children: Principals' and teachers' perspectives, *Health Education Journal* 70 (2011): 32–38.

48. R. Chatrath and coauthors, Physical fitness of urban American children, *Pediatric Cardiology* 23 (2002): 608–612; A. D. Salbe and coauthors, Assessing risk factors for obesity between childhood and adolescence: II. Energy metabolism and physical activity, *Pediatrics* 110 (2002): 307–314.

49. R. Boynton-Jarrett and coauthors, Impact of television viewing patterns on fruit and vegetable consumption among adolescents, *Pediatrics* 112 (2003): 1321–1326; K. A. Coon and coauthors, Relationships between use of television during

meals and children's food consumption patterns, *Pediatrics* 107 (2001): 167; C. J. Crespo and coauthors, Television watching, energy intake, and obesity in U.S. children: Results from the Third National Health and Nutrition Examination Survey, 1988–1994, *Archives of Pediatrics and Adolescent Medicine* 155 (2001): 360–365.

50. C. W. Enns, S. J. Mickle, and J. D. Goldman, Trends in food and nutrient intakes by children in the United States, *Family Economics and Nutrition Review* 14 (2002): 56–68.

51. R. Lowry and coauthors, Recent trends in participation in physical education among U.S. high school students, *Journal of School Health* 71 (2001): 145–152.

52. T. N. Robinson, Reducing children's television viewing to prevent obesity: A randomized controlled trial, Journal of the American Medical Association 282 (1999): 1561–1567; M. He and coauthors, Understanding screen-related sedentary behavior and its contributing factors among school-aged children: A social-ecological exploration, *American Journal of Health Promotion* 23 (2009): 299–308.

53. Committee on Public Education, American Academy of Pediatrics, 2001 [see reference 47]; B. A. Dennison, T. A. Erb, and P. L. Jenkins, Television viewing and television in bedroom associated with overweight risk among low-income preschool children, *Pediatrics* 109 (2002): 1028–1035.

54. M. I. Goran, Metabolic precursors and effects of obesity in children: A decade of progress, 1990–1999, *American Journal of Clinical Nutrition* 73 (2001): 158–171.

55. A. Must and S. E. Anderson, Effects of obesity on morbidity in children and adolescents, *Nutrition in Clinical Care* 6 (2003): 4–12; R. Sinha and coauthors, Prevalence of impaired glucose tolerance among children and adolescents with marked obesity, *New England Journal of Medicine* 346 (2002): 802–810.

56. J. B. Schwimmer, T. M. Burwinkle, and J. W. Varni, Health-related quality of life of severely obese children and adolescents, Journal of the American Medical Association 289 (2003): 1813–1819.

57. American Academy of Pediatrics, Policy statement, Prevention of pediatric overweight and obesity, *Pediatrics* 112 (2003): 424–430.

58. D. Spruijt-Metz and coauthors, Relation between mothers' child-feeding practices and children's adiposity, *American Journal of Clinical Nutrition* 75 (2002): 581–586; A. E. Field and coauthors, Peer, parent, and media influences on the development of weight concerns and frequent dieting among preadolescent and adolescent girls and boys, *Pediatrics* 107 (2001): 54–60; K. K. Davison and L. L. Birch, Weight status, parent reaction, and self-concept in five-year-old girls, *Pediatrics* 107 (2001): 46–53.

59. National Institute of Diabetes and Digestive and Kidney Diseases, National Institutes of Health, Helping Your Overweight Child, available at http://win.niddk.nih.gov/publications/over_child.htm.

60. B. J. Rolls, D. Engell, and L. L. Birch, Serving portion size influences 5-year-old but not 3-year-old children's food intakes, *Journal of the American Dietetic Association* 100 (2000): 232–234.

61. T. A. Nicklas and coauthors, Breakfast consumption with and without vitamin-mineral supplement use favorably impacts daily nutrient intake of ninth-grade students, *Journal of Adolescent Health* 27 (2000): 314–321.

62. C. S. Berkey and coauthors, Longitudinal study of skipping breakfast and weight change in adolescents, *International Journal of Obesity and Related Metabolic Disorders* 27 (2003): 1258–1266.

63. J. Bhattacharya, J. Currie, and S. J. Haider, Evaluating the impact of school nutrition programs: Final report, a report of the Economic Research Service, July 2004, available at http://webarchives.cdlib.org/sw1tx36512/http://www.ers.usda.gov/Publications/EFAN04008/.

64. S. M. Gross and B. Cinelli, Coordinated school health programs and dietetics professionals: Partners in promoting healthful eating, *Journal of the American Dietetic Association* 104 (2004): 793–798.

65. Alberta Public Health Association, Elimination of Soft Drink Promotion in Schools, Resolution 6 (2003).

66. Minister of Education, Making Ontario Schools Healthier Places to Learn (Ontario Ministry of Education, October 2004).

67. Position of the American Dietetic Association, 2004 [see reference 9].

68. A. J. Rainville, Nutritional quality of reimbursable school lunches compared with lunches brought from home in elementary schools in two southeastern Michigan districts, *Journal of Child Nutrition and Management* 1 (2000): 13–18.

69. P. M. Gleason and C. W. Suitor, Eating at school: How the National School Lunch Program affects children's diets, *American Journal of Agricultural Economics* 85 (2003): 1047–1051.

70. Position of the American Dietetic Association, Society of Nutrition Education, and American School Food Service Association, Nutrition services: An essential component of comprehensive school health programs, *Journal of the American Dietetic Association* 103 (2003): 505–514.

71. E. A. Bergman and coauthors, Time spent by schoolchildren to eat lunch, *Journal of the American Dietetic Association* 100 (2000): 696–698.

72. Position of the American Dietetic Association: Local support for nutrition integrity in schools, *Journal of the American Dietetic Association* 100 (2000): 108–111; K. W. Cullen and coauthors, Effect of a la carte and snack bar foods at school on children's lunchtime intake of fruits and vegetables, *Journal of the American Dietetic Association* 100 (2000): 1482–1486.

73. M. B. Wildey and coauthors, Fat and sugar levels are high in snacks purchased from student stores in middle schools, *Journal of the American Dietetic Association* 100 (2000): 319–322; L. Harnack and coauthors, Availability of a la carte food items in junior and senior high schools: A

needs assessment, *Journal of the American Dietetic Association* 100 (2000): 701–703.

74. K.W. Cullen and I. Zakeri, Fruits, vegetables, milk, and sweetened beverages consumption and access to a la carte/snack bar meals at school, *American Journal of Public Health* 94 (2004): 463–467; M.Y. Kubik and coauthors, The association of the school food environment with dietary behaviors of young adolescents, *American Journal of Public Health* 93 (2003): 1168–1173.

75. Committee on School Health, American Academy of Pediatrics, Soft drinks in schools, *Pediatrics* 113 (2004): 152–154; J. L. Kramer-Atwood and coauthors, Fostering healthy food consumption in schools: Focusing on the challenges of competitive foods, *Journal of the American Dietetic Association* 102 (2002): 1228–1233.

76. Position of the American Dietetic Association, Society for Nutrition Education, and American School Food Service Association, 2003 [see reference 70].

77. B. P. Roberts, A. S. Blinkhorn, and J. T. Duxbury, The power of children over adults when obtaining sweet snacks, *International Journal of Pediatric Dentistry* 13 (2003): 76–84; S. A. French, Pricing effects on food choices, *Journal of Nutrition* 133 (2003): 841S–843S.

78. U.S. Department of Agriculture (USDA), Fruits—What Foods Are in the Fruit Group?, available at http://www.choosemyplate.gov/food-groups/fruits.html; Committee on Nutrition, American Academy of Pediatrics, The use and misuse of fruit juice in pediatrics, *Pediatrics* 107: 1210–1213; Canadian Paediatric Society. Healthy Snacks for Children, available at http://www.caringforkids.cps.ca/handouts/healthy_snacks_for_children.

79. H. R. Melgar-Quinoñez and L. L. Kaiser, Relationship of child-feeding practices to overweight in low-income Mexican-American preschool-aged children, *Journal of the American Dietetic Association* 104 (2004): 1110–1119; P. K. Newby and coauthors, Beverage consumption is not associated with changes in weight and body mass index among low-income preschool children in North Dakota, *Journal of the American Dietetic Association* 104 (2004): 1086–1094; J. D. Skinner and B. R. Carruth, A longitudinal study of children's juice intake and growth: The juice controversy revisited, *Journal of the American Dietetic Association* 101 (2001): 432–437.

80. D. S. Ludwig, K. E. Peterson, and S. L. Gortmaker, Relation between consumption of sugar-sweetened drinks and childhood obesity: A prospective, observational analysis, *Lancet* 357 (2001): 505–508.

81. Position of the American Dietetic Association, Society of Nutrition Education, and American School Food Service Association, 2003 [see reference 70].

82. Position of the American Dietetic Association, Society for Nutrition Education, and American School Food Service Association, 2003 [see reference 70].

83. M. Story, D. Neumark-Sztainer, and S. French, Individual and environmental influences on adolescent eating behaviors, *Journal of the American Dietetic Association* 102 (2002): S40–S51.

84. D. Garriguet, 2006 [see reference 1].

85. D. Neumark-Sztainer and coauthors, Family meal patterns: Associations with sociodemographic characteristics and improved dietary intake among adolescents, *Journal of the American Dietetic Association* 103 (2003): 317–322.

86. E. Field and coauthors, 2001 [see reference 58]; K. K. Davison and L. L. Birch, 2001 [see reference 58].

87. Committee on the Scientific Evaluation of Dietary Reference Intakes, Food and Nutrition Board, Institute of Medicine, Dietary Reference Intakes for Vitamin A, Vitamin K, Arsenic, Boron, Chromium, Copper, Iodine, Iron, Manganese, Molybdenum, Nickel, Silicon, Vanadium, and Zinc (Washington, D.C.: National Academies Press, 2001), pp. 290–393.

88. J. S. Halterman and coauthors, Iron deficiency and cognitive achievement among school-aged children and adolescents in the United States, *Pediatrics* 107 (2001): 1381–1386.

89. Federal Update, Milk matters, *Journal of the American Dietetic Association* 102 (2002): 469.

90. G. Mrdjenovic and D. A. Levitsky, Nutritional and energetic consequences of sweetened drink consumption in 6- to 13-year-old children, *Journal of Pediatrics* 142 (2003): 604–610; Statistics Canada—Beverage consumption by children and teens, available at http://www.statcan.gc.ca/pub/82-003-x/2008004/article/10715/6500232-eng.htm.

91. H. J. Kalkwarf, J. C. Khoury, and B. P. Lanphear, Milk intake during childhood and adolescence, adult bone density, and osteoporotic fractures in US women, *American Journal of Clinical Nutrition* 77 (2003): 257–265.

92. S. A. Bowman, Beverage choices of young females: Changes and impact on nutrient intakes, *Journal of the American Dietetic Association* 102 (2002): 1234–1239.

93. J. James and coauthors, Preventing childhood obesity by reducing consumption of carbonated drinks: Cluster randomised controlled trial, British Medical Journal 328 (2004): 1237; D. S. Ludwig, K. E. Peterson, and S. L. Gortmaker, 2001 [see reference 80]; A. D. Danyliw and coauthors, Beverage intake patterns of Canadian children and relationship to overweight and obesity, Applied Physiology, *Nutrition and Metabolism* 37 (2012): 900–906.

94. Committee on the Scientific Evaluation of Dietary Reference Intakes, Food and Nutrition Board, Institute of Medicine, 2002, Chapter 5 [see reference 6].

95. D. Garriguet, 2006 [see reference 1].

96. D. Neumark-Sztainer and coauthors, Weight-control behaviors among adolescent girls and boys: Implications for dietary intake, *Journal of the American Dietetic Association* 104 (2004): 913–920.

97. D. Neumark-Sztainer and coauthors, 2004 [see reference 96].

98. A. E. Field and coauthors, Relation between dieting and weight change among preadolescents and adolescents, *Pediatrics* 112 (2003): 900–906.

99. L. A. Lytle and coauthors, How do children's eating patterns and food choices change over time? Results from a cohort study, *American Journal of Health Promotion* 14 (2000): 222–228.

100. M. Sigman-Grant, Strategies for counseling adolescents, *Journal of the American Dietetic Association* 102 (2002): S32–S39.

101. Federal Interagency Forum on Aging-Related Statistics, Older Americans 2004: Key Indicators of Well-Being, November 2004, available at http://www.agingstats.gov/Main_Site/Data/2004_Documents/entire_report.pdf; Trends in aging—United States and worldwide, Morbidity and Mortality Weekly Report 52 (2003): 101–106.

102. Statistics Canada, Life expectancy at birth, by sex, by province, available at http://www.statcan.gc.ca/tables-tableaux/sum-som/l01/cst01/health26-eng.htm.

103. T. Perls, Genetic and environmental influences on exceptional longevity and the AGE nomogram, *Annals of the New York Academy of Sciences* 959 (2002): 1–13.

104. C. E. Greenwood, Dietary carbohydrate, glucose regulation, and cognitive performance in elderly persons, *Nutrition Reviews* 61 (2003): S68–S74.

105. E. W. Gregg and coauthors, Relationship of changes in physical activity and mortality among older women, Journal of the American Medical Association 289 (2003): 2379–2386; W. J. Strawbridge and coauthors, Physical activity reduces the risk of subsequent depression for older adults, *American Journal of Epidemiology* 156 (2002): 328–334.

106. K. M. Tarpenning and coauthors, Endurance training delays age of decline in leg strength and muscle morphology, *Medicine and Science in Sports and Exercise* 36 (2004): 74–78; J. Haberer and coauthors, Clinical problem solving: A gut feeling, *New England Journal of Medicine* 349 (2003): 73–78; P. A. Ades and coauthors, Resistance training on physical performance in disabled older female cardiac patients, *Medicine and Science in Sports and Exercise* 35 (2003): 1265–1270.

107. R. D. Hansen and B. J. Allen, Habitual physical activity, anabolic hormones, and potassium content of fat-free mass in post-menopausal women, *American Journal of Clinical Nutrition* 75 (2002): 314–320.

108. A. S. Nicolas and coauthors, Successful aging and nutrition, *Nutrition Reviews* 59 (2001): S88–S92.

109. J. Kruger and coauthors, Strength training among adults aged ≥ 65 years—United States, 2001, *Morbidity and Mortality Weekly Report* 53 (2004): 25–28.

110. H. K. Kamel, Sarcopenia and aging, *Nutrition Reviews* 61 (2003): 157–167; C. W. Bales and C. S. Ritchie, Sarcopenia, weight loss, and nutritional frailty in the elderly, *Annual Review of Nutrition* 22 (2002): 309–323.

111. P. Jokl, P. M. Sethi, and A. J. Cooper, Master's performance in the New York City Marathon 1983–1999, *British Journal of Sports Medicine* 38 (2004): 408–412.

112. M. M. G. Wilson, R. Purushothaman, and J. E. Morley, Effect of liquid dietary supplements on energy intake in the elderly, *American Journal of Clinical Nutrition* 75 (2002): 944–947.

113. D. Benton and S. Nabb, Carbohydrate, memory, and mood, *Nutrition Reviews* 61 (2003): S61–S67.

114. N. R. Sahyoun and E. Krall, Lower dietary quality among older adults with self-perceived ill-fitting dentures, *Journal of the American Dietetic Association* 103 (2003): 1494–1499.

115. Committee on the Scientific Evaluation of Dietary Reference Intakes, Food and Nutrition Board, Institute of Medicine, 2002 [see reference 6].

116. Centers for Disease Control and Prevention, Prevalence of doctor-diagnosed arthritis and possible arthritis—30 states, 2002, *Morbidity and Mortality Weekly Report* 53 (2004): 383–386.

117. A. E. Wluka and coauthors, Supplementary vitamin E does not affect loss of cartilage volume in knee osteoarthritis: A 2 year double blind randomized placebo controlled study, *Journal of Rheumatology* 29 (2002): 2585–2591.

118. L. Hagfors and coauthors, Antioxidant intake, plasma antioxidants and oxidative stress in a randomized, controlled, parallel, Mediterranean dietary intervention study on patients with rheumatoid arthritis, *Nutrition Journal* 2 (2003), available at http://www.nutritionj.com/content/2/1/5; O. Adam, Dietary fatty acids and immune reactions in synovial tissue, *European Journal of Medical Research* 8 (2003): 381–387; L. Cleland, M. James, and S. Proudman, The role of fish oils in the treatment of rheumatoid arthritis, *Drugs* 63 (2003): 845–853.

119. L. Skoldstam, L. Hagfors, and G. Johansson, An experimental study of a Mediterranean diet intervention for patients with rheumatoid arthritis, *Annals of the Rheumatic Diseases* 62 (2003): 208–214.

120. V. B. Kraus and coauthors, Ascorbic acid increases the severity of spontaneous knee osteoarthritis in a guinea pig model, *Arthritis and Rheumatism* 50 (2004): 1822–1831.

121. D. J. Pattison, D. P. Symmons, and A. Young, Does diet have a role in the aetiology of rheumatoid arthritis? *Proceedings of the Nutrition Society* 63 (2004): 137–143; J. M. Kremer, n-3 Fatty acid supplements in rheumatoid arthritis, *American Journal of Clinical Nutrition* 71 (2000): 349S–351S.

122. S. P. Messier and coauthors, Exercise and dietary weight loss in overweight and obese older adults with knee osteoarthritis: The Arthritis, Diet, and Activity Promotion Trial, *Arthritis and Rheumatism* 50 (2004): 1501–1510; K. R. Baker and coauthors, The efficacy of home based progressive strength training in older adults with knee osteoarthritis: A randomized controlled trial, *Journal of Rheumatology* 28 (2001): 1655–1665.

123. J. Y. Reginster and coauthors, Naturocetic (glucosamine and chondroitin sulfate) compounds as structure-modifying drugs in the treatment of osteoarthritis, *Current Opinion in Rheumatology* 15 (2003): 651–655; National Institute of Arthritis and Musculoskeletal and Skin Diseases, National Institutes of Health, Glucosamine/Chondroitin Arthritis Intervention Trial (GAIT) begins patient recruitment, Press releases, 2000, available at http://www.niams.nih.gov/News_and_Events/Press_Releases/2000/12_11a.asp; T. E. McAlindon and coauthors, Glucosamine and chondroitin for treatment of osteoarthritis: A systematic quality assessment and meta-analysis, Journal of the American Medical Association 283 (2000): 1469–1475.

124. Standing Committee on the Scientific Evaluation of Dietary Reference Intakes, Food and Nutrition Board, Institute of Medicine, Dietary Reference Intakes for Calcium, Phosphorus, Magnesium, Vitamin D, and Fluoride (Washington, D.C.: National Academies Press, 1997).

125. C. Ho and coauthors, Practitioners' guide to meeting the vitamin B12 Recommended Dietary Allowance for people aged 51 years and older, *Journal of the American Dietetic Association* 99 (1999): 725–727.

126. T. S. Dharmarajan, G. U. Adiga, and E. P. Norkus, Vitamin B12 deficiency: Recognizing subtle symptoms in older adults, *Geriatrics* 58 (2003): 30–34, 37–38; H. W. Baik and R. M. Russell, Vitamin B12 deficiency in the elderly, *Annual Review of Nutrition* 19 (1999): 357–377.

127. M. A. Johnson and coauthors, Hyperhomocysteinemia and vitamin B-12 deficiency in elderly using Title IIIc nutrition services, *American Journal of Clinical Nutrition* 77 (2003): 211–220; H. W. Baik and R. M. Russell, 1999 [see reference 126].

128. I. H. Rosenberg, B vitamins, homocysteine, and neurocognitive function, *Nutrition Reviews* 59 (2001): S69–S74.

129. M. Meydani, Antioxidants and cognitive function, *Nutrition Reviews* 59 (2001): S75–S82.

130. J. L. Gottlieb, Age-related macular degeneration, Journal of the American Medical Association 288 (2002): 2233–2236.

131. N. I. Krinsky, J. T. Landrum, and R. A. Bone, Biologic mechanisms of the protective role of lutein and zeaxanthin in the eye, *Annual Review of Nutrition* 23 (2003): 171–201.

132. E. Cho and coauthors, Prospective study of dietary fat and the risk of age-related macular degeneration, *American Journal of Clinical Nutrition* 73 (2000): 209–218.

133. C. Chitchumroonchokchai and coauthors, Xanthophylls and α-tocopherol decrease UVB-induced lipid peroxidation and stress signaling in human lens epithelial cells, *Journal of Nutrition* 134 (2004): 3225–3232; A. Taylor and coauthors, Long-term intake of vitamins and carotenoids and odds of early age-related cortical and posterior subcapsular lens opacities, *American Journal of Clinical Nutrition* 75 (2002): 540–549; J. A. Simon and E. S. Hudes, Serum ascorbic acid and other correlates of self-reported cataract among older Americans, *Journal of Clinical Epidemiology* 52 (1999): 1207–1211.

134. S. M. Moeller and coauthors, Overall adherence to the Dietary Guidelines for Americans is associated with reduced prevalence of early age-related nuclear lens opacities in women, *Journal of Nutrition* 134 (2004): 1812–1819.

135. D. H. Holben and coauthors, Fluid intake compared with established standards and symptoms of dehydration among elderly residents of a long-term-care facility, *Journal of the American Dietetic Association* 99 (1999): 1447–1450.

136. D. J. Fleming and coauthors, Dietary factors associated with the risk of high iron stores in the elderly Framingham Heart Study cohort, *American Journal of Clinical Nutrition* 76 (2002): 1375–1384.

137. F. Girodon and coauthors, Impact of trace elements and vitamin supplementation on immunity and infections in institutionalized elderly patients: A randomized controlled trial, *Archives of Internal Medicine* 159 (1999): 748–754.

138. B. E. C. Nordin and coauthors, Effect of age on calcium absorption in post-menopausal women, *American Journal of Clinical Nutrition* 80 (2004): 998–1002; Position of the American Dietetic Association and Dietitians of Canada: Nutrition and women's health, *Journal of the American Dietetic Association* 104 (2004): 984–1001.

139. R. H. Fletcher and K. M. Fairfield, Vitamins for chronic disease prevention in adults, Journal of the American Medical Association 287 (2002): 3127–3129; W. C. Willett and M. J. Stampfer, What vitamins should I be taking, doctor? *New England Journal of Medicine* 345 (2001): 1819–1824.

140. N. B. Belloc and L. Breslow, Relationship of physical health status and health practices, *Preventive Medicine* 1 (1972): 409–421.

141. G. E. Vaillant and K. Mukamal, Successful aging, *American Journal of Psychiatry* 158 (2001): 839–847.

142. C. A. Jolly, Dietary restriction and immune function, *Journal of Nutrition* 134 (2004): 1853–1856; B. T. Larson and coauthors, Improved glucose tolerance with lifetime diet restriction favorably affects disease and survival in dogs, *Journal of Nutrition* 133 (2003): 2887–2892.

143. T. A. Gresl and coauthors, Dietary restriction and glucose regulation in aging rhesus monkeys: A follow-up report at 8.5 yr, *American Journal of Physiology: Endocrinology and Metabolism* 281 (2001): E757–E765; J. J. Ramsey and coauthors, Dietary restriction and aging in rhesus monkeys: The University of Wisconsin study, *Experimental Gerontology* 35 (2000): 1131–1149.

144. O. Lamas, J. A. Martinez, and A. Marti, Energy restriction restores the impaired immune response in overweight (cafeteria) rats, *Journal of Nutritional Biochemistry* 15 (2004): 418–425; R. M. Anson and coauthors, Intermittent fasting dissociates beneficial effects of dietary restriction on glucose metabolism and neuronal resistance to injury from calorie intake, *Proceedings of the National Academy of Sciences* 100 (2003): 6216–6220.

145. L. Fontana and coauthors, Long-term calorie restriction is highly effective in reducing the risk for atherosclerosis in humans, *Proceedings of the National Academy of Sciences* 101 (2004): 6659–6663.

146. W. S. Browner and coauthors, The genetics of human longevity, *American Journal of Medicine* 117 (2004): 882–883; J. M. Dhahbi and coauthors,

Caloric restriction alters the feeding response of key metabolic enzyme genes, *Mechanics of Aging and Development* 122 (2001): 1033–1048.

147. S. X. Cao and coauthors, Genomic profiling of short- and long-term caloric restriction effects in the liver of aging mice, *Proceedings of the National Academy of Sciences* 98 (2001): 10630–10635.

148. K. T. B. Knoops and coauthors, Mediterranean diet, lifestyle factors, and 10-year mortality in elderly European men and women, Journal of the American Medical Association 292 (2004): 1433–1439; G. Barja, Endogenous oxidative stress: Relationship to aging, longevity and caloric restriction, *Ageing Research and Reviews* 1 (2002): 397–411; B. J. Merry, Molecular mechanisms linking calorie restriction and longevity, *International Journal of Biochemistry and Cell Biology* 34 (2002): 1340–1354.

149. Alzheimer Society of Canada, Rising Tide: The Impact of Dementia on Canadian Society, available at http://www.alzheimer.ca/~/media/Files/national/Advocacy/ASC_Rising_Tide_Full_Report_e.ashx.

150. G. T. Grossberg, Diagnosis and treatment of Alzheimer's disease, *Journal of Clinical Psychiatry* 64 (2003): 3–6; R. C. Green and coauthors, Depression as a risk factor for Alzheimer's disease: The MIRAGE study, *Archives of Neurology* 60 (2003): 753–759; J. L. Cummings and G. Cole, Alzheimer disease, Journal of the American Medical Association 287 (2002): 2335–2338.

151. A. M. Clarfield, The decreasing prevalence of reversible dementias: An updated meta-analysis, *Archives of Internal Medicine* 163 (2003): 2219–2229.

152. C. Janus, Vaccines for Alzheimer's disease: How close are we? *CNS Drugs* 17 (2003): 457–474; M. W. Dysken and coauthors, Effect of Vitamin E and Memantine on Functional Decline in Alzheimer Disease: The TEAM-AD VA Cooperative Randomized Trial, Journal of the American Medical Association 311 (2014): 33–44.

153. M. A. Lovely, C. Xie, and W. R. Markesbery, Protections against amyloid beta peptide toxicity by zinc, *Brain Research* 823 (1999): 88–95.

154. G. Young and J. Conquer, Omega-3 fatty acids and neuropsychiatric disorders (review), *Reproduction Nutrition Development* 45 (2005): 1–28; F. Calon and coauthors, Docosahexaenoic acid protects from dendritic pathology in an Alzheimer's disease mouse model, *Neuron* 43 (2004): 633–645.

155. M. von Dongen and coauthors, Ginkgo for elderly people with dementia and age-associated memory impairment: A randomized clinical trial, *Journal of Clinical Epidemiology* 56 (2003): 367–376.

156. S. Gillette-Guyonnet and coauthors, Weight loss in Alzheimer disease, *American Journal of Clinical Nutrition* 71 (2000): 637S–642S; E. T. Poehlman and R. V. Dvorak, Energy expenditure, energy intake, and weight loss in Alzheimer disease, *American Journal of Clinical Nutrition* 71 (2000): 650S–655S.

157. V. A. Freedman, L. G. Martin, and R. F. Schoeni, Recent trends in disability and functioning among older adults in the United States:

A systematic review, *Journal of the American Medical Association* 288 (2002): 3137–3146.

158. M. A. Bernstein and coauthors, Higher dietary variety is associated with better nutritional status in frail elderly people, *Journal of the American Dietetic Association* 102 (2002): 1096–1104.

159. B. Bartali and coauthors, Age and disability affect dietary intake, *Journal of Nutrition* 133 (2003): 2868–2873.

160. B. A. Horwitz, C. A. Blanton, and R. B. McDonald, Physiologic determinants of the anorexia of aging: Insights from animal studies, *Annual Review of Nutrition* 22 (2002): 417–438; C. W. Bales and C. S. Ritchie, Sarcopenia, weight loss, and nutritional frailty in the elderly, I, *Annual Review of Nutrition* 22 (2002): 309–323.

161. S. B. Roberts, Energy regulation and aging: Recent findings and their implications, *Nutrition Reviews* 58 (2000): 91–97; F. Landi and coauthors, Body mass index and mortality among older people living in the community, *Journal of the American Geriatrics Society* 47 (1999): 1072–1076.

162. Government of Canada, Guide to Government of Canada Services for Seniors, available at http://publications.gc.ca/collections/collection_2008/servicecanada/SG5-18-2008E.pdf.

163. Position of the American Dietetic Association: Liberalized diets for older adults in long-term care, *Journal of the American Dietetic Association* 102 (2002): 1316–1323.

164. Economic Research Service of the U.S. Department of Agriculture, USDA report encourages Americans to remember nutritional needs when eating out, USDA News Release no. 0060.99 (1999), available at http://www.thefreelibrary.com/USDA+Encourages+Consumers+To+Remember+Nutritional+Needs+When+Dining...-a053950239

165. L. H. Clemens, D. L. Slawson, and R. C. Klesges, The effect of eating out on quality of diet in premenopausal women, *Journal of the American Dietetic Association* 99 (1999): 442–444.

166. United States Department of Agriculture, Safe Handling of Take-Out Foods(2013), available at http://www.fsis.usda.gov/wps/portal/fsis/topics/food-safety-education/get-answers/food-safety-fact-sheets/safe-food-handling/safe-handling-of-take-out-foods/.

Consumer Corner 14

1. Academy of Nutrition and Dietetics, *Premenstrual Syndrome* (2013), available at http://www.eatright.org/Public/content.aspx?id=11181&terms=PMS.

2. M. Landen and E. Eriksson, How does premenstrual dysphoric disorder relate to depression and anxiety disorders? *Depression and Anxiety* 17 (2003): 122–129.

3. American College of Obstetricians and Gynecologists, Fact Sheet: Tool Kit for Teen Care, 2nd edition, Premenstrual Syndrome and Premenstrual Dysphoric Disorder (2009), available at http://www.acog.org/~/media/Departments/Adolescent%20Health%20Care/Teen%20Care%20Tool%20Kit/PMS.pdf?dmc=1&ts=20140103T1619333966.

4. U. Halbreich, The etiology, biology, and evolving pathology of premenstrual syndromes, *Psychoneuroendocrinology* 28 (2003): 55–99.

5. C. A. Roca and coauthors, Differential menstrual cycle regulation of hypothalamic-pituitary-adrenal axis in women with premenstrual syndrome and controls, *Journal of Clinical Endocrinology and Metabolism* 88 (2003): 3057–3063.

6. G. B. Cross and coauthors, Changes in nutrient intake during the menstrual cycle of overweight women with premenstrual syndrome, *British Journal of Nutrition* 85 (2001): 475–482.

7. Academy of Nutrition and Dietetics, 2013 [see reference 1].

8. A. Bendick, The potential for dietary supplements to reduce premenstrual symptoms, *Journal of the American College of Nutrition* 19 (2002): 3–12.

Controversy 14

1. J. M. Sorenson, Herb–drug, food–drug, nutrient–drug, and drug–drug interactions: Mechanisms involved and their medical implications, *Journal of Alternative and Complementary Medicine* 8 (2002): 293–308.

2. L-N. Chan, Drug-nutrient interaction in clinical nutrition, *Current Opinion in Clinical Nutrition and Metabolic Care* 5 (2002): 327–332.

3. W. Abebe, Herbal medication: Potential for adverse interactions with analgesic drugs, *Journal of Clinical Pharmacy and Therapeutics* 27 (2002): 391–401.

4. A. W. Wallace, J. M. Victory, and G. W. Amsden, Lack of bioequivalence of gatifloxacin when coadministered with calcium fortified orange juice in healthy volunteers, *Journal of Clinical Pharmacology* 43 (2003): 92–96; L. E. Schmidt and K. Dalhoff, Food-drug interactions, *Drugs* 62 (2002): 1481–1502.

5. J. A. Cambria-Kiely, Effect of soy milk on warfarin efficacy, *Annals of Pharmacotherapy* 36 (2002): 1893–1896.

6. S. G. Stoney and coauthors, Oral contraceptive use is associated with increased cardiovascular reactivity in nonsmokers, *Annals of Behavioral Medicine* 23 (2001): 149–157.

7. Health Canada, *It's Your Health—Caffeine*, available at http://www.cg.cfpsa.ca/cg-pc/Comox/SiteCollectionDocuments/EN/Health%20Promotion/WW_Additional_Handouts/70%20-%20Caffeine_EN.pdf.

8. C. Papadelis and coauthors, Effects of mental workload and caffeine on catecholamines and blood pressure compared to performance variations, *Brain and Cognition* 51 (2003): 143–154; E. De Valck, E. De Groot, and R. Cluydts, Effects of slow-release caffeine and a nap on driving simulator performance after partial sleep deprivation, *Perceptual and Motor Skills* 96 (2003): 67–78; B. J. Fine and coauthors, Effects of caffeine or diphenhydramine on visual vigilance, *Psychopharmacology (Berlin)* 114 (1994): 233–238, as cited by H. R. Lieberman, The effects of ginseng, ephedrine, and caffeine on cognitive performance, mood, and energy, *Nutrition Reviews* 59 (2001): 91–102.

9. L. M. Juliano and R. R. Griffiths, A critical review of caffeine withdrawal: empirical validation

of symptoms and signs, incidence, severity, and associated features, *Psychopharmacology (Berlin)* 176 (2004), e-pub, available at http://link.springer.com/article/10.1007/s00213-004-2000-x#page-1; M. R. Yeomans and coauthors, Effects of caffeine on performance and mood depend on the level of caffeine abstinence, *Psychopharmacology (Berlin)* 164 (2002): 241–249.

10. M. R. Yeomans and coauthors, 2002 [see reference 9].

11. D. S. Michaud and coauthors, Coffee and alcohol consumption and the risk of pancreatic cancer in two prospective United States cohorts, *Cancer Epidemiology, Biomarkers, and Prevention* 10 (2001): 429–437; T. R. Hartley and coauthors, Hypertension risk status and effect of caffeine on blood pressure, *Hypertension* 36 (2000): 137–141.

12. M. C. Cornelis and coauthors, Coffee, CYP1A2 genotype, and risk of myocardial infarction, *Journal of the American Medical Association* 295 (2006): 1135–1141; A. Tavani and C. LaVeechia, Coffee and the risk of cancer and coronary heart disease, in T. Wilson and N. J. Temple, eds., *Beverages in Nutrition and Health* (Totowa, NJ: Humana Press, 2004), pp. 127–142; M. R. Olthof and coauthors, Consumption of high doses of chlorogenic acid, present in coffee, or of black tea increases plasma total homocysteine concentrations in humans, *American Journal of Clinical Nutrition* 73 (2001): 532–538.

13. M. F. Leitzmann and coauthors, A prospective study of coffee consumption and the risk of symptomatic gallstone disease in men, *Journal of the American Medical Association* 281 (1999): 2106–2112.

14. A. Rodgers, Effect of cola consumption on urinary biochemical and physiochemical risk factors associated with calcium oxalate urolithianis, *Urological Research* 27 (1999): 77–81.

15. K. Neilann and coauthors, Potential mechanisms of diet therapy for fibrocystic breast conditions show inadequate evidence of effectiveness, *Journal of the American Dietetic Association* 100 (2000): 1368–1380.

16. Standing Committee on the Scientific Evaluation of Dietary Reference Intakes, Food and Nutrition Board, Institute of Medicine, *Dietary Reference Intakes for Vitamin C, Vitamin E, Selenium, and Carotenoids* (Washington, D.C.: National Academies Press, 2000), pp. 152–153.

15 Hunger and the Global Environment

Do You Ever . . .

Read about starvation and strife in remote locations and feel well insulated here at home?

Feel overwhelmed when you think about the problems facing our world?

Purchase a meal, considering only its monetary price?

Wish that somebody would do something about the contaminants in air, water, and food that occasionally make headlines?

Keep Reading . . .

Learning Objectives

After completing this chapter, you should be able to

LO 15.1 Discuss the double threat of undernutrition and obesity and how this can impact the health and functioning of a group of people.

LO 15.2 Speculate how reducing a family's hunger level can lead to more positive outcomes for health and social well-being for that family.

LO 15.3 Explain why people in poverty are inclined to have larger families in spite of the scarcity of food.

LO 15.4 Describe why producing enough corn for people, livestock, and biofuels presents a problem for the environment.

LO 15.5 Define the term *ecological footprint* and describe ways to lessen one's ecological footprint.

Contents

One person in every five worldwide experiences persistent **hunger**—not the healthy appetite triggered by anticipation of a hearty meal but the painful condition caused by a chronic lack of food. Tens of thousands die of starvation each day—one every two seconds. Table 15–1 presents the current best estimate of the number of hungry people worldwide. The presence of hunger does not exclude the coexistence of nutrient deficiencies or overnutrition within the same country, the same area, or even the same family.*[1] Up to 80 percent of hungry children live in countries that produce surplus food, but the decisions of policymakers in those areas largely determine who among the population has access to the bounty.

Hunger in Canada

Hunger is a concern in Canada. Poverty among women with young children is one important factor related to hunger. According to Statistics Canada, in 2010 just over 8 percent of children under 18 years lived in low-income families.[2] The percentage is almost triple for children in female-headed single-parent low-income households.

Table 15–1		
Food and Agriculture Organization (FAO) 2012 Estimate of Undernourished Individuals by Region (Millions; Total = ~870 Million)		
Asia and Pacific	563	
Africa	239	
Latin America and the Caribbean	49	
Developed Countries	16	

Source: *Food and Agriculture Organization of the United Nations, 2012*, The State of Food Insecurity in the World, *http://www.fao.org/docrep/016/i3027e/i3027e.pdf*

---

*References are listed at the end of the chapter.

Helping at a local **food bank**, shelter, or emergency feeding centre can provide you with an opportunity to gain an understanding of local hunger issues associated with **food insecurity**. Terms relating to hunger are defined in Table 15–2.

The world's chronically hungry suffer from undernutrition, a condition of energy and nutrient deficiency that causes general weakness and fatigue. The greater the caloric deficit, the greater the susceptibility to nutrition-related health risks. Undernutrition stymies mental and physical development in children and makes people susceptible to potentially fatal infections such as dysentery, whooping cough, and tuberculosis.[3] Consequences of chronic hunger in children include infant mortality, stunted growth, iron-deficiency anemia, poor learning, extreme weakness, clinical signs of protein-energy malnutrition (PEM), increased susceptibility to disease, loss of the ability to stand or walk, and premature death.[4]

The tragedy described on these pages may seem at first to be beyond the influence of the ordinary person. What possible difference can one person make? Can one person's choice to recycle a bottle or to serve a meal to the homeless or to join a hunger-relief organization make a difference? In truth, such choices produce several benefits. For one, a single person's awareness and example, shared with others, can influence many people over time. For another, an action repeated becomes a beneficial habit. For still another, making choices with awareness of their impacts lends a sense of control over those impacts. That sense of personal control, in turn, helps people take effective action in many areas.

Students can play a powerful role in bringing about change. Students everywhere are helping to change governments, human predicaments, and environmental problems for the better. Student movements persuaded 127 universities and many institutions, corporations, and government agencies to put pressure on South Africa and succeeded in ending apartheid. Student pressure opened the way for the first deaf president at a university for the deaf. Students offer major services to communities through soup kitchens, home repair programs, and child education. The young people of today are the world's single best hope for a better tomorrow.

- "Never doubt that a small group of thoughtful, committed people can change the world. Indeed, it is the only thing that ever has."—Margaret Mead

The Challenge to Change

Banishing food insecurity for all of the world's citizens poses two major challenges. The first is to provide enough food to meet the needs of the earth's expanding population, without destroying natural resources needed to continue producing food. The second challenge is

Table 15–2

Hunger Terms

- **famine** widespread and extreme scarcity of food in an area that causes starvation and death in a large portion of the population.
- **food insecurity** the condition of limited or uncertain access to food of sufficient quality or quantity to sustain a healthy, active life.
- **food poverty** hunger occurring when enough food exists in an area but some of the people cannot obtain it because they lack money, are being deprived for political reasons, live in a country at war, or suffer from other problems such as lack of transportation.
- **food security** reliable access to enough nutritious food at all times to sustain a healthy, active life.
- **food shortage** hunger occurring when an area of the world lacks enough total food to feed its people.
- **hunger** lack or shortage of basic foods needed to provide the energy and nutrients that support health.
- **world food supply** the quantity of food, including stores from previous harvests, available to the world's people at a given time.
- **food banks** facilities that collect and distribute food donations to authorized organizations feeding the hungry.
- **food pantries** community food collection programs that provide groceries to be prepared and eaten at home.
- **emergency kitchens** programs that provide prepared meals to be eaten on-site; often called *soup kitchens*.

to ensure **food security**—that is, to make sure all people have access to enough food to live active, healthy lives. By all accounts, today's total **world food supply** can abundantly feed the entire current population, but this does not guarantee that people in need are able to get adequate food. If people do not have enough money to buy food or to buy the land, seeds, and tools to grow food or if natural or human-made disasters such as drought or war prevent them from getting food, hunger remains a problem.

Concerns for the future also exist. Many forces compound to threaten world food production and distribution in the next decade, and we may face more global food insecurity because of them:

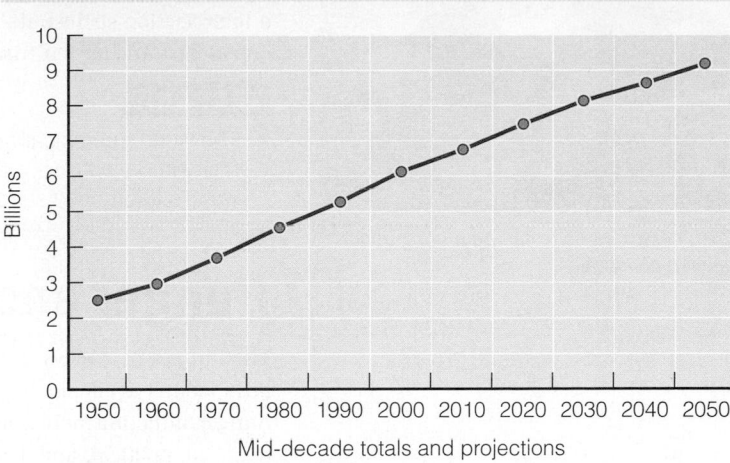

Figure 15–1

World Population Growth

Mid-decade totals and projections

- *Hunger, poverty, and population growth.* Millions of the world's people are starving. Fifteen children die of malnutrition every 30 seconds, but 125 children are born in that same 30 seconds. Every day, the earth gains another 220,000 new residents to feed (see Figure 15–1), most of them born in impoverished areas.[5]

- *Loss of food-producing land.* Food-producing land is becoming saltier, eroding, and being paved over. Each year, the world's farmers try to feed some 85 million additional people with 24 billion fewer tonnes of topsoil. This loss threatens overall food security.

- *Accelerating fossil fuel use.* Fossil fuel use is growing rapidly, with attendant pollution of air, soil, and water; ozone depletion; and global climate changes.

- *Increasing air pollution.* As populations and human activities increase, air quality diminishes in many areas around the globe.

- *Atmosphere and climate changes, glacier retreat, decreasing Arctic ice cover, droughts, and floods.* Climbing atmospheric levels of heat-trapping carbon dioxide are a concern. The concentration of carbon dioxide is now 26 percent higher than 200 years ago. Researchers suspect that a worldwide warming trend caused the record-breaking heat in the summer of 2003 that cost many thousands of European lives.[6] Climate changes also cause droughts and floods that destroy crops and people's homelands.[7] Diseases such as malaria that are now confined to tropical areas are expected to spread to other climate zones as they warm.

- *Ozone loss from the outer atmosphere.* The outer atmosphere's protective ozone layer is growing thinner, permitting harmful radiation from the sun to penetrate. This radiation increases the likelihood of skin cancers and cataracts in people and animals and may damage crops and ecosystems.

- *Water shortages.* The world's supplies of fresh water are dwindling and becoming polluted.[8]

- *Deforestation and desertification.* Forests are shrinking and deserts are growing.

- *Ocean pollution.* Ocean pollution is killing fish in large "dead zones" along the world's coasts; overfishing is depleting the fish that remain.[9] In North America, the U.S. Commission on Ocean Policy has deemed the U.S. systems of managing oceans and coasts fragmented and insufficient for the task; however, BP remains committed to remedying the damage its spill (April 2010) caused to the Gulf Coast.[10] Many other nations have weaker policies still or no policies at all.

- *Extinctions of species.* "Should we be alarmed at the current massive die-offs being noted in the animal and plant kingdoms? . . . Over 10,000 scientists in the World Conservation Union have compiled data showing that currently 51 per cent of known reptiles, 52 per cent of known insects, and 73 per cent of known flowering plants are in danger along with many mammals, birds and amphibians" (see http://www.globalresearch.ca/the-extinction-of-animal-and-plant-species/12965).

Each person's efforts can help bring about needed changes.

These global problems are all related and, often, so are their solutions. To think positively, this means that any initiative a person takes to help solve one problem will help solve many others. In particular, control of the earth's population is urgent, as a later section spells out. This chapter's Controversy shows how Canadian and U.S. consumers and agricultural practices affect the world's resources.

KEY POINT

- The world's chronically hungry people suffer the effects of undernutrition, and many in Canada live with food insecurity. Many forces combine to threaten the world's future food supply and its distribution.

Hunger and Malnutrition

The hunger of concern is a chronic, painful hunger people feel when no food or too little food is available. Severe deficiencies of vitamins and minerals accompany this hunger, afflicting more than 40 percent of the world's people to some degree due mainly to social, political, and armed conflict. An estimated 2 billion people, mostly women and children, suffer the effects of iron-deficiency anemia, and many more suffer milder degrees of insufficiency. Iodine deficiency remains the single greatest cause of preventable brain damage and mental retardation; 750 million adults suffer from goitre. Deficiency of vitamin A takes a terrible toll on the world's children—it stands out as the world's leading cause of blindness in young children and robs many millions of the ability to fight off infections. About 45 percent of the deaths among the world's children are attributable to malnutrition.[11] Worldwide, three-fourths of those who die each year from starvation and related illnesses are children and nearly half of under-five deaths occurred in sub-Saharan Africa.[12]

In developed countries, the primary cause of hunger is **food poverty**. People are hungry not because there is no food nearby to purchase but because they lack sufficient money with which to buy nutritious food and pay for other necessities, such as clothing, housing, medicines, and utilities. In 2010 about 9 percent of the Canadian population lived in a low-income situation.[13] The likelihood of food poverty increases with problems such as abuse of alcohol and other drugs, mental or physical illness, depression, lack of awareness of or access to available food programs, and the reluctance of people to accept what some perceive as "government handouts" or charity.[14] Similarly, according to the PROOF team of researchers (an international, interdisciplinary team of researchers who are committed to the reduction of household food insecurity), the 2011 CCHS revealed that one in six children were affected by food insecurity, representing about 12 percent of Canadian households (http://nutritionalsciences.lamp.utoronto.ca/food-insecurity).

Ideally, all people would always have enough nutritious food to support an active, healthy life; in other words, they would experience food security. Yet, according to Food Banks Canada's national survey of emergency food programs, HungerCount, the number of food bank users in Canada more than doubled from 378,000 in March 1989 to ~880,000 (38% of whom were children) in March 2012, the highest number on record and 30 percent higher than before the recession in 2008. These numbers are released on World Food Day (October 16) each year; watch for them in the coming year (see Figure 15–2).[15] Also, watch for Hunger Awareness Day/Week in May each year (see http://hungerawarenessweek.ca/about_hunger). Food poverty reaches into many segments of society, affecting not only the chronic poor (migrant workers, the unskilled and unemployed, the homeless, and some elderly) but also the so-called working poor. Some of these people are displaced farm families who work at minimum-wage jobs. Some are former blue-collar and white-collar workers forced out of their trades and professions. These people outnumber the chronic poor, and they are not on welfare—they have jobs, but the pay is too low to meet basic needs. The pay scale for low-skill jobs has increased only slightly in recent years, but living expenses have increased significantly, effectively reducing the real wages earned by workers.[16] Such families cannot afford to buy sufficient amounts of nourishing foods, even if they are skilled in food shopping.

FIGURE 15–2

Hunger Canada: Who Uses Food Banks (by Household Type)?

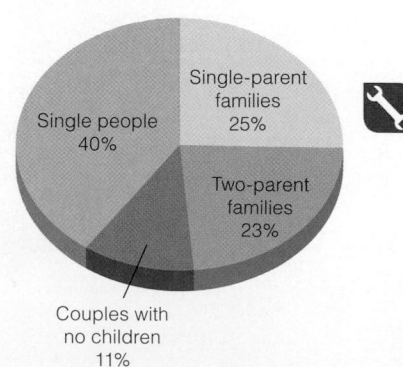

Source: Food Banks Canada (2012). HungerCount 2012. Toronto: Food Banks Canada

To stretch meagre food supplies, adults may skip meals or cut their portions. When desperate, they may be forced to break social rules—begging from strangers, stealing from markets, harvesting dead animals from roadsides, or scavenging through garbage cans, for example.[17] Such foods may be spoiled or contaminated, and eating them may easily inflict dangerous foodborne illnesses on people already bordering on malnutrition.

Children in such families sometimes go hungry for an entire day until the adults can obtain food. Indeed, when parents purchase inexpensive foods for their family, such as white bread, fats, crackers, and only a few servings of fruit and vegetables and milk alternatives, they must also keep in mind that children need other nutritious foods in their diet in order to be healthy.[18] The more severe their circumstances, the more likely children are to be in poor or just fair health and the greater the likelihood that they will be hospitalized.[19] Well-documented adverse effects suffered by children in poverty include cognitive deficits, behavioural problems, slow wound healing, and impaired immunity. These children often misbehave because of malnutrition or in rebellion against their circumstances, and relieving their poverty often improves their behaviour.[20]

For a sample of the many programs in Canada that promote food security, see Table 15–3, and to keep abreast of food insecurity in Canada, see Statistics Canada's website.[21] In 2005, two reports on household food insecurity in Canada were published.[22] The one by Dietitians of Canada (DC) was a position statement entitled "Individual and Household Food Insecurity in Canada, Position of Dietitians of Canada." The full report is available at the DC website (http://www.dietitians.ca), although a summary has also been published. According to these reports, the households most at risk include one-parent families with one or more young children, those receiving social assistance, and Aboriginal people living off reserves. DC also holds that access to adequate amounts of safe, nutritious, and culturally appropriate food at all times is a fundamental human right. More recently (April 2007), DC also released its position statement on community food security (CFS), advocating that "CFS involves long-term planning with a wide range of stakeholders working toward a healthy, just, and sustainable food system" (http://www.dietitians.ca/Dietitians-Views/Food-Security/Community-Food-Security.aspx). See especially Tables 2 and 3 of this position statement for numerous Canadian food security initiatives that involve dietitians. Eradicating hunger is in everyone's interest because the hunger of individual families affects the nation as a whole.

● Visit Food Banks Canada's website on World Food Day for the Hunger Count for each year: http://www.foodbankscanada.ca/Learn-About-Hunger/Publications/Research.aspx.

An estimated one out of five children in Canada lives in poverty.

KEY POINT

- Chronic hunger causes many deaths worldwide, especially among children. Intermittent hunger is frequently seen in Canadian and U.S. children. The immediate cause of hunger is poverty.

Table 15–3

More Examples of Canadian Programs That Promote Food Security

- Food Skills Programs: An example is *A Seat at the Table—Resource Guide for Local Governments to Promote Food Secure Communities*: http://www.phsa.ca/NR/rdonlyres/D49BA34E-B326-4302-8D0C-CC8E5A23A64F/0/ASeatattheTableResourceGuideforlocalgovernmentstopromotefoodsecurecommunities.pdf
- Community kitchens
- Community gardens
- FoodShare: http://www.foodshare.net
- Hunger Relief Advisory Committee of London
- Meals on Wheels: http://www.mealcall.org/canada
- School Feeding Programs: An example is http://www.breakfastforlearning.ca
- Wheels to Meals

School breakfasts and lunches provide low-income children with nourishment at little or no cost.

Canadian Programs Promoting Food Security, Including Nutrition North Canada

According to Food Banks Canada's 2012 national survey of emergency food programs, HungerCount, due in part to the recent economic downturn, there was an increase of almost 100,000 users in 2008, and 38 percent of those helped during 2012 were children.[23] In addition, the Canadian Living Foundation's "Breakfast for Learning" program is "Canada's only national, non-profit organization dedicated to supporting child nutrition."[24] Also, through a network of community breakfast clubs, the Children's Emergency Foundation provides help to children living in poverty.[25] Help from industry is also available, for example, the "ShareGoods" partnership between Food and Consumer Products of Canada (FCPC) and Food Banks Canada. In recent years, the FCPC "donated over 5 million bags of groceries to food banks in Canada."[26]

Food recovery programs collect and distribute good food that would otherwise go to waste; those donating the food often qualify for tax deductions for their donations. Table 15–4 presents a 14-step program for developing a hunger-free community. Although these efforts provide emergency relief to hungry people, they leave unsolved the greater problems of low wages and poverty among people who lack higher education or training.

In April of 2011 the Nutrition North Canada program was launched; just over 100 "isolated northern communities" are eligible for full or partial program subsidies. According to the Government of Canada website dedicated to this program, it "is a subsidy program that seeks to improve access to perishable healthy food in isolated northern communities" (http://nutritionnorthcanada.ca/eng/1366824567819/1366824594396). By October 2012, in some communities the price of two litres of milk had dropped by as much as 37 percent, while there was an average drop of eight percent in the cost of the "Revised Northern Food Basket" (http://news.gc.ca/web/article-eng.do?nid=697999).

KEY POINT

- Poverty and hunger coexist with affluence and bounty in Canada; working people as well as the unemployed experience poverty and hunger. Programs to relieve poverty and hunger are tremendously helpful.

food recovery collecting wholesome surplus food for distribution to low-income people who are hungry.

Chapter 15 Hunger and the Global Environment

Table 15–4

14 Ways Communities Can Address Their Local Hunger Problems

1. Establish a community-based emergency food-delivery network.
2. Assess food insecurity problems and evaluate community services. Create strategies for responding to unmet needs.
3. Establish a group of individuals, including low-income participants, to develop and to implement policies and programs to combat food insecurity, monitor responsiveness of existing services, and address underlying causes of hunger.
4. Participate in federally assisted nutrition programs that are easily accessible to targeted populations.
5. Integrate public and private resources, including local businesses, to relieve food insecurity.
6. Establish an education program that addresses the food needs of the community and the need for increased local citizen participation in activities to alleviate food insecurity.
7. Provide information and referral services for accessing both public and private programs and services.
8. Support programs to provide transportation and assistance in food shopping, where needed.
9. Identify high-risk populations and target services to meet their needs.
10. Provide adequate transportation and distribution of food from all resources.
11. Coordinate food services with parks and recreation programs and other community-based outlets to which area residents have easy access.
12. Improve public transportation to human services agencies and food resources.
13. Establish nutrition education programs for low-income citizens to enhance their food purchasing and preparation skills and to make them aware of the connections between diet and health.
14. Establish a program for collecting and distributing nutritious foods, either agricultural commodities in farmers' fields or prepared foods that would have been wasted.

Source: RCE: House Select Committee on Hunger, legislation introduced by Tony P. Hall, excerpted in the Sprouts edition of Seeds Magazine, January 1992, page 3 (Volume 14 No 1.) with permission (Seeds of Hope Publishers, 602 James Ave, Waco , TX 76706). For more on developing a hunger-free community, write Congressional Hunger Center, Hall of the States Building, 400 N. Capitol Street, NW Suite G100, Washington , D.C. 20001. Tel: 202-547-7022 Fax: 202-547-7575 www.hungercenter.org

What Is the State of World Hunger?

In the developing world, hunger and poverty are even more intense and the causes more diverse. The primary form of hunger is still food poverty, but the poverty is more extreme. Grasping the severity of poverty in the developing world can be difficult, but some statistics may help. One-fifth of the world's seven billion people have no land and no possessions *at all*. The "poorest poor" survive on less than one dollar a day each, they lack water that is safe to drink, and they cannot read or write. Many spend about 80 percent of all they earn on food, but still they are hungry and malnourished. It has been said that the average house cat in North America eats twice as much protein every day as one of these people, and the yearly cost of keeping that cat is greater than that person's annual income.

Poverty causes hunger, but hunger also worsens poverty by robbing a person of the good health and the physical and mental energy needed to be active and productive. The less active and productive people become, the lower their pay. Hungry people simply cannot work hard enough to get themselves out of poverty, and most have no borrowing power to obtain credit. Economists calculate that reducing world hunger and malnutrition by half would generate more than $120 billion in productivity.[27] Figure 15–3 highlights causes and outcomes of hunger in the world.

The majority of people currently living with food emergencies are concentrated in the nations of Africa and Asia (see Figure 15-4 on page 659). Recent advances in agricultural technology, economic development, and commitment to eradicating hunger have begun to improve some problems in some areas. In other areas, however, the number of hungry people continues to increase, and hunger remains an enormous

Four Common Methods of Food Recovery Are

- *Field gleaning*: Collecting crops from fields that either have already been harvested or are not profitable to harvest.
- *Perishable food rescue or salvage*: Collecting perishable produce from wholesalers and markets.
- *Prepared food rescue*: Collecting prepared foods from commercial kitchens.
- *Nonperishable food collection*: Collecting processed foods from wholesalers and markets.

Figure 15–3

Causes and Outcomes of Hunger

Regional quantity, quality, and availability of resources
• Is enough high-quality food available for all people in the region?
• Is drought or environmental degradation preventing production of adequate food?

Economic, organizational, and group discrimination factors that influence resource distribution
• Do unemployment and lack of borrowing power prevent escape from poverty?
• Does greed, government corruption, racial discrimination, ethnic or religious hatred, or a class system prevent equitable distribution of resources?
• Does the economy support necessary infrastructure, such as passable roads and fuel for food delivery?

An individual household's access to available resources
• Does the household have sufficient resources with which to obtain enough food?
• Is the household barred in some way from access to the food available?

Access to clean water and health service
• Does the family have access to enough clean water for its needs?
• Are immunizations and other basic health care available to prevent disease and disability?

Individual child-care practices and knowledge within the family
• Are some children fed, while others go hungry?
• Do mothers fail to breastfeed their newborns?
• Do parents make inappropriate substitutions for formula or mix formula with unclean water?
• Do parents understand the basic nutrition needs of their children and pregnant and lactating women?

Inadequate food or nutrient intakes lead to malnutrition, weakness, disease, and depressed appetite
• Are children and adults too weakened to compete for food?
• Are their appetites depressed as an effect of malnutrition?

Disease conditions worsen malnutrition
• When the resources the body uses to fight disease or obtain food are exhausted, death from disease or starvation results.

Source: Based on information from Position of the American Dietetic Association: Addressing world hunger, malnutrition, and food insecurity, Journal of the American Dietetic Association *103 (2003): 1046:1057.*

challenge. In these areas, hunger and poverty, population growth, political strife, armed conflicts, natural disasters, and environmental degradation are all linked, and they tend to worsen each other.

Food Shortage and Armed Conflict   The most visible form of hunger is **famine**, a true **food shortage** in an area that causes multitudes of people to starve and die (for definitions, see Table 15–2, page 652). The natural causes of famine—drought, flood, and pests—have, in recent years, taken second place behind the political and social causes. In parts of Africa, killer famines recur whenever human conflict converges with drought.[28] Additionally, racial discrimination and ethnic and religious hatred often underlie the food deprivation of whole groups of people.[29] For people of marginal

Figure 15–4
Hunger Hotspots (World Hunger Map 2013)

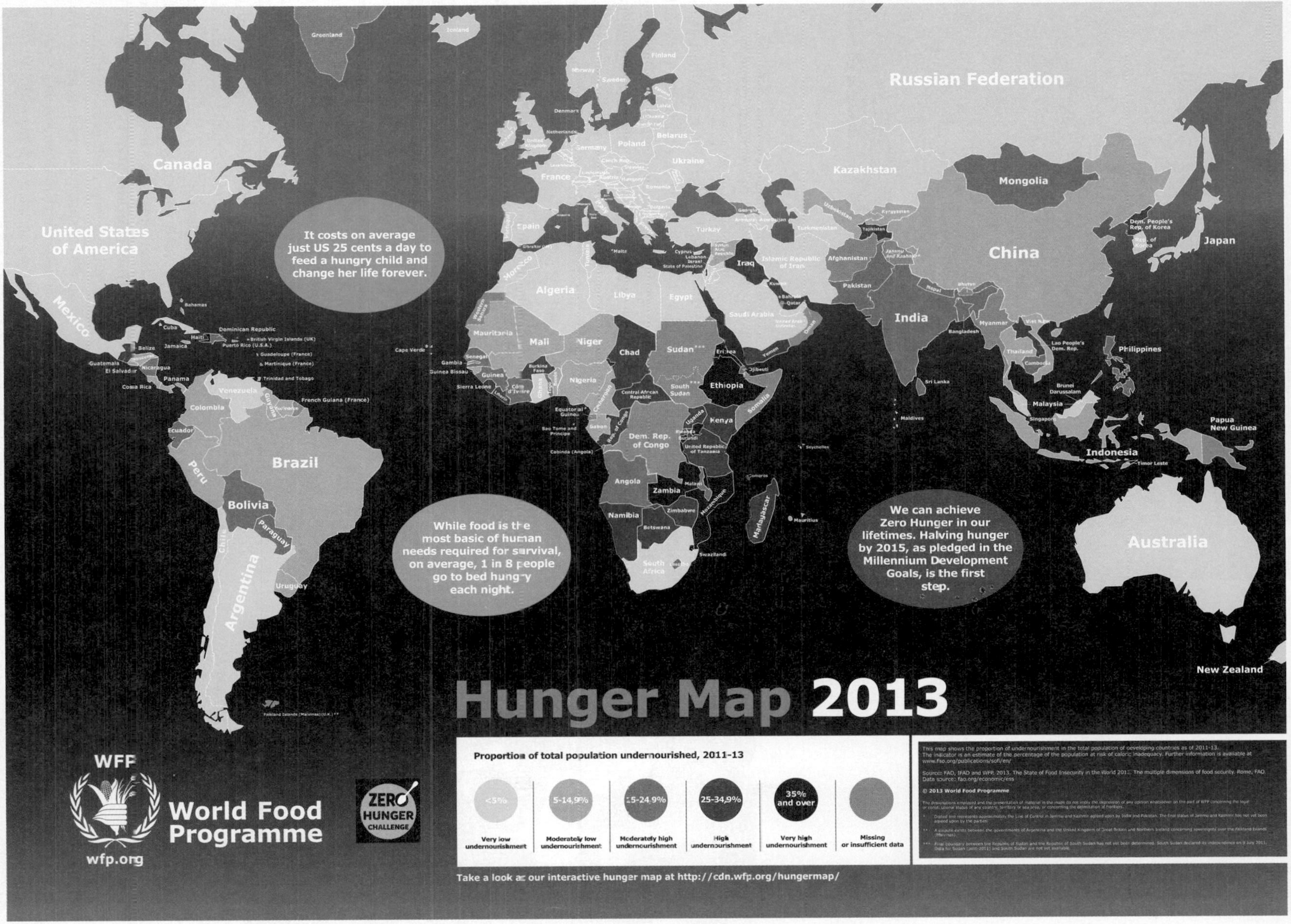

NOTE: Areas in dark red show where "very high undernourishment" exists (an interactive Hunger Map is also available at http://www.wfp.org/hunger/downloadmap).

The primary cause of hunger is poverty.

The hunger of conflict—people desperate for food in DR Congo.

existence, a sudden increase in food prices, a drop in workers' incomes, or a change in government policy can quickly leave millions hungry.

Since the 1990s, the violence of armed conflict has been a dominant cause of all the famines reported worldwide. Farmers become warriors and agricultural fields become battlegrounds while citizens go hungry. Warring factions often repel famine relief efforts in the hope of starving their opponents before they succumb to starvation themselves.

During natural disasters without war, food aid from other countries has provided a safety net for countries whose crops fail.[30] But food aid now does more than just offset poor harvests; it also delivers food relief to countries, such as Ethiopia, that are chronically short of food and without resources to buy it. Some people are concerned that as many nations cut their foreign aid, the supplies of needed food may become insufficient.

Chronic Hunger Although we usually associate world hunger with famine, the numbers affected by famine are relatively small compared with those suffering from less severe but chronic hunger. According to the World Food Programme, there are over 840 million hungry people.[31] Many more have food but lack iron, iodine, and vitamin A.[32] The prevalence and consequences of these deficiencies are enormous. The ravages to the body of nutrient deficiencies were spelled out in earlier chapters of this book.

Tens of thousands die of malnutrition every day. Most children who die of malnutrition do not starve to death—they die because their health has been compromised by dehydration from infections that cause diarrhea.[33] Currently, **oral rehydration therapy (ORT)** is saving an estimated one million lives each year by helping to stop the destructive spiral in which infection worsens diarrhea and diarrhea causes dehydration. The ORT solution increases a body's ability to absorb fluids 25-fold. Clean or boiled drinking water is essential for ORT, however, because contaminated water will reinfect the child.

Symptoms of malnutrition vary according to the nutrients lacking and the individual's stage of life. See Chapter 6 for effects of protein and energy deficiency; Chapters 7 and 8 for vitamin and mineral deficiencies; Chapter 11 for effects on immunity; Chapter 13 for effects on newborns and pregnant women; and Chapter 14 for effects on children, teens, and the elderly.

oral rehydration therapy (ORT) oral fluid replacement for children with severe diarrhea caused by infectious disease. ORT enables parents to mix a simple solution for their child from substances that they have at home.

Focus on Women Malnourished women in poverty bear sickly infants who cannot fend off the diseases of poverty, and many succumb within the first years of life. Up to 17 million children are born underweight annually.[34] Breastfeeding helps prolong an infant's life, but eventually the child must be weaned to thin gruels of scant quantity made with unclean water. All too often, children sicken and die soon after weaning. An estimated 250 million preschool children are vitamin A deficient and are at risk for the following: blindness, growth retardation, and poor resistance to common childhood infections such as measles. Because of poverty, infection, and malnutrition, the life expectancy in some African countries averages 50 years; in Uganda, it is only 42 years, little more than half of the life expectancy in Canada.

When crops fail or violence erupts in an already impoverished area, women are first to suffer. Seven out of 10 of the world's hungry people are women and girls, yet they receive only about half of the available food aid and must use it to feed their children as well as themselves. These facts are offered by the World Food Programme (WFP) to justify targeting women as direct recipients of food relief:

- Even when women are starving, they are likely to give what food is available to their hungry children. In contrast, when food is delivered to government agencies, much of it may be diverted from its intended recipients.
- In Asia and Africa, 60–80 percent of women are engaged in farming.
- In a third of households worldwide, women are the sole breadwinners.
- Given low-interest loans, basic equipment, and access to land ownership along with supports such as child care and education, women engage in sustainable activities that improve conditions in the community.

Universal education for girls and women is also a high priority.

World Food Supply Most disturbingly, misery and starvation exist side by side with adequate world food supplies. The world produces sufficient food to feed all of its hungry people; what is lacking is the political will to do so.[35]

In the decades after 1960, world food production grew faster than the world's population. These gains were largely the result of agricultural advances known as the *green revolution*, along with efforts to increase and diversify crop yields in agriculturally less advanced regions of the world. Today, the world's supply of grain, an index of the sufficiency of the world food supply, can still feed the world for several months. Wheat and corn, for example, the staple foods of many nations, are abundant and now cost less than half as much as 40 years ago.

The future may not be so bright, however. At its present rate of growth, the world's population will soon outstrip the current rate of food production.[36] The green revolution has passed, and old technology will not generate the greater crop yields needed to keep pace with the increasing numbers of people being born. A 2001 United Nations document states: "Only by doubling food production, improving distribution, and protecting the environment can we ensure food security for the 8 billion people that will inhabit the planet in 2025. Research suggests that the world's farmers will have to produce 40 percent more grain by 2020 to meet rising demand." Environmental degradation and dwindling water supplies may ultimately prevent further growth in the world's food output in many agricultural areas.

No part of the world is safely insulated against future food shortages. Developed countries may be the last to feel the effects, but they will ultimately go as the world goes.

> **KEY POINT**
>
> - Natural causes, such as drought, flood, and pests, and political and social causes, such as armed conflicts and overpopulation, all contribute to hunger and poverty in developing countries. To meet future demands for food, technology must continue to improve food production, food must be fairly distributed, and birthrates need to decline. The world's women and girls are major allies in the effort to fight hunger

To Prevent Death from Diarrheal Disease, Provide

- Adequate sanitation.
- Safe water.
- Oral rehydration therapy (ORT). A simple recipe for ORT calls for 1 c boiled water, 2 tsp sugar, and a pinch of salt.

Environmental Degradation and Hunger

Hunger and poverty interact with a third force—environmental degradation. Poor people often destroy the very resources they need for survival. Desperate to obtain money for food, they sell everything they own—even the seeds that would have produced next year's crops. They cut the available trees for firewood or timber to sell and then lose the soil to erosion. Without these resources, they become still poorer. Thus, poverty causes environmental ruin, and the ruin leads to hunger.

Soil Erosion Soil erosion affects agriculture in every nation. Deforestation of the world's rainforests dramatically adds to land loss. Without the forest covering to hold the soil in place, it washes off the rocks beneath, drastically reducing the land's productivity.

Around the world, irrigation and fertilizer can no longer compensate for these losses by improving crop yields because all of the land that can benefit from these measures is already receiving them. Compounding the problem, continuous irrigation leaves deposits of salt in the soil, and rising salt concentrations are lowering yields on close to a quarter of the world's irrigated cropland.

The U.S. government offers monetary incentives to farmers and ranchers who conserve wetlands and employ soil-conserving techniques on highly erodible croplands. In recent years, welcome evidence of slowing soil erosion has been attributed partly to conservation incentive policies and even more to agricultural innovations, as described in this chapter's Controversy.[37]

Grazing Lands and Fisheries Meat and fish outputs are also endangered. Grasslands for growing beef are already being fully used or overused on every continent. Despite persistent expansion of the world's fishing industry, for example, aquaculture, the Food and Agriculture Organization of the United Nations estimates that 30 percent of all assessed marine stocks have been overexploited.[38] Researchers report that populations of big fish, such as tuna, swordfish, cod, halibut, and shark, have declined by 90 percent over the last 50 years.[39] According to the Food and Agriculture Organization (FAO), an agency of the United Nations that monitors the world's food supplies, about 47–50 percent of major marine fish stocks are currently fully exploited, with no room for further expansion of fishing. Another 28 percent are overexploited or depleted and in danger of extinction unless given relief from overfishing.[40] The solution is simple: stop overfishing.[41] The problem is how to do so.

Not only are ocean fish being overfished, but, as previous chapters have pointed out, they are so contaminated from industrial pollution that pregnant women and young children must strictly limit their intakes, a fact that makes some dietitians hesitant to recommend fish for health. In California, when the blood of fish-eating people was tested, blood mercury exceeded established upper safe levels, sometimes enormously so, in 89 percent of participants.[42] Children were especially affected: average blood mercury levels of children in the study were more than *40 times* as high as the national average. On reducing fish intake, the subjects' mercury levels dropped quickly. The problem spans the globe: almost every major bay in Japan suffers serious pollution sufficient to interrupt the normal breeding cycles of food species in the region.[43]

Inland fisheries have also suffered tremendous drops in yield as a result of environmental damage. In the early 1990s, 14,000 Canadian lakes were declared biologically dead as a result of acid rain. The U.S. Food and Drug Administration (FDA) warns that eating too much fish from the Great Lakes threatens health because their flesh contains high levels of the industrial contaminant PCBs, once widely used in electrical equipment and as a lubricant.

Some ideas are now forthcoming to save the world's fish stocks. Seasonal quotas limit the number and type of fish that may be removed from a region to allow species to begin to recover their numbers; this measure has already proven successful for Alaskan

More about overgrazing appears in this chapter's Controversy feature.

To Protect Overfished Species, Consumers Can Choose These Fish Options

- Alaskan halibut
- Alaskan salmon
- Farm-raised tilapia and other farm-raised fish
- Sardines
- White sea bass

To Protect Yourself from Consuming Too Much Mercury, Health Canada Advises Limiting Consumption of Large Predatory Fish Such As

- Fresh and frozen tuna
- Shark
- Swordfish

halibut. Another essential step is to mark and enforce "no fishing zones" in large areas of the oceans, creating safe sanctuaries for fish breeding and development. Cracking down on illegal harvesting by commercial fisheries and reducing the size of fishing fleets would also reduce the pressure. Developing commercial fish aquaculture ("fish farms") and altering wild species through recombinant DNA technology may also help meet human demand. The FAO predicts that, unless tactics like these are put into place quickly and firmly, the world demand for fish will very soon outstrip the supply.

As groundwater is used up, deserts spread.

Climate, Air, and Fresh Water

Both air pollution and the resulting climate change also reduce food outputs. According to the United Nations Intergovernmental Panel on Climate Change, a major international collaboration involving more than 2,500 scientists from around the world, changes in climate are expected to result from a buildup of so-called greenhouse gases, such as carbon dioxide, methane, and nitrous oxide, and airborne particles.[44] These pollutants are produced by human industry, agriculture, and transportation activities. A rise of only a degree or so in average global temperature may reduce soil moisture, impair pollination of major food crops such as rice and corn, slow growth, weaken crops' resistance to disease, and disrupt many other factors affecting crop yields.

Dwindling supplies of fresh water are now limiting the numbers of people who can survive in some areas. Poor water management causes many of the world's water problems.[45] Each day, people dump approximately 1 million tonnes of waste into the world's rivers, lakes, and streams. As such pollution grows along with the population, vast quantities of the earth's fresh water will be unusable by the year 2050.[46] By 2025, if present patterns continue, two of every three persons on earth will live in water-stressed conditions.[47]

- Worldwide, 1.2 billion people live without access to clean, safe water.

According to *The 2012 Progress Report of the Federal Sustainable Development Strategy*, in terms of (a) air quality, Canada is "about one half of the way towards meeting its 2020 greenhouse gas emissions reduction target under the Copenhagen Accord," and (b) water quality, "For the period 2007 to 2009, freshwater quality was rated as excellent or good at 41% of stations, fair at 39% and marginal at 17%." The report further revealed that while Canadians are among the heaviest water users in the world, per capita residential water declined by almost 70 litres over the last decade (see Environment Canada, *The 2012 Progress Report of the Federal Sustainable Development Strategy*, http://www.ec.gc.ca/dd-sd/23E4714E-B774-4CC5-9337-F87B01556727/2012_Progress_Report_ofthe_FSDS.pdf).

Overpopulation

The world's population reached six billion in 1999 and seven billion in 2011, but the rate of growth has begun to taper off somewhat.[48] Still, at the present rate of increase, the human population will exceed the earth's estimated **carrying capacity** by 2033. Many authorities in many fields—and more every year—are calling for a reduction in the rate at which the world's population increases. Overpopulation may well be the most serious threat that humankind faces today.

The sheer magnitude of our annual population increase is difficult to comprehend. Each month the world adds the equivalent of another three cities the size of Toronto. During six months of the terrible 1992 famine in Somalia, an estimated 300,000 people starved to death. Yet it took the world only 29 *hours* to replace their numbers.

Population stabilization is one of the most pressing needs of our time because it appears to be the only way to enable the world's food output to keep up with demand. Without population stabilization, the world can neither support the lives of people already born nor halt environmental deterioration around the globe. And before the population problem can be resolved, it may be necessary to remedy the poverty problem. Of the many millions added to the population each year, 98 percent are born in the most poverty-stricken areas of the world.

Poverty and hunger exert a contradictory effect on people, driving them to bear more children. Figure 15–5 shows the high correlation of low income and high birthrate. Poverty and hunger are also correlated with lack of education, which includes lack of knowledge about controlling family size. A family in poverty also depends on its children to farm the land, haul water, and care for the adults in their

- Years needed for the world's population to reach

Its 1st billion	2,000,000 years
2nd billion	105 years
3rd billion	30 years
4th billion	15 years
5th billion	12 years
6th billion	11 years
7th billion	12 years

Is it any wonder that food and fresh water supplies may fall behind?

carrying capacity the total number of living organisms that a given environment can support without deteriorating in quality.

Figure 15–5

Income and Birthrate

Greater wealth means lower rates of birth. Each dot represents a country.

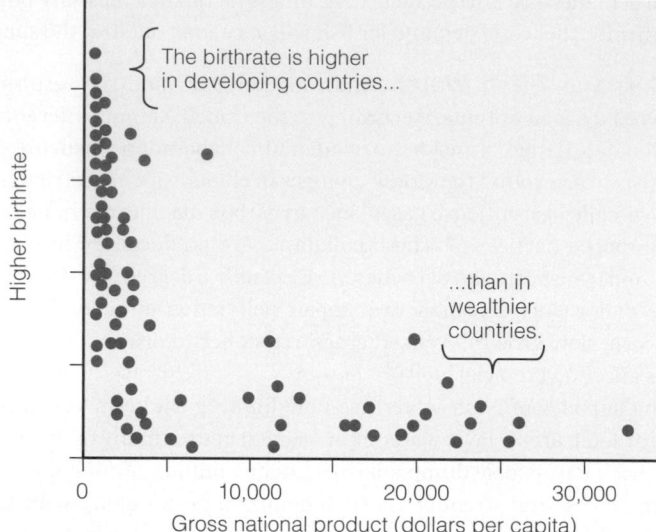

The birthrate is higher in developing countries...

...than in wealthier countries.

Higher birthrate

Gross national product (dollars per capita)

In some countries, every pair of little hands is needed to help feed the family.

sustainable able to continue indefinitely. In this context, the use of resources in ways that maintain both natural resources and human life; the use of natural resources at a pace that allows the earth to replace them. Examples: cutting trees no faster than new ones grow and producing pollutants at a rate with which the environment and human cleanup efforts can keep pace. In a sustainable economy, resources do not become depleted, and pollution does not accumulate.

old age. If a family faces ongoing poverty, and its young children are among the most likely to die from disease and other causes, the parents will choose to have many children as a form of "insurance" that some will survive to adulthood.

Relieving poverty and hunger, then, may be a necessary first step in curbing population growth. When people attain better access to health care, education, and family planning, the death rate falls. After a time, the birthrate follows suit. Thus, improvements in living standards help stabilize the population. Wealth distribution matters, too. In countries where economic growth has benefited only the rich, population growth has remained high. Examples include Brazil, Mexico, the Philippines, and Thailand, where large families continue to be a major economic asset for the poor.

KEY POINT

- Environmental degradation caused by the impacts of growing numbers of people is threatening the world's future ability to feed all of its citizens. Improvements in agriculture can no longer keep up with people's growing numbers. Human population growth is an urgent concern. Controlling population growth requires improving people's economic status and providing them with health care, education, and family planning.

Moving toward Solutions

Slowly but surely, improvements are becoming evident in developing nations. For example, most nations have seen a rise in their gross domestic product, a key measure of economic well-being. Adult literacy rates have increased by more than 50 percent in some areas since 1970, and the proportion of children being sent to school has risen, while the proportion of chronically undernourished people has declined. Today, optimism abounds, and keys to solving the world's environmental, poverty, and hunger problems are within the reach of both the poor and the rich nations—if they will make the effort required to employ them.

The poor nations need resources and the will to make contraceptive technology and information more widely available, educate their citizens, assist the poor, and adopt **sustainable** development practices that slow and reverse the destruction of their forests, waterways, and soil. The rich nations need to stem their wasteful and polluting uses of resources and energy, which are contributing to global environmental degradation.

Sustainable Development Worldwide

Many nations now agree that improving all nations' economies is a prerequisite to meeting the world's other urgent needs: population stabilization, arrest of environmental degradation, sustainable use of resources, and relief of hunger. At a summit of over a hundred nations, the United Nations Conference on Environment and Development, many nations agreed to a set of principles of sustainable development. The conferees defined sustainable development as development that would equitably meet both the economic and the environmental needs of present and future generations. To rephrase a well-known adage: If you give a man a fish, he will eat for a day. If you teach him to fish so that he can buy and maintain his own gear and bait, he will eat for a lifetime and help feed you.

- "For every person in the world to reach present U.S. levels of consumption with existing technology would require four more planet Earths."—E. O. Wilson, 2002

How Can People Engage in Activism and Simpler Lifestyles at Home?

Every segment of our society can play a role in the fight against poverty, hunger, and environmental degradation. The federal government; the provinces and territories; local communities; big business and small companies; educators; and all individuals, including dietitians and foodservice managers, have many opportunities to forward the effort.[49]

Government Action Government policies can change to promote sustainability. For example, the government can devote tax dollars and other resources to encouraging energy conservation and crop protection and to national and international education on sustainable development techniques.

Private and Community Enterprises Businesses in North America can take initiatives to help; some already have—AT&T, Prudential, Kellogg's Canada, Cargill Foods Ltd., and Kraft General Foods are major supporters of antihunger programs. Restaurants and other food facilities can participate in the nation's gleaning effort by giving their fresh leftover foods to community distribution centres. Food producers are more often choosing to produce their goods sustainably to meet a growing demand for products produced with integrity.[50]

Educators and Students Educators, including nutrition educators, have a crucial role to play. They can teach others about the underlying social and political causes of poverty, the root cause of hunger. At the college and university level, they can teach the relationships between hunger and birthrate, hunger and environmental degradation, hunger and the status of women, and hunger and global economics. Students can share the knowledge they gain with families, friends, and communities and take action at local and national levels.

Food and Nutrition Professionals Dietitians and foodservice managers can promote sustainable production of food and the saving of resources through reuse, recycling (including composting), energy conservation, and water conservation in both their professional and their personal lives.[51] In addition, health agencies in Canada urge their members to work for policy changes in private and government food assistance programs; to intensify education about hunger; and to be advocates at the local, provincial, and national levels to help end hunger in Canada.

Individuals: What Can You Do? In an effort to help our environment/reduce our ecological footprint globally (e.g., by eating meat-free meals more often, using less pesticides), students might consider, from a nutrition standpoint, visiting the David Suzuki Foundation website and taking the Nature Challenge (see http://www.davidsuzuki.org/what-you-can-do/nature-challenge). All individuals can become involved in these large trends. Many small decisions each day add up to large impacts on the environment. The Consumer Corner that follows sums up some of these decisions and actions.

KEY POINT

- Government, business, educators, and all individuals have many opportunities to promote sustainability worldwide and wise resource use at home.

use it! Consumer Corner

Saving Money and Protecting the Environment

Consumers can "tread lightly on the earth" through their daily choices. Consider this list:

- Shop "carless" and plan to make fewer shopping trips. Motor vehicles constitute the single largest source of air pollution, causing lung problems, reduced crop yields, and acid rain that damages forests.

- Ride a bike to work or classes.

- Choose foods that are low on the food chain more often (see the Controversy feature in this chapter).

- Limit use of imported canned beef products, including stews, chilli, corned beef, and pet foods. Many of these foods come at the expense of cleared rainforest land: 200 square feet of rain forest are lost *permanently* for every pound of beef produced.

- Choose small fish more often. Small fish eat tiny aquatic animals and plants—that is, they eat low on the food chain.

- Choose chicken from local farms.

- Shop at farmers' markets and road-side stands for local foods grown close to home.[*,1] Locally grown foods require less transportation, pack-aging, and refrigeration than shipped foods. Try picking your own from local farms—it's fun and saves money, too.[2]

- Avoid overly packaged items; buy bulk items with minimal packaging or reusable or recyclable packaging. Each can, foam tray, waxed or clay-coated cardboard container, plastic bottle, or glass jar requires land and many other resources to produce, and its disposal pollutes and costs more land.

- Use reusable pans and dishes rather than disposable items that are used

Consumer Corner references are listed separately at the end of the chapter.

once and thrown away. Use pumps instead of spray cans, which are hard to recycle because they are made of many materials.

- Carry reusable string or cloth grocery bags or bring plastic bags back to the store and refill them. Production of paper and plastic grocery bags rep-resents a huge drain on resources. Paper factories use chemicals such as toxic forms of chlorine bleach, which are released into waterways in quantities so large that the chemicals can destroy whole bays and fisheries.

- Use fast cooking methods. Stir-frying, pressure cooking, and microwaving all use less energy than conventional stovetop or oven cooking methods.

- Reduce use of aluminum foil, paper towels, plastic wraps, plastic storage bags, and other disposable items. Find permanent reusable replacements for each, such as reusable storage con-tainers and washable cloths.

- Use fewer electric gadgets. Mix bat-ters, chop vegetables, and open cans by hand.

- Purchase the most efficient large appliances possible—look for the Energy Star logo (see Figure 15–6). Products that rank highest in their category for energy efficiency earn this logo from National Resources Canada. By purchasing Energy Star products, consumers can save many energy dollars each year.

- Insulate your home.

- Consider using solar power, especially to heat water.

- Reduce, reuse, recycle.

The personal rewards of all of these behaviours are many, from saving money to the satisfaction of knowing that you are enjoying and preserving the earth (see Figure 15–7 for other suggestions). But do they really help? They do, if

enough people join in. To make the greatest impact, people can also support organizations that lobby for changes in economic policies toward developing countries. Another way to help solve these problems is to join with others to work for international hunger-relief organizations. Table 15–5 lists some of the major ones. Local food pantries welcome volunteers as well.

- "We do not inherit the earth from our ancestors, we borrow it from our children."
—Ascribed to Chief Seattle, a 19th-century Native American leader.

Figure 15–6
Energy Star

Products bearing the Energy Star logo rank highest for energy effi-ciency. For example, a non–Energy Star refrigerator uses as much energy as two refrigerators with the Energy Star label. Energy Star products range from large appli-ances to light bulbs and building materials. By choosing products with the Energy Star logo when replacing old equipment, the typ-ical household would save almost $400 per year in energy costs; in 2011, using Energy Star products resulted in energy savings equiva-lent to taking 66,000 cars off the road.

Figure 15–7

Individual Responsibility and Respect for the Environment

Reduce resource use, reduce fuel use, and reduce pollution with these individual actions.

Eat lower on the food chain—more grains, local chicken, and small fish, and less meat from large animals.

Eat local foods—visit your farmers' market.

Buy bulk items to save packaging.

Recycle glass, cans, paper, and plastic.

Buy fruits of differing ripeness.

Eat the most perishable foods first.

Shop carless. It can be a pleasure and a great source of exercise.

Buy recycled goods to close the loop.

Use reusable bags instead of throwaway bags.

Use items that don't use energy . . .

Use reusable items . . .

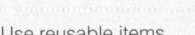

. . . instead of those that do use energy (even small appliances).

. . . instead of nonreusable items.

Use appliances that take less energy.

Run your refrigerator efficiently.

Even today's efficient refrigerators use substantial energy because they run day and night. Consumers can take several steps to minimize the energy a refrigerator uses:

- Set it at 3° or 4°C; set the freezer at −18°C.
- Clean the coils and the insulating gaskets around the doors regularly.
- Keep it in good repair.

The water heater can also waste a lot of energy. Keep the water heater set at 45°–50°C (no hotter) to save energy. For safe household dishes, sterilization is not necessary. Water of 45°–50°C enhances the action of dishwashing detergents, making microorganisms slippery and removing them from the dishes. These measures will keep food fresh and clean while keeping energy use low.

Table 15–5

Some Hunger-Relief Organizations People Can Donate To/Join

Canadian Feed The Children
174 Bartley Drive
Toronto, ON M4A 1E1
Toll-free: 1-800-387-1221
1-416-757-1220;
fax: 1-416-757-3318
http://www.canadianfeed
thechildren.ca

The Hunger Project—Canada
11 O'Connor Drive
Toronto, ON M4K 2K3
1-416-429-0023;
fax: 1-416-429-0023
http://thehungerproject.ca

World Vision Canada, English
1 World Drive
Mississauga, ON L5T 2Y4
Toll-free: 1-866-595-5550
1-905-565-6100;
fax: 1-866-219-8620
http://www2.worldvision.ca/
sponsorship/app?service5page

Action without Borders
350 Fifth Ave., Suite 6614
New York, NY 10118
1-212-843-3973
http://www.idealist.org

Bread for the World
50 F St. NW, Suite 500
Washington, D.C. 20010
1-800-82-BREAD or
1-800-822-7323
1-202-639-9400; fax:
1-202-639-9401
http://www.bread.org

Children's Hunger Relief Fund
182 Farmer's Lane
Suite 200
Santa Rosa, CA 95405
1-888-781-1585
http://www.childrenshungerrelief
.org

Congressional Hunger Center
2291/2 Pennsylvania Ave.
Washington, D.C. 20003
1-202-547-7022
http://www.hungercenter.org

Food Research and Action Center
1875 Connecticut Ave.
Suite 540
Washington, D.C. 20009
http://www.frac.org

OXFAM Canada
39 McArthur Avenue
Ottawa, ON K1L 8L7
1-613-237-5236
http://www.oxfam.ca

Pan American Health Organization
525 23rd St. NW
Washington, D.C. 20037
1-202-974-3000
http://www.paho.org

Second Harvest
1450 Lodestar Road, Unit 18
Toronto, ON M3J 3C1
1-416-408-2594
http://www.secondharvest.ca

Society of St. Andrew
3383 Sweet Hollow Rd.
Big Island, VA 24526
1-800-333-4597
http://www.endhunger.org

United Nations Food and
Agriculture Organization (FAO)
1001 22nd St. NW, Suite 300
Washington, D.C. 20437
1-202-653-2400
http://www.fao.org

United Nations International
Children's Emergency Fund
(UNICEF)
3 United Nations Plaza
New York, NY 10017-4414
1-212-326-7035
http://www.unicef.org

United Nations World Food
Programme
Via Cesare Giulio
Viola, 68
Parco dé Medici
Rome, Italy 00148
http://www.wfp.org

World Health Organization (WHO)
525 23rd St. NW
Washington, D.C. 20037
1-202-861-3200
http://www.who.org

World Hunger Year
505 Eighth Ave., 21st Floor
New York, NY 10018-6582
800-GleanIt
http://www.whyhunger.org

CONTROVERSY 15

Agribusiness and Food Production: How to Go Forward?

While some individuals are making their own personal lifestyles more environmentally benign, as suggested in the chapter, others are seeking ways to improve whole sectors of human enterprise, such as agriculture. To date, large agricultural enterprises have been among the world's biggest polluters and resource users. Is it possible for agriculture to become sustainable? Do our new technologies hold promise for advancing sustainability? How are small farmers faring? This Controversy addresses these questions.

Costs of Producing Food

The environmental and social costs of agriculture and the food industry take many forms. Among them are resource waste and pollution, energy overuse, and tolls on human workers in farm communities. Table C15–1 offers some terms important to these concepts.

Impacts on Land and Water

Producing food has always cost the earth dearly. To grow food, we clear land—prairie, wetland, or forest—causing losses of native ecosystems and wildlife. Then we plant crops or graze animals on the land. The soil loses nutrients as each crop is taken from it, so fertilizer is applied. Some fertilizer runs off and pollutes the waterways, causing overgrowth of algae and other imbalances. Some ploughed soil runs off, clouds the water, and interferes with the growth of aquatic plants and animals.

Then, to protect crops against weeds and pests, herbicides and pesticides are applied. In addition to killing weeds and pests, most herbicides and pesticides kill native plants, native insects, and animals that eat those plants and insects. Widespread use of pesticides and herbicides also causes resistant pests

and weeds to evolve. Pesticides pose hazards for farm workers who handle and apply them, and pesticide residues can become a problem for people who consume them along with foods.

Agricultural pesticides and herbicides, if not used conservatively, also pollute rivers, lakes, and groundwater. Pollution from "point sources," such as sewage plants or factories, is relatively easy to control, but runoff from fields and pastures enters waterways across broad regions and is nearly impossible to control.

Pure rivers represent irreplaceable water resources.

Finally, we irrigate, a practice that adds salts to the soil in many areas. The water evaporates, but the salts do not. As soils become salty, plant growth fails. Irrigation can also deplete the water supply over time because water is pulled from surface waters or from underground and then evaporates or runs off. This process, carried to an extreme, can dry up whole rivers and lakes and lower the water table of entire regions. The lower the water table, the more farmers must irrigate, and the more they irrigate, the more groundwater they use up.

Soil Depletion and Losses of Species

The soil can also be depleted by other agricultural practices, particularly

indiscriminate land clearing (deforestation), increased number of plants per acre (soil dilution) and overuse by cattle (overgrazing). In just the past 40 years, human agricultural activities have ruined more than 10 percent of the earth's fertile land, an area the size of China and India combined. Over 8 million hectares (20 million acres) have been so damaged that they may be impossible to reclaim. If soil erosion proceeds unchecked, by 2025 the world may be struggling to feed many more people with 40 percent less food-producing land per person.

Unsustainable agriculture has already destroyed many once-fertile regions, where high civilizations formerly flourished. The dry, salty deserts of North Africa were once ploughed and irrigated wheat fields, the breadbasket of the Roman Empire. Today's mistreatment of soil and water is causing destruction on a scale never known before.

Agriculture is also weakening its own underpinnings by failing to conserve species diversity. By the year 2050, some 40,000 plant species that exist today may become extinct. The United Nations Food and Agriculture Organization attributes many of the losses, which are occurring daily, to modern farming practices, as well as to population growth. The growing uniformity of global eating habits also contributes. As people everywhere eat the same limited array of foods, demand for local, genetically

Vast areas under plough are exposed to erosion, and those that must be irrigated can, over time, become salty and unusable.

NEL   Controversy 15 Agribusiness and Food Production: How to Go Forward?

669

diverse, native plants is insufficient to make them financially worth preserving. Yet, in the future, as the climate warms, those very plants may be needed as food sources. A wild species of corn that grows in a dry climate, for example, might contain just the genetic information necessary to help make the domestic corn crop resistant to drought.

Energy

Massive fossil fuel use is threatening our planet by causing ozone depletion, water pollution, ocean pollution, and other ills and by making global warming likely. In the United States, food industry consumes about 20 percent of all of the energy the nation uses. Each year the U.S. food industry spends 1,500 litres (over 350 gal) of energy from oil per person to produce, process, distribute, and prepare the country's food. Energy is used to run farm machinery and to produce fertilizers and pesticides. Energy is also used to prepare, package, transport, refrigerate, store, cook, and wash the foods.

The Problems of Livestock and Fishing

Raising livestock also takes a toll. Like plant crops, herds of livestock occupy land that once maintained itself in a natural state. The land suffers losses of native plants and animals, soil erosion, water depletion, and desert formation. If animals are raised in concentrated areas such as cattle feedlots or giant hog "farms" instead, huge masses of animal wastes produced in these overcrowded, factory-style farms leach into local soils and water supplies, polluting them. In an effort to control this source of pollution, the U.S. Environmental Protection Agency (EPA) offers incentives to livestock farmers who agree to clean up their wastes and allow their operations to be monitored for pollution.*,[1] The EPA may soon require more sustainable handling practices for animal wastes, such as diluting them for use as fertilizer on fields.[2] In addition to the waste problem, animals in such feedlots still

*Controversy references are listed separately at the end of the chapter.

Industrial farms generate huge masses of wastes that can contaminate local soil and water.
© iStockphoto/Thinkstock

have to be fed; grain is grown for them on other land (Figure C15–1 compares the grain required to produce various foods). That grain may require fertilizers, herbicides, pesticides, and irrigation, too. In the United States, one-fifth of all cropland is used to produce grain for livestock—more land than is used to produce grain for people.

Other environmental costs attend fishing. Fishing easily becomes over-fishing and depletes stocks of the very fish that people need to eat. Most nets also collect many nonfood species that are killed during harvest but returned to the sea instead of being put to use. Other aquatic animals are also vulnerable to injury and death from fishing activities, and populations of ecologically important nonfood animals, such as dolphins, are diminished. In short, our ways of producing foods are, for the most part, not sustainable.

Agribusiness

Farmers in the United States face serious challenges: not only are their costs for energy and other inputs increasing, but markets for U.S. farm products abroad are declining as a result of increased agricultural production and exports from other countries and economic problems that prevent grain-importing nations from purchasing U.S. products.[3] Many farms, especially

Kilograms of Grain Needed to Produce One Kilogram of Bread and One Kilogram of Animal Weight Gain

medium-sized family farms, are struggling to be profitable because of competition from foreign producers and a trend toward large food-producing operations.[4]

Faring somewhat better economically are huge centralized farms and ranches, many of which are being operated in Mexico or other developing nations; collectively, they are part of the massive food-producing enterprise called **agribusiness**. These operations in the

United States tend to use little local labour, and the profits they make tend not to stay in local communities. Their workers often endure unsafe conditions: nearly 500 pesticide poisonings among California farm workers were reported from 1997 to 2000, and many more unreported cases are believed to have occurred.[5] Agribusinesses located in countries outside the United States hire local labourers willing to work for much less than labourers in the United States.

Agribusinesses also tend to place a higher priority on producing abundant, inexpensive food than on protecting soil, water, and local biodiversity. As a result, no country on earth has more affordable abundant food than the United States.[6] When these large operations accomplish this feat through overuse of land, fertilizers, and pesticides, however, the resulting soil erosion, wasted irrigation water, and pollution problems can be enormous. Small U.S. farmers may be driven to adopt similar unsustainable practices or use their creativity to stay competitive.

Because of economies of scale, agribusinesses can price their products more attractively than can smaller, local farms. Thus, local U.S. grocers offer broccoli from Mexico, carrots from California, pineapples from Hawaii, and bananas from Central America at prices no local farmers can match, even if they could grow those products.

If food prices had to include a "tax" to pay for pollution cleanup, water protection, and land restoration, the prices of foods produced unsustainably would be much higher. If they included a living wage, education, and benefits for the migrant farm workers, they would be higher still.

The Future Is Now

For each of the problems just described, solutions are being devised, and some are already being put into practice. To fully exploit these new sustainable agriculture techniques across the country will require some new learning and change. Sustainable agriculture is not one system but a set of practices that can be matched to particular needs in local areas. The crop yields from farms that employ these practices often compare favourably with those from farms using less sustainable methods.[7] The first of these ideas, **sustainable**, **alternative**, or **low-input agriculture**, emphasizes careful use of natural processes wherever possible rather than chemically intensive methods.

Low-Input Agriculture

One form of low-input agriculture is **integrated pest management (IPM)**. Farmers using this system employ many techniques, such as crop rotation and natural predators, to control pests rather than depending on heavy use of pesticides alone. Not all crops can grow reliably without pesticides, but many can. Table C15–2 contrasts low-input agriculture methods with unsustainable methods. Many sustainable techniques are not really new—they would be familiar to our great-grandparents. Many farmers today are rediscovering the benefits of old techniques as they adapt and experiment with them in the search for sustainable methods.

Low-input agriculture has some apparent disadvantages, but advantages offset them. For example, as chemical use falls, yields per hectare also fall somewhat, but costs per hectare also fall, so the return per hectare may be the same as or greater than before. More money goes to farmers and less to fuels, fertilizers, pesticides, and irrigation. The result of such farming is to make both farmers and consumers better off financially and environmentally.

Low-input agriculture works. As the world's population grows and its land and water dwindle, the need to adopt sustainable agriculture and development around the globe grows urgent. More than 30,000 U.S. farmers are successfully using sustainable techniques such as those described in Table C15–2. They see it as a food production system that can indefinitely sustain a healthy food supply, restore soil and water resources, and revitalize farming communities while reducing reliance on fossil fuels.

According to Agriculture and Agri-Food Canada's "Planning for a Sustainable Future: A Federal Sustainable Development Strategy for Canada: 2013–2016," the Federal Sustainable Development Act defines sustainable development as "development that meets the needs of the present without compromising the ability of future generations to meet their own needs . . . the Government of Canada accepts the basic principle that sustainable development is based on an ecologically efficient use of natural, social and economic resources" (http://www.ec.gc.ca/dd-sd/A22718BA-0107-4B32-BE17-A438616C4F7A/FSDS%202013-2016%20Final%20E.pdf).

Precision Agriculture

An exciting development in agriculture is the application of powerful new computer technologies to food production. Through techniques collectively known as *precision agriculture*, farmers can adjust soil and crop management to meet the precise needs of various areas of the farm. For example, a farmer growing crops in a field with hills, which tend to stay drier, and with low-lying areas, which tend to stay wetter, can adjust irrigation water to meet the specific needs of each part of the field. Similarly, if one section of a field needs nitrogen fertilizer while another needs a different mix, the farmer can program a computer to apply fertilizer of just the right type and amount for each area.[8] Likewise, pesticide application can be programmed to prescribed patterns, avoiding areas too close to streams or other water sources. The system turns off the pesticide flow when it comes to a designated safety zone.

The *global positioning satellite (GPS)* system is at the heart of precision farming. In the GPS system, satellites beam accurate information about land positions and elevations of an area, such as a field, to receivers placed on farm equipment here on earth. The GPS system delivers a grid map, pinpointing locations on a farm. Farmers can use the GPS information grid to target, within a metre's accuracy, areas that need treatments. They can then program computerized farm equipment to apply

High-Input and Low-Input Agricultural Techniques Compared

Unsustainable Practice	Sustainable Practice
■ Growing the same crop repeatedly on the same patch of land. This takes more and more nutrients out of the soil, makes fertilizer use necessary; favours soil erosion; and invites weeds and pests to become established, making pesticide use necessary.	■ Rotating crops. This increases nitrogen in the soil, so there is less need to buy fertilizers. If used with appropriate ploughing methods, crop rotation reduces soil erosion. Crop rotation also reduces weeds and pests.
■ Using fertilizers generously. Excess fertilizer pollutes ground and surface water and costs both farmers' household money and consumers' tax money.	■ Reducing the use of fertilizers and using livestock manure more effectively. Storing manure during the nongrowing season and applying it during the growing season. ■ Alternating nutrient-devouring crops with nutrient-restoring crops, such as legumes. ■ Composting on a large scale, including all plant residues not harvested. Ploughing the compost into the soil to improve its water-holding capacity.
■ Feeding livestock in feedlots where their manure produces major water and soil pollutant problems. Piled in heaps, manure also releases methane, a global-warming gas.	■ Feeding livestock or bison on the open range, where their manure will fertilize the ground on which plants grow and will release no methane. Alternatively, at least collecting feedlot animals' manure and using it as fertilizer, or, at the very least, treating it before release.
■ Spraying herbicides and pesticides over large areas to wipe out weeds and pests.	■ Applying technology in weed and pest control. Using precision agriculture techniques if affordable or using rotary hoes twice instead of herbicides once. Spot treating weeds by hand. ■ Using genetically resistant crops. ■ Using biological controls such as predators that destroy the pests.
■ Ploughing the same way everywhere, allowing unsustainable water runoff and erosion.	■ Ploughing in ways tailored to different areas. Conserving both soil and water by using cover crops, crop rotation, no-till planting, and contour ploughing.
■ Injecting animals with antibiotics to prevent disease in livestock. ■ Irrigating on a large scale.	■ Maintaining animals' health so that they can resist disease. ■ Irrigating only during dry spells and only where needed.

chemicals or other treatments accordingly. Farmers can also use the information to adjust the depths to which they till the soil. The goal is to till deeply enough to prepare seedbeds properly and control weeds but to avoid excessive tilling that wastes fuel and worsens erosion. Finally, at harvest, a GPS system produces an accurate accounting of crop yield, hectare by hectare, so that spot adjustments can be made in the next planting season.

The future of precision agriculture seems bright, and the potential savings to farmers in terms of water, fertilizers, and pesticides are enormous. The accompanying reduction in polluting chemicals introduced into the environment means that everyone benefits. The high initial costs of the equipment

pose a potential barrier to some farmers, but incentive programs can often offset some of the costs.

Soil Conservation and Incentive Programs

The U.S. Conservation Reserve Program provides federal assistance to farmers and ranchers who wish to improve their conservation of soil, water, and related natural resources on environmentally sensitive lands. It encourages farmers to plant native grasses, wildlife habitat, or trees instead of cash crops on highly erodible cropland, wetlands, or other environmentally sensitive areas. It also encourages conservation techniques such as shallow tilling and planting grassy strips to move water off fields. In

exchange, farmers receive annual rental payments and other assistance over a 10–15-year contract period. The goals of the program are to

■ Reduce soil erosion.

■ Protect production of food and fibre.

■ Reduce sedimentation in streams and lakes.

■ Improve water quality.

■ Establish wildlife habitat.

■ Enhance forest and wetland resources.

About 25 percent of all U.S. land is considered highly erodible and thus qualifies for conservation incentives.

Other conservation programs offer incentives for improving air quality, water quality, or animal habitat or for instituting measures to achieve goals similar to those listed above. Others may purchase sensitive lands for conservation. Private foundations or other groups may fund such programs with help from local, state, or federal agencies.

Measuring the success of any conservation program presents challenges because it entails measuring the nature and extent of the changes in the practices of farmers and ranchers that occur in response to program incentives.[9] In addition, a program's success may be affected by weather conditions at the sites, changing local regulations, technology, and dozens of other variable factors. Based on soil loss alone, though, conservation programs do seem to be working to preserve soils. The amount of U.S. cropland lost annually to erosion fell by almost 50 percent between 1982 and 2007.[10]

Direct Sales from Farm to Consumer

Today's small farmer must cut costs and find creative means of boosting profits. One avenue to improved balance sheets is direct marketing to consumers. Farmers selling their broccoli, carrots, and apples at farmers' markets and roadside stands often net a higher profit, especially when consumers perceive an intrinsic benefit from making the extra effort to obtain such foods. For example, local food may offer a measure of protection against foodborne illnesses.[11] A recent outbreak of E. coli infection from imported spinach was traced to an infected farm California, for example. Local food has passed through fewer hands.

Another way small farmers can boost profits is to create extra value by packaging or processing their products in ways that benefit consumers. For example, when a grape grower establishes a winery that produces local wines or an apple producer begins making candy apples and apple pies, the farmers use their own produce to create a new "added-value" product line to increase profits.[12] Consumers appreciate knowing how their food and other products are grown and handled.

Urban consumers often relish a trip to "the country" to pick up fresh foods grown locally. For those interested in buying local foods who live in or are visiting Ontario, check out the "Local Food Maps throughout Ontario" website at http://brescia.uwo.ca/about/our_people/our_faculty/food_nutrition/local_food_maps_ontario.html.

Equally promising is the growing trend toward organic farming. Consumers pay substantially higher prices for certified organic products, so small farmers reap greater profits, and the environment benefits, too.

Agricultural Biotechnology

Although not every farmer worldwide may be in a position to reap benefits from the technologies of precision agriculture, the advances of biotechnology may prove to be an essential part of a worldwide move toward sustainable agriculture. If health and safety issues are addressed and resolved (see Controversy 12), rDNA technology promises economic, environmental, and agricultural benefits by shrinking the acreage needed for crops, reducing soil losses, minimizing use of chemical insecticides, and bettering crop protection.

Genetically modified microbes can offer benefits to sustainable agriculture if research and testing can ensure that rDNA microorganisms released into the environment will not turn out to be more harmful than the products they are intended to replace. Bioengineered microbes could contribute to the continuous renewal of the soil's fertility by fixing nitrogen and releasing other nutrients into the soil, thereby lessening the need for chemical fertilizers and easing the environmental burden. Scientific laboratories are also working to engineer microbes that can recycle agricultural, industrial, and household wastes into fertilizers, an obvious boon to the environment. Bacterial and fungal herbicides, fungicides, and insecticides are in advanced experimental stages. Such technologies promise to augment other integrated pest management systems of low-input agriculture such as crop rotation.

Energy Efficiency

Some 6,560 Calories of fuel are used to produce a can of corn (including the can and transportation), and 7,980 Calories are needed to produce a package of frozen corn (including packaging, freezing, and transportation). Much of this energy input could be reduced, as Table C15–3 shows. The last item in the table suggests that consumers should centre their diets on foods that require low energy inputs, a choice that is described next.

Eating Lower on the Food Chain

Studies of energy use in the U.S. food system have revealed which foods require the most and least energy to produce. The least energy is needed for grain: about one-third of a Calorie of fuel is burned to grow each Calorie of grain. Fruit and vegetables are intermediate, and most animal protein requires from

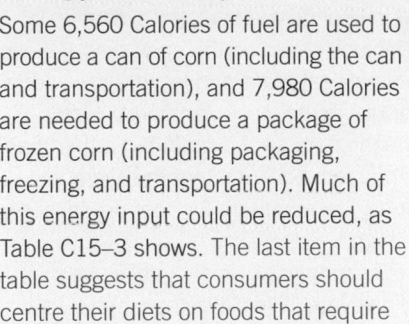

Table C15-3

Sustainable Energy-Saving Agricultural Techniques

- Use machinery scaled to the job at hand and operate it at efficient speeds.
- Combine operations. Harrow, plant, and fertilize in the same operation.
- Use diesel fuel. Use solar and wind energy on farms. Use methane from manure. Be open-minded to alternative energy sources.
- Use new disease- and pest-resistant plant varieties developed through genetic engineering.
- Save on technological and chemical inputs and spend some of the savings paying people to do manual jobs. Increasing labour inputs has been considered inefficient. Reverse this thinking: creating more jobs is preferable to using more machinery and fuel.
- Partially return to the techniques of using animal manure and crop rotation. This would save energy because chemical fertilizers require large energy inputs to produce.
- Choose crops that require low energy inputs (fertilizer, pesticides, irrigation).
- Educate people to cook food efficiently and to eat low on the food chain.

10 to 90 Calories of fossil energy per Calorie of usable food. An exception is livestock raised on the open range; these animals eat grass and require low energy inputs, as do most plant foods.[13] So much of our beef is grain fed rather than range fed, however, that the average energy requirement for beef production is high.

To support our meat intake, we maintain several billion livestock, about four times our own weight in animals. Livestock consume 10 times as much grain each day as we do. We could use much of that grain to make grain products for ourselves and share them. Such a shift in consumption could free up enough grain to feed 400 million people, would necessitate burning less fuel and using less water, and could also free up much more land. According to the United Nations, the "ecological footprint"—the productive land area needed to support a person's lifestyle—of each individual is four times as large in an industrialized country as in a developing one (see Figure C15–2). To help size up your own ecological footprint, take the quiz in Table C15–4.

Some meat eaters are choosing to cut down on their meat portions or to eat range-fed beef or bison only.

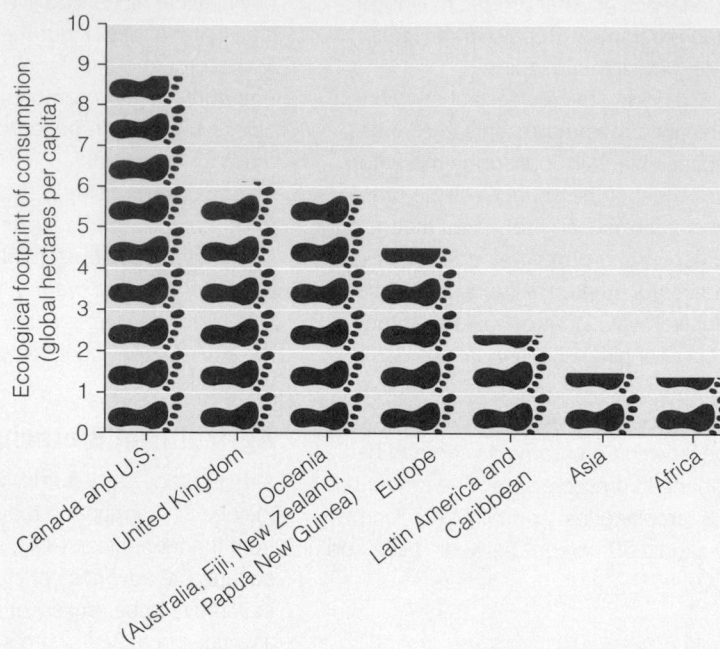

Figure C15–2

Ecological Footprints

Source: Global Footprint Network 2010. National Footprint Accounts, *2010 Edition. Available at www.footprintnetwork.org/en/index.php/GFN/page/ecological_footprint_atlas_2008*

Bison meat also offers nutrition advantages over grain-fed beef because it is lower in fat, and the fat has more polyunsaturated fatty acids, including the omega-3 type. Some people are switching to nonmeat, and even pure vegan, diets. The fish-farming industry shows promise of being able to feed large numbers of people in the future and could help greatly to provide nutritious meat at a price people and the environment could afford.

Table C15–4

How Big Is Your Ecological Footprint?

This quiz can help you evaluate your impact on the earth. The higher your score, the smaller your "footprint."

At home, do you	In the yard, do you
1. Recycle everything you can: newspapers, cans, glass bottles and jars, scrap metal, used oil, etc.?	6. Pull weeds instead of using herbicides?
2. Use cold water in the washer whenever possible?	7. Fertilize with manure and compost rather than with chemical fertilizers?
3. Avoid using appliances (such as electric can openers) to do things you can do by hand?	8. Compost your leaves and yard debris rather than burn them?
4. Reuse grocery bags to line your wastebasket? Reuse or recycle bread bags, butter tubs, etc.?	9. Take extra plastic and rubber pots back to the plant nursery?
5. Store food in reusable containers rather than plastic wrap, disposable bags and containers, or aluminum foil?	

(continued)

Table C15–4

How Big Is Your Ecological Footprint? (continued)

On vacation, do you	When buying, do you
10. Turn down the heat and turn off the hot water heater before you leave?	25. Buy as little plastic and foam packaging as possible?
11. Carry reusable cups, dishes, and flatware (and use them)?	26. Buy permanent, rather than disposable, products?
12. Dispose of trash appropriately (never litter)?	27. Buy paper rather than plastic, if you must buy disposable products?
13. Buy no souvenirs made from wild or endangered animals?	28. Buy fresh produce grown locally?
14. Stay on roads and trails and not trample dunes and fragile undergrowth?	29. Buy in bulk to avoid unnecessary packaging?

About your car, do you	In other areas, do you
15. Keep your car tuned up for maximum fuel efficiency?	30. Volunteer your time to conservation projects?
16. Use public transit whenever possible?	31. Encourage your family, friends, and neighbours to save resources, too?
17. Ride your bike or walk whenever possible?	32. Write letters to support conservation issues?
18. Plan to replace your car with a more fuel-efficient model when you can?	
19. Recycle your engine oil?	

At school or work, do you	Scoring
20. Recycle paper whenever possible?	First, give yourself 4 points for answering this quiz: ___
21. Use scrap paper for notes to yourself and others?	Then give yourself 1 point each for all of the habits you know people should adopt. This is to give you credit for your awareness, even if you haven't acted on it yet (total possible points = 32): ___
22. Print or copy on both sides of the paper?	Finally, give yourself 2 more points for each habit you have adopted—or honestly would if you could (total possible points = 64): ___
23. Reuse large envelopes and file folders?	Total score:
24. Use the stairs instead of the elevator whenever you can?	1–25: You are a beginner in stewardship of the earth. Try to improve.
	26–50: You are on your way and doing better than many consumers.
	51–75: Good. Pat yourself on the back and keep on improving.
	76–100: Excellent. You are a shining example for others to follow.

Source: Adapted from Conservation Action Checklist, produced by the Washington Park Zoo, Portland, Oregon, and available from Conservation International, 1015 18th St. NW, Suite 1000, Washington, D.C. 20036: 1-800-406-2306. (http://www.conservation.org). Call or write for copies of the original or for more information.

Conclusion

Although many problems are global in scope, the actions of individual people lie at the heart of their solutions. Do what you can to tread lightly on the earth. Beware of a perfectionist attitude, however, because believing that you "should" do more than a realistic amount can lead to defeat. Small improvements add up to large accomplishments, so any amount of progress is well worth celebrating. Celebrate the changes that are possible today by making them a permanent part of your life; do the same with changes that become possible tomorrow and every day thereafter. The results may add up to more than you dared to hope for.

Self-Check

Answers to these Self-Check questions are in Appendix D.

1. Which of the following is a symptom of food insecurity?
   a. You worry about gaining weight.
   b. You rely on neighbours to feed your children because there is not enough food in the house.
   c. You shop daily to get the best prices.
   d. You buy fresh rather than frozen foods.

2. According to Food Banks Canada, an estimated _____ Canadians used food banks in one month in 2012.
   a. 870,000
   b. 675,000
   c. 500,000
   d. 175,000

3. Today, famine is most often a result of
   a. poverty
   b. drought
   c. social causes such as war
   d. flood

4. Which of the following is an example of environmental degradation?
   a. soil erosion
   b. diminished grazing lands
   c. air pollution
   d. all of the above

5. Which of the following activities are recommended due to the small impact they have on the environment?
   a. Use the oven whenever possible.
   b. Line pans with aluminum foil to reduce cleanup effort.
   c. Use a pressure cooker or microwave to cook foods.
   d. Carry groceries home in paper bags rather than plastic.

6. Poverty and hunger drive people to bear more children.
   T   F

7. Most children who die of malnutrition starve to death.
   T   F

8. Grains require the least energy to produce.
   T   F

9. The higher a nation's economic status, the faster its population grows over the long run.
   T   F

10. Deficiency of vitamin A is the world's leading cause of blindness in young children.
    T   F

Endnotes

1. G. Gardner and B. Halweil, *Underfed and Overfed: The Global Epidemic of Malnutrition*, World Watch Paper 150 (Washington, D.C.: Worldwatch Institute, 2000).

2. Statistics Canada, Income in Canada 2010, available at http://www.statcan.gc.ca/pub/75-202-x/2010000/hl-fs-eng.htm.

3. G. Mudur, India's burden of waterborne diseases is underestimated, *British Medical Journal* 326 (2003): 1284; J. Liu and coauthors, Malnutrition at age 3 years and lower cognitive ability at age 11 years: Independence from psychosocial adversity, *Archives of Pediatrics and Adolescent Medicine* 157 (2003): 593–600.

4. S. Collins and M. Myatt, Short-term prognosis in severe adult and adolescent malnutrition during famine, *Journal of the American Medical Association* 284 (2000): 621–626.

5. World Health Organization, *Executive Summary, World Health Report 1998: Life in the 21st Century—A Vision for All*, available at http://www.who.int/whr/1998/en/.

6. S. Perkins, Dead heat: The health consequences of global warming could be many, *Science News* 166 (2004): 10–12; R. F. Keeling and H. E. Garcia, The change in oceanic O₂ inventory associated with recent global warming,

Proceedings of the National Academy of Sciences 99 (2002): 7848–7853.

7. S. Peng and coauthors, Rice yields decline with higher night temperature from global warming, *Proceedings of the National Academy of Sciences* 101 (2004): 9971–9975.

8. R. MacDonald, Providing the world with clean water, *British Medical Journal* 327 (2003): 1416–1418.

9. J. Raloff, Dead waters: Massive oxygen-starved zones are developing along the world's coasts, *Science News* 165 (2004): 360–362; J. Raloff, Limiting dead zones: How to curb river pollution and save the Gulf of Mexico, Science News 165 (2004): 378–380; Food and Agriculture Organization, *The State of Food and Agriculture 2013*, available at http://www.fao.org/publications/sofa/en/.

10. B. Harder, Sea change: Ocean report urges new policies, Science News 165 (2004): 259; British Petroleum (BP), *Gulf of Mexico Restoration*, available at http://www.bp.com/en/global/corporate/gulf-of-mexico-restoration.html.

11. World Health Organization, Children: Reducing Mortality (September 2013), available at http://www.who.int/mediacentre/factsheets/fs178/en/.

12. Food and Agriculture Organization, *The State of Food Insecurity in the World 2003*, available at http://www.fao.org/docrep/006/j0083e/j0083e00.htm; The UN Inter-agency Group for Child Mortality Estimation, *Levels and Trends in Child Mortality* (Report 2013), available at http://www.who.int/maternal_child_adolescent/documents/levels_trends_child_mortality_2013.pdf.

13. Statistics Canada, 2010 [see reference 2].

14. S. Bartlett and N. Burstein, Food Stamp Program access study: Eligible nonparticipants, a report of the Economic Research Service, May 2004, available at http://www.ers.usda.gov/publications/efan-electronic-publications-from-the-food-assistance-nutrition-research-program/efan03013-2.aspx#.UrxVVPRDs4g.

15. Food Banks Canada, *About Hunger in Canada*, available at http://www.foodbankscanada.ca/Learn-About-Hunger/About-Hunger-in-Canada.aspx.

16. K. Hanson and K. S. Hamrick, *Moving Public Assistance Recipients into the Labor Force, 1996–2000*, Report 40, electronic report, available at http://www.ers.usda.gov/publications/FANRR40/.

17. K. M. Kempson and coauthors, Food management practices used by people with limited resources to maintain food sufficiency as reported

by nutrition educators, *Journal of the American Dietetic Association* 102 (2002): 1795–1799.

18. Economic Research Service, U.S. Department of Agriculture, Low-income households' expenditures on fruits and vegetables, May 28, 2004, available at http://www.ers.usda.gov/publications/AER833/.

19. J. T. Cook and coauthors, Food insecurity is associated with adverse health outcomes among human infants and toddlers, *Journal of Nutrition* 134 (2004): 1432–1438.

20. E. J. Costello and coauthors, Relationships between poverty and psychopathology: A natural experiment, *Journal of the American Medical Association* 290 (2003): 2023–2029.

21. Statistics Canada, Household Food Insecurity 2011–2012, available at http://www.statcan.gc.ca/pub/82-625-x/2013001/article/11889-eng.htm.

22. Individual and Household Food Insecurity in Canada, Position of Dietitians of Canada, *Canadian Journal of Dietetic Practice and Research* 66 (2005): 43–46; V. Tarasuk, Household food insecurity in Canada, *Topics in Clinical Nutrition* 20 (2005): 299–312.

23. Food Banks Canada, 2012 [see reference 15].

24. Canadian Living Foundation, Breakfast for Learning, available at http://www.breakfastforlearning.ca.

25. Canadian Feed the Children, available at http://www.canadianfeedthechildren.ca/.

26. Food & Consumer Products of Canada, available at http://www.fcpc.ca/industry-facts-consumer-resources.

27. Food and Agriculture Organization, 2003 [see reference 12].

28. P. Moszynski, Darfur teetering "on the verge of mass starvation," *British Medical Journal* 328 (2004): 1275.

29. Position of the American Dietetic Association: Addressing world hunger, malnutrition, and food insecurity, *Journal of the American Dietetic Association* 103 (2003): 1047–1057.

30. S. Shapouri and S. Rosen, Fifty years of U.S. food aid and its role in reducing world hunger, *Amber Waves*, September 2004, available at http://webarchives.cdlib.org/sw1vh5dg3r/http://ers.usda.gov/Amberwaves/September04/Features/usfoodaid.htm.

31. World Food Programme, *Hunger—Who are the Hungry?* (2014), available at http://www.wfp.org/hunger/who-are.

32. U. Kapil and A. Bhavna, Adverse effects of poor micronutrient status during childhood and adolescence, *Nutrition Reviews* 60 (2002): S84–S90.

33. M. Pena and J. Bacallao, Malnutrition and poverty, *Annual Review of Nutrition* 22 (2002): 241–253.

34. World Food Programme [see reference 31].

35. Food and Agriculture Organization, 2003 [see reference 12].

36. United Nations Population Fund, *Global Population and Water*, 2003, available at http://www.unfpa.org/public/publications/pid/2400.

37. R. Claassen, Have conservation compliance incentives reduced soil erosion? *Amber Waves*, available at http://webarchives.cdlib.org/sw1vh5dg3r/http://ers.usda.gov/AmberWaves/June04/Features/HaveConservation.htm.

38. Food and Agriculture Organization, *The State of World Fisheries and Aquaculture* (2012), available at http://www.fao.org/fishery/en.

39. R. A. Myers and B. Worm, Rapid worldwide depletion of predatory fish communities, *Nature* 423 (2003): 280–283.

40. New international plan of action targets illegal, unregulated and unreported fishing, Press release, 2001, available at www.fao.org/WAICENT/OIS/PRESS_NE/PRESSENG/2001/pren0111.htm; Food and Agriculture Organization, Understanding the cultures of fishing communities: A key to fisheries management and food security, *The State of World Fisheries and Aquaculture*, 2000, available at http://www.fao.org/docrep/004/y1290e/y1290e00.htm.

41. L. R. Brown, as quoted in B. Harder, Catch zero: What can be done as marine ecosystems face a deepening crisis, *Science News* 164 (2003): 59–61.

42. J. M. Hightower and D. Moore, Mercury levels in high-end consumers of fish, *Environmental Health Perspectives* 111 (2003): 604–608.

43. B. M. Jenssen, Marine pollution: The future challenge is to link human and wildlife studies, editorial, *Environmental Health Perspectives* 111 (2003): A198; T. Suzuki, Oxygen-deficient waters along the Japanese coast and their effects upon the estuarine ecosystem, *Journal of Environmental Quality* 30 (2001): 291–302.

44. Intergovernmental Panel on Climate Change 2001, *IPCC Third Assessment Report*, available at https://www.ipcc.ch/ipccreports/tar/.

45. *The Role of Science in Solving the World's Emerging Water Problems*, Arthur M. Sackler Colloquia of the National Academy of Sciences, held in Irvine, California, October 8–10, 2004.

46. United Nations Populations Fund [see reference 36].

47. United Nations Environmental Programme, Major global trends: The state of the environment, *Global Environmental Outlook 2000*, overview available at http://www.unep.org/geo/GEO2000/pdfs/ov-e.pdf.

48. United Nations Environmental Programme, 2000 [see reference 47].

49. Position of the American Dietetic Association: Dietetic professionals can implement practices to conserve natural resources and protect the environment, *Journal of the American Dietetic Association* 101 (2001): 1221–1227.

50. Canadian Aquaculture Alliance, Salmon (2012), available at http://www.aquaculture.ca/files/species-salmon.php; T. Peterson, Fresh food for thought, *Business Week Online*, June 8, 2004, available at http://www.businessweek.com/stories/2004-06-07/fresh-food-for-thought.

51. R. Robinson and C. Smith, Integrating issues of sustainably produced foods into nutrition practice: A survey of Minnesota Dietetic Association members, *Journal of the American Dietetic Association* 103 (2003): 608–611.

Consumer Corner 15

1. C. Leitzmann, Nutrition ecology: The contribution of vegetarian diets, *American Journal of Clinical Nutrition* 78 (2003): 657S–659S.

2. *What Can You Do to Support Sustainable Agriculture?* UC Sustainable Agriculture Research and Education Program, available at http://www.sarep.ucdavis.edu.

Controversy 15

1. EPA, Animal Feeding Operations—Animal Feeding and Enforcement (2013), available at http://www.epa.gov/oecaagct/anafocom.html.

2. UC Davis, Sustainable Agriculture Research and Education program, available at http://www.sarep.ucdavis.edu/.

3. USDA, USDA Agricultural Projections to 2017, available at http://www.ers.usda.gov/publications/oce-usda-agricultural-projections/oce-2008-1.aspx#.UssZYLTtCZ9.

4. USDA, *Economics, Statistics and Market Information System* (2003–2007), available at http://usda.mannlib.cornell.edu/MannUsda/viewDocumentInfo.do?documentID=1521.

5. M. Reeves and K. S. Schafer, Greater risks, fewer rights: U.S. farmworkers and pesticides, *International Journal of Occupational and Environmental Health* 9 (2003): 30–39.

6. Groceries cost less in the U.S., News and Notes, *Progressive Farmer*, March 2001, p. 10.

7. BIFS program overview, University of California Sustainable Agriculture Research and Education Program, available at http://www.sarep.ucdavis.edu/sfr/bifs/overview.

8. J. Leidner, Sprayer mixes on the go, *Progressive Farmer*, February 2001, p. 26.

9. K. Smith and M. Weinberg, Measuring the success of conservation programs, *Amber Waves*, September 2004, available at http://webarchives.cdlib.org/sw1vh5dg3r/http:/ers.usda.gov/Amberwaves/September04/Features/measuringsuccess.htm.

10. USDA, Natural Resources Conservation Services—Soil Erosion on Cropland 2007, available at http://www.nrcs.usda.gov/wps/portal/nrcs/detail/national/technical/nra/nri/?cid=stelprdb1041887.

11. University of California Sustainable Agriculture Research and Education Program, Emerging Local Food Purchasing Initiatives in Northern California Hospitals, available at http://www.sarep.ucdavis.edu/sfs/files/Farm_To_Hospital_WebFinal.pdf.

12. J. L. Ohmart, Direct marketing with value-added products or: "give me the biggest one of those berry tarts!" 2003, a study with the University of California Sustainable Agriculture Research and Education Program, available at http://www.sarep.ucdavis.edu/sfs/dm/cs/e-com2; D. Miller, Cabernet among the corn, *Progressive Farmer*, mid-March 2001, pp. 34–36.

13. J. Robinson, *Grass-Fed Basics: Key Differences between Conventional and Pasture Animal Production, 2002–2003*, available at http://www.eatwild.com/basics.html.

Appendix Table of Contents

A. Canadian Nutrition Recommendations

B. Aids to Calculation

C. Canadian Diabetes Association—"Beyond the Basics" Chart

D. Answers to Self-Check Questions

E. Physical Activity and Energy Requirements

F. Dietary Approaches to Stop Hypertension (DASH)
   Eating Plan and Discretionary Calorie Allowance for Weight
   Management

G. Nutrition Resources
   (available online at http://www.nelson.com/nutrition3ce)

Canadian Nutrition Recommendations

This appendix presents a snapshot of the nutrition recommendations for Canadians, many of which are in the 2011 *Eating Well with Canada's Food Guide* (http://www.hc-sc.gc.ca/fn-an/food-guide-aliment/index-eng.php). Many others can be found in the Dietary Reference Intake (DRI) reports (see the inside front cover of the textbook). For a summary of the nutrition recommendations found in the Food Guide, also see Table 1–8 on page 17. Although a Food Choice System for Meal Planning for otherwise healthy Canadians similar to the U.S. Food Exchange System no longer exists, it is recommended that Canadians compare the portions they actually consume with the recommended number of servings provided by Canada's Food Guide. They can track their intake in relation to the Food Guide by using Dietitians of Canada's interactive EATracker activity (http://www.eatracker.ca) or the Diet Analysis Plus software (and end-of-chapter exercises) associated with this textbook. Links to Canadian, U.S., and international governmental agencies and professional organizations that may provide additional information are provided in Appendix G on this book's website (http://www.nelson.com/nutrition3ce).

Canadian Nutrition Recommendations

Canada's Food Guide nutrition recommendations for Canadians (see Table A–1) are intended to assist Canadians in choosing foods wisely for good health. The recommendations undergo periodic updates; obtain the latest edition of the Food Guide from the Health Canada website, http://www.hc-sc.gc.ca/index-eng.php.

TABLE A-1 Nutrition Recommendations for Canadians

- The Canadian diet should provide energy consistent with the maintenance of *body weight* within the recommended range.
- The Canadian diet should include *essential nutrients* in amounts specified in Dietary Reference Intake (DRI) reports (see the inside front cover of the text).
- The *sodium* content of the Canadian diet should be reduced.
- The Canadian diet should include no more than 5% of total energy as *alcohol*, or two drinks daily, whichever is less.
- The Canadian diet should contain no more *caffeine* than the equivalent of four regular cups of coffee per day.
- Community water supplies containing less than 1 mg/L of fluoride should be *fluoridated* to that level.

NOTE: Italics added to highlight areas of concern.

Source: Eating Well with Canada's Food Guide. *Health Canada, 2011. Reproduced with permission from Her Majesty the Queen in Right of Canada©, represented by the Minister of Health, 2013.*

Aids to Calculation

CONTENTS

Mathematical problems have been worked out for you as examples at appropriate places in the text. This appendix aims to help with the use of the metric system and with those problems not fully explained elsewhere.

Conversion Factors

Conversion factors are useful mathematical tools in everyday calculations, like the ones encountered in the study of nutrition. A conversion factor is a fraction in which the numerator (top) and the denominator (bottom) express the same quantity in different units. For example, 2.2 pounds (lb) and 1 kilogram (kg) are equivalent; they express the same weight. The conversion factor used to change pounds to kilograms or vice versa is

$$\frac{1 \text{ kg}}{2.2 \text{ lb}} \text{ or } \frac{2.2 \text{ lb}}{1 \text{ kg}}$$

Because both factors equal 1, measurements can be multiplied by the factor without changing the value of the measurement. Thus, the units can be changed.

The correct factor to use in a problem is the one with the unit you are seeking in the numerator (top) of the fraction. Following are some examples of problems commonly encountered in nutrition study; they illustrate the usefulness of conversion factors.

Example 1

Convert the weight of 130 pounds to kilograms.

1. Choose the conversion factor in which the unit you are seeking is on top:

$$\frac{1 \text{ kg}}{2.2 \text{ lb}}$$

2. Multiply 130 pounds by the factor:

$$130 \text{ lb} \times \frac{1 \text{ kg}}{2.2 \text{ lb}} = \frac{130 \text{ kg}}{2.2}$$

$$= 59 \text{ kg (rounded to the nearest whole number)}$$

Example 2

How many grams (g) of saturated fat are contained in a 3-ounce (oz) hamburger?

1. A 4-ounce hamburger contains 7 grams of saturated fat. You are seeking grams of saturated fat; therefore, the conversion factor is

$$\frac{7 \text{ g saturated fat}}{4 \text{ oz hamburger}}$$

2. Multiply 3 ounces of hamburger by the conversion factor:

$$4 \text{ oz hamburger} \times \frac{7 \text{ g saturated fat}}{4 \text{ oz hamburger}} = \frac{3 \times 7 \text{ g}}{4} = \frac{21 \text{ g}}{4}$$

$$= 5 \text{ g saturated fat (rounded to the nearest whole number)}$$

Energy Units

1 Calorie* (Cal) = 4.2 kilojoules

1 megajoule (MJ) = 240 Cal

1 kilojoule (kJ) = 0.24 Cal

1 gram (g) carbohydrate = 4 Cal = 17 kJ

1 g fat = 9 Cal = 37 kJ

1 g protein = 4 Cal = 17 kJ

1 g alcohol = 7 Cal = 29 kJ

Nutrient Unit Conversions

Sodium

To convert milligrams of sodium to grams of salt:

$$\text{mg sodium} \div 400 = \text{g salt}$$

The reverse is also true:

$$\text{g salt} \times 400 = \text{mg sodium}$$

Folate

To convert micrograms (µg) of synthetic folate in supplements and enriched foods to Dietary Folate Equivalents (µg DFE):

$$\text{µg synthetic folate} \times 1.7 = \text{µg DFE}$$

For naturally occurring folate, assign each microgram of folate a value of 1 µg DFE:

$$\text{µg folate} = \text{µg DFE}$$

Example 3

Consider a pregnant woman who takes a supplement and eats a bowl of fortified cornflakes, 2 slices of fortified bread, and a cup of fortified pasta.

1. From the supplement and fortified foods, she obtains synthetic folate:

Supplement	100 µg folate
Fortified cornflakes	100 µg folate
Fortified bread	40 µg folate
Fortified pasta	60 µg folate
	300 µg folate

2. To calculate the DFE, multiply the amount of synthetic folate by 1.7:

$$300 \text{ µg} \times 1.7 = 510 \text{ µg DFE}$$

3. Now add the naturally occurring folate from the other foods in her diet—in this example, another 90 µg of folate:

$$510 \text{ µg DFE} + 90 \text{ µg} = 600 \text{ µg DFE}$$

Notice that if we had not converted synthetic folate from supplements and fortified foods to DFE, then this woman's intake would appear to fall short of the 600-µg recommendation for pregnancy (300 µg + 90 µg = 390 µg). But, as this example shows, her intake does meet the recommendation. At this time, supplement and fortified food labels list folate in micrograms only, not micrograms DFE, making such calculations necessary.

Vitamin A

Equivalencies for vitamin A:

$$1 \text{ µg RAE} = 1 \text{ µg retinol}$$

$$= 12 \text{ µg beta-carotene}$$

$$= 24 \text{ µg other vitamin A carotenoids}$$

$$1 \text{ International Unit (IU)} = 0.3 \text{ µg retinol}$$

$$= 3.6 \text{ µg beta-carotene}$$

$$= 7.2 \text{ µg other vitamin A carotenoids}$$

To convert older RE values to micrograms RAE:

$$1 \text{ µg RE retinol} = 1 \text{ µg RAE retinol}$$

$$6 \text{ µg RE beta-carotene} = 12 \text{ µg RAE beta-carotene}$$

$$12 \text{ µg RE other vitamin A carotenoids} = 24 \text{ µg RAE other vitamin A carotenoids}$$

International Units

- 1 IU vitamin D = 1/40 µg vitamin D = 0.025 µg vitamin D
- 1 IU natural vitamin E = 0.67 mg alpha-tocopherol
- 1 IU synthetic vitamin E = 0.45 mg alpha-tocopherol
- vitamin A; see above

---

*Throughout this book and in the appendices, the term Calorie is used to mean kilocalorie. Thus, when converting Calories to kilojoules, do not enlarge the Calorie values—they are kilocalorie values.

Percentages

A percentage is a comparison between a number of items (perhaps your intake of energy) and a standard number (perhaps the number of Calories recommended for your age and gender—your energy DRI). The standard number is the number you divide by. The answer you get after the division must be multiplied by 100 to be stated as a percentage (*percent* means "per 100").

Example 4

What percentage of the DRI recommendation for energy is your energy intake?

1. Find your energy DRI value on the inside front cover. We'll use 2,368 Calories to demonstrate.
2. Total your energy intake for a day—for example, 1,200 Calories.
3. Divide your Calorie intake by the DRI value:

   1,200 Cal (your intake) ÷ 2,368 Cal (DRI) = 0.507

4. Multiply your answer by 100 to state it as a percentage:

   0.507 × 100 = 50.7 = 51% (rounded off to the nearest whole number)

   In some problems in nutrition, the percentage may be more than 100. For example, suppose your daily intake of vitamin A is 3,200 µg and your DRI is 900 µg. Your intake as a percentage of the DRI is more than 100 percent (i.e., you consume more than 100 percent of your recommendation for vitamin A). The following calculations show your vitamin A intake as a percentage of the DRI value:

   3,200 ÷ 900 = 3.6 (rounded)

   3.6 × 100 = 360% of DRI

Example 5

Food labels express nutrients and energy contents of foods as percentages of the Daily Values. If a serving of a food contains 200 milligrams of calcium, for example, what percentage of the calcium Daily Value does the food provide?

1. Find the calcium Daily Value on page B at the front of the book.
2. Divide the milligrams of calcium in the food by the Daily Value standard:

   $$\frac{200}{1,000} = 0.2$$

3. Multiply by 100:

   0.2 × 100 = 20% of the Daily Value

Example 6

This example demonstrates how to calculate the percentage of fat in a day's meals.

1. Recall the general formula for finding percentages of Calories from a nutrient:

   (One nutrient's Calories ÷ Total Calories) × 100 = Percentage of Calories from that nutrient

2. Say a day's meals provide 1,754 Calories and 54 grams of fat. First, convert fat grams to fat Calories:

   54 g × 9 Cal per g = 486 Cal from fat

3. Then apply the general formula for finding the percentage of Calories from fat:

   (Fat Calories ÷ Total Calories) × 100 = Percentage of Calories from fat

   (486 ÷ 1,754) × 100 = 27.7 (28%, rounded)

Weights and Measures

Length

1 inch (in) = 2.54 centimetres (cm)

1 foot (ft) = 30.48 cm

1 metre (m) = 39.37 in

Temperature

		Celsius	Fahrenheit	
Steam	100°C	212°F		Steam
Body temperature	37°C	98.6°F		Body temperature
Ice	0°C	37°F		Ice

- To find degrees Fahrenheit (°F) when you know degrees Celsius (°C), multiply by 9/5 and then add 32.
- To find degrees Celsius (°C) when you know degrees Fahrenheit (°F), subtract 32 and then multiply by 5/9.

Volume

Used to measure fluids or pourable dry substances such as cereal.

1 millilitre (mL) = $\frac{1}{5}$ teaspoon or 0.034 fluid ounce or $\frac{1}{1,000}$ litre

1 decilitre (dL) = $\frac{1}{10}$ litre

1 teaspoon (tsp or t) = 5 mL or about 5 grams (g; weight) salt

1 tablespoon (tbs or T) = 3 tsp or 15 mL

1 ounce, fluid (fl oz) = 2 tbs or 30 mL

1 cup (c) = 8 fl oz or 16 tbs or 250 mL

1 quart (qt) = 32 fl oz or 4 c or 0.95 litre

1 litre (L) = 1.06 qt or 1,000 mL

1 gallon (gal) = 16 c or 4 qt or 128 fl oz or 3.79 L

Weight

1 microgram (μg or mcg) = $\frac{1}{1,000}$ mg

1 milligram (mg) = 1,000 μg or $\frac{1}{1,000}$ g

1 gram (g) = 1,000 mg or $\frac{1}{1,000}$ kg

1 ounce, weight (oz) = about 28 g or $\frac{1}{16}$ lb

1 pound (lb) = 16 oz (wt) or about 454 g

1 kilogram (kg) = 1,000 g or 2.2 lb

Canadian Diabetes Association—"Beyond the Basics" Chart

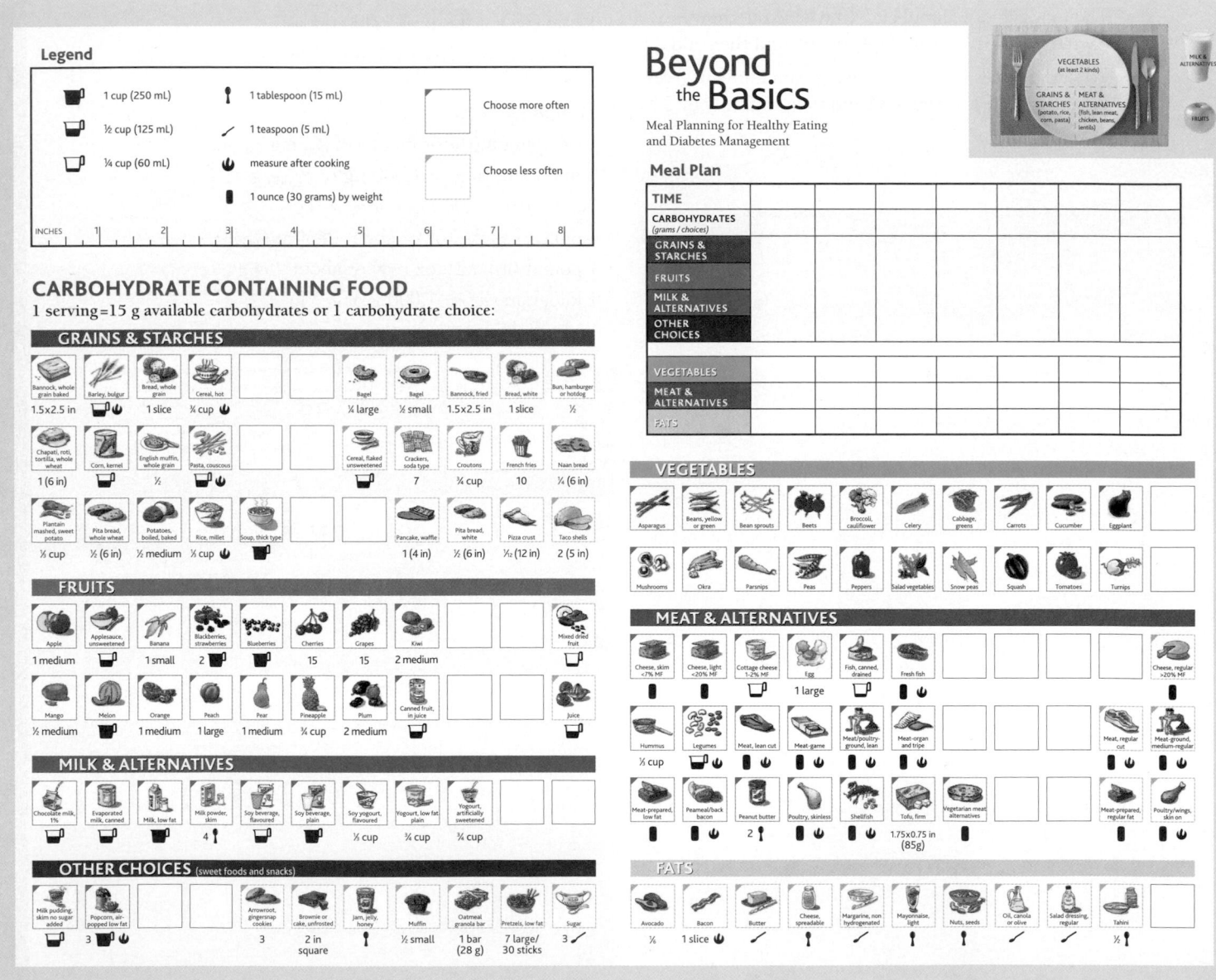

Finding Carbohydrate Values using the Nutrition Label:

The amount of carbohydrate in a food is listed on the Nutrition Facts Table.

- The amount listed is for the serving size given. Are you eating more, less, or the same? Compare your serving size to figure out the amount of carbohydrate you are eating.
- The total amount of carbohydrate in grams is listed first. This number includes starch, sugars and fibre. (Starch is not listed separately.)
- Fibre does not raise blood glucose and should be subtracted from the total carbohydrate (i.e. 36 g carbohydrate – 6 g Fibre = 30 g available carbohydrate).

Nutrition Facts	
Per 90 g serving (2 slices)	
Amount	% Daily Value
Calories 170	
Fat 2.7 g	4 %
Saturated 0.5 g + Trans 0 g	5 %
Cholesterol 0 mg	
Sodium 200 mg	8 %
Carbohydrate 36 g	13 %
Fibre 6 g	24 %
Sugars 3 g	
Protein 8 g	
Vitamin A 1 % Vitamin C	0 %
Calcium 2 % Iron	16 %

My goals:

Example: I will eat more vegetables by having at least one vegetable at lunch.

1. _____
2. _____
3. _____

Notes:

_____
_____
_____

Name	Date
Registered Dietitian	Phone	E-mail

OTHER USEFUL RESOURCES
available from the Canadian Diabetes Association

1. *Just the Basics: Healthy Eating for Diabetes Prevention and Management*
2. *The Glycemic Index*
3. *Basic carbohydrate counting for diabetes management*
4. *Sugars & Sweeteners*
5. *Alcohol + diabetes*
6. *Cholesterol + diabetes*
7. *Eating away from home*
8. *Managing weight + diabetes*
9. *High blood pressure + diabetes*

For more information about diabetes,
visit **diabetes.ca**
or call **1-800-BANTING** (226-8464)

Canadian Diabetes Association

211505 04-207 11/13 Q-60M

Beyond the Basics

Canadian Diabetes Association

Meal Planning for Healthy Eating and Diabetes Management

Healthy eating helps you manage your blood glucose and maintain a healthy weight. *Beyond the Basics: Meal Planning for Healthy Eating, Diabetes Prevention and Management,* will help you to choose the right foods and portions. Work with your Registered Dietitian to plan meals you enjoy.

Beyond the Basics teaches you about food groups. Each one adds to health. Foods to "Choose more often" ☐ are the healthier choices within each group. They are generally higher in vitamins, minerals, and fibre and have healthier fat. Foods to "Choose less often" are shown in ☐.

Foods that contain carbohydrate raise your blood glucose. These are **Grains & Starches, Fruits, Milk & Alternatives, and Other Choices**. One portion from any of these food groups contains about 15 grams (g) of available carbohydrate and counts as **1 carbohydrate choice**.

Grains & Starches includes grains, bread, pasta, potatoes, corn, and rice. Choose whole grains, such as whole wheat pasta and brown rice, more often to increase fibre intake. Most of these foods are low in fat.

Fruits are a good source of vitamins, minerals, and fibre. Choose fresh, frozen, and canned fruit (juice-packed) more often. These foods are high in fibre (except for juice) and low in fat.

Milk & Alternatives includes many sources and types of milk and fortified soy products, such as yogurt. "Choose more often" milk alternatives contain calcium and vitamin D and are lower in fat (skim, 1%, 2%).

Other Choices covers a wide variety of sweet foods and snacks.

Food groups that contain little or no carbohydrate are **Vegetables, Meat & Alternatives, Fats, and Extras.**

Vegetables are an excellent source of vitamins, minerals, and fibre. Choose dark green and brightly coloured vegetables often. Only parsnips, peas, and winter squash provide 15g of available carbohydrate when 1 cup (250 mL) is eaten.

Meat & Alternatives Choose lean meats, poultry without the skin, lower fat cheese and fish more often. This helps to reduce the total amount of fat you eat. Legumes (beans and lentils) are low in fat and high in fibre; they also contain some carbohydrate: 1 cup of legumes provides 15 g of available carbohydrate. "Choose more often" foods are low in saturated fat.

Fats Choose heart healthy unsaturated fats such as canola oil, olive oil, "non-hydrogenated" margarine, and small portions of nuts. Read labels and choose foods which say "low saturated fat" and "no trans fat".

✓ **Extras** Foods low in calories, carbohydrate, protein, and fat. Examples are sugar-free soft drinks and jello, broth, garlic, herbs and spices, and small amounts of mustard and ketchup.

✓ Use less salt in cooking and at the table. Ask a Registered Dietitian if you need "lower sodium" food products.

✓ Include physical activity every day.

211505   Date Printed: November 2013

CHAPTER 1
1. a
2. a
3. c
4. b
5. d
6. b
7. False. Heart disease and cancer are influenced by many factors, with genetics and diet among them.
8. True
9. False. The term *natural* has no legal definition.
10. True

CHAPTER 2
1. b
2. d
3. c
4. d
5. a
6. True
7. False. The DRI are estimates of the needs of healthy persons only. Medical problems alter nutrient needs.
8. False. People who choose to eat no meats or products taken from animals can still use Canada's Food Guide to ensure that their diets are adequate.
9. False. By law, food labels must state as a percentage of the Daily Values the amounts of vitamins A and C, calcium, and iron present in a food.
10. True

CHAPTER 3
1. a
2. d
3. c
4. c
5. d
6. False. Phagocytes are white blood cells that can ingest and destroy antigens in a process known as *phagocytosis*.
7. False. Hydrochloric acid initiates protein digestion and activates a protein-digesting enzyme in the stomach.
8. False. The digestive tract works efficiently to digest all foods simultaneously, regardless of composition.
9. True
10. False. Absorption of the majority of nutrients takes place across the specialized cells of the small intestine.

CHAPTER 4
1. b
2. a
3. c
4. b
5. a
6. True
7. False. Type 1 diabetes is most often controlled with insulin injections.
8. True
9. False. Whole-grain bread remains more nutritious despite the enrichment of white flour.
10. True

CHAPTER 5
1. c
2. a
3. c
4. b
5. d
6. True
7. False. Taking fish oil supplements is not recommended and may raise LDL cholesterol and have other harmful effects.
8. False. Consuming large amounts of *trans* fatty acids elevates serum LDL cholesterol and thus raises the risk of heart disease and heart attack.
9. False. When olestra is present in the digestive tract, fat-soluble vitamins, including vitamin E, become unavailable for absorption.
10. True

CHAPTER 6
1. b
2. b
3. d
4. a
5. d
6. True
7. False. Excess protein in the diet may have adverse effects such as obesity, enlarged liver or kidneys, worsened kidney disease, and accelerated bone loss.

8. False. Impoverished people living in inner cities and rural areas, as well as some elderly, homeless, and ill people in hospitals, have been diagnosed with PEM.
9. True
10. True

CHAPTER 7
1. b
2. c
3. d
4. a
5. c
6. d
7. False. No study to date has conclusively demonstrated that vitamin C can prevent colds or reduce their severity.
8. True
9. True
10. False. Vitamin A itself has no effect on acne.

CHAPTER 8
1. d
2. b
3. c
4. b
5. a
6. True
7. True
8. False. Calcium is the most abundant mineral in the body.
9. False. Butter, cream, and cream cheese contain negligible calcium, being almost pure fat. Many vegetables, such as broccoli, are good sources of available calcium.
10. False

CHAPTER 9
1. d
2. b
3. c
4. a
5. c
6. a
7. False. The thermic effect of food is believed to have negligible effects on total energy expenditure.
8. True
9. False. The BMI is unsuitable for use with athletes and adults over age 65.
10. True

CHAPTER 10
1. c
2. c
3. a
4. d
5. a

6. False. Weight training to improve muscle strength and endurance also helps maximize and maintain bone mass.
7. False. The average resting pulse for adults is around 70 beats per minute, but the rate is lower for active people.
8. True
9. True
10. True

CHAPTER 11
1. b
2. d
3. a
4. d
5. d
6. True
7. False. Laboratory evidence suggests that a high-calcium diet may help prevent colon cancer.
8. False. The DASH diet is designed to help people with hypertension control the disease.
9. False. Hypertension is more severe and occurs earlier in life among North Americans of African descent than those of European or Asian descent.
10. True

CHAPTER 12
1. b
2. c
3. d
4. a
5. c
6. False. Nature has provided many plants used for food with natural poisons to fend off diseases, insects, and other predators.
7. True
8. False. The canning industry chooses treatments that employ the high-temperature–short-time (HTST) principle.
9. True
10. True

CHAPTER 13
1. c
2. b
3. d
4. a
5. d
6. True
7. True
8. True
9. False. In general, the effect of nutritional deprivation of the mother is to reduce the quantity, not the quality, of her milk.
10. False. There is no proof for the theory that "stuffing the baby" at bedtime will promote sleeping through the night.

CHAPTER 14

1. c
2. d
3. c
4. c
5. b
6. d
7. False. Research to date does not support the idea that food allergies or intolerances cause hyperactivity in children, but studies continue.
8. True
9. False. Vitamin A absorption appears to increase with aging.
10. False. To date, no proven benefits are available from herbs or other remedies.

CHAPTER 15

1. b
2. a
3. c
4. d
5. c
6. True
7. False. Most children who die of malnutrition do not starve to death—they die because their health has been compromised by dehydration from infections that cause diarrhea.
8. True
9. False. The link between improved economic status and slowed population growth has been demonstrated in country after country.
10. True

Physical Activity and Energy Requirements

Chapter 9 described how to calculate your estimated energy requirements (EER) by using an equation that accounts for your gender, age, weight, height, and physical activity level. This appendix first helps you determine the correct physical activity factor to use in the equation, either by calculating your physical activity level or by guesstimating it. Then the appendix presents tables that provide a shortcut to estimating total energy expenditure.*

Calculating Your Physical Activity Level

To calculate your physical activity level, record all of your activities for a typical 24-hour day, noting the type of activity, the level of intensity, and the duration. Then, using a copy of Table E-1, find your activity in the first column (or an activity that is reasonably similar) and multiply the number of minutes spent on that activity by the factor in the third column. Write your answer in the last column and total the accumulated values for the day. Now add the subtotal of the last column to 1.1 (to account for basal energy and the thermic effect of food), as shown. This is your Physical Activity Level Score, and you are now close to having the number you need—the Physical Activity (PA) factor—for the equation in Chapter 9. Proceed, by using Table E–2, to find the PA factor for your gender that correlates with your Physical Activity Level Score. Then use your score in the energy equation on page 373 of Chapter 9.

Guesstimating Your Physical Activity Level

As an alternative to recording your activities for a day, you can use the first two columns of Table E-3 to decide if your daily activity is sedentary, low active, active, or very active. Find the PA factor for your gender that correlates with your typical physical activity level and use it in the energy equation on page 373 of Chapter 9. Warning: People generally overestimate their activity, guessing "active" most of the time. In reality, most people in Canada and the United States fall below the active level.

Using a Shortcut to Estimate Total Energy Expenditure

The DRI committee has developed estimates of total energy expenditures (and, therefore, energy requirements) based on the equations presented in Chapter 9. The DRI estimated numbers are provided in Table E-4 for women and Table E-5 for men. To use these tables to determine the energy (Calories) needed to maintain your current body weight:

1. Find the table appropriate for your gender.
2. Find your height in metres (or inches) in the left-hand column.

*This appendix, including the tables, is adapted from Committee on Dietary Reference Intakes, Dietary Reference Intakes for Energy, Carbohydrate, Fiber, Fat, Fatty Acids, Cholesterol, Protein, and Amino Acids (Washington, D.C.: National Academies Press, 2002).

3. Follow the row across to find your weight in kilograms (or pounds). (If you can't find your exact height and weight, choose a value between the two closest ones.)

4. Look down the column to find the number of Calories that corresponds to your activity level.

Importantly, the values given in the tables are for 30-year-old people. Women 19–29 should add 7 Calories per day for each year below age 30; older women should subtract 7 Calories per day for each year above age 30. Similarly, men 19–29 should add 10 Calories per day for each year below age 30; older men should subtract 10 Calories per day for each year above age 30.

TABLE E-1 Physical Activities and Their Scores

If your activity was equivalent to this . . .	Then list the number of minutes here and . . .	Multiply by this factor . . .	Add this column to get your Physical Activity Level Score:
Activities of Daily Living			
Gardening (no lifting)		0.0032	
Household tasks (moderate effort)		0.0024	
Lifting items continuously		0.0029	
Loading/unloading car		0.0019	
Lying quietly		0.0000	
Mopping		0.0024	
Mowing lawn (power mower)		0.0033	
Raking lawn		0.0029	
Riding in a vehicle		0.0000	
Sitting (idle)		0.0000	
Sitting (doing light activity)		0.0005	
Taking out garbage		0.0019	
Vacuuming		0.0024	
Walking the dog		0.0019	
Walking from house to car or bus		0.0014	
Watering plants		0.0014	
Additional Activities			
Billiards		0.0013	
Calisthenics (no weight)		0.0029	
Canoeing (leisurely)		0.0014	
Chopping wood		0.0037	
Climbing hills (carrying 11 lb load)		0.0061	
Climbing hills (no load)		0.0056	
Cycling (leisurely)		0.0024	
Cycling (moderately)		0.0045	
Dancing (aerobic or ballet)		0.0048	
Dancing (ballroom, leisurely)		0.0018	
Dancing (fast ballroom or square)		0.0043	
Golf (with cart)		0.0014	
Golf (without cart)		0.0032	
Horseback riding (walking)		0.0012	
Horseback riding (trotting)		0.0053	
Jogging (6 mph)		0.0088	
Music (playing accordion)		0.0008	
Music (playing cello)		0.0012	
Music (playing flute)		0.0010	

(continued)

TABLE E-1 Physical Activities and Their Scores (continued)

If your activity was equivalent to this . . .	Then list the number of minutes here and . . .	Multiply by this factor . . .	Add this column to get your Physical Activity Level Score:
Music (playing piano)		0.0012	
Music (playing violin)		0.0014	
Rope skipping		0.0105	
Skating (ice)		0.0043	
Skating (roller)		0.0052	
Skiing (water or downhill)		0.0055	
Squash		0.0106	
Surfing		0.0048	
Swimming (slow)		0.0033	
Swimming (fast)		0.0057	
Tennis (doubles)		0.0038	
Tennis (singles)		0.0057	
Volleyball (noncompetitive)		0.0018	
Walking (2 mph)		0.0014	
Walking (3 mph)		0.0022	
Walking (4 mph)		0.0033	
Walking (5 mph)		0.0067	
Subtotal			
Factor for basal energy and the thermic effect of food			1.1
Your Physical Activity Level Score			

Source: Adapted from National Academies Press, Committee on Dietary Reference Intakes, Dietary Reference Intakes for Energy, Carbohydrate, Fiber, Fat, Fatty Acids, Cholesterol, Protein, and Amino Acids *(Washington, D.C.: National Academies Press, 2002).*

TABLE E-2 Physical Activity Level Scores and Their PA Factors

Physical Activity Level Score	Description	Men: PA Factor	Women: PA Factor
1.0–1.39	Sedentary	1.0	1.0
1.4–1.59	Low active	1.11	1.12
1.6–1.89	Active	1.25	1.27

Source: Data from Committee on Dietary Reference Intakes, Dietary Reference Intakes for Energy, Carbohydrate, Fiber, Fat, Fatty Acids, Cholesterol, Protein, and Amino Acids *(Washington, D.C.: National Academies Press, 2002).*

TABLE E-3 Physical Activity Equivalents and Their PA Factors

Description	Physical Activity Equivalents	Men: PA Factor	Women: PA Factor
Sedentary	Only those physical activities required for normal independent living	1.0	1.0
	Activities equivalent to walking at a pace of 3–6.5 km/h for the following distances:		
Low active	2.5–5 km/day	1.11	1.12
Active	5–15 km/day	1.25	1.27
Very active	15 or more km/day	1.48	1.45

Source: Data from Committee on Dietary Reference Intakes, Dietary Reference Intakes for Energy, Carbohydrate, Fiber, Fat, Fatty Acids, Cholesterol, Protein, and Amino Acids *(Washington, D.C.: National Academies Press, 2002).*

TABLE E-4 Total Energy Expenditure (TEE in Calories per Day) for Women 30 Years of Age[a] at Various Levels of Activity and Various Heights and Weights

Height, m (in)	Physical Activity Level	Weight,[b] kg (lb)					
1.45 (57)		38.9 (86)	45.2 (100)	52.6 (116)	63.1 (139)	73.6 (162)	84.1 (185)
		Calories					
	Sedentary	1,564	1,623	1,698	1,813	1,927	2,042
	Low active	1,734	1,800	1,912	2,043	2,174	2,304
	Active	1,946	2,021	2,112	2,257	2,403	2,548
	Very active	2,201	2,287	2,387	2,553	2,719	2,886
1.50 (59)		41.6 (92)	48.4 (107)	56.3 (124)	67.5 (149)	78.8 (174)	90.0 (198)
		Calories					
	Sedentary	1,625	1,689	1,771	1,894	2,017	2,139
	Low active	1,803	1,874	1,996	2,136	2,276	2,415
	Active	2,025	2,105	2,205	2,360	2,516	2,672
	Very active	2,291	2,382	2,493	2,671	2,849	3,027
1.55 (61)		44.4 (98)	51.7 (114)	60.1 (132)	72.1 (159)	84.1 (185)	96.1 (212)
		Calories					
	Sedentary	1,688	1,756	1,846	1,977	2,108	2,239
	Low active	1,873	1,949	2,081	2,230	2,380	2,529
	Active	2,104	2,190	2,299	2,466	2,632	2,798
1.60 (63)		47.4 (104)	55.0 (121)	64.0 (141)	76.8 (169)	89.6 (197)	102.4 (226)
		Calories					
	Sedentary	1,752	1,824	1,922	2,061	2,201	2,340
	Low active	1,944	2,025	2,168	2,327	2,486	2,645
	Active	2,185	2,276	2,396	2,573	2,750	2,927
	Very active	2,474	2,578	2,712	2,914	3,116	3,318
1.65 (65)		50.4 (111)	58.5 (129)	68.1 (150)	81.7 (180)	95.3 (210)	108.9 (240)
		Calories					
	Sedentary	1,816	1,893	1,999	2,148	2,296	2,444
	Low active	2,016	2,102	2,556	2,425	2,594	2,763
	Active	2,267	2,364	2,494	2,682	2,871	3,059
	Very active	2,567	2,678	2,824	3,039	3,254	3,469
1.70 (67)		53.5 (118)	62.1 (137)	72.3 (159)	86.7 (191)	101.2 (223)	115.6 (255)
		Calories					
	Sedentary	1,881	1,963	2,078	2,235	2,393	2,550
	Low active	2,090	2,180	2,345	2,525	2,705	2,884
	Active	2,350	2,453	2,594	2,794	2,994	3,194
	Very active	2,662	2,780	2,938	3,166	3,395	3,623
1.75 (69)		56.7 (125)	65.8 (145)	76.6 (169)	91.9 (202)	107.2 (236)	122.5 (270)
		Calories					
	Sedentary	1,948	2,034	2,158	2,325	2,492	2,659
	Low active	2,164	2,260	2,437	2,627	2,817	3,007
	Active	2,434	2,543	2,695	2,907	3,119	3,331
	Very active	2,758	2,883	3,054	3,296	3,538	3,780
1.80 (71)		59.9 (132)	69.7 (154)	81.0 (178)	97.2 (214)	113.4 (250)	129.6 (285)
		Calories					
	Sedentary	2,015	2,106	2,239	2,416	2,593	2,769
	Low active	2,239	2,341	2,529	2,731	2,932	3,133
	Active	2,519	2,634	2,799	3,023	3,247	3,472
	Very active	2,855	2,987	3,172	3,428	3,684	3,940
1.85 (73)		63.3 (139)	73.6 (162)	85.6 (189)	102.7 (226)	119.8 (264)	136.9 (302)

[a]For each year below 30, add 7 Calories/day to TEE. For each year above 30, subtract 7 Calories/day from TEE.

[b]These columns represent BMIs of 18.5, 22.5, 25, 30, 35, and 40, respectively.

(continued)

TABLE E-4 — Total Energy Expenditure (TEE in Calories per Day) for Women 30 Years of Age[a] at Various Levels of Activity and Various Heights and Weights (continued)

Height, m (in)	Physical Activity Level	Weight,[b] kg (lb)					
		Calories					
	Sedentary	2,083	2,179	2,322	2,509	2,695	2,882
	Low active	2,315	2,422	2,624	2,836	3,049	3,262
	Active	2,605	2,727	2,904	3,141	3,378	3,615
	Very active	2,954	3,093	3,292	3,562	3,833	4,103
1.90 (75)		66.8 (147)	77.6 (171)	90.3 (199)	108.3 (239)	126.4 (278)	144.4 (318)
		Calories					
	Sedentary	2,151	2,253	2,406	2,603	2,800	2,996
	Low active	2,392	2,505	2,720	2,944	3,168	3,393
	Active	2,693	2,821	3,011	3,261	3,511	3,760
	Very active	3,053	3,200	3,414	3,699	3,984	4,270
1.95 (77)		70.3 (155)	81.8 (180)	95.1 (209)	114.1 (251)	133.1 (293)	152.1 (335)
		Calories					
	Sedentary	2,221	2,328	2,492	2,699	2,906	3,113
	Low active	2,470	2,589	2,817	3,053	3,290	3,526
	Active	2,781	2,917	3,119	3,383	3,646	3,909

[a]For each year below 30, add 7 Calories/day to TEE. For each year above 30, subtract 7 Calories/day from TEE.

[b]These columns represent BMIs of 18.5, 22.5, 25, 30, 35, and 40, respectively.

Source: Adapted from National Academies Press, Committee on Dietary Reference Intakes, Dietary Reference Intakes for Energy, Carbohydrate, Fiber, Fat, Fatty Acids, Cholesterol, Protein, and Amino Acids (Washington, D.C.: National Academies Press, 2002).

TABLE E-5 — Total Energy Expenditure (Calories per Day) for Men 30 Years of Age[a] at Various Levels of Activity and Various Heights and Weights

Height, m (in)	Physical Activity Level	Weight,[b] kg (lb)					
1.45 (57)		38.9 (86)	47.3 (100)	52.6 (116)	63.1 (139)	73.6 (163)	84.1 (185)
		Calories					
	Sedentary	1,777	1,911	2,048	2,198	2,347	2,496
	Low active	1,931	2,080	2,225	2,393	2,560	2,727
	Active	2,127	2,295	2,447	2,636	2,826	3,015
	Very active	2,450	2,648	2,845	3,075	3,305	3,535
1.50 (59)		41.6 (92)	50.6 (107)	56.3 (124)	67.5 (149)	78.8 (174)	90.0 (198)
		Calories					
	Sedentary	1,848	1,991	2,126	2,286	2,445	2,605
	Low active	2,009	2,168	2,312	2,491	2,670	2,849
	Active	2,215	2,394	2,545	2,748	2,951	3,154
	Very active	2,554	2,766	2,965	3,211	3,457	3,703
1.55 (61)		44.4 (98)	54.1 (114)	60.1 (132)	72.1 (159)	84.1 (185)	96.1 (212)
		Calories					
	Sedentary	1,919	2,072	2,205	2,376	2,546	2,717
	Low active	2,089	2,259	2,401	2,592	2,783	2,974
	Active	2,305	2,496	2,646	2,862	3,079	3,296
	Very active	2,660	2,887	3,087	3,349	3,612	3,875
1.60 (63)		47.4 (104)	57.6 (121)	64.0 (141)	76.8 (169)	89.6 (197)	102.4 (226)

[a]For each year below 30, add 10 Calories/day to TEE. For each year above 30, subtract 10 Calories/day from TEE.

[b]These columns represent BMIs of 18.5, 22.5, 25, 30, 35, and 40, respectively.

(continued)

Total Energy Expenditure (Calories per Day) for Men 30 Years of Age[a] at Various Levels of Activity and Various Heights and Weights (continued)

Height, m (in)	Physical Activity Level	Weight,[b] kg (lb)					
		Calories					
	Sedentary	1,993	2,156	2,286	2,468	2,650	2,831
	Low active	2,171	2,351	2,492	2,695	2,899	3,102
	Active	2,397	2,601	2,749	2,980	3,210	3,441
	Very active	2,769	3,010	3,211	3,491	3,771	4,051
1.65 (65)		50.4 (111)	61.3 (129)	68.1 (150)	81.7 (180)	95.3 (210)	108.9 (240)
		Calories					
	Sedentary	2,068	2,241	2,369	2,562	2,756	2,949
	Low active	2,254	2,446	2,585	2,801	3,017	3,234
	Active	2,490	2,707	2,854	3,099	3,345	3,590
	Very active	2,880	3,136	3,339	3,637	3,934	4,232
1.70 (67)		53.5 (118)	65.0 (137)	72.3 (159)	86.7 (191)	101.2 (223)	1 1 5.6 (255)
		Calories					
	Sedentary	2,144	2,328	2,454	2,659	2,864	3,069
	Low active	2,338	2,542	2,679	2,909	3,139	3,369
	Active	2,586	2,816	2,961	3,222	3,483	3,743
	Very active	2,992	3,265	3,469	3,785	4,101	4,417
1.75 (69)		56.7 (125)	68.9 (145)	76.6 (169)	91.9 (202)	107.2 (236)	122.5 (270)
		Calories					
	Sedentary	2,222	2,416	2,540	2,757	2,975	3,192
	Low active	2,425	2,641	2,776	3,020	3,263	3,507
	Active	2,683	2,927	3,071	3,347	3,623	3,900
	Very active	3,108	3,396	3,602	3,937	4,272	4,607
1.80 (71)		59.9 (132)	72.9 (154)	81.0 (178)	97.2 (214)	113.4 (250)	129.6 (285)
		Calories					
	Sedentary	2,301	2,507	2,628	2,858	3,088	3,318
	Low active	2,513	2,741	2,875	3,132	3,390	3,648
	Active	2,782	3,040	3,183	3,475	3,767	4,060
1.80 (73)		63.3 (139)	77.0 (162)	85.6 (189)	102.7 (226)	119.8 (264)	136.9 (302)
		Calories					
	Sedentary	2,382	2,599	2,718	2,961	3,204	3,447
	Low active	2,602	2,844	2,976	3,248	3,520	3,792
	Active	2,883	3,155	3,297	3,606	3,915	4,223
	Very active	3,344	3,667	3,877	4,251	4,625	4,999
1.90 (75)		66.8 (147)	81.2 (171)	90.3 (199)	108.3 (239)	126.4 (278)	144.4 (318)
		Calories					
	Sedentary	2,464	2,693	2,810	3,066	3,322	3,579
	Low active	2,693	2,948	3,078	3,365	3,652	3,939
	Active	2,986	3,273	3,414	3,739	4,065	4,390
	Very active	3,466	3,806	4,018	4,413	4,807	5,202
1.95 (77)		70.3 (155)	85.6 (180)	95.1 (209)	114.1 (251)	133.1 (293)	1 52.1 (335)
		Calories					
	Sedentary	2,547	2,789	2,903	3,173	3,443	3,713
	Low active	2,786	3,055	3,183	3,485	3,788	4,090
	Active	3,090	3,393	3,533	3,875	4,218	4,561

[a]For each year below 30, add 10 Calories/day to TEE. For each year above 30, subtract 10 Calories/day from TEE.

[b]These columns represent BMIs of 18.5, 22.5, 25, 30, 35, and 40, respectively.

Source: Adapted from National Academies Press, Committee on Dietary Reference Intakes, Dietary Reference Intakes for Energy, Carbohydrate, Fiber, Fat, Fatty Acids, Cholesterol, Protein, and Amino Acids (Washington, D.C.: National Academies Press, 2002).

Dietary Approaches to Stop Hypertension (DASH) Eating Plan and Discretionary Calorie Allowance for Weight Management

TABLE F-1   Discretionary Calorie Allowance as Outlined by the USDA Food Guide

This table shows the number of discretionary Calories remaining at each Calorie level if nutrient-dense foods provide the basis of the diet. The table shows an example of how these Calories may be divided between solid fats and added sugars. Those trying to lose weight may choose to omit discretionary Calories.

Discretionary Calories That Remain at Each Level

FOOD GUIDE CALORIE LEVEL												
	1,000	1,200	1,400	1,600	1,800	2,000	2,200	2,400	2,600	2,800	3,000	3,200
DISCRETIONARY CALORIES[a]												
	165	171	171	132	195	267	290	362	410	426	512	648

Example of division of discretionary Calories: solid fats are shown in grams (g), added sugars in grams (g) and teaspoons (tsp)

SOLID FATS[b]												
	11 g	14g	14g	11g	15g	18g	19g	22g	24g	24g	29g	34g
ADDED SUGARS[c]												
	20g	16g	16g	12g	20g	32g	36g	48g	56g	60g	72g	96g
	(5 tsp)	(4 tsp)	(4 tsp)	(3 tsp)	(5 tsp)	(8 tsp)	(9 tsp)	(12 tsp)	(14 tsp)	(15 tsp)	(18 tsp)	(24 tsp)

[a] The USDA Food Guide assumes foods will be nutrient dense (i.e., fat-free or low-fat and contain no added sugars). Solid fat and sugar Calories must always be counted as discretionary Calories. See Chapter 2 for more details.

[b] Solid fats: Amounts of solid fats listed in the table represent about 7–8% of Calories from saturated fat. Solid fats shown in this table represent the amounts of fats that may be added in cooking or at the table and fats consumed when higher-fat items are selected from the food groups. Most oils are not considered to be part of the discretionary Calorie allowance because they are a major source of the essential fatty acids and vitamin E in the food pattern.

[c] The amounts of added sugars suggested in the example are not specific recommendations for amounts of added sugars to consume but rather represent the amounts that can be included in each Calorie level without overconsuming Calories. The suggested amounts of added sugars may be helpful as part of the Food Guide to allow for some sweetened foods or beverages, without exceeding energy needs. This use of added sugars as a Calorie balance requires two assumptions: (1) that selections are made from all food groups in accordance with the suggested amounts and (2) that additional fats are used in the amounts shown, which, together with the fats in the core food groups, represent about 27–30% of Calories from fat.

Source: U.S. Department of Agriculture and U.S. Department of Health and Human Services, Dietary Guidelines for Americans, 2010, available at http://www.health.gov/dietaryguidelines/2010.asp.

TABLE F-2 The DASH Eating Plan at 1,600-, 2,000-, 2,600-, and 3,100-Calorie Levels[a]

The number of daily servings to choose from each food group depends on a person's energy requirement (see Chapter 9).

Food Groups	1,600 Calories	2,000 Calories	2,600 Calories	3,100 Calories	Serving Sizes	Examples and Notes	Significance of Each Food Group to the DASH Eating Plan
Grains[b]	6 servings	7–8 servings	10–11 servings	12–13 servings	1 slice bread, 1 oz dry cereal,[c] ½ cup cooked rice, pasta, or cereal	Whole-wheat bread, English muffin, pita bread, bagel, cereals, grits, oatmeal, crackers, unsalted pretzels, and popcorn	Major sources of energy and fibre
Vegetables	3–4 servings	4–5 servings	5–6 servings	6 servings	1 cup raw leafy vegetable, ½ cup cooked vegetable, 6 oz vegetable juice	Tomatoes, potatoes, carrots, green peas, squash, broccoli, turnip greens, collards, kale, spinach, artichokes green beans, lima beans, sweet potatoes	Rich sources of potassium, magnesium, and fibre
Fruit	4 servings	4–5 servings	5–6 servings	6 servings	6 oz fruit juice, 1 medium fruit; ¼ cup dried fruit; ½ cup fresh, frozen, or canned fruit	Apricots, bananas, dates, grapes, oranges, orange juice, grapefruit, grapefruit juice, mangoes, melons, peaches, pineapples, prunes, raisins, strawberries, tangerines	Important sources of potassium, magnesium, and fibre
Low-fat or fat-free dairy foods	2–3 servings	2–3 servings	3 servings	3–4 servings	8 oz milk, 1 cup yogurt, 1½ oz cheese	Fat-free or low-fat milk, fat-free or low-fat buttermilk, fat-free or low-fat regular or frozen yogurt, low-fat and fat-free cheese	Major sources of calcium and protein
Meat, poultry, fish	1–2 servings	2 or fewer servings	2 servings	2–3 servings	3 oz cooked meat, poultry, or fish	Select only lean; trim away visible fats; broil, roast, or boil instead of frying; remove skin from poultry	Rich sources of protein and magnesium
Nuts, seeds, legumes	3–4 servings/week	4–5 servings/week	1 serving	1 serving	⅓ cup or 1½ oz nuts, 2 tbs or ½ oz seeds, ½ cup cooked dry beans or peas	Almonds, filberts, mixed nuts, peanuts, walnuts, sunflower seeds, kidney beans, lentils	Rich sources of energy, magnesium, potassium, protein, and fibre
Fat and oils[d]	2 servings	2–3 servings	3 servings	4 servings	1 tsp soft margarine, 1 tbs low-fat mayonnaise, 2 tbs light salad dressing, 1 tsp vegetable oil	Soft margarine, low-fat mayonnaise, light salad dressing, vegetable oil (such as olive, corn, canola, or safflower)	DASH has 27% of Calories as fat (low in saturated fat), including fat in or added to foods
Sweets	0 servings	5 servings/week	2 servings	2 servings	1 tbs sugar, 1 tbs jelly or jam, ½ oz jelly beans, 8 oz lemonade	Maple syrup, sugar, jelly, jam, fruit-flavoured gelatin, jelly beans, hard candy, fruit punch, sorbet, ices	Sweets should be low in fat

[a]NIH publication no. 03-4082; N. M. Karanja and coauthors, Journal of the American Dietetic Association 8 (1999): S19–S27.

[b]Whole grains are recommended for most servings to meet fibre recommendations.

[c]Equals ½–1¼ cups, depending on cereal type. Check the product's Nutrition Facts label.

[d]Fat content changes serving counts for fats and oils: For example, 1 tbs of regular salad dressing equals 1 serving; 1 tbs of a low-fat dressing equals ½ serving; 1 tbs of a fat-free dressing equals 0 servings.

Source: U.S. Department of Agriculture and U.S. Department of Health and Human Services, Dietary Guidelines for Americans, 2010, available at http://www.health.gov/dietaryguidelines/2010.asp.

Glossary

A

absorb to take in, as nutrients are taken into the intestinal cells after digestion; the main function of the digestive tract with respect to nutrients. p. 86

acceptable daily intake (ADI) the estimated amount of a substance that can be consumed daily over a person's lifetime without any adverse effects. p. 151

acceptable macronutrient distribution ranges (AMDR) values for carbohydrate, fat, and protein expressed as percentages of total daily caloric intake; ranges of intakes set for the energy-yielding nutrients that are sufficient to provide adequate total energy and nutrients while reducing the risk of chronic diseases. p. 32

accredited approved; in the case of colleges and universities, certified by an agency such as provincial ministries of education; an accredited dietetic program at a university has been certified by an agency such as Dietitians of Canada. p. 27

acesulfame- (AY-sul-fame) **potassium**, also called **acesulfame-K** a zero-Calorie sweetener approved by Health Canada and the U.S. Food and Drug Administration (FDA). p. 151

acetaldehyde (ass-et-AL-deh-hide) a substance to which ethanol is metabolized on its way to becoming harmless waste products that can be excreted. p. 101

acid–base balance equilibrium between acid and base concentrations in the body fluids. p. 218

acid reducers prescription and over-the-counter drugs that reduce the acid output of the stomach; effective for treating severe, persistent forms of heartburn but not for neutralizing acid already present. Side effects are frequent and include diarrhea, other gastrointestinal complaints, and reduction of the stomach's capacity to destroy alcohol, thereby producing higher-than-expected blood alcohol levels from each drink. Also called *acid controllers*. p. 96

acidosis (acid-DOH-sis) the condition of excess acid in the blood, indicated by a below-normal pH (*osis* means "too much in the blood"). p. 219

acids compounds that release hydrogens in a watery solution. p. 218

acne chronic inflammation of the skin's follicles and oil-producing glands, which leads to an accumulation of oils inside the ducts that surround hairs; usually associated with the maturation of young adults. p. 621

acrylamide (ah-KRILL-ah-mide) a chemical produced in carbohydrate-rich foods, such as potatoes and grains, when cooked at high temperatures. A known animal carcinogen, acrylamide is also toxic to the nervous system of both animals and humans. Also used in manufacturing and construction. p. 484

acupuncture (ak-you-punk-chur) a technique that involves piercing the skin with long, thin needles at specific anatomical points to relieve pain or illness. Acupuncture sometimes uses heat, pressure, friction, suction, or electromagnetic energy to stimulate the points. p. 479

added sugars sugars and syrups added to a food for any purpose, such as to add sweetness or bulk or to aid in browning (baked goods). Also called *carbohydrate sweeteners*, they include glucose, fructose, corn syrup, concentrated fruit juice, and other sweet carbohydrates. p. 143

additives substances that are added to foods but are normally not consumed by themselves as foods. p. 532

adequacy the dietary characteristic of providing all of the essential nutrients, fibre, and energy in amounts sufficient to maintain health and body weight. p. 9

adequate intakes (AI) nutrient intake goals for individuals; the recommended average daily nutrient intake level based on intakes of healthy people (observed or experimentally derived) in a particular life stage and gender group and assumed to be adequate. Set whenever scientific data are insufficient to allow establishment of an RDA value. p. 32

adipose tissue the body's fat tissue, consisting of masses of fat-storing cells and blood vessels to nourish them. p. 33

advertorials lengthy advertisements in newspapers and magazines and on websites that read like feature articles but are written for the purpose of touting the virtues of products and may or may not be accurate. p. 21

aerobic (air-ROH-bic) requiring oxygen. Aerobic activity strengthens the heart and lungs by requiring them to work harder than normal to deliver oxygen to the tissues. p. 423

agribusiness agriculture practised on a massive scale by large corporations owning vast tracts of land and employing intensive technological, fuel, and chemical inputs. p. 669

AIDS acquired immune deficiency syndrome; caused by infection with human immunodeficiency virus (HIV), which is transmitted primarily by sexual contact, compromised epidermal layer coming in contact with infected blood, needles shared among drug users, or fluids transferred from an infected mother to her fetus or infant. p. 461

air displacement plethysmography (ADP) uses a piece of equipment referred to as the Bod Pod to measure air displacement by your body to estimate and track body composition changes over time. p. 375

alcohol dehydrogenase (dee-high-DRAH-gen-ace) **(ADH)** an enzyme system that breaks down alcohol. The antidiuretic hormone is also abbreviated ADH. p. 101

alcohol-related birth defects (ARBD) malformations in the skeletal and organ systems (heart, kidneys, eyes, ears) associated with prenatal alcohol exposure. p. 573

alcohol-related neurodevelopmental disorder (ARND) behavioural, cognitive, or central nervous system abnormalities associated with prenatal alcohol exposure. p. 573

alcoholism a dependency on alcohol marked by compulsive uncontrollable drinking with negative effects on physical health, family relationships, and social health. p. 573

alkalosis (al-kah-LOH-sis) the condition of excess base in the blood, indicated by an above-normal blood pH (alkalinity—*alka* means "base"; *osis* means "too much in the blood"). p. 219

allergy an immune reaction to a foreign substance, such as a component of food. Also called *hypersensitivity* by researchers. p. 609

aloe a tropical plant with widely claimed value as a topical treatment for minor skin injury. Some scientific evidence supports this claim; evidence against its use in severe wounds also exists. p. 480

alpha-lactalbumin (lact-AL-byoo-min) the chief protein in human breast milk. The chief protein in cow's milk is *casein* (CAY-seen). p. 580

alternative (low-input or sustainable) agriculture agriculture practised on a small scale using individualized approaches that vary with local conditions so as to minimize technological, fuel, and chemical inputs. p. 669

alternative therapy systems of theory and practice that have emerged independently of conventional biomedical approaches. Examples include acupuncture, biofeedback, chiropractic, faith healing, and many others. Also called *alternative medical systems.* p. 479

American Dietetic Association (ADA) the professional organization of dietitians in the United States. The Canadian equivalent is Dietitians of Canada (DC), which operates similarly.

amine (a-MEEN) **group** the nitrogen-containing portion of an amino acid. p. 207

amino acid chelates (KEY-lates) compounds of minerals (such as calcium) combined with amino acids in a form that favours their absorption. A *chelating agent* is a molecule that surrounds another molecule and can then either promote or prevent its movement from place to place (*chele* means "claw"). p. 356

amino acid pools amino acids dissolved in the body's fluids that provide cells with ready raw materials from which to build new proteins or other molecules. p. 223

amino (a-MEEN-o) **acids** the building blocks of protein. Each has an amine group at one end, an acid group at the other, and a distinctive side chain. p. 206

amniotic (AM-nee-OTT-ic) **sac** the "bag of waters" in the uterus in which the fetus floats. p. 557

anabolic steroid hormones chemical messengers related to the male sex hormone testosterone that stimulate building up of body tissues (anabolic means "promoting growth"; sterol refers to compounds chemically related to cholesterol). p. 445

anaerobic (AN-air-ROH-bic) not requiring oxygen. Anaerobic activity may require strength but does not work the heart and lungs very hard for a sustained period. p. 427

anaphylactic (an-ah-feh-LACK-tick) **shock** a life-threatening whole-body allergic reaction to an offending substance. p. 610

androstenedione (AN-droh-STEEN-dee-own) a precursor of testosterone that elevates both testosterone and estrogen in the blood of both males and females. Often called andro, it is sold with claims of producing increased muscle strength, but controlled studies disprove such claims. p. 445

anecdotal evidence information based on interesting and entertaining, but not scientific, personal accounts of events. p. 21

anemia the condition of inadequate or impaired red blood cells; a reduced number or volume of red blood cells along with too little hemoglobin in the blood. The red blood cells may be immature and, therefore, too large or too small to function properly. Anemia can

result from blood loss, excessive red blood cell destruction, defective red blood cell formation, and many nutrient deficiencies. Anemia is not a disease but a symptom of another problem; its name literally means "too little blood." p. 331

anencephaly (an-en-SEFF-ah-lee) an uncommon and always fatal NTD in which the brain fails to form. p. 561

aneurysm (AN-you-rism) the ballooning out of an artery wall at a point that is weakened by deterioration. p. 465

anorexia nervosa an eating disorder characterized by a refusal to maintain a minimally normal body weight, self-starvation to the extreme, and a disturbed perception of body weight and shape; seen (usually) in teenage girls and young women (*anorexia* means "without appetite"; *nervos* means "of nervous origin"). p. 406

antacids medications that react directly and immediately with the acid of the stomach, neutralizing it. Antacids are most suitable for treating occasional heartburn. p. 96

antibodies (AN-te-bod-ees) large proteins of the blood, produced by the immune system in response to an invasion of the body by foreign substances (antigens). Antibodies combine with and inactivate the antigens. p. 218

anticarcinogens compounds in foods that act in any of several ways to oppose the formation of cancer. p. 486

antidiuretic (AN-tee-dye-you-RET-ick) **hormone (ADH)** a hormone produced by the pituitary gland in response to dehydration (or a high sodium concentration in the blood). It stimulates the kidneys to reabsorb more water and so to excrete less. (This hormone should not be confused with the enzyme alcohol dehydrogenase, which is also abbreviated ADH.) p. 101

antigen a substance foreign to the body that elicits the formation of antibodies or an inflammation reaction from immune system cells. Food antigens are usually large proteins. p. 609

antimicrobial agents preservatives that prevent spoilage by mould or bacterial growth. Familiar examples are acetic acid (vinegar) and sodium chloride (salt). Others are benzoic, propionic, and sorbic acids; nitrites and nitrates; and sulphur dioxide. p. 533

antioxidant nutrients vitamins and minerals that oppose the effects of oxidants on human physical functions. The antioxidant vitamins are vitamin E, vitamin C, and beta-carotene. The mineral selenium also participates in antioxidant activities. p. 295

antioxidants (anti-OX-ih-dants) compounds that protect other compounds from damaging reactions involving oxygen by themselves

reacting with oxygen (*anti* means "against"; *oxy* means "oxygen"). *Oxidation* is a potentially damaging effect of normal cell chemistry involving oxygen. p. 63

aorta (ay-OR-tuh) the large, primary artery that conducts blood from the heart to the body's smaller arteries. p. 465

Apgar score a system of scoring an infant's physical condition right after birth. Heart rate, respiration, muscle tone, response to stimuli, and colour are ranked 0, 1, or 2. A low score indicates that medical attention is required to facilitate survival. p. 572

appendicitis inflammation and/or infection of the appendix, a sac protruding from the intestine. p. 122

appetite the psychological desire to eat; a learned motivation and a positive sensation that accompanies the sight, smell, or thought of appealing foods. p. 378

appliance thermometer a thermometer that verifies the temperature of an appliance. An *oven thermometer* verifies that the oven is heating properly; a *refrigerator/freezer thermometer* tests for proper refrigerator (< 4°C) or freezer (−17°C) temperature. p. 512

aquifers underground rock formations containing water that can be drawn to the surface for use. p. 312

arachidonic (ah-RACK-ih-DON-ik) **acid** an omega-6 fatty acid derived from linoleic acid. p. 177

arginine a nonessential amino acid falsely promoted as enhancing the secretion of human growth hormone, the breakdown of fat, and the development of muscle. p. 445

aristolochic acid a Chinese herb ingredient known to attack the kidneys and to cause cancer; U.S. consumers have required kidney transplants and must take lifelong antirejection medication after use. Banned by the FDA but available in supplements sold on the Internet. p. 293

arsenic a poisonous metallic element. In trace amounts, arsenic is believed to be an essential nutrient in some animal species. Arsenic is often added to insecticides and weed killers and, in tiny amounts, to certain animal drugs. p. 526

arteries blood vessels that carry blood containing fresh oxygen supplies from the heart to the tissues. p. 78

artesian water water drawn from a well that taps a confined aquifer in which the water is under pressure. p. 314

arthritis a usually painful inflammation of joints caused by many conditions, including infections, metabolic disturbances, or injury; usually results in altered joint structure and loss of function. p. 626

artificial colours certified food colours, added to enhance appearance. (Certified means approved by Health Canada.) Vegetable dyes, such as beta-carotene from carrots, are extracted from vegetables. Food colours are a mix of vegetable dyes and synthetic dyes approved by Health Canada for use in food. p. 533

artificial fats zero-energy fat replacers that are chemically synthesized to mimic the sensory and cooking qualities of naturally occurring fats but are totally or partially resistant to digestion. Also called *fat analogues*. p. 184

artificial flavours, flavour enhancers chemicals that mimic natural flavours and those that enhance flavour. p. 533

ascorbic acid one of the active forms of vitamin C (the other is *dehydroascorbic* acid); an antioxidant nutrient. p. 263

aspartame a compound of phenylalanine and aspartic acid that tastes like the sugar sucrose but is much sweeter. It is used in both Canada and the United States. p. 151

atherosclerosis (ath-er-oh-scler-OH-sis) the most common form of CVD; characterized by plaques along the inner walls of the arteries (*scleros* means "hard"; *osis* means "too much"). The term "arteriosclerosis" refers to all forms of hardening of the arteries and includes some rare diseases. p. 464

atrophy (AT-tro-fee) a decrease in size (e.g., of a muscle) because of disuse. p. 423

B

B-cells lymphocytes that produce antibodies. *B* stands for bursa, an organ in the chicken where B-cells were first identified. p. 84

baby water ordinary bottled water treated with ozone to make it safe but not sterile. p. 314

balance the dietary characteristic of providing foods of a number of types in proportion to each other, such that foods rich in some nutrients do not replace foods that are rich in other nutrients. Also called *proportionality*. p. 9

balance study a laboratory study in which a person is fed a controlled diet and the intake and excretion of a nutrient are measured. Balance studies are valid only for nutrients like calcium (chemical elements) that do not change while they are in the body. p. 35

basal metabolic rate (BMR) the rate at which the body uses energy to support its basal metabolism. p. 371

basal metabolism the sum total of all of the involuntary activities that are necessary to sustain life, including circulation, respiration, temperature maintenance, hormone secretion, nerve activity, and new tissue synthesis, but excluding digestion and voluntary activities. Basal metabolism is the largest component of the average person's daily energy expenditure. p. 371

bases compounds that accept hydrogens from solutions. p. 218

basic foods milk and milk products; meats and similar foods such as fish and poultry; vegetables, including dried beans and peas; fruit; and grains. These foods are generally considered to form the basis of a nutritious diet. Also called *whole foods*. p. 9

bee pollen a product consisting of bee saliva, plant nectar, and pollen that confers no benefit on athletes and may cause an allergic reaction in individuals sensitive to it. p. 445

beer belly central-body fatness associated with alcohol consumption. p. 101

behaviour modification alteration of behaviour using methods based on the theory that actions can be controlled by manipulating the environmental factors that cue, or trigger, the actions. p. 403

belladonna any part of the deadly night-shade plant; a fatal poison. p. 480

beriberi (berry-berry) the thiamin-deficiency disease; characterized by loss of sensation in the hands and feet, muscular weakness, advancing paralysis, and abnormal heart action. p. 269

best-before date/best if used by specifies the last date the food will be of the highest quality. After this date, quality is expected to diminish, although the food may still be safe for consumption if it has been handled and stored properly (check Table 12-5 for safe refrigerator storage times). Also called freshness date or quality assurance date. p. 530

beta-carotene an orange pigment with antioxidant activity; a vitamin A precursor made by plants and stored in human fat tissue. p. 247

bicarbonate a common alkaline chemical; a secretion of the pancreas; also the active ingredient of baking soda. p. 90

bile a cholesterol-containing digestive fluid made by the liver, stored in the gallbladder, and released into the small intestine when needed. It emulsifies fats and oils to ready them for enzymatic digestion. p. 90

binge drinkers people who drink four or more drinks in a short period. p. 101

binge eating disorder an eating disorder whose criteria are similar to those of bulimia nervosa, excluding purging or other compensatory behaviours. p. 406

bioaccumulation the accumulation of a contaminant in the tissues of living things at higher and higher concentrations along the food chain. p. 526

bioactive compounds defined by Health Canada as the naturally occurring chemical compounds contained in or derived from a plant, animal, or marine source that exert the desired health/wellness benefit (e.g., omega-3

fatty acids in flax or fish oils and beta-glucans from oats and barley). p. 63

bioelectrical impedance (im-PEE-dense) a technique for measuring body fatness by measuring the body's electrical conductivity. p. 375

biological role claim a carefully worded, prescribed statement on a food that meets strict criteria that outline the role a nutrient may have in our biological system. For example, an acceptable claim for the "carbohydrate" in foods is that it "supplies energy." p. 55

biotechnology the science of manipulating biological systems or organisms to modify their products or components or create new products; more properly called genetic engineering or *rDNA technology* (see Chapter 12's Controversy section). p. 525

bioterrorism the intentional spreading of disease-causing organisms or agricultural pests as a political weapon to produce fear and intimidate others. p. 459

biotin (BY-o-tin) a B vitamin; a coenzyme necessary for fat synthesis and other metabolic reactions. p. 280

bladder the sac that holds urine until time for elimination. p. 98

bleaching agents substances used to whiten foods such as flour and cheese. Peroxides are examples. p. 533

blind experiment an experiment in which the subjects do not know whether they are members of the experimental group or the control group. In a *double-blind experiment*, neither the subjects nor the researchers know to which group the members belong until the end of the experiment. p. 15

blood the fluid of the cardiovascular system; composed of water, red and white blood cells, other formed particles, nutrients, oxygen, and other constituents. p. 78

body composition the proportions of muscle, bone, fat, and other tissue that make up a person's total body weight. p. 364

body mass index (BMI) an indicator of obesity or underweight, calculated by dividing the weight of a person by the square of the person's height. p. 367

body system a group of related organs that work together to perform a function. Examples are the circulatory system, respiratory system, and nervous system. p. 77

bone density a measure of bone strength; the degree of mineralization of the bone matrix. p. 349

bone meal or powdered bone crushed or ground bone preparations intended to supply calcium to the diet. Calcium from bone is not well absorbed and is often contaminated with toxic materials such as arsenic, mercury, lead, and cadmium. p. 356

boron a nonessential mineral that is promoted as a "natural" steroid replacement. p. 445

bottled water drinking water sold in bottles. p. 312

botulism an often-fatal food poisoning caused by botulinum toxin, a toxin produced by the *Clostridium botulinum* bacterium that grows without oxygen in nonacidic canned foods. p. 508

bovine somatotropin (bST) (so-MAT-ah-TROW-pin) growth hormone of cattle, which can be produced for agricultural use by genetic engineering. Also called *bovine growth hormone (bGH)*. p. 525

bovine spongiform encephalopathy (BOW-vine SPON-jih-form en-SEH-fell-AH-path-ee) **(BSE)** an often-fatal illness of cattle affecting the nerves and brain. Also called *mad cow disease*. p. 515

bran the protective fibrous coating around a grain; the chief fibre donator of a grain. p. 124

branched-chain amino acids (BCAA) the amino acids leucine, isoleucine, and valine, which are present in large amounts in skeletal muscle tissue; supplements are falsely promoted as necessary for exercising muscles. p. 445

brewer's yeast a preparation of yeast cells, containing a concentrated amount of B vitamins and some minerals; falsely promoted as an energy booster. p. 445

broccoli sprouts the sprouted seed of *Brassica italica*, or the common broccoli plant, believed to be a functional food by virtue of its high phytochemical content. p. 63

brown bread bread containing ingredients such as molasses that lend a brown colour; may be made with any kind of flour, including white flour. p. 124

brown sugar white sugar with molasses added; 95 percent pure sucrose. p. 143

buffers molecules that can help keep the pH of a solution from changing by gathering or releasing H ions. p. 313

bulimia (byoo-LEEM-ee-uh) **nervosa** recurring episodes of binge eating combined with a morbid fear of becoming fat; usually followed by self-induced vomiting or purging. p. 406

butyrate (BYOO-tier-ate) a small fat fragment produced by the fermenting action of bacteria on viscous, soluble fibres; the preferred energy source for the colon cells. p. 123

C

caffeine a stimulant that may produce alertness and reduced reaction time in small doses but creates fluid losses with a larger dose. Overdoses cause headaches, trembling, an abnormally fast heart rate, and other undesirable effects. More about caffeine appears in Controversy 11. p. 445

caffeine water bottled water with caffeine added. p. 314

CAGE questions a set of four questions often used internationally for initial screening for alcoholism. The questions relate to C, Cutting down; A, Annoyance by criticism; G, Guilty feeling; and E, Eye-openers. p. 101

calcium compounds the simplest forms of purified calcium. They include calcium carbonate, citrate, gluconate, hydroxide, lactate, malate, and phosphate. These supplements vary in the amount of calcium they contain, so read the labels carefully. A 500-mg tablet of calcium gluconate may provide only 45 mg of calcium, for example. p. 356

caloric effect the drop in cancer incidence seen whenever intake of food energy (Calories) is restricted. p. 483

Calorie control control of energy intake; a feature of a sound diet plan. p. 9

Calorie-free fewer than 5 Calories per serving. p. 57

Calories/kcalories units of energy. Strictly speaking, the unit used to measure the energy in foods is a kilocalorie (*kcalorie* or *Calorie*): it is the amount of heat energy necessary to raise the temperature of a kilogram (a litre) of water by one degree Celsius. This book follows the common practice of using the term *Calorie** (abbreviated *Cal/kcal*) to mean the same thing. p. 7

Canada Prenatal Nutrition Program (CPNP) The women targeted by this program include pregnant adolescents, youth at risk of becoming pregnant, pregnant women who abuse alcohol or other substances, pregnant women living in violent situations, off-reserve Aboriginal and Inuit women, refugees, and pregnant women living in isolation or not having access to services; visit http://www.phac-aspc.gc.ca/hp-ps/dca-dea/prog-ini/cpnp-pcnp. p. 565

Canadian Food Inspection Agency (CFIA) "The role of the CFIA is to enforce food safety legislation. To this end, the CFIA implements activities which contribute to a safe food supply and accurate product information"; see http://www.inspection.gc.ca/food/safe-food-production-systems/food-recall-and-emergency-response/food-manual/eng/13784 02475724/1378403080658?chap=2. p. 504

cancer a disease in which cells multiply out of control and disrupt normal functioning of one or more organs. p. 480

canning a method of preserving food by killing all microorganisms present in the food and then sealing out air. The food, container, and lid are heated until sterile; as the food cools, the lid makes an airtight seal, preventing contamination. p. 531

capillaries minute, weblike blood vessels that connect arteries to veins and permit transfer of materials between blood and tissues (see Figures 3-3 and 3-4). p. 78

carbohydrate loading a regimen of moderate exercise, followed by eating a high-carbohydrate diet, that enables muscles to temporarily store glycogen beyond their normal capacity; also called *glycogen loading* or *glycogen supercompensation*. p. 430

carbohydrates compounds composed of single or multiple sugars. The name means "carbon and water," and a chemical shorthand for carbohydrate is CHO, signifying carbon (C), hydrogen (H), and oxygen (O). p. 113

carbonated water water that contains carbon dioxide gas, either naturally occurring or added, that causes bubbles to form in it; also called *bubbling* or *sparkling water*. Seltzer, soda, and tonic waters are legally soft drinks and are not regulated as water. p. 314

carcinogen (car-SIN-oh-jen) a cancer-causing substance (*carcin* means "cancer"; *gen* means "gives rise to"). p. 482

carcinogenesis the origination or beginning of cancer. p. 482

cardiac output the volume of blood discharged by the heart each minute. p. 425

cardiorespiratory endurance the ability to perform large-muscle dynamic exercise of moderate to high intensity for prolonged periods. p. 423

cardiovascular disease (CVD) disease of the heart and blood vessels; disease of the arteries of the heart is called *coronary heart disease* (CHD). p. 161

carnitine a nonessential nutrient that functions in cellular activities. Carnitine is claimed to "burn" fat and spare glycogen during endurance events, but it does neither. p. 280

carotenoid (CARE-oh-ten-oyd) a member of a group of pigments in foods that range in colour from light yellow to reddish orange and are chemical relatives of beta-carotene, many with a degree of vitamin A activity in the body (also defined in Controversy 2). p. 251

carpal tunnel syndrome a pinched nerve at the wrist, causing pain or numbness in the hand. It is often caused by repetitive motion of the wrist. p. 278

carrying capacity the total number of living organisms that a given environment can support without deteriorating in quality. p. 663

case studies studies of individuals. In clinical settings, researchers can observe treatments and their *apparent* effects. To prove that a treatment has produced an effect requires simultaneous observation of an untreated similar subject (a *case control*). p. 15

cataracts (CAT-uh-racts) clouding of the lens of the eye that can lead to blindness. Cataracts can be caused by injury; viral infection; toxic substances; genetic disorders; and, possibly, some nutrient deficiencies or imbalances. p. 627

cathartic a strong laxative. p. 406

cat's claw a herb from the rainforests of Brazil and Peru; claimed, but not proven, to be an "all-purpose" remedy. p. 480

CDC (Centers for Disease Control and Prevention) a branch of the Department of Health and Human Services that is responsible for monitoring foodborne diseases. p. 24

cell differentiation the process by which immature cells are stimulated to mature and gain the ability to perform functions characteristic of their cell type. p. 248

cell salts a mineral preparation supposedly prepared from living cells. No scientific evidence supports benefits from such preparations. p. 445

cells the smallest units in which independent life can exist. All living things are single cells or organisms made of cells. p. 76

cellulite a term popularly used to describe dimpled fat tissue on the thighs and buttocks; not recognized in science. p. 402

central obesity excess fat in the abdomen and around the trunk. p. 367

certified lactation consultant a health-care provider, often a registered nurse or a registered dietitian, with specialized training and certification in breast and infant anatomy and physiology who teaches the mechanics of breastfeeding to new mothers. p. 575

certified organic foods foods meeting strict Canadian production regulations, including prohibition of most synthetic pesticides, herbicides, fertilizers, drugs, and preservatives, as well as genetic engineering and irradiation. p. 541

cesarean (see-ZAIR-ee-un) **section** surgical childbirth, in which the infant is taken through an incision in the woman's abdomen. p. 564

chamomile flowers that may provide some limited medical value in soothing menstrual, intestinal, and stomach discomforts. p. 480

chaparral a herbal product made from ground leaves of the creosote bush and sold in tea or capsule form; supposedly, this herb has antioxidant effects, delays aging, "cleanses" the bloodstream, and treats skin conditions—all unproven claims. Chaparral has been found to cause acute toxic hepatitis, a severe liver illness. Deaths reported. p. 480

chelating (KEE-late-ing) **agents** molecules that attract or bind with other molecules and are therefore useful in either preventing or promoting movement of substances from place to place. p. 126

chlorophyll the green pigment of plants that captures energy from sunlight for use in photosynthesis. p. 113

cholesterol (koh-LESS-ter-all) a member of the group of lipids known as sterols; a soft, waxy substance made in the body for a variety of purposes and also found in animal-derived foods. p. 161

cholesterol-free less than 2 mg of cholesterol *and* 2 g or less saturated fat and *trans* fat combined per serving. p. 58

choline (KOH-leen) a nonessential nutrient used to make the phospholipid lecithin and other molecules. p. 280

chromium picolinate a trace element supplement; falsely promoted to increase lean body mass, enhance energy, and burn fat. p. 445

chronic diseases long-duration degenerative diseases characterized by deterioration of the body organs. Examples include heart disease, cancer, and diabetes. p. 3

chylomicrons (KYE-low-MY-krons) clusters formed when lipids from a meal are combined with carrier proteins in the cells of the intestinal lining. Chylomicrons transport food fats through the watery body fluids to the liver and other tissues. p. 170

chyme (KIME) the fluid resulting from the actions of the stomach upon food. p. 88

cirrhosis (seer-OH-sis) advanced liver disease, often associated with alcoholism, in which liver cells have died, hardened, turned an orange colour, and permanently lost their function. p. 101

clone an individual created asexually from a single ancestor, such as a plant grown from a single stem cell; a group of genetically identical individuals descended from a single common ancestor, such as a colony of bacteria arising from a single bacterial cell; in genetics, a replica of a segment of DNA, such as a gene, produced by genetic engineering. p. 541

coenzyme (co-EN-zime) a small molecule that works with an enzyme to promote the enzyme's activity. Many coenzymes have B vitamins as part of their structure (*co* means "with"). p. 267

coenzyme Q10 an enzyme made by cells and important for its role in energy metabolism. With diminished coenzyme Q10 function, oxidative stress increases, as may occur in aging. Preliminary research suggests that it may be of value for treating certain conditions; toxicity in animals appears to be low. No safe intake levels for humans have been established. p. 293

cognitive therapy psychological therapy aimed at changing undesirable behaviours by changing underlying thought processes contributing to these behaviours; in anorexia, a goal is to replace false beliefs about body weight, eating, and self-worth with health-promoting beliefs. p. 406

collagen (COLL-a-jen) the chief protein of most connective tissues, including scars, ligaments, and tendons, and the underlying matrix on which bones and teeth are built. p. 263

colon the large intestine. p. 88

colostrum (co-LAHS-trum) a milklike secretion from the breasts during the first day or so after delivery before milk appears; rich in protective factors. p. 581

comfrey leaves and roots of the comfrey plant are believed, but not proven, to promote cell proliferation. Toxic to the liver in doses ordinarily used. Deaths reported. p. 480

complementary proteins two or more proteins whose amino acid assortments complement each other in such a way that the essential amino acids missing from one are supplied by the other. p. 225

complex carbohydrates long chains of sugar units arranged to form starch or fibre; also called *polysaccharides*. p. 113

concentrated fruit juice sweetener a concentrated sugar syrup made from dehydrated, deflavoured fruit juice, commonly grape juice; used to sweeten products that can then claim to be "all fruit." p. 143

conditionally indispensable/essential amino acid an amino acid that is normally nonessential but must be supplied by the diet in special circumstances when the need for it exceeds the body's ability to produce it. p. 207

confectioner's sugar or **icing sugar** finely powdered sucrose; 99.9 percent pure. p. 143

congeners (CON-jen-ers) chemical substances other than alcohol that account for some of the physiological effects of alcoholic beverages, such as appetite, taste, and after-effects. p. 101

conjugated linoleic acid (CLA) a type of fat in butter, milk, and other dairy products believed by some to have biological activity in the body. Not a phytochemical but a biologically active chemical produced by animals. p. 63

constipation difficult, incomplete, or infrequent bowel movements, associated with discomfort in passing dry, hardened feces from the body. p. 122

contaminant any substance occurring in food by accident; any food constituent that is not normally present. p. 526

control group a group of individuals who are similar in all possible respects to the group being treated in an experiment but who receive a sham treatment instead of the real one. Also called *control subjects*. See also *experimental group* and *intervention studies*. p. 15

corn sweeteners corn syrup and sugar solutions derived from corn. p. 143

corn syrup a syrup, mostly glucose, partly maltose, produced by the action of enzymes on cornstarch. *High-fructose corn syrup* (*HFCS*) is a mixture of fructose, glucose (dextrose), and maltose. p. 143

cornea (KOR-nee-uh) the hard, transparent membrane covering the outside of the eye. p. 247

correlation the simultaneous change of two factors, such as the increase in weight with increasing height (a *direct* or *positive* correlation) or the decrease in cancer incidence with increasing fibre intake (an *inverse* or *negative* correlation). A correlation between two factors suggests that one may cause the other but does not rule out the possibility that both may be caused by chance or by a third factor. p. 15

correspondence school a school that gives home study/career course instruction by mail, sending lessons and exams to the student's home. p. 27

cortex the outermost layer of something. The brain's cortex is the part of the brain where conscious thought takes place. p. 83

cortical bone the ivorylike outer bone layer that forms a shell surrounding trabecular bone and that constitutes the shaft of a long bone. p. 349

creatine a nitrogen-containing compound that combines with phosphate to form a high-energy compound stored in muscle. Claims that creatine safely enhances energy during very high intensity exercise have been well documented; however, there are still reports of digestive side effects. p. 445

cretinism (CREE-tin-ism) severe mental and physical retardation of an infant caused by the mother's iodine deficiency during pregnancy. p. 329

critical period a finite period during development in which certain events may occur that will have irreversible effects on later developmental stages. A critical period is usually a period of cell division in a body organ. p. 558

cross-contamination the contamination of a food through exposure to utensils, hands, or other surfaces that were previously in contact with a contaminated food. p. 512

cruciferous vegetables vegetables with cross-shaped blossoms—the cabbage family. Their intake is associated with low cancer rates in human populations. Examples include broccoli, Brussels sprouts, cabbage, cauliflower, rutabagas, and turnips. p. 486

cuisines styles of cooking. p. 11

cyclamate a zero-Calorie sweetener used with restrictions in Canada and under consideration for use in the United States. p. 151

D

Daily Values nutrient standards that are printed on food labels. Based on nutrient and energy recommendations for a general 2,000-Calorie diet, they allow consumers to compare the nutrient and energy contents of packaged foods. p. 32

degenerative diseases chronic, irreversible diseases characterized by degeneration of body organs due in part to such personal lifestyle elements as poor food choices, smoking, alcohol use, and a lack of physical activity. Also called lifestyle diseases, chronic diseases, or the diseases of old age. p. 459

dehydration loss of water. The symptoms progress rapidly, from thirst to weakness to exhaustion and delirium, and end in death. p. 308

denaturation the irreversible change in a protein's shape brought about by heat, acids, bases, alcohol, salts of heavy metals, or other agents. p. 213

dental caries decay of the teeth (*caries* means "rottenness"). p. 149

desiccated liver dehydrated liver powder that supposedly contains all of the nutrients found in liver in concentrated form; possibly not dangerous but has no particular nutritional merit and is considerably more expensive than fresh liver. p. 445

dextrose an older name for glucose. p. 143

DHEA (dehydroepiandrosterone) a hormone made in the adrenal glands that serves as a precursor to the male hormone testosterone; banned by the U.S. Food and Drug Administration because it poses the risk of life-threatening diseases, including cancer. Falsely promoted to burn fat, build muscle, and slow aging. p. 446

diabetes (dye-uh-BEET-eez) a disease (technically termed *diabetes mellitus*) characterized by elevated blood glucose and inadequate or ineffective insulin, which impairs a person's ability to regulate blood glucose normally. p. 136

dialysis (die-AL-ih-sis) in kidney disease, treatment of the blood to remove toxic substances or metabolic wastes; more properly, hemodialysis, meaning "dialysis of the blood." p. 138

diarrhea frequent, watery bowel movements usually caused by diet, stress, or irritation of the colon. Severe, prolonged diarrhea robs the body of fluid and certain minerals, causing dehydration and imbalances that can be dangerous if left untreated. p. 97

diastolic (dye-as-TOL-ik) **pressure** the second figure in a blood pressure reading (the "lubb" of the heartbeat is heard), which reflects the arterial pressure when the heart is between beats. p. 474

diet the foods (including beverages) a person usually eats and drinks. p. 3

dietary antioxidant (anti-OX-ih-dant) a substance in food that significantly decreases the damaging effects of reactive compounds, such as reactive forms of oxygen and nitrogen on tissue functioning (*anti* means "against"; *oxy* means "oxygen"). p. 175

dietary folate equivalent (DFE) a unit of measure expressing the amount of folate available to the body from naturally occurring sources. The measure mathematically equalizes the difference in absorption between less absorbable food folate and highly absorbable synthetic folate added to enriched foods and found in supplements. p. 274

Dietary Reference Intakes (DRI) reports containing a set of five lists of values for measuring the nutrient intakes of healthy people in Canada and the United States. The five lists are estimated average requirements (EAR), recommended dietary allowances (RDA), adequate intakes (AI), tolerable upper intake levels (UL), and acceptable macronutrient distribution ranges (AMDR). Descriptions of the DRI values are found in Table 2-1. p. 31

dietary supplement a product, other than tobacco, that is added to the diet and contains one of the following ingredients: a vitamin, mineral, herb, botanical (plant extract), amino acid, metabolite, constituent, or extract or a combination of any of these ingredients. p. 7

dietetic technician a person who has completed a two-year academic degree from an accredited college or university and an approved dietetic technician program. p. 26

dietitian a person trained in nutrition, food science, and diet planning. See also *registered dietitian*. p. 26

Dietitians of Canada (DC) the professional organization of dietitians in Canada. p. 26

digest to break molecules into smaller molecules; a main function of the digestive tract with respect to food. p. 86

digestive system the body system composed of organs that break down complex food particles into smaller, absorbable products. The *digestive tract* and *alimentary canal* are names for the tubular organs that extend from the mouth to the anus. The whole system, including the pancreas, liver, and gallbladder, is sometimes called the *gastrointestinal*, or *GI, system*. p. 86

dipeptides (dye-PEP-tides) protein fragments that are two amino acids long (*di* means "two"). p. 214

diploma mill an organization that awards meaningless degrees without requiring its students to meet educational standards. p. 27

disaccharides pairs of single sugars linked together (*di* means "two"). p. 114

discretionary Calorie allowance the balance of Calories remaining in a person's energy allowance after accounting for the number of Calories needed to meet recommended nutrient intakes through consumption of nutrient-dense foods. p. 45

distilled water water that has been vapourized and recondensed, leaving it free of dissolved minerals. p. 314

diuretic (dye-you-RET-ic) a compound, usually a medication, causing increased urinary water excretion; a "water pill." p. 310

diverticula (dye-ver-TIC-you-la) sacs or pouches that balloon out of the intestinal wall, caused by weakening of the muscle layers that encase the intestine. The painful inflammation of one or more of these diverticula is known as *diverticulitis*. p. 122

DNA and **RNA (deoxyribonucleic acid and ribonucleic acid)** the genetic materials of cells necessary in protein synthesis; falsely promoted as ergogenic aids. p. 446

dolomite a compound of minerals (calcium magnesium carbonate) found in limestone and marble. Dolomite is powdered and is sold as a calcium-magnesium supplement but may be contaminated with toxic minerals, is not well absorbed, and interacts adversely with absorption of other essential minerals. p. 356

drink a dose of any alcoholic beverage that delivers 15 mL of pure ethanol. p. 101

drug any substance that when taken into a living organism may modify one or more of its functions. p. 63

drying a method of preserving food by removing sufficient water from the food to inhibit microbial growth. p. 532

dual energy X-ray absorptiometry (absorp-tee-OM-eh-tree) **(DEXA)** a noninvasive method of determining total body fat, fat distribution, and bone density by passing two low-dose X-ray beams through the body. Also used in evaluation of osteoporosis. p. 375

durable/best before date the anticipated amount of time that an unopened food product, when stored under appropriate conditions, will retain its freshness, taste, nutritional value, or any other qualities claimed by the manufacturer. p. 530

dysentery (DISS-en-terry) an infection of the digestive tract that causes diarrhea. p. 228

E

eating disorder a disturbance in eating behaviour that jeopardizes a person's physical or psychological health. p. 406

echinacea (EK-eh-NAY-see-ah) a herb popular before the advent of antibiotics for its "anti-infectious" properties and as an all-purpose remedy, especially for colds and allergy and for healing of wounds. Research is mixed on these claims. An insecticidal property opens questions about safety. Also called coneflower. p. 480

edema (eh-DEEM-uh) swelling of body tissue caused by leakage of fluid from the blood vessels; seen in protein deficiency (among other conditions). p. 218

EDNOS eating disorder not otherwise specified. p. 406

eicosanoids (eye-COSS-ah-noyds) biologically active compounds that regulate body functions. p. 176

electrolytes compounds that partly dissociate in water to form ions, such as the potassium ion (K^+) and the chloride ion (Cl^-). p. 312

electrons parts of an atom; negatively charged particles. Stable atoms (and molecules, which are made of atoms) have even numbers of electrons in pairs. An atom or molecule with an unpaired electron is an unstable free radical. p. 295

elemental diets diets composed of purified ingredients of known chemical composition; intended to supply all essential nutrients to people who cannot eat foods. p. 7

embolism an embolus that causes sudden closure of a blood vessel. p. 465

embolus (EM-boh-luss) a thrombus that breaks loose and travels through the blood vessels (*embol* means "to insert"). p. 465

embryo (EM-bree-oh) the stage of human gestation from the third to the eighth week after conception. p. 555

emergency kitchens programs that provide prepared meals to be eaten on-site; often called *soup kitchens*. p. 652

emetic (em-ETT-ic) an agent that causes vomiting. p. 406

emulsification the process of mixing lipid with water by adding an emulsifier. p. 167

emulsifier (ee-MULL-sih-fire) a compound with both water-soluble and fat-soluble portions that can attract fats and oils into water, combining them. p. 90

endorphins (en-DOOR-fins), **endogenous opiates** compounds of the brain whose actions mimic those of opiate drugs (morphine, heroin) in reducing pain and producing pleasure. In appetite control, endorphins are released on seeing, smelling, or tasting delicious food and are believed to enhance the drive to eat or continue eating. p. 378

endosperm the bulk of the edible part of a grain, the starchy part. p. 124

energy the capacity to do work. The energy in food is chemical energy; it can be converted to mechanical, electrical, heat, or other forms of energy in the body. Food energy is measured in Calories. p. 5

energy density a measure of the energy provided by a food relative to its weight (Calories per gram). p. 394

energy drinks sugar-sweetened beverages with supposedly ergogenic ingredients, such as vitamins, amino acids, caffeine, guarana, carnitine, ginseng, and others. While some are regulated as foods, others are regulated as natural health products. p. 446

energy-yielding nutrients the nutrients the body can use for energy. They may also supply building blocks for body structures. p. 6

enriched the addition of nutrients back to a food that may have been lost during processing, for example, the addition of thiamin, riboflavin, niacin, and iron to bleached wheat flour. Thus, you may see the term *enriched* on certain types of breads or cereals. p. 124

enriched foods and **fortified foods** foods to which nutrients have been added. If the starting material is a whole, basic food such as milk or whole grain, the result may be highly nutritious. If the starting material is a concentrated form of sugar or fat, the result may be less nutritious. p. 9

enterotoxins poisons that act upon mucous membranes, such as those of the digestive tract. p. 505

Environment Canada the federal agency that is responsible for regulating pesticides and establishing water quality standards. p. 504

environmental tobacco smoke (ETS) the combination of exhaled smoke (mainstream smoke) and smoke from lighted cigarettes, pipes, or cigars (sidestream smoke) that enters the air and may be inhaled by other people. p. 569

enzymes (EN-zimes) protein catalysts. A catalyst is a compound that facilitates a chemical reaction without itself being altered in the process. p. 209

EPA, DHA eicosapentaenoic (EYE-cossa-PENTA-ee-NO-ick) acid (20 carbons with 5 double bonds), docosahexaenoic (DOE-cossa-HEXA-ee-NO-ick) acid (22 carbons with 6 double bonds); omega-3 fatty acids made from linolenic acid in our body and available from the tissues of fish and marine oil supplements. p. 177

Ephedra **(ephedrine)** a dangerous and sometimes lethal herbal supplement previously sold for weight loss, muscle building, athletic performance, and other purposes. Although present in small doses in nasal decongestants, the addition of Ephedra to foods is not allowed in Canada, and it is now banned in the United States by the FDA. p. 446

epidemiological studies studies of populations; often used in nutrition to search for correlations between dietary habits and disease incidence; a first step in seeking nutrition-related causes of diseases. p. 15

epinephrine (EP-ih-NEFF-rin) the major hormone that elicits the stress response. p. 83

epiphyseal (eh-PIFF-ih-seal) **plate** a thick, cartilagelike layer that forms new cells that are eventually calcified, lengthening the bone (*epiphysis* means "growing" in Greek). p. 617

epithelial (ep-ith-THEE-lee-ull) **tissue** the layers of the body that serve as selective barriers to environmental factors. Examples are the cornea, the skin, the respiratory tract lining, and the lining of the digestive tract. p. 248

epoetin a drug derived from the human hormone erythropoietin and marketed under the trade name Epogen; illegally used to increase oxygen capacity. p. 446

ergogenic (ER-go-JEN-ic) **aids** products that supposedly enhance performance, although only a small number actually do so (e.g., creatine and caffeine); the term *ergogenic* implies "energy giving" (*ergo* means "work"; *genic* means "give rise to"). p. 446

erythritol, isomalt, lactitol, maltitol, mannitol, sorbitol, xylitol sugar alcohols that can be derived from fruit or commercially produced from a sugar; absorbed more slowly and metabolized differently from other sugars in the human body and not readily used by ordinary mouth bacteria. p. 151

erythrocyte (eh-REETH-ro-sight) **hemolysis** (HE-moh-LIE-sis, he-MOLL-ih-sis) rupture of the red blood cells, caused by vitamin E deficiency (*erythro* means "red"; *cyte* means "cell"; *hemo* means "blood"; *lysis* means "breaking"). p. 258

essential fatty acids fatty acids that the body needs but cannot make in amounts sufficient to meet physiological needs. p. 162

essential nutrients the nutrients the body cannot make for itself (or cannot make fast enough) from other raw materials; nutrients that must be obtained from food to prevent deficiencies. p. 6

estimated average requirements (EAR) the average daily nutrient intake estimated to meet the requirement of half of the healthy individuals in a particular life stage and gender group; used in nutrition research and policymaking and the basis upon which RDA values are set. p. 32

estimated energy requirement (EER) the average dietary energy intake predicted to maintain energy balance in a healthy adult of a certain age, gender, weight, height, and level of physical activity consistent with good health. p. 36

ethanol the alcohol of alcoholic beverages, produced by the action of microorganisms on the carbohydrates of grape juice or other carbohydrate-containing fluids. p. 101

ethnic foods foods associated with particular cultural subgroups within a population. p. 11

euphoria (you-FOR-ee-uh) an inflated sense of well-being and pleasure brought on by a moderate dose of alcohol and some other drugs. p. 101

evaporated cane juice raw sugar from which impurities have been removed. p. 143

exchange system a diet-planning tool that organizes foods with respect to their nutrient contents and Calorie amounts. p. 45

exercise planned, structured, and repetitive bodily movement that promotes or maintains physical fitness. p. 420

experimental group the people or animals participating in an experiment who receive the treatment under investigation. Also called *experimental subjects*. See also *control group* and *intervention studies*. p. 15

expiration date the last day that foods, such as meal replacements, should be consumed. All such foods should be discarded after this date. This term should not be confused with *best-before date* (see above), which applies to most conventional foods. p. 530

extra lean less than 5 g of fat *and* less than 2 g of saturated fat and *trans* fat combined *and* less than 95 mg of cholesterol per serving. p. 187

extracellular fluid fluid residing outside the cells that transports materials to and from the cells. p. 78

extreme obesity clinically severe overweight, presenting very high risks to health; the condition of having a BMI of 40 or above; also called *morbid obesity*. p. 400

extrusion a process by which the form of a food is changed, such as changing corn to corn chips; not a preservation measure. p. 532

F

famine widespread and extreme scarcity of food in an area that causes starvation and death in a large portion of the population. p. 652

fast foods restaurant foods that are available within minutes after customers order them—traditionally, hamburgers, French fries, and milkshakes; more recently, salads and other vegetable dishes as well. These foods may or may not meet people's nutrient needs, depending on the selections made and on the energy allowances and nutrient needs of the eaters. p. 9

fasting hypoglycemia hypoglycemia that occurs after 8 to 14 hours of fasting. p. 140

fat cells cells that specialize in the storage of fat and form the fat tissue. Fat cells also produce enzymes that metabolize fat and hormones involved in appetite and energy balance. p. 77

fat replacers ingredients that replace some or all of the functions of fat and may or may not provide energy. Often used interchangeably with *fat substitutes*, but the latter technically applies only to ingredients that replace all of the functions of fat and provide no energy. p. 184

fatfold test measurement of the thickness of a fold of skin on the back of the arm (over the triceps muscle), below the shoulder blade (subscapular), or in other places, using a caliper (depicted in Figure 9–8); also called *skinfold* test. p. 375

fats lipids that are solid at room temperature (20°C or 68°F). p. 161

fatty acids organic acids composed of carbon chains of various lengths. Each fatty acid has an acid end and hydrogens attached to all of the carbon atoms of the chain. p. 164

fatty liver an early stage of liver deterioration seen in several diseases, including kwashiorkor and alcoholic liver disease, in which fat accumulates in the liver cells. p. 101

FDA (U.S. Food and Drug Administration) the part of the U.S. Department of Health and Human Services' Public Health Service that is responsible for ensuring the safety and wholesomeness of all foods sold in interstate commerce except meat, poultry, and eggs (which are under the jurisdiction of the USDA); inspecting food plants and imported foods; and setting standards for food consumption.

feces waste material remaining after digestion and absorption are complete; eventually discharged from the body. p. 88

female athlete triad a potentially fatal triad of medical problems seen in female athletes: disordered eating, amenorrhea, and osteoporosis. p. 406

fertility the capacity of a woman to produce a normal ovum periodically and of a man to produce normal sperm; the ability to reproduce. p. 555

fetal alcohol syndrome (FAS) the cluster of symptoms including brain damage, growth retardation, mental retardation, and facial abnormalities seen in an infant or child whose mother consumed alcohol during her pregnancy. p. 572

fetus (FEET-us) the stage of human gestation from eight weeks after conception until the birth of an infant. p. 555

feverfew a herb sold as a migraine headache preventive. Some evidence exists to support this claim. p. 480

fibre the indigestible parts of plant foods, largely nonstarch polysaccharides that are not digested by human digestive enzymes, although some are digested by resident bacteria of the colon. Fibres include cellulose, hemicelluloses, pectins, gums, mucilages, and the nonpolysaccharide lignin. p. 116

fibrosis (fye-BROH-sis) an intermediate stage of alcoholic liver deterioration. Liver cells lose their function and assume the characteristics of connective tissue cells (fibres). p. 101

fight-or-flight reaction the body's instinctive hormone- and nerve-mediated reaction to danger. Also known as the *stress response*. p. 83

filtered water water treated by filtration, usually through *activated carbon filters* that reduce the lead in tap water, or by *reverse osmosis* units, which force pressurized water across a membrane, removing lead, arsenic, and some microorganisms from tap water. p. 314

fitness water lightly flavoured bottled water enhanced with vitamins, supposedly to enhance athletic performance. p. 314

flavonoid (FLAY-von-oyd) any member of a chemical family of yellow pigments in foods; phytochemicals that may exert physiological effects on the body. *Flavus* means "yellow." p. 63

flaxseed small brown seed of the flax plant; used in baking, cereals, or other foods; valued by industry as a source of linseed oil and fibre. p. 63

flexibility the capacity of the joints to move through a full range of motion; the ability to bend and recover without injury. p. 423

fluid and electrolyte balance the distribution of fluid and dissolved particles among body compartments. p. 218

fluid and electrolyte imbalance failure to maintain the proper amounts and kinds of fluids and minerals in every body compartment; a medical emergency. p. 313

fluorapatite (floor-APP-uh-tight) a crystal of bones and teeth, formed when fluoride displaces the "hydroxy" portion of hydroxyapatite. Fluorapatite resists being dissolved back into body fluid. p. 315

fluorosis (floor-OH-sis) discoloration of the teeth due to ingestion of too much fluoride during tooth development. p. 339

folate (FOH-late) a B vitamin that acts as part of a coenzyme important in the manufacture of new cells. The form added to foods and supplements is folic acid. p. 272

food medically, any substance that the body can take in and assimilate that will enable it to stay alive and to grow; the carrier of nourishment; socially, a more limited number of such substances defined as acceptable by each culture. p. 3

food aversion an intense dislike of a food, biological or psychological in nature, resulting from an illness or other negative experience associated with that food. p. 611

food banks facilities that collect and distribute food donations to authorized organizations feeding the hungry. p. 652

food group plan a diet-planning tool that sorts foods into groups based on their nutrient content and then specifies that people should eat certain minimum numbers of servings of foods from each group. p. 45

food insecurity the condition of limited or uncertain access to food of sufficient quality or quantity to sustain a healthy, active life. p. 652

food intolerance an adverse reaction to a food or food additive not involving an immune response. p. 611

food pantries community food collection programs that provide groceries to be prepared and eaten at home. p. 652

food poverty hunger occurring when enough food exists in an area but some of the people cannot obtain it because they lack money, are being deprived for political reasons, live in a country at war, or suffer from other problems such as lack of transportation. p. 652

food recovery collecting wholesome surplus food for distribution to low-income people who are hungry. p. 656

food security reliable access to enough nutritious food at all times to sustain a healthy, active life. p. 652

food shortage hunger occurring when an area of the world lacks enough total food to feed its people. p. 652

foodborne illness illness transmitted to human beings through food and water; caused by an infectious agent (*foodborne infection*) or a poisonous substance (*food intoxication*). Also called *food poisoning*. p. 505

foodways the sum of a culture's habits, customs, beliefs, and preferences concerning food. p. 11

fork thermometer a utensil combining a meat fork and an instant-read food thermometer. p. 512

formaldehyde a substance to which methanol is metabolized on the way to being converted to harmless waste products that can be excreted. p. 101

fortified the addition of nutrients to foods that did not contain them initially, for example, orange juice to which calcium was added. Thus, you may see the term *fortified* on such beverages. p. 124

foxglove a plant that contains a substance used in the heart medicine digoxin. p. 408

fraud or **quackery** the promotion, for financial gain, of devices, treatments, services, plans, or products (including diets and supplements) that alter or claim to alter a human condition without proof of safety or effectiveness. (The word *quackery* comes from the term *quacksalver*, meaning a person who quacks loudly about a miracle product—a lotion or a salve.) p. 21

free, without, no, zero none or a trivial amount. *Calorie free* means containing fewer than 5 Calories per serving; *sugar free* or *fat free* means containing less than half a gram per serving.

free radicals atoms or molecules with one or more unpaired electrons that make the atom or molecule unstable and highly reactive. p. 256

freezing a method of preserving food by lowering the food's temperature to a point that halts life processes. Microorganisms do not die but remain dormant until the food is thawed. p. 531

fresh raw, unprocessed, or minimally processed with no added preservatives.

fructose (FROOK-tose) a monosaccharide, sometimes known as fruit sugar (*fruct* means "fruit"; *ose* means "sugar"). p. 115

fructose, galactose, glucose the monosaccharides. p. 143

fruitarian includes only raw or dried fruit, seeds, and nuts in the diet. p. 235

functional foods defined by Health Canada as foods that appear similar to conventional foods, consumed as part of the usual diet, with demonstrated physiological benefits or with the ability to reduce chronic disease risks beyond basic nutrient functions. p. 63

G

galactose (ga-LACK-tose) a monosaccharide, part of the disaccharide lactose (milk sugar). p. 175

garlic oil an extract of garlic; may or may not contain the chemicals associated with garlic; claims for health benefits unproven. p. 293

gastric juice the digestive secretion of the stomach. p. 84

gastroesophageal (GAS-tro-eh-SOFF-ah-jee-al) **reflux disease (GERD)** a severe and chronic splashing of stomach acid and enzymes into the esophagus, throat, mouth, or airway that causes inflammation and injury to those organs. Untreated GERD may increase the risk of esophageal cancer; treatment may require surgery or management with medication. p. 97

gatekeeper with respect to nutrition, a key person who controls other people's access to foods and thereby affects their nutrition profoundly. Examples are the spouse who buys and cooks the food, the parent who feeds the children, and the caretaker in a daycare centre. p. 621

GE foods genetically engineered foods; food plants and animals altered by way of rDNA technology. p. 541

gelatin a soluble form of the protein collagen, used to thicken foods; sometimes falsely promoted as a strength enhancer. p. 446

generally recognized as safe (GRAS) list a list, established by the U.S. FDA, of food additives long in use and believed to be safe. p. 533

genes units of a cell's inheritance, made of the chemical DNA (deoxyribonucleic acid). Each gene directs the making of one or more proteins, which perform important tasks in the body. p. 4

genetic engineering (GE) the direct, intentional manipulation of the genetic material of living things in order to obtain some desirable trait not present in the original organism. Also called *recombinant DNA technology and biotechnology*. p. 541

genetic modification intentional changes to the genetic material of living things brought about through a range of methods, including rDNA technology, natural cross-breeding, and agricultural selective breeding. p. 541

genistein (GEN-ih-steen) a phytoestrogen found primarily in soybeans that both mimics and blocks the action of estrogen in the body. p. 63

genome (GEE-nome) the full complement of genetic material in the chromosomes of a cell. The study of genomes is *genomics*. p. 4

germ the nutrient-rich inner part of a grain. p. 124

germander an evergreen bush used in small quantities as a flavouring for alcoholic beverages. Recommended for gout and other ills, it causes often-irreversible liver damage and abnormalities. Deaths reported. p. 480

gestation the period of about 40 weeks (three trimesters) from conception to birth; the term of a pregnancy. p. 556

gestational diabetes abnormal glucose tolerance appearing during pregnancy. p. 574

ghrelin (GREH-lin) a hormone released by the stomach that signals the hypothalamus of the brain to stimulate eating. p. 377

ginkgo biloba an extract of a tree of the same name, claimed to enhance mental alertness but not proven to be effective or safe. p. 480

ginseng (JIN-seng) a plant root containing chemicals that have stimulant drug effects. Ginseng abuse syndrome is a group of symptoms associated with the overuse of ginseng, including high blood pressure, insomnia, nervousness, confusion, and depression. p. 480

glandular products extracts or preparations of raw animal glands and organs; sold with the false claim of boosting athletic performance but may present disease hazards if collected from infected animals. p. 446

glucagon (GLOO-cah-gon) a hormone secreted by the pancreas that stimulates the liver to release glucose into the blood when blood glucose concentration dips. p. 132

glucose (GLOO-cose) a single sugar used in both plant and animal tissues for energy, sometimes known as blood sugar or *dextrose*. p. 113

glucose polymers compounds that supply glucose, not as single molecules, but linked in chains somewhat like starch. The objective is to attract less water from the body into the digestive tract. p. 442

glutamine a conditionally indispensable amino acid, promoted as an ergogenic aid to assist in muscle cell repair after exercise and to maintain or boost immune function. p. 446

glycemic index (GI) a ranking of foods according to their potential for raising blood glucose relative to a standard such as glucose or white bread. p. 134

glycemic load a mathematical expression of both the glycemic index and the carbohydrate content of a food, meal, or diet (glycemic index multiplied by grams of carbohydrate). p. 134

glycerol (GLISS-er-all) an organic compound, three carbons long, of interest here because it serves as the backbone for triglycerides. p. 164

glycine a nonessential amino acid, promoted as an ergogenic aid because it is a precursor of creatine. p. 446

glycogen (GLY-co-gen) a highly branched polysaccharide composed of glucose that is made and stored by liver and muscle tissues of human beings and animals as a storage form of glucose. Glycogen is not a significant food source of carbohydrate and is not counted as one of the complex carbohydrates in foods. p. 116

glycolysis an important metabolic pathway in the cytoplasm of our cells that releases a small amount of energy by splitting glucose in half. p. 131

goitre (GOY-ter) enlargement of the thyroid gland due to iodine deficiency is *simple goitre*; enlargement due to an iodine excess is *toxic goitre*. p. 328

good source 10–19 percent of the Daily Value per serving.

good source of fibre 2.5–4.9 g per serving.

gout (GOWT) a painful form of arthritis caused by the abnormal buildup of the waste product uric acid in the blood, with uric acid salt deposited as crystals in the joints. p. 101

grams units of mass. A gram (g) is the mass of a cubic centimetre (cc) or millilitre (mL) of water under defined conditions of temperature and pressure. About 28 grams equals an ounce. p. 7

granulated sugar common table sugar, crystalline sucrose, 99.9 percent pure. p. 143

granules small grains. Starch granules are packages of starch molecules. Various plant species make starch granules of varying shapes. p. 116

green pills, fruit pills pills containing dehydrated, crushed vegetable or fruit matter. An advertisement may claim that each pill equals a pound of fresh produce, but, in reality, a pill may equal one small forkful—minus nutrient losses incurred in processing. p. 293

grehlin a hormone secreted by the stomach that is thought to be a "hunger hormone." p. 85

ground water water that comes from underground aquifers. p. 312

growth hormone a hormone (somatotropin) that promotes growth and is produced naturally in the pituitary gland of the brain. p. 525

growth hormone releasers herbs or pills that supposedly regulate hormones; falsely promoted as enhancing athletic performance. p. 446

growth spurt the marked rapid gain in physical size usually evident around the onset of adolescence. p. 617

guarana a reddish berry found in Brazil's Amazon basin that contains seven times as much caffeine as its relative, the coffee bean. It is used as an ingredient in carbonated sodas, and, taken in powder or tablet form, it supposedly enhances speed and endurance and serves as an aphrodisiac, a "cardiac tonic," an "intestinal disinfectant," and a "smart drug" touted to improve mental functions. High doses may stress the heart and can cause panic attacks. p. 446

H

hard water water with high calcium and magnesium concentrations. p. 311

hazard a state of danger; used to refer to any circumstance in which harm is possible under normal conditions of use. p. 504

Hazard Analysis Critical Control Point (HACCP) a systematic plan to identify and correct potential microbial hazards in the manufacturing, distribution, and commercial use of food products. *HACCP* may be pronounced "HASS-ip." p. 509

health claims claims linking food constituents with disease states; allowable on labels within the criteria established by Health Canada. p. 55

healthy low in fat, saturated fat, *trans* fat, cholesterol, and sodium and containing at least 10 percent of the Daily Value for vitamin A, vitamin C, iron, calcium, protein, or fibre.

Healthy Eating Index (HEI) a dietary assessment tool that evaluates a diet's adherence to the principles of the USDA Food Guide and the *Dietary Guidelines for Americans*, as well as the variety of foods the diet contains. p. 54

heart attack the event in which the vessels that feed the heart muscle become closed off by an embolism, thrombus, or other cause with resulting sudden tissue death. A heart attack is also called a *myocardial infarction* (*myo* means "muscle"; *cardial* means "of the heart"; *infarct* means "tissue death"). p. 466

heartburn a burning sensation in the chest (in the area of the heart) area caused by backflow of stomach acid into the esophagus. p. 95

heat stroke an acute and life-threatening reaction to heat buildup in the body. p. 437

heavy metal any of a number of mineral ions such as mercury and lead; so called because they are of relatively high atomic weight. Many heavy metals are poisonous. p. 527

heme (HEEM) the iron-containing portion of the hemoglobin and myoglobin molecules. p. 334

hemlock any part of the hemlock plant, which causes severe pain, convulsions, and death within 15 minutes. p. 480

hemoglobin (HEEM-oh-globe-in) the oxygen-carrying protein of the blood; found in the red blood cells (*hemo* means "blood"; *globin* means "spherical protein"). p. 330

hemorrhoids (HEM-or-oids) swollen, hardened (varicose) veins in the rectum, usually caused by the pressure resulting from constipation. p. 122

herbal medicine use of herbs and other natural substances with the intention of preventing or curing diseases or relieving symptoms. p. 479

herbal steroids or **plant sterols** mixtures of compounds from herbs that supposedly enhance human hormone activity. Products marketed as herbal steroids include astragalus, damiana, dong quai, fo ti teng, ginseng root, licorice root, palmetto berries, sarsaparilla, schizardra, unicorn root, yohimbe bark, and yucca. p. 446

hernia a protrusion of an organ or part of an organ through the wall of the body chamber that normally contains the organ. An example is a *hiatal* (high-AY-tal) *hernia*, in which part of the stomach protrudes up through the diaphragm into the chest cavity, which contains the esophagus, heart, and lungs. p. 96

hiccups spasms of both the vocal cords and the diaphragm, causing periodic, audible, short, inhaled coughs. Can be caused by irritation of the diaphragm, indigestion, or other causes. Hiccups usually resolve in a few minutes but can have serious effects if prolonged. Breathing into a paper bag (inhaling carbon dioxide) or dissolving a teaspoon of sugar in the mouth may stop them. p. 95

high-carbohydrate energy drinks fruit-flavoured commercial beverages used to restore muscle glycogen after exercise or as a pregame beverage. p. 431

high-density lipoproteins (HDL) lipoproteins that return cholesterol from the tissues to the liver for dismantling and disposal; contain a large proportion of protein. p. 171

high fibre 5 g or more per serving. (Foods making high-fibre claims must fit the definition of low fat, or the level of total fat must appear next to the high-fibre claim.) p. 57

high in 20 percent or more of the Daily Value for a given nutrient per serving; synonyms include "rich in" or "excellent source."

high-quality proteins dietary proteins containing all of the essential amino acids in relatively the same amounts that human beings require. They may also contain dispensable/nonessential amino acids. p. 223

high-temperature–short-time (HTST) principle the rule that every 10°C (18°F) rise in processing temperature brings about an approximately tenfold increase in microbial destruction while only doubling nutrient losses. p. 531

histamine a substance that participates in causing inflammation; produced by cells of the immune system as part of a local immune reaction to an antigen. p. 609

HMB (beta-hydroxy-beta-methyl-butyrate) a metabolite of the branched-chain amino acid leucine. Claims that HMB increases muscle mass and strength stem from "evidence" from the company that developed HMB as a supplement. p. 446

homocysteine (hoe-moe-SIS-teen) an amino acid produced as an intermediate compound during amino acid metabolism. A buildup of homocysteine in the blood is associated with deficiencies of folate and other B vitamins and may increase the risk of diseases. p. 278

honey a concentrated solution primarily composed of glucose and fructose, produced by enzymatic digestion of the sucrose in nectar by bees. p. 143

hormones chemicals that are secreted by glands into the blood in response to conditions in the body that require regulation. These chemicals serve as messengers, acting on other organs to maintain constant conditions. p. 82

human growth hormone (HGH) a hormone produced by the brain's pituitary gland that regulates normal growth and development (see text discussion); also called somatotropin. p. 446

hunger lack or shortage of basic foods needed to provide the energy and nutrients that support health. p. 652

hunger the physiological need to eat, experienced as a drive for obtaining food; an unpleasant sensation that demands relief. p. 377

husk the outer, inedible part of a grain. p. 124

hydrogenation (high-dro-gen-AY-shun) the process of adding hydrogen to unsaturated fatty acids to make fat more solid and resistant to the chemical change of oxidation. p. 180

hydroxyapatite (hi-DROX-ee-APP-uh-tight) the chief crystal of bone, formed from calcium and phosphorus. p. 315

hyperactivity (in children) a syndrome characterized by inattention, impulsiveness, and excessive motor activity; usually diagnosed

before age 7, lasts six months or more, and usually does not entail mental illness or mental retardation. Properly called *attention-deficit/hyperactivity disorder* (*ADHD*) and may be associated with minimal brain damage. p. 612

hypertension high blood pressure. p. 323

hypertrophy (high-PURR-tro-fee) an increase in size (e.g., of a muscle) in response to use. p. 423

hypoallergenic formulas clinically tested infant formulas that do not provoke reactions in 90 percent of infants or children with confirmed cow's milk allergy. p. 581

hypoglycemia (HIGH-poh-gly-SEE-mee-uh) a blood glucose concentration below normal, a symptom that may indicate any of several diseases, including impending diabetes. p. 140

hyponatremia (HIGH-poh-na-TREE-mee-ah) a decreased concentration of sodium in the blood (*hypo* means "below"; *natrium* means "sodium [Na]"; *emia* means "blood"). p. 439

hypothalamus (high-poh-THAL-uh-mus) a part of the brain that senses a variety of conditions in the blood, such as temperature, glucose content, salt content, and others. It signals other parts of the brain or body to adjust those conditions when necessary. p. 83

hypothermia a below-normal body temperature. p. 438

I

immune system a system of tissues and organs that defend the body against antigens, foreign materials that have penetrated the skin or body linings. p. 84

immunity protection from or resistance to a disease or infection by development of antibodies and by the actions of cells and tissues in response to a threat. p. 218

impaired glucose tolerance blood glucose levels higher than normal but not high enough to be diagnosed as diabetes; sometimes called *prediabetes*. p. 138

implantation the stage of development, during the first two weeks after conception, in which the fertilized egg (fertilized ovum or zygote) embeds itself in the wall of the uterus and begins to develop. p. 557

incidental additives substances that can get into food not through intentional introduction but as a result of contact with the food during growing, processing, packaging, storing, or some other stage before the food is consumed. Also called *accidental* or *indirect additives*. p. 536

indispensable/essential amino acids amino acids that either cannot be synthesized at all by the body or cannot be synthesized in amounts sufficient to meet physiological need. p. 207

infectious diseases diseases that are caused by bacteria, viruses, parasites, and other microbes and can be transmitted from one person to another through air, water, or food; by contact; or through vector organisms such as mosquitoes and fleas. p. 459

infomercials feature-length television commercials that follow the format of regular programs but are intended to convince viewers to buy products and not to educate or entertain them. The statements made may or may not be accurate. p. 21

initiation an event, probably occurring in a cell's genetic material, caused by radiation or by a chemical carcinogen that can give rise to cancer. p. 482

inosine an organic chemical that is falsely said to "activate cells, produce energy, and facilitate exercise." Studies have shown that it actually reduces the endurance of runners. p. 446

inositol (in-OSS-ih-tall) a nonessential nutrient found in cell membranes. p. 280

insoluble fibres the tough, fibrous structures of fruit, vegetables, and grains; indigestible food components that do not dissolve in water. p. 117

instant-read thermometer (e.g., tip-sensitive digital thermometer) a thermometer that, when inserted into food, measures its temperature within seconds; designed to test temperature of food at intervals and not to be left in food during cooking. p. 512

insulin a hormone secreted by the pancreas in response to a high blood glucose concentration. It assists cells in drawing glucose from the blood. p. 132

insulin resistance a condition in which a normal or high level of insulin produces a less-than-normal response by the tissues; thought to be a metabolic consequence of obesity. p. 137

integrated pest management (IPM) management of pests using a combination of natural and biological controls and minimal or no application of pesticides. p. 669

intervention studies studies of populations in which observation is accompanied by experimental manipulation of some population members—for example, a study in which half of the subjects (the *experimental subjects*) follow diet advice to reduce fat intakes while the other half (the *control subjects*) do not, and both groups' heart health is monitored. p. 15

intestine the body's long, tubular organ of digestion and the site of nutrient absorption. p. 80

intracellular fluid fluid residing inside the cells that provides the medium for cellular reactions. p. 80

intrinsic factor a factor found inside a system. The intrinsic factor necessary to prevent pernicious anemia is now known to be a compound that helps in the absorption of vitamin B_{12}. p. 276

invert sugar a mixture of glucose and fructose formed by the splitting of sucrose in an industrial process. Sold only in liquid form and sweeter than sucrose, invert sugar forms during certain cooking procedures and works to prevent crystallization of sucrose in soft candies and sweets. p. 143

ions (EYE-ons) electrically charged particles, such as sodium (positively charged) and chloride (negatively charged). p. 312

iron deficiency the condition of having depleted iron stores, which, at the extreme, causes iron-deficiency anemia. p. 331

iron-deficiency anemia a form of anemia caused by a lack of iron and characterized by red blood cell shrinkage and colour loss. Accompanying symptoms are weakness, apathy, headaches, pallor, intolerance to cold, and inability to pay attention. p. 331

iron overload the state of having more iron in the body than it needs or can handle, usually arising from a hereditary defect. Also called *hemochromatosis*. p. 332

irradiation the application of ionizing radiation to foods to reduce insect infestation or microbial contamination or to slow the ripening or sprouting process. Also called cold pasteurization. p. 519

irritable bowel syndrome intermittent disturbance of bowel function, especially diarrhea or alternating diarrhea and constipation; associated with diet, lack of physical activity, or psychological stress. p. 98

isomalt, lactitol, maltitol, mannitol, sorbitol, xylitol sugar alcohols that can be derived from fruits or commercially produced from a sugar; absorbed more slowly and metabolized differently from other sugars in the human body and not readily used by ordinary mouth bacteria. p. 151

IU (international unit) a measure of fat-soluble vitamin activity sometimes used on supplement labels. p. 251

J

jaundice (JAWN-dis) yellowing of the skin due to spillover of the bile pigment bilirubin (bill-ee-ROO-bin) from the liver into the general circulation. p. 262

K

kava the root of a tropical pepper plant, often brewed as a tea consumed for its calming effects. Limited scientific research supports use for anxiety relief. Adverse effects include skin rash, liver abnormalities, lethargy, and mental disorientation. p. 480

kefir (KEE-fur) a liquid form of yogurt, based on milk, probiotic microorganisms, and flavourings. p. 346

kelp tablets tablets made from dehydrated kelp, a kind of seaweed used by the Japanese as a foodstuff. p. 293

keratin (KERR-uh-tin) the normal protein of hair and nails. p. 248

keratinization accumulation of keratin in a tissue; a sign of vitamin A deficiency. p. 248

ketone bodies acidic compounds derived from fat and certain amino acids. Normally rare in the blood, they help feed the brain during times when too little carbohydrate is available. p. 385

ketosis (kee-TOE-sis) an undesirable high concentration of ketone bodies, such as acetone, in the blood or urine. p. 132

kidneys a pair of organs that filter wastes from the blood, make urine, and release it to the bladder for excretion from the body. p. 80

kombucha (KOM-boo-sha) a product of fermentation of sugar-sweetened tea by various yeasts and bacteria. Proclaimed as a treatment for everything from AIDS to cancer but lacking scientific evidence. Microorganisms in home-brewed kombucha have caused serious illnesses in people with weakened immunity. Also known as Manchurian tea, mushroom tea, or Kargasok tea. p. 480

Krebs cycle an important metabolic pathway in the mitochondria of our cells from which we derive most of the energy from molecules like glucose and fatty acids. p. 131

kudzu a weedy vine, whose roots are harvested and used by Chinese herbalists as a treatment for alcoholism. Kudzu reportedly reduces alcohol absorption by up to 50 percent in rats. p. 480

kwashiorkor (kwash-ee-OR-core, kwashee-or-CORE) a disease related to protein malnutrition, with a set of recognizable symptoms, such as edema. p. 227

L

laboratory studies studies that are performed under tightly controlled conditions and are designed to pinpoint causes and effects. Such studies often use animals as subjects. p. 15

lactase the intestinal enzyme that splits the disaccharide lactose to the monosaccharides glucose and galactose during digestion. p. 130

lactation production and secretion of breast milk for the purpose of nourishing an infant. p. 557

lactic acid a compound produced during the breakdown of glucose in anaerobic metabolism and produced by red blood cells under aerobic conditions. p. 428

lacto-ovo vegetarian includes dairy products, eggs, vegetables, grains, legumes, fruit, and nuts; excludes flesh and seafood. p. 235

lacto-vegetarian includes dairy products, vegetables, grains, legumes, fruit, and nuts; excludes flesh, seafood, and eggs. p. 235

lactoferrin (lack-toe-FERR-in) a factor in breast milk that binds iron and keeps it from supporting the growth of the infant's intestinal bacteria. p. 580

lactose a disaccharide composed of glucose and galactose; sometimes known as milk sugar (*lact* means "milk"; *ose* means "sugar"). p. 115

lactose intolerance impaired ability to digest lactose due to reduced amounts of the enzyme lactase. p. 130

lactose, maltose, sucrose the disaccharides. p. 143

large Intestine the portion of the intestine that completes the absorption process. p. 88

lean on a food label, less than 10 g of fat *and* less than 4 g of saturated fat and *trans* fat combined *and* less than 95 mg of cholesterol per serving.

learning disability a condition resulting in an altered ability to learn basic cognitive skills such as reading, writing, and mathematics. p. 612

leavened (LEV-end) literally, "lightened" by yeast cells, which digest some carbohydrate components of the dough and leave behind bubbles of gas that make the bread rise. p. 336

lecithin (LESS-ih-thin) a phospholipid manufactured by the liver and also found in many foods; a major constituent of cell membranes. p. 162

legumes (leg-GOOMS, LEG-yooms) beans, peas, and lentils, valued as inexpensive sources of protein, vitamins, minerals, and fibre that contribute little fat to the diet. p. 10

leptin an appetite-suppressing hormone produced in the fat cells that conveys information about body fatness to the brain; believed to be involved in the maintenance of body composition (*leptos* means "slender"). p. 379

less, fewer, reduced containing at least 25 percent less of a nutrient or Calories than a reference food. This may occur naturally or as a result of altering the food. For example, pretzels, which are usually low in fat, can claim to provide less fat than potato chips, a comparable food.

less saturated fat 25 percent or less saturated fat and *trans* fat combined than the comparison food.

levulose an older name for fructose. p. 143

licence to practice permission under provincial or federal law, granted on meeting specified criteria, to use a certain title (such as *dietitian*) and to offer certain services. Licensed dietitians may use the initials L.D. after their names. p. 25

life expectancy the average number of years lived by people in a given society. p. 622

life span the maximum number of years of life attainable by a member of a species. p. 622

lignans phytochemicals present in flaxseed, but not in flax oil, that are converted to phytosterols by intestinal bacteria and are under study as possible anticancer agents. p. 63

limiting amino acid an essential amino acid that is present in dietary protein in an insufficient amount, thereby limiting the body's ability to build protein. p. 223

linoleic (lin-oh-LAY-ic) **acid** (an omega-6 fatty acid) and **linolenic** (lin-oh-LEN-ic) **acid** (an omega-3 fatty acid) polyunsaturated fatty acids that are essential nutrients for human beings. The full name of linolenic acid is *alphalinolenic acid*. p. 176

lipids (LIP-ids) a family of organic (carbon-containing) compounds soluble in organic solvents but not in water. Lipids include triglycerides (fats and oils), phospholipids, and sterols. p. 161

lipoic (lip-OH-ic) **acid** a nonessential nutrient. p. 280

lipoprotein lipase (LPL) an enzyme mounted on the surface of fat cells that splits triglycerides in the blood into fatty acids and glycerol to be absorbed into the cells for reassembly and storage. p. 381

lipoproteins (LYE-poh-PRO-teens, LIH-poh-PRO-teens) clusters of lipids associated with protein, which serve as transport vehicles for lipids in blood and lymph. Major lipoprotein classes are the chylomicrons, the VLDL, the LDL, and the HDL. p. 170

listeriosis a serious foodborne infection that can cause severe illness, especially in the young and older individuals, and brain infection or death in a fetus or a newborn; caused by the bacterium *Listeria monocytogenes*, which is found in soil and water. p. 570

liver a large, lobed organ that lies just under the ribs. It filters the blood, removes and processes nutrients, manufactures materials for export to other parts of the body, destroys toxins or stores them to keep them out of the circulation, and excretes fat-soluble waste products into the small intestine. p. 80

lobelia (low-BEE-lee-uh) dried leaves and tops of lobelia ("Indian tobacco") plant are used to induce vomiting or treat a cough; abused for a mild euphoria. Causes breathing difficulty, rapid pulse, low blood pressure, diarrhea, dizziness, and tremors. Possible deaths reported. p. 480

longevity long duration of life. p. 622

low birthweight a birthweight of less than 2,500 g (5½ lb); used as a predictor of probable health problems in the newborn and as a probable indicator of poor nutrition status of the mother before and/or during pregnancy.

Low-birthweight infants are of two different types. Some are *premature infants*; they are born early and are the right size for their gestational age. Other low-birthweight infants have suffered growth failure in the uterus; they are small for gestational age (small for date) and may or may not be premature. p. 556

low Calorie 40 Calories or fewer per serving.

low cholesterol 20 mg or less of cholesterol and 2 g or less saturated fat per serving.

low-density lipoproteins (LDL) lipoproteins that transport lipids from the liver to other tissues such as muscle and fat; contain a large proportion of cholesterol. p. 171

low fat 3 g or less fat per serving.

low saturated fat 1 g or less saturated fat and less than 0.5 g of *trans* fat per serving.

low sodium 140 mg or less sodium per serving.

lungs the body's organs of gas exchange. Blood circulating through the lungs releases its carbon dioxide and picks up fresh oxygen to carry to the tissues. p. 80

lutein (LOO-teen) a plant pigment of yellow hue; a phytochemical believed to play roles in eye functioning and health. p. 63

lycopene (LYE-koh-peen) a pigment responsible for the red colour of tomatoes and other red-hued vegetables; a phytochemical that may act as an antioxidant in the body. p. 63

lymph (LIMF) the fluid that moves from the bloodstream into tissue spaces and then travels in its own vessels, which eventually drain back into the bloodstream. p. 78

lymphocytes (LIM-foh-sites) white blood cells that participate in the immune response: B-cells and T-cells. p. 84

M

ma huang a herbal preparation sold with promises of weight loss and increased energy but containing ephedrine, a banned cardiac stimulant with serious adverse effects. p. 446

macrobiotic diet a vegan diet composed mostly of whole grains, beans, and certain vegetables; taken to extremes, macrobiotic diets have resulted in malnutrition and even death. p. 235

macrophages (MACK-roh-fah-jes) large scavenger cells of the immune system that engulf debris and remove it (*macro* means "large"; *phagein* means "to eat"). p. 464

macular degeneration a common, progressive loss of function of the part of the retina that is most crucial to focused vision. This degeneration often leads to blindness. p. 253

major minerals essential mineral nutrients found in the human body in amounts larger than 5 grams. p. 305

malnutrition any condition caused by excess or deficient food energy or nutrient intake or by an imbalance of nutrients. Nutrient or energy deficiencies are classed as forms of undernutrition; nutrient or energy excesses are classed as forms of overnutrition. p. 3

maltose a disaccharide composed of two glucose units, sometimes known as malt *sugar*. p. 115

maple sugar a concentrated solution of sucrose derived from the sap of the sugar maple tree, mostly sucrose. This sugar was once common but is now usually replaced by sucrose and artificial maple flavouring. p. 143

marasmus (ma-RAZ-mus) the Calorie-deficiency disease; starvation. p. 227

margin of safety in reference to food additives, a zone between the concentration normally used and that at which a hazard exists. For common table salt, for example, the margin of safety is 1/5 (five times the concentration normally used would be hazardous). p. 533

medical nutrition therapy nutrition services used in the treatment of injury, illness, or other conditions; includes assessment of nutrition status and dietary intake and corrective applications of diet, counselling, and other nutrition services. p. 26

melatonin a hormone of the pineal gland believed to help regulate the body's daily rhythms, to reverse the effects of jet lag, and to promote sleep. Claims for life extension or enhancement of sexual prowess are without merit. p. 293

MEOS (microsomal ethanol oxidizing system) a system of enzymes in the liver that oxidize not only alcohol but also several classes of drugs. p. 101

metabolism the sum of all physical and chemical changes taking place in living cells; includes all reactions by which the body obtains and spends the energy from food. p. 83

metastasis (meh-TASS-ta-sis) movement of cancer cells from one body part to another, usually by way of the body fluids. p. 482

methanol an alcohol continuously produced in the body by all cells. p. 101

methylmercury any toxic compound of mercury to which a characteristic chemical structure, a methyl group, has been added, usually by bacteria in aquatic sediments. Methylmercury is easily absorbed from the intestine and causes nerve damage in people. p. 528

MFP factor a factor present in meat, fish, and poultry that enhances the absorption of nonheme iron present in the same foods or in other foods eaten at the same time. p. 334

micelles spheres of lipids that form in the aqueous medium of the small intestine; with the help of bile, lipids become emulsified. p. 168

microbes a shortened name for *microorganisms*; minute organisms too small to observe without a microscope, including bacteria, viruses, and others. p. 84

microorganisms bacteria, viruses, or other organisms invisible to the naked eye, some of which cause diseases. Also called *microbes*. p. 505

microvilli (MY-croh-VILL-ee, MY-croh-VILL-eye) tiny, hairlike projections on each cell of every villus that greatly expand the surface area available to trap nutrient particles and absorb them into the cells (singular: *microvillus*). p. 93

milk anemia iron-deficiency anemia caused by drinking so much milk that iron-rich foods are displaced from the diet. p. 584

mineral water water from a spring or well that typically contains 250 to 500 parts per million (ppm) of minerals. Minerals give water a distinctive flavour. Many mineral waters are high in sodium; read the Nutrition Facts table on bottled water labels. p. 314

minerals naturally occurring, inorganic, homogeneous substances; chemical elements. p. 305

miso fermented soybean paste used in Japanese cooking. Soy products are considered to be functional foods. p. 63

moderate drinkers people who do not drink excessively and do not behave inappropriately because of alcohol. A moderate drinker's health is not harmed by alcohol over the long term. p. 101

moderation the dietary characteristic of providing constituents within set limits, not to excess. p. 9

modified atmosphere packaging (MAP) a preservation technique in which a perishable food is packaged in a gas-impermeable container from which air has been removed or to which another gas mixture has been added. p. 530

molasses a syrup left over from the refining of sucrose from sugar cane; a thick, brown syrup. The major nutrient in molasses is iron, a contaminant from the machinery used in processing it. p. 143

monoglycerides (mon-oh-GLISS-er-ides) products of the digestion of lipids; consist of glycerol molecules with one remaining fatty acid attached (*mono* means "one"; *glyceride* means "a compound of glycerol"). p. 168

monosaccharides (mon-oh-SACK-ah-rides) single sugar units (*mono* means "one"; *saccharide* means "sugar unit"). p. 114

monounsaturated fats triglycerides in which most of the fatty acids have one point of unsaturation (are monounsaturated). p. 166

monounsaturated fatty acid (MUFA) a fatty acid containing one point of unsaturation. p. 165

more or **added fibre** at least 2.5 g more per serving than a reference food.

more, extra at least 10 percent more of the Daily Value than in a reference food. The nutrient may be added or may occur naturally.

MSG symptom complex the acute, temporary, and self-limiting reactions experienced by sensitive people upon ingesting a large dose of MSG. The name *MSG symptom complex*, given by the U.S. FDA, replaces the former *Chinese restaurant syndrome*. p. 536

mucus (MYOO-cus) a slippery coating of the digestive tract lining (and other body linings) that protects the cells from exposure to digestive juices (and other destructive agents). The adjective form is *mucous* (same pronunciation). The digestive tract lining is a *mucous membrane*. p. 90

muscle endurance the ability of a muscle to contract repeatedly within a given time without becoming exhausted. p. 423

muscle strength the ability of muscles to work against resistance. p. 423

mutual supplementation the strategy of combining two incomplete protein sources so that the amino acids in one food make up for those lacking in the other food. Such protein combinations are sometimes called *complementary proteins*. p. 225

myoglobin (MYE-oh-globe-in) the oxygen-holding protein of the muscles (*myo* means "muscle"). p. 330

N

natural foods a term that has no legal definition but is often used to imply wholesomeness. p. 9

natural health products (NHP) defined by Health Canada to include homeopathic preparations; substances used in traditional medicines (e.g., herbal remedies); minerals or trace elements; vitamins; amino acid; essential fatty acids; or other botanical, animal-, or microorganism-derived (e.g., probiotics) substances. These products are generally sold in medicinal or "dosage" form to diagnose, treat, or prevent disease; restore or correct function; or maintain or promote health. As a product group, NHPs include nutraceuticals. p. 64

natural water water obtained from a spring or well that is certified to be safe and sanitary. The mineral content may not be changed, but the water may be treated in other ways, such as with ozone or by filtration. p. 314

naturally occurring sugars sugars that are not added to a food but are present as its original constituents, such as the sugars of fruit or milk. p. 143

Neotame (NEE-oh-tame) an artificial sweetener composed of two amino acids (phenylalanine and aspartic acid) linked in such a way as to make them indigestible by human enzymes. p. 152

nephrons (NEFF-rons) the working units in the kidneys, consisting of intermeshed blood vessels and tubules. p. 98

neural tube the embryonic tissue that later forms the brain and spinal cord. p. 561

neural tube defects abnormalities of the brain and spinal cord apparent at birth and believed to be related to a woman's folate intake before and during pregnancy. p. 272

neurotoxins poisons that act upon the cells of the nervous system. p. 505

neurotransmitters chemicals that are released at the end of a nerve cell when a nerve impulse arrives there. They diffuse across the gap to the next cell and alter the membrane of that second cell to either inhibit or excite it. p. 83

niacin a B vitamin needed in energy metabolism. Niacin can be eaten preformed or can be made in the body from tryptophan, one of the amino acids. Other forms of niacin are *nicotinic acid, niacinamide,* and *nicotinamide.* p. 271

niacin equivalents (NE) the amount of niacin present in food, including the niacin that can theoretically be made from its precursor tryptophan that is present in the food. p. 272

night blindness slow recovery of vision after exposure to flashes of bright light at night; an early symptom of vitamin A deficiency. p. 247

nitrogen balance the amount of nitrogen consumed compared with the amount excreted in a given time period. p. 226

nonalcoholic a term used on labels of beverages, such as wine or beer, indicating that the product contains less than 0.5 percent alcohol. The terms *dealcoholized* and *alcohol removed* mean the same thing. *Alcohol-free* means that the product contains no detectable alcohol. p. 101

nonnutrients a term used in this book to mean compounds other than the six nutrients that are present in foods and have biological activity in the body. p. 8

norepinephrine (NOR-EP-ih-NEFF-rin) a compound related to epinephrine that helps elicit the stress response. p. 83

nori a type of seaweed popular in Asian, particularly Japanese, cooking. p. 346

nutraceutical defined by Health Canada as a product isolated or purified from foods that is generally sold in medicinal forms not usually associated with foods. A nutraceutical is demonstrated to have a physiological benefit or to provide protection against chronic disease. p. 64

nutrient additives vitamins and minerals added to improve nutritive value. p. 533

nutrient claims claims using approved wording to describe the nutrient values of foods, such as a claim that a food is "high" in a desirable constituent or "low" in an undesirable one. p. 56

nutrient content descriptors claims using approved wording to describe the nutrient values of foods, such as a claim that a food is "high" in a desirable constituent or "low" in an undesirable one. p. 55

nutrient density a measure of nutrients provided per Calorie of food. p. 19

nutrients components of food that are indispensable to the body's functioning. They provide energy, serve as building material, help maintain or repair body parts, and support growth. The nutrients include water, carbohydrates, fat, protein, vitamins, and minerals. p. 3

nutrition the study of the nutrients and other biologically active compounds in foods and in the body; sometimes also the study of human behaviours related to food. p. 3

Nutrition Facts on a food label, the panel of nutrition information required to appear on almost every packaged food. Grocers may also provide the information for fresh produce, meat, poultry, and seafood. p. 55

nutritional genomics the science of how nutrients affect the activities of genes and how genes affect the activities of nutrients. Also called *molecular nutrition* or *nutrigenomics.* p. 4

nutritional yeast a preparation of yeast cells, often praised for its high nutrient content. Yeast is a source of B vitamins, as are many other foods. Also called brewer's yeast; not the yeast used in baking. p. 293

nutritionist someone who engages in the study of nutrition. Some nutritionists have earned the designation R.D., whereas others are self-described experts whose training is questionable and who are not qualified to give advice. In U.S. states with responsible legislation, the term applies only to people who have a master of science (M.S.) or a doctor of philosophy (Ph.D.) degree from a properly accredited institution. p. 26

O

obesity overfatness with adverse health effects, as determined by reliable measures and interpreted with good medical judgment. Obesity is officially defined as a body mass index of 30 or higher. p. 365

octacosanol an alcohol extracted from wheat germ, often falsely promoted as enhancing athletic performance. p. 446

oils lipids that are liquid at room temperature (20°C or 68°F). p. 161

Olestra a noncaloric artificial fat made from sucrose and fatty acids; formerly called *sucrose polyester.* p. 184

omega-3 fatty acid a polyunsaturated fatty acid with its endmost double bond three carbons from the methyl end of the carbon chain. Linolenic acid is an example. p. 177

omega-6 fatty acid a polyunsaturated fatty acid with its endmost double bond six carbons from the methyl end of the carbon chain. Linoleic acid is an example. p. 177

omnivores people who eat foods of both plant and animal origin, including animal flesh. p. 11

open dating a general term referring to label dates that are stated in ordinary language that consumers can understand, as opposed to *closed dating,* which refers to dates printed in codes decipherable only by manufacturers. Open dating is used primarily on perishable foods and closed dating on shelf-stable products such as canned goods. p. 530

oral rehydration therapy (ORT) oral fluid replacement for children with severe diarrhea caused by infectious disease. ORT enables parents to mix a simple solution for their child from substances that they have at home. p. 660

organ and glandular extracts dried or extracted material from brain, adrenal, pituitary, or other glands or tissues providing few nutrients but posing a theoretical risk of "mad cow disease." p. 293

organic contain carbon. Four of the six classes of nutrients are organic: carbohydrate, fat, protein, and vitamins. Strictly speaking, organic compounds include only those made by living things and do not include carbon dioxide and a few carbon salts. p. 6

organic foods products grown and processed without the use of synthetic chemicals such as pesticides, herbicides, fertilizers, and preservatives and without genetic engineering or irradiation. p. 525

organosulphur compounds a large group of phytochemicals containing the mineral sulphur. Organosulphur phytochemicals are responsible for the pungent flavours and aromas of foods belonging to the onion, leek, chive, shallot, and garlic family and are thought to stimulate cancer defences in the body. p. 64

organs discrete structural units made of tissues that perform specific jobs. Examples are the heart, liver, and brain. p. 77

ornithine a nonessential amino acid falsely promoted as enhancing the secretion of human growth hormone, the breakdown of fat, and the development of muscle. p. 446

oryzanol a plant sterol that supposedly provides the same physical responses as anabolic steroids without the adverse side effects; also known as ferulic acid, ferulate, or FRAC. p. 446

osteomalacia (OS-tee-o-mal-AY-shuh) the adult expression of vitamin D–deficiency disease, characterized by an overabundance of unmineralized bone protein (*osteo* means "bone"; *mal* means "bad"). Symptoms include bending of the spine and bowing of the legs. p. 255

osteoporosis (OSS-tee-oh-pore-OH-sis) a reduction of the bone mass of older persons in which the bones become porous and fragile (*osteo* means "bones"; *poros* means "porous"); also known as *adult bone loss*. p. 317

outcrossing the unintended breeding of a domestic crop with a related wild species. p. 541

oven-safe thermometer a thermometer designed to remain in the food to give constant readings during cooking. p. 512

overload an extra physical demand placed on the body; an increase in the frequency, duration, or intensity of an activity. A principle of training is that for a body system to improve, it must be worked at frequencies, durations, or intensities that increase by increments. p. 423

overweight overfatness of a moderate degree; defined as a body mass index (BMI) of 25.0 through 29.9. p. 364

ovo-vegetarian includes eggs, vegetables, grains, legumes, fruit, and nuts; excludes flesh, seafood, and milk products. p. 235

ovum the egg, produced by the mother, that unites with a sperm from the father to produce a new individual. p. 557

oxidants compounds (such as oxygen itself) that oxidize other compounds. Compounds that prevent oxidation are called antioxidants, whereas those that promote it are called prooxidants (*anti* means "against"; *pro* means "for"). p. 295

oxidation interaction of a compound with oxygen; in this case, a damaging effect by a chemically reactive form of oxygen. p. 175

oxidative stress damage inflicted on living systems by free radicals. p. 295

oyster shell a product made from the powdered shells of oysters that is sold as a calcium supplement but is not well absorbed by the digestive system. p. 356

P

pack date the day the food was packaged or processed. When used on packages of fresh meats, pack dates can provide a general guide to freshness. p. 530

pancreas an organ with two main functions. One is an endocrine function—the making of hormones such as insulin, which it releases directly into the blood (*endo* means "into"). The other is an exocrine function—the making of digestive enzymes, which it releases through a duct into the small intestine to assist in digestion (*exo* means "out" into a body cavity or onto the skin surface). p. 82

pancreatic juice fluid secreted by the pancreas that contains both sodium bicarbonate, a neutralizing agent, and enzymes to digest carbohydrate, fat, and protein. p. 90

pangamic acid also called vitamin B$_{15}$ (but not a vitamin or even a specific compound—it can be anything with that label); falsely claimed to speed oxygen delivery. p. 446

pantothenic (PAN-to-THEN-ic) **acid** a B vitamin. p. 280

partial vegetarian a term sometimes used to mean an eating style that includes seafood, poultry, eggs, dairy products, vegetables, grains, legumes, fruit, and nuts; excludes or strictly limits certain meats, such as red meats. p. 235

partitioned foods foods composed of parts of whole foods, such as butter (from milk), sugar (from beets or cane), or corn oil (from corn). Partitioned foods are generally overused and provide few nutrients with many Calories. p. 9

pasteurization the treatment of milk with heat sufficient to kill certain pathogens (disease-causing microbes) commonly transmitted through milk; not a sterilization process. Pasteurized milk retains bacteria that cause milk spoilage. Raw milk, even if labelled "certified," transmits many foodborne diseases to people each year and should be avoided. p. 509

PCBs (polychlorinated biphenyls) stable oily synthetic chemicals used in hundreds of industrial and commercial operations that persist as pollution in the environment. PCBs cause cancer in animals and a number of other serious health effects. Environment Canada and Health Canada monitor their levels. p. 527

peak bone mass the highest attainable bone density for an individual; developed during the first three decades of life. p. 317

pellagra (pell-AY-gra) the niacin-deficiency disease (*pellis* means "skin"; *agra* means "rough"). Symptoms include the "4 Ds": diarrhea, dermatitis, dementia, and death. p. 271

pennyroyal relatives of the mint family brewed as tea or extracted as oil; used as mosquito repellent, claimed to treat various conditions. Tea produced multiple organ failure in infants; 1/2 tsp of oil caused convulsions and coma; 2 tbs caused the death of an 18-year-old expectant mother within 2 hours, despite hospitalization. p. 480

peptide bond a bond that connects one amino acid with another, forming a link in a protein chain. p. 209

percent fat free may be used only if the product meets the definition of *low fat* or *fat free*. Requires disclosure of grams of fat per 100 g food.

peristalsis (perri-STALL-sis) the wavelike muscular squeezing of the esophagus, stomach, and small intestine that pushes their contents along. p. 86

pernicious (per-NISH-us) **anemia** a vitamin B$_{12}$–deficiency disease caused by a lack of intrinsic factor and characterized by large, immature red blood cells and damage to the nervous system (*pernicious* means "highly injurious or destructive"). p. 276

persistent of a stubborn or enduring nature; with respect to food contaminants, the quality of remaining unaltered and unexcreted in plant foods or in the bodies of animals and human beings. p. 526

pesco-vegetarian same as partial vegetarian but eliminates poultry. p. 235

pesticides chemicals used to control insects, diseases, weeds, fungi, and other pests on crops and around animals. Used broadly, the term includes *herbicides* (to kill weeds), *insecticides* (to kill insects), and *fungicides* (to kill fungi). p. 523

pH a measure of acidity on a point scale. A solution with a pH of 1 is a strong acid; a solution with a pH of 7 is neutral; a solution with a pH of 14 is a strong base. p. 90

phagocytes (FAG-oh-sites) white blood cells that can ingest and destroy antigens. The process by which phagocytes engulf materials is called *phagocytosis*. The Greek word *phagein* means "to eat." p. 84

phosphate salt a product demonstrated to increase the levels of a metabolically important phosphate compound (diphosphoglycerate) in red blood cells and the potential of the cells to deliver oxygen to the body's muscle cells. However, it does not extend endurance or increase efficiency of aerobic metabolism, and it may cause calcium losses from the bones if taken in excess. p. 446

phospholipids (FOSS-foh-LIP-ids) one of the three main classes of dietary lipids. These lipids are similar to triglycerides, but each has a phosphorus-containing acid in place of one of the fatty acids. Phospholipids are present in *all* cell membranes. p. 162

photosynthesis the process by which green plants make carbohydrates from carbon dioxide and water using the green pigment chlorophyll to capture the sun's energy (*photo* means "light"; *synthesis* means "making"). p. 113

physical activity bodily movement produced by muscle contractions that substantially increase energy expenditure. p. 420

phytates (FYE-tates) compounds present in plant foods (particularly whole grains) that bind iron and may prevent its absorption. p. 334

phytochemicals nonnutrient compounds in plant-derived foods that have biological activity in the body (*phyto* means "plant"). p. 8

phytoestrogens (FIGH-toe-ESS-troh-gens) phytochemicals structurally similar to mammalian hormones, such as the female sex hormone estrogen. Phytoestrogens weakly mimic hormone activity in the human body. p. 64

pica (PIE-ka) a craving for nonfood substances. Also known as *geophagia* (gee-oh-FAY-gee-uh) when referring to clay eating and *pagophagia* (pag-oh-FAY-gee-uh) when referring to ice craving (*geo* means "earth"; *pago* means "frost"; *phagia* means "to eat"). p. 331

placebo a sham treatment often used in scientific studies; an inert harmless medication. The *placebo effect* is the healing effect that the act of treatment, rather than the treatment itself, often has. p. 15

placenta (pla-SEN-tuh) the organ of pregnancy in which maternal and fetal blood circulate in close proximity and exchange nutrients and oxygen (flowing into the fetus) and wastes (picked up by the mother's blood). p. 556

plant pesticides substances produced within plant tissues that kill or repel attacking organisms. p. 541

plant sterols lipid extracts of plants, called ferulic acid, oryzanol, phytosterols, or "adaptogens," marketed with false claims that they contain hormones or enhance hormonal activity. p. 447

plaques (PLACKS) mounds of lipid material mixed with smooth muscle cells and calcium that develop in the artery walls in atherosclerosis (*placken* means "patch"). The same word is also used to describe the accumulation of a different kind of deposits on teeth, which promote dental caries. p. 464

plasma the cell-free fluid part of blood and lymph. p. 78

platelets tiny cell-like fragments in the blood, important in blood clot formation (*platelet* means "little plate"). p. 465

point of unsaturation a site in a molecule where the bonding is such that additional hydrogen atoms can easily be attached. p. 165

polypeptides (POL-ee-PEP-tides) protein fragments of many (more than 10) amino acids bonded together (*poly* means "many"). A peptide is a strand of amino acids. A strand of between 4 and 10 amino acids is called an *oligopeptide*. p. 214

polysaccharides another term for complex carbohydrates; compounds composed of long strands of glucose units linked together (*poly* means "many"). Also called *complex carbohydrates*. p. 116

polyunsaturated fats triglycerides in which most of the fatty acids have two or more points of unsaturation (are polyunsaturated). p. 166

polyunsaturated fatty acid (PUFA) a fatty acid with two or more points of unsaturation p. 165

pop-up thermometer a disposable timing device commonly used in turkeys. The centre of the device contains a stainless steel spring that "pops up" when food reaches the right temperature. p. 512

postprandial hypoglycemia an unusual drop in blood glucose that follows a meal and is accompanied by symptoms such as anxiety, rapid heartbeat, and sweating; also called *reactive hypoglycemia*. p. 140

potassium iodide a medication approved by the U.S. FDA as safe and effective for the prevention of thyroid cancer caused by radioactive iodine that may be released during radiation emergencies. p. 329

precursors, provitamins compounds that can be converted into active vitamins. p. 246

preeclampsia (PRE-ee-CLAMP-see-uh) a potentially dangerous condition during pregnancy characterized by edema, hypertension, and protein in the urine. p. 574

pregame meal a meal eaten three to four hours before athletic competition p. 442

premenstrual syndrome (PMS) a cluster of symptoms that some women experience prior to and during menstruation. They include, among others, abdominal cramps, back pain, swelling, headache, painful breasts, and mood changes. p. 620

prenatal (pree-NAY-tal) before birth. p. 564

preservatives antimicrobial agents, antioxidants, chelating agents, radiation, and other additives that retard spoilage or preserve desired qualities, such as softness in baked goods. p. 533

prion (PREE-on) an infective agent consisting of an unusually folded protein that disrupts normal cell functioning, causing disease. p. 515

probiotics consumable products containing live microorganisms in sufficient numbers to alter the bacterial colonies of the body in ways believed to benefit health. A *prebiotic* product is a substance that may not be digestible by the host, such as fibre, but serves as food for probiotic bacteria and thus promotes their growth. p. 64

problem drinkers or **alcohol abusers** people who suffer social, emotional, family, job-related, or other problems because of alcohol. A problem drinker is on the way to alcoholism. p. 103

processed foods foods subjected to any process, such as milling, alteration of texture, addition of additives, cooking, or others. Depending on the starting material and the process, a processed food may or may not be nutritious. p. 9

promoters factors that do not initiate cancer but speed up its development once initiation has taken place. p. 482

proof a statement of the percentage of alcohol in an alcoholic beverage. Liquor that is 100 proof is 50 percent alcohol, 90 proof is 45 percent, and so forth. p. 101

prooxidant a compound that triggers reactions involving oxygen. p. 263

protein-energy malnutrition (PEM) the world's most widespread malnutrition problem, including both *marasmus* and *kwashiorkor* and states in which they overlap; also called *protein-Calorie malnutrition (PCM)*. p. 227

protein digestibility–corrected amino acid score (PDCAAS) a measuring tool used to determine protein quality. The PDCAAS reflects a protein's digestibility as well as the proportions of amino acids that it provides. p. 225

protein-sparing action the action of carbohydrate and fat in providing energy that allows protein to be used for purposes it alone can serve. p. 131

protein turnover the continuous breakdown and synthesis of body proteins involving the recycling of 300–400 g of amino acids each day. p. 216

proteins compounds composed of carbon, hydrogen, oxygen, and nitrogen and arranged as strands of amino acids. Some amino acids also contain the element sulphur. p. 206

public health nutritionist a dietitian or other person with an advanced degree in nutrition who specializes in public health nutrition. p. 26

public water water from a municipal or county water system that has been treated and disinfected. p. 314

purified water water that has been treated by distillation or other physical or chemical processes that remove dissolved solids. Because purified water contains no minerals or contaminants, it is useful for medical and research purposes. p. 314

pyloric (pye-LORE-ick) **valve** the circular muscle of the lower stomach that regulates the flow of partly digested food into the small intestine. Also called *pyloric sphincter*. p. 88

pyruvate a 3-carbon compound derived during the metabolism of glucose, certain amino acids, and glycerol; falsely promoted as burning fat and enhancing endurance. Common side effects include intestinal gas and diarrhea and possibly reduced physical performance. p. 447

R

radiolytic products chemicals formed in foods during the irradiation process; deemed harmless by experts. p. 519

randomized controlled trials (RCT) sometimes also referred to as clinical trials, studies in which the subjects are selected in such a way that they have an equal chance of being included in the experimental/treatment group or the control group. This type of study is considered the gold standard in research. p. 15

raw sugar the first crop of crystals harvested during sugar processing. Raw sugar cannot be sold in Canada or the United States because it contains too much filth (dirt, insect fragments, and the like). Sugar sold as "raw sugar" is actually evaporated cane juice. p. 143

recombinant DNA (rDNA) technology a technique of genetic modification whereby scientists directly manipulate the genes of living things; includes methods of removing genes, doubling genes, introducing foreign genes, and changing gene positions to influence the growth and development of organisms. p. 541

recommended dietary allowances (RDA) nutrient intake goals for individuals; the average daily nutrient intake level that meets the needs of nearly all (97 to 98 percent) healthy people in a particular life stage and gender group. Derived from the estimated average requirements. p. 32

reduced Calorie at least 25 percent lower in Calories than a "regular," or reference, food.

reduced or **less cholesterol** at least 25 percent less cholesterol than a reference food and 2 g or less saturated fat per serving.

reduced saturated fat at least 25 percent less saturated fat and reduced by more than 1 g saturated fat per serving compared with a reference food.

reduced sodium at least 25 percent lower in sodium than the regular product.

refined refers to the process by which the coarse parts of food products are removed. For example, the refining of wheat into flour involves removing three of the four parts of the kernel—the chaff, the bran, and the germ—leaving only the endosperm, composed mainly of starch and a little protein. p. 124

registered dietitian (R.D.) a dietitian who has graduated from a university or college after completing a program of dietetics. The program must be approved or accredited by Dietitians of Canada. The dietitian must also serve in an approved internship, coordinated program, or preprofessional practice program to practise the necessary skills and pass a national and provincial exam. p. 26

registration listing with a professional organization that requires specific course work, experience, and passing of an examination. p. 26

requirement the amount of a nutrient that will just prevent the development of specific deficiency signs; distinguished from the DRI recommended intake value, which is a generous allowance with a margin of safety. p. 35

residues whatever remains. In the case of pesticides, those amounts that remain on or in foods when people buy and use them. p. 523

resistant starch the fraction of starch in a food that is digested slowly, or not at all, by human enzymes. p. 128

retina (RET-in-uh) the layer of light-sensitive nerve cells lining the back of the inside of the eye. p. 247

retinol one of the active forms of vitamin A made from beta-carotene in animal and human bodies; an antioxidant nutrient. Other active forms are *retinal* and *retinoic acid*. p. 247

retinol activity equivalents (RAE) a new measure of the vitamin A activity of beta-carotene and other vitamin A precursors that reflects the amount of retinol that the body will derive from a food containing vitamin A precursor compounds. p. 251

rhodopsin (roh-DOP-sin) the light-sensitive pigment of the cells in the retina; it contains vitamin A (*rod* refers to the rod-shaped cells; *opsin* means "visual protein"). p. 247

riboflavin (RIBE-o-flay-vin) a B vitamin active in the body's energy-releasing mechanisms. p. 269

rickets the vitamin D–deficiency disease in children; characterized by abnormal growth of bone and manifested in bowed legs or knock-knees, outward-bowed chest, and knobs on the ribs. p. 254

risk factors factors known to be related to (or correlated with) diseases but not proven to be causal. p. 462

royal jelly a substance produced by worker bees and fed to the queen bee; often falsely promoted as enhancing athletic performance. p. 447

S

saccharin a zero-Calorie sweetener restricted in Canada but used freely in the United States. p. 151

safety the practical certainty that injury will not result from the use of a substance. p. 504

salts compounds composed of charged particles (ions). An example is potassium chloride (K^+Cl^-). p. 312

SAM-e an amino acid derivative that may have an antidepressant effect on the brain in some people but is not recommended as a substitute for standard antidepressant therapy. p. 293

sassafras root bark from the sassafras tree; once used in beverages but now banned as an ingredient in foods or beverages because it contains cancer-causing chemicals. p. 480

satiation (SAY-she-AY-shun) the perception of fullness that builds throughout a meal, eventually reaching the degree of fullness and satisfaction that halts eating. Satiation generally determines how much food is consumed at one sitting. p. 378

satiety (sah-TIE-eh-tee) the perception of fullness that lingers in the hours after a meal and inhibits eating until the next mealtime. Satiety generally determines the length of time between meals. p. 379

saturated fat-free less than 0.5 g of saturated fat and less than 0.5 g of *trans* fat.

saturated fats triglycerides in which most of the fatty acids are saturated. p. 166

saturated fatty acid (SAFA) a fatty acid carrying the maximum possible number of hydrogen atoms (having no points of unsaturation). p. 164

saw palmetto the ripe fruit or extracts of the saw palmetto plant. Claimed to relieve symptoms associated with enlarged prostate but reported as ineffective in research. p. 480

screenogenic an environment where, for example, children are constantly exposed to screens, such as those of computers, televisions, iPods, etc. p. 613

scurvy the vitamin C-deficiency disease. p. 262

segmentation alternating forward and backward movement allowing for greater contact between the partially digested food and intestinal juices and enzymes, thus resulting in virtually complete digestion of the food we eat. p. 86

selective breeding a technique of genetic modification whereby organisms are chosen for reproduction based on their desirability for human purposes, such as high growth rate, high food yield, or disease resistance, with the intention of retaining or enhancing these characteristics in their offspring. p. 541

self-efficacy a person's belief in his or her ability to succeed in an undertaking. p. 402

sell-by specifies the shelf life of the food. After this date, the food may still be safe for consumption if it has been handled and stored properly. Also called *pull date*. p. 530

senile dementia the loss of brain function beyond the normal loss of physical adeptness and memory that occurs with aging. p. 630

serotonin (SER-oh-tone-in) a neurotransmitter important in sleep regulation, appetite control, and mood regulation, among other roles. Serotonin is synthesized in the body from the amino acid tryptophan with the help of vitamin B_6. p. 277

set-point theory the theory that the body tends to maintain a certain weight by means of its own internal controls. p. 380

side chain the unique chemical structure attached to the backbone of each amino acid that differentiates one amino acid from another. p. 207

simple carbohydrates sugars, including both single sugar units and linked pairs of sugar units. The basic sugar unit is a molecule containing six carbon atoms, together with oxygen and hydrogen atoms. p. 113

single-use temperature indicator a type of instant-read thermometer that changes colour to indicate that the food has reached the desired temperature. Discarded after one use; they are often used in retail food markets to eliminate cross-contamination. p. 512

skullcap a native herb with no known medical uses but found in remedies. Other species may be harvested and sold as skullcap, so it has not been determined whether several deaths from liver toxicity reportedly from skullcap were, in fact, from another herb. p. 480

small intestine the seven-metre length of small-diameter intestine, below the stomach and above the large intestine, that is the major site of digestion of food and absorption of nutrients. p. 88

smoking point the temperature at which fat gives off an acrid blue gas. p. 180

social drinkers people who drink only on social occasions. Depending on how alcohol affects a social drinker's life, the person may be a moderate drinker or a problem drinker. p. 101

sodium bicarbonate baking soda; an alkaline salt believed to neutralize blood lactic acid and thereby reduce pain and enhance possible workload. "Soda loading" may cause intestinal bloating and diarrhea. p. 447

sodium free less than 5 mg per serving.

soft water water with a high sodium concentration. p. 311

soluble fibres food components that readily dissolve in water and often impart gummy or gel-like characteristics to foods. An example is pectin from fruit, which is used to thicken jellies and jams. Soluble fibres are indigestible by human enzymes but may be broken down to absorbable products by bacteria in the digestive tract. p. 117

soy drink a milklike beverage made from soybeans, claimed to be a functional food. Soy drink should be fortified with vitamin A, vitamin D, riboflavin, calcium, and vitamin B_{12} to approach the nutritional equivalency of milk. Also called *soy milk*. p. 64

Special Supplemental Food Program for Women, Infants, and Children (WIC) a USDA program offering low-income pregnant women and those with infants or preschool children coupons redeemable for specific foods that supply the nutrients deemed most necessary for growth and development. For more information, visit http://www.fns.usda.gov/wic/women-infants-and-children-wic.

sphincter (SFINK-ter) a circular muscle surrounding, and able to close, a body opening. p. 88

spina bifida (SPY-na BIFF-ih-duh) one of the most common types of NTDs in which gaps occur in the bones of the spine. Often the spinal cord bulges and protrudes through the gaps, resulting in a number of motor and other impairments. p. 561

spirulina a kind of alga ("blue-green manna") that supposedly contains large amounts of protein and vitamin B_{12}, suppresses appetite, and improves athletic performance. It does none of these things and is potentially toxic. p. 447

sports drinks (fluid replacers) beverages specifically developed for athletes to replace fluids and electrolytes and to provide glucose before, during, and after physical activity, especially endurance activity. p. 440

spring water water originating from an underground spring or well. It may be bubbly (carbonated) or "flat" or "still," meaning not carbonated. Brand names such as "Spring Pure" do not necessarily mean that the water comes from a spring. p. 314

St. John's wort a herb containing psychoactive substances that has been used for centuries to treat depression, insomnia, bedwetting, and "nervous conditions." Some scientific reports find St. John's wort equal in effectiveness to standard antidepressant medication for relief of depression. Long-term safety, however, has not been established. p. 480

staple foods foods used frequently or daily, for example, rice (in East and Southeast Asia) or potatoes (in Ireland). If well chosen, these foods are nutritious. p. 9

starch a plant polysaccharide composed of glucose. After cooking, starch is highly digestible by human beings; raw starch often resists digestion. p. 116

stem cell an undifferentiated cell that can mature into any of a number of specialized cell types. A stem cell of bone marrow may mature into one of many kinds of blood cells, for example. p. 541

sterol esters compounds derived from vegetable oils that lower blood cholesterol in human beings by competing with cholesterol for absorption from the digestive tract. The term *sterol esters* often refers to both stanol esters and sterol esters. p. 64

sterols (STEER-alls) one of the three main classes of dietary lipids. Sterols have a structure similar to that of cholesterol. p. 162

stevia (STEEV-ee-uh) the sweet-tasting leaves of a shrub sold as a dietary supplement but lacking U.S. FDA approval as a sweetener. However, small amounts of Steviol Glycosides (a purified Stevia extract) are allowed to be added to foods in Canada and may also be found in some natural health products. p. 151

stomach a muscular, elastic, pouchlike organ of the digestive tract that grinds and churns swallowed food and mixes it with acid and enzymes, forming chyme. p. 88

stone ground refers to a milling process using limestone to grind any grain, including refined grains, into flour. p. 124

stone-ground flour flour made by grinding kernels of grain between heavy wheels made of limestone, a kind of rock derived from the shells and bones of marine animals. As the stones scrape together, bits of the limestone mix with the flour, enriching it with calcium. p. 346

stroke the sudden shutting off of the blood flow to the brain by a thrombus, an embolism, or the bursting of a vessel (hemorrhage). p. 466

stroke volume the amount of oxygenated blood ejected from the heart toward body tissues at each beat. p. 425

subclinical, or marginal, deficiency a nutrient deficiency that has no outward clinical symptoms. The term is often used to market unneeded nutrient supplements to consumers. p. 295

subcutaneous fat fat stored directly under the skin (*sub* means "beneath"; *cutaneous* refers to the skin). p. 367

succinate a compound synthesized in the body and involved in the TCA cycle; falsely promoted as a metabolic enhancer. p. 447

sucralose a noncaloric sweetener derived from a chlorinated form of sugar that travels through the digestive tract unabsorbed. Approved for use in Canada and the United States. p. 151

sucrose (SOO-crose) a disaccharide composed of glucose and fructose; sometimes known as table, beet, or cane sugar or, often, simply *sugar*. p. 115

sucrose polyester any of a family of compounds in which fatty acids are bonded with sugars or sugar alcohols. Olestra is an example. p. 184

sugars simple carbohydrates, that is, molecules of either single sugar units or pairs of those sugar units bonded together. By common usage, *sugar* most often refers to sucrose. p. 113

superoxide dismutase (SOD) an enzyme that protects cells from oxidation. When it is taken orally, the body digests and inactivates this protein; it is useless to athletes. p. 447

surface water water that comes from lakes, rivers, and reservoirs. p. 312

sushi a Japanese dish that consists of vinegar-flavoured rice, seafood, and colourful vegetables, typically wrapped in seaweed. Some sushi is wrapped in raw fish; other sushi contains only cooked ingredients. p. 518

sustainable able to continue indefinitely. In this context, the use of resources in ways that maintain both natural resources and human life; the use of natural resources at a pace that allows the earth to replace them. Examples: cutting trees no faster than new ones grow and producing pollutants at a rate with which the environment and human cleanup efforts can keep pace. In a sustainable economy, resources do not become depleted, and pollution does not accumulate. p. 664

systolic (sis-TOL-ik) **pressure** the first figure in a blood pressure reading (the "dupp" of the heartbeat is heard), which reflects arterial pressure caused by the contraction of the heart's left ventricle. p. 474

T

tagatose an incompletely absorbed monosaccharide sweetener derived from lactose with a caloric value of 1.5 Calories per gram. About 80 percent of the ingested tagatose travels to the large intestine, where bacterial colonies ferment it. Tagatose is not readily used by mouth bacteria and so does not promote dental caries. p. 151

tannins compounds in tea (especially black tea) and coffee that bind iron. Tannins also denature proteins. p. 334

T-cells lymphocytes that attack antigens. *T* stands for the thymus gland of the neck, where the T-cells are stored and matured. p. 84

tetrahydrogestrinone (THG) an unapproved drug, once sold as an ergogenic aid, now banned by Health Canada. p. 447

textured vegetable protein processed soybean protein used in products formulated to look and taste like meat, fish, or poultry. p. 233

thermic effect of food (TEF) the body's speeded-up metabolism in response to having eaten a meal; also called diet-induced thermogenesis. p. 371

thermogenesis the generation and release of body heat associated with the breakdown of body fuels. *Adaptive thermogenesis* describes adjustments in energy expenditure related to changes in environment such as cold and to physiological events such as underfeeding or trauma. p. 380

thiamin (THIGH-uh-min) a B vitamin involved in the body's use of fuels. p. 269

thickening and stabilizing agents ingredients that maintain emulsions, foams, or suspensions or lend a desirable thick consistency to foods. Dextrins (short chains of glucose formed as a breakdown product of starch), starch, and pectin are examples. (Gums such as carrageenan, guar, locust bean, agar, and gum arabic are others.) p. 533

thrombosis a thrombus that has grown enough to close off a blood vessel. A *coronary thrombosis* closes off a vessel that feeds the heart muscle. A *cerebral thrombosis* closes off a vessel that feeds the brain (*coronary* means "crowning" [the heart]; *thrombo* means "clot"; the cerebrum is part of the brain). p. 465

thrombus a stationary blood clot. p. 465

tissues systems of cells working together to perform specialized tasks. Examples are muscles, nerves, blood, and bone. p. 77

tocopherol (tuh-KOFF-er-all) a kind of alcohol. The active form of vitamin E is alpha-tocopherol. p. 256

tofu (TOE-foo) a curd made from soybeans that is rich in protein, often rich in calcium, and variable in fat content; used in many Asian and vegetarian dishes in place of meat. p. 233

tolerable upper intake levels (UL) the highest average daily nutrient intake level that is likely to pose no risk of toxicity to almost all healthy individuals of a particular life stage and gender group. Usual intake above this level may place an individual at risk of illness from nutrient toxicity. p. 32

tolerance limit the maximum amount of a residue permitted in a food when a pesticide is used according to label directions. p. 523

toxicity the ability of a substance to harm living organisms. All substances are toxic if the concentration is high enough. p. 533

trabecular (tra-BECK-you-lar) **bone** the weblike structure composed of calcium-containing crystals inside a bone's solid outer shell. It provides strength and acts as a calcium storage bank. p. 349

trace minerals essential mineral nutrients found in the human body in amounts less than 5 grams. p. 305

training regular practice of an activity, which leads to physical adaptations of the body with improvement in flexibility, strength, or endurance. p. 419

***trans* fat free** less than 0.2 g of *trans* fat *and* less than 0.2 g of saturated fat per serving.

***trans* fats** fats that contain unusual fatty acids; *trans* fatty acids are largely formed during processing. p. 166

***trans* fatty acids** fatty acids with unusual shapes that can arise when polyunsaturated oils are hydrogenated. p. 182

transgenic organism an organism resulting from the growth of an embryonic, stem, or germ cell into which a new gene has been inserted. p. 541

triglycerides (try-GLISS-er-ides) one of the three main classes of dietary lipids and the chief form of fat in foods and in the human body. A triglyceride is made up of three units of fatty acids and one unit of glycerol. Triglycerides are also called *triacylglycerols*. p. 161

trimester a period representing gestation. A trimester is about 13 to 14 weeks. p. 558

tripeptides (try-PEP-tides) protein fragments that are three amino acids long (*tri* means "three"). p. 214

turbinado (ter-bih-NOD-oh) **sugar** raw sugar from which the filth has been washed; legal to sell in Canada and the United States. p. 143

type 1 diabetes the type of diabetes in which the pancreas produces no or very little insulin; often diagnosed in childhood, although some cases arise in adulthood. Formerly called *juvenile-onset* or *insulin-dependent diabetes*. p. 137

type 2 diabetes the type of diabetes in which the pancreas makes plenty of insulin, but the body's cells resist insulin's action; often diagnosed in adulthood. Formerly called *adult-onset* or *non-insulin-dependent diabetes*. p. 137

U

ulcer an erosion in the topmost, and sometimes underlying, layers of cells that form a lining. Ulcers of the digestive tract commonly form in the esophagus, stomach, or upper small intestine. p. 96

ultrahigh temperature (UHT) a process of sterilizing food by exposing it for a short time to temperatures above those normally used in processing. p. 529

unbleached flour a beige-coloured endosperm flour with texture and nutritive qualities that approximate those of regular white flour. p. 124

underwater weighing a measure of density and volume used to determine body fat content. p. 375

underweight too little body fat for health; defined as having a body mass index of less than 18.5. p. 364

unsaturated fatty acid a fatty acid that lacks some hydrogen atoms and has one or more points of unsaturation. An unsaturated fat is a triglyceride that contains one or more unsaturated fatty acids. p. 165

urban legends stories, usually false, that may travel rapidly throughout the world via the Internet, gaining strength of conviction solely on the basis of repetition. p. 21

urea (yoo-REE-uh) the principal nitrogen-excretion product of protein metabolism; generated mostly by removal of amine groups from unneeded amino acids or from amino acids being sacrificed to a need for energy. p. 220

urethane a carcinogenic compound that commonly forms in alcoholic beverages. p. 101

USDA (U.S. Department of Agriculture) the federal agency that is responsible for enforcing standards for the wholesomeness and quality of meat, poultry, and eggs produced in the United States;

conducting nutrition research; and educating the public about nutrition.

uterus (YOO-ter-us) the womb, the muscular organ within which the infant develops before birth. p. 556

V

valerian a preparation of the root of a herb used as a sedative and sleep agent. Safety and effectiveness of valerian have not been scientifically established. p. 480

variety the dietary characteristic of providing a wide selection of foods—the opposite of monotony. p. 9

vegans people who include only food from plant sources: vegetables, grains, legumes, fruit, seeds and nuts; also called *strict vegetarians*. p. 11

vegetarians people who exclude from their diets animal flesh and possibly other animal products such as milk, cheese, and eggs. p. 11

veins blood vessels that carry blood, with the carbon dioxide it has collected, from the tissues back to the heart (see Figure 3-3). p. 78

very low density lipoproteins (VLDL) lipoproteins that transport triglycerides and other lipids from the liver to various tissues in the body. p. 171

very low sodium 35 mg or less sodium per serving.

villi (VILL-ee, VILL-eye) fingerlike projections of the sheets of cells that line the intestinal tract. The villi make the surface area much greater than it would otherwise be (singular: *villus*). p. 93

visceral fat fat stored within the abdominal cavity in association with the internal abdominal organs; also called *intra-abdominal fat*. p. 367

viscous (VISS-cuss) having a sticky, gummy, or gel-like consistency that flows relatively slowly. p. 117

vitamin B$_6$ a B vitamin needed in protein metabolism. Its three active forms are *pyridoxine, pyridoxal, and pyridoxamine*. p. 277

vitamin B$_{12}$ a B vitamin that helps convert folate to its active form and also helps maintain the sheath around nerve cells. Vitamin B$_{12}$'s scientific name, not often used, is *cyanocobalamin*. p. 275

vitamin water bottled water with a few vitamins added; does not replace vitamins from a balanced diet and may worsen overload in people receiving vitamins from enriched food, supplements, and other enriched products such as "energy" bars. p. 314

vitamins organic compounds that are vital to life and indispensable to body functions but are needed only in minute amounts; noncaloric essential nutrients. p. 245

VO$_2$ max the maximum rate of oxygen consumption by an individual (measured at sea level). p. 426

voluntary activities intentional activities (such as walking, sitting, or running) conducted by voluntary muscles. p. 371

W

wasting the progressive, relentless loss of the body's tissues that accompanies certain diseases and shortens survival time. p. 366

water balance the balance between water intake and water excretion, which keeps the body's water content constant. p. 308

water intoxication/overhydration a dangerous dilution of the body's fluids resulting from excessive ingestion of plain water. Symptoms are headache, muscular weakness, lack of concentration, poor memory, and loss of appetite. p. 308

weight cycling repeated rounds of weight loss and subsequent regain, with reduced ability to lose weight with each attempt; also called *yo-yo dieting*. p. 402

weight training the use of free weights or weight machines to provide resistance for developing muscle strength and endurance. A person's own body weight may also be used to provide resistance as when a person does pushups, pullups, or situps. Also called *resistance training*. p. 424

well water water drawn from ground water by tapping into an aquifer. p. 314

Wernicke-Korsakoff (VER-nik-ee KOR-sah-koff) **syndrome** a cluster of symptoms involving nerve damage arising from a deficiency of the vitamin thiamin in alcoholism. Characterized by mental confusion, disorientation, memory loss, jerky eye movements, and staggering gait. p. 101

wheat flour any flour made from wheat, including white flour. p. 124

wheat germ oil the oil from the wheat kernel; often falsely promoted as an energy aid. p. 447

whey protein a by-product of cheese production; falsely promoted as increasing muscle mass. As for whey, it is the liquid left when most solids are removed from milk. p. 447

white flour an endosperm flour that has been refined and bleached for maximum softness and whiteness. p. 124

white sugar pure sucrose, produced by dissolving, concentrating, and recrystallizing raw sugar. p. 143

whole grain refers to a grain milled in its entirety (all but the husk), not refined. p. 124

whole-wheat flour flour made from whole-wheat kernels; a whole-grain flour. p. 124

witch hazel leaves or bark of a witch hazel tree; not proven to have healing powers. p. 480

world food supply the quantity of food, including stores from previous harvests, available to the world's people at a given time. p. 652

WHO (World Health Organization) "WHO is the directing and coordinating authority for health within the United Nations system. It is responsible for providing leadership on global health matters, shaping the health research agenda, setting norms and standards, articulating evidence-based policy options, providing technical support to countries and monitoring and assessing health trends"; see http://www.who.int/about/en/. A related organization is the FAO (Food and Agricultural Organization).

X

xerophthalmia (ZEER-ahf-THALL-me-uh) progressive hardening of the cornea of the eye in advanced vitamin A deficiency that can lead to blindness (*xero* means "dry"; *ophthalm* means "eye"). p. 248

xerosis (zeer-OH-sis) drying of the cornea; a symptom of vitamin A deficiency. p. 248

Z

zygote (ZYE-goat) the term that describes the product of the union of ovum and sperm during the first two weeks after fertilization. p. 557

Index

Hypertrophy, **423**

Hypoallergenic formulas, **581**

Hypoglycemia, **140**

Hyponatremia, **439**
    prevention of, 439–440
    symptoms of, 439

Hypothalamus, **83**

Hypothermia, **438**

I

Illicit drugs, 641

Illness, vegetarian diets and, 238

Immune system, **84**

Immunity, **218**
    immune factors in breast milk, 580–81
    nutrition and, 460–62, 461f
    vitamin A and, 248–49

Impaired fasting glucose (IFG), 139

Impaired glucose tolerance, **138**

Impaired iron status, **355t**

Implantation, **557**

Incidental additives, 536–37, **536**

Income and birthrate, 664f

Indispensable/essential amino acids, **207**, 207t

Individuality, nutrition and, 3

Infancy, vegetarian diets in, 237

Infant development, recommended foods in, 585t

Infant feeding, 577–88. *See also* Breast-feeding; Formula feeding
    foods in, recommended, 585t
    future health and, 587
    guidelines to, 588
    nutrient needs, 577–79, 578f
    solid foods, 584–86

Infant mortality rates, Canadian, 556f

Infectious diseases, **459**

Infomercials, **21t**

Ingredients list, 57–59

Inhibitory nerves, 104

Initiation, **482**

Inosine, **446t**

Inositol, **280**

Insoluble fibres, **117**

Instant-read thermometer, **512t**

Insulin, **82**, **132**

Insulin-dependent diabetes mellitus (IDDM). *See* Type 1 diabetes

Insulin resistance, **137**

Integrated Pan-Canadian Healthy Living Strategy 2005, 624

Integrated pest management (IPM), **669t**, 671

Internet
    genetic engineering sites, 549t
    nutrition information on, 23–24
    PubMed, 23, 24f
    reliable sites, 23t

Intervention studies, 14f, **15t**

Intestinal gas, 96t

Intestine, **80**
    large, **87**, 93
    small, **87**, 93, 94f

Intra-abdominal fat, **367**

Intracellular fluid, **80**

Intrinsic factor, **276**

Invert sugar, **143t**

Iodine, 328–30, 343t, 344t
    MDD for, 329

Ions, **312**

Iron, 330–35, *See also* Anemia; Iron deficiency
    absorbing, 334, 335t
    aging and, 328
    average amount young adult Canadians are consuming, 344t
    children and, 605t
    genes and iron absorption, 330
    hemoglobin and, **330**
    intake by 19–30-year-old Canadians *vs.* DRI report recommendations, 344t
    MDD for, 332
    myoglobin and, **330**
    overload, 332–34
    pregnancy and, 560t, 563–64
    recommendations and sources, 334
    Snapshot feature of, 333
    in solid foods for infants, 584, 586
    summary of, 343t
    teenagers and, 617
    vegetarian diets and, 238

Iron deficiency, **331**
    causes of, 332
    exercise-deficiency fatigue and, 332
    vs. iron-deficiency anemia, 331

Iron-deficiency anemia, **331**

Iron overload, **332**–34

Irradiation, **519t**

Irritable bowel syndrome, **98**

Isomalt, 150t, **151t**

IU (international unit), **251**

J

Jam and fruit spreads, sugar in, 143, 144f

Jaundice, **262**

Juice, cholesterol-reducing, 69

Juice safety, 517t

K

Kava, **480t**

Kefir, **63t**, **346**

Kelp tablets, **293t**

Keratin, **248**

Keratinization, **248**

Ketone bodies, **132**, **385**

Ketosis, **132**

Kidneys, **80**
    damage in susceptible individuals, **355t**
    hypertension and, 475–76

Kitchen food safety, 510–14
    hand washing and, 513f
    keeping cold food cold, 510, 512
    keeping hands and kitchen clean, 513–14
    keeping hot food hot, 510
    keeping raw food separate, 512
    quiz, 511t
    temperatures and thermometers, 512f, 512t

Kombucha, **480t**

Krebs cycle, **131**

Kudzu, **480t**

Kwashiorkor, **227**–30, 230t

L

Labelling, food, 54–59, 520. *See also* Food labels

Labels on vitamin supplements, 294f
    prenatal, 564f

Laboratory studies, **15t**

Lactase, **130**

Lactation, 574–76
    nutrition during, 575–76

Lactic acid, 428

Lactitol, **150t**, **151t**

Lactobacillus, 70

Lactoferrin, **580**

Lacto-ovo vegetarian, **235t**

Lactose, **115**, **143t**

Lactose intolerance, **130**–31

Lacto-vegetarian, **235t**

Large intestine, **88**, 93

Laxatives, nutritional effects of, 639t

LDL. *See* Low-density lipoproteins (LDL)

Lead, 526, 528t

Lead poisoning, 311, 479, 528t
    in children, 608–09, 609t
    role of chelating agents in, 126

Learning disability, **612**

Learning institutions, legitimate/fraudulent, 27t

Leavened, **336**

folate, 275
  iron, 333
  magnesium, 371
  niacin, 273
  phosphorus, 320
  potassium, 327
  riboflavin, 271
  thiamin, 270
  vitamin A and beta-carotene, 252
  vitamin B_6, 279
  vitamin B_{12}, 277
  vitamin D, 257
  vitamin K, 261
  vitamin C, 265
  zinc, 338
Social drinkers, **101t**, 102
Social meaning attached to food, 12
Social pressure, food choices and, 12
Sodium, 322–26. *See also* Salts
  in barbecue lunch, cutting sodium
    from, 324t
  blood pressure and, 323
  on Canadian labels, 324
  DASH Eating Plan and, 323, 476t,
    F-1–2
  depletion, 439
  hypertension and, 477
  intake (*see* Sodium intake)
  sources of, in Canadian diet, 325f
  water-weight and, 322
Sodium bicarbonate, **447t**
Sodium intake
  by 19–30-year-old Canadians *vs.* DRI
    report recommendations, 345t
  Canadian salt and, 323f
  controlling, 324–26
  Food Guide recommendations, 323
  guidelines, 322, 322t
  osteoporosis and, 353–54
  of young adult Canadians, 344t
Soft drinks, osteoporosis and, 353–54
Soft tissue health, vitamin D and, 255
Soft water, 310–11, **311**
Solanine, 522
Soil conservation and incentive
  programs, 672–73
Soil erosion, environmental degradation
  and, 662
Solid foods, 584–86
  food allergies and, 585–86
  infant food choices of, 586
  introducing, 584
  iron and, 584
  to omit, 586
  at one year age, 586, 586t
  physical readiness for, 585
  vitamin C and, 584
Soluble fibres, **117**
Sorbitol, **150t**

Soybeans, 67
Soy drink, **64t**, 67
Sphincter, **88**
Spina bifida, **561**, 562f
Spirulina, **447t**
Sports drinks, 440–41, **440t**
Spot reducing, 398
Spring water, **314t**
Stabilizing agents, **533t**
Stanol esters, 64t, 472
Staphylococcal food poisoning, **507t**
Staple foods, **9t**
Starch, **116**, 128
Stem cell, **541t**
Steroid alternative supplements, 451–52
Steroid hormone drugs, physical risks
  of, 451f
Sterol esters, **64t**, 69
Sterols, **162**
Stevia, **151t**, 153
Stocks, calcium in, 346
Stomach, **88**, 89f, 93
Stomach flu, **507t**
Stone-ground flour, **124t**, **346**
Storage system, 99–100
Storage times, food safety and, 513t
Stroke, **466**
Stroke volume, **425**
Subclinical deficiency, **295t**
Subcutaneous fat, **367**, 367f
Succinate, **447t**
Sucralose, **151t**, 153
Sucrose, **115**, **143t**
Sucrose polyester, **184t**
Sugar, **113**, 146–50. *See also* Artificial
    sweeteners; Sugar molecules
  added, **143**
  alcohols, evidence concerning, 150
  behaviour and, 148–49
  brown, **143t**
  calories in, **144t**
  carbohydrates in, 146
  confectioner's, **143t**
  dental caries and, 149–50, 149f
  digestion and absorption of, 115,
    128, 129f
  DRI recommended intakes of, 119t
  evidence concerning, 147–50
  in fruits, 115–16
  granulated, **143t**
  heart disease and, 148
  honey and, 143–45
  intake in Canada, 146, 146f
  invert, **143t**
  in jam and fruit spreads, 144f

liking for, 86
  magnifying sweetness without
    boosting calories, 146
  maple, **143t**
  molasses and, 143
  naturally occurring, **143**
  obesity and, 147
  as preservative, 534
  in processed foods, 144f
  terms that describe, 143t
  turbinado, **143t**
  type 2 diabetes and, 148
  using, personal strategy for, 150
  in vegetables, 141
  white, **143t**
Sugar alcohols, 150
  relative sweetness of, 150t
Sugar molecules, 114–15
  disaccharides, **114**, 115f
  fructose, **115**, **143t**
  galactose, **115**, **143t**
  maltose, **115**, **143t**
  monosaccharides, **114**, 115f
  sucrose, **115**, **143t**
Sugar substitutes. *See* Artificial
  sweeteners
Sulphate, 328, 342t
Sulphites, as antioxidants, 535
Sun exposure, synthesis and,
  256, 256f
Superoxide dismutase (SOD), **447t**
Supplements. *See also* Dietary
    supplements
  athletic performance and, 435
  ergogenic aids posing as, 452
  iron, 436–37
  prenatal, 564, 564f
  steroid alternative, 451–52
  vitamin E, 435–36
Surface water, **312t**
Surgery for weight loss, 400–01, 401f
Sushi, **518**
Sustainable, **664**
Swallowing and choking, 97f
Sweeteners. *See* Artificial sweeteners;
  Sugar
Synthesis, sun exposure and, 256, 256f
Systolic pressure, 468f, **474**,

T

Tagatose, **150t**, 153
Takeout foods, microbial growth
  and, 518
Tannins, **334**
T-cells, **84**
Tea, 66
  caffeine in, 637t
  phytochemicals in, 64–65t

Water-soluble vitamins, 262–80
 deficiencies, 282–85t
 functions, 282–85t
 toxicities, 282–85t
 vitamin B as individuals,
  269–80
 vitamin B in unison, 266–69
 vitamin C, 262–66
 vitamin-like bioactive
  compounds, 280
Web sites, reliable sites, 23t. *See also*
  Internet
Weight cycling, **402**
Weight gain, 398–99
 high energy density foods and, 399
 of infants and toddlers, 603f
 infant to 5 years, 557f
 meal spacing and, 399
 physical activity and, 398
 portion sizes and, 399
 during pregnancy, 556, 565–66,
  565t, 566f
 prepregnancy weight and, 556
 supplements, 399
 tobacco and, 399
Weight loss. *See also* Diet strategies for
  weight loss
 carbohydrates and, 123
 diet recommendations, 394t
 diet strategies, 391–96
 maintaining, 402
 moderate *vs.* rapid, 384–86
 physical activity and, 396–98
 schemes, rating sound and
  unsound, 393t
 surgery, 400–01, 401f
 urgent need indicators of, 368t

Weight management, 385
 accepting tips, 388t
 artificial sweeteners and, 153–54
 discretionary calorie allowance
  for, F-1
 fat replacers and, 186
 fibre and, 118
 food choices and, 12
 hypertension and, 469
 osteoporosis and, 352
 reasonable goals for, 388f
 Type 2 diabetes and, 139
 unreasonable expectations for, 388f
 vegetarian diets and, 235
Weights and measures, B-4
Weight training, **424**
Well-done meats, cancer and, 484
Well water, **314t**
Wernicke-Korsakoff syndrome, **101t**,
  108, 269
Wheat, 124–26, 124f
Wheat flour, 124, **124t**
Wheat germ oil, **447t**
Whey protein, **447t**
White flour, 124, **124t**
White sugar, **143t**
Whole foods, 9, 66
 cancer and, 479
Whole grain, **124t**
Whole-wheat flour, 124, **124t**
Wine, 66
 health effects of, 109
 nonalcoholic, 102
 as phytochemical, 66
Witch hazel, **480t**

Women. *See also* Pregnancy;
  Premenstrual syndrome (PMS)
 hunger and malnutrition
  in, 661
World food supply, **652t**, 661
World Health Organization, protein
  intake recommendations, 208t
World hunger, 657–61
World population growth, 653f
Worldwide hunger estimates, 651t

X

Xerophthalmia, **248**
Xerosis, **248**
Xylitol, **150t**

Y

Yogurt, fats in, 188–89, 189f

Z

Zinc, 336–39
 aging and, 628
 average amount young adult
  Canadians are consuming, 345t
 deficiency, 336
 food sources of, 337
 intake by 19–30-year-old Canadians
  vs. DRI report recommendations,
  345t
 MDD for, 337
 pregnancy and, 563–64
 Snapshot feature of, 338
 summary of, 343t
 toxicity, 336–37
 in vegetarian diets, 238
Zygote, **557**

Canadian Reference Standards for the Daily Values on Food Labels

These values were developed by Health Canada and are based on 2,000 Calories per day for adults and children over 2 years old. Chapter 2 provides more details.

Vitamins	Daily Value Reference Standard[a]
Vitamin A	1,000 RE
Vitamin D	5 µg
Vitamin E	10 mg
Vitamin K	80 µg
Thiamin	1.3 mg
Riboflavin	1.6 mg
Niacin	23 mg[b]
Folate	220 µg
Vitamin B_{12}	2 µg
Vitamin B_6	1.8 mg
Vitamin C	60 mg
Biotin	30 ug
Pantothenic acid	7 mg

Minerals	Daily Value Reference Standard
Calcium	1,100 mg
Phosphorus	1,100 mg
Magnesium	250 mg
Sodium	2,400 mg
Potassium	3,500 mg
Iron	14 mg
Zinc	9 mg
Iodide	160 µg
Selenium	50 ug
Copper	2 mg
Manganese	2 mg
Chromium	120 ug
Molybdenum	75 ug
Chloride	3,400 mg

[a]Regulations Amending the Food and Drug Regulations (Nutrition Labelling, Nutrient Content Claims and Health Claims). *Canadian Gazette Part II, Vol. 137, No. 1* pp.154–403. See Chapter 6—Elements Within the Nutrition Facts Table http://www.inspection.gc.ca/english/fssa/labeti/guide/ch6e.shtml#6.3.2
From 2003 *Guide to Food Labelling and Advertising,* Table 6-5 Recommended Daily Intake for Vitamins and Mineral Nutrients, Canadian Food Inspection Agency

[b]Niacin is expressed as Niacin Equivalents (NE).

Food Component	Amount	Calculation Factors
Fat	65 g	30 percent of Calories
The sum of saturated and *trans* fatty acids	20 g	10 percent of Calories
Cholesterol	300 mg	Same regardless of Calories
Carbohydrate (total)	300 g	60 percent of Calories
Total fibre	25 g	14 g per 1,000 Calories
Sodium	2,400 mg	Same regardless of Calories
Potassium	3,500 mg	Same regardless of Calories

GLOSSARY OF NUTRIENT MEASURES

kcal: Calories; a unit by which energy is measured (Chapter 1 provides more details).

g: grams; a unit of weight equivalent to about 0.03 ounces.

mg: milligrams; one-thousandth of a gram.

µg: micrograms; one-millionth of a gram.

IU: international units; an old measure of vitamin activity determined by biological methods (as opposed to new measures that are determined by direct chemical analyses). Many fortified foods and supplements use IU on their labels.
- For vitamin A, 1 IU = 0.3 µg retinol, 3.6 µg β-carotene, or 7.2 µg other vitamin A carotenoids
- For vitamin D, 1 IU = 0.02 µg cholecalciferol
- For vitamin E, 1 IU = 0.67 natural α-tocopherol (other conversion factors are used for different forms of vitamin E)

mg NE: milligrams niacin equivalents; a measure of niacin activity (Chapter 7 provides more details).
- 1 NE = 1 mg niacin
    = 60 mg tryptophan (an amino acid)

µg DFE: micrograms dietary folate equivalents; a measure of folate activity (Chapter 7 provides more details).
- 1 µg DFE = 1 µg food folate
    = 0.6 µg fortified food or supplement folate taken with food
    = 0.5 µg supplement folate taken on an empty stomach

µg RAE: micrograms retinol activity equivalents; a measure of vitamin A activity (Chapter 7 provides more details).
- 1 µg RAE = 1 µg retinol
    = 12 µg β-carotene
    = 24 µg other vitamin A carotenoids

mmol: millimoles; one-thousandth of a mole, the molecular weight of a substance. To convert mmol to mg, multiply by the atomic weight of the substance.
- For sodium, mmol × 23 = mg Na
- For chloride, mmol × 35.5 = mg Cl
- For sodium chloride, mmol × 58.5 = mg NaCl

Body Mass Index (BMI) Nomogram for Most Healthy Adults*

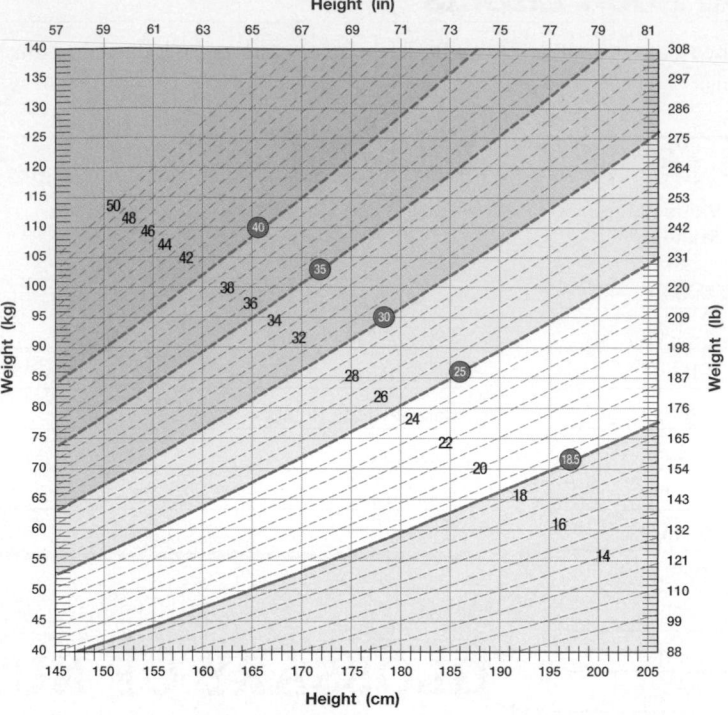

Source: Canadian Guidelines for Body Weight Classification in Adults. *Health Canada, 2003. Reproduced with permission from Her Majesty the Queen in Right of Canada©, represented by the Minister of Health, 2011.*

Body Mass Index-for-Age Percentiles: Boys and Girls, Age 2 to 19

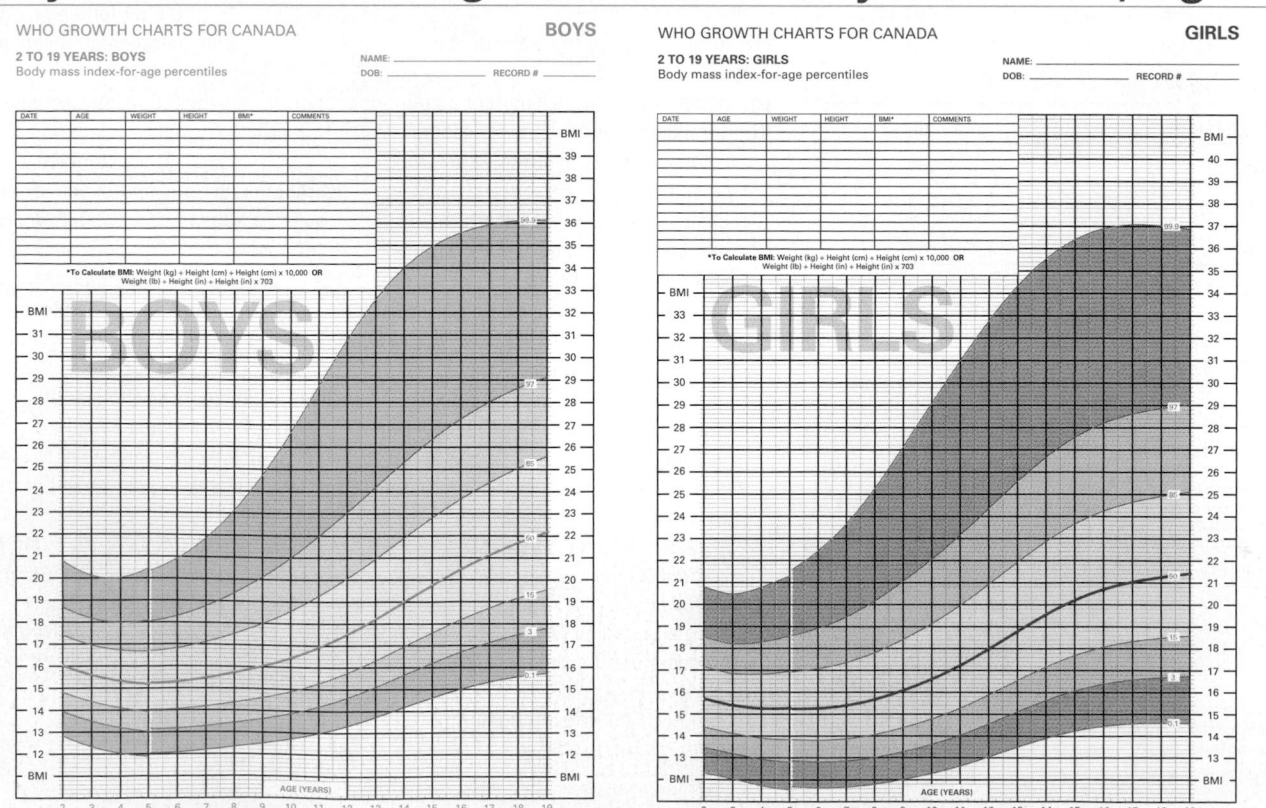

Source: *Developed by the National Center for Health Statistics in collaboration with the National Center for Chronic Disease Prevention and Health Promotion http://www.cdc.gov/growthcharts.*

*This nomogram is intended for use among Canadian adults, except for pregnant and lactating women.

Go Online and Make the Grade with CourseMate

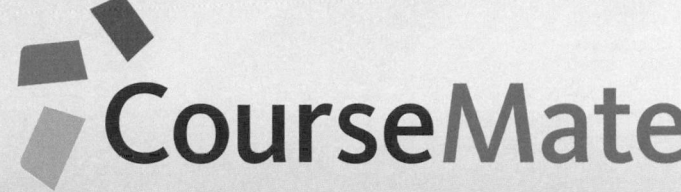
CourseMate

CourseMate brings course concepts to life with interactive learning, study, and exam preparation tools that support the textbook.

CourseMate includes:

- **Dynamic Teaching and Learning Tools**
  Quizzes, flashcards, and other multimedia help you prepare for class and review for tests.

- **An Interactive eBook**
  Take notes, highlight, search, and interact with embedded media specific to your textbook.

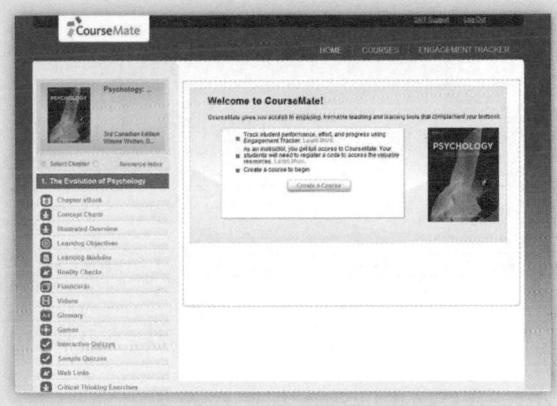

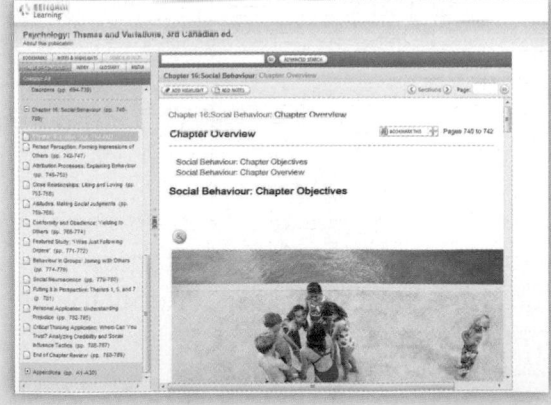

Study Smarter Online with CengageNow

CengageNow brings course concepts to life with interactive learning, study, and exam preparation tools that support your textbook.

CengageNow includes:

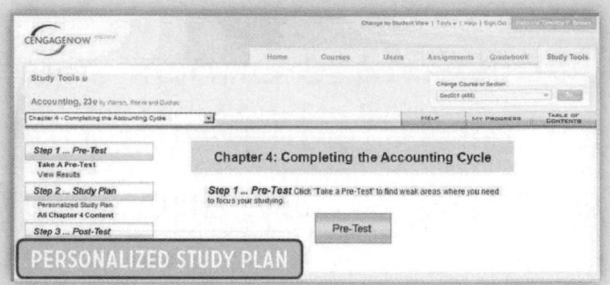

- **Chapter-Specific Pre-Tests and Post-Tests**
  Test your knowledge and receive immediate feedback. Plan your studying for maximum success.

- **Personalized Study Plan**
  Follow your personalized plan and review interactive tutorials, videos, animations, games, and other multimedia content to master course concepts and prepare for exams.

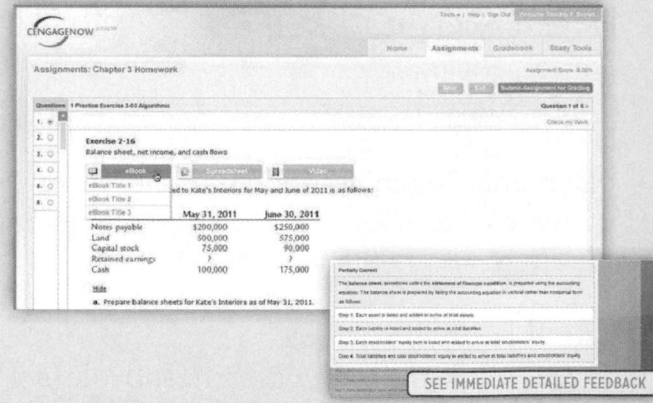

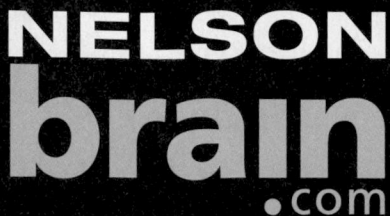